Preface

The second edition of COLLEGE CHEMISTRY is an extensive and thorough revision which seeks to bring the book completely up to date while retaining the basic organization and features which have contributed to the wide acceptance of the first edition.

COLLEGE CHEMISTRY differs from GENERAL CHEMISTRY by the same authors in that the study of the metals is organized according to the qualitative analysis scheme and includes analytical procedures for the qualitative analysis of the metals. The book is designed primarily for use in the course which integrates general chemistry and qualitative analysis. The periodic relationships of the elements receive ample attention, however.

As in the first edition, the book consists of five parts: Part 1, Principles of Chemistry and the Nonmetals; Part 2, The Metals; Part 3, Ionic Equilibria; Part 4, Semimicro Qualitative Analysis; and Part 5, Appendices. Predominantly descriptive chapters are interspersed with those devoted to the study of theory and principles. It is our experience that greater interest can be maintained and the subject matter more effectively assimilated with this approach than when large amounts of either description or theory are given at one time.

In Part 1, the discussion of atomic and molecular theory emphasizes modern theory and principles. A comprehensive introduction to the Periodic Table early in the book (Chapter 3) enables teachers and students to make extensive use of the Periodic Table at an early point in the course. More advanced topics on periodic relationships of elements are brought in later (Chapter 15). Other features in Part 1 of the second edition that will be welcomed by instructors are (1) a chapter on colloids that has been strengthened by a broader concept of colloids in accord with recent work in polymer and protein chemistry, (2) an expanded section on the nomenclature of compounds (Chapter 4) to include ternary compounds, (3) additional emphasis on formula writing and oxidation numbers, (4) the use throughout of atomic weights based on carbon-12 as the standard, and (5) a significant discussion of the recent work with the rare gases, which has demonstrated much greater reactivity for these elements than heretofore attributed to them.

Part 2 of the book takes up the metals as they are grouped according to the analytical scheme. Analytical properties of the metals are stressed in the presentation of the descriptive chemistry of the metals. Metals not included in the analytical scheme are considered in the last chapter of Part 2. A new chapter on coordination compounds in the second edition is in accord with the large and increasing interest in these compounds.

Part 3 consists of three chapters dealing with ionic equilibria in aqueous systems of weak electrolytes, of slightly soluble electrolytes, and of salts which hydrolyze. These chapters, in which the quantitative theory applicable to qualitative analysis is presented, are to be studied simultaneously with the chemistry involved in the analytical procedures. The hydrolysis chapter places a strong emphasis upon the hydration of ions in water solution.

Part 4 contains the analytical procedures, which are essentially those developed by A. A. Noyes. Inasmuch as the principal objective in an elementary course in qualitative analysis is to teach the chemistry of the common inorganic cations and anions, inorganic reagents are used almost exclusively in the qualitative procedures. However, thioacetamide (CH_3CSNH_2) is used for the sulfide precipitations. Emphasis is placed on understanding the reasons for the various steps utilized in the analytical procedures.

Every effort has been made to bring the material in the entire book completely up to date. Typical among the new developments discussed are the anthraquinone process for the production of hydrogen peroxide (Chapter 10), the DeNora cell for the production of sodium (Chapter 39), the synthesis of diamonds (Chapter 28), rocket propellants (Chapter 25), the exchange equilibrium process for production of heavy water (Chapter 10), solar battery and fuel cells (Chapter 20), and breeder reactors (Chapter 30). Additional emphasis has been placed on crystal structure (Chapter 9) and polymers (Chapter 31).

The factor and molar methods of solving chemical problems are employed to lead the student to a clearer understanding of the principles involved. End-of-chapter materials include numerous problems, with answers, to test his understanding.

The approach of this book makes it suitable for students majoring in fields such as chemistry, physics, geology, engineering, medicine, dentistry, medical technology, agriculture, and home economics. The development of the subject does not presuppose previous training in chemistry at the secondary school level but yet is paced to arouse and maintain the interest of those who have had an earlier introduction to the science.

Grateful acknowledgment is made to Dr. John C. Bailar, Jr., of the University of Illinois, consulting editor for D. C. Heath and Company, who went through the entire manuscript in detail and made many helpful suggestions. Our thanks also go to our colleagues and to the users of the previous edition for their many helpful suggestions and criticisms, which have been utilized in preparing the second edition.

William H. Nebergall
Frederic C. Schmidt
Henry F. Holtzclaw, Jr.

MODERN PERIODIC TABLE

The number of electrons in filled shells is shown in the column at the extreme left; the remaining electrons for each element are shown below the symbol and atomic number for each element. The atomic weights shown above the symbols are based on Carbon–12.

METALS — NONMETALS

TRANSITION METALS

PERIODS	I A	II A	III B	IV B	V B	VI B	VII B	VIII	VIII	VIII	I B	II B	III A	IV A	V A	VI A	VII A	0
1 0	1.00797 H [1] 1																1.00797 H [1] 1	4.0026 He[2] 2
2 2	6.939 Li [3] 1	9.0122 Be[4] 2											10.811 B [5] 3	12.01115 C [6] 4	14.0067 N [7] 5	15.9994 O [8] 6	18.9984 F [9] 7	20.183 Ne[10] 8
3 2, 8	22.9898 Na[11] 1	24.312 Mg[12] 2											26.9815 Al[13] 3	28.086 Si [14] 4	30.9738 P [15] 5	32.064 S [16] 6	35.453 Cl [17] 7	39.948 Ar[18] 8
4 2, 8	39.102 K [19] 8, 1	40.08 Ca[20] 8, 2	44.956 Sc [21] 9, 2	47.90 Ti [22] 10, 2	50.942 V [23] 11, 2	51.996 Cr[24] 13, 1	54.9380 Mn[25] 13, 2	55.847 Fe[26] 14, 2	58.9332 Co[27] 15, 2	58.71 Ni [28] 16, 2	63.54 Cu[29] 18, 1	65.37 Zn[30] 18, 2	69.72 Ga[31] 18, 3	72.59 Ge[32] 18, 4	74.9216 As[33] 18, 5	78.96 Se[34] 18, 6	79.909 Br[35] 18, 7	83.80 Kr[36] 18, 8
5 2, 8, 18	85.47 Rb[37] 8, 1	87.62 Sr [38] 8, 2	88.905 Y [39] 9, 2	91.22 Zr [40] 10, 2	92.906 Nb[41] 12, 1	95.94 Mo[42] 13, 1	(99) Tc[43] 14, 1	101.07 Ru[44] 15, 1	102.905 Rh[45] 16, 1	105.4 Pd[46] 18	107.870 Ag[47] 18, 1	112.40 Cd[48] 18, 2	114.82 In[49] 18, 3	118.69 Sn[50] 18, 4	121.75 Sb[51] 18, 5	127.60 Te[52] 18, 6	126.9044 I [53] 18, 7	131.30 Xe[54] 18, 8
6 2, 8, 18	132.905 Cs [55] 18, 8, 1	137.34 Ba[56] 18, 8, 2	[57-71] *	178.49 Hf[72] 32, 10, 2	180.948 Ta[73] 32, 11, 2	183.85 W [74] 32, 12, 2	186.2 Re[75] 32, 13, 2	190.2 Os[76] 32, 14, 2	192.2 Ir [77] 32, 15, 2	195.09 Pt [78] 32, 17, 1	196.967 Au[79] 32, 18, 1	200.59 Hg[80] 32, 18, 2	204.37 Tl [81] 32, 18, 3	207.19 Pb[82] 32, 18, 4	208.980 Bi [83] 32, 18, 5	(210) Po[84] 32, 18, 6	(210) At[85] 32, 18, 7	(222) Rn[86] 32, 18, 8
7 2,8,18,32	(223) Fr [87] 18, 8, 1	(226.05) Ra[88] 18, 8, 2	[89-103] †	[104]	[105]	[106]	[107]	[108]										

* LANTHANIDE SERIES	138.91 La[57] 18, 9, 2	140.12 Ce[58] 20, 8, 2	140.907 Pr[59] 21, 8, 2	144.24 Nd[60] 22, 8, 2	(145) Pm[61] 23, 8, 2	150.35 Sm[62] 24, 8, 2	151.96 Eu[63] 25, 8, 2	157.25 Gd[64] 25, 9, 2	158.924 Tb[65] 27, 8, 2	162.50 Dy[66] 28, 8, 2	164.930 Ho[67] 29, 8, 2	167.26 Er[68] 30, 8, 2	168.934 Tm[69] 31, 8, 2	173.04 Yb[70] 32, 8, 2	174.97 Lu[71] 32, 9, 2
† ACTINIDE SERIES	(227) Ac[89] 18, 9, 2	232.038 Th[90] 18, 10, 2	(231) Pa[91] 20, 9, 2	238.03 U [92] 21, 9, 2	(237) Np[93] 23, 8, 2	(242) Pu[94] 24, 8, 2	(243) Am[95] 25, 8, 2	(245) Cm[96] 25, 9, 2	(245) Bk[97] 26, 9, 2	(248) Cf [98] 28, 8, 2	(253) Es[99] 29, 8, 2	(254) Fm[100] 30, 8, 2	(256) Md[101] 31, 8, 2	(253) No[102] 32, 8, 2	(257) Lw[103] 32, 9, 2

College Chemistry
With Qualitative Analysis

COLLEGE CHEMISTRY

WITH QUALITATIVE ANALYSIS

Second Edition

WILLIAM H. NEBERGALL
Associate Professor of Chemistry, Indiana University

FREDERIC C. SCHMIDT
Professor of Chemistry, Indiana University

HENRY F. HOLTZCLAW, JR.
Professor of Chemistry, University of Nebraska

Under the editorship of JOHN C. BAILAR, JR.
Professor of Chemistry, University of Illinois

D. C. HEATH AND COMPANY BOSTON

Library of Congress Catalog Card Number: 63–9036

Printed August 1966

Contents

Part 2. THE METALS

Part 3. IONIC EQUILIBRIA

Part 4. SEMIMICRO QUALITATIVE ANALYSIS

Part 5. APPENDICES

PART 1

Principles of Chemistry and the Nonmetals

CHAPTER ONE

Some Fundamental Concepts

1.1 Chemistry

Such forms of matter as wood and glass, water and gasoline, salt and sugar, coal and granite, and iron and gold differ strikingly from each other in many properties. These differences in properties occur as a result of differences in the composition and structure of the various substances. In our study of chemistry, we shall be concerned with the composition and structure of matter. This is not the whole story of chemistry, however, for matter is not static. Much of our existence, in fact, depends upon the changes which occur in matter. Who has watched a burning piece of coal and not marveled at the apparent transformation of the hard black solid into a small quantity of ash? What changes in matter are taking place when iron rusts, milk sours, a storage battery produces an electric current, and food is digested and assimilated by the body? As we proceed in our study of chemistry, we shall look into the changes in the composition and structure of matter, the causes which produce these changes, the changes in energy which accompany them, and the principles and laws involved in these transformations. In brief, then, the science of **chemistry is the study of the composition, structure, and properties of matter, and the changes which it undergoes.**

The science of chemistry has become so vast during the last century that chemists usually specialize in one of several principal branches. **Analytical chemistry** is concerned with the identification, separation, and quantitative determination of the composition of different substances. **Physical chemistry** is primarily concerned with the structure of matter and the laws, principles, and theories which explain the transformations of one form of matter into another. **Organic chemistry** is the branch dealing with the study of the compounds of carbon, whereas **inorganic chemistry** is concerned with the chemistry of the elements, other than carbon, and their compounds. This division has come about because carbon forms a great many more compounds important to our civilization than any of the other elements. **Biochemistry** is the chemistry of the substances comprising living organisms, plants and animals. A course in **general chemistry** is a survey of all of the branches of chemistry and introduces the student to the entire field of the science.

1.2 Importance of Chemistry

Modern science, including chemistry, is constantly providing us with a supply of new things for better living, for a longer and healthier life, and an increased leisure in which to enjoy life. From the laboratory of the research chemist have come such familiar substances as penicillin, streptomycin, and the sulfa drugs to conquer disease and to save and prolong life. The modern automobile and airplane have become possible through the production of special alloys, high octane fuels, and synthetic rubber and other plastics. Synthetic fibers such as nylon and Dacron are competing with cotton and wool, while plastics and new types of glass are replacing steel, wood, bone, cork, and ceramics in an ever increasing number of applications. An increased production of foodstuffs to keep abreast of our rapidly growing population has been made possible by the development, production, and use of commercial fertilizers such as superphosphate of lime and insecticides such as DDT (dichlorodiphenyltrichloroethane).

The importance of chemistry is reflected in the number of people in the profession. There are more than ninety thousand members of the American Chemical Society, comprising about half the total number of chemists in the United States. An understanding of chemistry is important or is a necessity in many professions — medicine, geology, mineralogy, physics, biology, engineering, pharmacy, farming, homemaking.

1.3 Matter and Energy

All objects in the universe are composed of matter. **Matter** is that which occupies space and has mass. The property of occupying space is easily perceived by our senses of sight and feeling. The property of **mass** pertains to the quantity of matter that a body contains. The force required to give a body of matter a given acceleration, or the resistance of the body to being moved (inertia), is a measure of its mass.

Energy may be defined as the capacity for doing work. We are familiar with such forms of energy as heat, light, and electricity. Heat drives the steam engine, electricity causes electric motors to turn, and light is consumed in the manufacture of foods by plants. A body of matter may possess **potential energy** by virtue of its position, condition, or composition. Water at the top of a waterfall possesses energy as a result of its position; by falling it can do work on an electric generator, causing it to turn. A compressed spring, because of its compression, can do such work as making a clock run. Coal possesses chemical energy, a kind of potential energy, because of its characteristic composition. As the coal burns it produces heat energy which can be used to drive a steam engine.

If a body is allowed to fall, its potential energy is transformed into energy of motion. As the object reaches the ground, it has lost all of its potential energy, but it has gained ability to do work due to its motion. The energy which a body possesses because of its motion is called **kinetic energy.**

1.4 Law of Conservation of Matter

When a piece of coal is burned and all of the products (ash and gases) are collected and weighed, it is found that the products weigh more than the original piece of coal. If, however, the weight of the oxygen of the air that combines with the burning coal is taken into consideration, it may be shown that the weight of the products (ash and gases) is, within the limits of accuracy of our balances, equal to the weight of the reactants (coal and oxygen). This behavior of matter is in accord with what is called the **Law of Conservation of Matter: There is no detectable increase or decrease in the quantity of matter during a chemical change.**

1.5 Law of Conservation of Energy

Chemical changes are always accompanied by the conversion of chemical energy into other forms of energy, or of other forms of energy into chemical energy. Usually, heat energy is evolved or absorbed, but sometimes the conversion involves light or electrical energy instead of or in addition to heat energy. Many transformations of energy, of course, do not involve chemical changes. Electrical energy may be converted into mechanical, light, heat, or chemical energy. Mechanical energy is converted into electrical energy in the dynamo. Potential and kinetic energy can be converted into one another. Many other conversions are possible. All the energy involved in any change appears in some form after the change is completed. This leads to the **Law of Conservation of Energy: Energy cannot be created or destroyed, although it can be changed in form.**

Recently it has become necessary to regard matter and energy, not as distinct realities, but as different forms of a single reality. In the decomposition of atoms, such as takes place in the explosion of the atomic bomb, matter is actually converted into energy. The reverse conversion of energy into matter can be demonstrated. This interconversion of mass and energy takes place in ordinary chemical reactions, but the mass of the products differs so slightly from the mass of the reactants that it is impossible to measure the difference experimentally. The magnitude of mass change is so small that we may say, for practical purposes, that the law of conservation of matter holds in ordinary chemical reactions. However, to be more precise, we may combine the separate laws of conservation of matter and energy: **The total quantity of matter and energy available in the universe is fixed.**

1.6 Physical States of Matter

Matter can exist in three different states, designated as solid, liquid, and gas (Fig. 1–1), which can be distinguished by certain qualities.

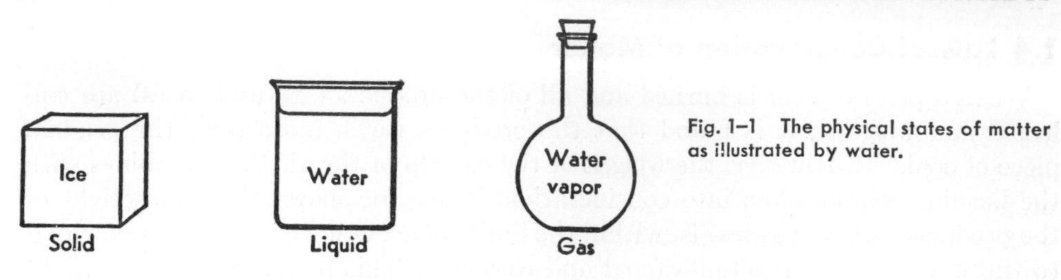

Fig. 1–1 The physical states of matter as illustrated by water.

A substance in the **solid state** is rigid, possesses a definite shape, and has a volume which is very nearly independent of changes in conditions such as temperature and pressure.

A **liquid,** such as water, possesses the property of flowing to take the shape of its container except that it assumes a horizontal surface (Fig. 1–2). Liquids are only slightly compressible and so for practical purposes have definite volumes.

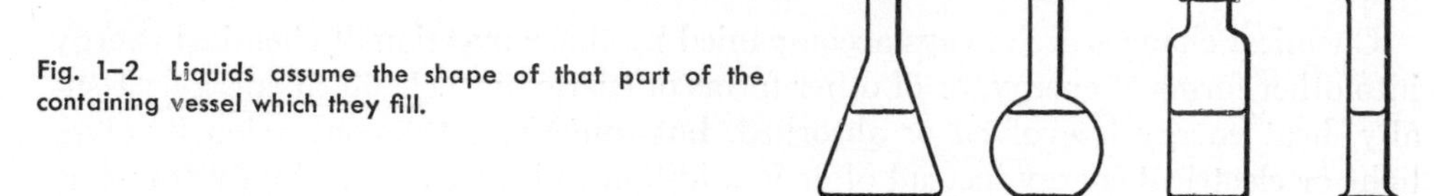

Fig. 1–2 Liquids assume the shape of that part of the containing vessel which they fill.

A substance in the **gaseous state** takes both the shape and volume of its container. Gases are readily compressible and capable of infinite expansion.

1.7 Chemical and Physical Changes

When carbon, a black solid substance, burns in air, an invisible gas consisting of both carbon and oxygen (carbon dioxide) is formed. When milk sours, the sugar in the milk is converted into an acid, and the composition and the properties of the acid differ greatly from those of the sugar. Iron rust formed by the corrosion of iron metal contains oxygen as well as iron, and it is therefore a different substance with different properties. All such changes are called **chemical changes.** A chemical change always produces at least one substance entirely different in composition and properties from those that existed before the change occurred. In addition, all chemical changes are accompanied by either the formation or absorption of some form of energy.

Changes that do not alter the composition of a substance are known as **physical changes.** The melting of ice, the freezing of water, the conversion of water to steam, the condensation of steam to water, the dissolving of sugar in water, and the heating of iron to redness, are all examples of physical change. In each of these there is a change in properties but there is no alteration of the chemical composition of the substances involved. Water, whether in the solid, liquid, or gaseous state, retains the same chemical composition. Sugar is the same chemical substance in solution in water as it is in the solid state and can readily be recovered as crystals by evaporation of the water. Iron, an emitter of light when red hot, is still the same substance that reflects light when cold.

1.8 Chemical and Physical Properties

The characteristics which enable us to distinguish one substance from another are known as **properties.** Those properties involved in a transformation of one substance into another are known as **chemical properties.** Thus, a chemical property is exhibited when coal burns, for the constituents of the coal combine with oxygen to form different substances. When iron rusts, it shows a chemical property as the iron combines with oxygen to form the reddish-brown iron oxide which we know as iron rust.

In addition to chemical properties, every substance also possesses definite physical properties. The **physical properties** of a substance are those which do not involve a change in composition of the material. Some familiar physical properties of matter are color, hardness, crystalline form, ductility, malleability, physical state, melting point, boiling point, density, electrical and thermal conductivity, and specific heat. Taste and odor are often classed as physical properties, but these sensations actually involve chemical changes. Changes in physical conditions such as temperature or pressure may modify the physical properties of a substance. For example, a substance in the gaseous state has certain physical properties such as density, specific heat, and thermal conductivity. By decreasing the temperature of the substance or compressing it to a smaller volume, it may be changed from the gaseous to the liquid state, in which condition it has an entirely different density, specific heat, and thermal conductivity.

A substance may be identified by its chemical and physical properties and by its composition because no two substances are alike in all respects.

1.9 Substances

A substance is any variety of matter all specimens of which have identical properties and composition. Pure water is an example of a substance. All samples of pure water, regardless of their source, have exactly the same composition, 2.01594 parts by weight of hydrogen to 15.9994 parts of oxygen, and are identical in melting point, boiling point, and all other properties. Pure iron, pure aluminum, pure carbon, pure sugar, and pure oxygen are representative substances. Two substances may be distinguished from each other by a study of their characteristic properties. Sugar and salt may be distinguished by taste, iron and gold by color, and silver and mercury by physical state.

1.10 Mixtures

A mixture is composed of two or more substances each of which retains its identity and specific properties. The composition of a mixture can be varied continuously. Black gunpowder is a mixture of carbon, sulfur, and potassium nitrate; granite is a mixture of quartz, feldspar, and mica; plumber's solder is a mixture of crystals of tin and lead; a solution of sugar and water is a mixture; and air is a mixture of nitrogen, oxygen, carbon dioxide, water vapor, and other gases. Milk, butter, cement, flour, gasoline, and coal are other examples of mixtures. In fact, most naturally occurring materials are mixtures.

Because each component of a mixture possesses its own set of characteristic properties, the various components can be separated by physical methods. The heterogeneous character of black gunpowder is readily detected by examining it under a microscope. Treatment of a sample of it with water causes the potassium nitrate to dissolve, leaving the sulfur and charcoal as solid particles; subsequent treatment of the residue with carbon disulfide causes the sulfur to dissolve, leaving only the carbon. The potassium nitrate and sulfur may be reclaimed as crystalline particles by evaporating their respective solutions to dryness. An intimate mixture of iron and sulfur may be separated by dissolving the sulfur in carbon disulfide, leaving the iron, or by removing the iron with a magnet, leaving the sulfur.

1.11 Elements

There are two classes of substances — elements and compounds. **Elements are pure substances which cannot be decomposed by a chemical change.** Familiar examples are iron, silver, gold, aluminum, sulfur, oxygen, and carbon.

One hundred and three elements are known at the present time; a list of these is printed on the inside front cover of this book. Eighty-eight elements have been found in nature and the other fifteen have been synthesized. Only about one-fourth of the elements ever occur in nature in the free state; the others are found only in combination. Eleven of the elements make up about 99 per cent of the earth's crust and the atmosphere (Table 1·1). Oxygen constitutes nearly one-half and silicon one-fourth of the total quantity of the elements in the world we know.

TABLE 1·1 The More Abundant Elements

Element	%	Element	%
Oxygen	49.20%	Chlorine	0.19%
Silicon	25.67	Phosphorus	0.11
Aluminum	7.50	Manganese	0.09
Iron	4.71	Carbon	0.08
Calcium	3.39	Sulfur	0.06
Sodium	2.63	Barium	0.04
Potassium	2.40	Nitrogen	0.03
Magnesium	1.93	Fluorine	0.03
Hydrogen	0.87	Strontium	0.02
Titanium	0.58	All others	0.47

1.12 Compounds

Compounds are substances which can be decomposed by chemical changes, and they are composed of two or more different elements. Elements in combination are different from elements in the free or uncombined state. The term "element" is used to designate an elementary substance whether free or present in compounds. For example, white crystalline sugar is a compound consisting of the element carbon, which is a black solid when free, and the two elements hydrogen and oxygen, which are colorless gases when uncombined. Water, a compound, can be decomposed by an electric current into its two constituent elements hydrogen and oxygen. Salt can be broken down by electrolysis into sodium and chlorine.

Whereas there are only 103 known elements, there are hundreds of thousands of chemical compounds representing different combinations of these elements. Each of these compounds possesses definite chemical and physical properties by which chemists can distinguish it from all other compounds.

1.13 Molecules

Water has a definite composition and set of chemical and physical properties which enable us to recognize it as a distinct substance. One might ask the question, "To what extent could a drop of water be subdivided before the smallest particle would be obtained which would still have the chemical properties of water?" The limit to which the subdivision could be carried is a particle called a **molecule** of water. Subdivision of a molecule of water would result in the formation of two new substances, hydrogen and oxygen, each with a set of properties quite different from water and each other. **The smallest particle of an element or compound that can have a stable, independent existence is called a molecule** (Fig. 1–3). Molecules are too small to be seen even with the most

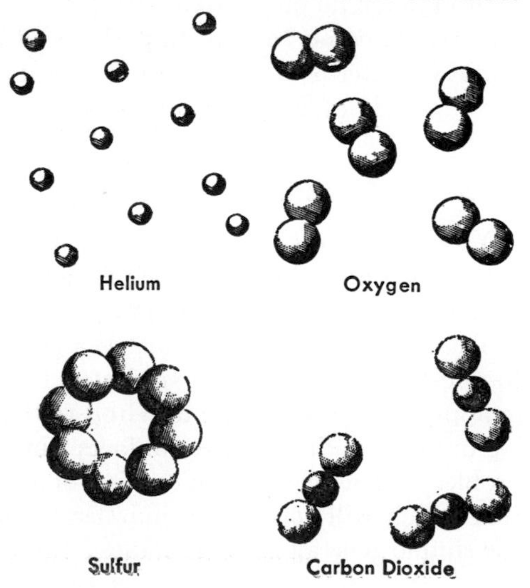

Fig. 1–3 Models of molecules of the elements helium, oxygen, and sulfur and of the compound carbon dioxide.

powerful microscope. An idea of the minute size of molecules can be appreciated from the fact that if a drop of water were to be magnified to the size of the earth, its constituent molecules would appear to be about the size of baseballs. One hundred million molecules of water laid side by side make a row about one inch long.

1.14 Atoms

We may define an atom as the smallest particle of an element which can enter into a chemical combination. For example, one atom of carbon can combine with two atoms of oxygen and form one molecule of carbon dioxide.

An atom of an element may or may not be capable of independent existence. In some cases, an atom of an element and a molecule of it are identical. When the molecule of an element contains only one atom it is said to be monatomic. Examples of elements which are composed of monatomic molecules are iron, copper, and helium. Hydrogen, oxygen, nitrogen, fluorine, chlorine, bromine, and iodine consist of diatomic molecules (two atoms per molecule). Molecules of phosphorus and sulfur contain four and eight atoms, respectively. It follows, then, that the term "molecule" applies to small particles of either elements or compounds, whereas the term "atom" always applies to the smallest particle of an element.

The word "atom," from the Greek word "atomos," means indivisible. The early Greek philosophers were the originators of the conception of atoms, and they taught that matter, being composed of atoms, is therefore finitely divisible. Although John Dalton, an English chemist and physicist, did not devise the atomic theory, it was he who revived the old Greek atomic hypothesis, and put it on a quantitative basis. For this reason Dalton is generally credited with being the father of the atomic theory (1808), the most important of all chemical theories. Dalton made no distinction between atoms and molecules as we do today, and he applied the name "atom" to particles of both elements and compounds. We shall see in Chapter 3 that even atoms are not the fundamental units of which matter is composed; atoms are complex systems and are made up of still smaller particles.

1.15 The Scientific Method

Your study of chemistry will be concerned with the hypotheses, theories, and laws which give this science its foundation and framework, into which bits of information fit to make an integrated area of knowledge.

The scientific method furnishes a simple and logical way of finding the answer to questions which can be subjected to inquiry and investigation. The first step in applying the **scientific method** to the solution of a problem involves the carrying out of experiments to gain facts which give information about all phases of the problem. The second step consists of an attempt to formulate a simple generalization which will correlate a number of these facts. If this attempt is successful, the simple generalization becomes a **law**. Usually, however, no general law can be formulated to correlate the facts, and then a provisional conjecture, known as a **hypothesis,** is advanced to explain the data. A hypothesis may be tested by further experiments and if it is capable of explaining a large body of facts in a given field, it is dignified by the name of **theory.** Theories serve as guides for further work by serving as the bases for predicting new information or the direction in which additional information must be sought. Finally, a theory must be established or modified in such a manner that it can be accepted as a general truth, which is often referred to as a **law.**

The theories and laws of chemistry are, in general, less precise than those of physics, making the study of chemistry somewhat more difficult. This lack of perfection, however, tends to stimulate interest in chemistry and points up the fact that there are still great opportunities for discovery in chemistry. Theories and laws help to simplify the study of chemistry by systematizing and ordering the vast body of chemical knowledge.

MEASUREMENTS IN CHEMISTRY

1.16 Units of Measurement

Chemistry is a quantitative science which is concerned with the measurement of quantities of matter and energy. In any kind of quantitative work it is necessary to have a system of units of measurement, and it is of great advantage to have a convenient system. In scientific work the **metric system** of weights and measures is used throughout the world. Calculations in the metric system are simple because the units are based upon the decimal system. However, in the **English system** the units are based on arbitrary standards of measurement and no simple relationship exists between them (Figs. 1–4 and 1–5). Calculations in American

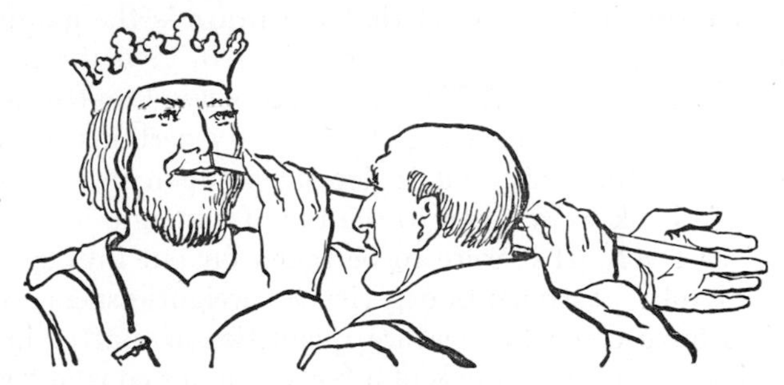

Fig. 1–4 The length of a yard was set by King Henry I. The yard was decreed to be the distance from the point of his nose to the end of his thumb.

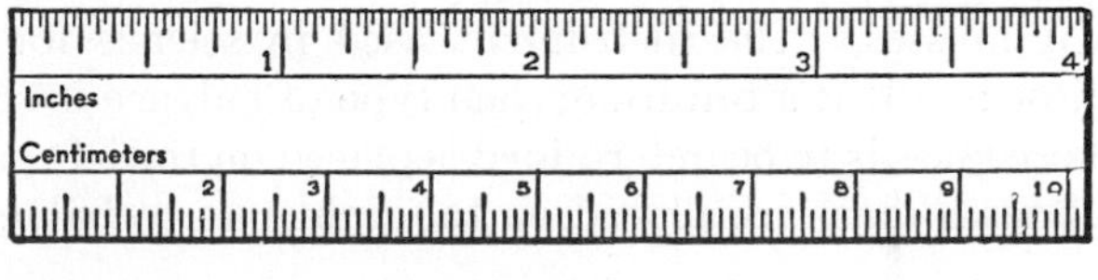

Fig. 1–5 The relationship between inches and centimeters.

engineering practice are based on the English system. In Table 1·2 are listed several important units of measurement in the two systems and their approximate relationship to each other.

TABLE 1·2 Units of Measurement

METRIC SYSTEM	ENGLISH SYSTEM
Units of Length	
Meter (m.) = 39.37 inches (in.)	Yard = 0.9144 m.
Centimeter (cm.) = 0.01 m.	Inch = 2.54 cm. (Fig. 1–5)
Millimeter (mm.) = 0.001 m.	
Kilometer (km.) = 1000 m.	Mile (U.S.) = 1.609 km.
Angstrom unit (A.U. or Å) = 10^{-8} cm.*	
Units of Volume	
Liter (l.) = volume of 1 kg. of water	Liquid quart (U.S.) = 0.9463 l.
Milliliter (ml.) = 0.001 l.	Cubic foot (U.S.) = 28.316 l.
Units of Weight	
Gram (g.) = weight of 1 ml. of water at 4° C	Ounce (oz.) (avoirdupois) = 28.35 g.
Milligram (mg.) = 0.001 g.	Pound (lb.) (avoirdupois) = 0.4536 kg.
Kilogram (kg.) = 1000 g.	Ton (short) = 2000 lb. = 907.185 kg.
Ton (metric) = 1000 kg. = 2204.62 lb.	Ton (long) = 2240 lb. = 1.016 metric tons

* See Appendix A for a discussion of exponential numbers.

1.17 Mass and Weight

We saw in Section 1.3 that the **mass** is the quantity of matter which a body contains and that the force required to give the body a given acceleration is a measure of its mass. The mass of a body of matter is an invariable quantity. On the other hand, the **weight** of a body pertains to the force of attraction of the earth for the body and is dependent upon its distance from the earth's center. If this book were taken to the top of a mountain it would weigh less than it does at sea level. If it were to be taken far out into space, its weight would become negligible. Astronauts experience "weightlessness" while in outer space. Scientists have come to measure quantities of matter in terms of mass rather than weight because the mass of a body remains constant whereas the weight of a body is an "accident of its environment."

The gravitational attraction of two bodies of matter is directly proportional to their masses. The instrument used in science for determining the mass of an object is called a **balance;** one type of balance is shown in Fig. 1–6. The object whose mass is to be determined is placed on the left pan of the balance. "Weights" of known mass are placed on the right pan to balance the object on the left pan.

"Weighing" an object on a balance makes use of the fact that the earth's force of attraction on objects of equal mass is the same, i.e., their weights are equal.

The **unit of mass** in the metric system is the **gram,** which is equal to one one-thousandth of the mass of the standard kilogram. The **standard kilogram** is a cylinder of platinum-iridium alloy which is kept at the International Bureau of Weights and Measures at Sèvres, France. The gram is very nearly equal to the weight of one cubic centimeter of water at 4° C, the temperature of its maximum density. The gram was originally intended to be exactly equal to the weight of one cubic centimeter of water at the temperature of its maximum density.

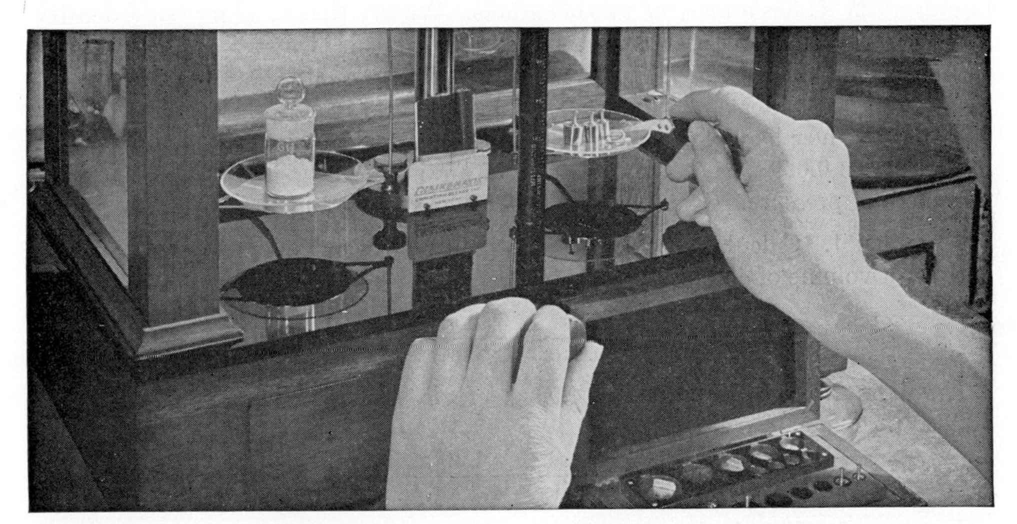

Fig. 1–6 On balances of this type chemists can weigh small objects to the nearest ten thousandth of a gram. *Murray Breeze Associates.*

1.18 Volume

It is oftentimes more convenient to measure the volume of a body of matter than to weigh it; this is particularly true of substances in the liquid or gaseous state. The **volume** of a body of matter is the space that it occupies. The unit of volume is the **liter,** which is the space occupied by one kilogram (1000 g.) of water at 4° C. One thousandth of a liter is known as the **milliliter** (Fig. 1–7).

Fig. 1–7 This drawing gives a comparison between a cubic centimeter block and a penny. One cubic centimeter is approximately one milliliter. One milliliter of water at 4° C weighs one gram.

Penny

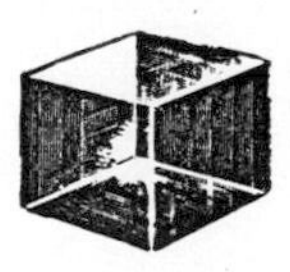

1 cubic centimeter

1.19 Density

One of the specific properties of a solid, liquid, or gas is its density. **Density is defined as mass per unit volume.** This may be expressed mathematically as follows:

$$\text{Density} = \frac{\text{mass}}{\text{volume}}, \quad \text{or} \quad D = \frac{M}{V}$$

Substances may be distinguished by measuring their densities because it is rare that any two substances have identical densities. One milliliter of mercury (a liquid) at 25° C has a mass of 13.5339 grams. We say that mercury has a density of 13.5339 g./ml. Because the milliliter and cubic centimeter are very nearly the same size, the density of mercury may be designated as 13.5339 g./cm.^{3}. The density of water at 25° C is 0.99707 g./cm.^{3} and at 4° C it is 1 g./cm.^{3}. At 0° C and 1 atmosphere of pressure one liter of hydrogen has a mass of 0.08987 gram; its density is 0.08987 g./l. The density of air is 1.2929 g./l. at 0° C and 1 atmosphere of pressure. The following problems are based upon density.

EXAMPLE 1. Calculate the density of a body that weighs (has a mass of) 320 g. and has a volume of 45 cm.^{3}.

$$\text{Density} = \frac{\text{mass}}{\text{volume}} = \frac{320 \text{ g.}}{45 \text{ cm.}^3} = 7.1 \text{ g./cm.}^3$$

EXAMPLE 2. What volume will 4.00 g. of air occupy? The density of air is 1.29 g./l.

$$\text{Volume} = \frac{\text{mass}}{\text{density}} = \frac{4.00 \text{ g.}}{1.29 \text{ g./l.}} = 3.10 \text{ l.}$$

EXAMPLE 3. What is the mass of a piece of iron which has a volume of 120 cm.^{3} and a density of 7.20 g./cm.^{3}?

$$\text{Mass} = \text{volume} \times \text{density} = 120 \text{ cm.}^3 \times 7.20 \text{ g./cm.}^3 = 864 \text{ g.}$$

EXAMPLE 4. The density of a solution of sulfuric acid which contains 38.0 per cent by weight of sulfuric acid (H_2SO_4) is 1.30 g./ml. How many grams of pure sulfuric acid are contained in 400 ml. of this solution?

One ml. of the solution of sulfuric acid has a mass of 1.30 g. Then 400 ml. of acid will have the mass:

$$\text{Mass} = \text{volume} \times \text{density} = 400 \text{ ml.} \times 1.30 \text{ g./ml.} = 520 \text{ g.}$$

Because 38.0 per cent by weight of the acid is pure H_2SO_4, the number of grams of H_2SO_4 in 400 ml. of the solution of the acid is

$$520 \text{ g.} \times \frac{38.0}{100} = 198 \text{ g.}$$

1.20 Specific Gravity

The term **specific gravity** (sp. gr.) denotes the ratio of the mass of a substance to that of an equal volume of a reference substance. The reference substance for solids and liquids is usually water.

$$\text{Specific gravity of a solid or liquid} = \frac{\text{mass of the solid or liquid}}{\text{mass of an equal volume of water}}$$

EXAMPLE. A pycnometer (see Section 1.21) weighs 210 g. when empty, 370 g. when filled with water, and 412 g. when filled with glycerine. Calculate the specific gravity of glycerine.

$$\text{Sp. gr. of glycerine} = \frac{\text{mass of glycerine}}{\text{mass of an equal volume of water}}$$
$$= \frac{(412 - 210)\text{ g.}}{(370 - 210)\text{ g.}} = \frac{202}{160} = 1.26$$

Common reference substances used in specifying the specific gravities for gases are air and hydrogen.

When measured in the metric system of units, the density of any substance has practically the same numerical value as the specific gravity referred to water as the reference substance.

The following example is based upon specific gravity.

EXAMPLE. Determine the mass of 50 ml. of kerosene, specific gravity 0.82.

1 ml. of kerosene has a mass of 0.82 g. Then 50 ml. has a mass of 50 ml. × 0.82 g./ml. = 41 g.

1.21 Measurement of the Density of a Liquid

Although the density of a liquid may be measured in many ways, the simplest method involves the use of a **pycnometer.** This instrument is a small bottle (10 ml. to 250 ml. capacity) with a ground-glass stopper which is bored with a moderately fine capillary. In determining the density of a liquid the pycnometer is first weighed empty; then it is filled with pure water and weighed again. The difference in weight when the pycnometer is filled with water and when it is empty equals the weight of water. The volume of the instrument is obtained by dividing the weight of the water by the density of water at the temperature at which the determination was made, usually 25° C. The pycnometer is then filled with the liquid whose density is to be determined, and it is weighed again. This weight minus that of the empty container equals the weight of the liquid. The density of the liquid is obtained by dividing its weight by the volume of the pycnometer.

1.22 Temperature and Its Measurement

The word **temperature** refers to the "hotness" or "coldness" of a body of matter. In temperature measurement some physical property of a substance which varies with temperature must be used. Practically all substances expand with an increase in temperature and contract when the temperature falls. The mercury or alcohol in our common glass thermometers rises when the temperature increases because its volume expands more than does the column of the glass container. Alcohol thermometers are designed for use where ease of reading is desired and accuracy is not important, hence the wide bore of these thermometers. The mercury thermometer has a smaller bore than the alcohol thermometer; hence it is usually more difficult to read. The bore of the mercury thermometer is made smaller because mercury expands about one-sixth as much as alcohol does, making the mercury thermometer inherently less accurate than an alcohol thermometer of the same bore.

1.23 Standard Reference Temperatures

In order that we may agree on a set of temperature values, it is necessary to have fixed temperatures which are readily determined. Two **fixed temperatures** which are commonly used are the freezing and boiling points of water at an atmospheric pressure of 760 mm. of mercury. On the Celsius (centigrade) scale the freezing point of water is taken as 0° and the boiling point as 100°. The space between these two fixed points is divided into 100 equal spaces or degrees. On the Fahrenheit scale the freezing point of water is 32° and the boiling point is 212°. The space between these two fixed points is divided into 180 equal spaces or degrees. Thus a degree Fahrenheit is 100/180, or 5/9, of a degree Celsius (Fig. 1–8). The relationships are shown in the following equations:

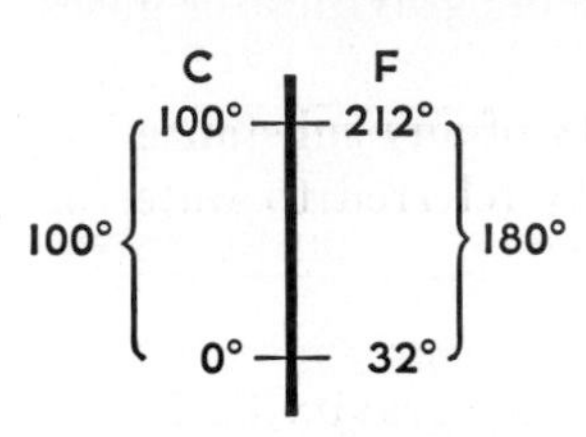

Fig. 1–8 Relationship between Celsius (centigrade) and Fahrenheit temperature scales.

$$\frac{F - 32}{180} = \frac{C}{100} \qquad C = \frac{5}{9}(F - 32) \qquad F = \frac{9}{5}C + 32$$

The readings below 0° on either scale are treated as negative. Temperatures in this book are in Celsius (centigrade) unless otherwise specified. The following examples illustrate conversions between the Celsius and Fahrenheit scales.

Example 1. Ethyl alcohol boils at 78.5° C at one atmosphere of pressure. What is its boiling point on the Fahrenheit scale?

$$F = \tfrac{9}{5}C + 32 = \tfrac{9}{5} \times 78.5 + 32 = 141 + 32 = 173°$$

Example 2. Convert 50° F to the Celsius (centigrade) scale.

$$C = \tfrac{5}{9}(F - 32) = \tfrac{5}{9}(50 - 32) = \tfrac{5}{9} \times 18 = 10°$$

1.24 The Measurement of Heat

Chemical reactions are accompanied by either the evolution or the absorption of heat energy. The unit of measurement of heat is the calorie. The **small calorie** is approximately equal to the quantity of heat which will raise the temperature of one gram of pure water one degree Celsius (centigrade). The amount of heat necessary to raise the temperature of 1 gram of water 1 degree Celsius is not quite the same at all temperatures, but for our purposes it is sufficiently accurate to assume that it is the same. The **large calorie** or kilocalorie (kcal.) is equal to 1000 small calories.

The **heat capacity** of a body of matter is the number of calories necessary to raise its temperature 1 degree Celsius. The heat capacity of 1 gram of water is one calorie, so the heat capacity of any amount of water is numerically equal to its weight in grams. The greater the mass of a substance, the greater its heat capacity. Every substance has its own heat capacity. Metals are much lower in heat capacity than is water. Only a very few substances have higher heat capacities than does water.

The specific heat of a substance is a physical property that may be used in describing the substance. The **specific heat** of a substance is the number of calories of heat required to raise the temperature of one gram of the substance one degree. The specific heat of copper is 0.09 calorie per gram per degree, that of aluminum is 0.21 calorie per gram per degree, and that of zinc is 0.093 calorie per gram per degree. The following problems are based upon the measurement of heat.

EXAMPLE 1. Calculate the quantity of heat required to raise the temperature of 400 g. of water from 10° C to 40° C.

$$\begin{aligned} \text{Heat required} &= \text{mass} \times \text{specific heat} \times \text{temperature change} \\ &= 400 \text{ g.} \times 1 \text{ cal./g. °C} \times (40 - 10) \text{ °C} = 12{,}000 \text{ cal.} \end{aligned}$$

EXAMPLE 2. Calculate the quantity of heat required to raise the temperature of 100 g. of mercury from 20° to 100° C. The specific heat of mercury is 0.033 calorie per gram per degree.

$$\begin{aligned} \text{Heat required} &= \text{mass} \times \text{specific heat} \times \text{temperature change} \\ &= 100 \text{ g.} \times 0.033 \text{ cal./g. °C} \times (100 - 20) \text{ °C} = 264 \text{ cal.} \end{aligned}$$

EXAMPLE 3. Calculate the temperature rise which results when 400 calories are supplied to 100 g. of ethyl alcohol, the specific heat of which is 0.58 cal./g. °C.

$$\text{Heat required} = \text{mass} \times \text{specific heat} \times \text{temperature change}$$

$$\begin{aligned} \text{Temperature change} &= \frac{\text{heat required}}{\text{mass} \times \text{specific heat}} \\ &= \frac{400 \text{ cal.}}{100 \text{ g.} \times 0.58 \text{ cal./g. °C}} = 6.9° \end{aligned}$$

EXAMPLE 4. The heat of combustion of carbon is 780 calories per gram. How much water could be heated from 22° C to 100° C using the heat from the burning of 100 g. of carbon?

$$\text{Heat produced} = 100 \text{ g.} \times 780 \text{ cal./g.} = 78{,}000 \text{ cal.}$$

$$\text{Heat required} = \text{mass} \times \text{specific heat} \times \text{temperature change}$$

$$\begin{aligned} \text{Mass} &= \frac{\text{heat required}}{\text{specific heat} \times \text{temperature change}} \\ &= \frac{78{,}000 \text{ cal.}}{1 \text{ cal./g. °C} \times (100 - 22) \text{ °C}} = 1000 \text{ g.} \end{aligned}$$

QUESTIONS

1. With what is the science of chemistry concerned?
2. List the five principal branches of chemistry and give the area covered by each branch.
3. Distinguish between the terms "mass" and "weight."
4. State the Law of Conservation of Matter, the Law of Conservation of Energy, and the combined Law of Conservation of Matter and Energy.
5. What is the meaning of the statement that matter and energy are not distinct realities but are different forms of a single reality?
6. Describe a chemical change that illustrates the Law of Conservation of Matter.
7. Classify each of the following as possessing potential or kinetic energy: a moving automobile; a book resting on a table; a stretched rubber band; falling water; gasoline.
8. Compare the three physical states of matter with regard to volume, shape, and compressibility.
9. Classify each of the following as a physical or chemical change: the formation of frost; the change of cider to vinegar; the change of electricity to light; the charging of a storage battery; the melting of iron; the explosion of a firecracker; the magnetization of a steel needle; the crystallization of sugar from solution.
10. Name some properties that are useful in identifying specimens of pure substances.
11. Classify each of the following as element, compound, or mixture: table salt, aluminum, bread, concrete, crude oil, sugar, potassium, alcohol, tincture of iodine, and air.
12. Define the terms "atom" and "molecule."
13. How do molecules of elements and compounds differ?
14. How would you separate a mixture of sand and sugar; salt and water; iron filings and sulfur?
15. The specific gravity of a substance is sometimes defined as the ratio of the density of the substance to the density of a reference substance. Is this definition compatible with the definition of specific gravity as given in Section 1.20? Explain your answer.
16. Show why the density of a substance, when measured in the metric system of units, has practically the same numerical value as the specific gravity referred to water as the reference substance.
17. Compare the units for density and for specific gravity.

PROBLEMS

1. A man weighs 70.00 kilograms. What will be his weight in pounds?
Ans. 154.3 lb.
2. Express 3.27 meters in centimeters, millimeters, and angstrom units.
Ans. 327 cm.; 3270 mm.; 3.27×10^{10} *Å*

3. Calculate the number of meters and centimeters in 4.20 yards.
Ans. *3.84 m.; 384 cm.*

4. Calculate the number of milliliters in a quart and in a cubic foot.
Ans. *946.3 ml.; 28,316 ml.*

5. Express 18.7 kg. in grams, milligrams, metric tons, and pounds.
Ans. *18,700 g.; 1.87×10^7 mg.; 1.87×10^{-2} metric tons; 41.2 lb.*

6. How many liters of water are there in a rectangular tank 80 centimeters long and 100 centimeters wide if it is filled to a depth of 10 centimeters? *Ans.* *80 l.*

7. What is the radius in meters of the Palomar 200-inch (diameter) telescope?
Ans. *2.54 m.*

8. Calculate the sp. gr. of a given liquid from the following data taken at 25° C.

Weight of pycnometer + liquid	14.6824 g.
Weight of pycnometer empty	9.2356 g.
Weight of pycnometer + pure water	18.5723 g.

Ans. *0.5834*

9. What is the density of a liquid if 60.0 cm.^{3} of it weighs 44.5 g.?
Ans. *0.742 g./cm.^{3}*

10. What is the density of a liquid if 500 cm.^{3} weighs 950 grams?
Ans. *1.90 g./cm.^{3}*

11. Find the volume of 365 g. of mercury (density = 13.5 g./cm.^{3}).
Ans. *27.0 cm.^{3}*

12. A piece of copper when put into water displaces 38.0 cubic centimeters. The specific gravity of pure copper is 8.94. Calculate the weight of the piece of copper. *Ans.* *340 g.*

13. What is the weight of each of the following?
(a) 25.50 cm.^{3} of a liquid, density = 1.836 g./cm.^{3} *Ans.* *46.82 g.*
(b) 100 cm.^{3} of a liquid, specific gravity = 0.935. *Ans.* *93.5 g.*
(c) 1 liter of mercury, density = 13.5 g./cm.^{3} *Ans.* *13.5 kg.*

14. Make the following temperature conversions:
(a) 32° F to degrees Celsius (centigrade). *Ans.* *0° C*
(b) 230° F to degrees Celsius. *Ans.* *110° C*
(c) − 40° F to degrees Celsius. *Ans.* *− 40° C*
(d) − 100° C to degrees Fahrenheit. *Ans.* *− 148° F*
(e) 21° C to degrees Fahrenheit. *Ans.* *70° C*

15. One British Thermal Unit (B.T.U.) is the quantity of heat necessary to raise the temperature of one pound of water one degree Fahrenheit. One degree Celsius (centigrade) is equal to 9/5 of a degree Fahrenheit, and one degree Fahrenheit is equal to 5/9 of a degree Celsius. Compute the number of calories that are equivalent to one B.T.U. *Ans.* *252.0 cal.*

16. Calculate the heat capacity of the following:
(a) 215 g. of water, specific heat 1 cal./g. °C. *Ans.* *215 cal./°C*
(b) 4 kg. of iron, specific heat 0.11 cal./g. °C *Ans.* *440 cal./°C*
(c) 100 ml. of mercury, sp. gr. 13.5, sp. heat 0.033 cal./g. °C
Ans. *44.6 cal./°C*

17. Calculate the quantity of heat required to raise the temperature of 400 g. of water from 25° C to 40° C. *Ans. 6000 cal.*

18. When 18 g. of water is formed from its elements, 68,317 calories are evolved. What would be the change in temperature of a piece of iron weighing 10.0 kilograms if heated by the quantity of heat liberated by the formation of 18.0 g. of water? The specific heat of iron is 0.115 calorie per gram per degree between 20° and 100° C. *Ans. 59.4° C*

19. If 700 calories are added to 40.0 g. of water at 15.0° C, what is the resulting temperature? *Ans. 32.5° C*

20. Calculate the resulting temperature when 300 g. of water at 15° C and 450 g. of water at 40° C are mixed. *Ans. 30° C*

21. Fifty grams of iron (specific heat = 0.115 cal./g. °C) at 50° C is mixed with 50 g. of water at 20° C. What will be the final temperature of the mixture? *Ans. 23° C*

22. A sphere of cork weighs 500 grams. The density of this cork is 0.25 g./cm.^{3}. Calculate the radius of this sphere. *Ans. 7.82 cm.*

23. A circular piece of copper weighs one metric ton. If this piece of metal were 1 cm. thick, what would be its diameter? The specific gravity of copper is 8.94. *Ans. 378 cm.*

REFERENCE

"Celsius versus Centigrade: The Nomenclature of the Temperature Scale of Science," H. F. Stimson, *Science*, **136** (3512) 254 (1962).

CHAPTER TWO

Symbols, Formulas, and Equations

The chemist makes constant use of chemical symbols, formulas, and equations when speaking and writing about matter and the changes which it undergoes. It is essential that the student become skilled in the use of the symbolism of the field before he can study chemistry effectively.

2.1 Symbols

As a matter of convenience in indicating the elements the chemist usually uses abbreviations, since they are more quickly written than names. These abbreviations are called **symbols.** For hydrogen, the symbol is H; for oxygen, O; and for carbon, C. Sometimes two letters are necessary to distinguish between two or more elements, the names of which begin with the same letter. For example, Ca is the symbol for calcium; Co for cobalt; Cr for chromium; Cl for chlorine; and Cd for cadmium. No symbol contains more than two letters and the first letter is always capitalized. Some symbols are abbreviations of the Latin names of the elements, as Fe for iron (Latin, ferrum). Na for sodium (Latin, natrium), and Cu for copper (Latin, cuprum). The symbols for the elements are given on the inside front cover of this book.

The symbol not only identifies the element, but also represents one atom of the element. To indicate more than one atom of an element a coefficient is placed in front of the symbol to designate a given number of atoms. Thus 2 Cu designates 2 atoms of copper, and 5 Fe designates 5 atoms of iron.

2.2 Formulas

A **formula** is a single symbol or a group of symbols which represents the composition of a substance. The symbols in a formula identify the elements present in the substance. Thus, NaCl is the formula for sodium chloride, which consists of equal numbers of atoms of the elements sodium and chlorine. Subscripts are used to indicate the relative numbers of atoms in the compound. A subscript is not used when only one atom of a given element is present. The formula for water, H_2O, indicates that each molecule contains two atoms of hydrogen and one atom of oxygen. Sulfuric acid is represented by the formula H_2SO_4, which indicates two atoms of hydrogen, one of sulfur, and four of oxygen. The formula for aluminum sulfate, $Al_2(SO_4)_3$, specifies two atoms of aluminum and three sulfate groups. Each sulfate group contains one atom of sulfur and four atoms of oxygen. Hence, the aluminum sulfate formula includes a total of two atoms of aluminum, three atoms of sulfur, and twelve atoms of oxygen.

The formula for a molecule of sulfur is S_8, showing that each molecule of this element consists of eight atoms. The molecular formulas for elementary hydrogen and oxygen (diatomic molecules) are H_2 and O_2, while that for helium (a monatomic molecule) is He. Note that H_2 and 2 H do not mean the same thing. H_2 represents a molecule of hydrogen consisting of two atoms of the element chemically combined. The expression 2 H, on the other hand, indicates that the two hydrogen atoms are not in combination as a unit but that they are separate particles.

Additional information which is useful in writing formulas for compounds will be presented in Chapter 4.

2.3 Chemical Equations

Atoms are the fundamental particles of the elements that enter into chemical changes. Substances that take part in chemical changes contain these atoms in the form of molecules or ions (atoms or groups of atoms that are electrically charged). Chemical changes involve the regrouping of atoms or ions to form new substances. The **chemical equation** is the chemist's shorthand expression for describing a chemical change, and symbols and formulas are used to indicate the composition of the substances involved in the change. The writer of an equation must know what substances react and what substances are formed, and he must be able to represent these substances correctly by formulas.

A statement of the decomposition of water by electrolysis, "When water is decomposed by an electric current, hydrogen and oxygen are formed," can be expressed as follows:

$$H_2O \rightarrow H_2 + O_2 \tag{1}$$

The formulas for the *reactants* are written to the left and the formulas for the *products* are written to the right of the arrow. The arrow is read as "gives," "produces," "yields," or "forms." The + sign on the right side of the expression is read as "and"; it does not imply mathematical addition. When the + sign appears between the formulas for two reactants on the left side of an equation, it implies "reacts with."

As it now stands expression (1) does not conform with the law of conservation of matter. Two atoms of oxygen in the molecule O_2 could not be formed from one molecule of water containing but one oxygen atom. The equation is *balanced* by introducing the proper number (coefficient) before each formula. Two molecules of water will each furnish one oxygen atom for the production of one diatomic oxygen molecule. Two water molecules will then supply four hydrogen atoms for the production of two diatomic molecules of hydrogen. The balanced equation is:

$$2\ H_2O \rightarrow 2\ H_2 + O_2 \tag{2}$$

It is important to remember that the subscripts in a formula cannot be changed in order to make an equation balance. Substances have definite atomic compositions that cannot be changed by merely changing the subscripts in their formulas.

Sometimes the symbol Δ is used in an equation to represent heat that must be supplied in order to make a reaction proceed. For example, potassium chlorate decomposes upon heating to form potassium chloride and oxygen:

(3)	$2\ KClO_3$	+ heat (or Δ) $\rightarrow$	$2\ KCl$	+	$3\ O_2$
	Potassium chlorate		Potassium chloride		Oxygen

When the fact that heat is produced during a chemical reaction is to be emphasized, the symbol Δ may be employed on the right of the arrow:

(4)	C	+	O_2	$\rightarrow$	CO_2	+ heat (or Δ)
	Carbon		Oxygen		Carbon dioxide	

A gaseous product formed by a reaction in a solution may be designated by an ascending arrow ($\uparrow$):

(5)	2 Na	+	$2\ H_2O$	$\rightarrow$	$2\ Na^+$	+	$2\ OH^-$	+	$H_2\uparrow$
	Sodium metal		Water		Sodium ion		Hydroxide ion		Hydrogen

2.4 Atomic Weights

It has been determined by experiment that an atom of hydrogen (the lightest element) weighs 1.7×10^{-24} g. (0.000 000 000 000 000 000 000 001 7 g.). It is obvious that such a method of expressing weights of atoms is inconvenient. Since the weights of the individual atoms of all the elements are of the same small order of magnitude, 10^{-24} g., it has been found more convenient to use relative weights in place of actual weights measured in grams or other units. **The relative weights of the atoms of the different elements are known as atomic weights and are proportional to the actual weights of the atoms.** For example, the atomic weight of hydrogen is 1.00797 on this arbitrary scale, that of carbon is 12.01115, and that of oxygen is 15.9994. Hence, carbon atoms weigh about twelve times as much as hydrogen atoms, and oxygen atoms are approximately sixteen times heavier than hydrogen atoms. Sulfur atoms weigh about twice as much as oxygen atoms, or 32.064 on this arbitrary scale. The standard used in expressing the atomic weights is a particular kind of carbon atom called the carbon-12 isotope. This will be discussed in Chapter 3 (see Section 3.9). Refer to the inside front cover of this book for a complete list of the atomic weights of the elements.

In addition to identifying the element and representing one atom of that element, a chemical symbol represents one chemical unit of weight of an element. The symbol O represents one atom of oxygen, or 15.9994 units of weight of oxygen. The unit of weight may be a gram, an ounce, a pound, etc. In quantitative work, the chemist finds it convenient to use the atomic weight of an element expressed in grams and called a **gram-atomic weight,** or **gram-atom.** Thus, one gram-atomic weight of oxygen and of hydrogen are 15.9994 g. and 1.00797 g., respectively.

2.5 The Avogadro Number

It can be shown experimentally that there is the same number of atoms, 6.023×10^{23}, in one gram-atomic weight of any element. This number is called **Avogadro's number** in honor of the Italian professor of physics Amedeo Avogadro (1776–1856). It is important to remember that one gram-atomic weight of any element, e.g., 15.9994 g. of oxygen, 32.064 g. of sulfur, and 1.00797 g. of hydrogen, contains 6.023×10^{23} atoms.

Knowing the atomic weight of an element and Avogadro's number, one can easily calculate the weight in grams of one atom of the element. The weight of one oxygen atom would be, therefore:

$$\frac{15.9994 \text{ g.}}{6.023 \times 10^{23}} = 26.56 \times 10^{-24} \text{ g.}$$

It is evident that atoms must be very small particles, since they have such extremely small weights.

2.6 Formula Weights, Molecular Weights, Moles

The sum of the atomic weights in the formula of a substance is its formula weight. Formula weights are relative, just as are the atomic weights upon which they are based. The formula weight of sulfuric acid (H_2SO_4) is $(2 \times 1.0) + (1 \times 32.1) + (4 \times 16.0) = 98.1$. For most of our work it will be permissible to round off the atomic weights of the elements at one digit after the decimal point, e.g., 1.00797 to 1.0 for hydrogen, 32.064 to 32.1 for sulfur, and 26.9815 to 27.0 for aluminum.

The formula weight of a substance expressed in grams is a **gram-formula weight** or a **mole** of that substance. Thus the gram-formula weight of sulfuric acid is 98.1 grams, whereas its formula weight is simply 98.1.

When the true formula for a molecule of a substance is known, the molecular weight can be calculated by adding the atomic weights of the atoms given in the formula of the substance. It is quite correct to speak of the molecular weight (or formula weight) of substances which consist of discrete molecules such as methane, CH_4; carbon dioxide, CO_2; and water, H_2O. On the other hand, ionic compounds such as NaCl, $KClO_3$, NaOH, and $CuSO_4$ do not consist of physically distinct and electrically neutral molecules (see Section 4.1) either in the crystalline state or in solution. Hence it is customary to use formula weights to represent the total composition of such substances. The use of the term "mole" in this book will be taken to mean a gram-formula weight of ionic compounds and a gram-molecular weight of molecular substances (either elements or compounds).

It is often convenient in quantitative chemical work to use millimoles in place of moles of a substance. **A millimole of a substance is its formula weight expressed in milligrams.** For example, the formula weight of H_2SO_4 is 98.1. Then one mole of H_2SO_4 is 98.1 g. and one millimole of it is 98.1 mg. In other words, one millimole is one-thousandth of a mole.

The following examples are based upon gram-atomic weights, gram-atoms, gram-formula weights, moles, and millimoles.

EXAMPLE 1. How many gram-atoms of sulfur are there in 80.3 g. of sulfur?

$$\text{Gram-atoms of S} = \frac{\text{grams of S}}{\text{gram-atomic weight of S}} = \frac{80.3\text{ g.}}{32.1\text{ g./gram-atom}}$$
$$= 2.50\text{ gram-atoms}$$

EXAMPLE 2. How many moles of sulfur are there in 80.3 g. of sulfur if the molecular formula of sulfur is S_8?

The gram-formula weight of S_8 is 8 × 32.1 g./gram-atom = 256.8 g.

$$\text{Moles of } S_8 = \frac{\text{grams of } S_8}{\text{gram-formula weight of } S_8} = \frac{80.3\text{ g.}}{256.8\text{ g./mole}} = 0.313\text{ mole}$$

EXAMPLE 3. How many moles are represented by 138 g. of ethyl alcohol, C_2H_5OH?

The formula weight of C_2H_5OH is calculated as follows:

$$\begin{array}{r} 2\ \text{C} = 2 \times 12.0 = 24.0 \\ 6\ \text{H} = 6 \times \ \ 1.0 = \ \ 6.0 \\ 1\ \text{O} = 1 \times 16.0 = 16.0 \\ \hline \text{Formula weight of } C_2H_5OH = 46.0 \end{array}$$

The gram-formula weight of ethyl alcohol is 46.0 g. and the number of moles contained in 138 g. of the compound is

$$\text{Moles of } C_2H_5OH = \frac{\text{grams of } C_2H_5OH}{\text{gram-formula weight of } C_2H_5OH} = \frac{138\text{ g.}}{46.0\text{ g./mole}}$$
$$= 3.00\text{ moles}$$

EXAMPLE 4. How many millimoles are contained in 0.160 gram of NaOH?

The formula weight of NaOH is (23.0 + 16.0 + 1.0) = 40.0.

$$\text{Millimoles of NaOH} = \frac{\text{milligrams of NaOH}}{\text{formula weight of NaOH in mg.}} = \frac{160\text{ mg.}}{40.0\text{ mg./millimole}}$$
$$= 4.00\text{ millimoles}$$

2.7 Percentage Composition from Formulas

The percentage by weight of each element in a compound may easily be calculated from the formula of the compound. This percentage will be equal to the fraction of the total weight of the compound which is attributable to the element, multiplied by 100. For example, suppose we calculate the percentage of hydrogen and that of oxygen in the compound water, H_2O.

$$\text{Percentage of hydrogen in } H_2O = \frac{2 \times \text{gram-atomic weight of H}}{\text{gram-formula weight of } H_2O} \times 100$$
$$= \frac{2 \times 1.0}{(2 \times 1.0) + (1 \times 16.0)} \times 100 = 11\%$$

$$\text{Percentage of oxygen in } H_2O = \frac{1 \times \text{gram-atomic weight of O}}{\text{gram-formula weight of } H_2O} \times 100$$

$$= \frac{1 \times 16.0}{(2 \times 1.0) + (1 \times 16.0)} \times 100 = 89\%$$

Samples of pure water, no matter what their source may be, contain the same elements, hydrogen and oxygen, united in the same proportion by weight, 11 parts of hydrogen to 89 parts of oxygen. A similar statement may be made about any pure compound. This is one of the fundamental concepts of chemistry and is known as the **Law of Definite Proportions,** or the **Law of Definite Composition.** This law may be stated as follows: **Different samples of a pure compound always contain the same elements in the same proportions by weight.** This law, among others, convinced John Dalton of the atomistic nature of matter, and led him to outline the atomic theory.

2.8 Derivation of Formulas

The first step in deriving the formula of a new compound is the determination of its percentage composition. The percentage composition of a compound can be determined experimentally by analysis or synthesis. A weighed sample of the compound may be separated into its constituent elements and the weight of each element in the sample determined. Thus, a 1.0000 g. sample of a certain compound is found to contain 0.2729 g. of carbon and 0.7271 g. of oxygen.

$$\text{Percentage of carbon in the compound} = \frac{0.2729 \text{ g.}}{1.0000 \text{ g.}} \times 100 = 27.29\%$$

$$\text{Percentage of oxygen in the compound} = \frac{0.7271 \text{ g.}}{1.0000 \text{ g.}} \times 100 = 72.71\%$$

The relative number of carbon and oxygen atoms in the compound may be obtained by dividing the above percentages by the weights (which are relative) of the respective atoms.

Element	*Percentage*	*Relative number of atoms*	*Divide by the smaller number*	*Smallest number of atoms*
Carbon	27.29	$\frac{27.29}{12.01} = 2.27$	$\frac{2.27}{2.27} = 1.00$	**1**
Oxygen	72.71	$\frac{72.71}{16.00} = 4.55$	$\frac{4.55}{2.27} = 2.00$	**2**

Thus for every 2.27 atoms of carbon there are 4.55 atoms of oxygen. Reduced to simple whole numbers, since only whole numbers of atoms can enter into chemical combination, there are twice as many oxygen atoms as carbon atoms in the compound, and the simplest formula for the compound must be CO_2. This **simplest formula** corresponds to a formula weight of 44. It can be shown by experiment that this compound has a molecular weight of 44. Thus in this case the simplest formula, the formula which indicates the ratio of the numbers of different kinds of atoms present, and the **molecular formula,** the formula which indicates the kinds of atoms present and the actual number of each kind per molecule, are one and the same. Had the molecular weight for the compound been 88, then the molecular formula would have contained twice as many atoms as the simplest formula; i.e., C_2O_4 rather than CO_2.

As another example of the determination of the formula of a compound, let us derive the formula for an oxide of iron which contains 69.94 per cent iron and 30.06 per cent oxygen.

Element	*Percentage*	*Relative number of atoms*	*Divide by the smaller number*	*Smallest number of atoms*
Iron	69.94	$\frac{69.94}{55.85} = 1.25$	$\frac{1.25}{1.25} = 1.0$	$2 \times 1.0 = 2$
Oxygen	30.06	$\frac{30.06}{16.00} = 1.88$	$\frac{1.88}{1.25} = 1.5$	$2 \times 1.5 = 3$

Unlike the previous example, step 2 did not give two integers, so a third step was necessary. This step involves multiplying both 1.0 and 1.5 by the smallest whole number which will give whole numbers of atoms of each element. Thus $2 \times 1.0 = 2$ and $2 \times 1.5 = 3$. Hence the simplest formula for the oxide is Fe_2O_3.

Let us derive the formula of a hydrated salt, $Na_2SO_4 \cdot x\ H_2O$, a 1.500 g. sample of which was found to contain 0.705 g. of water. The weight of Na_2SO_4 in the 1.500 g. sample = (1.500 − 0.705) g. = 0.795 g. The relative number of moles (formula weights) of Na_2SO_4 and H_2O in the salt may be calculated by dividing the weight of each of the compounds by its formula weight.

Compound	*Weight*	*Relative number of moles*	*Divide by the smaller number*	*Smallest number of moles*
Na_2SO_4	0.795 g.	$\frac{0.795\text{ g.}}{142\text{ g./mole}} = 0.0056$	$\frac{0.0056}{0.0056} = 1$	**1**
H_2O	0.705 g.	$\frac{0.705\text{ g.}}{18.0\text{ g./mole}} = 0.0392$	$\frac{0.0392}{0.0056} = 7$	**7**

Hence the simplest formula of the hydrated salt is $Na_2SO_4 \cdot 7\ H_2O$.

2.9 Calculations Based on Equations

There was little real progress in the development of chemistry before Lavoisier (1743–1794) put this science on a quantitative basis. In this chapter we shall become familiar with the quantitative aspects of chemistry through the study of calculations based on chemical equations.

Since symbols and formulas represent atomic and formula weights of substances, respectively, then a balanced chemical equation represents quantitative relationships for a given chemical change. Thus the equation for the thermal decomposition of potassium chlorate to form potassium chloride and oxygen

$$2\ KClO_3 + \Delta \rightarrow 2\ KCl + 3\ O_2 \uparrow$$

possesses the following quantitative significance: When decomposed by heating, two formula weights of potassium chlorate yield two formula weights of potassium chloride and three formula weights of oxygen (Fig. 2–1). The chemical units of formula weights may be grams, kilograms, ounces, pounds, tons, etc.

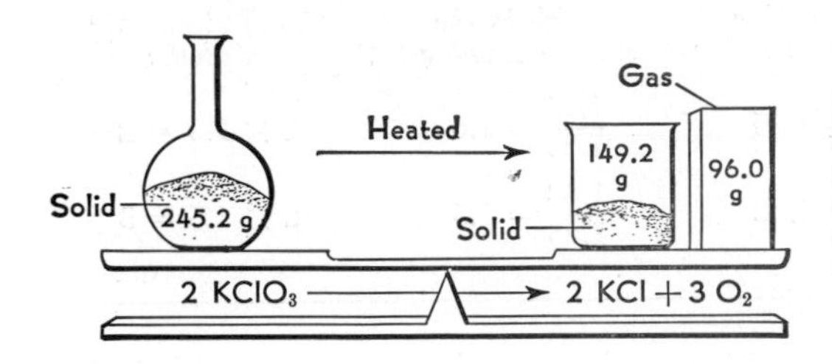

Fig. 2–1 When completely decomposed by heat, 245.2 grams of potassium chlorate yield 149.2 grams of potassium chloride and 96.0 grams of oxygen. Thermal decomposition of potassium chlorate always produces potassium chloride and oxygen in this same ratio to each other.

$2\ KClO_3$	$+ \Delta \rightarrow$	$2\ KCl$	+	$3\ O_2 \uparrow$
(2×122.6)		(2×74.6)		(3×32.0)
or 245.2 units		149.2 units		96.0 units

Example 1. We may calculate the weight of oxygen produced during the thermal decomposition of 100 g. of potassium chlorate:

a. *Unit Method.* If 245.2 g. of $KClO_3$ will produce 96.0 g. of O_2, then 1 g. of $KClO_3$ will produce (1/245.2)(96.0) g. of oxygen. 100 g. of $KClO_3$ will produce

$$100 \times \frac{1\text{ g.}}{245.2\text{ g.}} \times 96\text{ g.} = 39.2\text{ g. of oxygen}$$

This method is sometimes called the "unit method" because one calculates (in this case) the weight of oxygen produced from one unit (1 g.) of $KClO_3$.

b. *Molar Method*

$2\ KClO_3$	$+ \Delta \rightarrow$	$2\ KCl$	+	$3\ O_2 \uparrow$
2 moles		2 moles		3 moles

First, calculate the number of moles of $KClO_3$ in 100 g. of the compound.

$$\frac{100\text{ g.}}{122.6\text{ g./mole}} = 0.816\text{ mole of } KClO_3$$

Since, according to the equation, two moles of $KClO_3$ yields 3 moles of O_2, then 1 mole of $KClO_3$ would yield $\frac{3}{2} = 1.5$ moles of O_2. Thus 0.816 mole of $KClO_3$ would form $1.5 \times 0.816 = 1.224$ moles of O_2. The grams of O_2 in 1.224 moles $= 1.224$ moles $\times$ 32.00 g./mole = 39.2 g. of oxygen.

A summary of the method of solving the problem by the molar method is as follows:

$$\underbrace{\underbrace{\underbrace{\frac{100 \text{ g.}}{122.6 \text{ g./mole}}}_{\text{(moles of KClO}_3\text{ used)}} \times \frac{3}{2}}_{\text{(moles of O}_2\text{ produced)}} \times 32.00 \text{ g./mole}}_{\text{(grams of O}_2\text{ produced)}} = 39.2 \text{ g. of oxygen}$$

c. *Factor Method*

$$\underset{245.2 \text{ g.}}{2\ KClO_3} + \Delta \rightarrow 2\ KCl + \underset{96.0 \text{ g.}}{3\ O_2\uparrow}$$

If 245.2 g. of $KClO_3$ will produce 96.0 g. of oxygen, then 100 g. of $KClO_3$ will produce a smaller quantity of oxygen than will 245.2 g. of $KClO_3$. Multiplying the 96.0 g. of oxygen by a fraction made up of the two weights of $KClO_3$ and having a value less than unity (a proper fraction) will give the quantity of oxygen obtainable from 100 g. of $KClO_3$.

$$96.0 \text{ g.} \times \frac{100.0 \text{ g.}}{245.2 \text{ g.}} = 39.2 \text{ g. of oxygen}$$

EXAMPLE 2. Calculate the weight of limestone which is 95 per cent pure $CaCO_3$ that must be decomposed by heating to produce 500 g. of lime, CaO.

First write the balanced equation for the reaction.

$$\underset{\substack{1 \text{ mole} \\ 100.1 \text{ g.}}}{CaCO_3} + \Delta \rightarrow \underset{\substack{1 \text{ mole} \\ 56.1 \text{ g.}}}{CaO} + CO_2\uparrow$$

According to the equation, 100.1 g. of pure $CaCO_3$ produce 56.1 g. of CaO. It follows that a larger weight of $CaCO_3$ will be required in the production of 500 g. of CaO. Multiplying the 100.1 g. of $CaCO_3$ by an improper fraction made up of the two weights of CaO will give the weight of pure $CaCO_3$ necessary to prepare 500 g. of CaO.

$$100.1 \text{ g.} \times \frac{500 \text{ g.}}{56.1 \text{ g.}} = 893 \text{ g. of pure } CaCO_3$$

Thus 893 g. of pure $CaCO_3$ is required. The weight of limestone which is 95 per cent pure $CaCO_3$ required may be found by multiplying the 893 g. of pure $CaCO_3$ by an improper fraction made up of 100 per cent and 95 per cent.

$$893 \text{ g.} \times \frac{100 \text{ per cent}}{95 \text{ per cent}} = 940 \text{ g. of limestone}$$

EXAMPLE 3. Calculate the weight of carbon dioxide produced by the complete combustion of 10.0 lb. of ethane, C_2H_6, in air.

First write the equation for the reaction.

$$\underset{2\ \text{moles}}{2\ C_2H_6} + 7\ O_2 \rightarrow \underset{4\ \text{moles}}{4\ CO_2} + 6\ H_2O$$

Two moles of ethane will produce 4 moles of carbon dioxide.
One mole of ethane will produce 2 moles of carbon dioxide.
(1×30.0) units of ethane will produce (2×44.0) units of carbon dioxide.
30.0 lb. of ethane will produce 88.0 lb. of carbon dioxide.

Thus according to the equation 30.0 lb. of ethane will burn to give 88.0 lb. of carbon dioxide. It follows that 10.0 lb. of ethane will give

$$88.0\ \text{lb.} \times \frac{10.0\ \text{lb.}}{30.0\ \text{lb.}} = 29.3\ \text{lb. of carbon dioxide}$$

QUESTIONS

1. Give the name of the element corresponding to each of the following symbols: Ni, Fe, O, C, Cr, Mn, Pt, Au, Si, Sn, N, Ne, Cu, Bi, La, U, Cl, Hg, Pu.
2. What information is denoted by the formula H_2SO_4?
3. Give the meaning of the expressions 8 S and S_8.
4. Distinguish between the terms **symbol, formula,** and **equation.**
5. Read the following equations in words:

$$2\ KClO_3 + \Delta \rightarrow 2\ KCl + 3\ O_2\uparrow$$
$$S + O_2\uparrow \rightarrow SO_2\uparrow + \Delta$$

6. Explain why the following does not conform to the Law of Conservation of Matter and change the equation so that it does conform to the Law of Conservation of Matter:

$$C_{12}H_{22}O_{11} + O_2 \rightarrow 12\ CO_2 + 11\ H_2O + \Delta$$

7. What is the advantage of using the value 24.312 for the atomic weight of magnesium and 12.01115 for the atomic weight of carbon rather than the actual weights of the atoms?
8. What is meant by the statement that atomic weights are relative weights?
9. Balance the following equations:
   (a) $H_2 + Cl_2 \rightarrow HCl$
   (b) $PtCl_4 \rightarrow Pt + Cl_2$
   (c) $P + O_2 \rightarrow P_4O_{10}$
   (d) $Sb + O_2 \rightarrow Sb_4O_6$
   (e) $Fe + H_2O \rightarrow Fe_3O_4 + H_2$
   (f) $NaNO_3 \rightarrow NaNO_2 + O_2$
   (g) $Cu(NO_3)_2 \rightarrow CuO + NO_2 + O_2$
   (h) $Na_2HPO_4 \rightarrow Na_4P_2O_7 + H_2O$
   (i) $Ca_3(PO_4)_2 + H_3PO_4 \rightarrow Ca(H_2PO_4)_2$
   (j) $H_3PO_3 \rightarrow H_3PO_4 + PH_3$

10. Balance the following equations:
   (a) $CaO + C \rightarrow CaC_2 + CO$
   (b) $H_3PO_4 \rightarrow H_4P_2O_7 + H_2O$
   (c) $N_2 + H_2 \rightarrow NH_3$
   (d) $Ca_3(PO_4)_2 + C \rightarrow Ca_3P_2 + CO$
   (e) $MgO + Si \rightarrow Mg + SiO_2$
   (f) $PCl_5 + H_2O \rightarrow POCl_3 + HCl$
   (g) $Ca_3(PO_4)_2 + H_2SO_4 \rightarrow H_3PO_4 + CaSO_4$
   (h) $Ag + H_2S + O_2 \rightarrow Ag_2S + H_2O$
   (i) $Al_2O_3 + C + Cl_2 \rightarrow AlCl_3 + CO$
   (j) $Pb + H_2O + O_2 \rightarrow Pb(OH)_2$

PROBLEMS

1. Calculate the formula weight of each of the following:

N_2, H_3PO_4, H_2O_2, KNO_3, $C_{12}H_{22}O_{11}$, $Al_2(SO_4)_3$, $(NH_4)_2SO_3$.

Ans. $N_2 = 28.0134$; $H_3PO_4 = 97.9953$; $H_2O_2 = 34.0147$; $KNO_3 = 101.107$; $C_{12}H_{22}O_{11} = 342.3025$; $Al_2(SO_4)_3 = 342.148$; $(NH_4)_2SO_3 = 116.139$

2. Calculate the formula weight of each of the following minerals:
   (a) Carnallite, $KCl \cdot MgCl_2 \cdot 6\ H_2O$ — *Ans.* 277.865
   (b) Dolomite, $CaCO_3 \cdot MgCO_3$ — *Ans.* 184.41
   (c) Malachite, $Cu_2(OH)_2CO_3$ — *Ans.* 221.10
   (d) Tschermigite, $Al_2(SO_4)_3 \cdot (NH_4)_2SO_4 \cdot 24\ H_2O$ — *Ans.* 906.655
   (e) Beryl, $Be_3Al_2Si_6O_{18}$ — *Ans.* 537.505

3. Calculate the weight of:
   (a) 3 moles of K_3PO_4 — *Ans.* 636.832 g.
   (b) 0.06 mole of chlorine (Cl_2) — *Ans.* 4.254 g.
   (c) 4.5 gram-atoms of chlorine — *Ans.* 159.539 g.
   (d) 0.4 mole of $(NH_4)_2CO_3$ — *Ans.* 38.4346 g.

4. Calculate the number of moles in:
   (a) 6.0 g. of H_2O_2 — *Ans.* 0.18 mole
   (b) 210 g. of $MgCO_3$ — *Ans.* 2.49 moles
   (c) 4.8 g. of NH_3 — *Ans.* 0.28 mole
   (d) 9.0 g. of $Ca(OH)_2$ — *Ans.* 0.12 mole

5. Calculate the weight of one atom of lead from its gram-atomic weight and Avogadro's number. — *Ans.* 3.44×10^{-22} g.

6. Calculate each of the following:
   (a) The percentage of magnesium, of sulfur, and of oxygen in $MgSO_4$.
   Ans. $Mg = 20.2\%$; $S = 26.6\%$; $O = 53.2\%$
   (b) The percentage of water in $CuSO_4 \cdot 5\ H_2O$ — *Ans.* 36.1%
   (c) The percentage of ammonia in $CoCl_3 \cdot 6\ NH_3$ — *Ans.* 38.2%

7. Calculate the percentage composition of each of the following:
   (a) $Al(NO_3)_3$ — *Ans.* $Al = 12.7\%$; $N = 19.7\%$; $O = 67.6\%$
   (b) CH_3COOH — *Ans.* $C = 40.0\%$; $H = 6.7\%$; $O = 53.3\%$

(c) $C_6H_2(CH_3)(NO_2)_3$

Ans. $C = 37.0\%$; $H = 2.2\%$; $N = 18.5\%$; $O = 42.3\%$

(d) $(BiO)_2CO_3$ *Ans.* $Bi = 82.0\%$; $C = 2.3\%$; $O = 15.7\%$

8. (a) A compound has the following percentage composition: carbon, 92.3%; hydrogen, 7.7%. Calculate the simplest formula for the compound. (b) The molecular weight of the compound is 78.1. What is its true molecular formula?

Ans. (*a*) *CH*; (*b*) C_6H_6

9. Calculate the simplest formula for the compound which has the following percentage composition: K, 28.7%; H, 1.5%; P, 22.8%; O, 47.0%.

Ans. KH_2PO_4

10. A 24.00 g. sample of an oxide of iron contains 6.63 g. of oxygen. Calculate the simplest formula for the compound. *Ans.* Fe_3O_4

11. A sample containing 0.06 mole of a molecular compound weighs 2.25 g. Calculate the molecular weight of the compound. *Ans.* *37.5*

12. (a) What is the simplest formula of the compound which has the following percentage composition? Carbon, 24.3%; hydrogen, 4.1%; chlorine, 71.6%.

(b) The molecular weight of the compound is 99. What is its molecular formula? *Ans.* (*a*) CH_2Cl; (*b*) $C_2H_4Cl_2$

13. What weight of oxygen is contained in 20 g. of $KClO_3$? *Ans.* *7.8 g.*

14. Calculate the number of formula weights represented by 1.50 kg. of glycerine, $C_3H_5(OH)_3$. *Ans.* *16.3*

15. Determine the formula of a crystalline salt which has the following percentage composition: Na, 18.5%; S, 25.8%; O, 19.3%; H_2O, 36.4%.

Ans. $Na_2S_2O_3 \cdot 5\ H_2O$

16. Determine the simplest formula of a compound which has the following analysis: Na, 16.78%; NH_4, 13.16%; H, 0.74%; PO_4, 69.32%.

Ans. $NaNH_4HPO_4$

17. A 1.012 gram-atom sample of an element weighs 51.64 g. Calculate the atomic weight of this element. *Ans.* *51.03*

18. A certain compound contains 32.79% Na, 13.02% Al, and 54.19% F. Calculate the simplest formula of the compound. *Ans.* Na_3AlF_6

19. Determine the simplest formula of a compound which contains 35.56% K, 17.00% Fe, and 47.44% CN. *Ans.* $K_3Fe(CN)_6$

20. A 1.61 g. sample of an oxide of chromium contains 1.10 g. of chromium. Calculate the empirical formula of the compound. *Ans.* Cr_2O_3

21. What weight of Fe_2O_3 will contain 75.00 g. of oxygen? *Ans.* *249.5 g.*

22. Calculate the weight of hydrogen which would be formed by the reaction of 25 g. of zinc with excess HCl. The equation for the reaction is:

$$Zn + 2\ HCl \rightarrow ZnCl_2 + H_2$$ *Ans.* *0.77 g.*

23. Calculate the weight of mercuric oxide necessary to produce 22.0 g. of oxygen by the reaction: $2\ HgO + \Delta \rightarrow 2\ Hg + O_2$. *Ans.* *298 g.*

24. What weight of carbon dioxide will be formed by the combustion of 16.0 lb. of carbon ($C + O_2 \rightarrow CO_2$)? What weight of oxygen, purity 90% by weight, will be required in this reaction? *Ans.* *58.7 lb.*; *47.4 lb.*

25. How many tons of sulfur would have to be burned to produce 25.0 tons of sulfur dioxide ($S + O_2 \rightarrow SO_2$)? *Ans.* *12.5 tons*

26. What weight of sulfur which is 98% pure would be required in the production of 75.0 kilograms of H_2SO_4, if each atom of sulfur is converted into one molecule of H_2SO_4? *Ans.* *25.0 kg.*

27. What weight of chlorine would be required in the reaction of 10.0 metric tons of hydrogen ($H_2 + Cl_2 \rightarrow 2\ HCl$)? What weight of HCl would be produced, assuming the yield to be 90.0%? *Ans.* *355 tons; 328 tons*

28. (a) What weight of copper (II) nitrate, $Cu(NO_3)_2$, must be decomposed to produce 1500 g. copper (II) oxide, CuO?

$$Cu(NO_3)_2 \rightarrow CuO + NO_2 + O_2 \text{ (unbalanced)}$$ *Ans.* *3538 g.*

(b) What weight of nitrogen dioxide, NO_2, would be produced by the decomposition of 75.0 g. of copper (II) nitrate? *Ans.* *36.8 g.*

(c) How many moles of oxygen would be produced by the decomposition of 75.0 g. of copper (II) nitrate? *Ans.* *0.200 mole*

29. Write the balanced equation and calculate the number of moles of chlorine, Cl_2, required to react with 10.0 g. of sodium metal, Na, to produce sodium chloride, NaCl. How many grams of chlorine would this be? *Ans.* *0.217 mole; 15.4 g.*

30. A 12.0 g. sample of phosphorus (III) chloride, PCl_3, is allowed to react with water ($PCl_3 + 3\ H_2O \rightarrow H_3PO_3 + 3\ HCl$). What weight of HCl is produced and what weight of water enters the reaction? *Ans.* *9.56 g.; 4.71 g.*

31. A solution containing 50.0 g. of NaOH is mixed with one containing 50.0 g. of HCl ($NaOH + HCl \rightarrow NaCl + H_2O$). Which chemical is in excess and what weight of NaCl is produced? *Ans.* *HCl; 73.1 g.*

32. A mixture containing 4.03 g. of hydrogen and 34.00 g. of oxygen is ignited ($2\ H_2 + O_2 \rightarrow 2\ H_2O$). What is the composition of the system by weight after the reaction, assuming the reaction goes to completion?

Ans. *2.00 g. of oxygen and 36.03 g. of water*

REFERENCE

"History of the Chemical Sign Language," R. Winderlich (transl. by R. E. Oesper), *J. Chem. Educ.*, **30** (2) 58 (1953).

CHAPTER THREE

Structure of the Atom and the Periodic Law

A series of discoveries beginning during the latter part of the 19th century have modified the Daltonian concept of the atom by demonstrating that an atom is a complex unit made up of smaller discrete parts. Atoms are not simple, compact bodies as supposed by Dalton, but are complex systems composed of several fundamental particles of matter; the only ones we need consider are electrons, protons, and neutrons.

Knowledge of the structure of atoms has made it possible for the facts of chemistry to be systematized in such a way that the subject is easier to understand and remember. Chemical reactions that occur between atoms and the forces that hold atoms together in molecules can be explained in terms of atomic structure.

3.1 Electrons

Much information concerning the structure of atoms has resulted from experiments involving the conduction of electricity through gases at very low pressures. The apparatus used for experiments of this type, called a **discharge tube,** consists of a glass tube provided with two metal electrodes connected to a source of high voltage (Fig. 3–1a). When the tube is highly evacuated and a current at

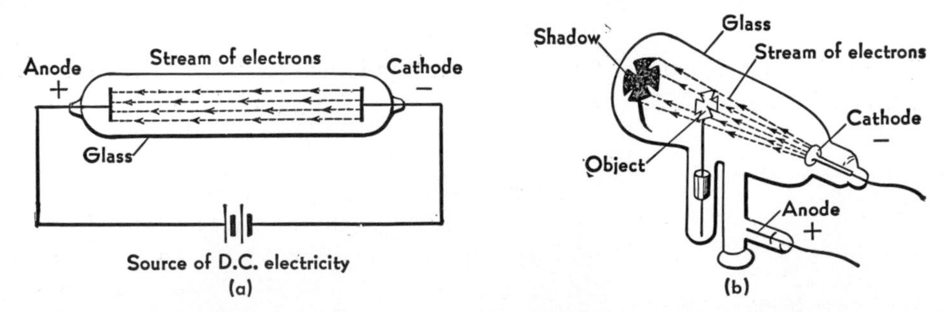

Fig. 3–1 Diagrams of two discharge tubes showing (a) streams of electrons flowing from the cathode to the anode, and (b) a shadow being cast by an object placed in a stream of electrons.

high potential is passed between the electrodes, streaks of light extend from the negative electrode (**cathode**) toward the positive electrode (**anode**). The rays appear to travel in straight lines from the cathode and they cause the wall at the opposite end of the tube, where they strike, to fluoresce or glow. These rays are called **cathode rays.**

Cathode rays have the following properties: (1) they travel in straight lines, as indicated by the fact that an object placed in their path casts a sharp shadow on the end of the tube (Fig. 3–1b), (2) they cause a light paddle-wheel which is placed in their path to rotate, (3) a piece of metal foil becomes hot when the rays strike it, and (4) they are deflected by negative magnetic and electrical fields (Fig. 3–2); the character of the deflection is the same as that shown by negatively charged particles in passing through such fields (a charged object will attract an object of opposite charge, whereas objects having charges of the same sign repel each other). These properties of cathode rays are best explained by assuming that they consist of streams of small particles of matter which are negatively charged. These particles are called **electrons.**

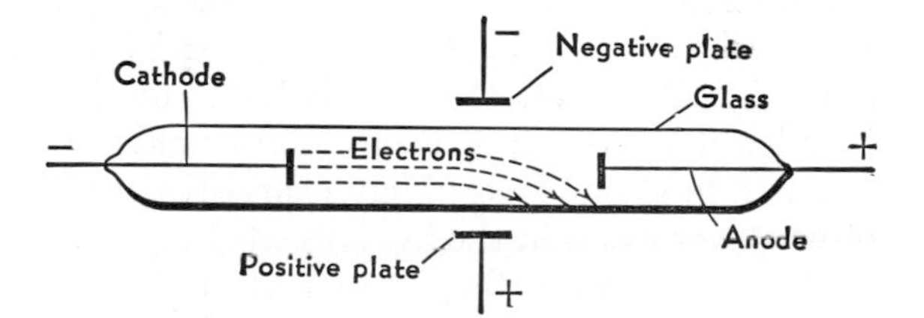

Fig. 3–2 Electrons are repelled by the negative plate and attracted by the positive plate.

In 1897 the English physicist Sir J. J. Thomson determined the ratio of the charge, e, to the mass, m, of electrons, and found it, e/m, to be identical for all cathode ray particles irrespective of the gas in the tube and the metal of which the electrodes are made. The charge on the electrons was measured by Millikan at the University of Chicago in 1909. From the values of e/m and e, the mass of the electron was calculated to be $\frac{1}{1837}$ of that of the hydrogen atom. On the atomic weight scale the mass of the electron is 0.00055.

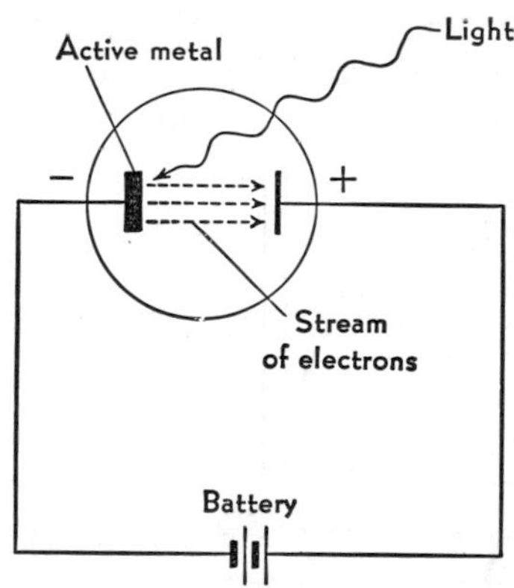

Fig. 3–3 Photoelectric circuit.

Electrons are emitted by certain metals when heated to high temperatures. This process is called **thermal emission** of electrons. The emission of electrons from electrically heated metal filaments in vacuum tubes is of great practical importance in the application of electronics, as in radio and television.

Electrons are also emitted from very active metals such as cesium, sodium, and potassium when they are exposed to light (Fig. 3–3). X-rays liberate electrons from all forms of matter. This type of electron emission is known as the **photoelectric effect** and is the basis of the "electric eye" photoelectric cell.

The fact that all electrons are identical, irrespective of their source or method of liberation from matter, and that they can be liberated from any kind of atom, proves quite conclusively that they are parts of all atoms.

3.2 Protons

In 1886 Goldstein, using a cathode ray tube of the type described in the preceding section but with a perforated cathode, observed rays passing through the holes in the cathode. Wien, in 1898, showed these rays to be composed of positively charged particles; they are called **positive rays.** The ratio of the charge on a positive particle to its mass was found to be much smaller than that for the electron and to vary with the nature of the gas in the tube. The charges on these positive particles, unlike those on electrons, were found to vary in magnitude. However, measurements showed the total charge on each particle to be either a positive charge of unit size, or some whole number multiple of this unit. The unit positive charge was shown to be equal in size but opposite in sign to that on the electron. The mass of the positive particle was found to be less when hydrogen was used in the discharge tube than when any other gas was employed. From the values of e and e/m for the positive particles when hydrogen is used, the value of m can be calculated; the mass is 1.0073 on the atomic weight scale. This particle is called the **proton;** it is one of the fundamental units of structure of all atoms.

The formation of positively charged particles from neutral atoms or molecules of whatever gas is in the discharge tube is caused by the loss of electrons by these neutral bodies when they are struck by high speed cathode rays. These charged atoms are known as **gaseous ions.** From the fact that any neutral atom can be made to form positive ions by the loss of one or more electrons, it follows that every atom must contain one or more positive units. The simplest atom is that of hydrogen. It contains one proton (hydrogen ion) and one electron.

3.3 Radioactivity and Atomic Structure

The first conclusive evidence that atoms are complex rather than "indivisible," as stated in the atomic theory of matter, came with the discovery of radioactivity by Becquerel, a French physicist, in 1896. The term **radioactivity** applies to the spontaneous decomposition of atoms of certain elements, such as radium and

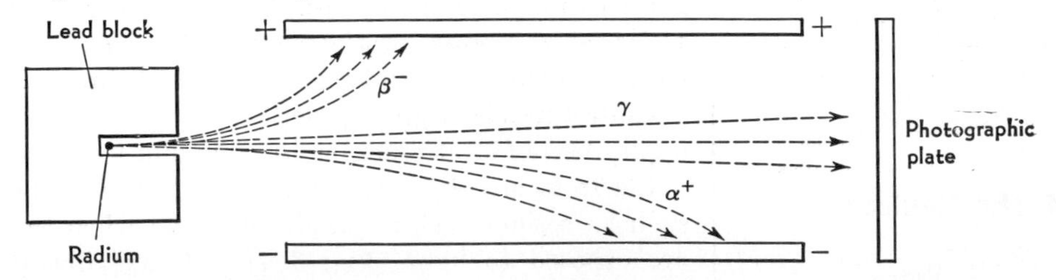

Fig. 3–4 The effect of an electric field on rays from radium. Beta, β, rays are electrons. Alpha, α, rays are nuclei of helium atoms. Gamma, γ, rays are similar to X-rays.

uranium, into simpler elements, and the simultaneous production of one or more of three kinds of radiations. These three types of rays may be studied and characterized by placing samples of the radioactive material in the bottom of a narrow hole bored in a block of lead, and allowing the emitted rays to pass through strong electric fields (Fig. 3–4). One type of ray is curved toward the negative part of the electric field and so must consist of positively charged particles. These are called **alpha (α) particles.** A second type of ray is deflected toward the positive part of the field and the path is bent much more than that of the alpha particles. These facts indicate that these particles are negatively charged and much smaller in mass than the alpha particles. They are called **beta (β) particles.** The third kind of ray is not deflected when it passes through an electric field. These rays proved to be similar to X-rays, but more penetrating (Fig. 3–5). They are called **gamma (γ) rays.**

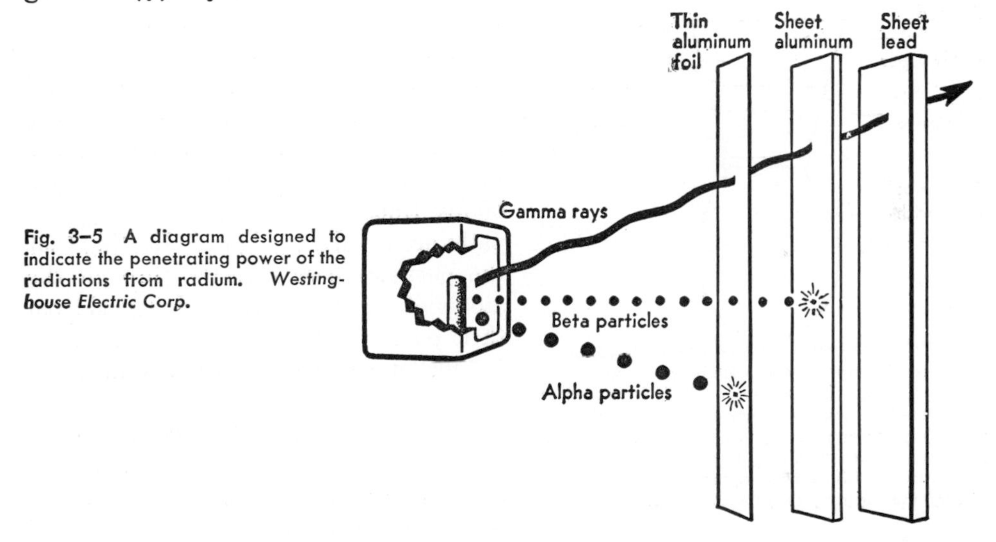

Fig. 3–5 A diagram designed to indicate the penetrating power of the radiations from radium. *Westinghouse Electric Corp.*

The α particles have been shown to have a mass of 4 and a charge of +2. They are helium ions, i.e., helium atoms that have lost two electrons each. The β particles are electrons with velocities approaching that of the speed of light (186,000 miles/second).

Convincing proof that atoms contain protons was obtained by Rutherford in 1919. Using high velocity α particles from radium as projectiles, he bombarded such atoms as nitrogen and aluminum and found that protons were ejected as a result of these collisions. These experiments indicated quite definitely that the electrically positive unit of the atom's structure is the proton.

3.4 The Neutron

In 1932 the English physicist Chadwick discovered a third type of fundamental unit of atomic structure. He observed that when atoms of beryllium (and other elements) are bombarded with high velocity α particles, uncharged particles are emitted. Chadwick called these neutral particles **neutrons;** they have a mass of 1.0087 on the atomic weight scale. It appears that under certain conditions a neutron may disintegrate and form a proton and an electron. This may be the origin of the electrons composing the β-rays which are emitted by radioactive elements.

3.5 The Nuclear Atom

Alpha particles pass through the air at very high velocities — on the average about 10,000 miles per second. Their paths may be photographed in an apparatus (cloud chamber) devised by C. T. R. Wilson (Fig. 3–6). As alpha particles pass through the air in the cloud chamber they ionize the air molecules in their paths. The air is supersaturated with water vapor and the ionized air molecules serve as nuclei upon which droplets of water condense. Thus a trail of small droplets of water (fog track) marks the path of a high velocity alpha particle through the cloud chamber. Photographs of fog tracks (Fig. 3–7) show that the paths are usually straight, indicating that the particles pass directly through the atoms of air without being deflected from their paths; however, a few paths show an abrupt change in direction near the end of the course.

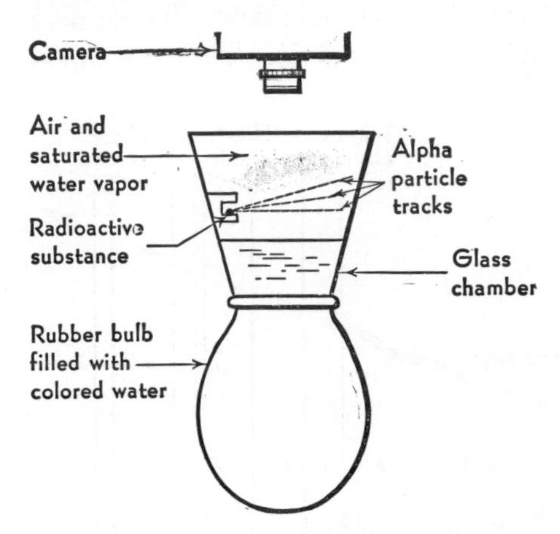

Fig. 3–6 A diagram to indicate how a Wilson cloud chamber works. Pressure on the bulb forces water into the glass chamber, compressing the air and water vapor within it. Upon sudden release of this pressure, condensation (fog) forms on the ions in the air. If the field is illuminated, the tracks of particles through the fog may be photographed.

When Rutherford projected a beam of α particles from a radioactive source upon a very thin solid (gold foil), he found that most of the particles passed through the solid without deflection, and that only a few of them were deviated from their paths. From the results of a series of such experiments Rutherford concluded that (1) the volume occupied by an atom must be largely empty space; this is indicated by the fact that most of the α particles pass through the foil undeflected, and (2) there must be located within each atom a heavy, positively charged body (the nucleus); this follows because an abrupt change in path (as noted for a few α particles) of a relatively heavy and positively charged α particle can result only from its close approach to a highly concentrated positive charge possessed by another particle (the atomic nucleus). The diameter of the nucleus was found to be about $\frac{1}{10,000}$ of the diameter of the atom; the diameter of an atom is of the order of 10^{-8} cm. Rutherford presumed the atom to consist of a very small, positively charged **nucleus** in which most of the mass of the atom is concentrated, surrounded by a number

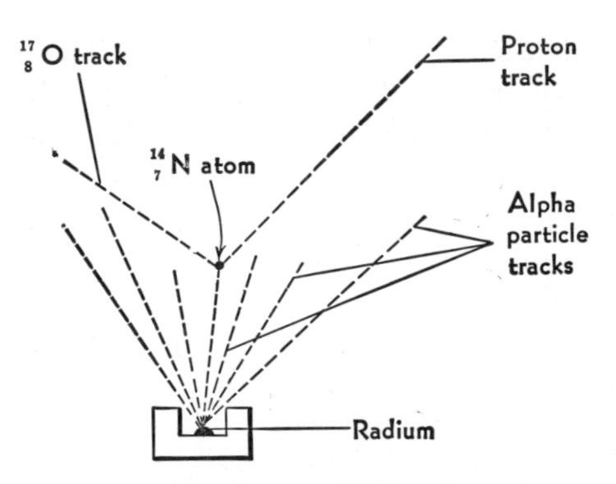

Fig. 3–7 A diagram that shows how the fog tracks look in a Wilson cloud chamber when an alpha particle hits and disrupts the nucleus of a nitrogen atom, forming an oxygen nucleus and a proton.

of electrons necessary to produce an electrically neutral whole. This is Rutherford's nuclear theory of the atom proposed in 1911.

From this same series of experiments, Rutherford showed that the number of positive charges on the nucleus (and thus the number of protons in the nucleus) is, in many cases, approximately one-half the atomic weight of the element. The number of charges on the nucleus of an atom of a given element is equal to the **atomic number** of that element. Long before Rutherford's experiments, however, the number representing the position of an element in the Periodic Table (first flyleaf of this book) had been called the atomic number of that element.

3.6 Moseley's Determination of Atomic Numbers

In 1914 Moseley worked out a method for determining the number of positive charges on the nucleus of an atom. This method involved the use of X-rays. A modern X-ray tube (Fig. 3–8) is a modified cathode ray tube in which electrons

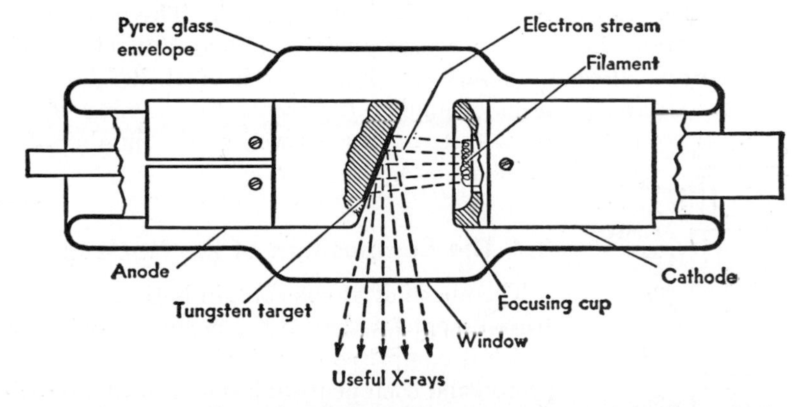

Fig. 3–8 In the Coolidge type X-ray tube, electrons strike a tungsten target causing the production of X-rays.

are obtained by thermal emission from a filament heated by an electric current. When a solid target is placed in the path of the high velocity electrons, electromagnetic radiations of short wave lengths are produced. These rays are very penetrating and are called **X-rays.** In order to study the X-rays produced when different elements (or their compounds) were made the targets in the X-ray tube, certain salt crystals were used as diffraction gratings to spread out the X-rays into a spectrum. This effect is similar to that produced when a beam of sunlight is resolved into a **spectrum** of its component colors when passed through a glass prism (Fig. 3–9).

When the spectra of X-rays produced in this manner are recorded on a photographic film, they produce lines which are characteristic of the material of which the target is made. Moseley arranged the X-ray spectra of different elements in order of increasing atomic weights, and found that with three exceptions the heavier the element the shorter the wave lengths of the principal lines in the spectra. The wave length of any element differed from that of the element next

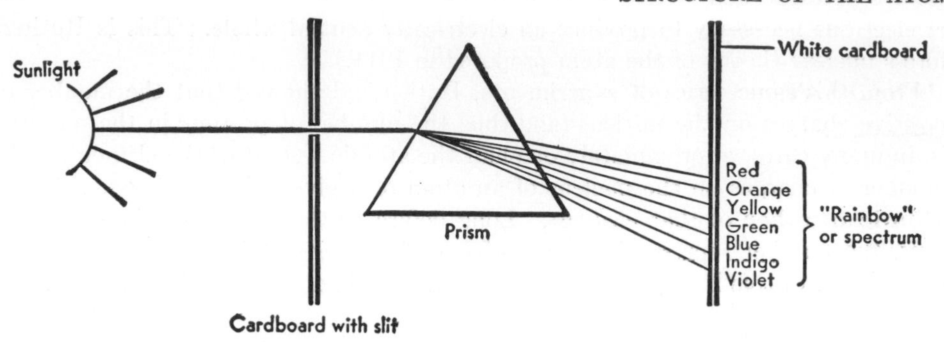

Fig. 3–9 When sunlight passes through a prism, it is separated into its component colors by refraction.

to it by the same amount (Fig. 3–10). This result indicated a constant difference of one proton in the nuclei of the atoms of elements adjacent in the series. It then became possible to arrange all the elements in order of increasing positive charge on the nuclei of their atoms, beginning with hydrogen as 1. **The atomic number of an element, then, is the number of positive charges on the nucleus of each of its atoms.** Because atoms are electrically neutral, it follows that the atomic number represents the number of electrons outside its nucleus as well as the number of protons in its nucleus.

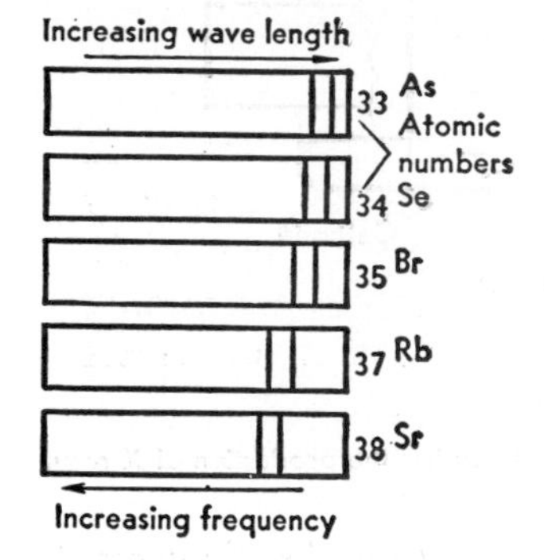

Fig. 3–10 The diagram represents several X-ray spectra as found by Moseley. Note the greater shift in wave length between Br and Rb. Element 36, krypton, was left out.

3.7 The Composition of the Nucleus

The nuclei of atoms contain both protons and neutrons except for that of the ordinary hydrogen atom, which is comprised of a single proton. Because each proton and each neutron has a mass of approximately 1 on the atomic weight scale, the atomic weight is equal to the number of protons and neutrons in the nucleus (neglecting the small mass of the electron). The composition of the atomic nuclei of the elements of atomic numbers one through ten is given in Table 3·1.

3.8 Isotopes

When we note that protons and neutrons each contribute very nearly one unit of atomic mass to atoms, we would expect to find the atomic weights of the elements to be approximately whole numbers. The fact that many atomic weights are far from being whole numbers led to the discovery that most elements are composed of mixtures of two or more kinds of atoms of different atomic masses, but similar in chemical properties. For example chlorine, with an atomic weight of 35.453, is composed of two kinds of chlorine atoms. These have masses very close to the whole numbers 35 and 37. Both types of chlorine atoms have an

TABLE 3·1 Nuclear Compositions

	Symbol	*Atomic Weight*	*Atomic Number*	*Number of Protons*	*Number of Neutrons*
Hydrogen	H	1.00797	1	1	0
Helium	He	4.0026	2	2	2
Lithium	Li	6.939	3	3	4
Beryllium	Be	9.0122	4	4	5
Boron	B	10.811	5	5	6
Carbon	C	12.01115	6	6	6
Nitrogen	N	14.0067	7	7	7
Oxygen	O	15.9994	8	8	8
Fluorine	F	18.9984	9	9	10
Neon	Ne	20.183	10	10	10

atomic number of 17, which means that they each have 17 protons in the nucleus. The difference must lie, then, in the number of neutrons in the nuclei of the different types of atoms; chlorine–35 has 18 neutrons and chlorine–37 has 20 neutrons. **Atoms of the same atomic number and different atomic weight are called isotopes.** It is important to remember that the only difference in composition between different isotopes of the same element is in the number of neutrons in the nucleus. The atomic weight of an element is an average of the weights of the isotopes of the element in the proportions in which they normally occur in nature. The atomic weight of 35.453 for chlorine indicates that the atoms of isotopic weight 35 are more abundant than the isotopes of weight 37.

A symbolism has been devised to distinguish between isotopes of an element. The two isotopes of chlorine are designated by the symbols $^{35}_{17}Cl$ and $^{37}_{17}Cl$. Note that the mass number is made the superscript and the atomic number the subscript.

3.9 Atomic Weight Scale

In Chapter 2 (see Section 2.4), mention was made that a carbon isotope is the present standard used in deriving the atomic weight scale. Carbon has three principal isotopes, $^{12}_{6}C$, $^{13}_{6}C$, and $^{14}_{6}C$. Each has six protons in the nucleus and six electrons outside the nucleus. Carbon–12 has, in addition, six neutrons in the nucleus, carbon–13 seven neutrons, and carbon–14 eight neutrons. The atomic weight scale is based upon the arbitrarily assigned value of the exact number 12 for the mass of the lightest and most abundant carbon isotope, $^{12}_{6}C$. The three isotopes of carbon occur in such proportion in a natural mixture that the average weight of the mixture, on the atomic weight scale, is 12.01115. Magnesium atoms weigh on the average a little more than twice as much as carbon atoms, or 24.312 units on the atomic weight scale, and hydrogen atoms, on the average, about one-twelfth as much as carbon atoms, or 1.00797. The table on the inside front cover lists the atomic weights of all the known elements, based upon the arbitrarily assigned value of **12** for ${}^{12}_{6}C$.

It is of interest to note that for many years two atomic weight scales have been utilized. The chemical atomic weight scale was based upon an arbitrarily assigned value of the exact number **16** for the average mass of ordinary oxygen (a mixture of three isotopes of oxygen, ${}^{16}_{8}O$, ${}^{17}_{8}O$, and ${}^{18}_{8}O$). The physical atomic weight scale was based upon an assigned value of the exact number **16** for the mass of the lightest and most abundant isotope of oxygen, ${}^{16}_{8}O$. The natural mixture of oxygen isotopes, assigned a value of exactly **16** on the chemical scale, had an average mass of 16.0044 units on the physical scale. Thus, one could multiply a chemical atomic weight by $\frac{16.0044}{16.0000}$, or 1.000275, to obtain the corresponding physical atomic weight. The need has long been felt, however, for one unified scale which would be satisfactory both to chemists and physicists. The scale based upon a value of **12** for the mass of the lightest carbon isotope, ${}^{12}_{6}C$, was suggested in 1957 and by August, 1961, was officially approved by both the International Union of Pure and Applied Chemistry and the International Union of Pure and Applied Physics.

3.10 Atomic Spectra and Electronic Structure

Sir Isaac Newton showed that sunlight is a mixture of different kinds of light. He separated white light into its spectrum of component colors by allowing it to pass through a refracting glass prism. Sunlight contains all wave lengths of visible light and hence gives the **continuous spectrum** so familiar in the rainbow. The sun's spectrum also contains invisible ultraviolet (very short wave lengths) and infrared waves (very long wave lengths) which may be detected and recorded photographically. Incandescent solids and liquids, and gases or vapors under great pressure, give continuous spectra. When an electric discharge is passed through a gas at low pressure, contained in a vacuum tube, the gas gives off light which when analyzed shows a spectrum made up of a number of bright lines (**a bright line spectrum**). These lines can be recorded photographically and the wave length of the light producing each line can be calculated from the positions of the lines on the photograph (Fig. 3–12).

Monatomic gases produce bright line spectra that consist of a set of lines which are characteristic of the elements composing the gas. Because these spectra are due to atoms they are called **atomic spectra.** Many attempts have been made to explain how an excited atom radiates energy and why it radiates the particular frequencies that it does. The first successful attempt was made by the Danish physicist Niels Bohr in 1913.

Bohr pictured the atom as a miniature solar system with the nucleus corresponding to the sun and the **orbital electrons** to the planets. However, planets attract each other because of gravitational forces, whereas the electrons in an atom repel one another; furthermore, the planets revolve in the same direction and in nearly the same plane, while electrons move in all directions and in all planes. While revolving in an orbit about the nucleus, the electron, according to Bohr, obeys the ordinary laws of mechanics. He suggested that an atom radiates energy as light only when the electron suddenly passes from one orbit to another where it has less energy (Fig. 3–11). The quantity of energy radiated is equal to the difference be-

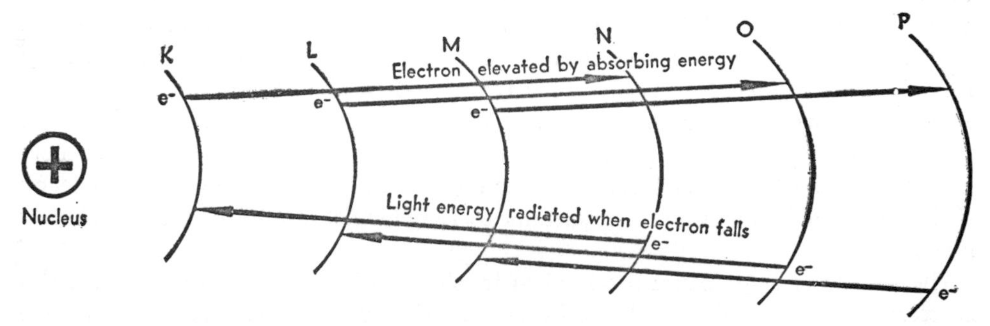

Fig. 3–11 Electron transitions which give rise to atomic spectra.

tween the energies the atom possessed before and after the electron changed orbits. He found it necessary to assume that the electron does not gain or lose energy continuously in passing from a lower orbit to a higher one during excitation of the atom or in dropping to a lower orbit from a higher one when radiating energy, but only in discrete quantities, called **quanta.** A quantum of energy is always directly proportional to the frequency of the radiation.

On the basis of his theory, Bohr was able to account satisfactorily for the bright lines in a number of different atomic spectral series. However, even after modification and expansion, Bohr's theory was inadequate in that it was able to account for the spectra of only the very simplest atomic systems such as the hydrogen atom. It is known now that the ordinary laws of mechanics do not adequately explain the properties of such small particles as electrons. Bohr's theory of the electron as a compact particle of matter moving in a circular or elliptical orbit about a nucleus has been largely supplanted by the highly mathematical theories of more modern quantum mechanics. Unfortunately, the quantum mechanical concept of the atom does not lend itself to a mechanical model that can be visualized.

For our purposes, the results of the Bohr theory and the quantum mechanical treatment indicate that the hydrogen atom consists of one proton (as a nucleus) and one electron moving about the proton. Larger atoms have several electrons moving about a positive nucleus which consists of several protons and neutrons. However, the exact path of the electron within its particular energy level cannot be determined. The German physicist Heisenberg expressed this in a form which has come to be known as the **Heisenberg Uncertainty Principle: It is impossible to determine accurately both the momentum and the position of an electron simultaneously.** (The momentum is the mass of the particle multiplied by its velocity.) The Heisenberg principle maintains that the more accurately we measure the momentum of a moving electron, the less accurately we can determine its position (and conversely). An experimental procedure which is designed to measure the position of an electron exactly will alter the momentum of the electron, and an experiment which seeks to measure accurately the momentum of an electron unavoidably changes its position. If measurements are obtained for both position and momentum at the same time, the values are inexact for one or the other or both. Therefore, since the exact position or path of an electron cannot be determined, the best that can be done is to speak of **the probability of finding an electron at a given location within the atom.**

The electrons, however, *are* located in definite *energy levels*. Inasmuch as the physical and chemical properties of an atom are primarily determined by the energies associated with the electrons in their movement within the atom, the energy of the electron is much more important to the chemist than the actual position of the electron.

The results of a quantum mechanical treatment of the problem show that the electron may be visualized as being in rapid motion within a relatively large region around the nucleus, but spending most of its time in certain high probability regions. For the hydrogen atom, the electron effectively occupies all the space within about 1 Å of the nucleus, with the greatest probability of being at a distance of about 0.5 Å; this gives the atom a spherical shape. Some chemists prefer to consider the electron in terms of a cloud of negative charge (electron cloud), with the cloud being dense in regions of high electron probability and more diffuse in regions of low probability. These **electron clouds** are spoken of as **atomic orbitals.**

The nuclei of atoms which are more complex than that of hydrogen are surrounded by orbital electrons which are arranged in a series of **shells** or **energy levels.** The closer an energy level is to the nucleus, the more strongly the electrons in that level are attracted to the nucleus because the electrostatic force of attraction between particles of opposite electrical charge increases rapidly with decreased distance of separation. The orbital electrons are classified in terms of their energy levels, i.e., on the basis of the firmness with which they are bound to the nucleus in the atom. The energy levels or shells are designated by the numbers 1, 2, 3, 4, 5, 6, and 7 or the letters K, L, M, N, O, P, and Q, starting with the one nearest the nucleus. The maximum number of electrons found to occupy the various electron shells is $2n^2$, where n is the number of the shell counting from the nucleus. Hence the shell nearest the nucleus, for which $n = 1$, can contain a maximum of $2(1)^2$ or 2 electrons; the second shell from the nucleus ($n = 2$), $2(2)^2$ or 8 electrons; and the third shell from the nucleus $2(3)^2$ or 18 electrons. Table 3·2 summarizes the maximum number of electrons possible for the first five major shells.

3.11 Atomic Structures

A single hydrogen atom consists of one proton and one electron. The proton may be represented by the letter p and the electron by e. The single electron moves in the K shell, around the proton.

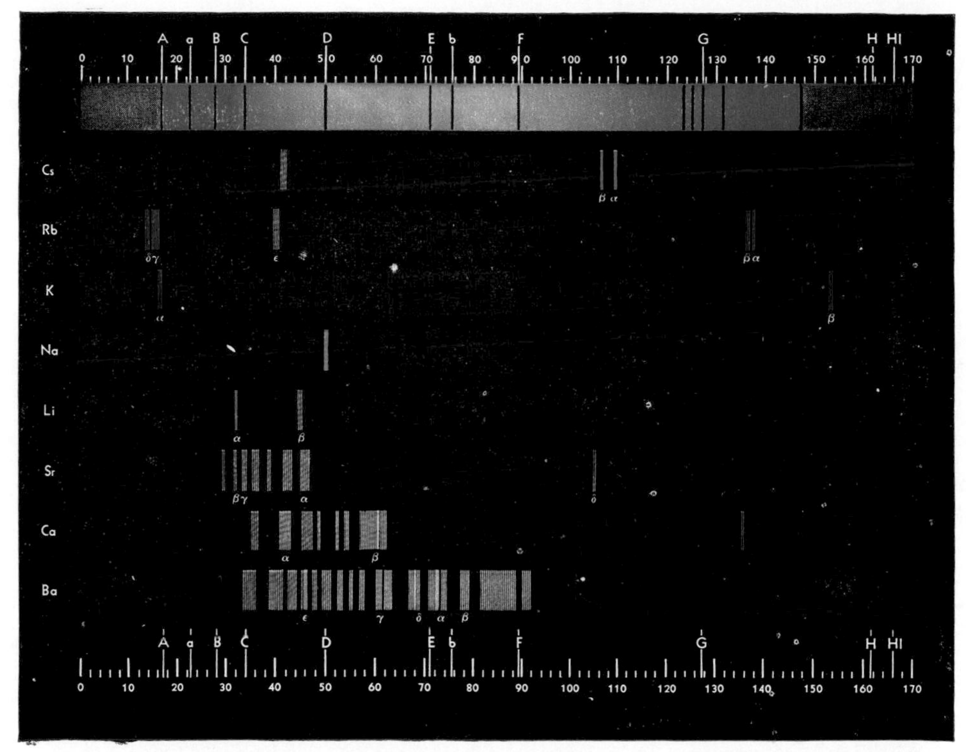

Fig. 3–12 Some Prominent Spectral Lines. At the top is the solar spectrum showing the dark Fraunhofer lines. The scale is an arbitrary one. The actual wave lengths may be estimated by noting that the B solar line has a wave length of approximately 6870 Å; the D line, 5896 Å; and the H line, 3968 Å.

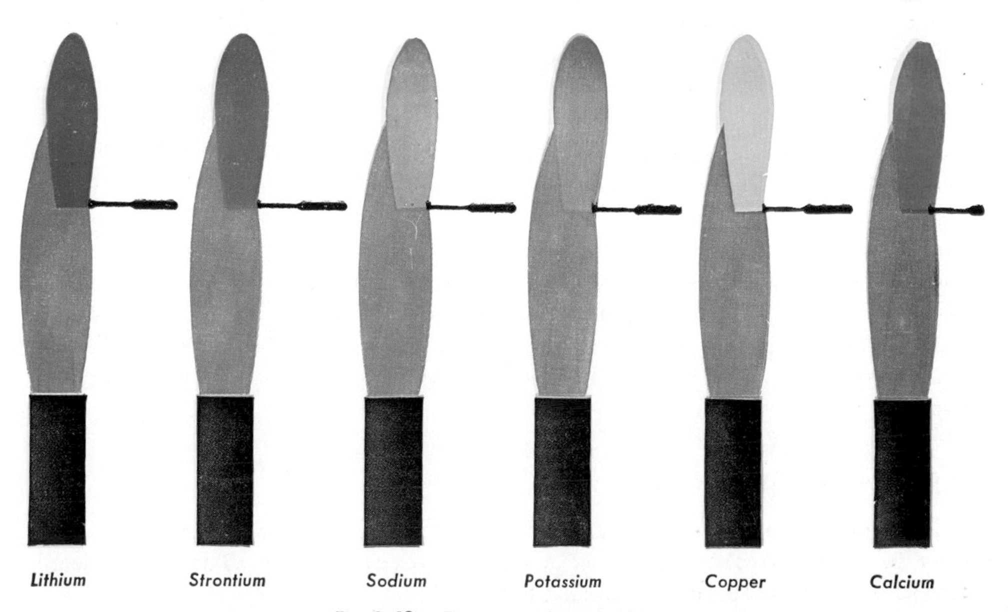

Fig. 3–13 Flame tests for metal ions.

TABLE 3·2

Energy Levels or Shells		*Maximum Number of Electrons*, $2n^2$
Letter Designation	n	
K	1	2
L	2	8
M	3	18
N	4	32
O	5	50 *

* As may be noted in Tables 3·3 and 3·7, no element so far known is large enough to contain more than 32 electrons in the O shell. The number 50, although hypothetical, is a logical prediction of the maximum number of electrons theoretically possible for the O shell.

Following hydrogen, the next simplest atom in terms of atomic structure is that of the **rare gas** helium, with an atomic number of two and an atomic weight of 4.0026. The helium atom contains two protons and two neutrons in its nucleus, and two electrons in the K electron shell, which is completely filled by these two electrons. The neutron is represented by the letter *n*.

1*p* 1 e

Hydrogen atom

The next atom in complexity after helium is that of the metal lithium, with an atomic number of three and an atomic weight of approximately seven. The nucleus of the isotope which weighs 7 on the atomic weight scale contains three protons and four neutrons, and there are three orbital electrons. Two of the orbital electrons make up the K shell. The third is in the next higher energy level, i.e., the L shell.

2*p* 2*n* 2 e

Helium atom

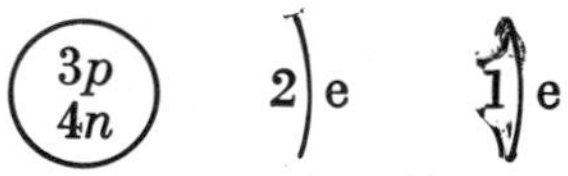

3*p* 4*n* 2 e 1 e

Lithium atom

An atom of the metal beryllium, atomic number four and atomic weight 9.0122, contains four protons and five neutrons in the nucleus, and four electrons, two each in the K and L shells.

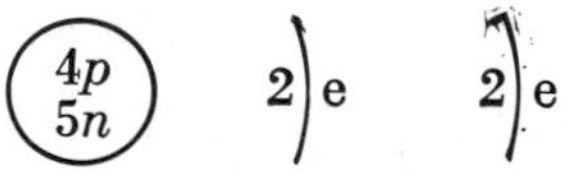

4*p* 5*n* 2 e 2 e

Beryllium atom

Boron (At. No. 5) has three electrons in its L shell; carbon (At. No. 6) has four; nitrogen (At. No. 7) has five; oxygen (At. No. 8) has six; fluorine (At. No. 9) has seven; and neon (At. No. 10) has eight electrons in its L shell. Just as the K shell is completely filled by two electrons, so the L shell is filled by eight, and neon resembles helium in having its electron shells completely filled.

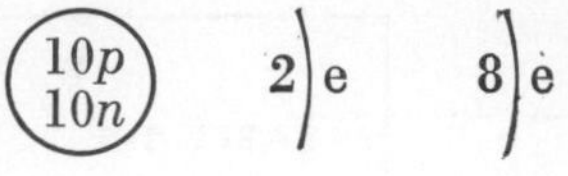

10*p* 10*n* | 2 e | 8 e

Neon atom

The sodium atom (At. No. 11) contains one more electron than the neon atom. This electron is found in the next higher energy level, i.e., the third or M shell. The sodium atom resembles the lithium atom in having one electron in its outermost shell.

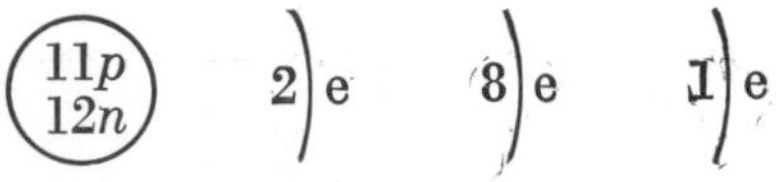

11*p* 12*n* | 2 e | 8 e | 1 e

Sodium atom

The magnesium atom (At. No. 12) has two electrons in its outer shell (the M shell), analogous to beryllium which also has two electrons in its outer shell (the L shell). Aluminum (At. No. 13), with three electrons in the outer shell, silicon with four, phosphorus with five, sulfur with six, chlorine with seven, and argon with eight, correspond respectively to boron, carbon, nitrogen, oxygen, fluorine, and neon. Any shell, other than the K shell (which is completely filled with two electrons), is complete with eight electrons if it is the outermost shell. Hence, argon has a complete outer electron configuration, with eight electrons in the M shell. The M shell, when it becomes an inner shell in larger atoms, can hold up to eighteen electrons.

Potassium and calcium (At. Nos. 19 and 20) have one and two electrons, respectively, in the N shell. Hence, potassium corresponds to lithium and sodium in outer configuration, whereas calcium corresponds to beryllium and magnesium.

Beginning with scandium (At. No. 21), the M shell, *which is now the second shell from the outside*, begins building from eight toward eighteen electrons, scandium having nine electrons in the M shell. The outer shell, N, remains the same as in calcium with two electrons.

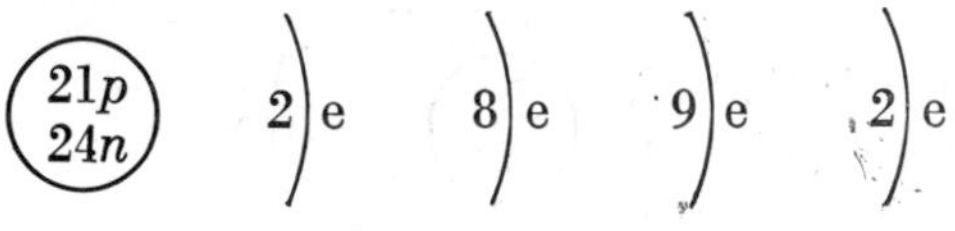

21*p* 24*n* | 2 e | 8 e | 9 e | 2 e

Scandium atom

Table 3·3 lists the atomic numbers and the numbers of electrons in the various electron shells of the atoms of the known elements.

3.12 The Periodic Law

The known elements vary greatly in their physical and chemical properties and in the nature of the compounds which they form. The study of the individual properties and compounds of each of the elements would prove to be extremely laborious and time consuming, but though every element is different from every other element, similarities make possible groupings that simplify the study. The most widely used grouping is that of the Periodic Table.

It became evident early in the development of chemistry that certain elements known at that time could be grouped together by reason of their similar properties. Lithium, sodium, and potassium (a portion of the group now referred to as the

TABLE 3·3 Electron Distribution in the Atoms of the Elements

Element	*At. No.*	*Electron Distribution*						
		K	*L*	*M*	*N*	*O*	*P*	*Q*
H	1	1						
He	2	2						
Li	3	2	1					
Be	4	2	2					
B	5	2	3					
C	6	2	4					
N	7	2	5					
O	8	2	6					
F	9	2	7					
Ne	10	2	8					
Na	11	2	8	1				
Mg	12	2	8	2				
Al	13	2	8	3				
Si	14	2	8	4				
P	15	2	8	5				
S	16	2	8	6				
Cl	17	2	8	7				
Ar	18	2	8	8				
K	19	2	8	8	1			
Ca	20	2	8	8	2			
Sc	21	2	8	9	2			
Ti	22	2	8	10	2			
V	23	2	8	11	2			
Cr	24	2	8	13	1			
Mn	25	2	8	13	2			
Fe	26	2	8	14	2			
Co	27	2	8	15	2			
Ni	28	2	8	16	2			
Cu	29	2	8	18	1			
Zn	30	2	8	18	2			
Ga	31	2	8	18	3			
Ge	32	2	8	18	4			
As	33	2	8	18	5			
Se	34	2	8	18	6			
Br	35	2	8	18	7			
Kr	36	2	8	18	8			
Rb	37	2	8	18	8	1		
Sr	38	2	8	18	8	2		
Y	39	2	8	18	9	2		
Zr	40	2	8	18	10	2		
Nb	41	2	8	18	12	1		
Mo	42	2	8	18	13	1		
Tc	43	2	8	18	14	1		
Ru	44	2	8	18	15	1		
Rh	45	2	8	18	16	1		
Pd	46	2	8	18	18	0		
Ag	47	2	8	18	18	1		
Cd	48	2	8	18	18	2		
In	49	2	8	18	18	3		
Sn	50	2	8	18	18	4		
Sb	51	2	8	18	18	5		
Te	52	2	8	18	18	6		
I	53	2	8	18	18	7		
Xe	54	2	8	18	18	8		
Cs	55	2	8	18	18	8	1	
Ba	56	2	8	18	18	8	2	
La	57	2	8	18	18	9	2	
Ce	58	2	8	18	20	8	2	
Pr	59	2	8	18	21	8	2	
Nd	60	2	8	18	22	8	2	
Pm	61	2	8	18	23	8	2	
Sm	62	2	8	18	24	8	2	
Eu	63	2	8	18	25	8	2	
Gd	64	2	8	18	25	9	2	
Tb	65	2	8	18	27	8	2	
Dy	66	2	8	18	28	8	2	
Ho	67	2	8	18	29	8	2	
Er	68	2	8	18	30	8	2	
Tm	69	2	8	18	31	8	2	
Yb	70	2	8	18	32	8	2	
Lu	71	2	8	18	32	9	2	
Hf	72	2	8	18	32	10	2	
Ta	73	2	8	18	32	11	2	
W	74	2	8	18	32	12	2	
Re	75	2	8	18	32	13	2	
Os	76	2	8	18	32	14	2	
Ir	77	2	8	18	32	15	2	
Pt	78	2	8	18	32	17	1	
Au	79	2	8	18	32	18	1	
Hg	80	2	8	18	32	18	2	
Tl	81	2	8	18	32	18	3	
Pb	82	2	8	18	32	18	4	
Bi	83	2	8	18	32	18	5	
Po	84	2	8	18	32	18	6	
At	85	2	8	18	32	18	7	
Rn	86	2	8	18	32	18	8	
Fr	87	2	8	18	32	18	8	1
Ra	88	2	8	18	32	18	8	2
Ac	89	2	8	18	32	18	9	2
Th	90	2	8	18	32	18	10	2
Pa	91	2	8	18	32	20	9	2
U	92	2	8	18	32	21	9	2
Np	93	2	8	18	32	23	8	2
Pu	94	2	8	18	32	24	8	2
Am	95	2	8	18	32	25	8	2
Cm	96	2	8	18	32	25	9	2
Bk	97	2	8	18	32	26	9	2
Cf	98	2	8	18	32	28	8	2
Es	99	2	8	18	32	29	8	2
Fm	100	2	8	18	32	30	8	2
Md	101	2	8	18	32	31	8	2
No	102	2	8	18	32	32	8	2
Lw	103	2	8	18	32	32	9	2

alkali metals), calcium, strontium, and barium (in the group called alkaline earth metals), and fluorine, chlorine, bromine, and iodine (in the halogen group) are examples of groups of elements exhibiting similar properties.

The German chemist Döbereiner, in 1829, was the first to suggest the existence of a relationship between the atomic weights and the properties of the elements. He showed that the atomic weight of strontium lies almost exactly midway between the atomic weights of two chemically similar elements, calcium and barium, and that the properties of strontium are intermediate between those of calcium and barium. He later recognized the existence of other **triads** of similar elements. Among these are the triads chlorine, bromine, and iodine; and lithium, sodium, and potassium. By 1854, other chemists showed that oxygen, sulfur, selenium, and tellurium could be classed as a family of elements, and that nitrogen, phosphorus, arsenic, antimony, and bismuth make up another family.

Fig. 3–14 To Dmitri Mendeleev (1834–1907) we owe the Periodic Law and an early form of the Periodic Table.

In 1865, Newlands in England recognized a correlation between the magnitude of the atomic weights and the properties of the elements. By 1870, Mendeleev (Fig. 3–14) in Russia and Lothar Meyer in Germany, working independently and apparently unaware of the work of Newlands, outlined the nature of this relationship between properties and atomic weights in some detail. Their conclusions led to a statement that the properties of the elements are periodic functions of their atomic weights. The idea is illustrated in the following two series of elements. Note that the elements have been arranged in order of increasing atomic weights from left to right.

Li	Be	B	C	N	O	F	Ne
6.939	9.0122	10.811	12.01115	14.0067	15.9994	18.9984	20.183
Na	Mg	Al	Si	P	S	Cl	Ar
22.9898	24.312	26.9815	28.086	30.9738	32.064	35.453	39.948

These two rows of elements comprise the second and third periods of the modern Periodic Table (first flyleaf of this book). Elements in each row differ decidedly in properties from one another. There is, however, an interesting and useful gradation in properties of elements in a given row as the atomic weight increases. Furthermore when the elements are arranged in order of increasing atomic weight, many elements in the same vertical columns have similar properties. For example, lithium (Li) is found to be very similar physically and chemically to sodium (Na), and beryllium (Be) very similar to magnesium (Mg).

The next heavier element after argon is potassium, which is similar to lithium and sodium. Beginning with potassium, however, eighteen elements must be added to the series in order of increasing atomic weights before rubidium (which is similar to potassium) is reached. These eighteen elements constitute a long period, in distinction to the two short periods which begin with lithium and sodium respectively. The other long periods are indicated in the Periodic Table. An explanation of the appearance of long and short periods in terms of atomic structure is made in Section 3.13.

The work of Moseley (Section 3.6) showed that atomic numbers rather than atomic weights are fundamental in determining the chemical properties of the elements. If you examine the Periodic Table, you will note that argon (At. Wt. 39.948) precedes potassium (At. Wt. 39.102), cobalt (At. Wt. 58.9332) precedes nickel (At. Wt. 58.71), tellurium (At. Wt. 127.60) precedes iodine (At. Wt. 126.9044), and thorium (At. Wt. 232.038) precedes protactinium (At. Wt. 231). The reversal, on the basis of atomic weights, is due to unusual percentages of isotopes in these pairs of elements. Consider, for example, argon (At. No. 18) and potassium (At. No. 19). The abundance of the isotopes of these elements is such that the average atomic weight of the naturally occurring mixture of isotopes is greater for argon than for potassium. Thus, argon consists almost entirely of the isotope with a mass number of 40, whereas potassium consists largely of the isotope with a mass number of 39. If the arrangement of the elements is in order of increasing atomic numbers, these eight elements fall into their proper positions in the table. The modern statement of the **Periodic Law** is: **The properties of the elements are periodic functions of their atomic numbers.**

The Periodic Table on the first flyleaf of this book is the **long period** form. It is also given on page 50 for convenient reference and study by the reader. The long period form is a modern version based on the table originally proposed by Mendeleev.

3.13 Electronic Structure and the Periodic Law

As we discuss in this section the relationship of the electronic structures of the atoms to the Periodic Table, you will find it exceedingly helpful to refer to it carefully as each idea is developed.

When the elements are arranged in order of increasing atomic numbers, elements with similar chemical properties recur at definite intervals, i.e., periodically. In regard to atomic structure, this suggests a periodicity in the number of electrons in the outer shells of the atoms of the elements. The electrons in the outermost shell of an atom are referred to as **valence electrons.** If elements having the same number of valence electrons are grouped together, the elements falling within each group are similar in chemical properties. Table 3·5 reviews the electron shells for the elements of atomic numbers 1 to 18, inclusive. Note the periodicity as regards the number of valence electrons.

It is seen that elements in any one vertical column (known as a **group** or **family**) have the same number of electrons in their outermost shells. We can now understand the similarity in chemical properties among elements of the same group because the number of electrons in the outermost shell of an atom is very important in determining its properties.

The horizontal rows of the Periodic Table are referred to as **periods.** Notice that the **first short period** of the table contains only the elements hydrogen and the rare gas helium. Helium has a complete outer shell (K shell) of two electrons.

TABLE 3·4 The Periodic Table of Elements (Long Period Form)

There are seven periods (horizontal rows) and eighteen groups (vertical columns) of elements. Atomic numbers are enclosed by brackets. Atomic weight values in parentheses are estimated and represent, in most cases, the isotopes of longest half-life. Atomic weights are based on carbon – 12.

	METALS												NONMETALS					
			TRANSITION METALS															
PERIODS	I A	II A	III B	IV B	V B	VI B	VII B	VIII	VIII	VIII	I B	II B	III A	IV A	V A	VI A	VII A	0
1 0	1.00797 H [1] 1																1.00797 H [1] 1	4.0026 He[2] 2
2 2	6.939 Li [3] 1	9.0122 Be[4] 2											10.811 B [5] 3	12.01115 C [6] 4	14.0067 N [7] 5	15.9994 O [8] 6	18.9984 F [9] 7	20.183 Ne[10] 8
3 2, 8	22.9898 Na[11] 1	24.312 Mg[12] 2											26.9815 Al[13] 3	28.086 Si [14] 4	30.9738 P [15] 5	32.064 S [16] 6	35.453 Cl [17] 7	39.948 Ar[18] 8
4 2, 8	39.102 K [19] 8, 1	40.08 Ca[20] 8, 2	44.956 Sc [21] 9, 2	47.90 Ti [22] 10, 2	50.942 V [23] 11, 2	51.996 Cr[24] 13, 1	54.9380 Mn[25] 13, 2	55.847 Fe[26] 14, 2	58.9332 Co[27] 15, 2	58.71 Ni [28] 16, 2	63.54 Cu[29] 18, 1	65.37 Zn[30] 18, 2	69.72 Ga[31] 18, 3	72.59 Ge[32] 18, 4	74.9216 As[33] 18, 5	78.96 Se[34] 18, 6	79.909 Br[35] 18, 7	83.80 Kr[36] 18, 8
5 2, 8, 18	85.47 Rb[37] 8, 1	87.62 Sr [38] 8, 2	88.905 Y [39] 9, 2	91.22 Zr [40] 10, 2	92.906 Nb[41] 12, 1	95.94 Mo[42] 13, 1	(99) Tc[43] 14, 1	101.07 Ru[44] 15, 1	102.905 Rh[45] 16, 1	105.4 Pd[46] 18	107.870 Ag[47] 18, 1	112.40 Cd[48] 18, 2	114.82 In[49] 18, 3	118.69 Sn[50] 18, 4	121.75 Sb[51] 18, 5	127.60 Te[52] 18, 6	126.9044 I [53] 18, 7	131.30 Xe[54] 18, 8
6 2, 8, 18	132.905 Cs [55] 18, 8, 1	137.34 Ba[56] 18, 8, 2	[57-71] *	178.49 Hf[72] 32, 10, 2	180.948 Ta[73] 32, 11, 2	183.85 W [74] 32, 12, 2	186.2 Re[75] 32, 13, 2	190.2 Os[76] 32, 14, 2	192.2 Ir [77] 32, 15, 2	195.09 Pt [78] 32, 17, 1	196.967 Au[79] 32, 18, 1	200.59 Hg[80] 32, 18, 2	204.37 Tl [81] 32, 18, 3	207.19 Pb[82] 32, 18, 4	208.980 Bi [83] 32, 18, 5	(210) Po[84] 32, 18, 6	(210) At[85] 32, 18, 7	(222) Rn[86] 32, 18, 8
7 2,8,18,32	(223) Fr [87] 18, 8, 1	(226.05) Ra[88] 18, 8, 2	[89-103] †	[104]	[105]	[106]	[107]	[108]										

* LANTHANIDE SERIES	138.91 La[57] 18, 9, 2	140.12 Ce[58] 20, 8, 2	140.907 Pr[59] 21, 8, 2	144.24 Nd[60] 22, 8, 2	(145) Pm[61] 23, 8, 2	150.35 Sm[62] 24, 8, 2	151.96 Eu[63] 25, 8, 2	157.25 Gd[64] 25, 9, 2	158.924 Tb[65] 27, 8, 2	162.50 Dy[66] 28, 8, 2	164.930 Ho[67] 29, 8, 2	167.26 Er[68] 30, 8, 2	168.934 Tm[69] 31, 8, 2	173.04 Yb[70] 32, 8, 2	174.97 Lu[71] 32, 9, 2
† ACTINIDE SERIES	(227) Ac[89] 18, 9, 2	232.038 Th[90] 18, 10, 2	(231) Pa[91] 20, 9, 2	238.03 U [92] 21, 9, 2	(237) Np[93] 23, 8, 2	(242) Pu[94] 24, 8, 2	(243) Am[95] 25, 8, 2	(245) Cm[96] 25, 9, 2	(245) Bk[97] 26, 9, 2	(248) Cf [98] 28, 8, 2	(253) Es[99] 29, 8, 2	(254) Fm[100] 30, 8, 2	(256) Md[101] 31, 8, 2	(253) No[102] 32, 8, 2	(257) Lw[103] 32, 9, 2

TABLE 3·5 Periodicity of Valence Electrons

Element	H							He
Electrons in shell	*1*							*2*
Element	Li	Be	B	C	N	O	F	Ne
Electrons in shells	2,*1*	2,*2*	2,*3*	2,*4*	2,*5*	2,*6*	2,*7*	2,*8*
Element	Na	Mg	Al	Si	P	S	Cl	Ar
Electrons in shells	2,8,*1*	2,8,*2*	2,8,*3*	2,8,*4*	2,8,*5*	2,8,*6*	2,8,*7*	2,8,*8*

The **second short period** contains eight elements, beginning with lithium and ending with the rare gas, neon. Neon has a complete outer shell (L shell) of eight electrons.

The **third short period** contains eight elements beginning with sodium and ending with the rare gas, argon, which contains eight electrons in the outer shell (M shell).

The **fourth period,** you will note, is the first of two long periods that contain eighteen elements each. This period includes a series of elements from scandium (At. No. 21) through copper (At. No. 29), which are known as **transition elements,** in which the second from the outer shell (the M shell, in this series) is building from eight to eighteen electrons. Before the transition series begins, however, two electrons enter the outer shell (the N shell) in potassium (At. No. 19) and calcium (At. No. 20), respectively. Following the transition series, the outer shell builds on up, reaching eight electrons with the rare gas, krypton (At. No. 36).

It is apparent from further inspection of the table that the **fifth period,** beginning with rubidium and ending with xenon, is similar to the fourth period. It has eighteen elements and contains a second transition series, yttrium (At. No. 39) through silver (At. No. 47), in which the second from the outer shell (the N shell) is building from eight to eighteen electrons, analogous to the first transition series in the preceding period.

The **sixth period** contains 32 elements. A third transition series is present, made up of lanthanum (At. No. 57) and the elements hafnium (At. No. 72) through gold (At. No. 79), in which the second shell from the outside (the O shell) builds from eight to eighteen electrons. Notice that the third transition series is split, however, and between lanthanum and hafnium is a series of fourteen elements, cerium (At. No. 58) through lutetium (At. No. 71). In these fourteen elements, the **third** shell from the outside (the N shell, which can hold a maximum of 32 electrons — see Table 3·2) builds from 18 to 32 electrons. Lutetium, therefore, has the structure 2, 8, 18, 32, 9, 2. These elements constitute the first **inner transition series** and are referred to as the **lanthanide series** or the **rare earth elements.** Inasmuch as lanthanum has a similar outer configuration, its properties are very much like those of the elements cerium through lutetium; hence, for convenience, it is often included in the lanthanide series even though in terms of electron structure it is more properly considered as the first element of the third transition series. Following lutetium, the elements hafnium through gold complete the third transition series, building the second from the outer shell (O shell) up to eighteen electrons. The outer shell (P shell) then builds up, reaching eight electrons with the rare gas, radon (At. No. 86).

The **seventh period** is incomplete. The first two members are francium (At. No. 87) and radium (At. No. 88), with K, L, M, N, O, P, and Q shells of 2, 8, 18, 32, 18, 8, 1 and 2, 8, 18, 32, 18, 8, 2 electrons, respectively. Actinium (At. No. 89), with the structure 2, 8, 18, 32, 18, 9, 2, is the first element of the fourth transition series. The next three naturally occurring elements — thorium, protactinium, and uranium — and the eleven transuranium elements, all artificially produced — neptunium, plutonium, americium, curium, berkelium, californium, einsteinium, fermium, mendelevium, nobelium, and lawrencium — constitute the second inner transition series, in which the third shell from the outside, the O shell, is building from 18 to 32 electrons. This series of elements, in which actinium is sometimes included because of its similarity in properties, is called the **actinide series.**

Although no additional elements are known beyond lawrencium (At. No. 103), which was produced for the first time in 1961, it is logical to assume that if elements 104, 105, 106, etc., are produced, they will be a part of the fourth transition series in which the second from the outer shell (the P shell, in this case) builds toward 18 electrons.

It is interesting to note that a number of irregularities occur in the atomic structures of the elements. For example, chromium (At. No. 24), which might be expected to have a structure 2, 8, 12, 2, instead has the structure 2, 8, 13, 1; copper (At. No. 29) would normally be expected to have a structure 2, 8, 17, 2, but actually is 2, 8, 18, 1; palladium (At. No. 46) might logically be 2, 8, 18, 16, 2, but is instead 2, 8, 18, 18, 0. The several irregularities occur because of similarities in energies of various of the electron shells. Very little difference in energy, for example, is involved between the M and N shells through the first transition series. At chromium, the M shell actually possesses a sufficiently lower energy to pull one of the electrons down from the N shell. For the next element, manganese (At. No. 25), the N shell is then somewhat lower in energy so that the regularity is restored with the additional electron going into the N shell to bring it back to two electrons.

The vertical columns (families or groups) of elements in the Periodic Table are numbered IA, IIA, IIIB, IVB, VB, VIB, VIIB, VIII, IB, IIB, IIIA, IVA, VA, VIA, VIIA, and O. The elements in a given "A" group show some resemblances to the corresponding elements in the "B" group of the same number.

3.14 Summary Classification of Elements in Terms of the Periodic Table

It is convenient to classify the elements in the Periodic Table into four categories, according to their atomic structures.

1. Rare gases — Elements in which the outer shell is complete with eight electrons (two electrons for helium). The rare gases are helium (He), neon (Ne), argon (Ar), krypton (Kr), xenon (Xe), and radon (Rn).

2. Representative elements — Elements in which the added electron enters the outermost shell but in which the outermost shell is incomplete. The representative elements are those in Groups IA, IIA, IIB, IIIA, IVA, VA, VIA, and VIIA of the Periodic Table.

3. Transition elements — Elements in which the second shell from the outside is building from eight to eighteen electrons. The four transition series are:

First transition series: Scandium (Sc) through copper (Cu).
Second transition series: Yttrium (Y) through silver (Ag).
Third transition series: Lanthanum (La); and hafnium (Hf) through gold (Au).
Fourth transition series (incomplete): Actinium (Ac); —.

4. Inner transition elements — Elements in which the third shell from the outside is building from eighteen to thirty-two electrons. The two inner transition series are:

First inner transition series: Cerium (Ce) through lutetium (Lu).
Second inner transition series: Thorium (Th) through lawrencium (Lw).

(Lanthanum and actinium, because of their similarities to the other members of the series, are sometimes included as the first elements of the first and second inner transition series, respectively).

3.15 Variation of Properties Within Periods and Groups

The properties of the elements are determined largely by their atomic structures. Differences in chemical properties are caused primarily by differences in three characteristics: (A) the magnitude of the nuclear charge and the number of electrons in the shells surrounding the nucleus, both of which are equal to the atomic number, (B) the number of shells of electrons and the number of electrons in these shells, particularly in the valence shells, and (C) the distances of the electrons in the various shells from each other and from the nucleus. These subjects and additional interesting matters concerning the Periodic Table will be discussed in Chapter 15.

3.16 Subshells and Orbitals

There are many more lines in the spectrum of an atom than can be accounted for in terms of electron transitions from the energy levels or shells which are designated by the numbers 1, 2, 3, 4, 5, 6, and 7. Many of these additional atomic spectral lines mean that the principal shell is divisible into **subshells.** The energies involved in similar electron transitions from different subshells of the same principal quantum shell differ slightly, and of course give rise to radiations of different wave lengths. The first principal shell has a single subshell, designated as the 1*s* shell, the second principal shell has two subshells, designated as 2*s* and 2*p*, the third principal shell has three subshells, designated as 3*s*, 3*p*, and 3*d*, and the fourth principal shell has four subshells — 4*s*, 4*p*, 4*d*, and 4*f*. The subshells are further divisible into **orbitals,** each of which can contain a maximum of two electrons. Thus, an *s* subshell, which is made up of one orbital, can contain a maximum of two electrons; a *p* subshell has three orbitals and can contain up to six electrons; a *d* subshell has five orbitals and can contain up to ten electrons; and an *f* subshell has seven orbitals and can contain a maximum of fourteen electrons. On the average, an *s* electron will approach the nucleus more closely than a *p* electron of the same major shell, a *p* electron more closely than a *d* electron, and a *d* electron more closely than an *f* electron.

A method of notation is commonly used in which a number in front of the subshell letter designates the number of the principal or major shell and a superscript designates the number of electrons in that particular subshell. For example, the notation $2p^4$ indicates four electrons in the *p* sublevel of the second principal shell from the nucleus; the notation $3d^8$ indicates eight electrons in the *d* sublevel of the third principal shell.

In arriving at the electronic structure of atoms of the various elements in terms of subshells, it is convenient to consider the subshells which electrons would enter if these atoms were built up in order of increasing atomic number, beginning with hydrogen. As each additional electron enters the atom, it will tend to occupy the available orbital of lowest energy, and electrons enter higher energy orbitals only after lower energy orbitals have been filled to capacity.

The energies corresponding to the various subshells of any given shell increase in the order $s < p < d < f$, so that in some cases the *d* or *f* subshells from a lower shell overlap with the *s* or *p* subshells from the next higher shell. For example, two electrons enter the 4*s* subshell in the calcium atom (At. No. 20), $1s^2$, $2s^22p^6$, $3s^23p^6$, $4s^2$ before an electron enters the 3*d* subshell in the scandium atom (At. No. 21), $1s^2$, $2s^22p^6$, $3s^23p^63d^1$, $4s^2$. Beginning with scandium, the series of nine elements in the first transition series of the Periodic Table occur (see Sections 3.13 and 3.14), in which additional electrons are added successively to the 3*d* subshell after two electrons have already occupied the 4*s* subshell. After the 3*d* subshell is filled to its capacity with ten electrons, the 4*p* subshell fills up. The electron configurations of the elements potassium to gallium are given in Table 3·6. Note that the electron configurations of chromium and copper do not conform with the generalization stated above. With chromium the third subshell becomes half-filled (5 electrons) and with copper the third subshell becomes completely filled (10 electrons). The extra electron needed for this to occur appears to come from the 4*s* orbital, leaving it with only one electron. It has been shown by quantum mechanics that half-filled and completely filled subshells represent the conditions of greatest stability.

The subshells listed in order of increasing energy are:

$$1s<2s<2p<3s<3p<4s<3d<4p<5s<4d<5p<6s<4f<5d<6p<7s<5f<6d$$

The energies of the 4*f* and 5*d* subshells, and of the 5*f* and 6*d* subshells, are of nearly the same magnitude. In certain atoms their order of occupancy is reversed.

3.17 An Energy-Level Diagram

Although it is not possible to depict the electron energy levels exactly, a diagram representing roughly the energy values of all electrons in all the atoms is given in Fig. 3–15, page 56. The energy of an electron in an orbital is indicated by the vertical coordinate in the diagram, the orbital of lowest energy and greatest stability being the $1s$ orbital at the bottom of the diagram. Levels of nearly the same energy content are connected by vertical lines at the right of the figure. In general, added electrons may be expected to occupy the orbitals in order as they

TABLE 3·6

Atomic Number	*Element*	*Electron Configuration*
19	Potassium	$1s^2$ $2s^2$ $2p^6$ $3s^2$ $3p^6$ $3d^0$ $4s^1$
20	Calcium	$3d^0$ $4s^2$
21	Scandium	$3d^1$ $4s^2$
22	Titanium	$3d^2$ $4s^2$
23	Vanadium	$3d^3$ $4s^2$
24	Chromium	$3d^5$ $4s^1$
25	Manganese	$3d^5$ $4s^2$
26	Iron	$3d^6$ $4s^2$
27	Cobalt	$3d^7$ $4s^2$
28	Nickel	$3d^8$ $4s^2$
29	Copper	$3d^{10}$ $4s^1$
30	Zinc	$3d^{10}$ $4s^2$
31	Gallium	$3d^{10}$ $4s^2$ $4p^1$

appear in the diagram, starting at the bottom and working up, each set of orbitals being filled before electrons enter the next set immediately above. This scheme holds strictly only for the elements of low atomic numbers; and as the atomic number increases, the relative energies of the levels change somewhat, but not all change to the same extent. This means that the elements of higher atomic number have electron arrangements slightly different from that depicted in the energy-level diagram.

The device shown in Fig. 3–16, page 56, is useful in arriving at the electronic configuration of an atom. Orbitals are occupied by electrons in the order indicated by the connecting lines. An exception to the diagram occurs where a single $5d$ electron is added before any $4f$ orbitals are occupied. The remaining nine $5d$ electrons enter this subshell after the $4f$ subshell has been completely filled with fourteen electrons. Similarly, one or more electrons enter the $6d$ subshell before any occupy the $5f$ subshell.

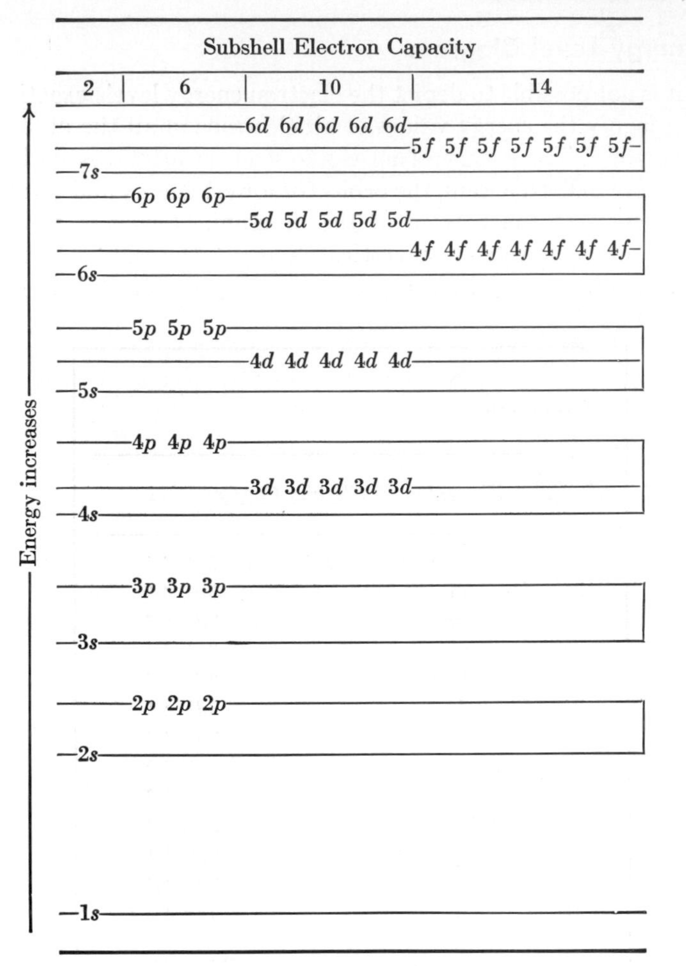

Fig. 3–15 Energy-level diagram for atomic orbitals.

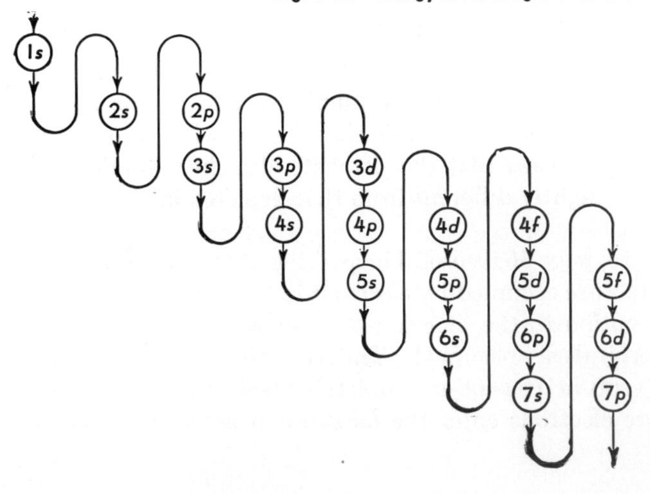

Fig. 3–16 Order of occupancy of atomic orbitals.

Period																		
1	H $1s^1$																H $1s^1$	He $1s^2$
2	Li $2s^1$	Be $2s^2$											B $2p^1$	C $2p^2$	N $2p^3$	O $2p^4$	F $2p^5$	Ne $2p^6$
3	Na $3s^1$	Mg $3s^2$											Al $3p^1$	Si $3p^2$	P $3p^3$	S $3p^4$	Cl $3p^5$	Ar $3p^6$
4	K $4s^1$	Ca $4s^2$	Sc $3d^1$	Ti $3d^2$	V $3d^3$	Cr $3d^5$	Mn $3d^5$	Fe $3d^6$	Co $3d^7$	Ni $3d^8$	Cu $3d^{10}$	Zn $3d^{10}$	Ga $4p^1$	Ge $4p^2$	As $4p^3$	Se $4p^4$	Br $4p^5$	Kr $4p^6$
5	Rb $5s^1$	Sr $5s^2$	Y $4d^1$	Zr $4d^2$	Nb $4d^4$	Mo $4d^5$	Tc $4d^6$	Ru $4d^7$	Rh $4d^8$	Pd $4d^{10}$	Ag $4d^{10}$	Cd $4d^{10}$	In $5p^1$	Sn $5p^2$	Sb $5p^3$	Te $5p^4$	I $5p^5$	Xe $5p^6$
6	Cs $6s^1$	Ba $6s^2$	*	Hf $5d^2$	Ta $5d^3$	W $5d^4$	Re $5d^5$	Os $5d^6$	Ir $5d^7$	Pt $5d^9$	Au $5d^{10}$	Hg $5d^{10}$	Tl $6p^1$	Pb $6p^2$	Bi $6p^3$	Po $6p^4$	At $6p^5$	Rn $6p^6$
7	Fr $7s^1$	Ra $7s^2$	†															

*	La $5d^1$	Ce $4f^2$	Pr $4f^3$	Nd $4f^4$	Pm $4f^5$	Sm $4f^6$	Eu $4f^7$	Gd $4f^7$	Tb $4f^9$	Dy $4f^{10}$	Ho $4f^{11}$	Er $4f^{12}$	Tm $4f^{13}$	Yb $4f^{14}$	Lu $4f^{14}$
†	Ac $6d^1$	Th $6d^2$	Pa $5f^2$	U $5f^3$	Np $5f^4$	Pu $5f^6$	Am $5f^7$	Cm $5f^7$	Bk $5f^8$	Cf $5f^{10}$	Es $5f^{11}$	Fm $5f^{12}$	Md $5f^{13}$	No $5f^{14}$	Lw $5f^{14}$

Fig. 3–17 The order of occupancy of atomic orbitals and the Periodic Table, as the atoms are built up in order of increasing atomic number ("Aufbau Principle").

TABLE 3·7 Electron Distribution, in Terms of Subshells, for the Known Elements

		K	L		M			N				O				P			Q
		1s	2s	2p	3s	3p	3d	4s	4p	4d	4f	5s	5p	5d	5f	6s	6p	6d	7s
H	1	1																	
He	2	2																	
Li	3	2	1																
Be	4	2	2																
B	5	2	2	1															
C	6	2	2	2															
N	7	2	2	3															
O	8	2	2	4															
F	9	2	2	5															
Ne	10	2	2	6															
Na	11	2	2	6	1														
Mg	12	2	2	6	2														
Al	13	2	2	6	2	1													
Si	14	2	2	6	2	2													
P	15	2	2	6	2	3													
S	16	2	2	6	2	4													
Cl	17	2	2	6	2	5													
Ar	18	2	2	6	2	6													
K	19	2	2	6	2	6		1											
Ca	20	2	2	6	2	6		2											
Sc	21	2	2	6	2	6	1	2											
Ti	22	2	2	6	2	6	2	2											
V	23	2	2	6	2	6	3	2											
Cr	24	2	2	6	2	6	5	1											
Mn	25	2	2	6	2	6	5	2											
Fe	26	2	2	6	2	6	6	2											
Co	27	2	2	6	2	6	7	2											
Ni	28	2	2	6	2	6	8	2											
Cu	29	2	2	6	2	6	10	1											
Zn	30	2	2	6	2	6	10	2											
Ga	31	2	2	6	2	6	10	2	1										
Ge	32	2	2	6	2	6	10	2	2										
As	33	2	2	6	2	6	10	2	3										
Se	34	2	2	6	2	6	10	2	4										
Br	35	2	2	6	2	6	10	2	5										
Kr	36	2	2	6	2	6	10	2	6										
Rb	37	2	2	6	2	6	10	2	6			1							
Sr	38	2	2	6	2	6	10	2	6			2							
Y	39	2	2	6	2	6	10	2	6	1		2							
Zr	40	2	2	6	2	6	10	2	6	2		2							
Nb	41	2	2	6	2	6	10	2	6	4		1							
Mo	42	2	2	6	2	6	10	2	6	5		1							
Tc	43	2	2	6	2	6	10	2	6	6		1							
Ru	44	2	2	6	2	6	10	2	6	7		1							
Rh	45	2	2	6	2	6	10	2	6	8		1							
Pd	46	2	2	6	2	6	10	2	6	10									
Ag	47	2	2	6	2	6	10	2	6	10		1							
Cd	48	2	2	6	2	6	10	2	6	10		2							
In	49	2	2	6	2	6	10	2	6	10		2	1						
Sn	50	2	2	6	2	6	10	2	6	10		2	2						
Sb	51	2	2	6	2	6	10	2	6	10		2	3						
Te	52	2	2	6	2	6	10	2	6	10		2	4						
I	53	2	2	6	2	6	10	2	6	10		2	5						
Xe	54	2	2	6	2	6	10	2	6	10		2	6						
		2	8		18			18				8							

Table 3·7 (continued)

		K	*L*	*M*	*N*				*O*				*P*			*Q*
					4*s*	4*p*	4*d*	4*f*	5*s*	5*p*	5*d*	5*f*	6*s*	6*p*	6*d*	7*s*
Cs	55	2	8	18	2	6	10		2	6			1			
Ba	56	2	8	18	2	6	10		2	6			2			
La	57	2	8	18	2	6	10		2	6	1		2			
Ce	58	2	8	18	2	6	10	2	2	6			2			
Pr	59	2	8	18	2	6	10	3	2	6			2			
Nd	60	2	8	18	2	6	10	4	2	6			2			
Pm	61	2	8	18	2	6	10	5	2	6			2			
Sm	62	2	8	18	2	6	10	6	2	6			2			
Eu	63	2	8	18	2	6	10	7	2	6			2			
Gd	64	2	8	18	2	6	10	7	2	6	1		2			
Tb	65	2	8	18	2	6	10	9	2	6			2			
Dy	66	2	8	18	2	6	10	10	2	6			2			
Ho	67	2	8	18	2	6	10	11	2	6			2			
Er	68	2	8	18	2	6	10	12	2	6			2			
Tm	69	2	8	18	2	6	10	13	2	6			2			
Yb	70	2	8	18	2	6	10	14	2	6			2			
Lu	71	2	8	18	2	6	10	14	2	6	1		2			
Hf	72	2	8	18	2	6	10	14	2	6	2		2			
Ta	73	2	8	18	2	6	10	14	2	6	3		2			
W	74	2	8	18	2	6	10	14	2	6	4		2			
Re	75	2	8	18	2	6	10	14	2	6	5		2			
Os	76	2	8	18	2	6	10	14	2	6	6		2			
Ir	77	2	8	18	2	6	10	14	2	6	7		2			
Pt	78	2	8	18	2	6	10	14	2	6	9		1			
Au	79	2	8	18	2	6	10	14	2	6	10		1			
Hg	80	2	8	18	2	6	10	14	2	6	10		2			
Tl	81	2	8	18	2	6	10	14	2	6	10		2	1		
Pb	82	2	8	18	2	6	10	14	2	6	10		2	2		
Bi	83	2	8	18	2	6	10	14	2	6	10		2	3		
Po	84	2	8	18	2	6	10	14	2	6	10		2	4		
At	85	2	8	18	2	6	10	14	2	6	10		2	5		
Rn	86	2	8	18	2	6	10	14	2	6	10		2	6		
Fr	87	2	8	18	2	6	10	14	2	6	10		2	6		1
Ra	88	2	8	18	2	6	10	14	2	6	10		2	6		2
Ac	89	2	8	18	2	6	10	14	2	6	10		2	6	1	2
Th	90	2	8	18	2	6	10	14	2	6	10		2	6	2	2
Pa	91	2	8	18	2	6	10	14	2	6	10	2	2	6	1	2
U	92	2	8	18	2	6	10	14	2	6	10	3	2	6	1	2
Np	93	2	8	18	2	6	10	14	2	6	10	4	2	6	1	2
Pu	94	2	8	18	2	6	10	14	2	6	10	6	2	6		2
Am	95	2	8	18	2	6	10	14	2	6	10	7	2	6		2
Cm	96	2	8	18	2	6	10	14	2	6	10	7	2	6	1	2
Bk	97	2	8	18	2	6	10	14	2	6	10	8	2	6	1	2
Cf	98	2	8	18	2	6	10	14	2	6	10	10	2	6		2
Es	99	2	8	18	2	6	10	14	2	6	10	11	2	6		2
Fm	100	2	8	18	2	6	10	14	2	6	10	12	2	6		2
Md	101	2	8	18	2	6	10	14	2	6	10	13	2	6		2
No	102	2	8	18	2	6	10	14	2	6	10	14	2	6		2
Lw	103	2	8	18	2	6	10	14	2	6	10	14	2	6	1	2
		2	8	18	32				32				9			2

Table 3·7, pages 58 and 59, lists the electron structures, in terms of subshells, for each of the known elements. Note that for each transition series of elements, ten *d* electrons are added to the second from the outer shell to bring the shell from eight to eighteen electrons. For each inner transition series, fourteen *f* electrons are added to the third from the outer shell to bring that shell from eighteen to thirty-two electrons. (See also Table 3·3 and Sections 3.13 and 3.14.)

Figure 3–17 on page 57 shows in Periodic Table form the orbitals which the added electrons would enter if the atoms were built up in order of increasing atomic number ("Aufbau Principle").

3.18 The Nature of Atomic Orbitals

The orbitals which are occupied by electrons in different energy levels differ from each other with regard to their size, shape, and orientation in space. The larger the number of the principal shell, the greater is the volume of the corresponding orbital. For example, a 2*s* electron has a larger orbital than a 1*s* electron, and a 3*s* electron has a larger orbital than a 2*s* electron. It should be noted, however, that the orbitals of the higher principal shells overlap those of the lower shells, meaning that outer electrons penetrate the regions occupied by inner electrons. With regard to shape, the orbital of an *s* electron is spherical (Fig. 3–18), while that of a *p* electron is a sort of dumbbell, represented by two spheres (Fig. 3–19a), or in

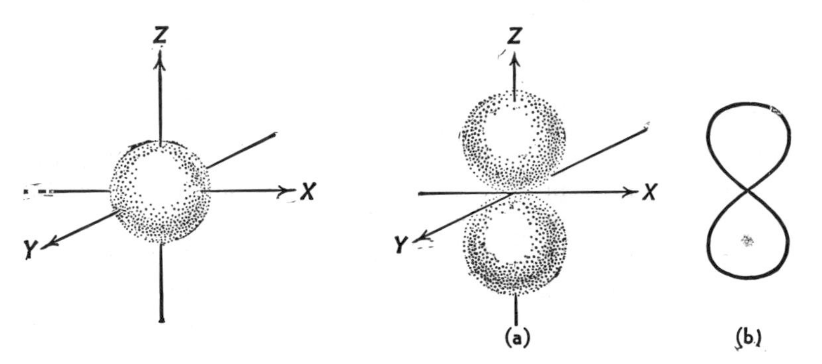

Fig. 3–18 Atomic *s* orbitals.

Fig. 3–19 Atomic *p* orbitals.

cross section by a figure eight loop (b). The orbitals of *d* and *f* electrons are still more complicated in shape (see Section 34.5).

The number of possible orientations of atomic orbitals in space depends to an extent upon the shape of the orbital. No matter how a sphere (*s* orbital) is oriented, it still presents the same appearance to an outside observer. Orbitals of the *s* type are said, therefore, to be spherically symmetrical and without directional characteristics. The situation becomes more complex with *p* orbitals, which occur in sets of three. Although it is not possible to determine the direction of any one orbital in a given set, the axes (with the nucleus of the atom at the intersection) along which the three *p* orbitals lie are mutually at right angles to each other

(Fig. 3–20). The three *p* orbitals are designated in the diagram as p_x, p_y, and p_z to emphasize their directional character.

It was mentioned in Section 3.16 that each atomic orbital can accommodate two electrons. It has been found that all electrons spin either clockwise or counter-clockwise, and that the two electrons of a given orbital are identical in all respects except that they are spinning in opposite directions. According to the **Pauli**

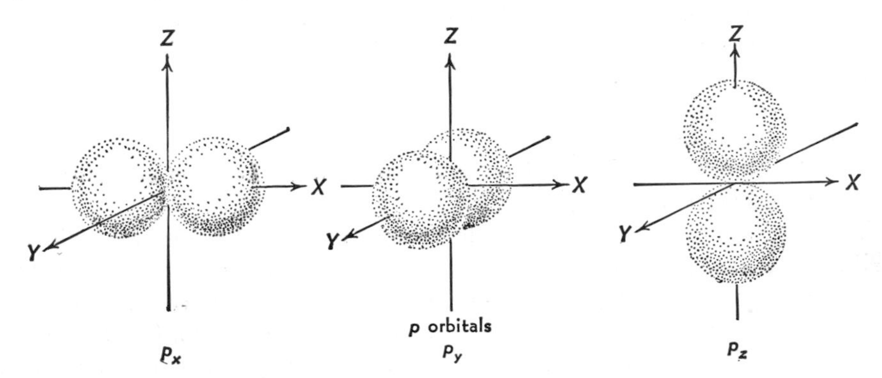

Fig. 3–20 Directional characteristics of atomic *p* orbitals.

Exclusion Principle, no two electrons in the same atom may have identical energies. The fact that the two electrons of an atomic orbital have opposed spins prevents them from having identical energies.

QUESTIONS

1. Describe the production of cathode rays in a simple vacuum discharge tube.
2. What is the experimental evidence that electrons are small negatively charged particles?
3. Explain: thermal emission of electrons; the photoelectric effect.
4. What is the evidence that all atoms contain electrons?
5. Relate the proton to the hydrogen atom. What is the evidence that all atoms contain protons?
6. Describe the three types of rays emitted by radioactive substances.
7. Explain the formation of "fog tracks" in a Wilson cloud chamber.
8. What experimental evidence led Rutherford to propose his nuclear theory of the atom?
9. What is the significance of atomic numbers? How were they determined by Moseley?
10. List the name, mass, charge, and symbol of each of the fundamental particles of matter necessary to describe the composition of atoms.
11. How can atoms contain electrically charged particles and still be electrically neutral?
12. Define the following terms: atomic number, atomic weight, nuclear charge, isotopes.

13. Give one reason why the atomic weights of many of the elements are other than whole numbers even though the component particles of atoms have weights which are nearly whole numbers.

14. (a) Why is 12.01115 listed in the atomic weight table as the atomic weight of carbon, whereas the arbitrary standard for the atomic weight scale is the exact number 12 for the mass of the carbon-12 isotope?

(b) Carbon, as it occurs in nature, contains approximately 99% $^{12}_{6}C$, 1% $^{13}_{6}C$, and an infinitesimal trace of $^{14}_{6}C$. Based upon the recognized standard specifying the exact number 12 for the mass of $^{12}_{6}C$, calculate the average atomic weight for the mixture and compare this with the atomic weight which is listed for carbon in the atomic weight table.

15. State the Periodic Law. How can the Periodic Law be accounted for in terms of atomic structure?

16. Give the meaning of the following terms as applied to the Periodic Table, and illustrate each with specific examples: period, group, short period, long period, transition series, inner transition series, rare gases, representative elements.

17. Find four places in the Periodic Table where the positions of the elements are not in keeping with their atomic weights. Account for the positions of these elements.

18. Give the nuclear composition of the following isotopes:

$$^{1}_{1}H,\ ^{2}_{1}H,\ ^{3}_{1}H;\ ^{16}_{8}O,\ ^{17}_{8}O,\ ^{18}_{8}O;\ \text{and}\ ^{20}_{10}Ne,\ ^{22}_{10}Ne$$

19. Why would more energy be required in the removal of an electron from a K electron shell than from an L shell?

20. What is the relationship between the number of electrons of a neutral atom and its atomic number?

21. How many electrons are found in the outermost energy level of each of the rare gases, He, Ne, Ar, Kr, Xe, and Rn?

22. Make drawings to represent the complete nuclear composition and electronic structure (using principal electron shells) of the isotopes listed in question 18.

23. Explain the use of atomic spectra in the determination of electron arrangements in atoms.

24. Distinguish between principal electron shells and subshells; subshells and orbitals.

25. What do the following notations mean: $1s^1$; $2p^6$; $3d^0$, $4f^{10}$; $3s^2\ 3p^2\ 3d^5$?

26. Represent the electronic structure of each of the inert gases in terms of subshell notation (s, p, d, and f).

27. By means of standard notation ($1s^2$, $2s^2$, $2p^6$, etc.), give the electron distribution in terms of s, p, d, and f subshells for each of the following, and classify each as to whether it is a representative element, a transition element, an inner transition element, or a rare gas: C, Sr, Gd, Co, Rn, Lw.

28. (a) Give the electron distribution, in terms of s, p, d, and f subshells, for the following pairs of atoms: Rb (in group IA of the Periodic Table) and Ag (group IB); Ca (group IIA) and Zn (group IIB); Mn (group VIIB) and Br (group VIIA).

(b) What similarities are evident in the outer one or two subshells for the elements of each of the pairs referred to in part (a)? (The energy-level diagram of Fig. 3–15 should be considered in answering this question.)

29. Formulate definitions for rare gases, representative elements, transition elements, and inner transition elements in terms of *s*, *p*, *d*, and *f* subshells.

REFERENCES

"Atomic Weight Scales Unified?" (Based upon an interview with Dr. Edward Wichers of the National Bureau of Standards), *Chem. Eng. News*, Sept. 8, 1958; p. 76.

"IUPAC Revises Atomic Weight Values," *Chem. Eng. News*, Nov. 20, 1961; p. 42.

"Interpreting Electronic Structures," J. A. Campbell, *J. Chem. Educ.*, **26** (9) 477 (1949).

"Electronic Structure of the Atom," D. C. Devault, *J. Chem. Educ.*, **21** (11) 526 (1944); **21** (12) 575 (1944).

"Periodic System of the Elements," M. E. Weeks, *Discovery of the Elements*, Sixth Edition, Publ. by the Journal of Chemical Education, Easton, Pa., 1956; chapter 24, pp. 653–669.

"The Prehistory of the Periodic System of the Elements," J. W. van Spronsen, *J. Chem. Educ.*, **36** (11) 565 (1959).

"The Carbon-12 Scale of Atomic Masses," A. Labbauf, *J. Chem. Educ.*, **39** (6) 282 (1962).

CHAPTER FOUR

Chemical Bonding

The union of atoms of elements to form compound substances is accompanied by the establishment of chemical bonds between the atoms of these elements. When the atoms separate, these chemical bonds are destroyed. Before the discovery of the electrical structure of the atom the nature of the forces holding atoms together was a mysterious one. Now it is believed that these forces are electrical in nature and that the chemical reactions that occur between atoms involve changes in their electronic structures.

4.1 Chemical Bonding by Electron Transfer; Ionic Bonding

The electrons which are involved in bond formation between atoms are found in the outermost shell (and sometimes in the next to the outermost shell) of the neutral atom; these are called **valence electrons.** The atoms of elements which have only one or two electrons in their outermost shells (the active metals) may lose electrons when they combine with atoms of other elements. An atom which has lost one or more valence electrons possesses a positive charge, and is called a **positive ion.** The sodium atom loses its one valence electron and acquires a +1 charge when it enters into chemical combination with an atom of another element such as chlorine. The magnesium atom may lose its two valence electrons and assume a +2 charge.

$$\underset{\text{Sodium atom}}{Na} \rightarrow \underset{\text{Sodium ion}}{Na^+} + e^-$$

$$\underset{\text{Magnesium atom}}{Mg} \rightarrow \underset{\text{Magnesium ion}}{Mg^{++}} + 2e^-$$

The smaller the number of valence electrons in the atom, the greater the tendency for the element to form positive ions during chemical combination with atoms of other elements. The energy required to remove an electron from a neutral atom and form a positive ion is called its **ionization potential.** Some metals have small ionization potentials and readily form positive ions. The nonmetals, which have more electrons in their outer shells than the metals, have large ionization potentials and show little tendency toward the formation of positive ions. The rare gases (He, Ne, Ar, Kr, Xe, and Rn) have the largest ionization potentials and the most stable electronic structures of the elements.

Atoms which lack one or two electrons of having an outermost shell of eight electrons readily gain sufficient electrons from certain other atoms, such as sodium and magnesium, to make a full complement of eight electrons in the outside shell. Neutral atoms become **negative ions** by gaining electrons. The nonmetals, such as F, Cl, Br, I, O, and S, readily form negative ions.

$$\underset{\text{Chlorine atom}}{Cl} \quad + e^- \quad \rightarrow \quad \underset{\text{Chloride ion}}{Cl^-}$$

$$\underset{\text{Sulfur atom}}{S} \quad + 2e^- \quad \rightarrow \quad \underset{\text{Sulfide ion}}{S^=}$$

The attraction of a neutral atom for electrons is known as its **electron affinity.** The nonmetals have high electron affinities and the metals have very low electron affinities. Thus only the nonmetals tend to form negative ions during chemical combination.

When a positive ion and a negative ion are brought close together, strong electrostatic attractive forces between the charges of opposite sign are set up, and the ions are held together by **ionic bonding.** The term **electrovalence** is sometimes employed to designate this type of bonding.

The changes in electronic structure which take place during chemical reactions can be expressed simply by adopting a system of notation in which the symbol of an atom represents all of the atom except the valence electrons; the symbol is written surrounded by its valence electrons. Valence electrons are designated by the symbols (·), (x), and (o). Different symbols for electrons are used to indicate their sources; it must be remembered, however, that all electrons are identical regardless of their origin.

Valence electronic symbols may be written to show the formation of ionic compounds by electron transfer.

$$\underset{\text{Sodium atom}}{Na\cdot} \quad + \quad \underset{\text{Chlorine atom}}{{}^{\times}\overset{\times\times}{\underset{\times\times}{Cl}}{}_{\times}^{\times}} \quad \rightarrow \quad \underset{\text{Sodium chloride (ionic)}}{Na^+\left[{}^{\times}_{\cdot}\overset{\times\times}{\underset{\times\times}{Cl}}{}_{\times}^{\times}\right]^-}$$

$$\underset{\text{Magnesium atom}}{Mg:} \quad + \quad \underset{\text{Oxygen atom}}{\overset{\times\times}{\underset{\times\times}{O}}{}_{\times}^{\times}} \quad \rightarrow \quad \underset{\text{Magnesium oxide (ionic)}}{Mg^{++}\left[:\overset{\times\times}{\underset{\times\times}{O}}{}_{\times}^{\times}\right]^=}$$

$$\underset{\text{Calcium atom}}{\cdot Ca\cdot} \quad + \quad \underset{\text{Fluorine atoms}}{2\,{}^{\times}\overset{\times\times}{\underset{\times\times}{F}}{}_{\times}^{\times}} \quad \rightarrow \quad \underset{\text{Calcium fluoride (ionic)}}{\left[{}_{\times}^{\times}\overset{\times\times}{\underset{\times\times}{F}}{}^{\times}_{\cdot}\right]^- Ca^{++}\left[{}^{\times}_{\cdot}\overset{\times\times}{\underset{\times\times}{F}}{}_{\times}^{\times}\right]^-}$$

The atom and the ion of an element have distinct physical and chemical properties. Sodium is a soft, silvery-white metal that burns vigorously in air and reacts rapidly with water. Chlorine is a greenish-yellow gas which is extremely corrosive to most metals and is very poisonous. Sodium chloride, table salt, is formed in a vigorous reaction between sodium atoms and chlorine atoms. This compound, which contains ions of sodium and chlorine, exists as a crystalline solid with properties quite different from those of sodium and chlorine as elements. Chlorine is poisonous but sodium chloride is a substance essential to life.

A crystal of sodium chloride consists of a regular geometrical arrangement of sodium and chloride ions (Fig. 4–1). Each sodium ion is surrounded by six chloride

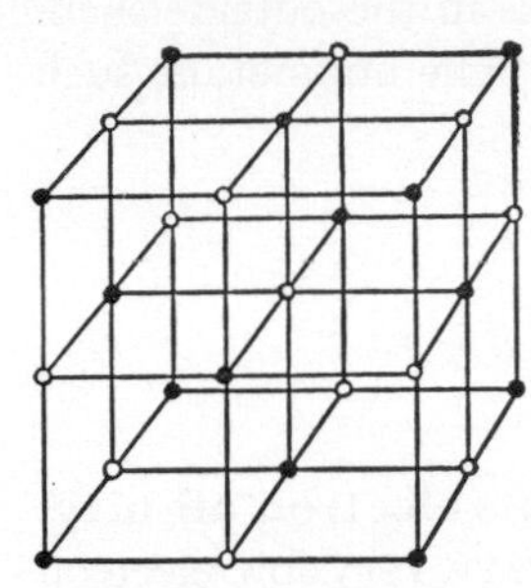

Fig. 4–1 The arrangement of sodium and chloride ions in a crystal of sodium chloride (common salt). The small spheres represent sodium ions and the large spheres chloride ions in the perspective drawing (right).

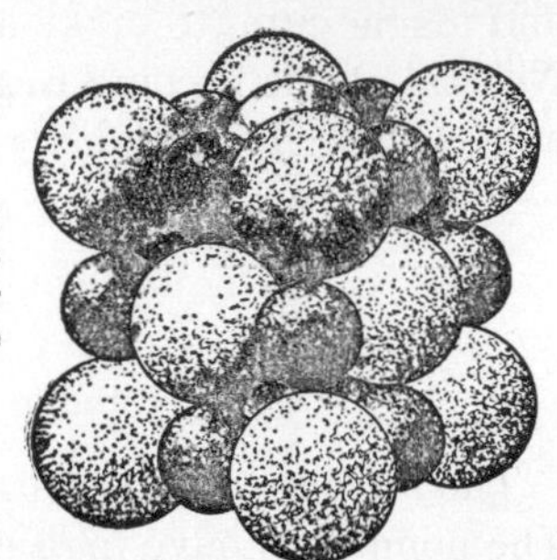

ions and each chloride ion is surrounded by six neighboring sodium ions. The force which holds the ions together in the crystal is the electrostatic attraction between ions of opposite charge. Any given ion in the crystal exerts a similar force on all of its six immediate neighbors of opposite charge, and it is therefore impossible to identify any one sodium ion and chloride ion as constituting a molecule of sodium chloride. In truly ionic compounds, then, no molecules are present and a crystal of an ionic compound is an aggregation of charged particles. The formula of an ionic compound represents the relative number of ions necessary to give an algebraic balance of ionic charges. Since a crystal of sodium chloride is electrically neutral, it must contain the same number of Na^+ and Cl^- and its formula is NaCl. A crystal of sodium oxide contains twice as many Na^+ as $O^=$, and its formula is Na_2O. It follows that the term "molecular weight" has no significance in connection with ionic substances. The formula NaCl represents one formula weight of sodium chloride; but it cannot be said to represent a molecular weight, for there are no molecules of sodium chloride.

Ionic compounds are usually hard, crystalline solids with high melting points and low volatility. They conduct electricity when melted or dissolved in a suitable solvent, conditions under which the ions become mobile.

4.2 Ions with a Rare Gas Structure

When the sodium atom loses its one valence electron, it then has an electronic configuration identical with that of the rare gas neon. Magnesium atoms acquire this same electronic configuration by losing their two valence electrons.

	Nucleus		
Neon atom, Ne	$10p$ $10n$	2 e	8 e
Sodium ion, Na^+	$11p$ $12n$	2 e	8 e
Magnesium ion, Mg^{++}	$12p$ $12n$	2 e	8 e

Lithium ions (Li^+) and beryllium ions (Be^{++}) have the same electron arrangements as the helium atom; Na^+ and Mg^{++}, the same as neon; K^+ and Ca^{++}, the same as argon; Rb^+ and Sr^{++}, the same as krypton; Cs^+ and Ba^{++}, the same as xenon; and Fr^+ and Ra^{++}, the same as radon. The electron distribution in atoms of the rare gases is reviewed in Table 4·1.

TABLE 4·1 Electron Distribution in the Rare Gases

Shell	*K*	*L*	*M*	*N*	*O*	*P*
He	2					
Ne	2	8				
Ar	2	8	8			
Kr	2	8	18	8		
Xe	2	8	18	18	8	
Rn	2	8	18	32	18	8

The negative chloride and sulfide ions resemble the argon atom in electronic structure.

	Nucleus			
Argon atom, Ar	18*p* 22*n*	2 e	8 e	8 e
Chloride ion, Cl^-	17*p* 18*n*	2 e	8 e	8 e
Sulfide ion, $S^{=}$	16*p* 16*n*	2 e	8 e	8 e

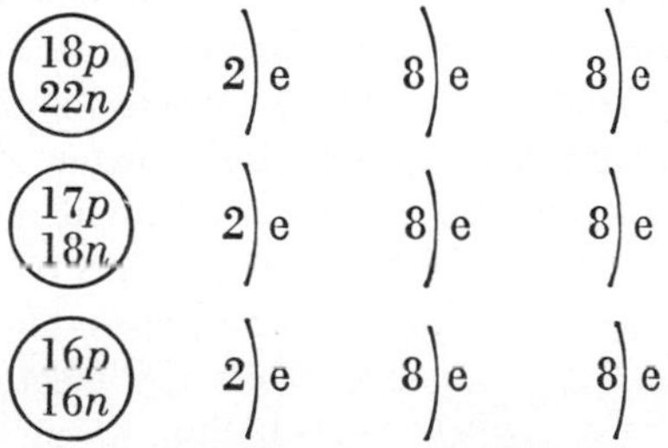

Furthermore, each of the negative ions F^-, Br^-, I^-, H^-, $O^{=}$, and $N^{\equiv}$ has an electronic structure like that of one of the rare gases. It is a remarkable fact that every positive and negative ion mentioned above contains the same number of electrons as one of the rare gases. The rare gas arrangement of electrons is undeniably one of stability. This is evidenced by the lack of chemical reactivity of the rare gases and by the high ionization potentials associated with these arrangements. Overemphasis of the rare gas arrangements must, however, be avoided because there are many ions, all positive ones, with other electron arrangements that are stable in aqueous solution. Some examples of such ions are Cu^{++}, Zn^{++}, Ag^+, Cd^{++}, Hg^{++}, Au^+, Cr^{++}, Cr^{+++}, Mn^{++}, Fe^{++}, Fe^{+++}, Ni^{++}, Co^{++}, and there are many others.

4.3 Chemical Bonding by Sharing Electrons; Covalent Bonds

In Section 4.1 we have considered chemical compounds which contain ions held together by strong electrostatic forces. There are many compounds, however, which do not contain ions. These nonionic compounds consist of atoms bonded tightly together in the form of molecules. The bonds holding the atoms together are called **shared-electron-pair bonds** or **covalent bonds.** The simplest substance in which the atoms are covalently bonded is the hydrogen molecule, H_2. Each hydrogen atom has one electron in its K shell. The electrons from two hydrogen atoms may form a pair which is shared by the two nuclei (Fig. 4–2).

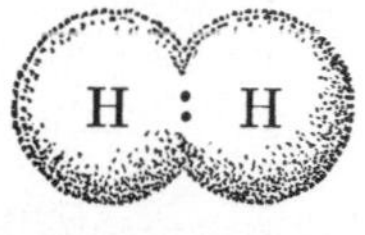

H : H

$$\underset{\text{Hydrogen atoms}}{H\cdot \; + \; {}^{\times}H} \quad \longrightarrow \quad \underset{\text{Hydrogen molecule}}{H{\stackrel{\cdot}{\times}}H}$$

Fig. 4–2 Combination of two hydrogen atoms to form a hydrogen molecule, H_2, by covalent bonding.

The two electrons are held jointly by the two nuclei, and serve to bond them together. The bond is very strong, as evidenced by the large amount of energy required to break it — 103.4 kilocalories per mole. This same quantity of energy is evolved when a mole of molecular hydrogen is formed from hydrogen atoms.

It is evident that the bonding in the hydrogen molecule cannot be the result of electron transfer, as in ionic compounds, because the two hydrogen atoms have identical ionization potentials and electron affinities. Note that no ions are formed when two atoms unite by the sharing of a pair of electrons; the product of the union is a molecule. We saw in the preceding section that there is a strong tendency for certain metals and the nonmetals to gain stability by assuming the electronic arrangement of a rare gas through the transfer of electrons. This same tendency is operative when atoms unite to form covalent molecules by electron-pair sharing.

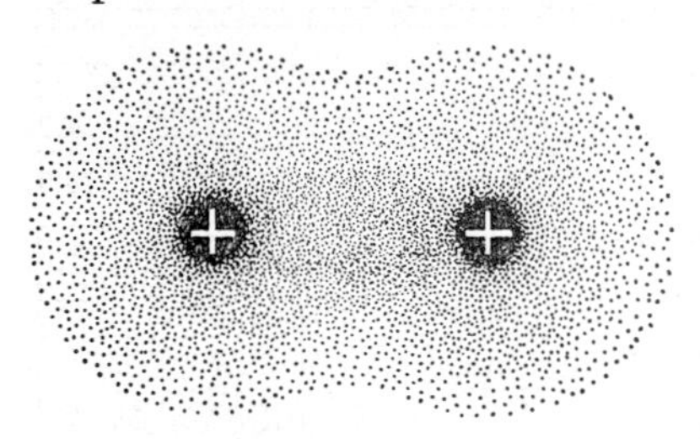

Fig. 4–3 Distribution of charge within the hydrogen molecule.

When the two electrons of the covalent bond are counted for each atom, each hydrogen atom has the electronic arrangement of the stable helium atom. The 1*s* orbital of each hydrogen atom in the H_2 molecule is, in effect, occupied by both electrons of the shared pair. The electron pair occupies the whole molecule, spending an equal amount of time near each nucleus. Figure 4–3 illustrates the distribution of charge in the H_2 molecule. The shading represents the intensity of negative charge, that is, the relative probability of finding the electron pair at a given location.

The bonding in a molecule of chlorine, Cl_2, furnishes a second example of covalent bonding. Each atom of chlorine has seven electrons in its outer shell and differs from the rare gas argon in its electronic structure by one electron. The sharing of one pair of electrons between two atoms in a molecule of chlorine gives each atom the stable electronic structure of an atom of argon.

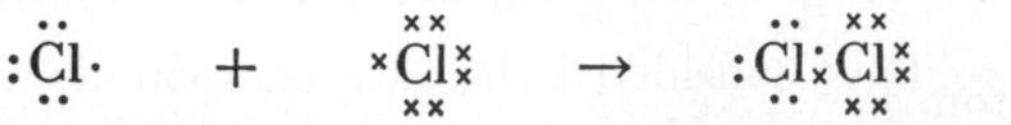

$$\underset{\text{Chlorine atoms}}{:\ddot{\underset{\cdot\cdot}{Cl}}\cdot \; + \; {}^{\times}\overset{\times\times}{\underset{\times\times}{Cl}}{}^{\times}_{\times}} \quad \longrightarrow \quad \underset{\text{Chlorine molecule}}{:\ddot{\underset{\cdot\cdot}{Cl}}{\stackrel{\cdot}{\times}}\overset{\times\times}{\underset{\times\times}{Cl}}{}^{\times}_{\times}}$$

The bonding in the other halogen molecules F_2, Br_2, and I_2 is like that in the chlorine molecule.

Many atoms share more than one pair of electrons, if that is necessary to give each atom a full complement of eight electrons in its valence shell. For example, the atoms in the nitrogen molecule, N_2, share three pairs of electrons. This makes a total of eight electrons in the valence shell of each nitrogen atom.

$$:\overset{\cdot}{\underset{\cdot}{N}}\cdot \quad + \quad \times\overset{\times}{\underset{\times}{N}}\overset{\times}{\underset{\times}{}} \quad \rightarrow \quad :N\overset{\cdot\times}{\underset{\cdot\times}{\vdots\times}}N\overset{\times}{\underset{\times}{}}$$

The two atoms in the N_2 molecule are said to be held together by a triple covalent bond.

In covalent molecules, the valence of an atom is regarded as the number of electron pairs shared by the atom. Thus hydrogen and chlorine each have a valence of one whereas nitrogen has a valence of three in their diatomic molecules H_2, Cl_2, and N_2, respectively.

4.4 Covalent Bonds Between Unlike Atoms

Unlike atoms may also combine through covalent bond formation. For example, one hydrogen atom combines with one chlorine atom with the formation of a molecule of hydrogen chloride, the atoms of which are covalently bonded.

$$H\cdot \quad + \quad \times\overset{\times\times}{\underset{\times\times}{Cl}}\overset{\times}{\underset{\times}{}} \quad \rightarrow \quad H\overset{\cdot}{\underset{\times}{}}\overset{\times\times}{\underset{\times\times}{Cl}}\overset{\times}{\underset{\times}{}}$$

Although the electrons of the pair are shared between the hydrogen atom and chlorine atom, they are not shared equally, as they are in H_2 and Cl_2. A chlorine atom attracts electrons more strongly than does a hydrogen atom, causing the electrons of the shared pair to be associated with the chlorine nucleus more than half of the time. This results in the development of a "partial" positive charge on the hydrogen atom and a "partial" negative charge on the chlorine atom. This does not imply, however, that the hydrogen atom has lost its electron; it means that the electrons of the pair spend more time on the average in the vicinity of the chlorine nucleus than near the hydrogen nucleus. Another way of stating this is to say that the electron density, or the density of the electron cloud, is greater around the chlorine nucleus than around the hydrogen nucleus.

The oxygen atom has six valence electrons and completes an octet of electrons (eight electrons) by sharing electron pairs with two hydrogen atoms in the covalent water molecule.

$$\begin{array}{c} H\overset{\times}{\underset{\cdot}{}}\overset{\times\times}{\underset{\cdot\times}{O}}\overset{\times}{\underset{\times}{}} \\ H \end{array}$$

Water

The nitrogen atom with five valence electrons shares electron pairs with three hydrogen atoms in the covalent ammonia molecule, NH_3. In a molecule of methane,

CH_4, the carbon atom with four valence electrons completes its octet by forming covalent bonds with four atoms of hydrogen.

```
   H            H
   ×·           ·×
 H×N××        H×C×H
   ·×           ·×
   H            H
Ammonia      Methane
```

The carbon dioxide molecule contains one atom of carbon with four valence electrons and two atoms of oxygen, each with six valence electrons. The sharing of two electron pairs between the carbon atom and each of the two oxygen atoms gives each of the three atoms in the molecule an octet of electrons.

```
 ××      ××
×O××:C:××O×
×        ×
```

Carbon dioxide

4.5 Covalently Bonded Atoms Without Rare Gas Structure

As has been pointed out, stable compounds do exist in which the atoms do not all have the rare gas arrangement. For example, boron, with three valence electrons, shares electron pairs with three chlorine atoms in the molecule BCl_3. Although this union of atoms gives each chlorine atom an argon structure, boron with six electrons in its outer shell does not have the electron arrangement of a rare gas. Furthermore, atoms of the elements in which the outermost electron shell is the M shell or higher can participate in covalent bonding with other atoms in which more than four pairs of electrons are shared. For example, the phosphorus atom in liquid or gaseous PCl_5 shares five pairs of electrons, or ten electrons in all, whereas atoms of the rare gases are restricted to a maximum of eight electrons in the outer shells of the free elements. The outermost or M shell of phosphorus has a theoretical maximum capacity of eighteen electrons, or nine electron pairs, but no examples are known in which this condition is fulfilled. Sulfur shares six electron pairs (twelve electrons) in the SF_6 molecule; and iodine, seven electron pairs in IF_7. In some cases, the number of electrons in the outer shell exceeds eight, even though some of the pairs are not shared. This is the case with IF_5 and XeF_4.

```
                                 ××
                                ×Cl×
                   ××           ·× ××
 ·B·   +   3 ×Cl×      →        B×Cl×
                   ××           ·× ××
                                ×Cl×
                                 ××
```

Boron trichloride

The formation of covalent compounds such as BCl_3, PCl_5, SF_6, and IF_7 conforms to a rule which supplements the rare gas structure or octet rule; namely, that electrons tend to occur in pairs in molecular structures. In other words, we may state that **the atoms in most covalent molecules appear to have reached a stable condition by sharing pairs of electrons with each other.** Thus the boron atom, which can form only three bonds by sharing its electrons because it has only three valence electrons, attains a condition of stability by forming three electron-pair bonds in the molecule BCl_3.

4.6 Electronegativity of the Elements

We have seen that the chlorine atom in the hydrogen chloride molecule attracts the electrons of the electron-pair bond more strongly than does the hydrogen atom so that the electrons are not shared equally by the two atoms. This power of attraction that an atom shows for electrons in a covalent bond is known as electronegativity. **Electronegativity** is a measure of the attraction of an atom for the electrons in its outer shell. The values of the electronegativities of many of the elements are given in Table 4·2, page 72. These values are based upon an arbitrary scale, meaning that we cannot say, for example, that fluorine (4.0) is twice as electronegative as boron (2.0). The electronegativity values are not a measure of absolute electronegativity, but they do provide a measure of differences in electronegativity. For example, the difference in electronegativity between boron (2.0) and nitrogen (3.0) is the same as that between nitrogen (3.0) and fluorine (4.0).

Note that the nonmetals have higher electronegativity values than the metals. Fluorine, the most chemically active nonmetal, has the highest electronegativity (4.0), and cesium, the most chemically active metal (with the possible exception of francium), has the lowest electronegativity (0.7). Because the metals have relatively low electronegativities and tend to assume positive charges in compounds, they are often spoken of as being **electropositive;** conversely, nonmetals are said to be **electronegative.**

4.7 Polarity of Substances and the Chemical Bond

A system is said to be **polar** if its center of positive charge does not coincide with its center of negative charge. An extreme case of polarity is represented by an ionic compound such as sodium chloride (Na^+Cl^-), in which the sodium ion is completely positive and the chloride ion is completely negative. When a covalent bond is formed between atoms of different electronegativities, the pair of electrons will be more closely associated with the more electronegative atom, and the resulting covalent bond will be somewhat polar. We have noted that in the hydrogen chloride molecule, the chlorine atom attracts the pair of electrons of the covalent bond more strongly than does the hydrogen atom (Section 4.4). The hydrogen-chlorine bond is polar, the chlorine atom becoming somewhat negative and the hydrogen atom becoming somewhat positive as the bond is formed. Since the centers of positive and negative electricity do not coincide, the molecule of hydrogen chloride is electrically unsymmetrical. Because of the separation of centers of charge, molecules held together by polar bonds tend to turn when placed in an electric field so that the positive end of the molecule is oriented toward the negative plate and the negative end toward the positive plate (Fig. 4–4, page 73).

The greater the difference between the electronegativities of the two atoms involved in the bond, the greater the polarity of the bond. Thus the polarity of the bond in the hydrogen halides increases in the order HI, HBr, HCl, and HF corresponding to an increase in electronegativity of the halogen: I(2.5), Br(2.8), Cl(3.0), and F(4.0). If the difference in electronegativity between the two atoms

TABLE 4·2 Electronegativity Values of the Elements, According to the Periodic Table Arrangement

H																	He
2.1																	. . .
Li	Be											B	C	N	O	F	Ne
1.0	1.5											2.0	2.5	3.0	3.5	4.0	. . .
Na	Mg											Al	Si	P	S	Cl	Ar
0.9	1.2											1.5	1.8	2.1	2.5	3.0	. . .
K	Ca	Sc	Ti	V	Cr	Mn	Fe	Co	Ni	Cu	Zn	Ga	Ge	As	Se	Br	Kr
0.8	1.0	1.3	1.5	1.6	1.6	1.5	1.8	1.8	1.8	1.9	1.6	1.6	1.8	2.0	2.4	2.8	. . .
Rb	Sr	Y	Zr	Nb	Mo	Tc	Ru	Rh	Pd	Ag	Cd	In	Sn	Sb	Te	I	Xe
0.8	1.0	1.2	1.4	1.6	1.8	1.9	2.2	2.2	2.2	1.9	1.7	1.7	1.8	1.9	2.1	2.5	. . .
Cs	Ba	La-Lu	Hf	Ta	W	Re	Os	Ir	Pt	Au	Hg	Tl	Pb	Bi	Po	At	Rn
0.7	0.9	1.1-1.2	1.3	1.5	1.7	1.9	2.2	2.2	2.2	2.4	1.9	1.8	1.8	1.9	2.0	2.2	. . .
Fr	Ra	Ac-Lw															
0.7	0.9	1.1-															

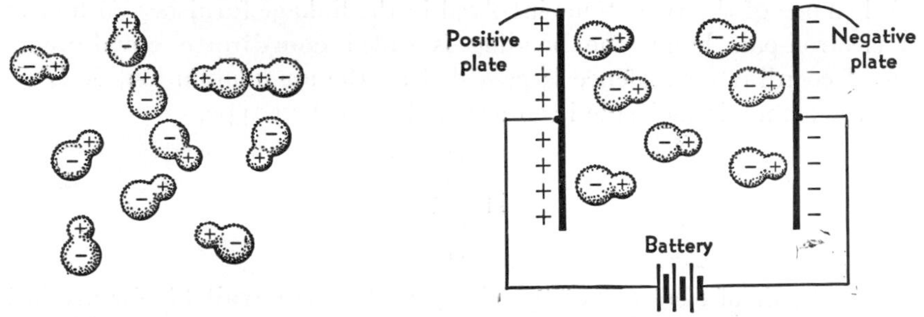

Polar molecules randomly oriented in the absence of an electric field.

Polar molecules lined up in an electric field.

Fig. 4–4 Polar molecules, such as hydrogen chloride, tend to line up in an electric field with the positive ends oriented toward the negative plate and the negative ends toward the positive plate.

is sufficiently large, the electron furnished by the atom of lower electronegativity will be transferred completely to the more electronegative atom, and ionic bonding, rather than covalent bonding, will result. The other extreme may be achieved when identical atoms share a pair of electrons as in the case of H:H, where the bonding is covalent with no polarity. It becomes apparent then that there is no sharp dividing line between compounds in which the bonding is covalent and those in which the bonding is ionic. In the intermediate cases the molecules will have bonds which possess some of the nature of both covalent and ionic bonds and are often referred to as **covalent bonds with partial ionic character** or **polar covalent bonds.**

It is possible to have molecules in which the bonds are of the polar covalent type but where the molecules as a whole are nonpolar. If a molecule contains several polar covalent bonds directed in such a way as to give a symmetrical molecule, then the molecule is nonpolar. This is illustrated by $HgCl_2$, in which each of the covalent bonds is polar while the molecule as a whole is nonpolar. The centers of positive and negative electricity for the molecule are identical. Each chlorine is negative with respect to positive mercury, and each mercury-chlorine bond has some polar character. However, these bond polarities counterbalance each other because the bonds are directed in such a manner as to give an electrically symmetrical molecule.

$$\mathrm{Cl}^{-}\longleftarrow{}^{+}\mathrm{Hg}^{+}\longrightarrow{}^{-}\mathrm{Cl}$$

Covalent compounds may exist as solids, liquids, or gases at ordinary temperatures. In general, they have low melting points and are volatile. Their solutions conduct electricity only when they form ions by reacting with the solvent (see Chapter 12).

4.8 Coordinate Covalence

We have noted that covalent bonding involves the sharing of electron pairs between atoms with each atom involved in the bond furnishing one electron to the pair. When one of the two atoms involved in the linkage furnishes both electrons of the electron-pair bond, the bonding is called **coordinate covalence.** An example of coordinate covalence is provided by the ammonium ion, NH_4^+. The bonds in the ammonia molecule itself are of the covalent type.

$$\begin{array}{c} H \\ \cdot\times \\ H{}^{\cdot}_{\times}N{}^{\times}_{\times} \\ \cdot\times \\ H \end{array}$$

The unshared pair of electrons of the nitrogen atom are available for use in bond formation as indicated by the readiness with which ammonia will combine with a hydrogen ion to form the ammonium ion.

$$\begin{array}{c} H \\ \cdot\times \\ H{}^{\cdot}_{\times}N{}^{\times}_{\times} \\ \cdot\times \\ H \\ \text{Ammonia} \\ \text{molecule, } NH_3 \end{array} \quad + \quad H^+ \quad \rightarrow \quad \begin{array}{c} \left[\begin{array}{c} H \\ \cdot\times \\ H{}^{\cdot}_{\times}N{}^{\times}_{\times}H \\ \cdot\times \\ H \end{array}\right]^+ \\ \text{Ammonium} \\ \text{ion, } NH_4^+ \end{array}$$

Because NH_3 is a neutral molecule, the union with a hydrogen ion (proton) gives a unit positive charge to the resulting ammonium ion. In a similar fashion water molecules combine with hydrogen ions to form hydronium ions.

$$\begin{array}{c} \times\times \\ H{}^{\cdot}_{\times}O{}^{\times}_{\times} \\ \cdot\times \\ H \\ \text{Water} \\ \text{molecule} \end{array} \quad + \quad H^+ \quad \rightarrow \quad \begin{array}{c} \left[\begin{array}{c} \times\times \\ H{}^{\cdot}_{\times}O{}^{\times}_{\times}H \\ \cdot\times \\ H \end{array}\right]^+ \\ \text{Hydronium} \\ \text{ion, } H_3O^+ \end{array}$$

The formation of a coordinate covalent bond is possible only between an atom with an unshared pair of electrons in its valence shell and an atom or ion that needs a pair of electrons to acquire a stable electronic configuration. The chief difference between the coordinate covalent bond and the covalent bond is in the mode of formation. Once established, they are indistinguishable.

4.9 Oxidation Numbers

The term **valence,** discussed in Section 4.3, does not indicate the positive and negative nature of the atoms in a compound. The **oxidation number,** sometimes referred to as the **oxidation state,** is related to the valence but not identical to it and is used to designate the positive and negative character of the atoms.

When valence electrons are removed or shifted away from an atom during a chemical reaction, the atom is assigned a **positive oxidation number** and is said to be in a **positive oxidation state.** When electrons are gained by or shifted toward an atom during a chemical reaction, the atom is given a **negative oxidation number** and is said to be in a **negative oxidation state.** The numerical value of the oxidation number depends upon the number of electrons involved per atom in the transfer or shift to or away from the atom.

For ionic materials, the oxidation number of an element is equal to the charge on the ion. In sodium chloride, NaCl, the oxidation number for sodium is +1 and for chlorine is −1; in magnesium oxide, MgO, the oxidation number for magnesium is +2 and for oxygen is −2; in calcium bromide, $CaBr_2$, the oxidation number for calcium is +2 and for bromine is −1.

For covalent materials, the oxidation number concept is more arbitrary but is nevertheless useful in writing formulas and, as we shall see in Chapter 14, in balancing oxidation-reduction equations. In covalent compounds containing two elements, the more electronegative element (see Table 4·2) is assigned a negative oxidation number. The more positive element is assigned a positive oxidation number. In the covalent molecule of hydrogen chloride, HCl, the hydrogen atom has an oxidation number of +1 due to a shift (but not a transfer) of the valence electron of the hydrogen toward the more electronegative chlorine atom. The chlorine atom in HCl has an oxidation number of −1. In methane, CH_4, the electronegativity of carbon is greater than that of hydrogen; in this compound, therefore, it is customary to speak of the oxidation number of carbon as −4 and that of hydrogen as +1; the electrons are shifted toward the carbon atom. In carbon dioxide, CO_2, the electronegativity of oxygen is greater than that of carbon; therefore, in this compound the oxidation number of oxygen is −2 and that of carbon is +4. In water, H_2O, each hydrogen atom has an oxidation number of +1 and oxygen an oxidation number of −2. It is convenient to indicate the oxidation number of an atom by placing the proper number and sign over its symbol. Some examples are given below.

$$\overset{+1\,-1}{NaCl} \qquad \overset{+1\,-1}{HCl} \qquad \overset{+1\,-2}{H_2O} \qquad \overset{-3\,+1}{NH_3} \qquad \overset{+2\,-2}{CaS} \qquad \overset{+1\,-1}{ICl} \qquad \overset{+4\,-1}{CCl_4}$$

Elements in the free state are always assigned an oxidation number of zero. The zero oxidation number for free elements is based upon the fact that all of the atoms of an element have the same electronegativity; there is no transfer or net shift of electrons occurring during bond formation between atoms of the same element. But the number of bonds (shared pairs of electrons) associated with each atom in a molecule is equal to the valence of the atom. Thus the valence of an atom may be different from its oxidation number as seen from the following examples.

		Valence	Oxidation number
H_2	$H\overset{\circ}{\underset{\times}{}}H$	1	0
Cl_2	$\underset{\times\times}{\overset{\times\times}{{}^{\times}_{\times}Cl}}\overset{\circ}{\underset{\times}{}}\underset{\circ\circ}{\overset{\circ\circ}{Cl{}^{\circ}_{\circ}}}$	1	0
N_2	${}^{\circ}_{\circ}N\underset{\circ\times}{\overset{\circ\times}{{}^{\circ\times}_{\circ\times}}}N{}^{\times}_{\times}$	3	0

Many elements exhibit more than one oxidation number in their various compounds. For example, iron has an oxidation number of +2 in $FeCl_2$ and an oxidation number of +3 in $FeCl_3$. Tin exhibits oxidation numbers of +2 and +4 in $SnCl_2$ and $SnCl_4$, respectively. The oxidation number of chlorine in each of the above examples is −1. Chlorine, however, exhibits an oxidation number of +1 in NaOCl, +3 in $NaClO_2$, +5 in $NaClO_3$, and +7 in $NaClO_4$.

If the oxidation numbers are known for all but one kind of atom in a compound, the remaining oxidation number can be calculated. **The algebraic sum of the positive oxidation numbers and the negative oxidation numbers of the atoms present in a compound must always be zero.** In Na_2SO_4, for example, the oxidation number for sulfur can be calculated from the known oxidation numbers for sodium and oxygen. The two sodium atoms, each with an oxidation number of +1, total +2; the four oxygen atoms, each with an oxidation number of −2, total −8. For the sum of the oxidation numbers to be zero, sulfur must have an oxidation number of +6. For Na_2SO_3, a similar calculation shows the oxidation number of sulfur in that compound to be +4. In H_2S, the oxidation number of sulfur is −2.

Several common oxidation numbers are given in Table 4·3.

It should be emphasized that, although the concept of oxidation numbers is of great convenience in writing formulas and in balancing oxidation-reduction equations, the concept is quite arbitrary.

4.10 Application of Oxidation Numbers to Writing Formulas

One can write the formulas of a great many compounds by knowing the oxidation numbers of the constituent elements of each compound. The principal oxidation number of an element is, in general, evident from the position of the element in the Periodic Table and from a knowledge of the electronic structure of the atom. The writing of formulas by using oxidation numbers is possible because the algebraic sum of the units of positive and negative oxidation number must be equal to zero.

TABLE 4·3 Examples of Common Oxidation Numbers

Element	*Oxidation Number*
H	+1 (except −1 in hydrides; for example, NaH)
Li	+1
Na	+1
K	+1
Mg	+2
Ca	+2
Zn	+2
Al	+3
Cl	−1 (−1 in compounds with only two elements; variable oxidation numbers in compounds containing more than two elements, such as $NaClO_3$ and $NaClO_4$)
Br	−1 (as for Cl)
I	−1 (as for Cl)
O	−2 (except −1 in peroxides; for example, H_2O_2)
Hg	+1 and +2
Fe	+2 and +3
Sn	+2 and +4

EXAMPLE 1. Let us write the formula for aluminum oxide by using the oxidation numbers of its constituent elements. Place the element with the positive oxidation number before the one with the negative oxidation number: $\overset{+3-2}{AlO}$. Because +3 plus −2 does not give 0, then AlO is not the correct formula for aluminum oxide. By inspection it is readily seen that 2 atoms of aluminum would give a total of 6 units of positive oxidation number, that three atoms of oxygen would give 6 units of negative oxidation number, and that the algebraic sum of the oxidation numbers would be zero. The correct simplest formula for aluminum oxide is, therefore, Al_2O_3.

EXAMPLE 2. Write the formula for magnesium chloride. The formula cannot be $\overset{+2\ -1}{MgCl}$, because +2 and −1 do not add up to 0. For the total of the oxidation numbers to be zero for the compound, the ions must be in a ratio of one magnesium ion to two chloride ions, or $MgCl_2$.

4.11 Ions Containing More than One Atom

Many ions, referred to as **polyatomic ions,** contain more than one atom. Several examples, selected from many such ions, are given in Table 4·4.

TABLE 4·4 Some Common Polyatomic Ions

Ammonium	NH_4^+	Carbonate	$CO_3^=$	Phosphate	PO_4^{-3}
Acetate	$C_2H_3O_2^-$	Sulfate	$SO_4^=$	Arsenate	AsO_4^{-3}
Nitrate	NO_3^-	Sulfite	$SO_3^=$	Arsenite	AsO_3^{-3}
Nitrite	NO_2^-	Thiosulfate	$S_2O_3^=$		
Hydroxide	OH^-	Peroxide	$O_2^=$		
Hypochlorite	ClO^-	Chromate	$CrO_4^=$		
Chlorite	ClO_2^-	Dichromate	$Cr_2O_7^=$		
Chlorate	ClO_3^-	Silicate	$SiO_3^=$		
Perchlorate	ClO_4^-				
Permanganate	MnO_4^-				

For ions containing more than one atom, the sum of the positive and negative oxidation numbers of the constituent atoms must equal the charge on the ion. Hence, for the OH^- ion, the −2 oxidation number of oxygen and the +1 oxidation number of hydrogen add up to give the −1 charge for the ion.

It is customary in writing formulas of compounds which include more than one unit of a given polyatomic ion to enclose the formula of the ion in parentheses and to indicate with a subscript the number of such ions in the compound. Examples are $(NH_4)_2CO_3$ and $Al_2(SO_4)_3$. In $(NH_4)_2CO_3$, two ammonium ions, each with a +1 ionic charge, are necessary to balance the −2 ionic charge of the carbonate ion. In $Al_2(SO_4)_3$, two aluminum ions, each with a charge of +3, and three sulfate ions, each with a charge of −2, are required to balance the charges. It should be noted that the sum of the total positive and negative oxidation numbers for the various atoms, as well as the sum of the total charges on the ions, equals zero for each compound.

The following examples illustrate the process of writing formulas for compounds containing polyatomic ions.

EXAMPLE 1. Write the formula for iron perchlorate, given that the oxidation number for iron in the compound is +3.

Consideration of the charge of +3 for the iron ion and the charge of −1 for the perchlorate ion shows the formula $\overset{+3}{Fe}(\overset{-1}{ClO_4})$ to be incorrect. By using three perchlorate ions and one iron ion, the sum of the positive and negative charges becomes zero; the correct formula is $Fe(ClO_4)_3$.

EXAMPLE 2. Write the formula for calcium phosphate.

Inasmuch as the charge for the calcium ion is +2 and the charge on the phosphate ion is −3, the formula cannot be $\overset{+2}{Ca}(\overset{-3}{PO_4})$ because the algebraic sum of the charges on the ions must be zero for the compound. By using three calcium ions and two phosphate ions, the algebraic sum becomes zero, $3(+2) + 2(-3) = 0$. Thus, $Ca_3(PO_4)_2$ is the correct formula for calcium phosphate.

4.12 The Names of Compounds

Binary Compounds. Binary compounds are those containing two different elements. The name of a binary compound consists of the name of the more electropositive element followed by the name of the more electronegative element with its ending replaced by the suffix "ide." Some examples are:

$NaCl$, sodium chloride
KBr, potassium bromide
CaI_2, calcium iodide
AgF, silver fluoride
HCl, hydrogen chloride
Na_2O, sodium oxide
CdS, cadmium sulfide
Mg_3N_2, magnesium nitride
Ca_3P_2, calcium phosphide
Al_4C_3, aluminum carbide
LiH, lithium hydride
Mg_2Si, magnesium silicide

A few polyatomic ions have special names and are treated as if they were single atoms in naming their compounds; thus $NaOH$ is called sodium hydroxide; HCN, hydrogen cyanide; and NH_4Cl, ammonium chloride.

If a binary hydrogen compound is an acid when it is dissolved in water, the prefix "hydro" is used and the suffix "ic" replaces the suffix "ide."

HCl, hydrochloric acid
HBr, hydrobromic acid
H_2S, hydrosulfuric acid
HCN, hydrocyanic acid

When an element of variable valence forms more than one compound with another element, the compounds may be distinguished from each other by means of the Greek prefixes *mono-* (meaning one), *di-* (two), *tri-* (three), *tetra-* (four), *penta-* (five), *hexa-* (six), *hepta-* (seven), and *octa-* (eight). The prefixes precede the name of the constituent to which they refer. The prefix "mono" is sometimes omitted.

CO, carbon monoxide	N_2O_5, dinitrogen pentoxide
CO_2, carbon dioxide	PbO, lead monoxide
NO_2, nitrogen dioxide	PbO_2, lead dioxide
N_2O_4, dinitrogen tetroxide	Pb_3O_4, trilead tetroxide

A second method of naming different binary compounds containing the same elements involves the use of Roman numerals placed in parentheses to indicate the oxidation number of the more positive element, and following the names of the elements to which they refer. This method of naming binary compounds is usually applied to those in which the electropositive element is a metal.

$FeCl_2$, iron (II) chloride	Hg_2O, mercury (I) oxide
$FeCl_3$, iron (III) chloride	HgO, mercury (II) oxide

Although the system of nomenclature used in this book is, for the most part, an improved system as formulated by a committee of the International Union of Pure and Applied Chemistry, it is essential that the student become familiar also with the "old" system because it will be constantly encountered.

According to the "old" system, when two elements form more than one compound with each other, and when both elements are nonmetals, the distinction is made by indicating only the number of atoms of the more electronegative element by Greek prefixes. NO_2, N_2O_3, N_2O_4, and N_2O_5 are nitrogen dioxide, trioxide, tetroxide, and pentoxide, respectively. When the more electropositive element is a metal, the lower oxidation number of the metal is indicated by using the suffix "ous" on the name of the metal. The higher oxidation number is designated by the suffix "ic." Thus $FeCl_2$ is ferrous chloride, and $FeCl_3$ is ferric chloride, Hg_2O is mercurous oxide, and HgO is mercuric oxide.

Ternary Compounds. Ternary compounds are those containing three different elements. It has already been noted that some ternary compounds, such as NH_4Cl, KOH, and HCN, are named as if they were binary compounds. Chlorine, nitrogen, sulfur, phosphorus, and several other elements each form oxyacids (ternary compounds with hydrogen and oxygen) which differ from each other in their oxygen content. Usually the most common acid of a series bears the name of the acid-forming element ending with the suffix "ic." This may be noted in the names chloric acid ($HClO_3$), sulfuric acid (H_2SO_4), nitric acid (HNO_3), and phosphoric acid (H_3PO_4). The names of acids containing one oxygen atom more than the "ic" acid retain the suffix "ic" and have the prefix "per" added. The name perchloric acid for $HClO_4$ illustrates this rule. An acid which contains one less oxygen atom than the "ic" acid is named with the suffix "ous." Examples are chlorous acid ($HClO_2$), sulfurous acid (H_2SO_3), nitrous acid (HNO_2), and phosphorous acid (H_3PO_3). Acids with one less oxygen atom than the "ous" acid are named by adding the prefix "hypo" and retaining the ending "ous." Thus, $HClO$ is hypochlorous acid and H_2SO_2 is hyposulfurous acid.

Metal salts of the oxyacids (compounds in which a metal replaces the hydrogen of the acid) are named by naming the metal and then the acid radical. The ending "ic" of the oxyacid name is changed to "ate" and the ending "ous" of the acid is changed to "ite" for the salt. The salts of perchloric acid are perchlorates, those of sulfuric acid are sulfates, those of nitrous acid are nitrites, and those of hyposulfurous acid are hyposulfites. This system of naming applies to all inorganic oxyacids and their salts. The names of the oxyacids of chlorine and the corresponding sodium salts are given in Table 4·5.

TABLE 4·5 Names of Oxychlorine Acids and the Corresponding Sodium Salts

Acids	*Salts*
$HClO$, hypochlorous acid	$NaClO$, sodium hypochlorite
$HClO_2$, chlorous acid	$NaClO_2$, sodium chlorite
$HClO_3$, chloric acid	$NaClO_3$, sodium chlorate
$HClO_4$, perchloric acid	$NaClO_4$, sodium perchlorate

QUESTIONS

1. Define the following in terms of electrons: valence, single bond, double bond, and triple bond.
2. Relate valence to the number of electrons in the outermost shell of a neutral atom.
3. How is the number of valence electrons in an atom of an element related to its tendency to gain or lose electrons during compound formation?
4. How are positive and negative ions formed from neutral atoms?
5. What kind of elements tend to form positive ions? negative ions?
6. Explain the meaning of the term "ionization potential." How is the tendency of an element to form positive (or negative) ions related to its ionization potential?
7. Relate the electronic structure of positive and negative ions to that of the rare gases. Cite several examples of ions which have a rare gas electronic structure and several ions which do not.
8. How does the sodium ion differ from the sodium atom both physically and chemically? the chloride ion from the chlorine atom (or molecule)?
9. What is the nature of the bonding force which holds the sodium and chloride ions together in a crystal of sodium chloride?
10. Why may we not look upon sodium chloride as being a molecular compound?
11. Compare metals and nonmetals with regard to electron affinity.
12. Define the term covalence. Give examples of covalent bonding between like atoms and between unlike atoms.
13. What is meant by the electronegativity of an element?
14. How do the electronegativities of the metals compare with those of the nonmetals?

15. Give an example of a nonpolar covalent bond, a polar covalent bond, and a bond of extreme polarity.

16. Relate bond polarity to electronegativity differences between the atoms involved in the bond.

17. When is the formation of a coordinate covalent bond possible? Give an example.

18. From the electronegativity scale, which of the following compounds would you expect to be covalent and which ones ionic?

Methane, CH_4	Cesium iodide, CsI
Iodine monochloride, ICl	Sodium oxide, Na_2O
Silane, SiH_4	Carbon disulfide, CS_2
Barium chloride, $BaCl_2$	Cyanogen, C_2N_2
Silicon tetrachloride, $SiCl_4$	Potassium sulfide, K_2S

19. Write valence electronic structures for each of the following: KF, $CaBr_2$, PH_3, H_2O, H_3O^+, NH_4^+, $SiCl_4$, HI, Br_2, SF_6, BF_3, and ICl.

20. Name the following compounds: KCl, NaBr, CaF_2, AgI, HBr, CaO, ZnS, AlN, Ba_3P_2, NaH, Ca_2Si, NaCN, PCl_3, PCl_5, $FeBr_3$, $Ca(OH)_2$, NH_4CN, $HBrO_3$, KNO_2, KNO_3, Na_2SO_3, $Ca(ClO)_2$, KIO_4.

21. With the aid of oxidation numbers, write formulas for the following compounds: sodium fluoride, calcium hydride, aluminum oxide, tin (II) fluoride, uranium hexafluoride, calcium phosphate, sodium nitrite, potassium carbonate, potassium hypobromite, sodium chlorate, iron (II) sulfate, tin (IV) chloride, sulfurous acid, mercury (II) chloride, ammonium perchlorate, sodium oxide, calcium chlorite.

22. Calculate the oxidation number for each element in each of the substances listed in questions 19 and 20.

23. Calculate the oxidation number of nitrogen in each of the following: N_2O, NO, N_2O_3, N_2O_4, HNO_3, HNO_2, NH_3, NH_4Cl, N_2H_4, NH_2OH, AlN.

24. Write formulas for the following compounds: sodium acetate, calcium nitrate, aluminum hydroxide, lead (II) hydroxide, barium hypochlorite, potassium chlorite, hydrogen perchlorate, sodium permanganate, zinc oxide, phosphorus (III) chloride, iron (II) phosphate, barium carbonate, sodium sulfite, lead (II) sulfate, tin (IV) sulfate, cobalt (III) fluoride, sodium arsenate, potassium silicate, sodium peroxide, sodium thiosulfate, mercury (II) sulfide, cadmium chloride, silver carbonate, magnesium sulfate, chromium (III) oxide, hydrogen phosphate.

REFERENCES

"Principles of Chemical Bonding," R. T. Sanderson, *J. Chem. Educ.*, **38** (8) 382 (1961).

"The Building-up Principle and Atomic and Ionic Structure," D. F. Swinehart, *J. Chem. Educ.*, **27** (11) 622 (1950).

"The Use of Electronic Structure in Interpreting Chemical Reactions," W. F. Kieffer, *J. Chem. Educ.*, **25** (10) 537 (1948).

"The Role of Electrons in Interatomic Relations," W. F. Ehret, *J. Chem. Educ.*, **25** (5) 291 (1948).

"A Nomograph for Percentage of Ionic Character," W. H. Nebergall and W. A. Lindeke, *J. Chem. Educ.*, **26** (4) 223 (1949).

"The Evolution of Valence Theory and Bond Symbolism," H. Mackle, *J. Chem. Educ.*, **31** (12) 618 (1954).

"A Schematic Representation of Valence," R. T. Sanderson, *J. Chem. Educ.*, **35** (11) 541 (1958).

"Revised Inorganic (Stock) Nomenclature for the General Chemistry Student," R. C. Brasted, *J. Chem. Educ.*, **35** (3) 136 (1958).

"Nomenclature of Inorganic Chemistry" (Report of the Commission on the Nomenclature of Inorganic Chemistry, International Union of Pure and Applied Chemistry), *J. Am. Chem. Soc.*, **82**, 5523 (1960).

CHAPTER FIVE

Oxygen and Ozone

OXYGEN

We may well begin our study of the chemical elements with oxygen because it is the most abundant of all the elements. It is essential to the processes of respiration in air-breathing animals and the combustion of fuels and other substances, and its discovery marks the beginning of modern chemistry.

5.1 History

The credit for the discovery of oxygen is usually given to Priestley, an English clergyman and scientist, who in 1774 prepared oxygen by focusing the sun's rays upon mercury (II) oxide by means of a "burning glass" (Fig. 5–1). He tested the gas with a burning candle and noted that it burned more brightly than in ordinary air. Shortly thereafter, Lavoisier (Fig. 5–2) correctly interpreted the role played by oxygen in the processes of combustion and respiration. For these important advances, he is often spoken of as the father of modern chemistry. Because sulfur and phosphorus burn in this gas and form substances which give acidic solutions in water, Lavoisier named the gas **oxygen,** a term derived from the Greek, meaning "acid producer." He assumed oxygen to be an essential constituent of all acids. This assumption was incorrect because many acids contain no oxygen.

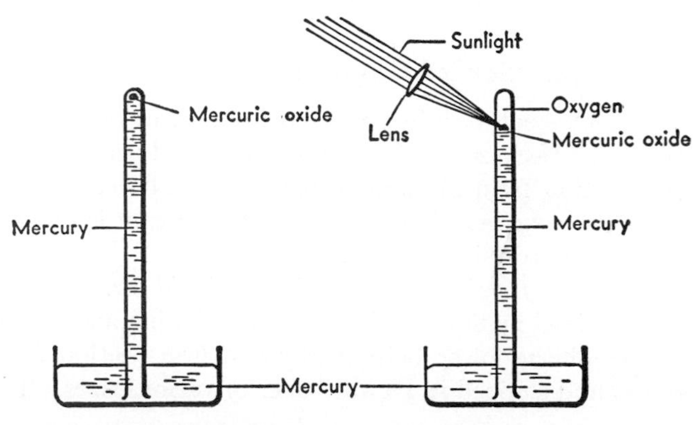

Fig. 5–1 Priestley prepared oxygen by the method illustrated here.

Fig. 5–2 An artist's concept of Antoine Laurent Lavoisier (1743–1794) explaining his theory of the composition of matter. Lavoisier is often called the "Father of Chemistry." *The Bettmann Archive*

5.2 Occurrence

Oxygen is the most abundant and widely distributed of the terrestrial elements on the surface of the earth. It forms about 23 per cent of the air as the free element, 89 per cent of water, in which it is combined with hydrogen, and 50 per cent of the earth's crust by weight. About 90 per cent of the volume of the earth's crust is occupied by oxygen, which is combined with other elements, principally silicon. In combination with carbon, hydrogen, and nitrogen, oxygen constitutes a large part of the weight of the bodies of plants and animals.

5.3 Preparation of Oxygen

This element may be prepared from air or from certain oxygen-containing compounds. Because of the abundance, ready availability, cheapness, and ease of preparation from air and water, nearly all commercial oxygen is obtained from these two sources. Approximately 97 per cent is produced from air and 3 per cent by the electrolysis of water.

1. *By the fractional evaporation of liquid air.* Commercial quantities of oxygen are obtained by first cooling and compressing air until it liquefies and then evaporating off the lower boiling nitrogen (see Section 24.2). As a liquid, oxygen is stored and shipped in Dewar flasks of various sizes. These are equipped to be self-

refrigerating by the evaporation of some of the oxygen. Much commercial oxygen, however, is stored and shipped as a compressed gas in steel cylinders. Liquid oxygen is one of the propellant components for today's rockets (see Sections 5.13 and 25.13).

2. *Preparation from water by electrolysis.* Pure water is a very poor conductor of electricity; but when a small amount of an acid, base, or salt is dissolved in water, the resulting solution readily conducts an electric current. Acids, bases, and salts are three important classes of compounds, called **electrolytes,** that furnish positive and negative ions in solution. When a current of electricity is passed through a conducting solution between two electrodes, the ions of the electrolyte are the agencies that carry the current; they migrate toward the electrodes. The positive ions (**cations**) move toward the negative electrode (**cathode**), and the negative ions (**anions**) move toward the positive electrode (**anode**). When an electric current is passed through water containing a small amount of an acid, base, or salt, such as H_2SO_4, NaOH, or Na_2SO_4, bubbles of hydrogen are formed at the cathode and oxygen is evolved at the anode (Fig. 5–3). The process is called **electrolysis.** Measurements show that the volume of hydrogen produced is twice that of the oxygen. The net reaction can be summarized by the equation

$$2\,H_2O + \text{electrical energy} \rightarrow 2\,H_2\uparrow + O_2\uparrow$$

although, as we shall see in Section 20.5, the reactions taking place at the electrodes are somewhat more complex than suggested by this simple equation. It is important to note that the energy change involved in this reaction is an absorption of electrical energy. The same amount of energy is liberated as heat and light if the hydrogen and oxygen produced by electrolysis are recombined by combustion to form water. The use of this process for the industrial production of oxygen is limited because of the excessive cost of the electricity which is required.

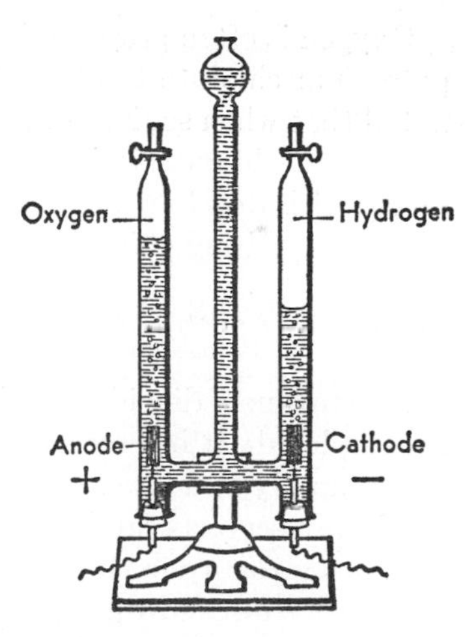

Fig. 5–3 Electrolysis of water.

3. *By heating certain metal oxides.* The oxides of mercury, silver, gold, and platinum lose oxygen when heated. For example, when red mercury (II) oxide is heated (Fig. 5–4), metallic mercury and oxygen are formed.

$$\underset{\text{Mercury (II) oxide}}{2\,HgO} + \Delta \rightarrow 2\,Hg + O_2$$

This is the method used by Priestley and Lavoisier. It is too expensive to be used except for its historic interest. Equations similar to that for the thermal decomposition of mercury (II) oxide can be written for silver oxide, Ag_2O; the oxides of gold, Au_2O and Au_2O_3; and the oxides of platinum, PtO and PtO_2.

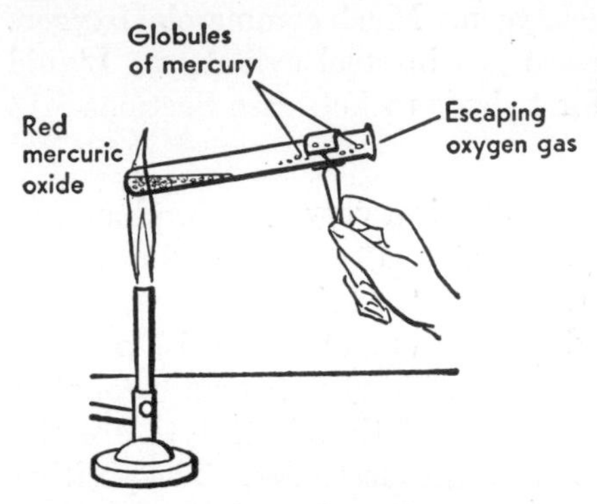

Fig. 5–4 When mercury (II) oxide is strongly heated, it decomposes, yielding oxygen gas and liquid mercury.

When metal oxides containing a high proportion of oxygen are heated, part of their oxygen is liberated.

$$2\,BaO_2 + \Delta \rightarrow 2\,BaO + O_2$$
Barium peroxide — Barium oxide

4. *By heating certain salts which contain oxygen.* The nitrate salts of metals yield oxygen upon being heated.

$$2\,NaNO_3 + \Delta \rightarrow 2\,NaNO_2 + O_2$$
Sodium nitrate — Sodium nitrite

$$2\,Cu(NO_3)_2 + \Delta \rightarrow 2\,CuO + 4\,NO_2 + O_2$$
Copper (II) nitrate — Copper (II) oxide — Nitrogen dioxide

Oxygen is often prepared in the laboratory on a small scale (Fig. 5–5) by heating potassium chlorate to about 50° above its melting point of 368.4°. It should be noted that when sodium nitrate is heated, only part of the oxygen is lost, but when potassium chlorate is heated, all the oxygen escapes. If manganese dioxide is mixed with the chlorate, the latter decomposes quite rapidly near 270°, nearly 100° below its melting point.

$$2\,KClO_3 + \Delta \xrightarrow{MnO_2} 2\,KCl + 3\,O_2$$
Potassium chlorate — Potassium chloride

The manganese dioxide may be reclaimed chemically unchanged after the reaction is completed; it has served to "catalyze" the reaction by causing it to take place more rapidly at a lower temperature. Many other metal oxides, such as Fe_2O_3 and Cr_2O_3 also serve as catalysts for the decomposition of potassium chlorate. **A catalyst is a substance that either increases or decreases the speed of a reaction without undergoing a permanent chemical change itself. Positive catalysts** increase the speed of reactions; **negative catalysts** decrease the speed of reactions. Manganese dioxide acts as a positive catalyst in the thermal decomposition of potassium chlorate. Catalysts are usually specific in their action; a substance that will catalyze one reaction is often without effect upon another.

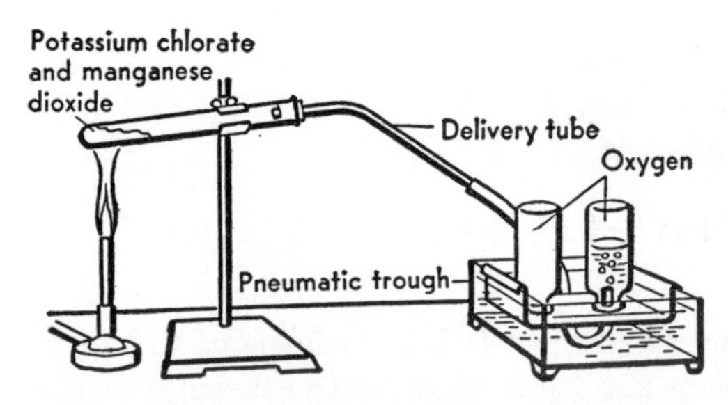

Fig. 5–5 Oxygen is usually prepared in the laboratory as indicated in this diagram. The manganese dioxide remains after the potassium chlorate has decomposed.

The preparation of oxygen by heating potassium chlorate can be very dangerous when done by beginners. Explosions can occur when combustible material such as carbon, sulfur, and rubber come in contact with fused potassium chlorate. The danger involved in this experiment cannot be overemphasized. Proceed with caution when preparing oxygen by this method.

5. *By the action of water upon sodium peroxide.* A convenient but expensive method for the preparation of oxygen involves the action of water upon sodium peroxide, a solid formed by burning sodium in an excess of oxygen or air.

$$\underset{\text{Sodium peroxide}}{2\ Na_2O_2} + 2\ H_2O \rightarrow \underset{\text{Sodium hydroxide}}{4\ Na^+ + 4\ OH^-} + O_2\uparrow$$

The fact that the sodium hydroxide is in water solution as independent ions is indicated by designating it as $Na^+ + OH^-$ rather than by the formula NaOH. Evaporation of the solution to dryness would cause the ions to associate and form solid sodium hydroxide (usually written as NaOH).

5.4 Physical Properties

Oxygen is a colorless, odorless, and tasteless gas that is slightly more dense than air. One liter of oxygen measured at 0° and 760 mm. weighs 1.429 g. A corresponding volume of air weighs 1.292 g. Although oxygen is only slightly soluble in water (30 ml. of gas in one liter of water at 20°) its solubility is very important to marine life. Oxygen is pale blue in the liquid state and boils at −183° at atmospheric pressure. Solid oxygen, also pale blue, melts at −218.4°. The oxygen molecule is diatomic (O_2) and it is **paramagnetic,** i.e., attracted by a magnetic field, particularly when in the solid or liquid state.

5.5 Chemical Properties

Oxygen is an active element that combines either directly or indirectly with nearly all the other elements, the only exceptions being the inert gases. The product formed when an element combines with oxygen is called an **oxide. The process of combining with oxygen is called oxidation,** a term which is later used in this book with a much broader meaning.

1. *Action with metals.* The metals down to and including copper in the activity series (see Section 6.9) combine directly with oxygen to form oxides. The action is slow in most cases at ordinary temperatures. Many of the more active metals burn readily when heated in the presence of pure oxygen.

$$2\ Na + O_2 \rightarrow Na_2O_2 \text{ (Sodium peroxide)}$$
$$2\ Ca + O_2 \rightarrow 2\ CaO \text{ (Calcium oxide)}$$
$$2\ Mg + O_2 \rightarrow 2\ MgO \text{ (Magnesium oxide)}$$
$$4\ Al + 3\ O_2 \rightarrow 2\ Al_2O_3 \text{ (Aluminum oxide)}$$
$$3\ Fe + 2\ O_2 \rightarrow Fe_3O_4 \text{ (Iron (II, III) oxide)}$$

The oxide (Fe_3O_4) formed by burning iron in oxygen is different from the one (Fe_2O_3) produced when iron rusts. In the compound Fe_3O_4, one atom of iron shares two electrons with the oxygen whereas the other two atoms of iron share three electrons each. The two different valence states for iron in the compound, which may also be represented as $FeO \cdot Fe_2O_3$, are indicated in the name iron (II, III) oxide. The name of FeO is simply iron (II) oxide, and that of Fe_2O_3 is iron (III) oxide.

2. *Action with nonmetals.* Many of the nonmetals combine directly with oxygen to form oxides. Although oxygen does not combine directly with the halogens (fluorine, chlorine, bromine, and iodine), oxides of these elements are known. Some typical reactions of nonmetals with oxygen are as follows:

$$2\ H_2 + O_2 \rightarrow 2\ H_2O \text{ (Water)}$$
$$C + O_2 \rightarrow CO_2 \text{ (Carbon dioxide)}$$
$$S + O_2 \rightarrow SO_2 \text{ (Sulfur dioxide)}$$
$$P_4 + 5\ O_2 \rightarrow P_4O_{10} \text{ (Phosphorus (V) oxide)}$$

Elements which exhibit more than one oxidation number may form more than one oxide. Carbon forms CO and CO_2; sulfur forms SO_2 and SO_3; and phosphorus forms P_4O_6 and P_4O_{10}.

3. *Action with compounds.* If a compound is composed of elements which will combine with oxygen, the compound will also react with oxygen; oxides of the constituent elements are produced. For example, hydrogen sulfide contains the elements hydrogen and sulfur, both of which will react directly with oxygen when they are free. Thus hydrogen sulfide burns in oxygen when ignited and forms water and sulfur dioxide.

$$2\ H_2S + 3\ O_2 \rightarrow 2\ H_2O + 2\ SO_2$$

Additional examples of compounds that react with oxygen and the equations for the reactions follow.

$$\underset{\text{Carbon disulfide}}{CS_2} + 3\ O_2 \rightarrow CO_2 + 2\ SO_2$$

$$\underset{\text{Sugar}}{C_{12}H_{22}O_{11}} + 12\ O_2 \rightarrow 12\ CO_2 + 11\ H_2O$$

$$\underset{\text{Methane}}{CH_4} + 2\ O_2 \rightarrow CO_2 + 2\ H_2O$$

$$\underset{\text{Zinc sulfide}}{2\ ZnS} + 3\ O_2 \rightarrow 2\ ZnO + 2\ SO_2$$

Certain oxides, in which all the valence electrons of the element with which the oxygen is combined are not already involved in bonding, will unite with oxygen. Examples are given below:

$$\underset{\text{Carbon monoxide}}{2\ CO} + O_2 \rightarrow 2\ CO_2$$

$$\underset{\text{Phosphorus (III) oxide}}{P_4O_6} + 2\ O_2 \rightarrow P_4O_{10}$$

Compounds such as carbon dioxide (CO_2), sand (SiO_2), sulfur trioxide (SO_3), and magnesium oxide (MgO) do not react with oxygen, because in these compounds all of the valence electrons of the element with which the oxygen is combined are already involved in bonding.

5.6 The Action of Water on Oxides of Certain Elements

When the oxides of certain elements such as sodium, potassium, calcium, and magnesium are dissolved in water, the solutions turn red litmus blue. This behavior is characteristic of aqueous solutions of bases. The equations for the reaction of sodium oxide and calcium oxide with water are written as follows:

$$Na_2O + H_2O \rightarrow 2\ Na^+ + 2\ OH^- \text{ (Sodium hydroxide)}$$
$$CaO + H_2O \rightarrow Ca^{++} + 2\ OH^- \text{ (Calcium hydroxide)}$$

Sodium oxide and calcium oxide are often called **basic oxides** or **basic anhydrides** because they may be considered to be hydroxide bases minus water. Elements whose oxides are basic in character are called metals. However, there are many oxides of metals, such as Fe_3O_4, which are not significantly soluble in water and thus cannot be considered as being basic oxides.

Oxides of certain other elements such as carbon, sulfur, and phosphorus dissolve in water to form solutions which turn blue litmus red. This behavior is characteristic of aqueous solutions of acids. The reactions of these oxides with water are indicated by the following equations:

$$CO_2 + H_2O \rightarrow H_2CO_3 \text{ (Carbonic acid)}$$
$$SO_2 + H_2O \rightarrow H_2SO_3 \text{ (Sulfurous acid)}$$
$$P_4O_{10} + 6\ H_2O \rightarrow 4\ H_3PO_4 \text{ (Phosphoric acid)}$$

Acidic oxides are also called **acid anhydrides** because they may be considered to be acids minus water. Elements whose oxides are acidic in character are called nonmetals.

5.7 Acids, Bases, and Salts

There are three very important classes of chemical compounds which are called acids, bases, and salts. We shall note their general characteristics here and study them in more detail later (Chapter 21).

Acids comprise a class of compounds which we recognize not only by the ability of their aqueous solutions to turn blue litmus red, but also by their sour taste and their ability to neutralize bases. The sour taste of vinegar is due to acetic acid ($HC_2H_3O_2$), and that of lemon juice to citric acid ($H_3C_6H_5O_7$). Common laboratory acids include hydrochloric (HCl), sulfuric (H_2SO_4), and nitric (HNO_3). Great caution must be exercised in tasting all chemicals because many of them are either poisonous or corrosive.

Hydrogen is a characteristic constituent of all acids in aqueous solution. When an acid such as HCl dissolves in water, it ionizes. The ionization of HCl is shown by the equation:

$$HCl + H_2O \rightarrow \underset{\text{Hydronium ion}}{H_3O^+} + \underset{\text{Chloride ion}}{Cl^-}$$

Or in terms of valence electron symbols:

$$\mathrm{H}\!:\!\overset{\times\times}{\underset{\times\times}{\mathrm{Cl}}}\!\!\times\!\!\times \quad + \quad \mathrm{H}\!:\!\overset{\times\times}{\underset{\underset{\mathrm{H}}{\cdot\times}}{\mathrm{O}}}\!\!\times\!\!\times \longrightarrow \left[\mathrm{H}\!:\!\overset{\overset{\mathrm{H}}{\times\times}}{\underset{\underset{\mathrm{H}}{\cdot\times}}{\mathrm{O}}}\!\!\times\!\!\times\right]^{+} \quad + \quad :\!\overset{\times\times}{\underset{\times\times}{\mathrm{Cl}}}\!\!\times\!\!\times^{-}$$

The hydrogen leaves its valence electron with the chlorine atom which thus becomes a chloride ion, Cl^-. The hydrogen ion (the hydrogen atom minus its valence electron) does not exist free in solution, but combines with a water molecule to form the **hydronium ion,** H_3O^+. The hydration of the hydrogen ion is not unique, for all ions in aqueous solution probably form complexes with water. Although we know that the hydrogen ion is always hydrated in aqueous solution, it is usually designated as H^+ in order to simplify the writing and balancing of equations. Thus the equation for the ionization of HCl in water can be written

$$HCl \rightarrow H^+ + Cl^-$$

The hydrogen ion is responsible for the characteristic properties of acids in aqueous solution, i.e., the sour taste and the ability to turn blue litmus red and to neutralize bases.

Sodium hydroxide, NaOH, and potassium hydroxide, KOH, are two examples of the class of compounds called bases. The term **base** was formerly applied only to compounds which give hydroxide ions, OH^-, when dissolved in water. However, the significance of the term in its present usage is much broader, as we shall see in Section 21.3.

The hydroxide ion is responsible for the characteristic properties of bases in aqueous solution, i.e., the ability to turn red litmus blue, feel soapy on the skin, taste bitter, and neutralize acids. When an acid is neutralized by a base, the characteristic properties of each are lost, and a salt and water are formed. For example, hydrochloric acid is neutralized by sodium hydroxide with the formation of sodium chloride (table salt) and water.

$$\underset{\text{Sodium hydroxide}}{(Na^+) + OH^-} \quad + \quad \underset{\text{Hydrochloric acid}}{H^+ + (Cl^-)} \quad \rightarrow \quad \underset{\text{Sodium chloride}}{(Na^+) + (Cl^-)} \quad + \quad \underset{\text{Water}}{H_2O}$$

The sodium ions and chloride ions do not undergo a change during the reaction and this fact is indicated by enclosing their symbols in parentheses in the equation. In fact, the neutralization of an acid by a base can be written $H^+ + OH^- \rightarrow H_2O$. Upon evaporation of the above solution to dryness, crystalline sodium chloride is obtained. Sodium chloride is an example of a class of compounds called **salts.**

5.8 Heat of Reaction

Heat is evolved in most reactions involving the union of oxygen with an element or compound. Reactions accompanied by the production of heat are said to be **exothermic.** The burning of magnesium, hydrogen, carbon, sulfur, methane, carbon disulfide, and sugar are all exothermic reactions. Once started, exothermic reactions may proceed in the absence of any supply of energy from the outside.

Hydrogen will continue to burn in oxygen with the evolution of heat until the supply of hydrogen or oxygen is exhausted.

Reactions accompanied by the absorption of heat are called **endothermic reactions.** Reactions of this kind require a continuous supply of energy from the outside to keep them going. For example, the decomposition of potassium chlorate into potassium chloride and oxygen will continue only so long as the compound is heated.

Compounds which are formed by highly exothermic reactions, such as water and carbon dioxide, are stable toward heat; they are said to be thermally stable. This means that a very high temperature is required to decompose them into their constituent elements. Compounds resulting from endothermic reactions, such as hydrogen peroxide (H_2O_2), are thermally unstable, i.e., their internal energies tend to break the bonds holding the atoms together in the molecule.

The quantity of heat liberated or absorbed during a chemical change is referred to as the **heat of reaction.** The heat involved in the formation of compounds from their constituent elements is known as **heat of formation.** Customarily, when energy is liberated during a reaction, the heat of reaction is given a negative sign; conversely, when energy is absorbed, the heat of reaction is given a positive sign. Inasmuch as 68,317 calories of heat are liberated when a mole of water is formed from hydrogen and oxygen, the heat of formation of water from hydrogen and oxygen is −68,317 calories per mole; that of carbon dioxide is −94,052 calories; and that of magnesium oxide is −143,840 calories. The same amount of energy is required to decompose a compound into its constituent elements as is involved in the formation of the compound. This follows from the Law of Conservation of Energy. Thus, a quantity of electrical energy equivalent to 68,317 calories is needed to decompose one mole of water by the electrolytic method.

5.9 Combustion

The term **combustion** is applied to chemical reactions that are accompanied by the evolution of both light and heat. Common examples of combustion are the burning of wood, coal, or magnesium in air. Combustion, however, is not restricted to reactions involving oxygen. For example, hydrogen will burn in an atmosphere of chlorine, hydrogen chloride being formed ($H_2 + Cl_2 \rightarrow 2\ HCl$).

Before combustion can take place, the substances involved must be heated to the **kindling temperature,** i.e., the temperature at which the burning is sufficiently rapid to proceed without further addition of heat from the outside. The kindling temperature for many substances, especially solids, is not definite but depends upon the extent of subdivision and other factors. For example, iron in the form of fine wire will burn readily when heated in a Bunsen flame and then placed in pure oxygen. However, a rod of iron a few millimeters in diameter will not ignite under the same conditions.

Spontaneous combustion may occur when the heat evolved during a reaction is not carried away from the system but accumulates and raises the temperature of the reacting substances to the kindling temperature. For example, linseed oil unites with oxygen of the air at ordinary temperatures (**slow oxidation**) in an exothermic reaction. Rags soaked with linseed oil and stored in locations where there is insufficient circulation of air to carry off the heat produced by slow oxidation may ignite spontaneously, i.e., the heat of reaction accumulates and raises the temperature of the system above the kindling point. Many costly and disastrous fires have been started by spontaneous combustion of such materials as uncured hay stored in unventilated barns and waste rags containing paints or drying oils.

Whenever combustion takes place extremely rapidly, the heat of reaction is liberated almost instantly and usually a large increase in gaseous volume results. Such reactions are known as **explosions.** The mixture of gasoline and air in the cylinder of an automobile engine explodes when ignited by a spark. The rapid burning of gunpowder results in an explosion. Disastrous explosions sometimes occur in flour mills and coal mines when dry dust is ignited. Any process, whether it be a chemical reaction or simply the overheating of a steam boiler, which leads to a sudden, large increase in gaseous volume can create an explosion.

5.10 Flames

The combustion of many materials is accompanied by the production of flames. When wood or coal is heated, combustible gases are liberated. The burning of these gases produces the effect that we call a **flame.** When charcoal and coke burn, there is no flame. The reason for this is that the volatile substances were driven off during the production of the charcoal and coke by heating them in the absence of air.

When hydrogen gas burns, a nearly colorless flame is produced. However, the flame produced by burning wood or coal is colored yellow. Some of the carbon-containing compounds in the gas from coal or wood decompose, and some free carbon is liberated. The carbon particles emit light when heated sufficiently and thus impart color to the flame.

5.11 Speed of Reaction

Oxygen combines slowly with finely divided bituminous, or soft, coal at ordinary temperatures with the production of little heat and no light. Such a change is called **slow oxidation.** When ignited, coal may burn quietly with a flame, considerable heat and light being produced. Finely divided coal and oxygen unite explosively when ignited by a spark. It is evident, then, that the speed of a given reaction may vary greatly. The rate at which substances are used up or are formed during a chemical change is known as the **speed of reaction.** Among the factors which influence the speed of a reaction are: the temperature, the concentration of the reactants, and the presence or absence of a catalyst (see Chapter 16).

1. *Temperature.* In general, substances react faster when heated. Many reaction rates, roughly speaking, are doubled for each 10° rise in temperature.

2. *Concentration.* The fact that a heated iron wire will burn in pure oxygen but not in air, which is only 21 per cent oxygen by volume, shows the effect of concentration upon the speed of oxidation of iron. The speed of a reaction increases as the concentration of the reactants is increased. Reactions between substances take place only when they are in contact, and the more intimate the contact the more rapid the reaction may become. Powdered coal burns more rapidly than the same mass of coal in the form of a single piece which has much less surface in contact with the oxygen. Wood in the form of shavings burns much more rapidly than a massive chunk of the same material.

3. *Catalysts.* The effect of manganese dioxide as a catalyst upon the thermal decomposition of potassium chlorate was mentioned in Section 5.3. The success of many industrial processes is due to the use of catalysts for controlling reaction rates that are too fast or too slow to be commercially feasible otherwise.

5.12 The Importance of Oxygen to Life

The energy required to maintain the normal temperature of the human body and for muscular activity is derived from the slow oxidation of materials in the body. Oxygen passes into the blood in the lungs where it combines with hemoglobin, producing red oxyhemoglobin. In this form oxygen is carried to the various tissues of the body, where it is consumed in reactions with oxidizable materials, producing mainly carbon dioxide and water. The blood, which now contains hemoglobin and carbon dioxide, returns through the veins to the lungs. There it gives up carbon dioxide and collects another supply of oxygen. Slow oxidation in the body involves a series of complicated reactions catalyzed by a group of substances called enzymes. The digestion and assimilation of food regenerates the materials which are consumed by oxidation in the body, and the same amount of energy is liberated as would be obtained if the food had been burned by rapid oxidation outside the body.

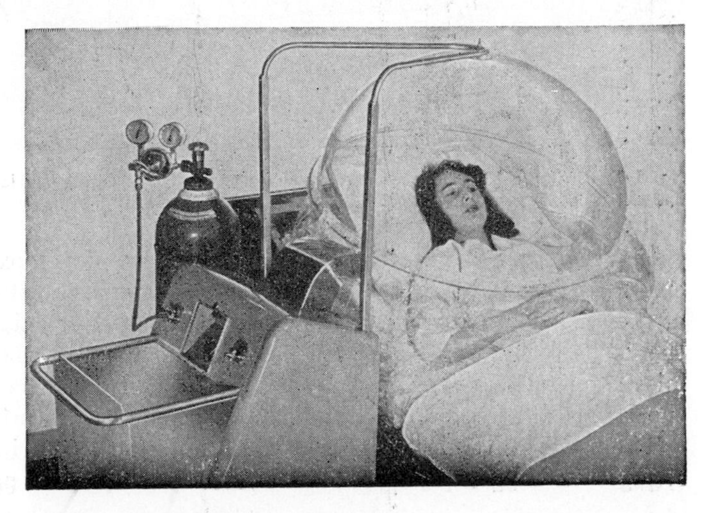

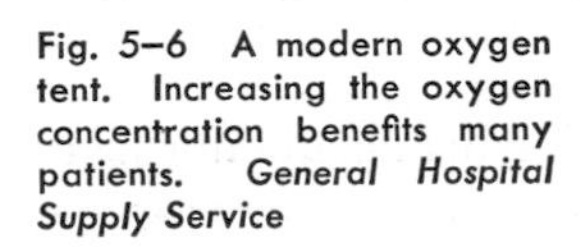

Fig. 5–6 A modern oxygen tent. Increasing the oxygen concentration benefits many patients. ***General Hospital Supply Service***

5.13 Uses of Oxygen

The many applications of oxygen make use of the oxygen in the air, oxygen-enriched air, or pure oxygen. Animals use the oxygen in the air in the metabolic process known as respiration. Oxygen in the air is essential in combustion processes such as the burning of fuels for the production of heat; it is also essential in the decay of organic matter. Oxygen-enriched air is used in medical practice (Fig. 5–6) when the blood receives an inadequate supply of oxygen because of such things as shock, pneumonia, tuberculosis, and heart ailments; it is also used in high altitude flying for the same reason. Pure oxygen is important in certain metallurgical processes such as the removal of carbon from iron in the production of steel. Large quantities of pure oxygen are consumed in the cutting and welding of metals with oxyhydrogen and oxyacetylene torches (Fig. 5–7). Throughout the world almost half the pure oxygen produced is used in making other chemicals.

Fig. 5–7 Cutting a 12-inch plate of steel with an oxyacetylene machine. Notice the stream of molten metal and oxide flowing from the underside. *Air Reduction Sales Co.*

Liquid oxygen is one of the most commonly employed oxidizing agents in rocket engines for use in burning the fuel in regions beyond the atmosphere, where oxygen of the air is not available for the combustion process. Liquid oxygen was used in the Atlas rocket which put the first American into orbit. It is estimated that missile operations consume an average of about 2,000 tons of oxygen per day in the United States and about 5,000 tons per day world-wide (see Section 25.13).

The usage of oxygen is sufficient that more than 3,000 industrial plants are now engaged in oxygen production. Commercial oxygen is produced in two grades, a higher purity oxygen which is 99.5 per cent pure or higher, and a lower purity oxygen in the range 95.0 to 98.5 per cent pure. In 1961, the world consumed 72,475 tons of purified oxygen per day.

OZONE

5.14 Allotropy

When dry oxygen is passed between the two electrically charged plates of an apparatus called an **ozonizer** (Fig. 5–8), a decrease in volume of the gas occurs and a new pale blue gaseous substance possessing a pungent (sharp, irritating) odor is formed. This substance is known as **ozone**; its molecules are each composed of three oxygen atoms; i.e., it is triatomic.

$$3\ O_2 + 68{,}000\ \text{cal.} \rightarrow 2\ O_3$$

Ozone and oxygen are allotropic forms of the same element. The term **allotropy** is used to designate the existence of an element in two or more forms in the same physical state. Ordinary oxygen, O_2, and ozone, O_3, are different forms of the element, both gases under ordinary conditions of temperature and pressure.

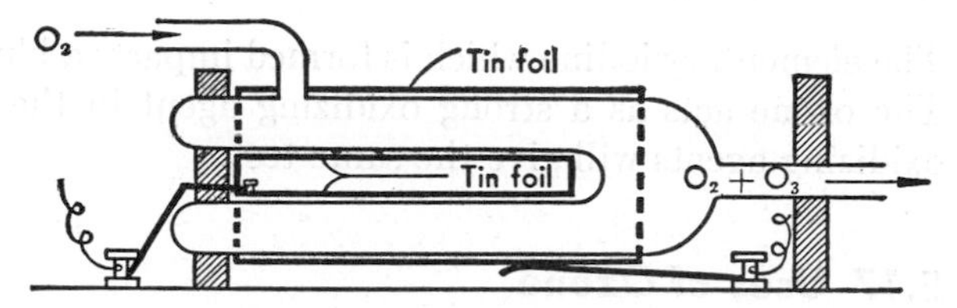

Fig. 5–8 Laboratory form of ozone apparatus.

5.15 Preparation

The formation of ozone from oxygen is an endothermic reaction in which the energy may be furnished in the form of an electrical discharge, heat, or ultraviolet light. Ozone is prepared commercially from oxygen by means of an electrical ozonizer which is more complicated in design and more efficient than the laboratory apparatus. An alternate method of commercial production of ozone is by electrolysis of very cold, rather concentrated sulfuric acid. Ozone is also formed, but in small quantities not suitable for commercial production, during the slow oxidation of phosphorus, by a jet of burning hydrogen, by lightning, and by most electrical discharges in air. Trace amounts of ozone are apparently formed as ultraviolet light from the sun falls upon the oxygen in the upper atmosphere.

5.16 Properties of Ozone

Ozone is a pale blue gas which has a pungent odor. As would be expected from its formula, O_3, it is 1.5 times as dense as molecular oxygen, O_2.

Because energy is absorbed when ozone is formed from oxygen, it is not surprising that ozone is more active chemically than oxygen and that it decomposes readily into oxygen.

$$2\ O_3 \rightarrow 3\ O_2 + 68{,}000\ \text{cal.}$$

As a general rule, substances formed by endothermic reactions tend to be less stable than those formed by exothermic reactions, as mentioned in Section 5.8. Ozone is a stronger oxidizing agent than oxygen because of its higher energy content. In fact, ozone is nearly as strong an oxidizing agent as fluorine, which is the strongest one known. Silver and mercury are not attacked by air at ordinary temperatures whereas both are readily oxidized superficially when placed in an atmosphere containing ozone. The presence of ozone in gas mixtures can readily be detected by passing the gas through a solution of potassium iodide containing some starch emulsion.

$$\underset{\text{Potassium iodide}}{(2\ K^+) + 2\ I^-} + O_3 + H_2O \rightarrow (2\ K^+) + 2\ OH^- + \underset{\text{Iodine}}{I_2} + O_2\uparrow$$

The elementary iodine which is formed imparts a blue color to the starch emulsion. The ozone acts as a strong oxidizing agent in the above reaction. Many other oxidizing agents will give the same test.

5.17 Uses of Ozone

The uses of ozone are dependent upon its activity as an oxidizing agent. Its use as a bleaching agent for oils, waxes, fabrics, and starch involves the oxidation of colored substances to colorless compounds.

5.18 Bonding in Oxygen and Ozone

From the fact that the oxygen atom possesses six valence electrons we might expect the sharing of two pairs of electrons between the two atoms in the diatomic molecule.

$$\overset{\times\times}{{}^{\times}_{\times}O}{}^{\times\circ}_{\times\circ}\overset{\circ\circ}{O}{}^{\circ}_{\circ}$$

This structure would give each oxygen atom a completed octet of electrons in its outer shell. However, in Section 5.4 the paramagnetic character of oxygen was noted. In order that an atomic or molecular system show paramagnetism, it must contain one or more unpaired electrons. The paramagnetic character of the diatomic oxygen molecule corresponds to that of a structure with two unpaired electrons. It is probable that the structure contains two 3-electron bonds and one electron-pair bond. The 3-electron bond involves one unpaired electron. While two of the three electrons are in an orbital about the nucleus of one of the atoms, the third electron is occupying the corresponding orbital of the other atom.

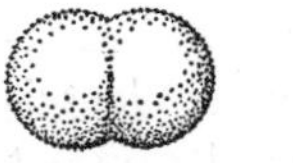

$:O\because\therefore O:$

Fig. 5–9 Oxygen molecule.

The valence electronic structure of ozone, the triatomic form of oxygen, is given below. The ozone molecule is angular, as shown, and the two bonds are indistinguishable due to a phenomenon called **resonance** (see Section 23.1).

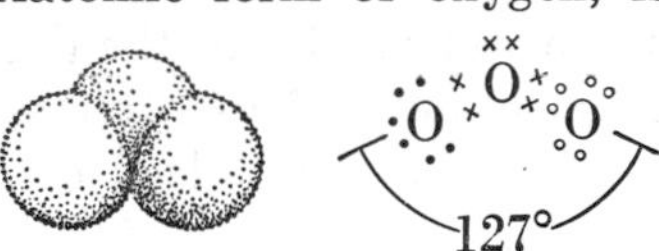

Fig. 5–10 Ozone molecule.

QUESTIONS

1. Describe the preparation of oxygen by the electrolysis of water.

2. Write equations for the preparation of oxygen from: $NaNO_3$, $Cu(NO_3)_2$, $KClO_3$, H_2O, and Na_2O_2.

3. Why is manganese dioxide of value in the preparation of oxygen from $KClO_3$?

4. "Catalysts are specific in their action." Explain.

5. Why must care be exercised in the preparation of oxygen by heating $KClO_3$?

6. Give equations for the action of oxygen upon each of the following: H_2, Na, Mg, Fe, C, S, P, H_2S, CS_2, CH_4, CO, and P_4O_6.

7. Define and illustrate each of the following: base, basic anhydride, acid, acid anhydride, and neutralization.

8. Define the term "combustion." Is combustion restricted to reactions involving oxygen? Explain.

9. When may spontaneous combustion occur?

10. Why will magnesium ribbon burn more rapidly in pure oxygen than in air?

11. Why will wood shavings ignite and burn more rapidly than a log of wood?

12. Give examples of "slow oxidation" and "rapid oxidation." Why will H_2O, SiO_2, and CO_2 not burn?

13. Discuss the essentiality of oxygen to animal life.

14. Define and illustrate allotropy.

15. Why is ozone a more active oxidizing agent than oxygen?

16. Describe a chemical test for ozone.

17. Account for the paramagnetism of molecular oxygen in terms of its electronic structure.

18. Explain the separation of oxygen from air by fractional evaporation of liquid air.

PROBLEMS

1. What weight of potassium chlorate would be required to give sufficient oxygen to burn 35.0 g. of methane, CH_4? *Ans.* *357 g.*

2. Which contains more oxygen, 100 g. of $NaClO_3$ or 100 g. of $KClO_3$? *Ans.* *100 g. of $NaClO_3$*

3. What will be the approximate increase in the speed of a reaction when the temperature is raised 40°? *Ans.* *16 times*

4. How many grams of oxygen are contained in 85 g. of BaO_2? How many grams of oxygen will be liberated upon heating 85 g. of BaO_2? *Ans.* *16.1 g.; 8.05 g.*

5. How many grams of oxygen will be formed by the action of 18 g. of Na_2O_2 upon water? From the density of oxygen, calculate how many liters this would be at 0° and 760 mm. pressure. *Ans. 3.69 g.; 2.58 l.*

6. An oxide of lead contains 90.5% lead. Derive the formula of this compound. *Ans.* Pb_3O_4

7. What weight of H_2SO_4 could be produced from the SO_2 resulting from the roasting of 5000 kg. of ZnS, assuming the entire process to be 75.00% efficient? *Ans. 3800 kg.*

8. What weight of H_2S can be completely oxidized to sulfur dioxide by the oxygen liberated when 325 g. of Na_2O_2 reacts with water? *Ans. 47.3 g.*

9. The heat of formation of water from hydrogen and oxygen is 66,970 calories per mole at 100°. How much water can be heated from 25° to 100° by the heat evolved during the formation of 10.00 moles of water from hydrogen and oxygen? *Ans. 8.929 kg.*

10. How much electrical energy, measured in calories, would be required in the electrolytic decomposition of sufficient water to give 10 g. of oxygen at 25°? The heat of formation of water at 25° is 68,317 calories per mole. *Ans. 42.7 kcal.*

11. What weight of NaOH would be required to neutralize the HCl in 100 g. of a 25.0% aqueous solution of the acid? *Ans. 27.4 g.*

12. How many gram-atoms of oxygen are there in 1.05 moles of ozone? How many moles of oxygen will be formed by the decomposition of this quantity of ozone? *Ans. 3.15 gram-atoms; 1.58 moles*

13. What is the total weight of the products formed when 25.0 g. of carbon disulfide is completely oxidized by oxygen of the air? *Ans. 56.5 g.*

14. How much iron can be burned to magnetic oxide of iron, Fe_3O_4, by 1000 g. of 98.0% pure oxygen? *Ans. 2.57 kg.*

REFERENCES

"Catalysis and the Elementary Chemistry Course," J. A. Campbell, *J. Chem. Educ.*, **23** (12) 582 (1946).

"Lavoisier," D. I. Duveen, *Sci. American*, May, 1956; p. 84.

"Priestley," Mitchell Wilson, *Sci. American*, Oct., 1954; p. 68.

"The Discovery of Oxygen," J. R. Partington, *J. Chem. Educ.*, **39** (3) 123 (1962).

"Oxygen," M. E. Weeks, *Discovery of the Elements*, Sixth Edition, Publ. by the Journal of Chemical Education, Easton, Pa., 1956; pp. 209–229.

"Oxygen, Chemical Raw Material," M. Sittig, *Chem. Eng. News*, Nov. 27, 1961; p. 92.

"Lavoisier. The Crucial Year. The Background and Origin of His First Experiments on Combustion in 1772." Henry Guerlac, Cornell University Press, Ithaca, New York, 1961.

CHAPTER SIX

Hydrogen

Early in the sixteenth century a Swiss-German physician by the name of Paracelsus noted that an inflammable gas was formed by the reaction of sulfuric acid with iron. However, it was not until 1766 that Cavendish (Fig. 6–1), an Englishman, recognized this gas as a distinct substance and prepared it by the action of various acids on certain metals (Fig. 6–2). Lavoisier named the gas **hydrogen,** meaning "water producer," because water is formed when hydrogen burns. Since its atom is composed of one proton and one electron, hydrogen is the simplest in structure of all the elements.

Fig. 6–1 Henry Cavendish was probably the first to recognize that hydrogen is a distinct substance. He called it "inflammable air." ***Fisher Scientific Co.***

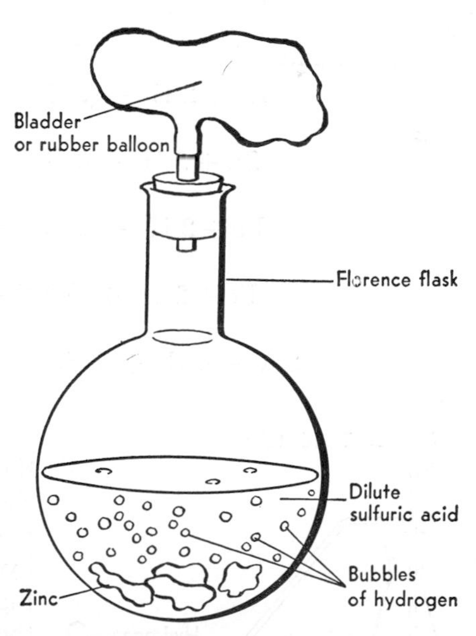

Fig. 6–2 Cavendish used apparatus such as this to collect hydrogen. When he saw the bubbles of hydrogen forming on the zinc, he came to the erroneous conclusion that the hydrogen came from the zinc. Cavendish used iron, zinc, and tin at different times. He used hydrochloric acid in some instances. He collected his samples of hydrogen in bladders.

6.1 Occurrence

Because it is a chemically active element, hydrogen is found in the free state in only negligible quantities. It occurs free in very small amounts in the atmosphere, in the gases of active volcanoes, in natural gas, coal mines, and meteorites. The atmosphere of the sun and other stars appears to be composed largely of hydrogen.

More compounds containing hydrogen are known than those of any other one element. In the combined form hydrogen comprises nearly eleven per cent of the weight of water, its most abundant compound. Hydrogen is found combined with carbon and oxygen in the tissues of all plants and animals. It is an important part of petroleum, cellulose and starch, $(C_6H_{10}O_5)_x$, sugar, $C_{12}H_{22}O_{11}$, fats, oils, alcohols, acids and bases, and many other substances.

6.2 Preparation of Hydrogen

There are many ways of liberating hydrogen from its compounds, particularly from acids, bases, and water. Where small quantities of hydrogen are required, as in the laboratory, it is usually generated from acids. When commercial quantities of hydrogen are needed, water is generally used as the raw material because it is abundant and cheap.

1. *Preparation from acids.* Hydrogen is conveniently prepared in the laboratory by the reaction of an active metal with an acid. Zinc and iron are most frequently used with dilute solutions of hydrochloric or sulfuric acid.

$$Zn + 2\ H^+ + (2\ Cl^-) \rightarrow \underset{\text{Zinc chloride}}{Zn^{++} + (2\ Cl^-)} + H_2\uparrow$$

$$Zn + 2\ H^+ + (SO_4^=) \rightarrow \underset{\text{Zinc sulfate}}{Zn^{++} + (SO_4^=)} + H_2\uparrow$$

$$Fe + 2\ H^+ + (2\ Cl^-) \rightarrow \underset{\text{Iron (II) chloride}}{Fe^{++} + (2\ Cl^-)} + H_2\uparrow$$

$$Fe + 2\ H^+ + (SO_4^=) \rightarrow \underset{\text{Iron (II) sulfate}}{Fe^{++} + (SO_4^=)} + H_2\uparrow$$

$$2\ Al + 6\ H^+ + (3\ SO_4^=) \rightarrow \underset{\text{Aluminum sulfate}}{2\ Al^{+3} + (3\ SO_4^=)} + 3\ H_2\uparrow$$

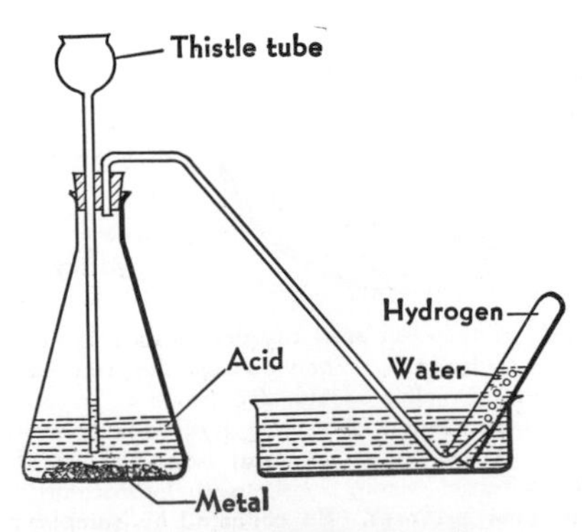

Fig. 6–3 Hydrogen generator

In each of these reactions the metal has taken the place of the hydrogen of the acid. Such chemical changes are known as **displacement reactions.** In the laboratory preparation of hydrogen, an apparatus like that shown in Fig. 6–3 is used. The acid is poured through the thistle tube upon the metal, and the hydrogen is collected by the downward displacement of water. It is the hydrogen ion of dilute aqueous acids that reacts with active metals. The negative ion does not enter the reaction. However, upon evaporating the solution to dryness after the reaction is complete, a crystalline **salt** composed of the metal ion and the negative ion of the acid is obtained. In three of the reactions given here, the salts are zinc chloride, iron (II) sulfate, and aluminum sulfate.

2. *By the electrolysis of water.* The decomposition of water into its constituent elements by means of a direct current of electricity was described in Section 5.3. Hydrogen is liberated at the cathode when water containing a small amount of sulfuric acid or sodium hydroxide is electrolyzed.

$$2\ H_2O + \text{electrical energy} \rightarrow 2\ H_2\uparrow + O_2\uparrow$$

3. *By the electrolysis of sodium chloride solutions.* When an aqueous solution of common salt is electrolyzed, hydrogen is formed along with sodium hydroxide and chlorine.

$$(2\ Na^+) + 2\ Cl^- + 2\ H_2O + \text{electrical energy} \rightarrow (2\ Na^+) + 2\ OH^- + Cl_2\uparrow + H_2\uparrow$$

This is a commercial method for producing caustic soda, NaOH, and chlorine; hydrogen is a by-product (Section 20.4). The salt solution used must be fairly concentrated, otherwise oxygen is liberated.

4. *By the action of certain metals and nonmetals on water.* Very active metals, such as sodium, potassium, and calcium, rapidly displace hydrogen from water at room temperature as shown in Fig. 6–4.

$$2\ Na + 2\ HOH \rightarrow 2\ Na^+ + 2\ OH^- + H_2\uparrow$$
$$2\ K + 2\ HOH \rightarrow 2\ K^+ + 2\ OH^- + H_2\uparrow$$
$$Ca + 2\ HOH \rightarrow Ca^{++} + 2\ OH^- + H_2\uparrow$$

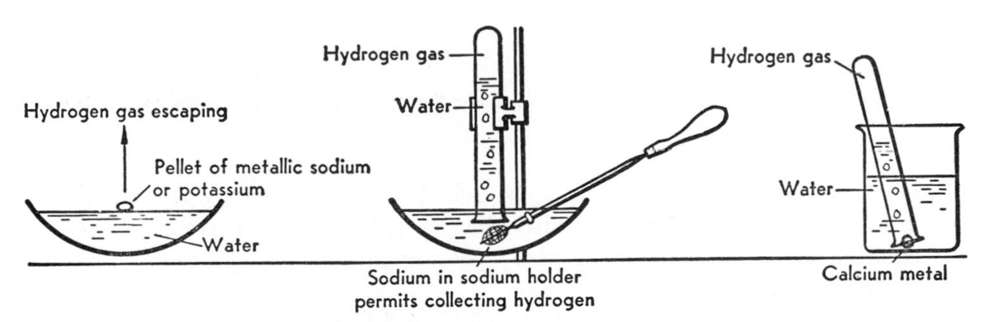

Fig. 6–4 Sodium, potassium, lithium, and calcium will react with water, yielding hydrogen.

The reaction of a small piece of sodium or potassium with water produces sufficient heat to ignite the hydrogen as it is produced. It is dangerous to bring large pieces of either metal into contact with water because explosions will result. An alloy of lead and sodium, and one of mercury and sodium, which react with water less vigorously than does pure sodium, are sometimes used for the preparation of hydrogen in small quantities.

Other less active metals will displace hydrogen from water at higher temperatures. Iron and magnesium react only slowly with boiling water, but when steam is passed over magnesium or red-hot iron, hydrogen is liberated rapidly (Fig. 6–5).

$$Mg + H_2O \rightarrow H_2 + MgO \text{ (Magnesium oxide)}$$
$$3\ Fe + 4\ H_2O \rightarrow 4\ H_2 + Fe_3O_4 \text{ (Iron (II, III) oxide)}$$

Note that all of the hydrogen of water has been replaced by the metals in the above reactions whereas the active metals sodium and potassium replaced only half of it.

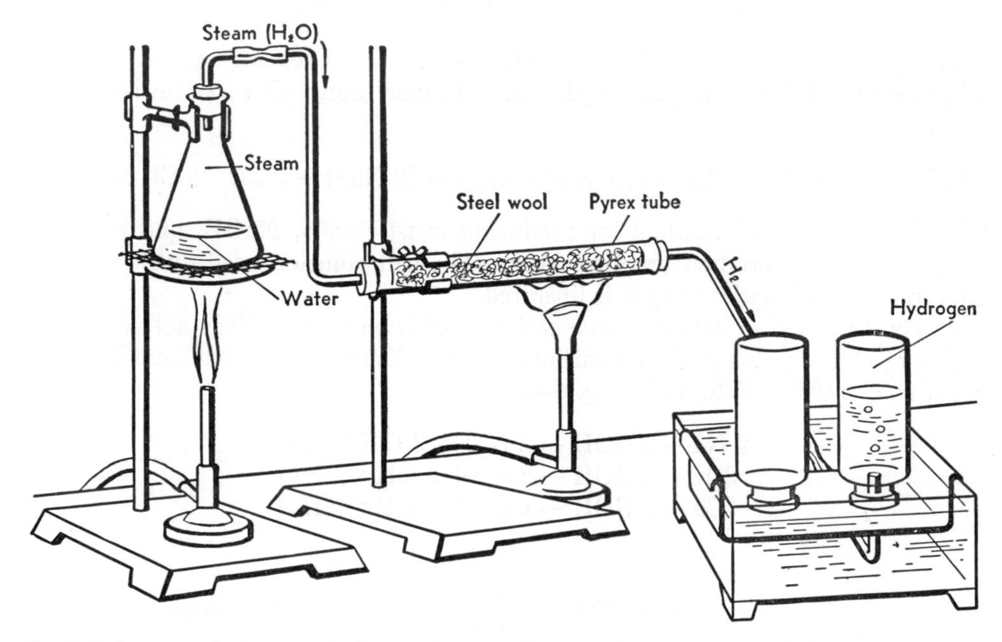

Fig. 6–5 Some metals, for example Mg and Fe, less active than calcium, will react with the oxygen in steam, setting hydrogen free and forming metallic oxides.

Some of the hydrogen that is used in industry is produced by the reaction of iron with steam. After a mass of iron has been largely converted to Fe_3O_4 by this reaction, the iron is regenerated by passing carbon monoxide, CO, over the heated iron oxide.

$$Fe_3O_4 + 4\ CO \rightarrow 3\ Fe + 4\ CO_2$$

By the alternate use of steam and carbon monoxide the iron can be used over and over again.

Carbon, a nonmetal, when white hot will react with steam, producing a mixture of carbon monoxide and hydrogen, commonly known as "water gas."

$$C + H_2O \rightarrow CO + H_2$$

Because both carbon monoxide and hydrogen will burn in oxygen or air and produce much heat, water gas is a valuable industrial fuel. When water gas is mixed with steam and passed over a catalyst such as iron oxide or thorium oxide at a fairly high temperature (500°), carbon dioxide and hydrogen are produced by the reaction

$$CO + H_2O + (H_2) \rightarrow CO_2 + H_2 + (H_2)$$

Large quantities of hydrogen produced in this way are used in the synthesis of ammonia, NH_3, and wood alcohol, CH_3OH.

5. *By the action of certain elements on active bases.* Certain elements, such as aluminum, zinc, and silicon, react with sodium hydroxide, or other active bases, in concentrated aqueous solution with the liberation of hydrogen.

$$2\ Al + (2\ Na^+) + 2\ OH^- + 6\ H_2O \rightarrow (2\ Na^+) + \underset{\text{Sodium aluminate}}{2\ Al(OH)_4^-} + 3\ H_2 \uparrow$$

$$Zn + (2\ Na^+) + 2\ OH^- + 2\ H_2O \rightarrow (2\ Na^+) + \underset{\text{Sodium zincate}}{Zn(OH)_4^{=}} + H_2 \uparrow$$

$$Si + (2\ Na^+) + 2\ OH^- + H_2O \rightarrow (2\ Na^+) + \underset{\text{Sodium silicate}}{SiO_3^{=}} + 2\ H_2 \uparrow$$

Aluminum and zinc do not displace hydrogen from water because a film of oxide forms on the metal surface which prevents direct contact of the metal with the water. Acids and active bases dissolve the oxide film and thus allow the metal to displace hydrogen from the acid or from water.

6. *By the action of certain metal hydrides on water.* Compounds of active metals and hydrogen, such as calcium hydride and sodium hydride, react readily with water liberating hydrogen.

$$CaH_2 + 2\ H_2O \rightarrow Ca^{++} + 2\ OH^- + 2\ H_2 \uparrow$$
$$NaH + H_2O \rightarrow Na^+ + OH^- + H_2 \uparrow$$

Metal hydrides are expensive but convenient sources of very pure hydrogen. Calcium hydride is sold in commercial quantities.

7. *Other methods.* Hydrogen is produced commercially in the largest quantities from **hydrocarbons** (compounds which contain only carbon and hydrogen), which are the principal components of petroleum and natural gas. Methane, the simplest hydrocarbon, is decomposed into carbon and hydrogen when heated in the presence of a suitable catalyst, according to the equation

$$CH_4 \rightarrow C + 2\ H_2$$

Such catalyzed thermal decompositions are called **cracking reactions.** The carbon produced by the cracking of methane is an important commercial product which is called **carbon black.**

When a mixture of methane and steam is heated to a high temperature in the presence of catalysts, a mixture of carbon monoxide, carbon dioxide, and hydrogen is produced.

$$CH_4 + H_2O \rightarrow CO + 3\ H_2$$
$$CO + H_2O \rightarrow CO_2 + H_2$$

These are typical reactions and other hydrocarbons may be substituted for methane in this industrial method for the production of hydrogen.

6.3 Physical Properties of Hydrogen

Hydrogen is a colorless, odorless, and tasteless gas consisting of diatomic molecules, H_2. It is the lightest known substance, with a density of 0.08987 g. per liter. Because of its low density it can be collected by the downward displacement of air. The fact that hydrogen is so much lighter than air (which has a density of 1.293 g. per liter) makes it useful for inflating balloons.

By cooling and compressing hydrogen it can be changed to a liquid which boils at − 252.7°. The low temperature of liquid hydrogen makes possible its use in cooling other materials to low temperatures. It may be used to transform all other gases into solids with the single exception of helium. Hydrogen freezes to a transparent solid at − 259.14°.

Hydrogen diffuses (Section 7.10) faster than any other gas because its molecules are smaller in mass than those of any other gas. The diffusion of hydrogen can be demonstrated by lowering an inverted beaker of hydrogen over a porous clay cup (Fig. 6–6a). Hydrogen diffuses through the porous wall of the cup faster than the air within the cup diffuses outward. Consequently, a pressure develops in the cup, which causes the water in the bottle to be forced out through the jet. If the beaker of hydrogen is taken away from the porous cup, which now contains both hydrogen and air (Fig. 6–6b), the hydrogen diffuses out of the porous cup faster than air diffuses inward. Thus, a partial vacuum is created within the cup which results in air being forced into the bottle of water through the jet tube.

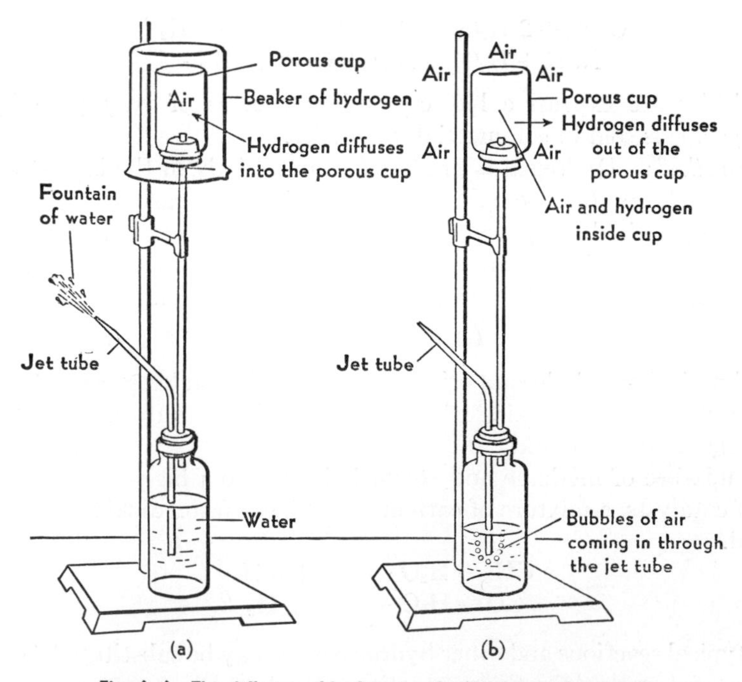

Fig. 6–6 The diffusion of hydrogen; the "hydrogen fountain."

6.4 The Adsorption of Hydrogen by Metals

Hydrogen is readily adsorbed by certain metals, the effect being most pronounced with gold, platinum, tungsten, and especially palladium. **Adsorption is the adhesion of molecules of a gas, liquid, or dissolved substance to the surface of a solid.** The quantity of hydrogen adsorbed by a given mass of metal depends upon the condition of the metal, such as extent of subdivision, and the temperature and pressure under which the adsorption takes place. At room temperature one volume of finely divided palladium (called palladium black) adsorbs nearly 900 volumes of hydrogen. Adsorbed hydrogen is very active chemically as indicated by its rapid union with oxygen, whereas ordinary hydrogen and oxygen do not noticeably combine unless the mixture is ignited. There is evidence that adsorbed hydrogen is ionized or activated in some way because metals such as platinum are good catalysts for many chemical reactions involving hydrogen as a reactant. Because of this property of adsorption, hydrogen readily passes through the heated walls of containers made of metals which strongly adsorb it.

6.5 Chemical Properties of Hydrogen

At ordinary temperatures, hydrogen is relatively inactive chemically but when heated it enters into many chemical reactions.

1. *Reaction with oxygen.* When a mixture of hydrogen and oxygen is ignited, an explosion occurs, and water is formed.

$$2\ H_2 + O_2 \rightarrow 2\ H_2O + \text{heat}$$

Because of the violence of the explosion, great caution should be used in handling hydrogen (or any other combustible gas). The fact that water is formed when hydrogen is burned in air or oxygen may be demonstrated (Fig. 6–7) by allowing a jet of hydrogen to burn inside an inverted, cold, dry bell jar.

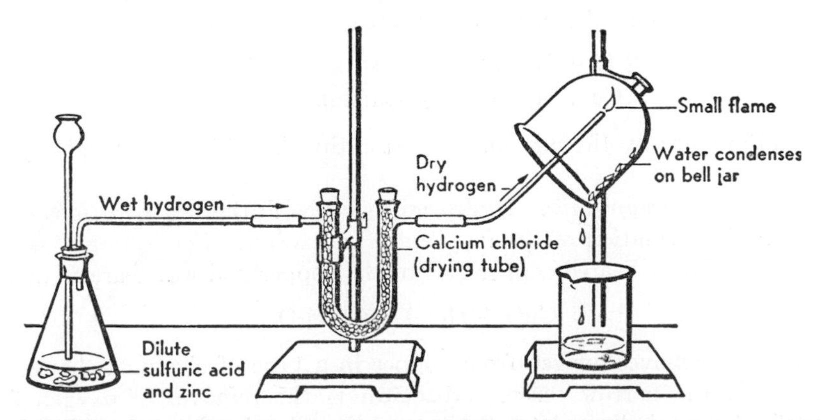

Fig. 6–7 When hydrogen burns in air, water vapor is formed. The bell jar serves as a condenser.

The very high heat of combustion of hydrogen in pure oxygen is used in the oxyhydrogen blowtorch, which makes it possible to achieve temperatures up to 2800°. The hot flame of this blowtorch can be used in "cutting" thick sheets of many metals.

When hydrogen gas, consisting of diatomic molecules, is passed through an electric arc, energy is absorbed by the hydrogen, which is broken up into monatomic hydrogen molecules.

$$H_2 + \text{heat} \rightarrow 2\ H$$

The single atoms of hydrogen readily recombine upon collision with one another and release the heat which was absorbed during dissociation in the electric arc.

$$2\ H \rightarrow H_2 + \text{heat}$$

The energy released in this reaction added to that arising from the burning of the hydrogen in pure oxygen is utilized in the atomic hydrogen torch (Fig. 6–8), which is used to attain temperatures up to 5000°. This torch is useful in cutting and welding metals which melt at high temperatures.

2. *Reaction with other nonmetals.* Hydrogen combines by direct union with several nonmetals, in addition to oxygen, under suitable conditions to form covalent compounds.

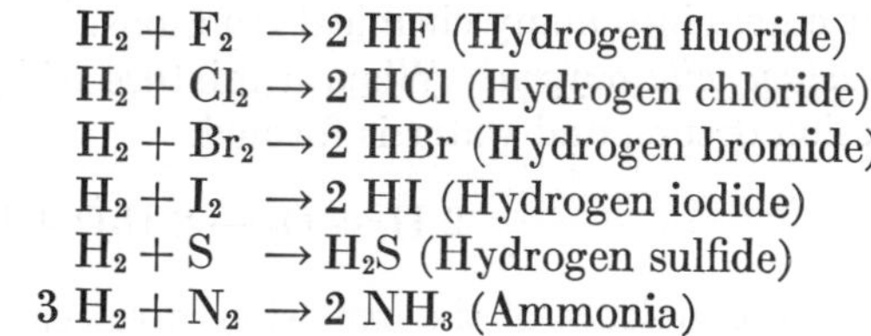
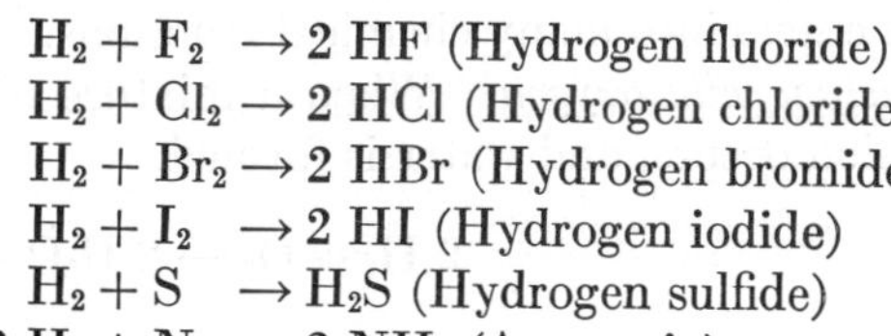
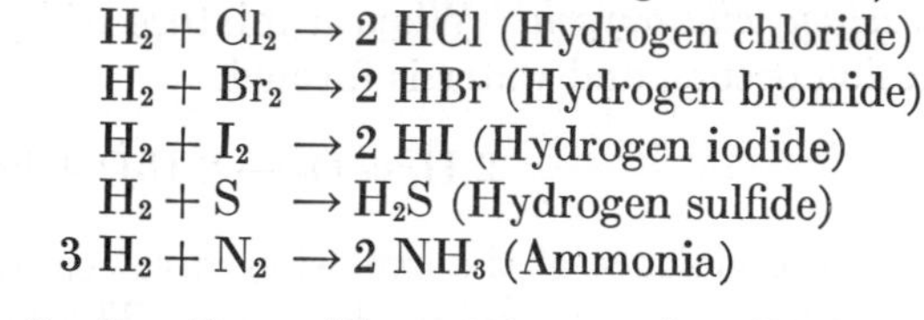

$$H_2 + F_2 \rightarrow 2\ HF \text{ (Hydrogen fluoride)}$$
$$H_2 + Cl_2 \rightarrow 2\ HCl \text{ (Hydrogen chloride)}$$
$$H_2 + Br_2 \rightarrow 2\ HBr \text{ (Hydrogen bromide)}$$
$$H_2 + I_2 \rightarrow 2\ HI \text{ (Hydrogen iodide)}$$
$$H_2 + S \rightarrow H_2S \text{ (Hydrogen sulfide)}$$
$$3\ H_2 + N_2 \rightarrow 2\ NH_3 \text{ (Ammonia)}$$

Fig. 6–8 Atomic hydrogen torch.

3. *Reaction with certain metals.* Hydrogen also reacts with some of the active metals, forming crystalline ionic **hydrides.** In contrast, the compounds of hydrogen and nonmetals, such as H_2O, HCl, and NH_3, are covalent.

$$2\ Li + H_2 \rightarrow 2\ LiH \text{ (Lithium hydride)}$$
$$Ca + H_2 \rightarrow CaH_2 \text{ (Calcium hydride)}$$

These reactions are exothermic and the resulting hydrides are relatively stable toward heat.

4. *Reaction with compounds.* Hydrogen reacts with the heated oxides of many metals with the formation of the free metal and water. For example, when hydrogen is passed over heated copper (II) oxide, copper and water are formed.

$$CuO + H_2 \rightarrow Cu + H_2O$$

Here hydrogen removes oxygen from copper in a type of chemical change called reduction. In the narrow sense, **reduction** is the removal of oxygen from a compound. As we shall see later (Chapter 14), reduction has a broader meaning than the mere removal of oxygen from a compound. Hydrogen is said to act as a **reducing agent** in the reaction. The copper (II) oxide, which furnishes the oxygen for the oxidation of the hydrogen, is called an **oxidizing agent.** Reduction is the opposite of oxidation and the two processes always occur simultaneously.

Hydrogen may also react with certain metal oxides with the formation of a lower oxide. For example,

$$MnO_2 + H_2 \rightarrow MnO + H_2O$$

6.6 Reversible Reactions

When hydrogen is passed over heated magnetic oxide of iron, Fe_3O_4, reduction takes place with the formation of iron and steam.

$$Fe_3O_4 + 4\ H_2 \rightarrow 3\ Fe + 4\ H_2O \quad (1)$$

This reaction is exactly the reverse of the one described in Section 6.2, i.e., the production of hydrogen by passing steam over heated iron.

$$3\ Fe + 4\ H_2O \rightarrow Fe_3O_4 + 4\ H_2 \quad (2)$$

In both of the above reactions a stream of gas is passed over a heated solid in a tube. In reaction (1), hydrogen is in excess and the steam is swept out of the reaction tube by the current of hydrogen. Thus reaction (1) can go to completion. In reaction (2) the hydrogen is swept out of the tube by the steam and thus this reaction can go to completion. If a mixture of iron and steam is heated in a closed tube, neither the steam nor hydrogen which forms can escape. At first, reaction (2) will be the only one to take place because only iron and steam are present, but as this reaction proceeds, iron and steam will be used up while Fe_3O_4 and hydrogen are being formed. It follows that the rate of reaction (2) will decrease while that of reaction (1) is increasing, and after a time, the two reaction rates will become equal. The two reactions will reach a state of **chemical equilibrium.** The quantity of each of the four substances in the closed tube remains unchanged at equilibrium, because each is constantly being formed at the same rate that it is being consumed. Reactions of this type are said to be **reversible,** and it is customary to represent the reversibility by means of double arrows in the equation:

$$3\ Fe + 4\ H_2O \rightleftharpoons Fe_3O_4 + 4\ H_2$$

A more complete account of the very important phenomenon of chemical equilibrium is given in Chapter 16.

6.7 Uses of Hydrogen

Although hydrogen was once extensively used to inflate airships such as blimps and dirigibles, it has largely been replaced by the heavier gas helium. Because of its inertness, helium is much safer than the highly combustible hydrogen

Fig. 6–9 Explosion of hydrogen on the airship *Hindenburg* at Lakehurst, New Jersey, May 6, 1937. This picture was taken immediately following the explosion of one compartment; two other compartments exploded almost at once, resulting in the complete destruction of this giant airliner. *International News Photos*

(Fig. 6–9). Mention has already been made of the use of hydrogen in both the oxyhydrogen and the atomic hydrogen torch. Vegetable oils are changed from liquids to solids by treating the liquid oils with hydrogen under pressure and in the presence of nickel as a catalyst. The chemical change which occurs (called **hydrogenation**) involves the union of hydrogen with the oil. The resulting solid fats are used in cooking. Crisco, Spry, and Swiftning are examples of hydrogenated oils. Large quantities of hydrogen are united directly with nitrogen to produce ammonia and with chlorine to produce hydrogen chloride. An increasingly important use of hydrogen is in the catalytic conversion of coal dust to liquid hydrocarbons, which supplement petroleum as a source of liquid fuel. Methyl alcohol is produced synthetically by the catalyzed reaction of hydrogen with carbon monoxide ($2\ H_2 + CO \rightarrow CH_3OH$). **Water gas,** a mixture of hydrogen with carbon monoxide, is an important industrial fuel. Hydrogen is used in the reduction of certain metal oxides to obtain the free metal. The use of hydrogen in the hydrogen bomb is discussed in a later chapter (Nuclear Chemistry).

6.8 Isotopes of Hydrogen

By means of an instrument known as the mass spectrograph, it has been shown that hydrogen is composed of three isotopes. They are ordinary hydrogen, or **protium,** ${}^1_1H$; heavy hydrogen, or **deuterium,** ${}^2_1H$; and **tritium,** ${}^3_1H$.

1p 1e — 1n 1p 1e — 2n 1p 1e

Ordinary hydrogen. Deuterium Tritium

For every 10^7 atoms of ordinary hydrogen there is only one atom of tritium, and for every 5,000 atoms of ordinary hydrogen there is only one atom of deuterium in a sample of hydrogen as it is ordinarily prepared in the laboratory. The chemical properties of the different isotopic forms of hydrogen are essentially the same; they have identical electronic structures. The differences in their atomic masses give rise to differences in physical properties, however. Deuterium and tritium have lower vapor pressures than does ordinary hydrogen, so the heavier isotopes are concentrated in the last portions of liquid hydrogen as it evaporates.

Deuterium is of interest in connection with heavy water (Section 10.12), and tritium with the hydrogen bomb.

6.9 The Activity or Electromotive Series of the Metals

We noted in Section 6.2 that certain metals, such as sodium and potassium, react readily with cold water by displacing hydrogen and forming metal hydroxides. It was also pointed out that magnesium and iron react with water only when they are heated. Sodium and potassium react much more vigorously with acids than do magnesium and iron. From experimental observations of this sort it is possible to arrange the metals in order of their chemical activities (see Table 6·1 on page 110).

Potassium is the most reactive of the common metals. Each succeeding metal in the series is less reactive, and gold, the least reactive of all, is found at the bottom of the series. In general, any metal in the series will displace any other element below it in the series from water solutions of its soluble compounds. For example, any metal above hydrogen in the series is capable of liberating hydrogen from aqueous acids (water solutions of acids). The metals below hydrogen cannot displace hydrogen from water or from aqueous acids. Another example is the displacement of copper by iron from aqueous solutions of copper (II) salts (Fig. 6–10, page 110).

$$\underset{}{Fe} + \underset{\text{Copper (II) sulfate}}{CuSO_4} \rightarrow \underset{\text{Iron (II) sulfate}}{FeSO_4} + \underline{Cu}$$

or

$$Fe + Cu^{++} \rightarrow Fe^{++} + \underline{Cu}$$

The symbol for copper is underscored ($\underline{Cu}$) to show that copper is formed as a solid precipitate during the reaction. In a similar manner, silver is displaced by copper (Fig. 6–11, page 110), and gold is displaced by silver.

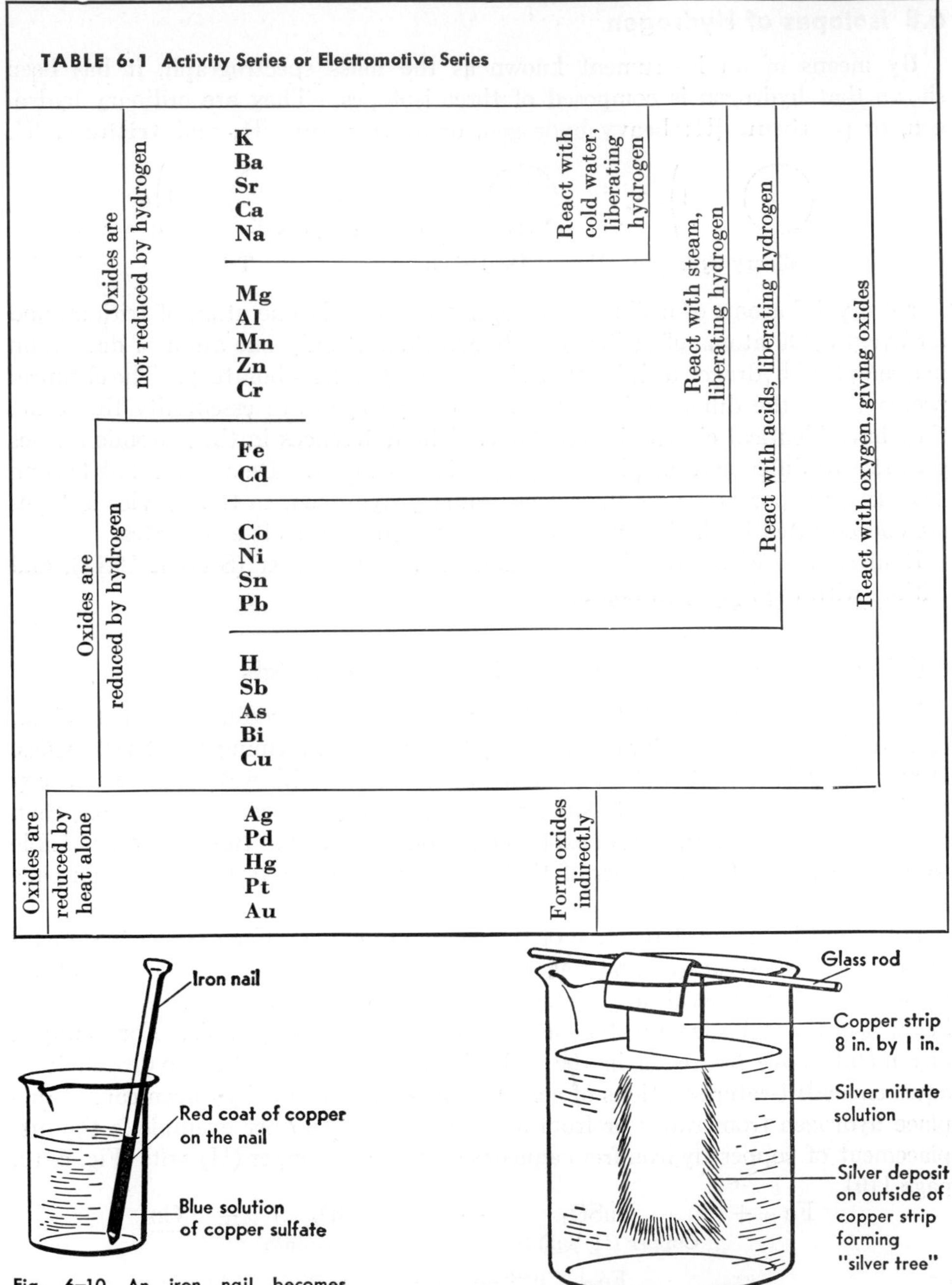

TABLE 6·1 Activity Series or Electromotive Series

Metals	Oxides	Reactions
K, Ba, Sr, Ca, Na	Oxides are not reduced by hydrogen	React with cold water, liberating hydrogen; React with steam, liberating hydrogen; React with acids, liberating hydrogen; React with oxygen, giving oxides
Mg, Al, Mn, Zn, Cr	Oxides are not reduced by hydrogen	React with steam, liberating hydrogen; React with acids, liberating hydrogen; React with oxygen, giving oxides
Fe, Cd	Oxides are reduced by hydrogen	React with steam, liberating hydrogen; React with acids, liberating hydrogen; React with oxygen, giving oxides
Co, Ni, Sn, Pb	Oxides are reduced by hydrogen	React with acids, liberating hydrogen; React with oxygen, giving oxides
H, Sb, As, Bi, Cu	Oxides are reduced by hydrogen	React with oxygen, giving oxides
Ag, Pd, Hg, Pt, Au	Oxides are reduced by heat alone	Form oxides indirectly

Fig. 6–10 An iron nail becomes coated with metallic copper when immersed in a solution of copper sulfate.

Fig. 6–11 When a strip of copper is immersed in silver nitrate solution, silver, a less active metal than copper, is replaced and deposited on the surface of the copper. The deposit is called a "silver tree," because, as it grows, it sends out crystals that look like branches.

The decreasing activity of the metals down the series is reflected in the decrease in tendency to form positive ions in solution. Thus, zinc has a greater tendency to lose electrons than copper and goes into solution as positive ions more readily than does copper.

$$Zn \rightarrow Zn^{++} + 2e^-$$
$$Cu \rightarrow Cu^{++} + 2e^-$$

The reactivity of the metals toward oxygen, sulfur, and the halogens is less for each succeeding metal in passing down the series. The heat of formation and stability of the compounds formed decreases in a similar manner. It is evident then that the activity series is very useful because it indicates the possibility of a reaction of a given metal with water, acids, salts of other metals, oxygen, sulfur, and the halogens (fluorine, chlorine, bromine, and iodine). It should be noted, however, that the order in which the elements are placed in the series will depend somewhat upon the conditions under which the activity is observed. A series determined from observation of the activity of the metals with respect to their ions in water solution will be slightly different from that showing the order of activity at high temperatures and in the absence of a solvent. The series is not applicable to reactions in solvents other than water (e.g., in fused salts, in gaseous conditions, etc.) except in a general way.

QUESTIONS

1. What is the atomic structure of hydrogen? In what way is the hydrogen nucleus unique?
2. Account for the almost complete absence of free hydrogen in nature.
3. Write ionic equations for the preparation of hydrogen by the action of Na, Mg, Al, Fe, and Zn upon hydrochloric acid; upon sulfuric acid. Name the salts produced in these reactions.
4. What is a displacement reaction? Give an example.
5. What ion is common to aqueous solutions of all acids? Write equations for the ionization of hydrogen chloride and hydrogen sulfate in water.
6. What happens to the electrical energy that is used in the electrolysis of water?
7. Give the equation for the electrolysis of an aqueous solution of sodium chloride of fairly high concentration.
8. Name three metals that will displace hydrogen from (a) cold water; (b) steam; (c) acids. Give equations.
9. What is meant by a "reversible" reaction? What is meant by the term "chemical equilibrium"?
10. Give the composition, mode of preparation, and one use of water gas.
11. Give equations for the reaction of Al, Zn, and Si with sodium hydroxide.
12. Explain: "Metal hydrides are convenient and portable sources of hydrogen."
13. Explain how the "hydrogen fountain" functions.

14. Why are higher temperatures attainable by the atomic hydrogen flame than by the oxyhydrogen flame?

15. Give equations for the reaction of hydrogen with each of the following: O_2, F_2, Cl_2, Br_2, I_2, N_2, and Na.

16. Distinguish between exothermic and endothermic reactions.

17. Relate compound stability to heat of formation.

18. Define and illustrate: oxidation, oxidizing agent, reduction, reducing agent.

19. What is the name and structure of each of the three isotopes of hydrogen?

20. With the aid of the activity series, decide whether or not each of the following reactions will take place.

(a) $Sr + 2\ H_2O \rightarrow Sr^{++} + 2\ OH^- + H_2 \uparrow$
(b) $Cu + 2\ H^+ \rightarrow Cu^{++} + H_2 \uparrow$
(c) $2\ Al + Fe_2O_3 \rightarrow Al_2O_3 + 2\ Fe$
(d) $2\ Pb + O_2 \rightarrow 2\ PbO$
(e) $SnO + H_2 \rightarrow Sn + H_2O$
(f) $2\ Au_2O_3 + heat \rightarrow 4\ Au + 3\ O_2$
(g) $H_2 + Cu^{++} \rightarrow Cu + 2\ H^+$
(h) $Na_2O + H_2 \rightarrow Na + H_2O$
(i) $2\ Ag + Cu^{++} \rightarrow Cu + 2\ Ag^+$

21. With the aid of the activity series, determine whether or not each of the following reactions will take place.

(a) $Ni + 2H^+ \rightarrow Ni^{++} + H_2$
(b) $Mg + Pb^{++} \rightarrow Mg^{++} + Pb$
(c) $3\ Fe + 4\ H_2O \rightarrow Fe_3O_4 + 4\ H_2$
(d) $Cd + Zn^{++} \rightarrow Cd^{++} + Zn$
(e) $2\ Bi + 6\ H^+ \rightarrow 2\ Bi^{+++} + 3\ H_2$
(f) $NiO + H_2 \rightarrow Ni + H_2O$
(g) $2\ Ag_2O + heat \rightarrow 4\ Ag + O_2$
(h) $MgO + H_2 \rightarrow Mg + H_2O$
(i) $Cu + 2\ H^+ \rightarrow Cu^{++} + H_2$

PROBLEMS

1. How many grams of hydrogen can be displaced from an excess of acid by 8.24 g. of zinc? If the acid were hydrochloric, what weight of zinc chloride would be produced in the reaction? *Ans. 0.254 g.; 17.2 g.*

2. Calculate the per cent of hydrogen in H_3PO_4. What weight of H_3PO_4 contains 18.24 g. of hydrogen? *Ans. 3.09%; 591.1 g.*

3. What weight of hydrogen can be produced from one kilogram of sodium hydride reacting with water? What volume would this mass of hydrogen occupy at 0° and 760 mm. pressure? (The density of hydrogen is 0.08987 g./l. at 0° and 760 mm. pressure.) *Ans. 84.0 g.; 935 l.*

4. What is the weight of 85.0 l. of hydrogen at 0° and 760 mm.? *Ans. 7.64 g.*

5. How many grams of oxygen would be required to burn 150 g. of hydrogen? What weight of water would be produced? *Ans. 1.19 kg.; 1.34 kg.*

6. Calculate the number of gram-atoms of K, Zn, and Al, respectively, required to liberate 10.0 liters of hydrogen (density 0.08987 g./l.) from an excess of acid. *Ans. 0.892; 0.446; 0.297*

7. What weight of CaH_2 would be needed to fill a balloon of 10,000 liter capacity with hydrogen (density 0.08987 g./l.), assuming the reaction of the hydride with water to give a yield of 95.0%? *Ans. 9880 g.*

8. What weight of silicon would be required in a reaction with aqueous sodium hydroxide to give the same weight of hydrogen as that liberated when 10.0 g. of aluminum reacts with aqueous potassium hydroxide? *Ans. 7.81 g.*

9. What weight of "water gas" is formed by the reaction of 120 kg. of steam with white hot carbon, assuming the process to give a yield of 65.0%? *Ans. 130 kg.*

10. Calculate the weight of methane, CH_4, that must be cracked to yield one metric ton of carbon. *Ans. 1.34 metric tons*

11. Determine the weight of fluorine, F_2, required in the burning of 50.0 liters of hydrogen (density 0.08987 g./l.). What weight of HF will be produced in the reaction? *Ans. 84.7 g.; 89.2 g.*

12. What weight of HBr can be formed from the hydrogen liberated by the action of 12.0 g. of sodium upon an excess of water? *Ans. 42.2 g.*

13. Calculate the number of gram-atoms of iron needed in a reaction with aqueous copper (II) sulfate to precipitate 100.0 g. of copper metal. *Ans. 1.57*

14. A 10.0 g. copper strip is placed in a beaker containing an excess of aqueous silver nitrate. What weight of metallic silver will eventually be deposited from the solution? *Ans. 34.0 g.*

15. What weight of tin (II) oxide can be reduced by 80.0 g. of hydrogen gas, assuming a 100% yield? *Ans. 5.35 kg.*

REFERENCES

"Significance of Hydrogen Isotopes," H. C. Urey (Willard Gibbs Medal Address), *Ind. Eng. Chem.*, 26 (7) 803 (1934).

"Hydrogen," M. E. Weeks, *Discovery of the Elements*, Sixth Edition, Publ. by the Journal of Chemical Education, Easton, Pa., 1956; pp. 197–205.

CHAPTER SEVEN

The Gaseous State and the Kinetic-Molecular Theory

7.1 Physical States of Matter

We noted in Section 1.6 that matter exists in three different physical states, which are designated as **solid, liquid,** and **gas.** Water in the solid state is known as ice, in the liquid state as water, and in the gaseous state as water vapor or steam. When water in the form of ice takes up heat energy, it changes to the liquid state; and when liquid water is heated, it changes into the gaseous state. These changes take place in the reverse direction when heat energy is removed. Such changes in physical state are possible for a great many but not all substances. For example, we have observed in our study of the preparation of oxygen that solid mercury (II) oxide and potassium chlorate decompose upon heating. However, any substance which can exist in the gaseous state can be liquefied and solidified under suitable conditions of temperature and pressure.

The gaseous state of matter will be considered first because it is the easiest physical state to study and understand.

7.2 Behavior of Matter in the Gaseous State

The volume of a gas, unlike that of a solid or liquid, may be decreased greatly by increasing the pressure upon it. This property is known as **compressibility.** Increasing the weight on a piston, such as shown in Fig. 7–1, will cause the volume of the gas confined in the cylinder to decrease until the pressure of the gas is sufficient to support the piston and the weight.

When gases are heated they expand to larger volumes unless confined. This can be shown by heating the gas contained in the cylinder illustrated in Fig. 7–1. When the gas is heated, it expands, raising the piston; but the pressure remains constant. This is a case of expansion at constant pressure. If the piston is kept from moving by adding more weight to it, then the volume remains constant. In this case the pressure of the gas increases with rise in temperature at constant volume. **Expansibility** is a characteristic property of all gases.

A small quantity of a pungent gas released into a room in which the air is still can in time be detected in other parts of the room. When a sample of gas is introduced into an evacuated container, it quickly distributes itself and fills the

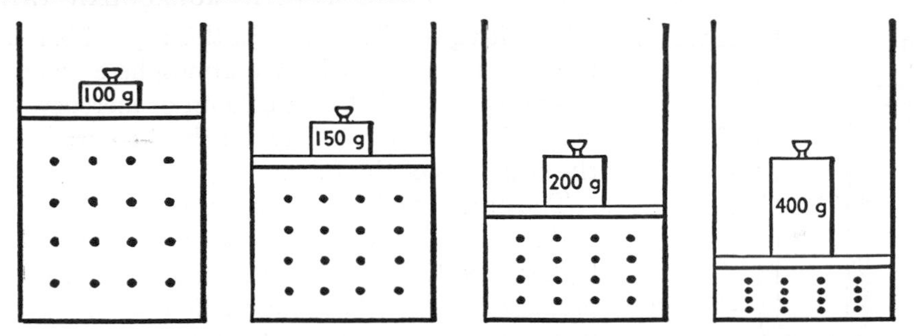

Fig. 7–1 These figures illustrate what happens when a fixed quantity of gas kept at constant temperature is confined in a cylinder and is subjected to more and more pressure by placing heavier and heavier weights on the movable gas-tight piston. Of course, the number of molecules represented is but a minute fraction of the actual number in such a volume.

container completely. These are examples of the diffusion of gases. The fact that two gases introduced into the same container quickly mix by diffusion shows each gas to be permeable to the other. Thus gases possess the properties of **diffusibility** and **permeability.**

The different gases which compose the atmosphere differ in density, but diffusion prevents a separation of the gases, i.e., the composition of the atmosphere does not vary with altitude. Mixtures of gases are homogeneous; they do not tend to separate into layers because of differences in densities.

7.3 Measurement of Gas Pressures

The pressure exerted by the atmosphere (a mixture of gases) may be measured by a simple mercury **barometer** (Fig. 7–2). Such an instrument can be prepared by filling a glass tube, closed at one end and about 80 cm. long, with mercury and inverting it in a dish of mercury. The mercury falls in the tube until the pressure exerted by the column of mercury is exactly equal to the pressure exerted by the air upon the surface of the mercury in the dish. (Pressure means the force exerted upon a unit area of surface, e.g., pounds per square inch, etc.) The mercury vapor pressure in the space above the mercury in the closed tube is negligible. The pressure of the atmosphere varies with the location on the surface of the earth and with climatic changes. The average pressure of the atmosphere at sea level at a latitude of 45° will support a column of mercury 760 mm. in height. The height of the column of mercury is the distance between the surface of the mercury in the tube and that in the open vessel. A mercury barometer may consist of two arms, one closed and one open to the atmosphere or connected to a container

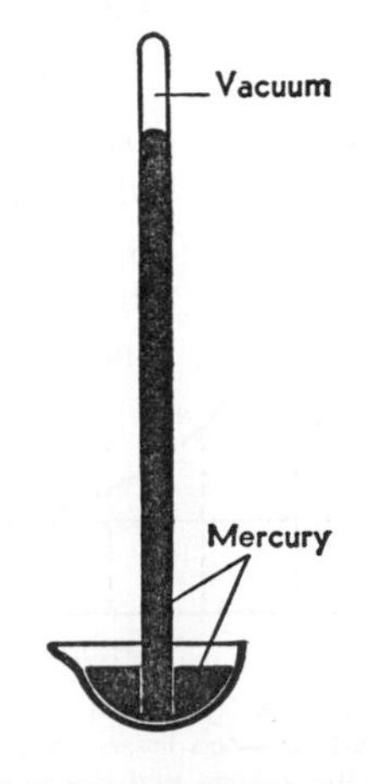

Fig. 7–2 Mercury barometer.

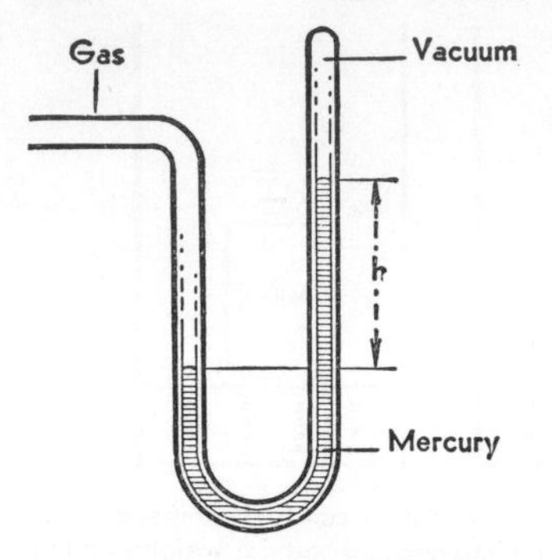

Fig. 7–3 A two-arm mercury barometer.

filled with gas (Fig. 7–3). In this type of barometer the pressure exerted by the atmosphere or another gas is equal to that of a column of mercury whose height is the distance between the mercury levels in the two arms of the tube.

The pressure of the atmosphere, as you may know, varies with the distance above sea level. At a higher elevation, the air is less dense, and thus the pressure is less. The atmospheric pressure at 20,000 feet is only half of that at sea level because about half of the entire atmosphere is below this elevation. Portable **aneroid barometers** (Fig. 7–4) are made with scales graduated for measuring elevations. Mountain climbers and aviators use such barometers to determine height above sea level.

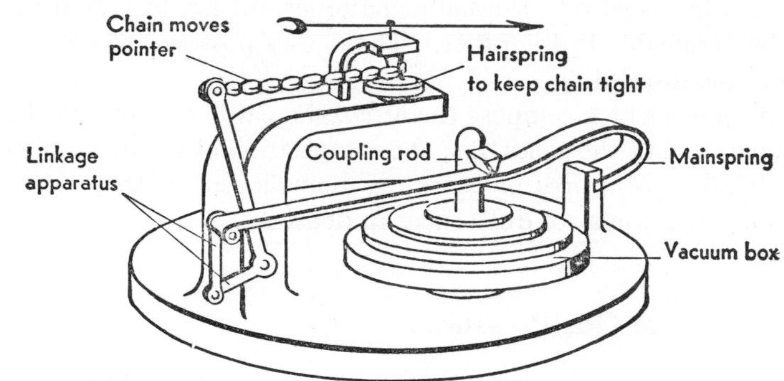

Fig. 7–4 A diagram of the operation of an aneroid barometer. Changes in air pressure cause changes in thickness of the vacuum box to which the coupling rod is attached.

7.4 Relation of Volume to Pressure; Boyle's Law

It has been observed from experiment that the volume of a given mass of gas, at constant temperature, is reduced to half when the pressure on the gas is doubled. Conversely, the volume is doubled by a decrease in pressure to one-half. Observations of this sort were summarized by Robert Boyle in 1660 in a form now known as **Boyle's Law: The volume of a given mass of gas held at constant temperature is inversely proportional to the pressure under which it is measured.** (Fig. 7–5). The following problems will serve to illustrate Boyle's Law.

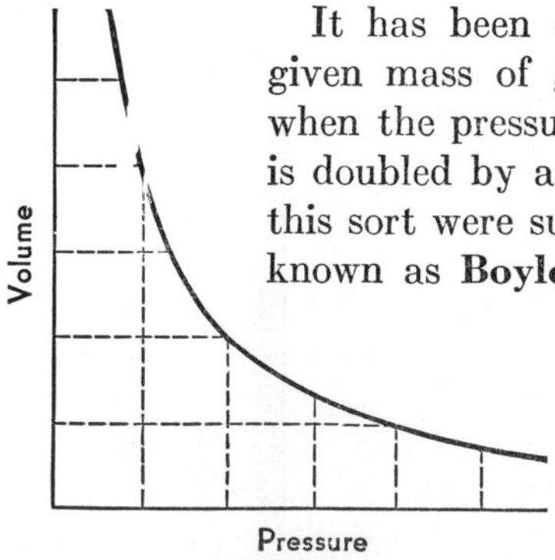

Fig. 7–5 A graphical illustration of Boyle's Law — an inverse proportion between the volume and pressure of a gas at constant temperature.

EXAMPLE 1. A sample of gas has a volume of 400 ml. when measured at 25° and 760 mm. pressure. What volume will it occupy at 25° and 190 mm. pressure?

A decrease in pressure from 760 mm. to 190 mm. means that the volume of the gas will increase, the temperature remaining constant. The new volume will be determined by the ratio of the two pressures. By making the larger pressure the numerator and the smaller pressure the denominator of the ratio, and multiplying the original volume by this ratio, the new volume may be found.

$$400 \text{ ml.} \times \frac{760 \text{ mm.}}{190 \text{ mm.}} = 1600 \text{ ml.}$$

Thus, the new volume is four times the original volume as the result of decreasing the pressure to one-fourth its initial value. Note that because the term "mm." appears in both numerator and denominator of the expression, it cancels out and leaves only the term "ml." as the unit of measurement in the answer to the problem.

EXAMPLE 2. What final pressure must be applied to a sample of gas having a volume of 200 ml. at 20° and 750 mm. pressure to permit the expansion of the gas to a volume of 600 ml. at 20°?

A decrease in pressure is required to permit the volume of a gas to increase at constant temperature. The new pressure will be determined by the ratio of the two volumes. By making the smaller volume the numerator and the larger volume the denominator of the ratio, and multiplying the original pressure by this ratio, the new pressure may be found.

$$750 \text{ mm.} \times \frac{200 \text{ ml.}}{600 \text{ ml.}} = 250 \text{ mm.}$$

The new pressure must be one-third the initial pressure to permit the volume to increase threefold.

7.5 The Kelvin Temperature Scale

By experiment it has been found that when 273 ml. of gas at 0° is warmed to 1°, its volume increases by 1 ml. to 274 ml.; at 20° its volume increases to 293 ml.; at 273° its volume increases to 546 ml. (double that at 0°), and so on, provided that in each case the pressure remains constant. Note that the volume of the gas at 0° increases $\frac{1}{273}$ of its volume for each increase of 1° on the Celsius (centigrade) scale. The volume of a gas decreases at the same rate when the temperature falls. If the temperature of 273 ml. of a gas could be lowered from 0° to −273°, then the gas should have no volume at −273° because its volume should decrease at the rate of $\frac{1}{273}$ of its volume at 0° for each degree of fall in temperature. Before the temperature of −273° is reached all gases become liquids, to which this rate of change in volume does not apply. The temperature −273° (or more exactly −273.16° C) is called **absolute zero** and is the zero point on the **Kelvin scale** of temperature (Fig. 7–6). The freezing point of water is therefore 273° Kelvin (0° C), and the boiling point is 373° Kelvin (100° C). Temperatures on the Kelvin scale are designated as °K. The size of the degree on the Kelvin scale is the same as on the Celsius scale. A temperature on the Celsius scale is converted to the Kelvin

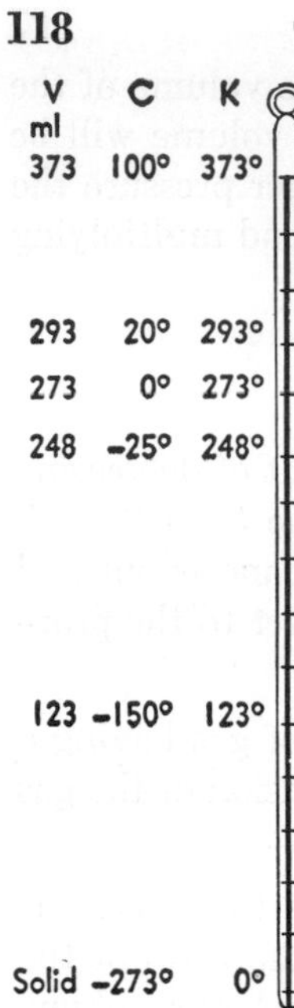

Fig. 7–6 The volume of a gas is directly proportional to its Kelvin temperature.

scale by adding 273° to the Celsius reading. For example, 25° C = (25 + 273)° K = 298° K.

7.6 Relation of Volume to Temperature; Charles' Law

Studies of the effect of temperature upon the volume of confined gases at constant pressure by Charles in 1787 led to the generalization known as **Charles' Law,** which we can state in modern terms as follows: **The volume of a given mass of gas is directly proportional to its temperature on the Kelvin scale when the pressure is held constant** (see Figs. 7–6 and 7–7). The following problems are based upon this law.

EXAMPLE 1. A sample of gas occupies 200 ml. at 10° and 750 mm. pressure. What volume will the gas have at 20° and 750 mm.?

The Celsius temperatures are first converted to the Kelvin scale, 10° C + 273° = 283° K, and 20° C + 273° = 293° K. When the temperature of a gas is raised, the gas expands, and the ratio of temperatures used in solving for the final volume must be an improper fraction, i.e., the larger temperature must be in the numerator:

$$200 \text{ ml.} \times \frac{293° \text{ K}}{283° \text{ K}} = 207 \text{ ml.}$$

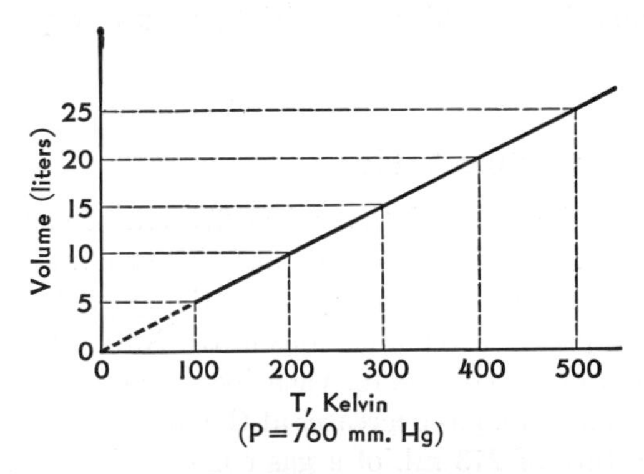

Fig. 7–7 A graphical illustration of Charles' Law — a direct proportion between the volume of a gas and Kelvin temperature at constant pressure.

EXAMPLE 2. A sample of gas occupies 100 ml. at 27° and 740 mm. pressure. What temperature will the gas have when its volume is changed to 80 ml. at 740 mm.?

The initial temperature of 27° C is equal to 300° K. The temperature must decrease to cause a reduction in volume at constant pressure. Thus, the ratio of volumes must be a proper fraction, i.e., the larger volume must be in the denominator:

$$300° \text{ K} \times \frac{80 \text{ ml.}}{100 \text{ ml.}} = 240° \text{ K}$$

Subtracting 273° from 240° K, we find the final Celsius temperature to be − 33°.

7.7 Standard Conditions of Temperature and Pressure

From the foregoing considerations of the variation of the volume of a given mass of gas with changes in pressure and temperature, it should be clear that the volume and the density (mass per unit volume) of a gas vary with these conditions. Thus, to be able to compare different gases with regard to their densities or to fix a definite density for any gas, it is necessary to adopt a set of **standard conditions of temperature and pressure** (S.T.P.) for all measurements of gases. Accordingly, 0° C temperature and 760 mm. pressure are universally used as standard conditions.

7.8 Correction of the Volume of a Gas to Standard Conditions

Let us suppose that a sample of gas is found to occupy 500 ml. under laboratory conditions of 27° C and 740 mm. pressure. Correct the volume to standard conditions of 0° C and 760 mm. First, convert the Celsius temperatures to the Kelvin scale: 27° C = (27 + 273)° K = 300° K, and 0° C = (0 + 273)° K = 273° K. A decrease in temperature from 300° K to 273° K will cause a decrease in the volume of the gas. Multiply the original volume by a fraction made up of the two temperatures and having a value less than unity:

$$500 \text{ ml.} \times \frac{273° \text{ K}}{300° \text{ K}}$$

The increase in pressure from 740 mm. to 760 mm. will also decrease the volume of the gas, and this factor may be included in the same expression with the temperature factor to obtain the corrected volume:

$$500 \text{ ml.} \times \frac{273° \text{ K}}{300° \text{ K}} \times \frac{740 \text{ mm.}}{760 \text{ mm.}} = 443 \text{ ml.}$$

It is common practice to correct the volume of a gas to standard conditions, or to any other conditions of temperature and pressure, in one operation.

7.9 The Pressure of a Mixture of Gases; Dalton's Law

Suppose, for example, that we have gas A at a pressure of 100 mm. in a 1-liter container, and gas B also at a pressure of 100 mm. and contained in a second 1-liter vessel. After transferring gas B to the 1-liter vessel containing gas A, the tempera-

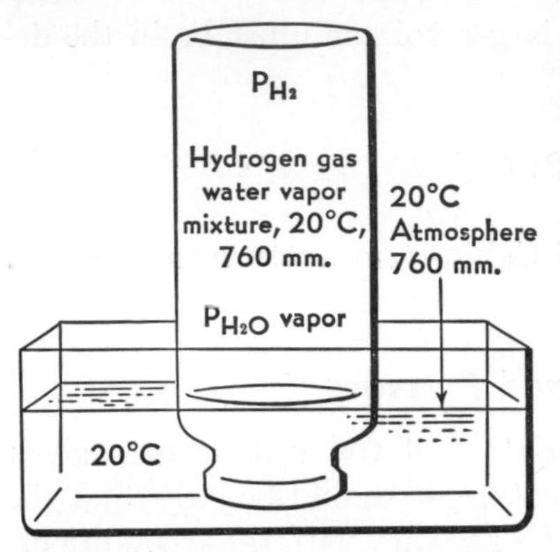

Fig. 7–8 In this illustration a mixture of hydrogen gas and water vapor is under a pressure of 760 mm. How could you find the pressure of the hydrogen alone?

ture being held constant, the total pressure of the mixture is found to be 200 mm. In the absence of chemical interaction between the components of a mixture of gases, the individual gases do not interfere with the pressures of one another. The pressure exerted by each gas in a mixture is called the partial pressure of that gas, and the total pressure of the mixture of gases is the sum of the partial pressures of all the gases present in the mixture. This law is known as **Dalton's Law of Partial Pressures** and may be stated in the following manner: **The total pressure of a mixture of gases is equal to the sum of the partial pressures of the component gases.**

A convenient method of measuring the pressure which a gas is exerting is to collect the gas over water and adjust the water level (Fig. 7–8) so that it is the same both inside and outside the gas container. The gas is then at atmospheric pressure, which can be read on a laboratory barometer.

When a gas is collected over water, it will soon become saturated with water vapor. The total pressure of the mixture will be equal to the sum of the partial pressure of the gas and that of the water vapor. The pressure of the pure gas is therefore equal to the total pressure minus the water vapor pressure. Suppose that 200 ml. of hydrogen is collected over water at a temperature of 26° and a pressure of 750 mm. The pressure of water vapor at 26° is 25 mm. What is the pressure of the hydrogen in the dry state at 26°? According to Dalton's Law of Partial Pressures, the pressure of the dry hydrogen is the difference between the total pressure (750 mm.) and the vapor pressure of water at 26° (25 mm.), or

$$P_{H_2} = P_{\text{Total}} - P_{H_2O\text{ vapor}} = 750\text{ mm.} - 25\text{ mm.} = 725\text{ mm.}$$

The vapor pressure of water at various temperatures is given in Table 7·1. This table and Fig. 7–9 illustrate the increase in vapor pressure as the temperature increases.

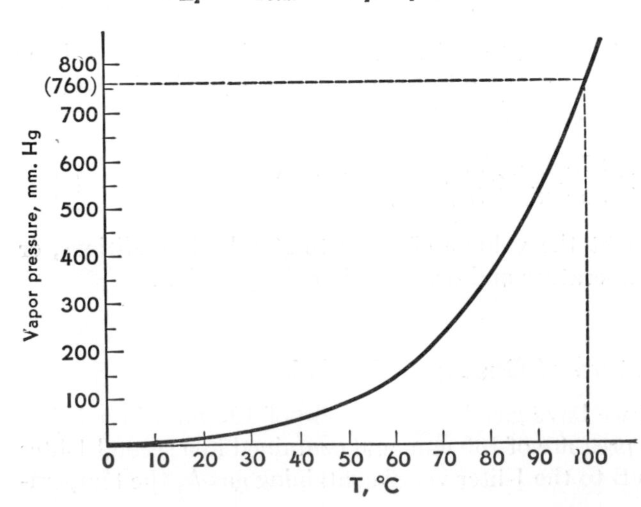

Fig. 7–9 A graph illustrating change of vapor pressure of water with temperature.

TABLE 7·1 Vapor Pressure of Ice and Water in Millimeters of Mercury

Temperature	*Pressure*	*Temperature*	*Pressure*	*Temperature*	*Pressure*
−10°	2.1	18°	15.5	80°	355.1
−5°	3.2	19°	16.5	90°	525.8
−2°	4.0	20°	17.5	95°	633.9
−1°	4.3	21°	18.7	96°	657.6
0°	4.6	22°	19.8	97°	682.1
1°	4.9	23°	21.1	98°	707.3
2°	5.3	24°	22.4	99°	733.2
3°	5.7	25°	23.8	99.1°	735.9
4°	6.1	26°	25.2	99.2°	738.5
5°	6.5	27°	26.7	99.3°	741.2
6°	7.0	28°	28.3	99.4°	743.9
7°	7.5	29°	30.0	99.5°	746.5
8°	8.0	30°	31.8	99.6°	749.2
9°	8.6	31°	33.7	99.7°	751.9
10°	9.2	32°	35.7	99.8°	754.6
11°	9.8	33°	37.7	99.9°	757.3
12°	10.5	34°	39.9	100.0°	760.0
13°	11.2	35°	42.2	100.1°	762.7
14°	12.0	40°	55.3	100.2°	765.5
15°	12.8	50°	92.5	100.3°	768.2
16°	13.6	60°	149.4	100.5°	773.7
17°	14.5	70°	233.7	101.0°	787.5

Suppose that 500 ml. of oxygen is collected over water at a temperature of 23° and a barometric pressure of 800 mm. The vapor pressure of water at 23° is 21.1 mm. Calculate the volume of dry oxygen corrected to standard conditions. The gas collected over water is a mixture of oxygen and water vapor. The pressure of the dry oxygen is the total pressure minus the vapor pressure of water or

$$P_{O_2} = P_{\text{Total}} - P_{H_2O\text{ vapor}} = 800\text{ mm.} - 21\text{ mm.} = 779\text{ mm.}$$

A decrease in temperature from 23° C (296° K) to 0° C (273° K) causes a decrease in volume. To correct for the temperature change, multiply the original volume by 273° K/296° K. A decrease in pressure from 779 mm. to 760 mm. causes an increase in volume. To correct for the pressure change, multiply the original volume by 779 mm./760 mm.

$$\text{Volume of dry oxygen at S.T.P.} = 500\text{ ml.} \times \frac{273^\circ\text{ K}}{296^\circ\text{ K}} \times \frac{779\text{ mm.}}{760\text{ mm.}} = 473\text{ ml.}$$

7.10 Diffusion of Gases; Graham's Law

When a sample of gas is set free in one part of a closed container, it very quickly diffuses throughout the container (see Fig. 7–10 on page 122). If a mixture of

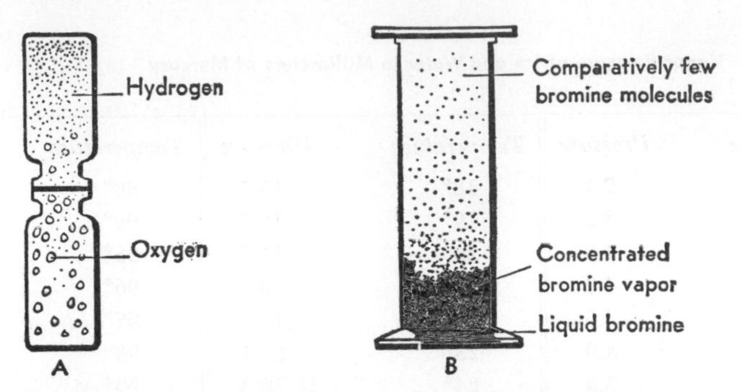

Fig. 7–10 A. Despite the differences in density of these gases, the molecules intermingle. They must have considerable kinetic energy because some of the oxygen molecules move upwards in spite of gravity and some of the hydrogen molecules move down in spite of the buoyant force of the heavier oxygen gas. B. Bromine vaporizes and its heavier molecules diffuse upward among the air molecules.

gases is placed in a container the walls of which are porous to gases, diffusion of the gases through the porous walls will take place. The lighter gases will diffuse through the small openings of the porous walls more rapidly than the heavier ones. Graham, in 1832, studied the rates of diffusion of different gases and showed that **the rates of diffusion of gases are inversely proportional to the square roots of their densities (or molecular weights).** The density of oxygen is almost exactly sixteen times that of hydrogen. Thus,

$$\frac{\text{Rate of diffusion of hydrogen}}{\text{Rate of diffusion of oxygen}} = \frac{\sqrt{1.429 \text{ g./l.}}}{\sqrt{0.08987 \text{ g./l.}}} = \frac{\sqrt{32}}{\sqrt{2}} = \frac{4}{1}$$

This means that hydrogen diffuses four times as rapidly as oxygen. The rates of diffusion must depend upon the velocities of the molecules; the rate of diffusion is greater for molecules of smaller mass and higher velocities than for molecules of larger mass and lower velocities (see Section 7.11).

Practical application of differences in diffusion rates of gaseous substances is made in the separation of light isotopes from heavy ones. Fractional diffusion through a porous barrier from a region of higher pressure to one of lower pressure is used for the large-scale separation of gaseous $^{235}_{92}UF_6$ from $^{238}_{92}UF_6$ at the Oak Ridge atomic energy installation. It is said that for separation to be complete, each UF_6 molecule must be diffused some two million times.

7.11 The Kinetic-Molecular Theory

The idea that the properties of gases such as compressibility, expansibility, and diffusibility could be accounted for by considering the gas molecules to be in continuous motion occurred to several people (Bernoulli in 1738, Poule in 1851, and Kronig in 1856). During the latter half of the nineteenth century, Clausius, Maxwell, Boltzmann, and others developed this hypothesis into the detailed **kinetic-molecular theory** of gases, which is summarized as follows.

(1) Gases are composed of separate particles called molecules. The volume actually occupied by the individual molecules of a gas under ordinary conditions is very small compared with the total volume of the gas. Thus the molecules of a gas are relatively far apart; and they have very little attraction for one another, except when near the liquefaction point.

(2) The molecules of a gas are in continuous motion (Fig. 7–11) with varying velocities. They move in straight lines in all directions and behave as perfectly elastic bodies when they collide with the walls of the container or with each other.

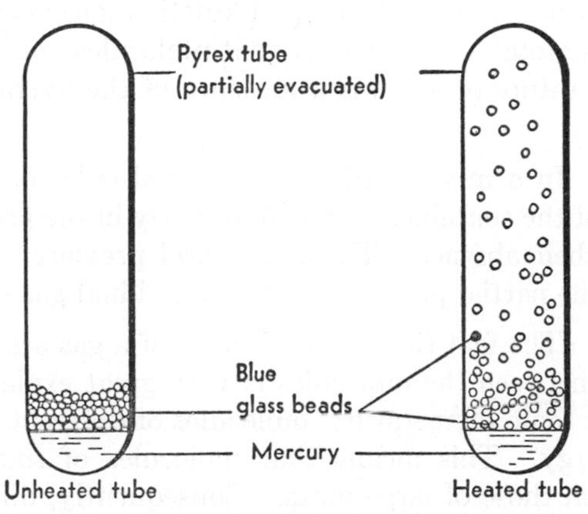

Fig. 7–11 The glass beads in the tube dance when the mercury is heated sufficiently to provide an appreciable vapor pressure of mercury. The beads finally move toward the top of the tube. This demonstration provides evidence for the motion of gaseous mercury molecules.

(3) The average kinetic energy (energy due to their motion) of the molecules of different gases is the same at the same temperature, regardless of differences in mass. The kinetic energy of gaseous molecules increases with a rise in temperature, and decreases as the temperature falls. The kinetic energy of a molecule is equal to $\frac{1}{2}mv^2$, where (m) is mass and (v) is velocity. It follows that molecules of small mass, like hydrogen, must move with higher velocities than molecules of larger mass, like oxygen, because they have the same kinetic energy at the same temperature.

7.12 Relation of the Behavior of Gases to the Kinetic-Molecular Theory

The gas laws may be readily explained in light of the kinetic theory.

1. *Boyle's Law.* The pressure exerted by a gas upon the walls of its container is caused by the bombardment of the walls by rapidly moving molecules and varies directly with the number of molecules confined within a given volume. Reducing the volume of a given mass of gas to one-half will double the number of molecules per unit volume. It follows that the number of impacts per unit time upon the same area of wall surface will also be doubled. The increased number of

impacts per unit area results in twice as much pressure. These results are in accordance with Boyle's law relating volume and pressure.

2. *Charles' Law.* It is a common observation that a rise in temperature increases the pressure of a gas at constant volume. The increase in pressure of a gas with increase in temperature reflects the increase in average kinetic energy of the molecules as the temperature is raised. An increase in average velocity of the molecules results in more frequent and harder impacts upon the walls of the container, i.e., greater pressure.

A study of the effect of temperature upon kinetic-molecular motion leads to the belief that heat is the total kinetic energy that molecules possess by virtue of their motion. The temperature of a gas is a measure of the average kinetic energy of the molecules.

3. *Dalton's Law.* In a mixture of gases the molecules of one component will bombard the walls of the container just as frequently in the presence of other kinds of molecules as in their absence. Thus, the total pressure of a mixture of gases will be the sum of the partial pressures of the individual gases.

4. *Graham's Law.* The fact that the molecules of a gas are in rapid motion and that the free space between the molecules is very great explains the phenomenon of diffusion. At the same temperature, molecules of different gases have the same average kinetic energy. This means that molecules of small mass move with higher velocities than those of large mass. Consequently, diffusion rates of gases are related inversely to their molecular weights and densities.

Hydrogen is the lightest and therefore diffuses most rapidly of all the gases. The average velocity of its molecules at room temperature is about one mile per second and that of oxygen molecules is about one-fourth mile per second. However, diffusion rates are much lower than these velocities due to collisions between molecules, of which there are about 11 billion per molecule per second in hydrogen gas at standard conditions. Hydrogen molecules travel about 17×10^{-6} cm. between collisions and, on the average, are halted about 60 thousand times in traveling one centimeter.

7.13 Deviations from the Gas Laws

When gases under ordinary conditions of temperature and pressure are compressed, the volume is reduced by crowding the molecules closer together. This reduction in volume is really a reduction in the amount of empty space between the molecules. At high pressures, the molecules are crowded so closely together that the volume which they occupy is a large fraction of the entire volume of the gas. Because the volume of the molecules themselves is not compressed, only a small fraction of the entire volume can be affected by an increase in pressure. Thus at high pressures the whole volume is not inversely proportional to the pressure as predicted by Boyle's Law.

The molecules in a gas at relatively low pressures and high temperatures have practically no attraction for one another because they are far apart. However, as the molecules are crowded closer together at low temperatures and high pressures, the force of attraction between the molecules increases. This attraction has the same effect as an increase in external pressure; it causes a slightly greater decrease in volume than corresponds to the increase in external pressure. The compression caused by intermolecular attraction is more pronounced at lower temperatures because the molecules move more slowly and have a smaller tendency to fly apart after collision with one another.

Strictly speaking, then, the gas laws apply exactly only to gases whose molecules do not attract one another and which occupy no part of the whole volume. Because there are no gases which have these properties, we can speak of them only as **ideal** or **perfect gases.** Under ordinary conditions, however, the deviations from the gas laws are so slight that they may be neglected.

QUESTIONS

1. Explain the following terms as applied to the gaseous state: compressibility, expansibility, diffusibility, permeability, and homogeneity.
2. Describe a mercury barometer and explain how it functions in measuring gas pressures.
3. State Boyle's Law. Set up a mathematical expression of this law in the form of a proportion using V_1 for the initial volume, V_2 for the final volume, P_1 for the initial pressure, and P_2 for the final pressure.
4. State Charles' Law. The fraction $\frac{1}{273}$ is sometimes called the coefficient of volume expansion of gases. Explain. Why does this coefficient not apply at very low temperatures and high pressures?
5. What are the standard conditions of temperature and pressure and why is it important to have a set of standard conditions?
6. State and illustrate Dalton's Law of Partial Pressures.
7. Summarize the kinetic-molecular theory as it applies to gases.
8. Explain Boyle's Law, Charles' Law, and Dalton's Law in terms of the kinetic-molecular theory.

PROBLEMS

1. The volume of a mass of gas is 500 ml. at 760 mm. pressure. What volume will it occupy at 380 mm., the temperature remaining constant? *Ans. 1000 ml.*
2. The volume of a mass of gas is 3.50 l. at 735 mm. and 25°. What volume will it occupy at standard pressure and 25°? *Ans. 3.38 l.*
3. A given mass of air occupies 1500 ml. at one atmosphere (760 mm.) of pressure. What pressure must be applied to reduce the volume to 300 ml. at constant temperature? *Ans. 5 atm.*
4. Using the coefficient of expansion of gases ($\frac{1}{273}$), what change in temperature (at constant pressure) would be required to double the volume of a gas measured at 0°? *Ans. 546° K or 273° C*
5. The volume of a given mass of gas is 325 ml. at 5° and 750 mm. What will be its volume measured at 25° and 750 mm.? *Ans. 348 ml.*

6. The volume of a gas measured at 30° and 760 mm. is 10 l. What final temperature would be required to reduce the volume to 9 l. at constant pressure?

Ans. *273° K or 0° C*

7. A gas occupies 85 ml. at 0° and 720 mm. What final temperature would be required to increase the pressure to 760 mm., the volume being held constant?

Ans. *288° K or 15° C*

8. The volume of a gas is 400 ml. at 27° and 742 mm. What volume will the gas occupy at S.T.P.? *Ans.* *355 ml.*

9. The volume of a gas is 700 ml. at S.T.P. What volume will it occupy at 20° and 770 mm.? *Ans.* *742 ml.*

10. A gas occupies 300 ml. at – 10° and 720 mm. What volume will the gas occupy at 20° and 740 mm.? *Ans.* *325 ml.*

11. The volume of a gas collected over water at 32.0° and 720 mm. is 1350 ml. What will the volume of the gas be when dried and measured at S.T.P.? (Vapor pressure of water at 32° = 35.7 mm.) *Ans.* *1090 ml.*

12. Which of the following gases will diffuse more rapidly than oxygen: C_2H_2, Cl_2, H_2S, N_2, NO_2, CH_4? *Ans.* C_2H_2, N_2, CH_4

13. If the average velocity of hydrogen molecules is one mile per second at room temperature, what will be the average velocity of nitrogen molecules at the same temperature? *Ans.* *0.268 mile per second*

14. A gas of unknown composition diffuses at the rate of 10 ml./sec. in a diffusion apparatus in which CH_4 gas diffuses at the rate of 20 ml./sec. Calculate the approximate molecular weight of the gas of unknown composition. *Ans.* *64*

15. Calculate the relative rates of diffusion of the gases CO_2 and Ar.

Ans. *Ar diffuses 1.05 times faster than* CO_2

16. A 500 ml. volume of oxygen measured at S.T.P. is warmed to the normal boiling point of water. Calculate the new volume of the gas, assuming no change in pressure. *Ans.* *683 ml.*

17. Calculate the volume occupied by the oxygen produced by the thermal decomposition of 100 g. of $KClO_3$, assuming the oxygen to be measured at 25° and 755 mm. (Density of oxygen at S.T.P. is 1.429 g./l.) *Ans.* *30.1 l.*

18. A given mass of nitrogen has a volume of 300 ml. at 0° and 750 mm. To what temperature must the nitrogen be heated in order that it occupy 400 ml. at 750 mm.? *Ans.* *364° K or 91° C*

19. Air at S.T.P. has a density of 1.292 g./l. What will 4.00 liters of air weigh at 20.0° and 750 mm.? *Ans.* *4.75 g.*

20. What volume is occupied by 10.0 g. of nitrogen at 25.0° and 800 mm.? (The density of nitrogen is 1.2506 g./l. at S.T.P.) *Ans.* *8.29 l.*

21. Carbon dioxide has a density of 1.9766 g./l. at S.T.P. Calculate the pressure exerted by 1.000 g. of carbon dioxide at 0°, when contained in a 100 ml. vessel.

Ans. *3840 mm.*

22. The volume of a mass of dry nitrogen is 200 ml. at 15.0° and 740 mm. What will be the volume of this gas maintained over water at 25.0° and 750 mm.? (See Table 7·1.) *Ans.* *211 ml.*

23. Calculate the weight of dry hydrogen in 400 ml. of moist hydrogen gas col-

lected over water at 23.0° and 740 mm. (The density of hydrogen is 0.08987 g./l. at S.T.P.) *Ans. 0.0314 g.*

24. The density of air at S.T.P. is 1.292 g./l. What will be its density at 136.5° K and 380 mm.? *Ans. 1.292 g./l.*

25. Air contains, on the average, 0.03 per cent by volume of carbon dioxide at S.T.P. Calculate the weight of carbon dioxide in 500 l. of air measured at 20.0° and 760 mm. (The density of CO_2 is 1.9766 g./l. at S.T.P.) *Ans. 0.276 g.*

26. Calculate the partial pressures of oxygen and of nitrogen in the air at a total pressure of 760 mm., if the air has a 20.8 volume per cent of oxygen and 79.2 volume per cent of nitrogen. *Ans. 158 mm.; 602 mm.*

27. A sample of oxygen is collected over water at a temperature of 20.0°, pressure of 764 mm., and volume of 570 ml. What volume would the dry oxygen have under the same conditions of temperature and pressure? (See Table 7·1).

Ans. 557 ml.

28. Calculate the relative rates of diffusion of NH_3 and He; CO_2 and H_2; Cl_2 and F_2. *Ans. 2.06; 4.67; 1.37*

29. Calculate the relative rates of diffusion of $^{235}_{92}UF_6$ and $^{238}_{92}UF_6$.

Ans. 1.004

30. A gas of unknown identity diffuses at the rate of 100 ml. per second in a diffusion apparatus in which a second gas whose molecular weight is 76.0 diffuses at the rate of 64.0 ml. per second. Calculate the molecular weight of the first gas.

Ans. 31.1

31. The time of outflow of a gas through a small opening is 26.6 minutes, while that of hydrogen is 6.50 minutes. Calculate the molecular weight of the first gas.

Ans. 33.8

32. One liter of gaseous CCl_4 is collected at 400° K and 800 mm. What will be the volume of this mass of gas measured at 600° K and standard pressure?

Ans. 1.58 l.

33. What pressure will a given mass of gas measuring 100 ml. at S.T.P. exert when expanded to 250 ml. with no change in temperature? *Ans. 304 mm.*

34. The density of ammonia at S.T.P. is 0.7710 g./l. What weight of ammonia will be required to produce a pressure of 2.00 atmospheres at a temperature of 546° K when contained in a 500 ml. vessel? *Ans. 0.386 g.*

REFERENCES

"Some Early Thermometers," E. H. Brown, *J. Chem. Educ.*, **11** (8) 448 (1934).

"Kinetic-Molecular Theory and Its Relation to Heat Phenomena," J. A. Timm, *J. Chem. Educ.*, **12** (1) 31 (1935).

"Robert Boyle and His Background," D. Reilly, *J. Chem. Educ.*, **28** (4) 178 (1951).

"Thomas Graham's Study of the Diffusion of Gases," A. Ruckstuhl, *J. Chem. Educ.*, **28** (11) 594 (1951).

CHAPTER EIGHT

Gram-Molecular Volume of Gases and Molecular, Atomic, and Equivalent Weights

8.1 Reactions Involving Gases; Gay-Lussac's Law

From studies of the volumetric relations in which gaseous substances interact, the early chemists came to the conclusion that gases combine or react in definite and simple proportions by volume. For example, it has been determined by experiment that one volume of nitrogen will combine with three volumes of hydrogen to give two volumes of ammonia gas, providing the volumes of the reactants and product are measured under the same conditions of temperature and pressure.

$$\underset{\text{1 Volume}}{N_2} + \underset{\text{3 Volumes}}{3\,H_2} \rightarrow \underset{\text{2 Volumes}}{2\,NH_3}$$

The term "volume" is used here in a general sense, and if the volume of nitrogen is measured in liters, then the volumes of hydrogen and ammonia must also be measured in liters. Note that the relative numbers of volumes are numerically the same as the relative numbers of molecules of the substances participating in the reaction. Such observations from experiment were summarized by **Gay-Lussac** (Fig. 8–1) in the **Law of Combining Volumes: The volumes of gases involved in a reaction, at constant temperature and pressure, can be expressed as a ratio of small whole numbers.** It is important to remember that this law applies only to substances in the gaseous state measured at constant temperature and pressure, and that the volumes of any solids or liquids involved in the reactions are not considered. When liquids or solids undergo chemical reaction, no generalizations can be made concerning the volumes of the reactants and products involved in the reactions. Additional examples illustrating Gay-Lussac's Law are as follows.

Fig. 8–1 Joseph Louis Gay-Lussac (1788–1850) contributed much to our knowledge of chemistry, particularly relating to the volumes of gases. *Fisher Scientific Co.*

(1) Two volumes of hydrogen and one volume of oxygen react to give two volumes of steam.

$$\underset{\text{2 Volumes}}{2\,H_2} + \underset{\text{1 Volume}}{O_2} \rightarrow \underset{\text{2 Volumes}}{2\,H_2O}$$

(2) One volume of hydrogen combines with one volume of chlorine to form two volumes of hydrogen chloride.

$$\underset{\text{1 Volume}}{H_2} + \underset{\text{1 Volume}}{Cl_2} \rightarrow \underset{\text{2 Volumes}}{2\,HCl}$$

(3) Carbon (a solid) reacts with one volume of oxygen to give one volume of carbon dioxide.

$$\underset{\text{A solid}}{C} + \underset{\text{1 Volume}}{O_2} \rightarrow \underset{\text{1 Volume}}{CO_2}$$

(4) Four volumes of steam react with iron (a solid) to yield four volumes of hydrogen and Fe_3O_4 (a solid).

$$\underset{\text{4 Volumes}}{4\,H_2O} + \underset{\text{A solid}}{3\,Fe} \rightarrow \underset{\text{4 Volumes}}{4\,H_2} + \underset{\text{A solid}}{Fe_3O_4}$$

The simplest ratio, of course, for the reacting gaseous volumes in this case is one to one.

8.2 An Explanation of Gay-Lussac's Law; Avogadro's Law

The law of combining volumes of gases can be satisfactorily explained in terms of the molecular structure of gases if we assume that **equal volumes of all gases, measured under the same conditions of temperature and pressure, contain the same number of molecules.** Avogadro enunciated this hypothesis in 1811 to account for the behavior of gases. His hypothesis, which has since been experimentally proven, is now accepted as fact and is known as **Avogadro's Law.**

Consider the union of hydrogen and chlorine to produce hydrogen chloride, the volumes of the reactants and product being measured under the same conditions of temperature and pressure:

1 volume of hydrogen + 1 volume of chlorine → 2 volumes of hydrogen chloride

According to Avogadro's Law, equal volumes of hydrogen, chlorine, and hydrogen chloride contain the same number of molecules. During reaction, then, two molecules of hydrogen chloride are formed from one molecule each of hydrogen and chlorine. Now each molecule of hydrogen chloride must contain at least one atom of hydrogen and one atom of chlorine; hence, two molecules of hydrogen chloride will contain at least two atoms of hydrogen and two atoms of chlorine, which must have been present in one molecule of hydrogen and one molecule of chlorine.

1 volume of hydrogen + 1 volume of chlorine → 2 volumes of hydrogen chloride

1 molecule of hydrogen + 1 molecule of chlorine → 2 molecules of hydrogen chloride

No similar gaseous reaction has been found in which one molecule of hydrogen (or chlorine) contains enough of the element to form more than two molecules of product. We can assume, therefore, that each molecule of hydrogen (and chlorine) contains two and only two atoms. Furthermore, when an electric arc is passed through hydrogen one volume of hydrogen becomes two volumes (the initial and final volumes being corrected to the same conditions of temperature and pressure). This fact means that each of the original hydrogen molecules has dissociated into two new molecules.

$$\underset{\text{1 Volume}}{H_2} \rightarrow \underset{\text{2 Volumes}}{2\,H}$$

The new molecules are apparently monatomic because higher energies do not cause further dissociation. In a similar manner, it can be shown that elementary oxygen, nitrogen, fluorine, chlorine, bromine, and iodine consist of diatomic molecules.

The volumetric relationship involved in the formation of hydrogen chloride from hydrogen and chlorine may be represented graphically (Fig. 8–2). The ad-

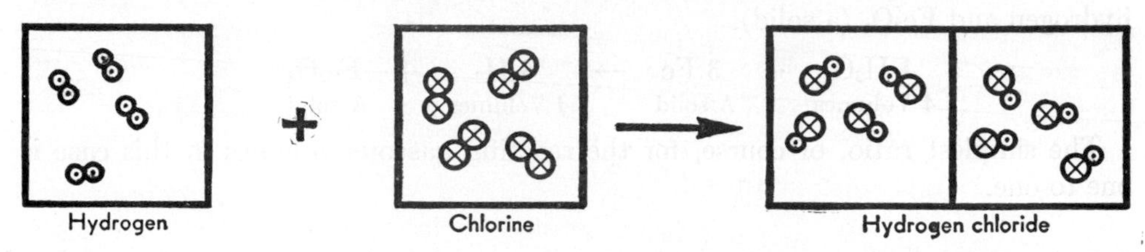

Fig. 8–2 One volume of hydrogen combines with one volume of chlorine. Two volumes of hydrogen chloride, HCl, are formed.

herence of other gaseous reactions to Gay-Lussac's Law can be explained and pictured graphically in a manner similar to that described for the reaction of hydrogen with chlorine. Dalton had considered and rejected the idea that equal volumes of gases contain the same number of atoms; it did not occur to him that elements might exist as polyatomic molecules (H_2, O_2).

Gay-Lussac's Law can be used to determine the volumes of gases involved in a reaction. For example, let us calculate the number of liters of hydrogen that will combine with 20.0 liters of nitrogen to form ammonia, the gaseous volumes being measured at S.T.P. First, write down the equation for the reaction.

$$\underset{\text{1 Volume}}{N_2} + \underset{\text{3 Volumes}}{3\,H_2} \rightarrow \underset{\text{2 Volumes}}{2\,NH_3}$$

From the equation we see that one volume of nitrogen will combine with three volumes of hydrogen. Therefore, 20 l. of nitrogen will combine with

$$20\text{ l.} \times \frac{3\text{ volumes}}{1\text{ volume}} = 60\text{ l. of hydrogen}$$

8.3 Relative Densities of Gases

It follows from the fact that molecules of different substances have different masses and that equal volumes of different gases under the same conditions of temperature and pressure contain the same number of molecules, that the densities of different gases will not be the same. For example, the density of oxygen at S.T.P. is 1.429 grams per liter, whereas that of hydrogen is 0.0899 gram per liter. Because equal volumes of different gases contain the same number of molecules, the ratio of the densities of two gases is the same as the ratio of their molecular weights.

$$\frac{\text{density of oxygen}}{\text{density of hydrogen}} = \frac{1.429 \text{ g./l.}}{0.0899 \text{ g./l.}} = \frac{\text{molecular weight of oxygen}}{\text{molecular weight of hydrogen}} = \frac{32.00}{2.016}$$

Suppose we calculate the molecular weight of carbon dioxide, the density of which is 1.977 g./l. at S.T.P. Noting that carbon dioxide has a greater density than oxygen (1.429 g./l.), it follows that its molecular weight should be greater than that of oxygen (32.00). We may obtain the molecular weight of carbon dioxide by multiplying that of oxygen by the ratio of the two densities.

$$32 \times \frac{1.977 \text{ g./l.}}{1.429 \text{ g./l.}} = 44$$

It should be obvious to the student that if the molecular weights of two gases are known and if the density of one of them is known, the density of the other may be calculated easily.

8.4 Gram-Molecular Volume of Gases

As we shall see in Section 8.5, the volume occupied by one gram-molecular weight of a substance in the gaseous state is important in the experimental determination of the molecular weight of the substance. We can calculate the volume that one gram-molecular weight of a gas will occupy under standard conditions if we know its density at S.T.P. and its molecular weight. For example, oxygen has a density of 1.429 g./l. at S.T.P. and its molecular weight is 32.00. Calculate the volume occupied by one gram-molecular weight of oxygen at S.T.P. One mole (32.00 g.) of oxygen will occupy more space than 1.429 g. of the gas, which has a volume of one liter. Therefore, set up the expression in such a manner as to give a larger volume:

$$1 \text{ liter} \times \frac{32.00 \text{ g.}}{1.429 \text{ g.}} = 22.4 \text{ liters}$$

The volume occupied by one gram-molecular weight of a substance as a gas is known as its gram-molecular volume (G.M.V.). A gram-molecular weight of any substance contains 6.023×10^{23} molecules of that substance (Section 2.5), and the same number of molecules of different gases occupy equal volumes under the same conditions of temperature and pressure. The highly important and interesting fact follows, then, that the **gram-molecular volume at any given temperature and pressure is the same for all gases; it is 22.4 l. at 0° C. and 760 mm.** (Fig. 8–3). Just as most gases show deviations from the

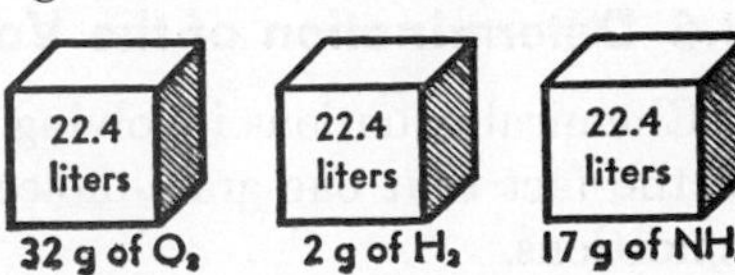

Fig. 8–3 A gram-molecular weight of any gas occupies a volume of approximately 22.4 liters at standard conditions and is the weight in grams of 6.023×10^{23} molecules of that gas.

Gas Laws (Section 7.13), they also show slight deviations from Avogadro's Law. Thus the gram-molecular volume is not quite the same for different gases, and therefore not always *exactly* equal to 22.4 liters.

8.5 Determination of Molecular Weights of Gases

The molecular weight of a gas can be found readily by determining experimentally the weight of a known volume of the gas under laboratory conditions of temperature and pressure and, using these data, calculating the weight of 22.4 l. of the gas corrected to standard conditions. For example, a sample of gas occupies 400 ml. at 20.0° and 740 mm. and weighs 0.842 g. What is the molecular weight of the gas? The volume of the gas at standard conditions can be found by multiplying the measured volume by fractions determined by the temperature change and the pressure change. The temperature change is from 293° K to 273° K, which will cause a decrease in volume; such a change will require a fraction whose value is less than unity. An increase in pressure from 740 mm. to 760 mm., which will cause a decrease in volume, thus requires a fraction with a value less than unity.

$$400 \text{ ml.} \times \frac{273^\circ \text{ K}}{293^\circ \text{ K}} \times \frac{740 \text{ mm.}}{760 \text{ mm.}} = 364 \text{ ml.}$$

The weight of 364 ml. of the gas at standard conditions is 0.842 g. Therefore, the weight of 22,400 ml. (22.4 l.) of the gas at S.T.P. can be found by multiplying the weight of 364 ml. of the gas by a fraction whose value is greater than unity and made up of the two volumes.

$$0.842 \text{ g.} \times \frac{22{,}400 \text{ ml.}}{364 \text{ ml.}} = 52.0 \text{ g.}$$

The weight of 22.4 l. of the gas at S.T.P. is 52.0 g. This weight is numerically equal to the molecular weight of the gas, 52.0. Molecular weights obtained by this method are only approximate because the gram-molecular volume is not exactly 22.4 l. for all gases.

This method of determining molecular weights is applicable only to gases and to substances that can be vaporized without decomposition. Many substances decompose before they are completely changed to the vapor state, and many others vaporize at such high temperatures that it is either impossible or impractical to determine their molecular weights by this method. For substances that are soluble in suitable solvents, the molecular weights may be determined by the use of the depression of the freezing point, elevation of the boiling point, or the osmotic pressure of their solutions (Chapter 11).

8.6 Determination of the Volumes of Gases Involved in a Reaction

Chemical equations involving gases may be quantitatively interpreted in terms of the fact that one gram-molecular weight of a gas occupies 22.4 l. at standard conditions.

What volume of oxygen, measured at 0° and 760 mm., would be formed by complete decomposition of 21.66 g. of mercury (II) oxide? The equation for the reaction is

$2\,HgO$	$\rightarrow 2\,Hg +$	O_2
2 moles		1 mole
2×216.6 g.		32 g. (22.4 l. at S.T.P.)

This equation shows that two moles (gram-formula weights) of mercury (II) oxide (weight, 433.2 g.) will liberate one mole of oxygen (volume, 22.4 l. at S.T.P.). If 433.2 g. of HgO yield 22.4 l. of oxygen, then 21.66 g. will give

$$22.4 \text{ l.} \times \frac{21.66 \text{ g.}}{433.2 \text{ g.}} = 1.12 \text{ l. of oxygen}$$

8.7 General Gas Law Equation

The conditions relating to pressure, volume, temperature, and number of moles of a gas can be combined into one equation, referred to as the **General Gas Law Equation** or the **Ideal Gas Law Equation.**

Boyle's Law states that the volume V of a particular number of moles n of an ideal gas is inversely proportional to the pressure P at constant temperature T. Using the symbol $\propto$ for "is proportional to," this can be written

$$V \propto \frac{1}{P} \quad \text{at constant T and n}$$

Charles' Law states that the volume V of n moles of an ideal gas is directly proportional to the Kelvin temperature T at constant pressure P.

$$V \propto T \quad \text{at constant P and n}$$

According to Avogadro's Law, the volume of a gas is proportional to the number of molecules, and hence the number of moles n, of the gas at constant pressure P and temperature T.

$$V \propto n \quad \text{at constant P and T}$$

In general, it can be shown that

$$V \propto \left(\frac{1}{P}\right)(T)(n)$$

or

$$V = R\left(\frac{1}{P}\right)(T)(n)$$

or

$$PV = nRT$$

where R is the proportionality constant and is often referred to as the **universal gas constant.**

The numerical value of R can be obtained by substituting actual experimental values for P, V, n, and T. At standard conditions, P = 760 mm. or 1 atmosphere, T = 273° K, and one mole of any gas occupies a volume of 22.4 liters. Substituting these values in PV = nRT:

$$(1 \text{ atm.})(22.4 \text{ l.}) = (1 \text{ mole})(R)(273° \text{ K})$$

$$R = \frac{(1 \text{ atm.})(22.4 \text{ l.})}{(1 \text{ mole})(273° \text{ K})} = 0.082 \frac{\text{l.-atm.}}{\text{mole-°K}}$$

(or 0.082 liter-atmospheres per mole per degree Kelvin)

The numerical value of R for other units of P, V, n, and T will be different. It is important to remember that in using a particular numerical value for R, the values of P, V, n, and T must always be expressed in terms of the units used in evaluating R.

The following problem illustrates the use of the general gas law equation.

Calculate the volume occupied by 15.0 grams of nitrogen gas at 15° C and 735 mm. pressure.

$$P = 735 \text{ mm.} = \tfrac{735}{760} \text{ atm.}$$

$$n = \frac{15.0}{28.0} \text{ moles} = \text{number of moles in 15.0 g. nitrogen}$$

$$R = 0.082 \frac{\text{l.-atm.}}{\text{mole-°K}}$$

$$T = 15° \text{ C} = (273 + 15)° \text{ K}$$

Substituting in PV = nRT:

$$\left(\frac{735}{760} \text{ atm.}\right)(V) = \left(\frac{15.0}{28.0} \text{ moles}\right)\left(0.082 \frac{\text{l.-atm.}}{\text{mole-°K}}\right)(273 + 15)° \text{ K}$$

$$V = \left(\frac{15.0}{28.0} \text{ mole}\right)\left(0.082 \frac{\text{l.-atm.}}{\text{mole-°K}}\right)(288° \text{ K})\left(\frac{1}{\frac{735}{760} \text{ atm.}}\right) = 13.1 \text{ liters}$$

8.8 Determination of Atomic Weights

A general method of determining the atomic weight of an element is based upon determination of the molecular weights of different compounds of the element. Because an atom is the smallest portion of an element that can be contained in a molecule of a compound, it follows that the gram-molecular weight of any compound of an element must contain one or some whole multiple of the gram-atomic weight of that element. Thus, the smallest weight of an element ever found in a gram-molecular weight of any of its compounds will be the gram-atomic weight of the element. Hence it is usually possible to obtain the atomic weight of an element by determining the smallest weight of that element in a gram-molecular volume of several of its volatile compounds. Atomic weights found by this method are only approximate because Avogadro's Law is not absolutely accurate.

To illustrate the determination of atomic weights by this method, let us consider the gram-molecular weights and analyses of several compounds of chlorine.

An inspection of Table 8·1 shows that the weight of chlorine in a gram-molecular weight of these volatile compounds, and hence in a gram molecular volume at S.T.P., is 35.5 g. or a simple whole number multiple of this number. Therefore, it is logical to conclude that the atomic weight of chlorine is very close to 35.5 if the data are sufficient.

TABLE 8·1 Composition of Some Chlorine Compounds

	Molecular Weight	*Total Weight of Chlorine in Molecular Weight*	*Formula*
Hydrogen chloride	36.5	35.5	HCl
Methyl chloride	50.5	35.5	CH_3Cl
Chlorine dioxide	67.5	35.5	ClO_2
Phosgene	99.0	71.0 (2 × 35.5)	$COCl_2$
Phosphorus trichloride	137.4	106.4 (3 × 35.5)	PCl_3
Carbon tetrachloride	153.8	141.8 (4 × 35.5)	CCl_4
Phosphorus pentachloride	208.3	177.3 (5 × 35.5)	PCl_5

8.9 Atomic Weights from Specific Heats

The discovery by Dulong and Petit in 1819 that **the product of the specific heats** (Section 1.24) **and atomic weights of solid elements is very nearly a constant, approximately 6.4,** was a milestone in the development of the atomic theory of the structure of matter (Fig. 8–4). This law has been found to be approximately valid for all solid elements having atomic weights greater than 40 and for most metallic elements. It does not hold (at room temperature) for such elements as carbon, silicon, phosphorus, or sulfur. Suppose we calculate the approximate atomic weight of iron, which has a specific heat of 0.115 cal. per gram per degree.

$$\text{Atomic weight} \times \text{specific heat} = 6.4$$

$$\text{Atomic weight} = \frac{6.4}{\text{specific heat}} = \frac{6.4}{0.115} = 56$$

The value 56 is not the exact atomic weight of iron because the law of Dulong and Petit is only approximately valid. Prior to this discovery of Dulong and Petit, atomic weights could only be conjectured from experimentally derived equivalent weights (next section) by certain unproved assumptions. With the aid of this law, decisions could be made as to which multiple of the equivalent weight of an element represented its atomic weight. Although proposed originally as an empirical rule, the law of Dulong and Petit has been shown in recent years to have theoretical significance as well.

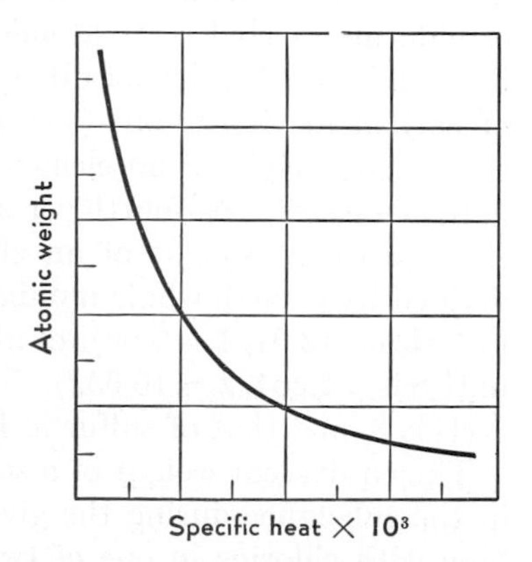

Fig. 8–4 Variation of specific heat with atomic weight.

A method for a more accurate determination

of atomic weights involving equivalent weights of the elements is described in Section 8.12.

8.10 Equivalent Weights of the Elements

The term **equivalent** was first used in a chemical sense by Henry Cavendish, in 1767, in reference to the relative quantities of potassium carbonate and calcium hydroxide required to neutralize the same quantity of acid. The fundamental definition of equivalent weight is this: **The equivalent weight of a substance is the number of parts of it by weight which combine with or are otherwise chemically equivalent to 8.00 parts by weight of oxygen.** This fundamental definition will be expanded in Section 11.16. **A gram-equivalent weight** of a substance is its equivalent weight expressed in grams. In forming H_2O, two gram-atoms of hydrogen (2×1.008 g.) combine with one gram-atom of oxygen (16.00 g.); therefore, 1.008 g. of hydrogen combine with (are equivalent to) 8.00 g. of oxygen. Hence, a gram-equivalent weight of hydrogen is 1.008 g., which is also its gram-atomic weight. One gram-atom of magnesium (24.312 g.) combines with one gram-atom of oxygen (16.00 g.) in forming MgO; therefore, 12.16 g. of magnesium combine with 8.00 g. of oxygen. A gram-equivalent of magnesium is 12.16 g., which is one-half its gram-atomic weight. Likewise, an equivalent weight of sodium is the same as its atomic weight because two atoms of sodium combine with one atom (two equivalent weights) of oxygen in forming Na_2O. In CO_2 one atom of carbon is in union with two atoms of oxygen. Two atoms of oxygen represent four equivalent weights of it; therefore, the equivalent weight of carbon in CO_2 is one-fourth its atomic weight.

For fixing equivalent weights, any element of known equivalent weight can be used as a standard but only because its equivalent weight has been determined in relation to the value 8.00 for oxygen. Thus, the combining capacity of hydrogen can be used in determining the equivalent weights of other elements with which it combines (or is equivalent to) because it has been established that 1.008 g. of hydrogen are equivalent to 8.00 g. of oxygen. It follows that the equivalent weight of chlorine in HCl is its atomic weight (35.45), that of sulfur in H_2S is one-half its atomic weight, that of nitrogen in NH_3 is one-third its atomic weight, and that of carbon in CH_4 is one-fourth its atomic weight. We observe, then, that the equivalent weight of an element is either equal to its atomic weight, or it is one-half, one-third, one-fourth, or some other simple fraction of it. In other words, the equivalent weight of an element is numerically equal to its atomic weight divided by a small whole number — its valence. The equivalent weight of carbon in CH_4 is ($12.01/4 = 3.00$), of nitrogen in NH_3 is ($14.007/3 = 4.002$), and of sulfur in H_2S is ($32.064/2 = 16.032$). The valence of carbon in CH_4 is 4, that of nitrogen in NH_3 is 3, and that of sulfur in H_2S is 2.

The equivalent weight of a substance depends upon the change that takes place in the substance during the given reaction. For example, phosphorus may combine with chlorine in one of two ways, depending upon the conditions of the reaction, with the formation of either PCl_3 or PCl_5. The equivalent weight of chlorine in both compounds is its atomic weight (35.45). This means that the equivalent weight of phosphorus in PCl_3 is one-third its atomic weight (30.97/3 = 10.32), while in PCl_5 it is one-fifth its atomic weight (30.97/5 = 6.19).

8.11 Determination of Equivalent Weights

The equivalent weight of an element can be determined accurately by experiment. This is done by finding the weight of the element which will combine with or displace one equivalent weight of an element of known equivalent weight.

Let us calculate the equivalent weight of aluminum from the observation that when 6.74 g. of the metal are burned in oxygen, 12.74 g. of aluminum oxide are formed. The weight of oxygen which combines with 6.74 g. of aluminum is the weight of the aluminum oxide minus the weight of the aluminum, or

$$(12.74 \text{ g.} - 6.74 \text{ g.}) = 6.00 \text{ g. of oxygen}$$

The equivalent weight of aluminum is that weight of it which combines with 8.00 g. of oxygen. If 6.74 g. of aluminum combine with 6.00 g. of oxygen, then a greater weight of aluminum will be required to combine with 8.00 g. of oxygen. Hence, multiply 6.74 g. of aluminum by the ratio 8.00 g./6.00 g. to find the equivalent weight of aluminum.

$$6.74 \text{ g.} \times \frac{8.00 \text{ g.}}{6.00 \text{ g.}} = 8.99 \text{ g.}$$

Thus, the equivalent weight of aluminum is 8.99.

Suppose that a 1.6345 g. sample of pure zinc displaced 0.0504 g. of hydrogen from a dilute solution of an acid. What is the equivalent weight of the zinc? The gram-equivalent weight of zinc is that weight of it which will displace 1.008 g. of hydrogen. If 1.6345 g. of zinc displace 0.0504 g. of hydrogen, then a greater mass of zinc would be required in the displacement of 1.008 g. of hydrogen. Multiplying 1.6345 g. of zinc by the improper fraction made up of the two weights of hydrogen will give the gram-equivalent weight of zinc.

$$1.6345 \text{ g.} \times \frac{1.008 \text{ g.}}{0.0504 \text{ g.}} = 32.7 \text{ g.}$$

Thus, the equivalent weight of zinc is 32.7.

8.12 Determination of Atomic Weights from Equivalent Weights

The exact atomic weight of an element may be calculated after the experimental determination of (1) the exact equivalent weight, and (2) the approximate atomic weight. The calculation of the exact atomic weight of an element is illustrated by the following example. Suppose that the least weight found for the element carbon in a gram-molecular weight of any of the volatile compounds is 12.071. This weight is the approximate atomic weight of carbon. A very careful determination of the equivalent weight of carbon shows it to be 3.0027. This weight is one which can be accurately determined and it is, therefore, very nearly exact. Dividing its approximate atomic weight by its exact equivalent weight gives us the valence of carbon.

$$\frac{12.071}{3.0027} = 4.02$$

It is evident that the exact atomic weight of carbon divided by its exact equivalent weight should give the number 4 (instead of 4.02), because valences are whole numbers, and the only reason it does not is that 12.071 is not the exact atomic weight. We may now calculate the exact value of the atomic weight of carbon by multiplying the equivalent weight, 3.0027, by 4, which gives 12.011, the accepted value for the atomic weight of carbon (Section 3.9).

QUESTIONS

1. State Gay-Lussac's Law. Does this law pertain to substances in the liquid and solid states as well as the gaseous state? Explain.

2. What information is given by a balanced chemical equation involving gases that can be used in determining volumetric relations?

3. Show graphically the explanation of Gay-Lussac's Law as applied to the following reactions involving gases:

   (a) $N_2 + 3\ H_2 \rightarrow 2\ NH_3$

   (b) $2\ H_2 + O_2 \rightarrow 2\ H_2O$

4. How can it be shown experimentally that molecular iodine is diatomic?

5. Explain why the ratio of the relative densities of two gases is equal to the ratio of the molecular weights of the two gaseous substances.

6. What is the volume occupied by one gram-molecular weight of a gas called? What is its value at S.T.P.? How is it found from the density and molecular weight of a gas?

7. Relate the weight of an element present in a gram-molecular weight of any of its compounds to the atomic weight of that element.

8. State Avogadro's Law and the Law of Dulong and Petit.

9. Define the term "equivalent weight of an element." Relate atomic weights to equivalent weights and valence.

10. Which equivalent weights may be used as standards in determining other equivalent weights?

11. Why are equivalent weights more fundamental as regards quantities of elements undergoing chemical change than are atomic weights?

PROBLEMS

1. How many moles are represented by each of the following measured at S.T.P.?

   (a) 150 ml. of acetylene, C_2H_2. *Ans.* 6.70×10^{-3} *mole*

   (b) 0.0300 l. of phosphine, PH_3. *Ans.* 1.34×10^{-3} *mole*

   (c) 10.2 l. of helium, He. *Ans.* *0.455 mole*

   (d) 6.40 ml. of diborane, B_2H_6. *Ans.* 2.86×10^{-4} *mole*

   (e) 1000 ml. of silane, SiH_4. *Ans.* 4.46×10^{-2} *mole*

2. Calculate the density of the gas propane (C_3H_8) at S.T.P. *Ans. 1.97 g./l.*

3. Calculate the volume occupied by one mole of hydrogen at S.T.P. (density = 0.0899 g./l.), one mole of oxygen at S.T.P. (density = 1.429 g./l.), and one mole of methane gas (CH_4) at S.T.P. (density = 0.715 g./l.). What is this volume called? *Ans. 22.4 l.*

4. Calculate the number of molecules in one liter of a gas at 27.0° and 740 mm. *Ans. 2.38×10^{22}*

5. What volume is occupied by 14.0 g. of nitrogen
   (a) at S.T.P.? *Ans. 11.2 l.*
   (b) at 23.0° and 800 mm.? *Ans. 11.5 l.*
   (c) at the normal boiling point of water and 2.0 atmospheres of pressure? *Ans. 7.65 l.*

6. What volume would be occupied by each of the following gases at S.T.P.?
   (a) 0.600 mole of chlorine, Cl_2. *Ans. 13.4 l.*
   (b) 2.40 moles of nitrogen dioxide, NO_2. *Ans. 53.8 l.*
   (c) 16.0 grams of oxygen, O_2. *Ans. 11.2 l.*
   (d) 6.00 grams of hydrogen, H_2. *Ans. 66.7 l.*

7. How many grams of nitrogen, N_2, are there in 89.6 l. of the gas at S.T.P.? *Ans. 122 g.*

8. (a) Calculate the weight of 10.0 l. of methane, CH_4, at S.T.P. *Ans. 7.16 g.*
   (b) Calculate the weight of 15.5 l. of N_2 at −10.0° and 720 mm. *Ans. 19.1 g.*
   (c) Calculate the volume of 40.0 g. of NH_3 at 500° and 1000 atmospheres pressure (1 atm. = 760 mm.). *Ans. 0.149 l.*

9. Calculate the specific gravity of carbon dioxide at S.T.P. (a) referred to hydrogen at S.T.P. as a standard and (b) referred to air at S.T.P. as a standard (density of air at S.T.P. = 1.29 g./l.). Are these values of specific gravity equal numerically to the density of carbon dioxide at S.T.P.? Under what conditions are the numerical values for the density and the specific gravity of a substance equal? *Ans. (a) 22; (b) 1.5*

10. How many grams of carbon are there in 85.0 liters of CH_4 measured at S.T.P.? *Ans. 45.5 g.*

11. Calculate the density of each of the following gases at S.T.P. and at 15.0° and 780 mm.: CO, CO_2, NH_3, CH_4, He.

Ans.:

	S.T.P.	*15.0° and 780 mm.*
CO	*1.25 g./l.*	*1.22 g./l.*
CO_2	*1.96 g./l.*	*1.91 g./l.*
NH_3	*0.760 g./l.*	*0.740 g./l.*
CH_4	*0.716 g./l.*	*0.696 g./l.*
He	*0.179 g./l.*	*0.174 g./l.*

12. Calculate the weight of ethane, C_2H_6, required to produce a pressure of 760 mm. at 25.0° when contained in a one liter vessel. *Ans. 1.23 g.*

13. What pressure is exerted by 22.0 g. of carbon dioxide when contained in a 10.0 liter vessel at 27.0°? *Ans. 1.23 atm.*

14. A volume of 11,200 ml. of a gas measured at S.T.P. weighed 15 g. Calculate the approximate molecular weight of the gas. *Ans. 30*

15. A quantity of a gaseous compound weighing 2.714 g. had a volume of 1500 ml. at 25.0° and 742 mm. Calculate the approximate molecular weight of the compound. *Ans. 45.3*

16. How many grams of hydrogen will be required to fill a spherical balloon three meters in diameter at 20.0° and 700 mm. pressure? *Ans. 1090 g.*

17. A mixture of 0.100 g. of hydrogen and 0.200 g. of nitrogen is stored at S.T.P. What volume must the container have, assuming no interaction of the two gases? *Ans. 1.28 l.*

18. The atomic weight of chlorine is 35.5, and the weight of 22.4 l. of chlorine at S.T.P. is 71.0 g. What must be the formula for molecular chlorine? *Ans.* Cl_2

19. The simplest formula of a certain compound is CH_2 and the weight of a molar volume of the compound is 28.0 g. What must be the molecular formula of the compound? *Ans.* C_2H_4

20. The gram-formula weight of one form of elementary phosphorus is 123.9 g. Calculate the formula of molecular phosphorus. *Ans.* P_4

21. A 100 ml. flask contains only CH_4 at a temperature of 100° and a pressure of 760 mm. How many molecules are in the flask? *Ans.* 1.97×10^{21}

22. The weight of 22.4 ml. of a certain vapor at 20.0° and 737 mm. is 0.110 g. What is the molecular weight of the vapor? *Ans. 122*

23. A certain compound containing only carbon and hydrogen is found to have a vapor density of 2.550 g./l. at 100° and 760 mm. If the atomic ratio of carbon to hydrogen is one to one, what is the molecular formula of the compound? *Ans.* C_6H_6

24. How many liters of oxygen will be required to burn 45 liters of hydrogen ($2\ H_2 + O_2 \rightarrow 2\ H_2O$)? How many liters of air (21 per cent oxygen by volume) would be required? How many liters of water vapor will be formed? *Ans. 22.5 l.; 107 l.; 45 l.*

25. Calculate the volume of oxygen required to burn 12.0 liters of ethane gas (C_2H_6) to produce carbon dioxide and water. *Ans. 42.0 l.*

26. What volume of oxygen (measured at S.T.P.) can be produced by the decomposition of 135 g. of $KClO_3$ ($2\ KClO_3 \rightarrow 2\ KCl + 3\ O_2$)? *Ans. 37.0 l.*

27. How many grams of hydrogen would be required to reduce 50.0 g. of lead (II) oxide ($PbO + H_2 \rightarrow Pb + H_2O$)? This weight of hydrogen would be equal to how many moles? How many liters would this be at S.T.P.? *Ans. 0.452 g.; 0.224 mole; 5.02 l.*

28. How many liters of hydrogen gas, measured at 23.0° and 750 mm., can be obtained by the reaction of 50.0 g. of aluminum with an excess of dilute sulfuric acid? *Ans. 66.4 l.*

29. What volume of chlorine at S.T.P. can be obtained by the electrolysis of 100 g. of sodium chloride in a process that is 80% efficient? (Metallic sodium and chlorine gas, Cl_2, are the products of the electrolysis.) *Ans. 15.3 l.*

30. What volume of hydrogen, measured at S.T.P., would be formed by the action of 12.0 g. of CaH_2 upon an excess of water? *Ans. 12.8 l.*

31. Calculate the volume of hydrogen, measured at 25.0° and 730 mm., which would be produced by the reaction of 60.0 g. of iron with excess steam.

Ans. *36.5 l.*

32. What is the equivalent weight of a metal, 0.135 g. of which combines with 0.120 g. of oxygen? *Ans.* *9.0*

33. A 12.075 g. sample of a metal displaced 0.3723 g. of hydrogen gas from hydrochloric acid. What is the equivalent weight of the metal? The valence of the metal is 2. What is its atomic weight? *Ans.* *32.69; 65.37*

34. The approximate atomic weight of an element is 26.80, and its exact equivalent weight is 8.99. What is the valence and the exact atomic weight of the element?

Ans. *3; 26.97*

35. What is the equivalent weight of the phosphorus in each of the following compounds? (a) PH_3; (b) P_4O_6; (c) P_4O_{10}. *Ans.* *(a) 10.32; (b) 10.32; (c) 6.19*

36. Calculate the equivalent weight of nitrogen in each of the following compounds: (a) N_2O; (b) NO; (c) NO_2; (d) N_2O_3; (e) N_2O_5; (f) NH_3.

Ans. *(a) 14.007; (b) 7.003; (c) 3.502; (d) 4.668; (e) 2.801; (f) 4.668*

37. What fraction of the atomic weight represents the equivalent weight of each of the metals in the following equations?

(a) $Na + 2\ H_2O \rightarrow 2\ Na^+ + 2\ OH^- + H_2$ *Ans.* $\frac{1}{1}$

(b) $Si + 2\ OH^- + H_2O \rightarrow SiO_3^= + 2\ H_2$. *Ans.* $\frac{1}{4}$

(c) $Mg + H_2O \rightarrow MgO + H_2$ *Ans.* $\frac{1}{2}$

(d) $2\ Al + 6\ H^+ \rightarrow 2\ Al^{+3} + 3\ H_2$ *Ans.* $\frac{1}{3}$

38. Calculate the equivalent weight of tin in $SnCl_2$ and in $SnCl_4$.

Ans. *59.35; 29.67*

39. Analysis of a sample of a compound shows it to contain 42.41 g. of bismuth and 4.87 g. of oxygen. What are the equivalent weight and valence of bismuth in the compound? *Ans.* *69.7; 3*

40. A 5.00 gram sample of an oxide of lead contains 4.53 g. of lead. Calculate the equivalent weight of the lead in the compound. *Ans.* *77.1*

41. A certain metal forms two different binary compounds with chlorine, one containing 14.81% and the other 34.24% chlorine. The specific heat of the metal is 0.033 calorie per gram per degree. Calculate the atomic weight of the metal, and give the simplest formulas for the two chlorides of the metal.

Ans. *204; MCl, MCl_3*

42. The specific heat of a given metal is 0.031 calorie per gram per degree. Calculate the approximate atomic weight of the metal. *Ans.* *206*

43. A metallic chloride contains 34.06% of a metal whose specific heat is 0.114 calorie per gram per degree. Calculate (a) the atomic weight, and (b) the valence of the metal. *Ans.* *(a) 56.1; (b) 3*

REFERENCES

"Gram-Equivalent Weights," W. B. Meldrum, *J. Chem. Educ.*, **32** (1) 48 (1955).

"Berzelius — Pioneer Atomic Weight Chemist," W. M. MacNevin, *J. Chem. Educ.*, **31** (4) 207 (1954).

CHAPTER NINE

The Liquid and Solid States

9.1 The Kinetic-Molecular Theory and the Liquid State

We learned in Section 7.11 that the molecules of a substance in the gaseous state are in constant and very rapid motion and that the space between the molecules is large compared to the sizes of the molecules themselves. As the molecules of a gas are brought closer together by increased external pressure, the average distance between the molecules is decreased and **intermolecular attractive forces** become stronger. As a gas is cooled, the average velocity of the molecules decreases and their tendency to move apart after collision decreases. If the pressure is sufficiently high and the temperature is low enough, the intermolecular attraction overcomes the tendency of the molecules to fly apart, and the gas condenses to a liquid. Although molecules in the liquid state cling to one another, they still retain a limited amount of motion as reflected in the capacity of liquids to flow, to take the shape of a container, to diffuse, and to evaporate.

The molecules in a liquid are held in such close contact by their mutual attractive forces that the volume of any liquid decreases very little with increased pressure; liquids are relatively incompressible as compared to gases. The molecules in a liquid are able to move past one another in random fashion and thus possess the property of diffusion. Because of the much more limited freedom of molecular motion existing in liquids, they diffuse much more slowly than do gases.

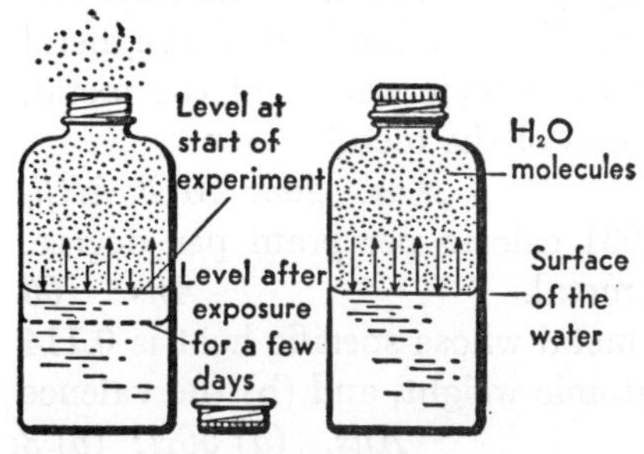

Fig. 9–1 Molecules of water can escape from the open bottle and evaporation occurs. Molecules of water do not escape from the covered bottle and dynamic equilibrium occurs.

9.2 Evaporation of Liquids

From experience we know that water placed in an open vessel decreases in volume upon standing. We say that **evaporation** has occurred. Evaporation may be explained in terms of the motion of molecules. At any given temperature above absolute zero the molecules of a liquid move — some slowly, some at intermediate rates, some very fast. An average velocity can be calculated. A rapidly moving molecule near the surface of the liquid may possess sufficient kinetic energy to overcome the attraction of its neighbors and escape, i.e., **evaporate,** to the space above the liquid (Fig. 9–1). Other fast moving molecules will leave the liquid phase and appear in the gaseous phase above the liquid as the process of evaporation continues. When the space above the liquid is confined, molecules cannot escape into the open but strike the walls of the container, rebound, and may strike the surface of the liquid, where they are trapped. The return of the molecules from the vapor to the liquid is known as **condensation.** As evaporation

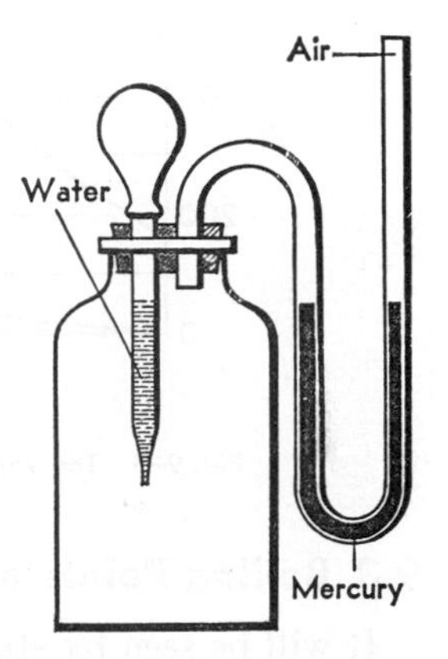

Fig. 9–2 A manometer being used to measure the vapor pressure of water. Squeezing the bulb forces water into the bottle. As the water comes to equilibrium with its vapor, the vapor molecules exert a pressure on their surroundings which include the surface of mercury in the left arm of the manometer. The surface of mercury in the left arm is pushed down and the surface of mercury in the other arm is pushed up. The difference in the levels of mercury in the two arms is a measure of the vapor pressure of the water.

proceeds, the number of molecules in the vapor state increases, and in turn, the rate of condensation increases. The rate of condensation will soon become equal to the rate of evaporation and the vapor in the closed container will be in equilibrium with its liquid (Fig. 9–1). This is called a **dynamic equilibrium** because the opposing changes involved are in full operation.

$$\text{Liquid} \underset{\text{condensation}}{\overset{\text{evaporation}}{\rightleftarrows}} \text{Vapor}$$

At equilibrium the space above the liquid is saturated with respect to molecules of the vapor. The pressure exerted by the vapor in equilibrium with its liquid, at a given temperature, is called the **vapor pressure** of the liquid (Fig. 9–2). Some vapor pressure data for water, alcohol, and ether are given in Table 9·1 and Fig. 9–3 on page 144.

TABLE 9·1 Vapor Pressures (mm. of Hg) of Some Common Substances at Various Temperatures

	0° C	*20° C*	*40° C*	*60° C*	*80° C*	*100° C*
Water	4.6	17.5	55.0	149.2	355.5	760.0
Alcohol	12.2	43.9	135.3	352.7	812.6	1,693.3
Ether	185.3	442.2	921.1	1,730.0	2,993.6	4,859.4

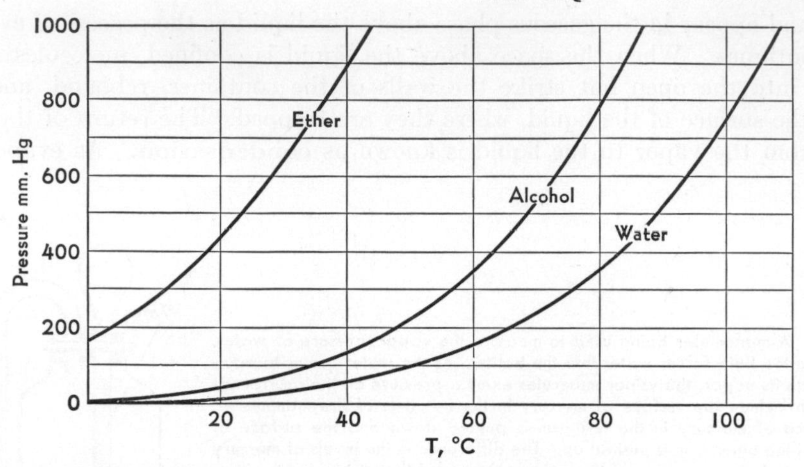

Fig. 9–3 The vapor pressures of three common substances at various temperatures.

9.3 Boiling Points of Liquids

It will be seen by studying Table 9·1 and Fig. 9–3 that, at a given temperature, the vapor pressure of ether is greater than that of alcohol, and that of alcohol is greater than that of water. These differences in vapor pressure are related to the intermolecular attractive forces which, of the three substances, are smallest for ether and greatest for water. Thus the equilibrium vapor pressure of a liquid is dependent upon the particular kind of molecule composing the liquid.

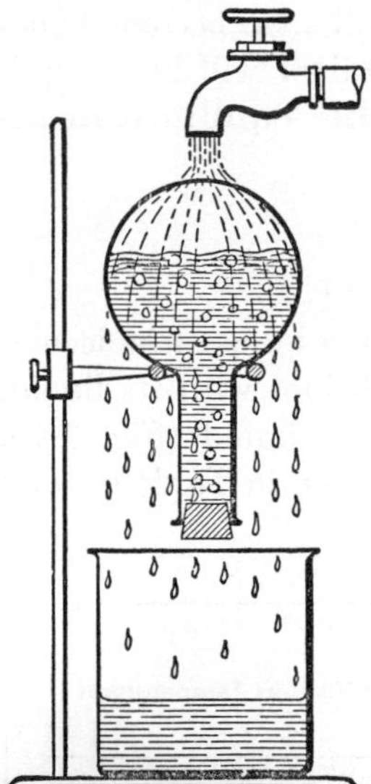

Fig. 9–4 The boiling temperature of water is lowered by lowering the pressure of the water vapor which is in equilibrium with the boiling water in the flask.

The data in Table 9·1 and Fig. 9–3 show that the vapor pressure of a liquid increases as the temperature is raised; this is due to an increase in the rate of molecular motion which accompanies an increase in temperature. The result is a more rapid escape of molecules from the surface of the liquid and thus a higher equilibrium vapor pressure.

When bubbles of vapor form within a liquid and rise to the surface where they burst and release the vapor, the liquid is said to boil. A liquid exposed to the air will boil when its equilibrium vapor pressure becomes equal to the pressure of the atmosphere. The **normal boiling point** of a liquid is that temperature at which its equilibrium vapor pressure becomes exactly equal to the standard atmospheric pressure of 760 mm. A liquid may boil at temperatures higher than normal under external pressures greater than one atmosphere; conversely, the boiling point of a liquid may be lowered below normal by decreasing the pressure on the surface of the liquid below one atmosphere (Fig. 9–4). Thus at high altitudes where the atmospheric pressure is less than 760 mm., water boils at temperatures below its normal boiling point of 100°. Food cooked with water cooks more slowly at high altitudes because the temperature of boiling water is lower than it would be at locations nearer sea level. The temperature of boiling water in pressure cookers is higher than normal due to higher equilibrium vapor pressures, thus making it possible to cook foods faster than in open vessels.

9.4 Intermolecular Forces and Boiling Point

We saw in the preceding section that differences in vapor pressures of liquids are related to differences in the forces of attraction between molecules of the liquids. What is the nature of these attractive forces and why do they differ in magnitude for molecules of different substances? All molecules exert an attraction for one another. This attraction is weak and is significant only when the molecules are very close together, i.e., very nearly in contact with one another. The attraction, known as **van der Waals attraction,** has its origin in the electrostatic attraction of the positive nucleus of one molecule for the electron cloud of a neighboring molecule (Fig. 9–5). The van der Waals attraction is opposed by (1) the

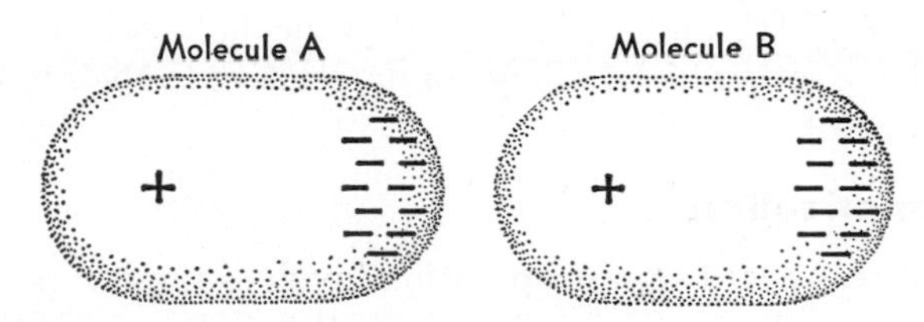

Fig. 9–5 Diagram showing van der Waals attraction due to nearly instantaneous fluctuating dipoles.

repulsive force of the electron clouds of the adjacent molecules and (2) the repulsion of the nuclei of neighboring atoms for one another. However, the attractive forces are somewhat stronger than the repulsive forces. It is the van der Waals attraction that causes substances such as the rare gases and the halogens to condense to liquids and freeze into solids when the temperature is lowered sufficiently.

The magnitude of the van der Waals attraction increases with increase in the number of electrons per molecule, and therefore with the molecular weight. This increase in intermolecular attraction with molecular weight is reflected in the increase in boiling point in a series of related substances such as He, Ne, Ar, Kr, Xe, Rn and H_2, F_2, Cl_2, Br_2, I_2 (see Table 9·2, p. 146).

It was noted in Section 4.7 that molecules whose centers of positive and negative electric charge do not coincide possess a permanent electric **dipole moment.** The HCl molecule, because chlorine has a greater electronegativity than hydrogen, has a partial negative charge on the chlorine atom and a partial positive charge on the hydrogen atom; the HCl molecule has a permanent dipole moment. The electrostatic attraction of the positive end of one HCl molecule for the negative end of another constitutes an attractive force in addition to the van der Waals attraction; this also causes an increase in boiling point.

TABLE 9·2 Molecular Weights and Boiling Points

Substance	He	Ne	Ar	Kr	Xe	Rn
Molecular weight	4.0	20.18	39.94	83.7	131.1	222
Boiling point, °C	−268.9	−245.9	−185.7	−152.9	−107.1	−61.8
Substance	H_2	F_2	Cl_2	Br_2	I_2	
Molecular weight	2.016	38.0	70.91	159.8	253.8	
Boiling point, °C	−252.7	−187	−34.6	58.78	184.4	

In general, liquids composed of discrete molecules which have no permanent dipole moments have low boiling points relative to their molecular weights because only the weak van der Waals attraction must be overcome during vaporization. In such molecules the centers of positive and negative electric charge coincide. Examples are the molecules of the inert gases and the halogens, and other symmetrical molecules such as CH_4, SiH_4, CF_4, SiF_4, SF_6, and UF_6. Molecular substances such as H_2O, HF, and C_2H_5OH (ethyl alcohol), which have permanent dipole moments, have rather high boiling points, relative to their molecular weights.

9.5 Heat of Vaporization

In Section 9.2 it was noted that evaporation involves the escape of the molecules of high kinetic energy (hotter molecules) from the surface of a liquid. The loss of the hotter molecules through evaporation results in a lower average kinetic energy for those remaining behind and, consequently, a lowering of the temperature of the liquid through evaporation. The cooling effect due to evaporation of water makes the air seem cold when one comes out of water.

Before a liquid can evaporate at a constant temperature, heat must be supplied in sufficient quantities to offset the cooling effect brought about by the escape of the molecules possessing high kinetic energies. The heat energy that must be supplied to evaporate a given mass of liquid at a constant temperature is known as the **heat of vaporization.** The heat of vaporization of water is 540 calories per gram, and that of ammonia is 327 calories per gram. The quantity of heat evolved during the condensation of a liquid is the same as that absorbed during evaporation.

The operation of modern mechanical refrigerators is based upon the heat absorbed by the vaporization of liquids (Fig. 9–6). Heat energy is removed from within the refrigerator by the evaporation of a liquid such as ammonia. The refrigerant is then transported in the gaseous state outside the refrigerator where the gas is again liquefied by the combined effect of compressing and cooling. To be an effective refrigerant, a substance must be readily convertible from the gaseous to the liquid state at the working temperature and it must have a high heat of vaporization.

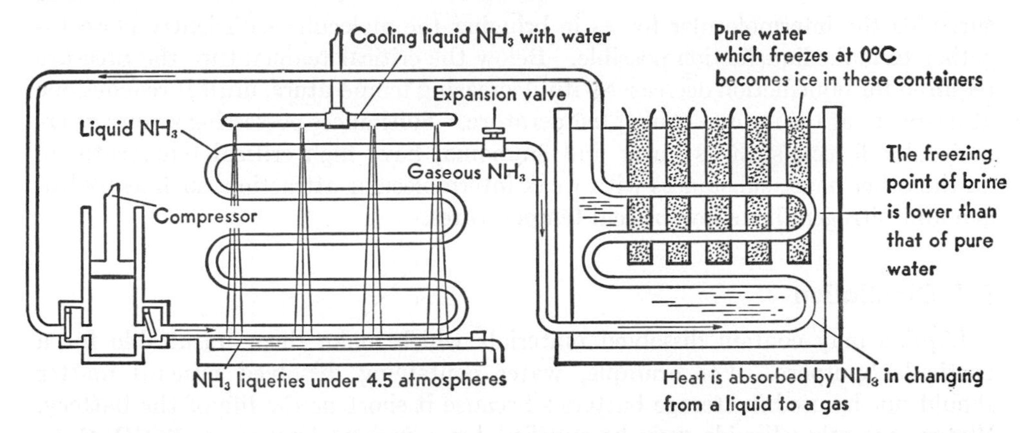

Cooling liquid NH_3 with water
Pure water which freezes at 0°C becomes ice in these containers
Expansion valve
Liquid NH_3
Gaseous NH_3
Compressor
The freezing point of brine is lower than that of pure water
NH_3 liquefies under 4.5 atmospheres
Heat is absorbed by NH_3 in changing from a liquid to a gas

Fig. 9–6 Ammonia is the refrigerant used in many commercial ice factories. A pressure of about 4.5 atmospheres liquefies gaseous ammonia in the compressor. The liquid ammonia is cooled by water running over the coil of pipes. An expansion valve releases the pressure on the liquid ammonia; and the ammonia passes into the coils immersed in brine, where it absorbs heat as it vaporizes. The temperature of the brine is lowered to about — 10° C; pure water in the molds freezes. The ammonia gas is returned to the compressor and is liquefied again, making this a continuous process.

9.6 Critical Temperature and Pressure

We noted in Section 9.1 that compressing a gas and lowering its temperature favor the transition from the gaseous to the liquid state. It is not possible in some cases to achieve liquefaction of a gas by simply compressing it. For each substance there exists a temperature, called the **critical temperature,** above which it cannot be liquefied by the application of pressure. The pressure required to liquefy a gas at its critical temperature is called the **critical pressure.** The critical temperatures and critical pressures of some common substances are given in Table 9·3.

Above the critical temperature of a substance the average kinetic energy of molecules is sufficient to overcome their mutual attractive forces, and the molecules will not cling together closely enough to form a liquid no matter how great the pressure. If the temperature is decreased, the average kinetic energy of the molecules is decreased. At the critical temperature the intermolecular forces are sufficiently large, relative to the average kinetic energy, that the gas can be liquefied provided the substance is under a pressure equal to or greater than its critical pressure. The pres-

TABLE 9·3 Critical Temperatures and Pressures of Some Common Substances

	Critical Temperature (°K)	*Critical Pressure (atm.)*
Hydrogen	33.24	12.8
Nitrogen	126.0	33.5
Oxygen	154.3	49.7
Carbon dioxide	304.2	73.0
Ammonia	405.5	111.5
Water	647.1	217.7
Sulfur dioxide	430.3	77.7

sure aids the intermolecular forces in bringing the molecules sufficiently close together to make liquefaction possible. Below the critical temperature the pressure required for liquefaction decreases with decreasing temperature, until it reaches one atmosphere at the normal boiling temperature. Substances possessing strong intermolecular forces, such as water and ammonia, have high critical temperatures; on the other hand, substances with weak intermolecular attraction, such as hydrogen and nitrogen, have low critical temperatures.

9.7 Distillation

Liquids may contain dissolved materials which make them unsuitable for a particular purpose. For example, water containing dissolved mineral matter should not be used in storage batteries because it shortens the life of the battery. Water and other liquids may be purified by a process known as **distillation.** By heating ordinary water in a distillation flask (Fig. 9–7), the liquid is converted

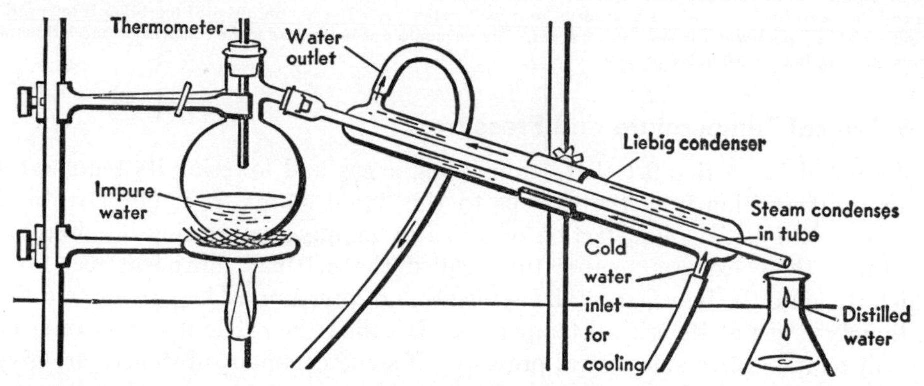

Fig. 9–7 When water is distilled in this apparatus, nonvolatile substances remain in the distilling flask. The water is vaporized, condensed, and collected in the receiving flask.

to vapor which passes over into the condenser. The vapor is condensed to the liquid in the water-cooled condenser, and the liquid flows into the receiving vessel. The dissolved mineral matter such as calcium sulfate, magnesium chloride, etc. is not volatile at the boiling point of water and remains in the distillation flask. Distillation makes use of the facts that the addition of heat to a liquid speeds up the rate of evaporation, an endothermic change, and that cooling a vapor favors condensation, an exothermic change. The separation of volatile substances by distillation is described in Section 11.6.

9.8 Surface Tension

The molecules within the bulk of a liquid are attracted equally in all directions by neighboring molecules; the resultant force on any one molecule within the liquid is therefore zero. However, the molecules on the surface of a liquid are attracted only inward and sideways. This unbalanced molecular attraction pulls some of the surface molecules into the bulk of the liquid, and a condition of equilibrium is reached when the surface is reduced to a minimum. The surface of the liquid, therefore, behaves as if it were under a strain or tension. This contracting force is called **surface tension.** A small drop of liquid tends to assume a spherical shape because in a sphere the ratio of surface to volume is a minimum. We may define surface tension as the force which causes the surface of a liquid to contract. A liquid surface acts as if it were a stretched membrane. A steel needle carefully placed on water will float. Some insects can move on the surface of water, being supported by the surface tension. One of the forces causing water to rise in capillary tubes is its surface tension. Water is brought up to the surface of the soil and to the roots of plants by this capillary action.

9.9 The Kinetic-Molecular Theory and the Solid State

When the temperature of water is lowered to 0° and then more heat is removed, the molecular motion decreases until the molecules take up relatively fixed and ordered positions relative to each other, with only vibratory motion remaining. When this happens, the water is said to freeze, i.e., change from the liquid to the solid state, and form ice crystals which are hard and rigid. The rigidity and small compressibility of crystalline solids reflect the resistance of the molecules to change of position. However, the facts that diffusion takes place to a slight extent in the solid state and that crystalline compounds show a perceptible vapor pressure indicate that the molecules are not motionless. As the temperature of a solid is lowered, the motion of the molecules gradually decreases until at absolute zero it ceases.

9.10 Crystalline Solids

Most solid substances are crystalline in nature. Although some solids, such as sugar and table salt in the form in which we are familiar with them, are composed of single crystals, most crystalline solids with which we come in daily contact are aggregates of many interlocking small crystals. Common examples of the latter are chunks of ice and objects made of metals. **A crystal may be defined as a homogeneous body having the natural shape of a polyhedron.** Crystals are three-dimensional figures bounded by plane surfaces. The angles at which the surfaces intersect are always the same for a given substance, and are characteristic of that substance. Fig. 9–8 illustrates the appearance of single crystals of sodium chloride, copper metal, and calcite ($CaCO_3$).

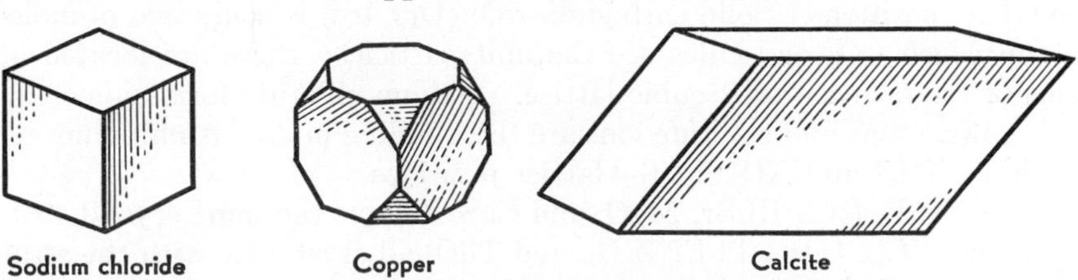

Fig. 9–8 An illustration of the appearance of single crystals of sodium chloride, copper metal, and calcite ($CaCO_3$).

It has been found by the X-ray study of crystalline forms of matter that every crystal consists of atoms, molecules, or ions arranged in a three-dimensional pattern that repeats itself regularly throughout the entire crystal. Crystals of each substance are built up according to a fundamental geometric pattern known as the **crystal lattice.** The smallest fraction of the crystal lattice which contains a representative portion of the crystal structure is referred to as the **unit cell.** The unit cell, if indefinitely repeated in three dimensions, will reproduce the crystal. The nature of the solid is determined, therefore, by the size, shape, and content of its unit cell. The unit cell is a parallelepiped for which the size and shape are defined by the lengths (a, b, c) of the three axes and the angles (α, β, γ) between the axes (Fig. 9–9).

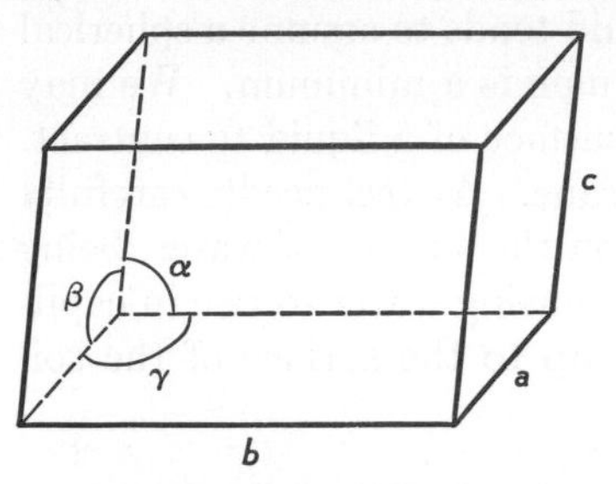

Fig. 9–9 The unit cell.

The unit cells for known crystals can be grouped into seven types:

			Example
Cubic	$a = b = c$	$\alpha = \beta = \gamma = 90°$	Rock salt (NaCl)
Tetragonal	$a = b \neq c$	$\alpha = \beta = \gamma = 90°$	White tin
Orthorhombic	$a \neq b \neq c$	$\alpha = \beta = \gamma = 90°$	Mercury (II) chloride
Monoclinic	$a \neq b \neq c$	$\alpha = \gamma = 90°;\ \beta \neq 90°$	Potassium chlorate
Triclinic	$a \neq b \neq c$	$\alpha \neq \beta \neq \gamma \neq 90°$	Potassium dichromate
Hexagonal	$a = b \neq c$	$\alpha = \beta = 90°;\ \gamma = 120°$	Silica (SiO_2)
Rhombohedral	$a = b = c$	$\alpha = \beta = \gamma \neq 90°$	Calcite ($CaCO_3$)

Variations of the seven types of unit cell give rise to fourteen observed crystal lattices, shown in Fig. 9–10. Three of these are shown again in Fig. 9–11. A crystal lattice is said to be **body-centered** if each unit cell contains at its center an atom of the same kind as at the corners. The lattice is **face-centered** if the unit cell contains at the midpoints of its faces atoms of the same kind as at the corners.

The structure of a crystal is determined by various factors. Among these are the relative numbers and sizes of the building units and the types of bonds holding the building units together in the crystal. The building units may be atoms, ions, or molecules. Copper forms atomic crystals which are built up of copper atoms packed together in a regular pattern (face-centered cubic) with the atoms occupying the lattice positions. Solid carbon dioxide (Dry Ice) is composed of molecular crystals in which CO_2 molecules are the unit particles; these are located at the positions of the face-centered cubic lattice. Sodium chloride forms ionic crystals in which sodium ions and chloride ions are the building units. Ammonium nitrate crystals have NH_4^+ and NO_3^- at the lattice positions.

Crystals of NaF, KCl, RbBr, MgO, and CaS all have the same crystal structure as NaCl; and $SrCl_2$, CdF_2, PbF_2, ZrO_2, and ThO_2 all crystallize with the structure characteristic of CaF_2 (Fig. 9–12, page 152). Different compounds which crystallize with the same structure are said to be **isomorphous.**

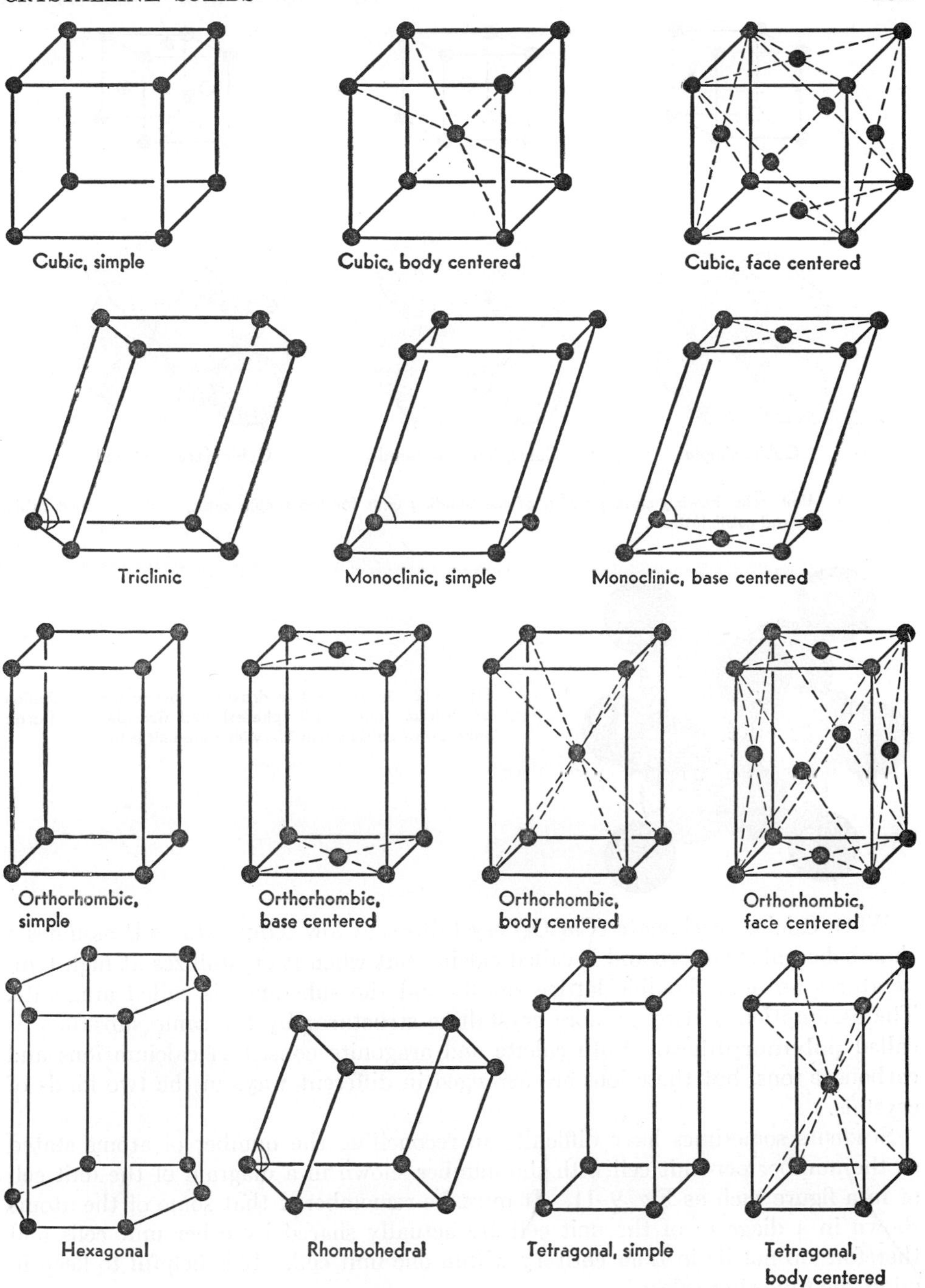

Fig. 9–10 The fourteen possible crystal lattices.

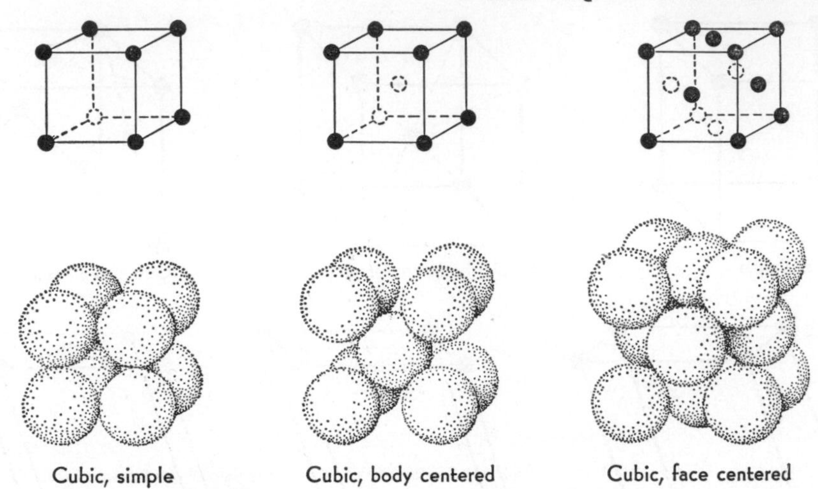

Fig. 9–11 Unit cells showing close packing of the building units for the simple cubic, body-centered cubic, and face-centered cubic lattices.

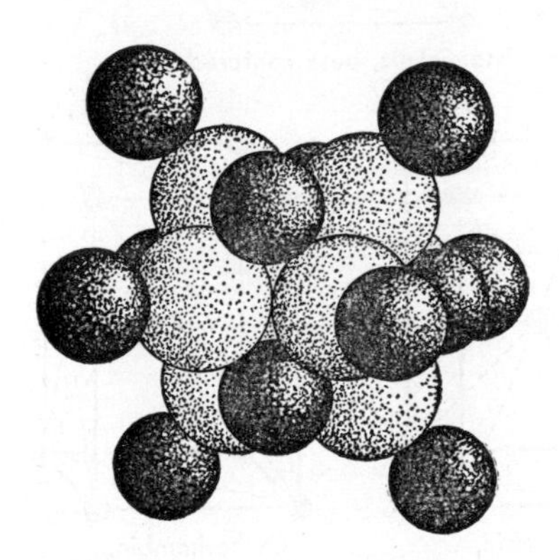

Fig. 9–12 A perspective drawing showing the distribution of calcium ions (small spheres) and fluoride ions (large spheres) of calcium fluoride within the unit cube.

When calcium carbonate ($CaCO_3$) crystallizes at low temperatures it assumes a rhombohedral structure and is called calcite, but when it crystallizes at high temperatures an orthorhombic lattice results and the substance is called aragonite. The assumption of two or more crystalline structures by the same substance is called **polymorphism.** Both calcite and aragonite consist of calcium ions and carbonate ions, but these ions are arranged in different ways in the two kinds of crystals.

Students sometimes have difficulty in reconciling the number of atoms stated as the number per unit cell with the number shown in a diagram of the unit cell or in a figure such as Fig. 9–11. It must be remembered that some of the atoms shown in a diagram of the unit cell are actually shared by other unit cells and therefore do not lie in their entirety within one unit cell. It is helpful to keep in mind the following rules:

(1) An atom which lies completely within the unit cell belongs to that unit cell only.

(2) An atom lying on a face of a unit cell belongs equally to two unit cells and therefore counts as one-half of one atom for a particular unit cell.

(3) An atom lying on an edge is shared equally by four unit cells and thus counts as one-fourth of an atom for a particular unit cell.

(4) An atom lying at a corner is shared equally by eight unit cells and counts as one-eighth of an atom for each particular unit cell.

9.11 Melting of Solids

When a crystalline solid is heated sufficiently, the vibrational energy of some of the molecules becomes great enough to overcome the intermolecular forces holding the molecules in their fixed positions in the crystal lattice, and the solid begins to melt (fuse). If heating is continued, all of the solid will pass into the liquid state even though the temperature does not rise. If, however, the heating is stopped and no heat is withdrawn, the solid and liquid phases will remain in equilibrium, the rate of melting just being balanced by the rate of freezing. The changes will continue, but the quantities of solid and liquid will remain constant. The temperature at which the liquid and solid phases of a given substance are in equilibrium is known as the **freezing point** of the liquid, or the **melting point** of the solid.

The temperature at which a solid melts reflects the strength of the forces of attraction between the building units present in the crystal. Crystals composed of small symmetrical molecules, such as H_2, N_2, O_2, and F_2, have low melting points because the intermolecular forces are of the weak electronic van der Waals type. Crystalline solids built up of unsymmetrical molecules with permanent dipole moments melt at higher temperatures; examples are ice and sugar. Diamond is an atomic crystal in which the small carbon atoms are held together in the crystal lattice by strong covalent bonds; the melting point of diamond is very high. The atoms in the crystals of metals are strongly bonded together by metallic bonds (Section 33.9), which are modified covalent bonds. In general the metals have high melting points. The electrostatic forces of attraction between the ions in ionic solids are quite strong; thus ionic crystals have high melting points.

9.12 Heat of Fusion

When the temperature of a crystalline solid reaches the melting point, it remains constant until all of the solid has changed to the liquid state. The quantity of heat that must be supplied to change a unit mass of a substance from the solid to the liquid state at constant temperature is known as the **heat of fusion** of the substance. The heat of fusion of ice is approximately 80 calories per gram. It represents the difference between the heat content of water, in which the molecules have considerable freedom of motion, and that of ice, in which the molecules vibrate about fixed positions in the crystal. The quantity of heat liberated during crystallization (freezing) is exactly the same as that absorbed during fusion.

9.13 Vapor Pressure of Solids

The fact that snow and ice evaporate at temperatures below their melting point and that certain solids such as naphthalene (moth balls) have characteristic odors is evidence that molecules of such solids may pass directly into the vapor state. It is those solids in which the intermolecular forces are weak which exhibit measurable vapor pressures at room temperature. As one might predict, the vapor pressure of a solid increases with rise in temperature. The vapor pressure of solid iodine is 0.2 mm. at 20° and 90 mm. at 114°, its melting point. If iodine crystals are heated in a container to a temperature just below the melting point, evaporation of the solid proceeds rapidly and the vapor may condense in the form of crystals in a cooler part of the container (Fig. 9–13). The complete process of a solid passing directly into the vapor state without melting and the recondensation of the vapor into the solid state is called **sublimation.** Many substances, such as iodine, may be purified, i.e., separated from impurities which have low vapor pressures, by sublimation.

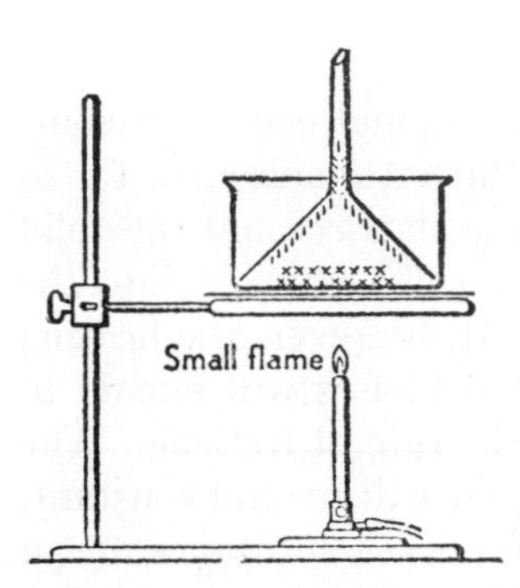

Fig. 9–13 A method of demonstrating the sublimation of iodine.

9.14 Undercooled Liquids; Amorphous Solids

The temperature of many liquids may be lowered below their freezing points before crystallization begins. A liquid existing at a temperature below its freezing point is said to be **undercooled,** or **supercooled.** An undercooled liquid is in a metastable condition, i.e., it is not at equilibrium with its solid. Mechanical agitation, such as vigorous stirring, or the introduction of a "seed" crystal of the substance, often induces crystallization by providing an ordered structure to which the slow-moving molecules can become attached.

Liquid materials, such as fused glass, containing large cumbersome particles which cannot move readily into the positions of a regular crystal lattice often show great tendencies to undercool. As the temperature is lowered, the presence of the large and irregular structural units composing the material causes the undercooled liquid to become less and less mobile, and finally to become rigid, a characteristic of the solid state. Such solids are often spoken of as **amorphous solids** or **glasses.** True solids are crystalline in structure with a definite internal ordered arrangement of their building units; they have sharp melting points and resist change of shape under pressure. Amorphous solids, on the other hand, are entirely lacking in a definite internal structure; they do not melt but soften and become less viscous when heated (Fig. 9–14).

Crystalline solids such as NaCl or $NaClO_3$ melt sharply when heated because the Na—Cl or Na—ClO_3 bonds are all of the same strength and thus all break at once. The gradual softening of glasses as opposed to the sharp melting of crystalline solids results from the structural nonequivalence of the atoms. When a

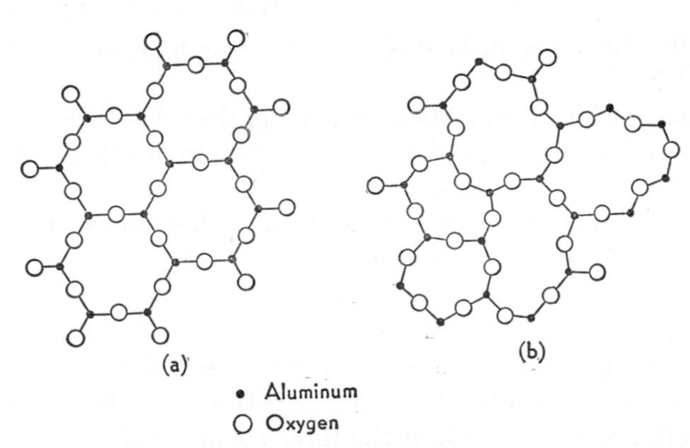

Fig. 9–14 (a) An illustration showing the ordered arrangement in two dimensions in a crystal of aluminum oxide. (b) An illustration showing the disorder in vitreous (amorphous) aluminum oxide.

glass is heated, the weakest bonds break first; and as the temperature is further increased, stronger bonds are broken. This causes a gradual decrease in the size and an increase in the mobility of the structural units as the temperature is raised.

QUESTIONS

1. Compare the structure of solids, liquids, and gases with regard to freedom of motion of their molecules.
2. What is meant by the phrase "intermolecular forces"?
3. In terms of the kinetic-molecular theory, explain the cooling effect of evaporation.
4. What feature characterizes the equilibrium as being dynamic in the case of a vapor in equilibrium with its liquid?
5. How are vapor pressures and intermolecular forces in liquids related?
6. Define the term boiling point. Why is the boiling point of a liquid lowered by reducing the external pressure?
7. Account for the fact that steam produces much more severe burns than does boiling water.
8. What properties must a substance possess to make it an effective refrigerant?
9. Explain the separation of a volatile substance from a nonvolatile one by distillation.
10. Why can a needle, which is almost eight times as dense as water, be made to "float" on water?
11. How do crystalline solids and amorphous solids differ with regard to internal structure?
12. Relate the magnitude of the melting point of a solid to the mutual attractive forces between its building units.
13. Explain in terms of internal structure the high melting point (and hardness) of diamond.
14. How do we know that certain solids such as ice and naphthalene have vapor pressures?

15. What is the difference in heat content between a gram of water at 0° and a gram of ice at 0°?

16. What is meant by "purification by sublimation"?

17. Liquid materials made up of what type of molecules tend to undercool and form glasses?

18. Contrast crystalline and amorphous solids with regard to melting points.

19. What is the origin of van der Waals forces?

20. Distinguish between isomorphism and polymorphism.

21. Methane (CH_4), ammonia (NH_3), and water (H_2O), have very similar molecular weights. Yet methane has a boiling point of −161.5° C., ammonia −33.4° C., and water +100° C. What does this suggest with respect to polar character and intermolecular attractions for each of the three compounds?

PROBLEMS

1. How much heat is liberated when 450 g. of steam at 100° is changed to water at 30°? *Ans. 274,000 cal.*

2. How much heat is required to (a) melt 100 g. of ice? (b) change 100 g. of water at 100° to steam at 100°? *Ans. (a) 8,000 cal. (b) 54,000 cal.*

3. How much heat is required to convert 15 g. of ice at −8° to steam at 105°? The specific heat of ice is 0.50 cal. per g. per degree; of water is 1.0; of steam is 0.48. *Ans. 11 kcal.*

4. What weight of hydrogen must be burned in an excess of oxygen (heat of formation of water at 25° is 68,317 cal./mole) to furnish a quantity of heat necessary to convert 200 g. of water at 100° to steam at 100°? The heat of vaporization of water is 540 cal./g. at 100°. *Ans. 3.18 g.*

5. A 200.0 g. sample of hydrogen is burned in just sufficient oxygen for complete combustion. The heat of formation of water is 68,317 cal./mole at 25°. What amount of heat is evolved during the overall process? *Ans. 6,778 kcal.*

6. What mass of water could be heated from 0° to 25° by the amount of heat evolved during the freezing of a kilogram of water at 0°? The heat of fusion of water is 79.71 cal./g. *Ans. 3.19 kg.*

7. The specific heat of copper is 0.0931 cal. per g. per degree. What weight of steam at 100° (heat of vaporization of water is 540 cal./g.) must be condensed to supply sufficient heat to raise the temperature of 100 g. of copper from 99° to 100°, assuming that the water formed by the condensation of the steam is at 100°? *Ans. 17.4 mg.*

8. How much higher is the heat content of 1000 kg. of steam at 100° than the same mass of ice at −10°? The specific heat of ice is 0.50 cal./g./degree. *Ans.* 7.2×10^5 *kcal.*

9. Calculate the amount of heat necessary to raise $\frac{1}{2}$ mole of water in the solid state at − 10° to steam at 140°. The specific heat of ice between − 10° and 0° is 0.50 cal./g./degree; the specific heat of steam is 0.48 cal./g./degree. *Ans. 6.7 kcal.*

10. The unit cell of sodium chloride contains four sodium ions and four chloride ions. The edge of this cubic cell is 5.638×10^{-8} cm. and the density of sodium chloride is 2.163 g./cm.^{3}. From these data, calculate Avogadro's Number.

Ans. 6.03×10^{23}

REFERENCES

"The Structure of Liquids," J. D. Bernal, *Sci. American*, Aug., 1960; p. 124.
"The Growth of Crystals," R. L. Fullman, *Sci, American*, March, 1955; p. 74.
"Growing Crystals," F. P. Fehlner, *J. Chem. Educ.*, **33** (9) 449 (1956).
"Diffusion in Metals," B. D. Cullity, *Sci. American*, May, 1957; p. 103.

CHAPTER TEN

Water and Hydrogen Peroxide

WATER

Of all the hundreds of thousands of chemical substances, none is more important than water. It covers nearly three-fourths of the earth's surface; it is present in the atmosphere and the earth's crust; and it comprises a large part of all plant and animal matter.

10.1 The Composition of Water

Until the latter part of the eighteenth century, water was thought to be an element. Henry Cavendish in 1781 showed that water is formed when hydrogen burns in air, and a few years later, Lavoisier determined the composition of water by weight.

The formula of water is H_2O, and the relative weights of hydrogen and oxygen in the compound have been determined with great accuracy by two American chemists to be 1.008:8.000. Professor Morley, at Cleveland, spent twelve years of intensive work in determining the weights of hydrogen and oxygen which combine to form water. The last and most accurate determinations were made at the U.S. Bureau of Standards by Professor W. A. Noyes. He synthesized water by reducing copper (II) oxide by hydrogen according to the equation:

$$CuO + H_2 \rightarrow Cu + H_2O$$

The composition of water has also been accurately determined by weighing the amounts of hydrogen and oxygen liberated from water by electrolysis.

10.2 Physical Properties of Water

It is essential that we have a thorough knowledge of the properties of water because it is the most widely used of all substances and because it is a standard for the determination of a number of physical constants and units.

Pure water is an odorless, tasteless, and colorless liquid. Natural waters have a bluish-green color in large bodies. The pleasant taste of drinking water is due to dissolved gases from the air and to salts from the earth.

The freezing point of water is 0° C, and its boiling point at 760 mm. is 100° C. (Recall that the boiling point at 760 mm. atmospheric pressure is the **normal boil-**

ing point; see Section 9.3.) The vapor pressures of ice and water at various temperatures are listed in Table 7·1 on page 121.

The unit of mass in the metric system of measurement is chosen so that 1 ml. of water at 4° C (the temperature of its maximum density) has a mass of 1.00000 g. The unit of heat measurement is defined in reference to water: a calorie is the quantity of heat required to raise the temperature of one gram of water from 14.5° to 15.5°. Water is the reference substance in the measurement of the specific gravity of liquids and solids (Section 1.20). The heat of fusion of water (as ice) is 80 cal./g. at 0° and its heat of vaporization is 540 cal./g. at 100°.

10.3 Water, a Basic Natural Resource

It is a remarkable fact that the use of water in the United States averages about 2500 tons per year for each man, woman, and child. Although there is enough water in the oceans to cover the entire earth to a depth of two miles, for the most part, man's needs can be satisfied only by fresh water. It could well be, then, that water as a natural resource could present a critical problem of supply as the population of the country increases. In fact, it is already critical in many parts of the United States (Colorado, New Mexico, Arizona, California, etc.).

About a half-gallon of water per day is required to satisfy the biological needs of a human being. Nearly 150 gallons of water per day per person are used in maintaining cleanliness, in the cooking of food, and in the heating and air conditioning of homes. These quantities are dwarfed by the 750 gallons of water used per person per day in industries in the United States. Five gallons of water are used in the production of one gallon of milk, ten gallons for one of gasoline, 80 gallons for one kilowatt of electricity, and 65,000 gallons for one ton of steel. More water is used for irrigation in the United States than for any other purpose; the average consumption is 750 gallons per person per day for this purpose.

Fresh water, unlike most mineral resources, is renewable in that it is a part of a gigantic endless cycle. Water evaporates into the atmosphere, the energy required being supplied by radiation from the sun; it is transported in the atmosphere by the winds; and it finally precipitates as rain or snow. The maximum supply of fresh water in an area is the amount of precipitation. A large part of the water which precipitates is lost to man's daily use, however, through evaporation and transpiration by plants.

At the present time, the oceans are becoming increasingly important potential sources of water for our needs because of recent advances in devising desalting processes which are economical and practical. The United States government is participating in the establishment of several desalting plants in various parts of the country and has authorized an expenditure of 75 million dollars on the salt water research program for the six years 1962 through 1967.

10.4 Natural Waters

All natural waters are impure since they contain dissolved substances. Rain water is relatively pure, the chief impurities being dissolved gases. After rain falls for a while, the air has been washed free of dust and bacteria, and any rain that falls thereafter is quite free of such impurities. Sea water contains about 3.6 per cent of dissolved solids, principally common salt. The impurities in water on the earth's surface depend upon the nature of the soil and rocks which it has passed over or through. These impurities may be classified as follows:

1. *Suspended solids:* sand, clay, mud, silt, organic material (such as bits of leaves), and microorganisms.
2. *Dissolved gases:* oxygen, nitrogen, carbon dioxide, oxides of nitrogen, ammonia, and hydrogen sulfide.
3. *Dissolved salts:* chlorides, sulfates, and hydrogen carbonates of sodium, potassium, calcium, magnesium, aluminum, and iron.
4. *Dissolved organic substances* resulting from the decay of vegetable and animal matter.

10.5 Purification of Water

Water is purified for city water supplies by first allowing it to stand in large reservoirs where most of the mud, clay, and silt settle out, a process called **sedimentation,** and then it is filtered through beds of sand and gravel. Often, prior to filtration, lime and aluminum sulfate are added to the water in the settling reservoirs or filters. These chemicals react in water to form aluminum hydroxide, an insoluble gelatinous precipitate, which carries down much of the suspended matter, including most of the bacteria, as it slowly settles. The equation for the precipitation of aluminum hydroxide is

$$\underset{\text{Aluminum sulfate}}{2\,Al^{+++} + (3\,SO_4^{=})} + \underset{\text{Calcium hydroxide}}{3\,Ca(OH)_2} \rightarrow \underset{\text{Aluminum hydroxide}}{\underline{2\,Al(OH)_3}} + \underset{\text{Calcium sulfate}}{3\,Ca^{++} + (3\,SO_4)^{=}}$$

It is common practice to kill the bacteria which remain after filtration by adding chlorine to the water.

Relatively pure water for laboratory use is commonly prepared by distillation (see Section 9.7). Because the basic constituents of glass slowly dissolve in water, glass equipment is not satisfactory for the preparation and storage of very pure water. Distillation apparatus made of fused silica or pure tin is often used in making pure water. Gases from the air, particularly carbon dioxide, often contaminate distilled water and must be removed for some laboratory operations.

10.6 Hard Water

Water containing soluble calcium, magnesium, and iron salts is known as **hard water.** The negative ions present in hard water are usually chloride, sulfate, and hydrogen carbonate. Hardness in water is objectionable for two reasons: (1) The calcium, magnesium, and iron ions in it form insoluble soaps by reaction with soluble soaps such as sodium stearate, $C_{17}H_{35}COONa$.

$$2\,C_{17}H_{35}COO^- + (2\,Na^+) + Ca^{++} \rightarrow \underline{Ca(C_{17}H_{35}COO)_2} + (2\,Na^+)$$

Fig. 10–1 Boiler scale collected in service pipes. The tube at the right shows the enlargement and final failure due to boiler scale.

Insoluble soaps have no cleansing power, and due to their sticky nature adhere to fabrics, giving them a dingy appearance. Soap in excess of that needed to precipitate the calcium and magnesium must be added in order to obtain cleansing action. (2) Hard water is responsible for the formation of scale in boilers (Fig. 10–1). Upon heating to a high temperature, much of the mineral matter dissolved in hard water is precipitated as scale [insoluble metal carbonates such as calcium carbonate, magnesium carbonate, and iron (II) carbonate]. This scale is a poor conductor of heat and thus causes a waste of fuel. Furthermore, boiler explosions are often due to the presence of scale. Since the scale is not a good heat conductor, the metal must be very hot (often red hot) in order to bring the water to the desired temperature. If the scale cracks, the water seeps through and comes in contact with the hot metal.

$$4\ H_2O + 3\ Fe\ (hot) \rightarrow Fe_3O_4 + 4\ H_2$$

The hydrogen gas, as it is formed, breaks the scale loose and more water gets in producing still more hydrogen, thereby setting the stage for a violent explosion.

It is important that the substances responsible for hardness in water be removed before the water is used for washing or in boilers. The removal of the metallic ions responsible for the hardness in hard water is known as **water-softening.**

When hydrogen carbonate ions are present, boiling the water drives off carbon dioxide and the metal carbonates precipitate.

$$Ca^{++} + 2\ HCO_3^- \xrightarrow{\Delta} \underline{CaCO_3} + CO_2\uparrow + H_2O$$

The carbonates of calcium and magnesium thus precipitated form the deposits found in teakettles and boilers. Such water is said to possess **carbonate,** or **temporary, hardness** — temporary, because most of the hardness can be removed by boiling the water. The hydrogen carbonate ion may also be converted to the carbonate ion by the addition of a basic substance. On a commercial basis, calcium hydroxide is added in the exact quantity needed to react with the hydrogen carbonates.

$$Ca^{++} + 2\ OH^- + Ca^{++} + 2\ HCO_3^- \rightarrow 2\ \underline{CaCO_3} + 2\ H_2O$$

Similar equations may be written where the positive ions are Mg^{++} and Fe^{++}. The precipitated carbonates are readily removed from the water by filtration. An aqueous solution of ammonia is a basic solution which is often used in the home to remove temporary hardness.

$$Ca^{++} + 2\ HCO_3^- + 2\ NH_3 \rightarrow \underline{CaCO_3} + 2\ NH_4^+ + CO_3^=$$

Water which contains chloride or sulfate ions in addition to the calcium, magnesium, or iron ions is said to possess **noncarbonate hardness.** Chloride and sulfate ions are not removed by boiling as is the hydrogen carbonate ion. Noncarbonate hardness may be removed by the addition of washing soda (sodium carbonate).

$$Ca^{++} + (SO_4^=) + (2\ Na^+) + CO_3^= \rightarrow \underline{CaCO_3} + (2\ Na^+) + (SO_4^=)$$
$$Ca^{++} + (2\ Cl^-) + (2\ Na^+) + CO_3^= \rightarrow \underline{CaCO_3} + (2\ Na^+) + (2\ Cl^-)$$

The sodium sulfate and sodium chloride which are produced do not interfere with the cleansing action of soap, nor do they form boiler scale.

Crude sodium hydroxide (caustic soda) is often used on a large scale to remove both temporary and noncarbonate hardness.

$$Ca^{++} + 2\ HCO_3^- + (2\ Na^+) + 2\ OH^- \rightarrow \underline{CaCO_3} + (2\ Na^+) + CO_3^= + 2\ H_2O$$

The Na_2CO_3 which is produced in the removal of temporary hardness then reacts to remove the noncarbonate hardness.

$$Ca^{++} + (SO_4^=) + (2\ Na^+) + CO_3^= \rightarrow \underline{CaCO_3} + (2\ Na^+) + (SO_4^=)$$

Trisodium phosphate and borax are also used in the softening of hard water by forming insoluble calcium and magnesium phosphates and borates. Polymetaphosphates, such as $(NaPO_3)_x$, form soluble complexes with Ca^{++} and Mg^{++}, and thus prevent them from reacting with soap.

Ion exchange, discussed in the next section, provides another useful method of softening water.

10.7 Ion Exchangers

The softening of hard water is often accomplished by a process called **ion exchange.** Both naturally occurring sodium aluminosilicates, known as **zeolites,** and synthetic resins are used as exchangers. When water containing calcium and magnesium ions filters slowly through thick layers of coarse granules of the zeolites, the sodium in the compound is replaced by calcium or magnesium, and the water is softened.

$$2\ NaAlSi_2O_6 + Ca^{++} \rightarrow Ca(AlSi_2O_6)_2 + 2\ Na^+$$

The calcium aluminosilicate can be reconverted into the sodium compound by treating the zeolite with a concentrated solution of sodium chloride.

$$Ca(AlSi_2O_6)_2 + 2\ Na^+ \rightarrow 2\ NaAlSi_2O_6 + Ca^{++}$$

Note that this reaction is the reverse of the preceding one; the reversibility can be represented by double arrows. The direction the reaction takes is controlled by the excess of either Ca^{++} or Na^+ ions.

$$2\ Na\ Zeolite + Ca^{++} \rightleftharpoons Ca(Zeolite)_2 + 2\ Na^+$$

After the sodium zeolite is regenerated, it is ready for use once more. This method of water-softening is effective for the removal of both carbonate and noncarbonate hardness. One charge of zeolite in an ion-exchanger may be used as long as twenty years (Fig. 10–2).

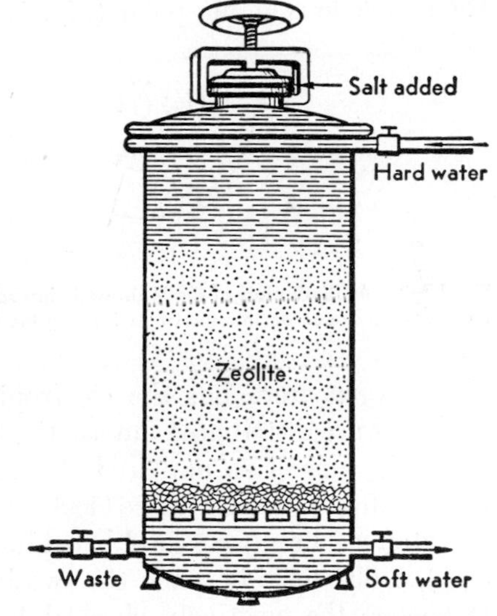

Fig. 10–2 Water softening. When regeneration is necessary, the soft water valve is closed and a concentrated NaCl solution is run through the zeolite and out the waste line until the regeneration of the zeolite is complete.

Synthetic resin ion-exchangers have been developed which remove both cations (positive ions) and anions (negative ions) from hard water; that is, they demineralize the water completely. Examples of these resins are Amberlite and Zeo-Carb. Metal ions displace hydrogen ions from one type of resin.

$$2\ RCOOH + Ca^{++} + (SO_4^{=}) \rightarrow (RCOO)_2Ca + 2\ H^+ + (SO_4^{=})$$

Another type of resin then removes the ions of the acid from the water.

$$2\ RNH_2 + 2\ H^+ + SO_4^{=} \rightarrow (RNH_3)_2SO_4$$

Hence, by passing a hard water (or a salt solution) first through an exchanger which replaces all metal ions with H^+, then through a resin which removes the resulting acids, the water can be completely demineralized. The result is essentially the same as that achieved through distillation of water. In recent years the use of ion-exchangers in the treatment of water for industrial and domestic purposes has grown tremendously.

10.8 The Structure of Water

Water has remarkable solvent properties and it has an abnormally low vapor pressure, high boiling point, and high heat of vaporization. These properties are closely related to the structure of the water molecule.

The atoms in a molecule of water are held together by bonds that are somewhat polar in character because oxygen is more electronegative (3.5) than hydrogen (2.1). This means that the oxygen atom possesses a net negative charge and each hydrogen atom a net positive charge. If the molecule were linear ($\overset{+}{H}—\overset{=}{O}—\overset{+}{H}$), then the two bond polarities would cancel each other, and the molecule would be nonpolar. Actually, the two bonds make an angle of 105° with each other, and the molecule is highly polar (Fig. 10–3).

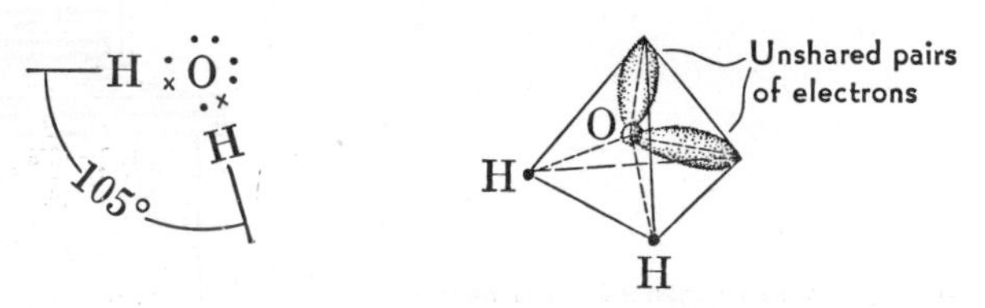

Fig. 10–3 An illustration of the V-shaped character of the water molecule including the two unshared pairs of electrons which can be thought of as forming the other two corners of a tetrahedron.

The oxygen atom has the electronic structure $1s^2$, $2s^2 2p^4$. The four *p*-subshell electrons are distributed among the three *p*-orbitals in this manner — $2p_x^2\ 2p_y^1\ 2p_z^1$. Thus there are two unpaired electrons in the oxygen atom. When combination with hydrogen occurs, these electrons are paired with 1*s* electrons from two hydrogen atoms. Because p_y and p_z orbitals are at right angles to each other (see Section 3.18), a 90° angle between the two bonds in the H_2O molecule would be expected. However, the positively charged hydrogen atoms repel each other and increase the angle from 90° to the observed 105°.

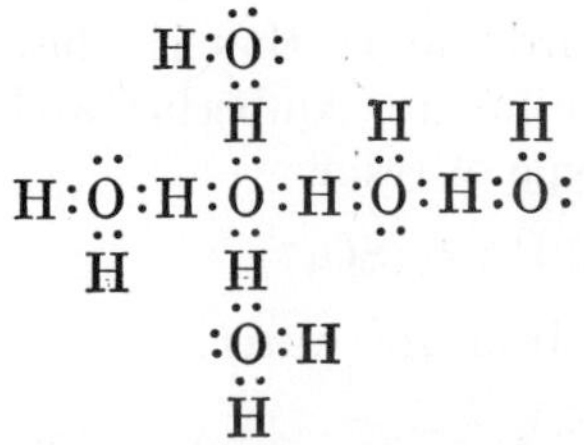

The positive hydrogen of one water molecule attracts the negative oxygen of a neighboring water molecule forming what is known as a *hydrogen bond* (see Section 18.4). This bond, even though weak, is effective in producing associated molecules or **polymers** (Fig. 10–4).

```
   H:Ö:
     ..
     H     H    H
 ..  ..    ..   ..
H:O:H:O:H:O:H:O:
 ..  ..    ..
 H   H
     ..
    :O:H
     ..
     H
```

Fig. 10–4 Association of water into clusters of water molecules through hydrogen bonding.

$$x\ H_2O \rightleftharpoons (H_2O)_x + \text{heat}$$

The value of x depends upon such conditions as temperature and the presence of substances dissolved in the water. As the temperature is raised, some of the hydrogen bonds are disrupted, and the larger associated units are broken down into smaller ones. In the vapor state, water is composed almost entirely of single H_2O molecules. Association of the polar molecules is responsible for the abnormally low vapor pressure, high boiling point, and high heat of vaporization of water relative to the same properties of nonassociated compounds of similar formulas, such as H_2S, H_2Se, and H_2Te. These abnormal physical properties are due to the fact that energy is required to break the hydrogen bonds holding the units together in the associated molecules.

The abnormally large dielectric constant of water, which is responsible for the remarkable power of water to dissolve ionic substances (Chapter 12), is due to the association of polar molecules. The size of the dipole moment depends upon the charges and the distance between them. Thus the product of the charge on either end of a dipole and the effective distance between the centers of the charges is the **dipole moment.** The dipole moment of a complex made up of two water molecules is more than double that of a single molecule.

Crystal chemistry has shown that the water molecules in ice are so arranged that each oxygen atom has four hydrogen atoms as close neighbors, two attached by electron pair bonds and two more by hydrogen bonds (Fig. 10–5). Such an arrangement leads to an open structure, i.e., one with relatively large holes in it. This makes ice (Fig. 10–6, page 166) a substance with a relatively low density. When ice melts, some of the hydrogen bonds are broken; the open structure is destroyed; and the water molecules pack more closely together. This accounts for the fact that water is more dense than ice.

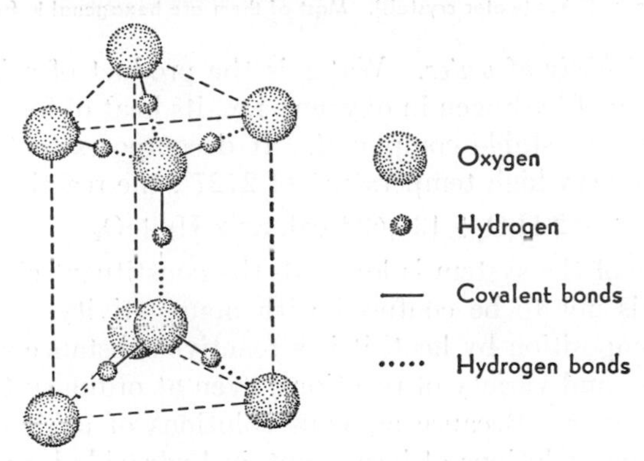

Fig. 10–5 An illustration of the structure of water in ice, showing each oxygen atom with four hydrogen atoms as close neighbors, two attached by electron pair bonds and two by hydrogen bonds. This is only a portion of a continuous lattice; the oxygen atoms shown on the corners of the prism are also parts of other prisms.

10.9 Chemical Properties of Water

Water is a very important medium in which chemical reactions take place. The majority of the chemical changes that we study in a course in general chemistry are reactions taking place in aqueous solution.

Fig. 10–6 These are snowflakes (water crystals). Most of them are hexagonal in form. *Ewing Galloway*

1. *The thermal stability of water.* Water is the product of a highly exothermic reaction, the burning of hydrogen in oxygen; i.e., its heat of formation is high and it is accordingly a very stable compound. It decomposes to the extent of only 11.1 per cent at the very high temperature of 2727°, the reaction being reversible.

$$2\ H_2O + 136{,}634\ \text{cal.} \rightleftharpoons 2\ H_2 + O_2$$

As the temperature of the system is lowered, the constituent elements recombine. Thermal stability is not to be confused with nonreactivity. Although water is stable toward decomposition by heat, it is a reactive substance and enters readily into a great number and variety of reactions, even at ordinary temperatures.

2. *Ionization of water.* Because aqueous solutions of acids contain hydrogen ions, H^+, and aqueous solutions of bases contain hydroxide ions, OH^-, one might ask whether or not these ions are present in pure water, which is neutral. Hydrogen ions and hydroxide ions are present in water in equal but very small concentrations. Pure water conducts electricity, but very poorly, because it dissociates only to a slight extent into hydrated hydrogen ions (hydronium ions, $H^+ \cdot H_2O$ or H_3O^+) and hydroxyl ions.

$$2\ H_2O \rightleftharpoons H_3O^+ + OH^-$$

The addition of an acid to water causes an increase in the hydronium ion concentration and a corresponding decrease in the hydroxide ion concentration, but not to zero. In basic solutions the hydroxide ion concentration is large and the hydrogen ion concentration is very small. Many of the chemical properties of water depend upon the hydrogen ion and hydroxide ion content. A more complete account of the ionization of water is given in a later chapter (Ionic Equilibria Involving Weak Electrolytes).

3. *Action of water with metals.* The reactivity of various metals with water was mentioned in connection with the preparation of hydrogen (Chapter 6). Only those metals which lie above cobalt in the activity series (Section 6.9) will displace hydrogen from water. The more active metals react with cold water and the less active ones require steam.

$$2\ Na + 2\ H_2O\ (\text{cold}) \rightarrow 2\ Na^+ + 2\ OH^- + H_2 \uparrow$$
$$3\ Fe + 4\ H_2O\ (\text{steam}) \rightarrow Fe_3O_4 + 4\ H_2 \uparrow$$

Magnesium reacts with hot water to give the hydroxide.

$$Mg + 2\ H_2O\ (\text{hot}) \rightarrow \underline{Mg(OH)_2} + H_2 \uparrow$$

When magnesium burns in steam, the oxide rather than the hydroxide results. Magnesium hydroxide, if it were formed, would immediately lose water at the high temperature of the reaction, to produce MgO.

$$Mg(OH)_2 + \text{heat} \rightarrow MgO + H_2O$$

4. *Action of water with nonmetals.* Fluorine, chlorine, and bromine react with water at ordinary temperatures. The equation for the reaction of chlorine with water is

$$Cl_2 + H_2O \rightarrow \underset{\text{Hydrochloric acid}}{H^+ + Cl^-} + \underset{\text{Hypochlorous acid}}{HClO}$$

Hydrochloric acid is completely ionized in dilute aqueous solution, a property characteristic of **strong acids.** On the other hand, hypochlorous acid is only slightly ionized; most of it is in the form of molecules in aqueous solution, a property characteristic of **weak acids.**

Hot carbon reacts with steam and produces carbon monoxide and hydrogen.

$$C + H_2O \rightarrow CO + H_2$$

This is an oxidation-reduction reaction. Carbon is oxidized and water is reduced. Carbon is the reducing agent and water is the oxidizing agent (see Section 6.5).

5. *Reaction of water with compounds.* The oxides of the alkali metals (Li, Na, K, Rb, and Cs) combine in exothermic reactions with water to form bases.

$$Na_2O + H_2O \rightarrow 2\ Na^+ + 2\ OH^-$$

The alkali metal hydroxides are too stable to be decomposed by heating, even at their boiling points, which are high. The oxides of the alkaline earth metals (Be, Mg, Ca, Sr, Ba, and Ra) react less readily with water and give hydroxides which are only slightly soluble in water.

$$BaO + H_2O \rightarrow Ba(OH)_2$$
$$SrO + H_2O \rightarrow Sr(OH)_2$$
$$CaO + H_2O \rightarrow Ca(OH)_2$$

The alkaline earth hydroxides may be decomposed into metal oxides and water by heating. They are less stable thermally than the alkali hydroxides. Beryllium and magnesium oxides, which are highly insoluble in water, react with water only slowly and incompletely. Metal oxides are often referred to as **basic anhydrides,** inasmuch as they react with water to form bases.

The oxides of certain nonmetals react with water to form acids. Some examples are:

$$SO_2 + H_2O \rightarrow H_2SO_3 \text{ (Sulfurous acid)}$$
$$CO_2 + H_2O \rightarrow H_2CO_3 \text{ (Carbonic acid)}$$
$$P_4O_{10} + 6\ H_2O \rightarrow 4\ H_3PO_4 \text{ (Phosphoric acid)}$$

Nonmetal oxides are referred to as **acidic anhydrides,** inasmuch as they react with water to form acids.

6. *Hydrolysis.* Water also enters into reactions with certain compounds and ions in an important way called **hydrolysis.** Reactions of this type will be considered in detail in a later chapter (Hydrolysis).

7. *Hydrates.* When aqueous solutions of many soluble salts are evaporated, the salt separates as crystals which contain the salt and water combined in definite proportions by weight. Such compounds are known as **hydrates** and the water is called **water of hydration.** The formation of hydrates is not limited to salts but is common with acids and bases and even elements. Furthermore, it is not confined to crystals. Familiar examples of hydrates are blue vitriol, $CuSO_4 \cdot 5\ H_2O$; Epsom salts, $MgSO_4 \cdot 7\ H_2O$; alum, $KAl(SO_4)_2 \cdot 12\ H_2O$; Glauber's salt, $Na_2SO_4 \cdot 10\ H_2O$; $H_2SO_4 \cdot H_2O$; $Ba(OH)_2 \cdot 8\ H_2O$; and $Cl_2 \cdot 6\ H_2O$.

When blue crystals of copper (II) sulfate 5-hydrate, $CuSO_4 \cdot 5\ H_2O$, are heated, water is given off, the crystalline structure characteristic of the hydrated salt breaks down, and the white anhydrous salt, $CuSO_4$, remains.

$$CuSO_4 \cdot 5\ H_2O \rightleftharpoons CuSO_4 + 5\ H_2O$$

The above reaction is reversible in that the addition of water to the anhydrous salt will produce the original hydrated salt.

Crystal chemistry has shown that in $CuSO_4 \cdot 5\ H_2O$ the copper (II) ion, Cu^{++}, is combined with four water molecules, and the sulfate ion ($SO_4^{=}$) with one. We may formulate the hydrate, then, as $[Cu(H_2O)_4][SO_4(H_2O)]$. All ions are undoubtedly hydrated in aqueous solution, but in many cases the water of hydration is lost when the compound separates from solution.

10.10 Deliquescence and Efflorescence

Hydrates exhibit vapor pressures as can be demonstrated by placing a crystal of a hydrate in the vacuum above the mercury in a barometer tube, the mercury level being depressed to an extent dependent upon the magnitude of the **vapor pressure of the hydrate.** The vapor pressure of a hydrate increases with a rise in temperature and decreases as the temperature is lowered.

When a hydrate exhibits a vapor pressure higher than the partial pressure of water in the atmosphere, it will lose a part or all of its water of hydration when exposed to the air. Hydrates which lose water of hydration when exposed to the air are said to **effloresce,** and **efflorescence** (Fig. 10–7) is said to have taken place. $Na_2SO_4 \cdot 10\ H_2O$ effloresces rapidly when exposed to the air when the partial pressure of the water vapor in the air is less than 14 mm., the vapor pres-

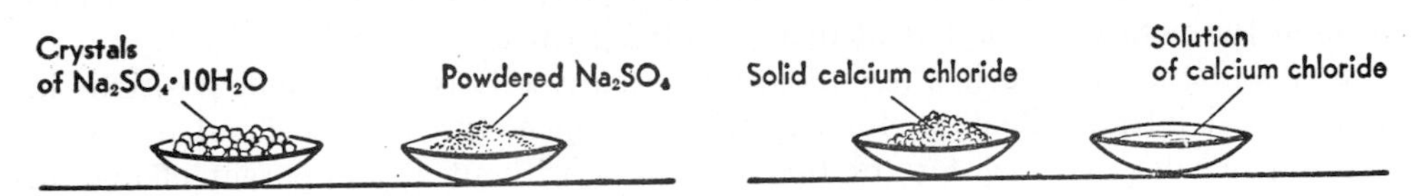

Fig. 10–7 Efflorescent crystals lose water and crumble to a powder. Some deliquescent substances take up enough water from the air to dissolve.

sure of the hydrate. $CuSO_4 \cdot 5\ H_2O$ is stable in air as long as the partial pressure of the water in the air is greater than 7.8 mm. It follows that some hydrates are stable when the humidity is high but decompose when it is low. A salt, such as copper (II) sulfate, may form more than one hydrate, each of which possesses its own definite vapor pressure at a given temperature. The following hydrates of copper (II) sulfate are known: $CuSO_4 \cdot 5\ H_2O$; $CuSO_4 \cdot 3\ H_2O$; and $CuSO_4 \cdot H_2O$.

When certain substances of low vapor pressure, such as $CaCl_2 \cdot H_2O$, are exposed to the air, they form higher hydrates. Such salts may be used in the removal of moisture from air or other gases. A substance that can remove moisture from the air is said to be **hygroscopic.** Concentrated sulfuric acid, a liquid, and phosphorus (V) oxide, a solid, are powerful drying agents, or **desiccants.** Certain water-soluble hygroscopic solids remove sufficient water from the air to dissolve completely in this water and form solutions. Such substances are said to be **deliquescent,** and the process is termed **deliquescence** (Fig. 10–7). Very soluble salts, such as $CaCl_2 \cdot 6\ H_2O$, are often extremely deliquescent.

10.11 The Structure of Hydrates

It appears that water may exist in a crystal in five different forms.

1. *Water of hydroxylation.* The structural unit when water is present in a compound as water of **hydroxylation** is the OH^- ion. This is the case with many metal hydroxides such as NaOH, $Mg(OH)_2$, and $Al(OH)_3$. Removal of water of hydroxylation disrupts the crystal. The crystal structure characteristic of Al_2O_3, which may be formed by dehydrating $Al(OH)_3$, is entirely different from that of aluminum hydroxide.

2. *Water of coordination.* Water of this type is joined to the metal ion by coordinate bonds. A crystal of $BeSO_4 \cdot 4\ H_2O$ has as its building units $[Be(H_2O)_4]^{++}$ and $SO_4^=$, and one of $NiSO_4 \cdot 6\ H_2O$ contains $[Ni(H_2O)_6]^{++}$ and $SO_4^=$ as structural units. Water of coordination is essential to the stability of the crystal and the crystal lattice collapses when even a part of the water is driven off.

3. *Anion water.* This type of water is attached to the anion by hydrogen bonding (see Sections 10.8 and 18.4). A crystal of $CuSO_4 \cdot 5\ H_2O$ has four of the five water molecules attached to the copper ion as water of coordination; the fifth molecule of water is attached to the sulfate ion as anion water.

4. *Lattice water.* In some hydrates, water molecules occupy definite positions in the crystal lattice but are not attached directly to either cation or anion. In

$KAl(SO_4)_2 \cdot 12\ H_2O$, six water molecules are attached to the aluminum ion by coordinate bonding; the other six are lattice water, arranged in definite positions around the potassium ion but at distances too great to be attached directly.

5. *Zeolitic water.* Such water molecules occupy relatively random positions in the crystal lattice. Zeolites, for example, are open, three-dimensional networks of SiO_4 tetrahedra which lose or take up water without any apparent change in crystal structure.

10.12 Heavy Water

Water which is composed of deuterium, ${}^2_1H$, and oxygen is known as **heavy water** or deuterium oxide, D_2O. Heavy water is present in ordinary water in the ratio of one part in 6,900. Heavy water was first obtained by the electrolysis of ordinary water. Deuterium oxide is decomposed more slowly than ordinary water during electrolysis; therefore, the heavy water tends to remain behind in the residual water and become concentrated as electrolysis proceeds. Heavy water is now produced in the atomic energy program by an exchange equilibrium process which is less costly and more efficient than the electrolytic method. In the new process, advantage is taken of the fact that when liquid water and gaseous hydrogen sulfide are mixed, the deuterium concentrates in the water at low temperatures and in the hydrogen sulfide at elevated temperatures.

$$H_2S + D_2O \underset{\text{cold}}{\overset{\text{hot}}{\rightleftarrows}} D_2S + H_2O$$

By passing water and hydrogen sulfide through each other in opposite directions at an elevated temperature, the hydrogen sulfide becomes saturated with water and through exchange is enriched with respect to D_2S. However, when the resulting mixture of steam and hydrogen sulfide is drawn off and condensed to the liquid state by cooling, the reverse exchange process takes place producing water which is enriched with respect to D_2O and which thereby contains a larger proportion of D_2O than before. The process is operated to yield a D_2O concentrate of about 15 per cent, which is then enriched to 99.8 per cent D_2O by fractional distillation and electrolysis. To produce one ton of D_2O, a plant must process 45,000 tons of water and must cycle 150,000 tons of H_2S. The cost of producing D_2O by this process is estimated to be $13.50 per pound. Several hundred tons of heavy water can now be produced per year.

Heavy water resembles ordinary water in appearance but differs from it slightly in other physical properties (Table 10·1).

Because heavy water is about 10 per cent heavier than ordinary water, it is possible to detect the presence of as little as one part of it in 100,000 parts of an aqueous solution. For this reason, heavy water and deuterium serve as valuable tracers in the study of both chemical and physiological changes. By replacing ordinary hydrogen with deuterium in the molecules of food, the processes of digestion and metabolism in the body can be studied.

TABLE 10·1 Some Physical Properties of Water and Heavy Water

	Ordinary Water	Heavy Water
Density, 20°	0.997	1.108
Boiling point, °C	100.00	101.41
Melting point, °C	0.00	3.79
Heat of vaporization, cal./mole	9,720	9,944
Heat of fusion, cal./mole	1,436	1,500

Salts have slightly lower solubilities in D_2O than H_2O, and the rates of reactions of D_2O are somewhat smaller than those of similar reactions involving H_2O.

HYDROGEN PEROXIDE

Hydrogen forms a second compound with oxygen, called **hydrogen peroxide,** H_2O_2, in which there is twice as much oxygen for the same weight of hydrogen as there is in water. Hydrogen peroxide was first prepared in 1818 by Thénard, who obtained it by treating barium peroxide with hydrochloric acid. Very small quantities of it are present in dew, rain, and snow, probably as a result of the action of ultraviolet light upon moist oxygen.

10.13 Preparation

In the nineteenth century, hydrogen peroxide was produced exclusively on a commercial scale by the reaction of an acid upon barium peroxide, which is readily formed by heating barium oxide in air ($2\ BaO + O_2 \rightarrow 2\ BaO_2$). When sulfuric acid is used on barium peroxide, the equation is

$$BaO_2 + 2\ H^+ + SO_4^= \rightarrow \underline{BaSO_4} + H_2O_2$$

Barium sulfate is nearly insoluble and can be separated from the solution by filtration. As usually prepared, the hydrogen peroxide thus produced is quite dilute.

Hydrogen peroxide can be prepared in the laboratory by adding sodium peroxide to cold water or cold dilute hydrochloric acid.

$$Na_2O_2 + 2\ H_2O \rightarrow 2\ Na^+ + 2\ OH^- + H_2O_2$$

Electrochemical processes for the production of hydrogen peroxide were introduced into the United States in 1926, and by 1955 probably accounted for 80 to 90 per cent of U.S. production. Electrochemical methods involve the electrolysis of solutions of sulfuric acid or ammonium hydrogen sulfate. When sulfuric acid solutions having a density of about 1.4 are electrolyzed, peroxydisulfuric acid, $H_2S_2O_8$, is formed at the anode and hydrogen is evolved at the cathode.

$$2\ H_2SO_4 + \text{electrical energy} \rightarrow H_2S_2O_8 + H_2 \uparrow$$

The peroxydisulfuric acid is subsequently hydrolyzed (allowed to react with water) to produce hydrogen peroxide.

$$H_2S_2O_8 + 2\ H_2O \rightarrow 2\ H_2SO_4 + H_2O_2$$

The sulfuric acid formed is recycled, i.e., it is used over again in the production of more hydrogen peroxide. The net reaction involved in the process is expressed in the equation

$$2\ H_2O + \text{electrical energy} \rightarrow H_2O_2 + H_2 \uparrow$$

Only water and electrical energy are consumed in the process, and consequently, the plants have been located near sources of low-cost electricity.

For military uses and for some uses as a chemical reagent, solutions up to 90 per cent are required rather than the 27 to 35 per cent aqueous solution which is produced directly by the electrolytic process. Purification and concentration of dilute solutions of hydrogen peroxide are accomplished by multiple vacuum distillation. Reduced pressures are necessary because hydrogen peroxide decomposes when heated.

Recently, a different industrial method for the production of hydrogen peroxide has rapidly gained importance and now accounts for most of the production of hydrogen peroxide. In this process, an organic compound referred to as an anthraquinone is reduced by hydrogen in a benzene solution, using palladium as a catalyst, to a kind of compound known as a *dihydro*anthraquinone. When the dihydroanthraquinone is then allowed to react with oxygen, the original anthraquinone is obtained along with hydrogen peroxide. The anthraquinone is then used over again in the production of more hydrogen peroxide.

$$\underset{\text{2-ethyl anthraquinone}}{C_{16}H_{12}O_2} + H_2 \xrightarrow{\text{Pd catalyst}} \underset{\text{2-ethyl dihydroanthraquinone}}{C_{16}H_{12}(OH)_2}$$

$$C_{16}H_{12}(OH)_2 + O_2 \longrightarrow C_{16}H_{12}O_2 + H_2O_2$$

When the hydrogen peroxide reaches a concentration, in the benzene solution, of about 5.5 grams per liter, it is extracted with water to produce an 18 per cent water solution of hydrogen peroxide which may be further concentrated by vacuum distillation.

When very pure, H_2O_2 is quite stable, and solutions of 85–90 per cent concentration are produced and used. However, when impurities are present, the concentrated solutions are dangerously explosive. For storage purposes, a negative catalyst (**stabilizer**), such as a small amount of acid or an organic compound (acetanilide), is added. Bases and heavy metal ions, such as Cu^{++}, act as positive catalysts in the decomposition of hydrogen peroxide into water and oxygen.

10.14 Properties

Pure hydrogen peroxide is a colorless, syrupy liquid with a sharp odor and astringent taste. It has a density of 1.438 g./cm.[3] at 20° C, boils at 62.8° at 21 mm., and freezes at – 1.70°. It is miscible (mutually soluble) with water, alcohol, and ether in all proportions. As stated in the above section, hydrogen peroxide is thermally unstable, and decomposes with the evolution of much heat.

$$2\ H_2O_2 \rightarrow 2\ H_2O + O_2 \uparrow\ + 47{,}950\ \text{cal.}$$

Its instability may be explained by the fact that its formation is a highly endothermic process.

Hydrogen peroxide is an active oxidizing agent. It oxidizes sulfurous acid to sulfuric acid and sulfides to sulfates.

$$H_2SO_3 + H_2O_2 \rightarrow H_2SO_4 + H_2O$$

$$\underset{\text{(black)}}{PbS} + 4\ H_2O_2 \rightarrow \underset{\text{(white)}}{PbSO_4} + 4\ H_2O$$

In its use as an oxidizing agent, it has an advantage over other oxidizing agents because the only by-product of the oxidizing reactions is water.

Hydrogen peroxide not only acts as an oxidizing agent with strong reducing agents, but also as a reducing agent with strong oxidizing agents. For example, it will reduce silver oxide to the metal.

$$Ag_2O + H_2O_2 \rightarrow 2\ Ag + H_2O + O_2 \uparrow$$

Hydrogen peroxide reduces many other substances with the evolution of oxygen. These substances include the oxides of mercury, gold, and platinum, and the strong oxidizing agents, manganese dioxide and potassium permanganate. The reaction of hydrogen peroxide with the permanganate ion in acid solution is according to the equation

$$6\ H^+ + 2\ MnO_4^- + 5\ H_2O_2 \rightarrow 5\ O_2 \uparrow\ + 2\ Mn^{++} + 8\ H_2O$$

Hydrogen peroxide is a weak acid; in water it ionizes to a slight extent in two steps.

$$H_2O_2 \rightleftharpoons H^+ + HO_2^-\ \text{(Hydroperoxide ion)}$$

$$HO_2^- \rightleftharpoons H^+ + O_2^=\ \text{(Peroxide ion)}$$

Its acidic character is demonstrated in the following equation.

$$\underset{\text{Base}}{Ba(OH)_2} + \underset{\text{Acid}}{H_2O_2} \rightarrow \underset{\text{Salt}}{\underline{BaO_2}} + \underset{\text{Water}}{2\ H_2O}$$

Hydrogen peroxide may be detected by the formation of a blue color when it is treated with a potassium iodide and starch solution.

$$H_2O_2 + (2\ K^+) + 2\ I^- \rightarrow (2\ K^+) + 2\ OH^- + I_2$$

Ozone (Section 5.16) does not interfere with the test for hydrogen peroxide if iron (II) sulfate is added to the test solution before the potassium iodide is introduced.

10.15 The Structure of Peroxides

The valence electronic structures for hydrogen peroxide and a diagram of its molecular structure are given in Fig. 10–8. Its structure can be likened to that of a sheet of paper folded to an angle of 94°, with the oxygen atoms located in the fold and one hydrogen atom located in each plane.

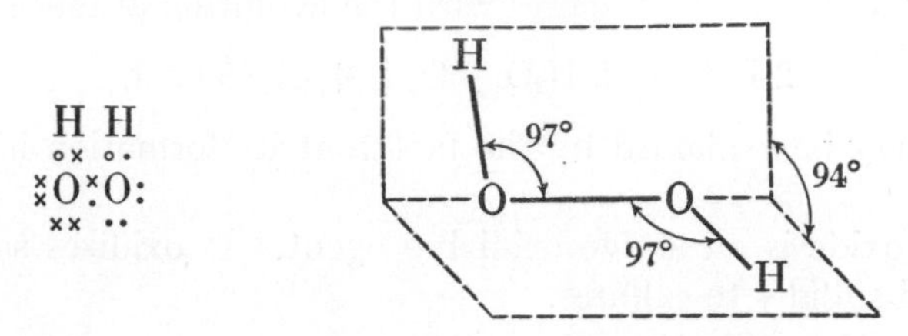

Fig. 10–8 The molecular structure of hydrogen peroxide, H_2O_2.

Note that the two atoms of oxygen are connected through an electron-pair bond and that the combining capacity (or valence) of the peroxide group is two. This is true of other peroxides as well and is illustrated once again by barium peroxide (BaO_2) in the following diagrams. The usual valence of *single* oxygen atoms is two, as indicated in the valence electronic structures for barium oxide (BaO) and manganese dioxide (MnO_2).

$Ba^{++}\left[:\ddot{O}:\ddot{O}:\right]^{=}$	$Ba^{++}\left[:\ddot{O}:\right]^{=}$	$:\ddot{O}::Mn::\ddot{O}:$
Barium peroxide	Barium oxide	Manganese dioxide

Manganese dioxide, unlike barium peroxide, does not yield hydrogen peroxide when treated with acids. This fact indicates that MnO_2 is a dioxide rather than a peroxide; i.e., the two oxygen atoms are not joined together, but are each joined to the manganese.

10.16 Uses of Hydrogen Peroxide

Three per cent solutions of hydrogen peroxide by weight are used in the home as a mild antiseptic, a deodorizer, a germicide, and a bleach for hair. Its effective action as a bactericidal agent is questionable, however. A 30 per cent solution of hydrogen peroxide is commonly used in the laboratory as an oxidizing agent. In commerce, the principal consumption of hydrogen peroxide is as an oxidizing agent, particularly as a bleaching agent. Substances of animal origin such as wool and hair, which are harmed by most other bleaching agents, are often bleached by hydrogen peroxide. At present, most cotton cloth is bleached with hydrogen peroxide because of the innocuous character of the decomposition products and the permanency of the whiteness produced by peroxide bleaching.

Ninety per cent hydrogen peroxide is used as an oxidizing agent in certain high explosives and in the combustion of fuel in propelling rockets and guided missiles. It is an ideal liquid oxidant because it has a high energy release on reaction, it is relatively stable to shock, and it is noncorrosive, nontoxic, and has a high boiling point and low freezing point (see Section 25.13).

Concentrated hydrogen peroxide may be used as a monopropellant, in which it is decomposed under pressure yielding a gaseous mixture of oxygen and superheated steam, as well as the oxidizing agent for the burning of a fuel.

Hydrogen peroxide is also used as a polymerization catalyst, particularly in the production of "cold rubber." Polymers so produced have superior physical properties.

10.17 The Law of Multiple Proportions

We have seen that hydrogen and oxygen form two distinctly different compounds, water and hydrogen peroxide. One mole of water (18.0153 g.) contains 2.0159 g. of hydrogen and 15.9994 g. of oxygen; on the other hand, one mole of hydrogen peroxide (34.0157 g.) contains the same weight of hydrogen (2.0159 g.) but twice as much oxygen (31.9998 g.). Many elements form more than one compound in which the proportions by weight of the constituent elements are not the same. Additional examples are: Na_2O and Na_2O_2; BaO and BaO_2; FeO, Fe_2O_3, and Fe_3O_4; and N_2O, NO, NO_2, N_2O_3 and N_2O_5. This fact led Dalton (1804) to formulate the **Law of Multiple Proportions: When two elements, A and B, form more than one compound by combining with each other, the weights of element B which combine with a given weight of element A stand in a ratio which can be expressed by small whole numbers.** The ratio for the weights of oxygen which combine with a given weight of hydrogen in the compounds H_2O_2 and H_2O, is 2:1.

QUESTIONS

1. List the following physical constants for water: boiling point, freezing point, density, specific heat, heat of vaporization, and heat of fusion.
2. Account for the polar character of the water molecule in terms of its structure.
3. Describe the hydrogen bond.
4. Account for the abnormally high boiling point of water.
5. Under what conditions does water exist as single H_2O molecules?
6. Why do gasoline motors run better during humid weather than dry?
7. Account for the high thermal stability of water.
8. Define and illustrate the terms "acidic anhydride" and "basic anhydride."
9. Why is $Mg(OH)_2$ formed when magnesium reacts with water whereas MgO is produced when it burns in steam?
10. Distinguish between strong and weak acids in terms of degree of ionization in water.
11. Which metal oxides react with water to form bases?
12. How can the fact that hydrates exert vapor pressure be conveniently demonstrated?

13. Relate vapor pressure of hydrates to temperature.

14. In terms of relative vapor pressures, explain why $Na_2SO_4 \cdot 10\ H_2O$ effloresces in dry air.

15. Why is $CuSO_4 \cdot 5\ H_2O$ stable in moist air?

16. Explain the action of drying agents.

17. Distinguish between the terms "hygroscopic" and "deliquescent."

18. List the classes of impurities commonly found in natural waters.

19. Explain the use of aluminum sulfate and calcium hydroxide in the purification of water.

20. What metal ions are responsible for the hardness of water?

21. Water possessing temporary hardness may be softened by boiling. Explain.

22. How may the noncarbonate hardness of water be removed?

23. What properties make the use of hard water objectionable?

24. Explain the action of ion exchangers in the softening of water.

25. What is heavy water and how is it prepared?

26. How is hydrogen peroxide prepared in the laboratory? How is it prepared commercially? Write equations.

27. Why is hydrogen peroxide purified by distillation under reduced pressure? What are "stabilizers"?

28. What is the advantage of using hydrogen peroxide as an oxidizing agent over other such agents?

29. Under what conditions does hydrogen peroxide act as a reducing agent? Illustrate.

30. Write an equation showing that H_2O_2 is an acid.

31. Distinguish between dioxides and peroxides in terms of electronic structures.

32. State the Law of Multiple Proportions. Explain how water and hydrogen peroxide illustrate this law.

33. Two sulfides of iron have the following compositions:

Fe	63.40 per cent	46.67 per cent
S	36.60 per cent	53.33 per cent
	100.00 per cent	100.00 per cent

Show how these compounds illustrate the Law of Multiple Proportions.

PROBLEMS

1. How many liters of hydrogen would be released at 25.0° C. and one atmosphere pressure when 36.0 g. of sodium reacts with water? *Ans. 19.1 l.*

2. What is the per cent of water by weight in each of the following compounds?
   (a) $CuSO_4 \cdot 5\ H_2O$ *Ans. 36.1%*
   (b) $KAl(SO_4)_2 \cdot 12\ H_2O$ *Ans. 45.6%*
   (c) $Ba(OH)_2 \cdot 8\ H_2O$ *Ans. 45.7%*
   (d) $CaSO_4 \cdot 2\ H_2O$ *Ans. 20.9%*

3. How many moles of phosphoric acid, H_3PO_4, can be produced from 15.0 g. of P_4O_{10}? What is the minimum weight of water necessary to effect this conversion? *Ans. 0.211 mole; 5.71 g.*

4. What weight of a solution of hydrogen peroxide (30% H_2O_2 by weight) is necessary to convert 1.50 moles of sulfurous acid to sulfuric acid? *Ans. 170 g.*

5. Calculate how many moles and how many grams of each of the following hydrates would have to be dehydrated to produce 1.00 kg. of the anhydrous salt:

(a) $MgSO_4 \cdot 7\ H_2O$ *Ans. 8.31 moles; 2050 g.*
(b) $Na_2SO_4 \cdot 10\ H_2O$ *Ans. 7.04 moles; 2270 g.*
(c) $CuSO_4 \cdot 3\ H_2O$ *Ans. 6.27 moles; 1340 g.*
(d) $CuSO_4 \cdot H_2O$ *Ans. 6.27 moles; 1110 g.*

6. How many grams of the metal hydroxide can be produced when water is added to each of the following?

(a) 3.00 moles of Na_2O *Ans. 240 g.*
(b) 15.0 g. of SrO *Ans. 17.6 g.*
(c) 45.0 g. of K_2O *Ans. 53.6 g.*
(d) 1.25 moles of CaO *Ans. 92.6 g.*

7. What weight of hydrogen is obtained when 37.5 g. of magnesium is burned in steam, producing magnesium oxide and hydrogen? *Ans. 3.11 g.*

8. Calculate the number of moles of hydrogen peroxide which can be prepared from 750 g. of barium peroxide and an excess of sulfuric acid, assuming complete conversion with no decomposition of the peroxides. *Ans. 4.43 moles*

9. What volume of oxygen is produced when 35.0 g. of hydrogen peroxide decomposes to give oxygen and water at 50.0° C and 740 mm. pressure? *Ans. 14.0 l.*

10. Calculate the number of moles of sulfurous acid which can be prepared by adding 50.0 liters of sulfur dioxide at 25.0° C and 730 mm. pressure to an excess of water. *Ans. 1.96 moles*

REFERENCES

"Water, a Basic Natural Resource," R. E. Keirstead, *J. Chem. Educ.*, **32** (2) 99 (1955).
"Our National Water Resources," A. P. Black, *J. Chem. Educ.*, **35** (5) 227 (1958).
"Sea Water Conversion: A Key to Water Conservation?" K. Hickman, *J. Chem. Educ.*, **35** (5) 221 (1958).
"Demineralization of Saline Waters," W. S. Gillam and J. W. McCutchan, *Science*, **134** (3485) 1041 (1961).
"Fresh Water from Saline Waters," B. F. Dodge, *Am. Scientist*, **48**, 476 (1960).
"Fresh Water from Salt," D. S. Jenkins, *Sci. American*, March, 1957; p. 37.
"The Growth of Snow Crystals," B. J. Mason, *Sci. American*, Jan., 1961; p. 120.
"How Water Freezes," B. Chalmers, *Sci. American*, Febr., 1959; p. 114.
"The Biology of Heavy Water," J. J. Katz, *Sci. American*, July, 1960; p. 106.
"Hydrogen Peroxide," C. N. Satterfield, *Chem. Eng. News*, **32** (27) 2726 (1954).
"Peroxide Catches Up," (Staff), *Chem. Eng. News*, Febr. 12, 1962; p. 33.

CHAPTER ELEVEN

Solutions

11.1 The Nature of Solutions

When crystals of sugar are stirred with a sufficient quantity of water, the sugar disappears and a clear mixture of sugar in water is formed. The sugar is said to have **dissolved** (or gone into solution) in the water. The solution consists of two components, the **solute** (the dissolved sugar) and the **solvent** (the water). In this solution the molecules of sugar are uniformly distributed among the molecules of water; i.e., the solution is a homogeneous mixture of sugar and water molecules. The molecules of sugar diffuse continuously through the water, and although they are heavier than the single molecules of water, the sugar does not settle out on standing (Fig. 11–1).

An aqueous solution of sugar which contains only a small amount of sugar (the solute) in comparison with the amount of water is said to be **dilute;** the addition of more sugar makes the solution more **concentrated.** The solution is said to be **saturated** when the concentration of dissolved solute is that which can exist **in equilibrium with excess undissolved solute.** The **solubility** of a given solute is defined as the quantity of the solute which will dissolve in a specified quantity of solvent to produce a saturated solution. The composition of a solution may be varied continuously between certain limits. Thus solutions are not compounds because the latter always contain the same elements in the same proportions by weight.

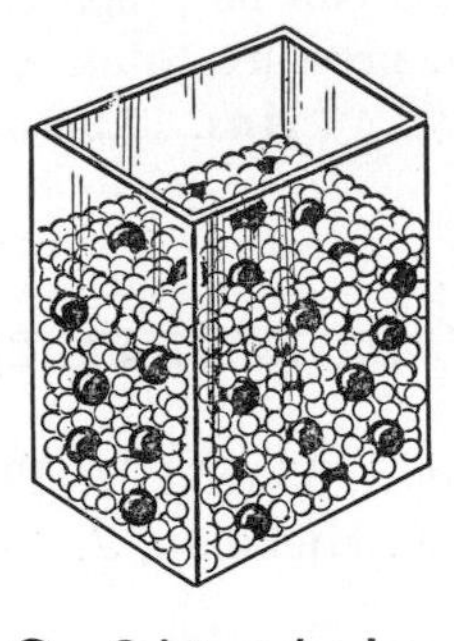

Fig. 11–1 A model of liquid solution, showing solute molecules distributed among solvent molecules.

When sodium chloride, an ionic substance, dissolves in water, sodium ions and chloride ions become uniformly distributed throughout the water. This solution is a homogeneous mixture of water molecules, sodium ions, and chloride ions. As in the case of the molecular solute (sugar), there is diffusion of the solute particles (ions) through the water, and no settling of the ions upon standing.

All solutions are characterized by (1) homogeneity, (2) absence of settling, and (3) the molecular or ionic state of subdivision of the components.

11.2 Kinds of Solutions

Because solutions may be classified in terms of the physical state of both the solute and solvent, many kinds of solutions are possible. In view of the fact that **solutions are defined as homogeneous mixtures,** it is not surprising that almost any gas, liquid, or solid will act as a solvent for other gases, liquids, and solids. Air is a homogeneous mixture of gases; it is a gaseous solution. Oxygen (a gas), alcohol (a liquid), and sugar (a solid) will each dissolve in water (a liquid) and form liquid solutions. Liquid solutions exhibit the general properties characteristic of liquids. The most common and important solutions with which we work in chemistry are those in which the solvent is a liquid. The use of water as a solvent is so general that the word "solution" has come to imply a water solution unless some other solvent is designated. Alloys are frequently solid solutions of one solid dissolved in another; nickel coins contain nickel dissolved in copper.

11.3 Importance of Solutions

Many reactions take place at an appreciable rate only when the reactants are in solution. For example, when powdered barium chloride and sodium sulfate are mixed at ordinary temperatures, there is no perceptible reaction. However, when aqueous solutions of these compounds are mixed, the reaction takes place very rapidly as is indicated by the immediate formation of a precipitate of barium sulfate.

$$Ba^{++} + (2\ Cl^{-}) + (2\ Na^{+}) + SO_4^{=} \rightarrow \underline{BaSO_4} + (2\ Na^{+}) + (2\ Cl^{-})$$

When solutions of these two ionic compounds are brought together, their ions mix freely by diffusion, and when the barium ions collide with sulfate ions, they may remain associated in the form of slightly soluble barium sulfate. When reactants are in the solid state, reaction is possible only for the molecules or ions in the surface layers of the particles because collision between the molecules (or ions) is necessary before reaction can take place. In addition, the movement of the unit particles in solids is greatly restricted, and the chances of collision with molecules or ions in adjacent solid particles is very slight.

Solutions are important in the separation of substances of wide differences in solubility in a given solvent. Thus barium sulfate, which is only slightly soluble in water, is readily separated from the quite soluble sodium chloride by filtration; the sodium and chloride ions pass through the pores of filter paper with the water and the crystals of barium sulfate are retained by the paper. **Precipitation analysis,** a part of the field of analytical chemistry, is based upon the separation of compounds which differ greatly in their solubilities.

Solutions are extremely important in life processes. For example, oxygen and carbon dioxide are carried throughout the body in solution in the blood. **Digestion** is a process in which foods are converted into a form which will pass through the walls of the digestive tract and dissolve in the blood.

The action of natural waters in dissolving substances from air and earth is one of the important processes involved in the conversions of rocks to soil, in altering the fertility of the soil, and in changing the form of the earth's surface. The deposits of many minerals in the earth's crust are the result of reactions that have taken place in solution, or by the evaporation of solutions.

SOLUTIONS OF GASES IN LIQUIDS

11.4 Conditions Affecting Solution of Gases in Liquids

The extent to which a gas dissolves in a liquid is dependent upon the following factors: (1) the nature of the gas and the solvent, (2) the pressure at which the gas is supplied to the liquid, and (3) the temperature of the system.

The solubility of a gas in a given liquid may be considered as a specific property of the gas because its solubility will differ from that of other gases in the same liquid. For example, one liter of water dissolves 0.0489 liter of oxygen at 0° and 760 mm., whereas under the same conditions one liter of water dissolves 1.713 liters of carbon dioxide, 79.789 liters of sulfur dioxide, and 1176.0 liters of ammonia.

The solubility of a gas in a liquid can be increased by increasing the pressure under which the gas is supplied to the solution. This relationship is quantitatively expressed by **Henry's Law** as follows: **The weight of a gas that dissolves in a definite volume of liquid is directly proportional to the pressure at which the gas is supplied to the liquid.** This law means that if 1 g. of a gas dissolves in 1 liter of water at one atmosphere of pressure (760 mm.)., 5 g. will dissolve at 5 atmospheres of pressure (3800 mm.). The effect of pressure does not follow Henry's Law when a chemical reaction takes place between the gas and the solvent. Thus, the solubility of ammonia in water does not increase as rapidly with increasing pressure as predicted by the law because ammonia reacts to some extent with water and forms ammonium ions and hydroxide ions.

The effect of increased pressure upon the solubility of a gas in a liquid is illustrated by the behavior of carbonated beverages. Carbon dioxide is forced into the liquid beverage under pressure, and the bottle is tightly capped to prevent escape of carbon dioxide and maintain the pressure. When the cap is removed, the pressure is decreased, and some of the gas escapes. The escape of bubbles of the gas from the liquid is known as **effervescence.**

Finally, the solubility of gases in liquids decreases with an increase in temperature. For example, carbon dioxide at 760 mm. pressure dissolves in 1 liter of water to the extent of 1.713 liters at 0°, 1.194 l. at 10°, 0.878 l. at 20°, and 0.359 l. at 60°. This relationship is not one of inverse proportion, however, and the solubility of a gas in a liquid at a given temperature must be determined experimentally. Many gases may be expelled from solvents by boiling their solutions. Thus, oxygen, nitrogen, carbon dioxide, and sulfur dioxide can be removed from water by boiling it for a few minutes.

SOLUTIONS OF LIQUIDS IN LIQUIDS

11.5 Miscibility of Liquids

Some liquids will mix with water in all proportions. Such liquids are usually either ionic in solution, so that the charged ions attract the oppositely charged ends of the polar water molecules, or they are polar substances (see Section 4.7) with polar character similar to that of water. For such polar liquids, the negative ends of the one kind of polar molecules attract the positive ends of the other kind of polar molecules, with about the same degree of attraction that like molecules of either substance attract each other. Hence, the two kinds of molecules mix easily in all proportions. Liquids which mix with water in all proportions are said to be **miscible** with water. Ethyl alcohol, sulfuric acid, and glycerine are examples. Nonpolar covalent liquids, such as gasoline, carbon disulfide, and carbon tetrachloride, do not have a net charge separation within the molecule and hence do not effectively attract the polar water molecules. Thus, the water molecules have appreciable attractions only for other water molecules and effectively "squeeze out" the molecules of the nonpolar liquid so that these liquids are very nearly insoluble in the water. Such liquids are said to be **immiscible** with water. Still others, such as ether and bromine, have slight solubilities in water. Two layers are formed when two **immiscible** liquids are in contact with each other. In cases of partial miscibility, each layer is a solution of one liquid in the other.

11.6 Fractional Distillation

It will be recalled from Chapter 9 that a pure liquid exhibits a definite vapor pressure at a given temperature and that the normal boiling point of a pure liquid is the temperature at which the vapor pressure of the liquid is 760 mm. The total pressure exerted by the vapor of a solution of a liquid in a liquid depends upon the concentration of its components and it may be (A) greater than that of either component taken separately, (B) less than that of either component, or (C) intermediate in value between those of the two liquids concerned. Usually, the boiling point of a mixture of two liquids lies between the boiling points of the two components. The boiling point of the mixture is the temperature at which the total vapor pressure of the mixture is equal to the atmospheric pressure.

When a mixture of two liquids is boiled, the vapor produced at the boiling point is richer in the lower boiling component than the original mixture. When this vapor is condensed (Fig. 11–2), the resulting distillate is richer in the liquid of the higher vapor pressure (lower boiling point) than the original mixture. This means that the composi-

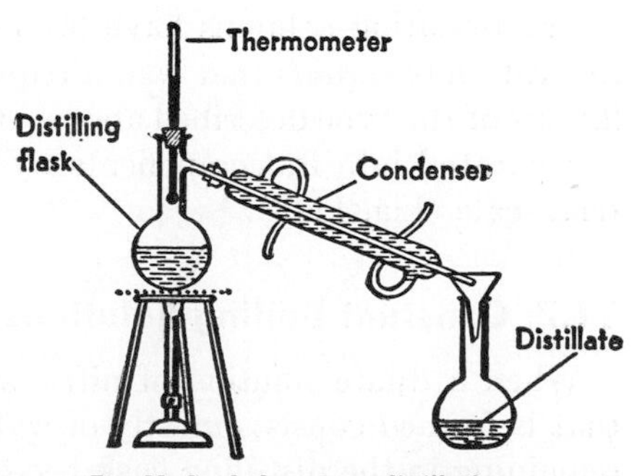

Fig. 11–2 Laboratory distillation.

tion of the mixture is constantly changing and that the boiling point rises as distillation is continued. The vapor (and distillate) contains more and more of the less volatile component and less and less of the more volatile component. By changing the receiver at intervals, successive fractions, each increasingly richer in the less volatile component, are obtained. If this process (**fractional distillation**) is repeated several times, relatively pure samples of the two liquids may be obtained.

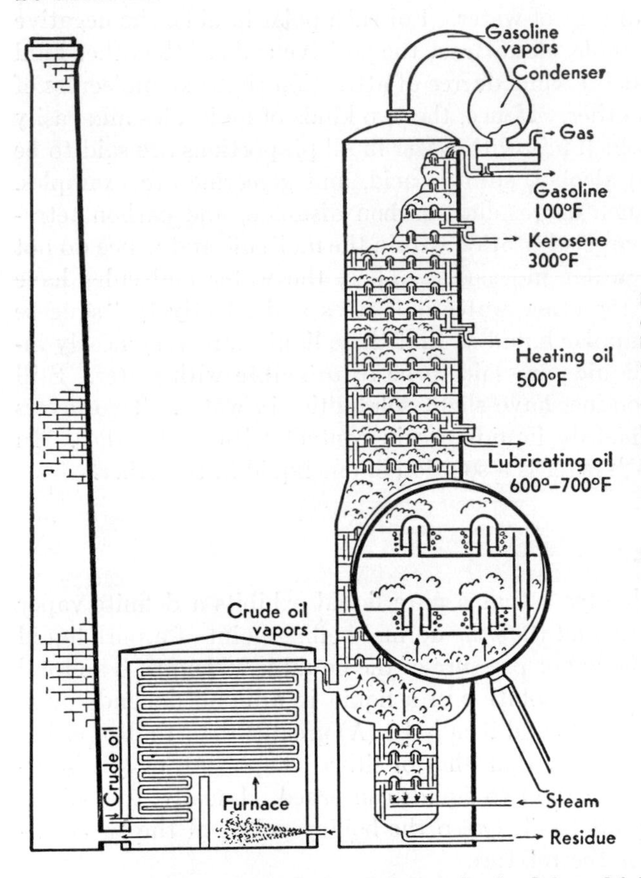

Fig. 11–3 Fractional distillation of crude oil. Oil is heated to about 800° F in the furnace and vaporizes when it enters the tower at the right. The vapors rise through a series of trays in the tower. As the vapors gradually cool, fractions of higher, then of lower, boiling points condense to liquids and are drawn off. The fraction of highest boiling point is drawn off at the bottom as a residue. It is heavy fuel oil. In modern refineries these fractions, which still consist of mixtures of hydrocarbons, are further processed.

Fractionating columns have been devised in which a single operation achieves separation of liquids that would require a great number of simple fractional distillations of the type described above. Crude oil, a complex mixture of hydrocarbons, is separated into its components by fractional distillation on an enormous industrial scale (Fig. 11–3).

11.7 Constant Boiling Solutions

When a dilute solution of nitric acid is distilled, the first fraction of distillate that is formed consists mostly of water. As distillation is continued, the solution remaining in the distilling flask becomes richer in nitric acid. After a time a concentration of 68 per cent HNO_3 is reached, and thereafter the solution boils at a constant temperature of 120.5° (760 mm.). At this temperature the solution and the vapor have the same composition, and the solution distills without a change in composition.

If a nitric acid solution more concentrated than 68 per cent is distilled, the vapor which is first formed contains a large amount of HNO_3. The solution which remains in the distilling flask contains, therefore, a greater percentage of water than at first, and the concentration of the nitric acid in the distilling flask decreases as the distillation is continued. Finally, a concentration of 68 per cent HNO_3 is reached and the solution again boils at the constant temperature of 120.5°. The 68 per cent nitric acid is called a constant boiling solution. At this specific concentration the solution has a lower vapor pressure, and thus a higher boiling point, than at any other possible concentration. **Solutions which distill without change in composition or temperature are called azeotropic mixtures.**

Other common and important substances that form azeotropic mixtures with water are HCl (20.24 per cent and 110°) and H_2SO_4 (98.3 per cent and 338°).

SOLUTIONS OF SOLIDS IN LIQUIDS

11.8 The Effect of Temperature on the Solubility of Solids

When a solid dissolves in a liquid, a change in the physical state of the solid analogous to melting takes place. Energy is absorbed in overcoming the forces which hold the molecules, atoms, or ions in their lattice positions in the crystal. This is an endothermic change that accompanies the dissolution of all solids in liquids. The physical process of solution is often accompanied by a second change, that of a chemical reaction between the solute and the solvent. This second change is commonly exothermic in character. In some cases, the heat evolved in the chemical change is greater than that absorbed in the physical change. In such cases the heat of solution is negative, i.e., the net process of solution is exothermic. In other cases the heat of solution is positive, i.e., the net process is endothermic (see Section 5.8). Furthermore, heat is either absorbed or evolved during the process of crystallization of a solid from solution, a process opposite to that of solution.

The opposed processes of dissolution and crystallization under conditions of equilibrium between a solid and its saturated solution may be represented as follows:

(1) solute + solvent $\rightleftharpoons$ solution + heat (negative heat of solution)
(2) solute + solvent + heat $\rightleftharpoons$ solution (positive heat of solution)

The addition of heat (a rise in temperature) in system (2) causes more of the solute to dissolve; the added heat is absorbed by the system when the equilibrium shifts to the right. This is the case with most solid-liquid solutions. In system (1) the solubility decreases with a rise in temperature.

The dependence of solubility upon temperature for a number of solid inorganic

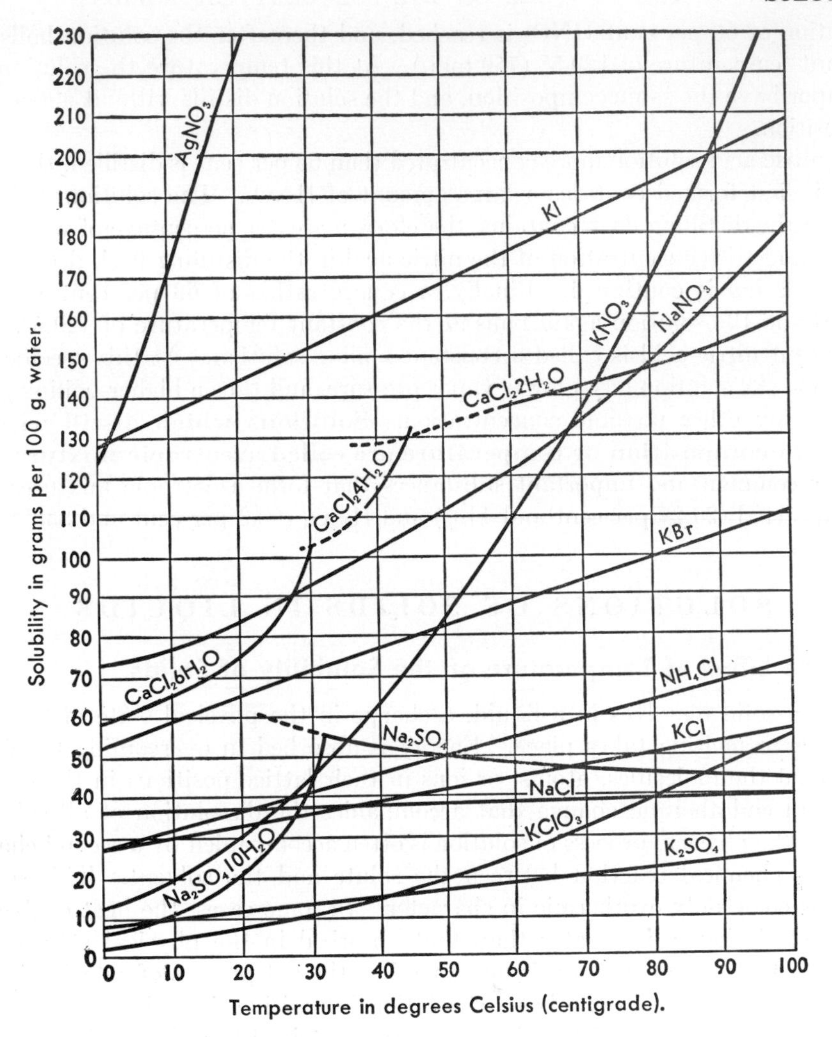

Fig. 11–4 Graph showing the effect of temperature on the solubility of several inorganic substances.

substances is represented graphically by the solubility curves in Fig. 11–4. Note that the solubility of sodium chloride increases very slightly with a rise in temperature whereas that of potassium nitrate increases rapidly. A sharp break in a solubility curve indicates the formation of a compound whose solubility is different from that of the substance from which it was formed. When $Na_2SO_4 \cdot 10\ H_2O$ (Glauber's salt) is heated to 32.4°, it loses its water of crystallization and forms the anhydrous salt, Na_2SO_4. The curve up to 32.4°, the **transition point,** represents the effect of a rise in temperature upon the solubility of $Na_2SO_4 \cdot 10\ H_2O$ and the curve for temperatures above this point represents the effect of a rise in temperature upon the solubility of Na_2SO_4.

11.9 Saturated Solutions

It was noted in Section 11.1 that sugar dissolves in water at a given temperature until the point of saturation is reached. When more crystals of sugar are added to the solution, they fall to the bottom of the container, and it appears that the dissolving process stops. Actually, molecules of sugar continue to leave the crystalline solid under the solvent action of the water and go into solution. However, as the molecules of sugar in solution move about by diffusion, some of them collide with the solid and take up positions in the crystal lattice. This process is the opposite of dissolution and is called crystallization. There is a sufficiently large number of molecules returning to the solid state from the saturated solution so that the process of crystallization just counterbalances that of dissolution, and we have a state of dynamic equilibrium. The same reasoning holds when no crystals are formed — for example, ether in water. A saturated solution is one which is in equilibrium with the undissolved solute. If a crystal of imperfect shape is placed in a solution saturated with respect to the crystalline material, it will slowly "mend" its shape by loss of particles to the solution and gain of particles from the solution. This is experimental evidence that a saturated solution in contact with its solid solute is a system in dynamic equilibrium.

11.10 Supersaturated Solutions

When saturated solutions of solid solutes are prepared at elevated temperatures and then permitted to cool, the excess solute usually separates from the solution by crystallizing. However, if a saturated solution is prepared at an elevated temperature and excess solute removed, crystallization often does not take place when the solution is allowed to cool undisturbed. The solution contains more of the solute than it does when it is in equilibrium with the undissolved state and is called a **supersaturated solution.** Such solutions are metastable (unstable) systems. Agitation of the solution or the addition of a "seed" crystal of the solute may start crystallization of the excess solute; after crystallization, a saturated solution in equilibrium with the crystals of solute remains.

11.11 Rate of Solution

Rate of solution pertains to the amount of solute entering the solution per unit of time. It depends upon several factors. First, more soluble substances dissolve more rapidly than less soluble ones. Because the dissolution of a solid can take place only at the surface of the particles, the more finely divided the solute is (the greater the surface area per unit mass of the substance), the greater will be its rate of solution. The rate of diffusion of the molecules away from the solid solute is relatively slow and so the solution in the immediate vicinity of the solid phase approaches the saturation concentration. Stirring or shaking the mixture brings unsaturated solution in contact with the solute and thus increases the rate of solution; heating results in convection currents which produce the same effects as agitation of the mixture, and heating also usually increases the solubility of the solid.

THE CONCENTRATION OF SOLUTIONS

11.12 Standard Solutions

The solubility of a solid substance in a pure solvent at a given temperature is a quantitatively definite physical property of the substance. The solubility of sodium chloride is 35.8 g. per 100 g. of water at 20°; that of NaF is 4.2 g.; and that of silver bromide is 0.00002 g. It is obvious, then, that the solubilities of various substances differ greatly. A general idea of relative solubilities is conveyed by use of the terms **quite soluble, moderately soluble,** and **slightly soluble** or **insoluble.** Strictly speaking, no substance is absolutely insoluble, although for all practical purposes many substances appear to be so. The relative concentrations of solutions may be expressed by the terms **dilute** (containing a small proportion of solute) and **concentrated** (containing a large proportion of solute).

Chemists usually work with unsaturated solutions of known concentration. **Solutions of known concentration are called standard solutions.**

The concentrations of solutions may be expressed in a number of ways. It is very important that the methods of expressing concentrations of solutions be thoroughly mastered.

11.13 Concentration Expressed in Physical Units

One method of expressing concentration in physical units involves the weight of solute in a given weight of solvent; for example, 1 g. of NaCl in 100 g. of water. A second system expresses concentration by percentage composition by weight. A 10 per cent NaCl solution by weight contains 10 g. of NaCl in 100 g. of solution (90 g. of water).

EXAMPLE 1. Calculate the weight of NaCl solution (10 per cent NaCl by weight) that will contain 50 g. of NaCl.

If 100 g. of solution contain 10 g. of NaCl (10 per cent of 100 g.), then

$$100 \text{ g. of solution} \times \frac{50 \text{ g. of NaCl}}{10 \text{ g. of NaCl}} = 500 \text{ g. of solution}$$

Hence, 500 g. of 10 per cent sodium chloride solution will contain 50 g. of NaCl (and 450 g. of water).

In order to calculate the weight of solute in a given volume of solution from the percentage composition by weight, it is necessary to know the specific gravity (or density) of the solution.

EXAMPLE 2. Calculate the weight of hydrogen chloride (HCl) in 100 ml. of concentrated hydrochloric acid of specific gravity 1.19 and containing 37.23 per cent HCl by weight.

Solution:

One ml. of the solution weighs 1.19 g.
100 ml. of the solution weigh 100 ml. × 1.19 g./ml. = 119 g.

Because the solution is 37.23 per cent HCl by weight,

119 g. of the solution contain 119 g. × 0.3723 = 44.3 g. of HCl.

EXAMPLE 3. What volume of concentrated hydrochloric acid of specific gravity 1.19 and containing 37.23 per cent HCl by weight contains 100 g. of HCl?

Solution:

One ml. of acid contains 1.19 g. × 0.3723 = 0.443 g. of HCl. To obtain the volume of acid that would contain 100 g. of HCl, multiply the 1 ml. by an improper fraction made up of 100 g. and 0.443 g.

$$1 \text{ ml.} \times \frac{100 \text{ g.}}{0.443 \text{ g.}} = 226 \text{ ml.}$$

Thus, 226 ml. of the concentrated hydrochloric acid contain 100 g. of HCl.

11.14 Molar Solutions

It is frequently desirable to express concentration in terms of gram-formula weights, instead of grams, of solute. **A solution containing one gram-formula weight, or mole, of the solute in one liter of solution is called a one-molar solution.** Note that a liter of solution rather than a liter of solvent is specified in this definition. Because gram-formula weights of different molecular substances contain the same number of molecules, it follows that equal volumes of one-molar solutions will contain the same number of molecules of the solute. It should be obvious that by using the molar method of expressing concentration of solutions, it is easy to select a desired number of moles, molecules, or ions of the solute by measuring out the appropriate volume of solution. For example, if 1 mole of sodium hydroxide is needed for a given reaction, one can use 1 liter of a one-molar (1 M) solution or 2 liters of a 0.5 M solution of the base. If the 2 liters of 0.5 M sodium hydroxide solution were to be used in a reaction with 0.4 M hydrochloric acid, 2.5 liters of the acid would be needed because 2.5 liters of 0.4 M acid will furnish one mole of the solute HCl.

$$\underset{(2 \text{ l.} \times 0.5 \text{ M})}{\underset{1 \text{ mole}}{NaOH}} + \underset{(2.5 \text{ l.} \times 0.4 \text{ M})}{\underset{1 \text{ mole}}{HCl}} \rightarrow NaCl + H_2O$$

Fig. 11–5 A volumetric flask is used in preparing solutions of known concentration.

In preparing a 1 M solution of sodium hydroxide, 40.0 g. (1 mole) of pure sodium hydroxide is weighed out accurately and dissolved in sufficient water to form one liter of solution. A 1 M solution of hydrochloric acid contains 36.5 g. of the acid per liter. A 2 M solution of sodium hydroxide contains 80.0 g. (2 moles) of NaOH per liter, and a 0.1 M solution contains

4.0 g. of NaOH per liter. **Volumetric flasks** are used to measure volumes of solutions accurately (Fig. 11–5, page 187).

11.15 Problems Based on Molarity of Solutions

The molarity of a solution is the number of moles of solute per liter of solution.

EXAMPLE 1. Calculate the molarity of a solution, 2.0 liters of which contain 2.6 moles of solute.

$$\text{Molarity} = \frac{\text{moles of solute}}{\text{liters of solution}} = \frac{2.6 \text{ moles}}{2.0 \text{ liters}} = 1.3 \text{ moles/liter} = 1.3 \text{ M}$$

The molarity of a solution is also the number of millimoles of solute per milliliter of solution. This follows because a millimole is one-thousandth of a mole and a milliliter is one-thousandth of a liter.

EXAMPLE 2. Calculate the molarity of a solution, 20 ml. of which contain 5.0 millimoles of solute.

$$\text{Molarity} = \frac{\text{millimoles of solute}}{\text{milliliters of solution}} = \frac{5.0 \text{ millimoles}}{20 \text{ ml.}} = 0.25 \text{ millimole/ml.} = 0.25 \text{ M}$$

EXAMPLE 3. Calculate the molarity of a solution which contains 4.0 g. of NaOH in 2.0 liters of solution. The gram-formula weight of NaOH is (23.0 + 16.0 + 1.0) g. = 40.0 g.

$$\text{Number of moles of NaOH} = \frac{\text{grams of NaOH}}{\text{gram-formula weight}} = \frac{4.0 \text{ g.}}{40 \text{ g./mole}} = 0.10 \text{ mole}$$

$$\text{Molarity} = \frac{\text{moles of solute}}{\text{liters of solution}} = \frac{0.10 \text{ mole}}{2.0 \text{ liters}} = 0.05 \text{ mole/liter} = 0.05 \text{ M}$$

EXAMPLE 4. How many grams of H_2SO_4 are contained in 0.80 liter of 0.050 M sulfuric acid?

One liter of 0.050 M acid would contain 0.050 mole of H_2SO_4

0.80 liter of 0.050 M acid would contain 0.080 l. × 0.050 mole/l. = 0.040 mole of H_2SO_4

One mole of H_2SO_4 is 98 g.

0.040 mole of H_2SO_4 is 0.040 mole × 98. g./mole = 3.9 g.

Thus, 3.9 g. of H_2SO_4 are contained in 0.80 liter of 0.050 M sulfuric acid.

EXAMPLE 5. Calculate the molarity of a concentrated sulfuric acid solution of specific gravity 1.84 and containing 98.0 per cent H_2SO_4 by weight.

The weight of 1 ml. of acid is 1.84 g.

The weight of 1 liter (1000 ml.) of the acid is 1000 ml. × 1.84 g./ml. = 1840 g.

The weight of H_2SO_4 in one liter of the acid is 1840 g. × 0.980 = 1800 g.

The gram-formula weight of H_2SO_4 is 98.0 g.

$$\text{Moles of } H_2SO_4 \text{ in 1800 g. of } H_2SO_4 = \frac{1800 \text{ g.}}{98.0 \text{ g./mole}} = 18.4 \text{ moles}$$

Because the concentrated sulfuric acid contains 18.4 moles of H_2SO_4 in 1 liter of solution, its concentration is 18.4 M.

11.16 Equivalent Weights of Compounds

It can be shown by experiment that the sodium hydroxide in 1 liter of a 1 M solution of the base will completely neutralize the hydrochloric acid in 1 liter of a 1 M solution of the acid; however, 2 liters of 1 M sodium hydroxide are required in the complete neutralization of the acid in 1 liter of 1 M sulfuric acid. This arises from the fact that one mole of sulfuric acid reacts with two moles of sodium hydroxide, whereas one mole of hydrochloric acid reacts with only one mole of sodium hydroxide.

$$HCl + NaOH \rightarrow NaCl + H_2O$$
$$H_2SO_4 + 2\ NaOH \rightarrow Na_2SO_4 + 2\ H_2O$$

Each mole of sulfuric acid supplies two hydrogen ions, each of which can neutralize one hydroxide ion: $H^+ + OH^- \rightarrow H_2O$. In other words, one mole of sodium hydroxide is chemically equivalent to half a mole of sulfuric acid.

The fundamental definition of equivalent weight (Section 8.10) is this: The equivalent weight of a substance is the number of parts by weight of it which combine with or are otherwise chemically equivalent to 8.00 parts by weight of oxygen. This fundamental definition may be expanded to one which seems to be applicable in all ordinary cases: **Gram-equivalent weight** (often shortened to just gram-equivalent) **is the number of grams of a substance, in a chemical reaction, associated with the transfer of N electrons or protons or with the neutralization of N negative or positive charges, where N is Avogadro's number, 6.023×10^{23}.**

In an acid-base reaction, protons, H^+, are transferred from the acid to the base and it is upon the number of these that the calculation of the gram-equivalent weight of the acid and base is based. When hydrochloric acid reacts with sodium hydroxide, one proton is transferred from the hydronium ion (the acid) to the hydroxide ion (the base).

$$H_3O^+ + OH^- \rightarrow 2\ H_2O$$

When one mole of hydrochloric acid reacts with one mole of sodium hydroxide, N protons (6.023×10^{23}) are transferred from the hydronium ion to the hydroxide ion. It follows, then, that one gram-equivalent weight of hydrochloric acid is equal to one mole (36.5 g.), and one gram-equivalent weight of sodium hydroxide is equal to one mole (40.0 g.). When one mole of sulfuric acid reacts with two moles of sodium hydroxide ($H_2SO_4 + 2\ NaOH \rightarrow Na_2SO_4 + 2\ H_2O$), 2 N protons are transferred from the acid to the base. Hence one gram-equivalent weight of sulfuric acid is equal to one-half mole (98.0 g. ÷ 2 = 49.0 g.) of the acid.

It should be emphasized that the number of protons actually transferred in the reaction determines the equivalent weight. For example, phosphoric acid may react with sodium hydroxide in one of three ways:

$$(1)\ H_3PO_4 + NaOH \rightarrow NaH_2PO_4 + H_2O$$
$$(2)\ H_3PO_4 + 2\ NaOH \rightarrow Na_2HPO_4 + 2\ H_2O$$
$$(3)\ H_3PO_4 + 3\ NaOH \rightarrow Na_3PO_4 + 3\ H_2O$$

The numbers of protons transferred in the three reactions are N, 2 N, and 3 N, respectively. Thus the equivalent weight of H_3PO_4 in the three cases is equal to 1 mole, one-half mole, and one-third mole, respectively.

In the reaction (1) above, N protons were transferred in the formation of NaH_2PO_4; so a gram-equivalent weight of this salt is equal to one mole of it. Likewise, a gram-equivalent of Na_2HPO_4 is one-half mole, and that of Na_3PO_4 is one-third mole because 2 N protons and 3 N protons were transferred during their formation, respectively.

When solutions of silver nitrate ($AgNO_3$) and sodium chloride (NaCl) are mixed, silver chloride precipitates. The reaction may be written

$$Ag^+ + Cl^- \rightarrow \underline{Ag^+Cl^-}$$

The silver ion and chloride ion combine to yield an ionic compound of low solubility. The ions form a crystal lattice and are neutralized electrostatically. The gram-equivalent weight is calculated from the number of charges neutralized in this way. When one mole each of silver nitrate and sodium chloride react, N positive charges and N negative charges are neutralized. Hence the gram-equivalent weight of $AgNO_3$ and that of NaCl are each equal to one mole, i.e., to 169.87 g. and 58.44 g., respectively.

Barium chloride precipitates the sulfate ion from a sodium sulfate solution according to the equation

$$Ba^{++} + SO_4^{=} \rightarrow \underline{Ba^{++}SO_4^{=}}$$

When one mole of barium ion, Ba^{++}, reacts with one mole of sulfate ion, $SO_4^{=}$, 2 N positive charges and 2 N negative charges are neutralized; hence the gram-equivalent weight of $BaCl_2$ will be one-half the gram-formula weight, and that of Na_2SO_4 will be one-half the gram-formula weight.

11.17 Normal Solutions

When concentration is expressed as the number of gram-equivalent weights of solute per liter of solution, equal volumes of solutions containing the same number of gram-equivalent weights of different substances are chemically equivalent. **A solution which contains one gram-equivalent weight of solute in one liter of solution is called a one-normal solution.** A one-normal (1 N) solution of sulfuric acid contains one gram-equivalent weight (98 g./2 = 49 g.) of H_2SO_4 per liter; a 2 N solution contains 98 g. of H_2SO_4, and a 0.01 N solution contains 0.49 g. of H_2SO_4. It should be evident that a 1 M solution of hydrochloric acid is also 1 N because a gram-equivalent weight of HCl is equal to one mole of it. However, a 1 M solution of sulfuric acid is 2 N because the gram-formula weight of H_2SO_4 is equal to two gram-equivalent weights of it.

It must be emphasized that the gram-equivalent weight to be used in determining the normality of a solution must be deduced from the reaction, not merely from the formula of the substance. For example, the gram-equivalent weight of H_3PO_4 in making up a 1 N solution of phosphoric acid is equal to one mole when it is to be used in the reaction

$$H_3PO_4 + NaOH \rightarrow NaH_2PO_4 + H_2O$$

However, if the reaction involves one mole of H_3PO_4 with two of NaOH,

$$H_3PO_4 + 2\ NaOH \rightarrow Na_2HPO_4 + 2\ H_2O$$

then the gram-equivalent weight of H_3PO_4 is equal to one-half a mole.

11.18 Problems Based on Normality

The normality of a solution is the number of gram-equivalent weights of solute per liter of solution.

EXAMPLE 1. Calculate the normality of a solution which contains 0.40 gram-equivalent of solute in 2.0 liters of solution.

$$\text{Normality} = \frac{\text{gram-equivalents of solute}}{\text{liters of solution}} = \frac{0.40 \text{ g.-equiv.}}{2.0 \text{ liters}} = 0.20 \text{ N}$$

The normality of a solution is also the number of milligram-equivalents of solute per milliliter of solution, because a milligram is one-thousandth of a gram and a milliliter is one-thousandth of a liter.

EXAMPLE 2. What is the normality of 10 ml. of a solution which contains 20 milligram-equivalents of solute?

$$\text{Normality} = \frac{\text{milligram-equivalents of solute}}{\text{milliliters of solution}} = \frac{20 \text{ mg.-equiv.}}{10 \text{ ml.}} = 2.0 \text{ N}$$

EXAMPLE 3. Calculate the normality of a solution of hydrochloric acid which contains 3.65 g. of HCl in 0.50 liter of solution.

The gram-equivalent of HCl is equal to one mole, 36.5 g.

$$\text{Number of gram-equivalents of HCl} = \frac{\text{grams of HCl}}{\text{gram-equivalent weight}}$$

$$= \frac{3.65 \text{ g.}}{36.5 \text{ g./g.-equiv.}} = 0.10$$

$$\text{Normality} = \frac{\text{gram-equivalents of solute}}{\text{liters of solution}} = \frac{0.10 \text{ g.-equiv.}}{0.50 \text{ l.}} = 0.20 \text{ N}$$

EXAMPLE 4. How many grams of H_2SO_4 are contained in 1.2 liters of 0.50 N sulfuric acid?

One liter of 0.50 N acid would contain 0.50 gram-equivalent of H_2SO_4.

1.2 liters of 0.50 N acid would contain 1.2 l. $\times$ 0.50 g.-equiv./l. = 0.60 g.-equiv. of H_2SO_4.

The gram-equivalent of H_2SO_4 is one-half the gram-formula weight (98 g./2 = 49.0 g.).

0.60 g.-equiv. of H_2SO_4 is 0.60 g.-equiv. × 49.0 g./g.-equiv. = 29.4 g. Inasmuch as only two significant figures are justified by the data used, the answer must be rounded off to 29 g. Thus, we calculate that 1.2 liters of 0.50 N sulfuric acid contains 29 g. of H_2SO_4.

EXAMPLE 5. What is the normality of a solution of barium hydroxide, 100.0 ml. of which contain 17.14 mg. of $Ba(OH)_2$?

The milligram-equivalent of $Ba(OH)_2$ is one-half its milligram-formula weight (171.4 mg./2 = 85.7 mg.).

$$\text{Number of milligram-equivalents} = \frac{\text{milligrams of solute}}{\text{milligram-equivalent weight}}$$

$$= \frac{17.14 \text{ mg.}}{85.7 \text{ mg./mg.-equiv. wt.}} = 0.200 \text{ mg.-equiv.}$$

$$\text{Normality} = \frac{\text{milligram-equivalents of solute}}{\text{milliliters of solution}} = \frac{0.200 \text{ mg.-equiv.}}{100.0 \text{ ml.}} = 0.0020 \text{ N}$$

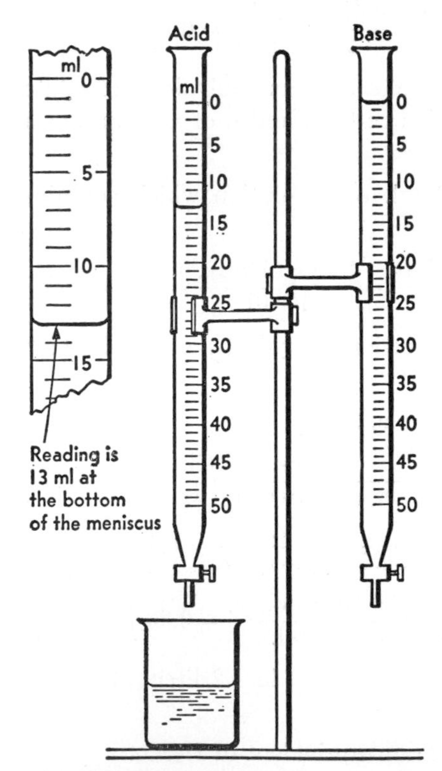

Fig. 11–6 Burets are used for accurately measuring the volume of a solution. Accurate reading (see insert) is necessary.

11.19 Acidimetry and Alkalimetry

The determination of the concentration of acidic solutions of unknown normality by means of standard basic solutions is known as **acidimetry.** The quantity of acid in a solution of known volume is determined by measuring the volume of base of known normality (standard solution) required to neutralize the acid. An indicator (see chapter on ionic equilibrium) which changes color at the point of the neutralization or **end point** is used to indicate that equivalent amounts of acid and base have been brought together. The base is added drop by drop to the acid from a **buret** (Fig. 11–6); this process is called **titration.** The use of standard acid solutions to determine the concentration of basic solutions of unknown normality is called **alkalimetry.**

EXAMPLE 1. Let us suppose that 20 ml. of 0.1 N hydrochloric acid are required in the titration of 50 ml. of a basic solution of unknown normality. Calculate the normality of the basic solution.

1 ml. of 0.1 N hydrochloric acid contains 0.1 milligram-equivalent of HCl.

20 ml. of 0.1 N hydrochloric acid contains 20 ml. × 0.1 mg.-equiv./ml. = 2.0 milligram-equivalents of HCl.

For the complete neutralization of 2.0 milligram-equivalents of acid, 2.0 milligram-equivalents of base are required.

Because this quantity of base is contained in 50 ml. of solution,

$$\text{Normality of base} = \frac{\text{milligram-equivalents}}{\text{milliliters of solution}} = \frac{2.0 \text{ mg.-equiv.}}{50 \text{ ml.}} = 0.04 \text{ N}$$

EXAMPLE 2. Let us calculate the volume of 0.10 N silver nitrate required to precipitate the chloride ions in 200 ml. of 0.05 N sodium chloride solution ($Ag^+ + Cl^- \rightarrow \underline{AgCl}$).

200 ml. of 0.05 N NaCl contain 200 ml. × 0.05 mg.-equiv./ml. = 10 mg.-equivalents.

Hence, 10 mg.-equivalents of $AgNO_3$ will be required to react with 10 mg.-equivalents of NaCl.

Each ml. of 0.10 N $AgNO_3$ solution contains 0.10 mg.-equivalent of $AgNO_3$.

The number of ml. of 0.10 N silver nitrate solution that will contain 10 mg.-equivalents of $AgNO_3$ is therefore

$$\frac{10 \text{ mg.-equivalents}}{0.10 \text{ mg.-equiv./ml.}} = 100 \text{ ml. of } AgNO_3$$

11.20 Problems Based on Dilution of Solutions

When a solution is diluted, the volume is increased by adding more solvent and the concentration is decreased, but the total amount of solute is constant.

EXAMPLE 1. A liter of 5.0 M silver nitrate is diluted to a volume of 2.0 liters by adding water. What is the molarity of the diluted silver nitrate?

One liter of a 5.0 M solution contains 1.0 liter × 5.0 moles/liter = 5.0 moles of solute.

After dilution, 2 liters of solution contain 5.0 moles of solute.

$$\text{Molarity after dilution} = \frac{\text{moles of solute}}{\text{liters of solution}} = \frac{5.0 \text{ moles}}{2.0 \text{ liters}} = 2.5 \text{ M}$$

EXAMPLE 2. What volume of water would be required to dilute 10 ml. of 0.40 N acid to a concentration of 0.10 N?

10 ml. of 0.40 N acid contains 10 ml. × 0.40 mg.-equiv./ml. = 4.0 mg.-equiv. of pure acid.

After dilution, each ml. of solution will contain 0.10 mg.-equivalent and the total quantity of solute will be 4.0 mg.-equiv.

$$\text{Volume after dilution} = \frac{4.0 \text{ mg.-equiv.}}{0.10 \text{ mg.-equiv./ml.}} = 40 \text{ ml.}$$

The volume of water required in the dilution is equal to the final volume of the solution minus the original volume: 40 ml. − 10 ml. = 30 ml.

EXAMPLE 3. A solution of 0.40 M hydrochloric acid having a volume of 100 ml. is mixed with 50 ml. of 0.20 M sodium hydroxide solution. Calculate the molarity of each solute in the resulting solution.

100 ml. of 0.40 M hydrochloric acid contains 100 ml. $\times$ 0.40 millimole/ml. = 40 millimoles of HCl.

50 ml. of 0.20 M sodium hydroxide contains 50 ml. $\times$ 0.20 millimole/ml. = 10 millimoles of NaOH.

10 millimoles of NaOH will neutralize 10 millimoles of HCl, forming 10 millimoles of NaCl, and leaving 40 − 10 = 30 millimoles of HCl in excess.

The total volume after mixing is 100 ml. + 50 ml. = 150 ml.

$$\text{Molarity of HCl} = \frac{30 \text{ millimoles of HCl}}{150 \text{ ml. of solution}} = 0.20 \text{ M}$$

$$\text{Molarity of NaCl} = \frac{10 \text{ millimoles of NaCl}}{150 \text{ ml. of solution}} = 0.067 \text{ M}$$

THE EFFECT OF SOLUTES UPON THE PROPERTIES OF THE SOLVENT

11.21 Vapor Pressures of Solvents

It has been found from experiment that when a nonvolatile substance is dissolved in a liquid, the vapor pressure of the liquid is lowered. Solid solutes exhibit only negligible vapor pressures so they may be considered as being nonvolatile. Thus, the vapor pressure of an aqueous sugar solution is less than that of pure water. The vapor pressure of a liquid is determined by the frequency of escape of molecules from the surface of the liquid. The presence of sugar molecules in the solution lowers the frequency of escape of water molecules from the surface of the liquid. This is the cause of the lowering of the vapor pressure, and the kind or size of solute molecule has little to do in determining the extent of this effect. It turns out that the decrease in vapor pressure is proportional to the number of molecules of solute that is dissolved in a definite number of molecules of the solvent. These considerations lead to **Raoult's Law,** which is stated as follows: **The lowering of the vapor pressure of a solvent is directly proportional to the weight of the solute which is dissolved in a definite weight of the solvent.**

11.22 Elevation of the Boiling Point of the Solvent

It was seen in Section 9.3 that the boiling point of a liquid is the temperature at which the vapor pressure of the liquid becomes equal to the pressure upon its surface. Because the addition of a solute lowers the vapor pressure of a liquid, a higher temperature is required to bring the vapor pressure of the liquid up to the atmospheric pressure and make the solution boil. According to Raoult's Law, the lowering of the vapor pressure of a solvent is directly proportional to the weight of solute which is dissolved in a definite weight of solvent. It follows, then, that the elevation of the boiling point of the solvent is also proportional to the weight of the solute which is dissolved in a definite weight of solvent. For solutes which are nonelectrolytes (substances which do not give ions in solution) and nonvolatile, the elevation of the boiling point of the solvent is the same when solutions of equimolecular concentrations are considered. For example, one gram-molecular weight of sucrose ($C_{12}H_{22}O_{11}$) and one gram-molecular weight of glucose ($C_6H_{12}O_6$), each dissolved in 1000 g. of water, form solutions which have the same boiling points, 100.512° at 760 mm. The elevation of the boiling point of the water, then, is $100.512° - 100° = 0.512°$. It should be evident from these considerations that two gram-molecular weights of solute in 1000 g. of water give a solution which boils at $100° + (2 \times 0.512°) = 101.02$.

It should be emphasized that the extent to which the vapor pressure of a solvent is lowered and the boiling point is elevated depends upon the number of solute particles present in a given amount of solvent and not upon the mass or size of the particles. Properties of solutions which depend upon the number and not the kind of particles concerned are spoken of as **colligative** properties. It is not surprising to find that a mole of sodium chloride, which consists of two ions, causes nearly twice as great a rise in boiling point as does a mole of a nonelectrolyte. One mole of sugar contains 6.023×10^{23} particles (as molecules), whereas one mole of sodium chloride contains $2 \times 6.023 \times 10^{23}$ particles (as ions). Hence, calcium chloride ($CaCl_2$), which consists of three ions, causes nearly three times as great a rise in boiling point as does sugar. Why the elevation is not exactly twice (for NaCl) or three times (for $CaCl_2$) that of the molecular boiling point elevation is explained in Section 12.11.

11.23 Depression of the Freezing Point of a Solvent

It is a common observation that solutions freeze at lower temperatures than do pure liquids. We use aqueous solutions of various "antifreezes" such as alcohol and ethylene glycol in place of pure water in automobile radiators because they freeze at lower temperatures. Sea water, with its large salt content, freezes at a lower temperature than fresh water. The depression of the freezing point of a solvent by an added solute is a reflection of the vapor pressure lowering caused by the solute. In Section 9.11 we saw that the freezing point of a pure liquid is the temperature at which it is in equilibrium with its solid. A pure liquid and its solid have the same vapor pressure at the freezing point. Pure water and ice have the same vapor pressure at 0°, but the water in a solution has a lower vapor pressure than ice at this temperature. Consequently, if ice and an aqueous solution at 0° are placed in contact, the ice will melt. As the temperature is lowered below 0° the vapor pressure of the ice decreases more rapidly than does that of the water in the solution. At a temperature somewhat below 0°, the ice and the water have the same vapor pressure, and this is the temperature at which the solution and ice are in equilibrium; it is the freezing point of the solution.

It has been found that one gram-molecular weight of such nonelectrolytes as sucrose, glycerine, and alcohol, when dissolved in 1000 g. of water, gives solutions which freeze at $-1.86°$. A gram-formula weight of sodium chloride in 1000 g. of water will show nearly twice the freezing point depression characteristic of molecular compounds. Each ion individually produces about the same effect as a molecule upon the freezing point of a solution. In Section 12.11, we will consider why the lowering produced by sodium chloride is not exactly twice that produced by a similar amount of a nonelectrolyte.

11.24 Determination of Molecular Weights of Substances in Solution

We have seen in the preceding sections that the lowering of the vapor pressure and freezing point, and the elevation of the boiling point of a solution, depend upon the number of solute particles in a definite weight of solvent, and not upon the nature of the particles. It is evident, from the previous discussion, that the gram-molecular weight (6.023×10^{23} molecules) of any nonelectrolyte is that weight which, when dissolved in 1000 g. of water, lowers the freezing point 1.86°. Similarly, the gram-molecular weight of any nonvolatile nonelectrolyte is that weight which when dissolved in 1000 g. of water raises the boiling point 0.512°. Molecular weights of nonelectrolytes are often determined by observing the effect that they have upon the freezing point or boiling point of a solvent. Let us suppose that 5.00 g. of a nonelectrolyte dissolved in 100 g. of water lowers the freezing point of the water 0.31°. We know that the molecular weight of this substance is that weight which, when dissolved in 1000 g. of water, would lower the freezing point of water 1.86°. First calculate the weight of the substance that would lower the freezing point of 1000 g. of water 0.31°.

$$\frac{1000 \text{ g.}}{100 \text{ g.}} \times 5.00 \text{ g.} = 50.0 \text{ g.}$$

Now, calculate the weight of substance required to lower the freezing point of 1000 g. of water 1.86°; this weight will be the gram-molecular weight of the substance.

$$\frac{1.86°}{0.31°} \times 50.0 \text{ g.} = 300 \text{ g.}$$

Hence, the molecular weight of the substance is 300.

11.25 Molal Solutions

A solution which contains one mole of solute in 1000 g. of solvent is called a one-molal solution. This is another method of expressing concentration and different from the molar methods in that the final volume of the solution is usually greater than 1 liter. It is correct to say that a one-molal aqueous solution of a nonelectrolyte boils at 100.512° and freezes at $-1.86°$. Each solvent has a different **molal freezing-point depression constant** (K_f) and **molal boiling-point elevation constant** (K_b); these constants for several solvents are listed in Table 11·1.

TABLE 11·1 Boiling-Point Elevation and Freezing-Point Depression

Solvent	*Boiling Point (760 mm.), °C*	K_b	*Freezing Point °C*	K_f
Water	100.0	0.512	0	1.86
Acetic acid	118.1	3.07	16.6	3.9
Benzene	80.1	2.53	5.48	5.12
Chloroform	61.26	3.63	−63.5	4.68
Nitrobenzene	210.9	5.24	5.67	8.1

11.26 Osmotic Pressure of Solutions

When a solution and its pure solvent are separated by a semipermeable membrane (one through which the solvent but not the solute can pass), the pure solvent will diffuse through the membrane and dilute the solution. This process is known as osmosis. Actually the solvent diffuses through the membrane in both directions simultaneously; however, the rate of flow is greater from the pure solvent to the solution than in the opposite direction. The force causing diffusion of liquids, called **osmotic pressure,** may be measured in the following way: A piece of cellophane is securely fastened over the end of a thistle tube and the bowl of the thistle tube is filled with a concentrated sugar solution. When the thistle tube is inverted in a beaker of water (Fig. 11–7), water will flow through the membrane into the solution

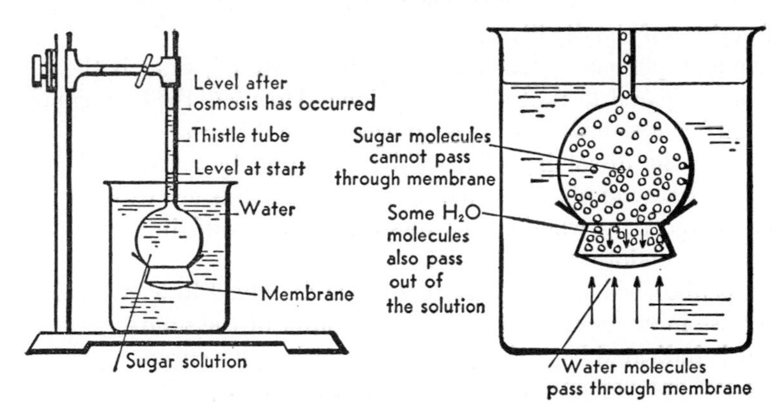

Fig. 11–7 Apparatus designed to demonstrate osmosis.

and a slow rise of liquid in the tube will be observed. If the cellophane is sufficiently strong to withstand the pressure and if the stem of the tube is long enough, the liquid will rise until its hydrostatic pressure is equal to the osmotic pressure. When this condition is achieved, the vapor pressure of the water in the solution under pressure equals the vapor pressure of the pure water outside the tube; it is a condition of equilibrium. The height to which the liquid will rise depends upon the concentration of the solution; the osmotic pressure is proportional to the number of solute particles in a definite volume of liquid. When gram-molecular weights of different nonelectrolytes are dissolved in 1000 g. of water, these solutions exert the same osmotic pressures, approximately 22.4 atmospheres.

QUESTIONS

1. How do solutions differ from compounds? from ordinary mixtures?
2. Explain the following terms as applied to solutions: solute, solvent, dilute, concentrated, and saturated.
3. What are the principal characteristics of solutions?
4. There being three different physical states in which matter can exist, how many different types of solutions are possible on the basis of this classification?
5. Why are the majority of chemical reactions carried out in solutions?
6. Account for the presence of tremendous quantities of soluble substances in sea water.
7. Relate the solubility of gases to (a) the nature of the gas and its solvent, (b) the pressure at which the gas is supplied to a liquid, (c) the temperature, and (d) the reaction of the gas with its solvent liquid.
8. How may many gases be expelled from their liquid solvents?
9. What is meant by "miscible" liquids? "immiscible" liquids? "partially miscible" liquids? Give examples.
10. How may the "boiling point" of a liquid-liquid solution be defined?
11. Describe the fractional distillation of a 50 per cent mixture of isopropyl alcohol (boiling point 82.5°) and water with regard to the composition of the first and last fractions of the distillate.
12. When a 50 per cent nitric acid solution is distilled, what is the composition of the vapor compared to that of the solution? How will the boiling point change as distillation is continued? What is an azeotropic mixture?
13. Why can the dissolving of a solid in a liquid be considered analogous to melting? What second change often occurs when solids are dissolved in liquids?
14. What determines whether the dissolving of a solid in a liquid will be an exothermic or an endothermic process?
15. Heat is absorbed when a certain solid is dissolved in a given liquid. How will an increase in temperature affect the solubility of the solid?
16. What is indicated by a sharp break in a solubility curve?
17. How can one demonstrate that a saturated solution in contact with excess solid solute is in "dynamic" equilibrium?
18. Distinguish between crystallization from a solution and crystallization from a melt.
19. Why is a supersaturated solution considered as an unstable system?
20. What factors determine the rate of solution of a solid in a liquid?
21. Define the following terms: molar solution, equivalent weight of a compound, and normal solution.

22. Compare the number of molecules in 1 molar solutions of sucrose ($C_{12}H_{22}O_{11}$) and glucose ($C_6H_{12}O_6$).

23. What is the advantage of the use of normal solutions over that of molar solutions?

24. What is meant by titration? end point?

25. Define the term "normal solution" in terms of milliequivalent weights and milliliters.

26. Explain the lowering of the vapor pressure of a liquid by a nonvolatile solute in terms of the kinetic-molecular theory.

27. State and explain Raoult's Law.

28. What are "colligative" properties? Give examples.

29. Why will ice melt when placed in an aqueous solution at 0°?

30. Why will a mole of sodium chloride depress the freezing point of 1000 g. of water about twice as much as a mole of glycerine?

31. Distinguish between molar and molal solutions.

32. What is meant by a molal freezing-point depression constant?

PROBLEMS

1. What weights of KNO_3 and water are contained in 138 g. of a 15.0 per cent solution of KNO_3 by weight? *Ans. 20.7 g. of KNO_3; 117.3 g. of H_2O*

2. How many grams of a 6.0 per cent KOH solution by weight are necessary to yield 120 grams of KOH? *Ans. 2000 g.*

3. How would you prepare 120.00 g. of a 4.00 per cent $BaCl_2$ solution by weight starting with $BaCl_2 \cdot 2\ H_2O$ and water?
Ans. Dissolve 5.63 g. of $BaCl_2 \cdot 2\ H_2O$ in 114.37 g. of water

4. How much sulfuric acid (95.0% by weight) is needed in the preparation of 1000 g. of a 10.0% solution of the acid by weight? *Ans. 105 g.*

5. The density of a 25.0% by weight solution of aqueous ammonia is 0.910 g./ml. What volume of ammonia gas (S.T.P.) would be required in the preparation of 200 ml. of this solution? *Ans. 59.8 l.*

6. How many grams of HCl are contained in 65.0 ml. of hydrochloric acid of specific gravity 1.19 and containing 37.2% HCl by weight? *Ans. 28.8 g.*

7. Calculate the volume of sulfuric acid of specific gravity 1.070 and containing 10.00% H_2SO_4 by weight, that would contain 115.0 g. of pure H_2SO_4.
Ans. 1,075 ml.

8. It is desired to prepare 1.00 liter of a 10.0% solution of NaOH by weight from solid NaOH of 95.0% purity by weight. What weight of the solid NaOH would be required? The specific gravity of 10.0% NaOH at 25° is 1.109.
Ans. 117 g.

9. Concentrated hydrochloric acid is 37.0% HCl by weight and has a specific gravity of 1.19. What volume of this acid must be diluted to one liter to produce a 0.100 N solution of the acid? *Ans. 8.29 ml.*

10. How many liters of HCl measured at S.T.P. are required in the preparation of 2000 ml. of 2.00 M hydrochloric acid? *Ans. 89.6 l.*

11. Calculate the weight of solute in each of the following solutions:

(a) 2.50 l. of 0.750 M HNO_3. *Ans. 118 g.*
(b) 300 ml. of 0.0400 M $C_{12}H_{22}O_{11}$. *Ans. 4.10 g.*
(c) 10.0 ml. of 0.0300 M $Ca(OH)_2$. *Ans. 0.0222 g.*
(d) 16.80 l. of 1.75 M K_2SO_4. *Ans. 5,120 g.*

12. What volume of 0.10 M potassium sulfate would contain 75 g. of potassium sulfate? *Ans. 4.3 l.*

13. Calculate the molarity of each of the following solutions:

(a) 4.5 g. of H_2SO_4 in 1.0 liter of solution. *Ans. 0.046 M*
(b) 130 g. of NaOH in 5.0 liters of solution. *Ans. 0.65 M*
(c) 8.0 g. of HCl in 75 ml. of solution. *Ans. 2.9 M*
(d) 40.0 mg. of HNO_3 in 10.0 ml. of solution. *Ans. 0.0635 M*
(e) 7.0 millimoles of HI in 100 ml. of solution. *Ans. 0.070 M*

14. Calculate the molarity of a solution of potassium permanganate, $KMnO_4$, for which the density is 1.04 g./ml. and which contains 5.00% of the salt by weight. *Ans. 0.329 M*

15. Calculate the molarity of a 500 ml. volume of solution containing 2.5 g. of 98.0% phosphoric acid, H_3PO_4. *Ans. 0.050 M*

16. A 12.0 g. sample of blue vitriol, $CuSO_4 \cdot 5\ H_2O$, is dissolved in 100 g. of water. Calculate the percentage by weight of $CuSO_4$ in the solution and the molality of the solution in terms of $CuSO_4$. *Ans. 6.85%; 0.463 molal*

17. A 10.0% solution of K_2CO_3 by weight has a specific gravity of 1.09. Calculate the molarity of the solution. *Ans. 0.789 M*

18. A 600 ml. volume of gaseous ammonia measured at 27.0° and 764 mm. pressure was absorbed in 100 ml. of water. How many ml. of 0.0100 N hydrochloric acid would be required in the neutralization of this aqueous ammonia, and what would be its normality? Assume no change in volume when the gaseous ammonia is added to the water. *Ans. 2,450 ml.; 0.245 N*

19. How many moles of sodium hydroxide would be required to react with all the hydrogen ions from:

(a) 2 moles of HCl? *Ans. 2 moles*
(b) 1 mole of H_2SO_4? *Ans. 2 moles*
(c) 0.5 mole of H_3PO_4? *Ans. 1.5 moles*

20. It is desired to produce 1.000 liter of 0.500 N nitric acid by diluting 10.00 N nitric acid. Calculate the volume of the concentrated acid and the volume of water required in the dilution. *Ans. 50 ml. of HNO_3; 950 ml. of H_2O*

21. What weight of $K_4Fe(CN)_6$ is there in 100 ml. of a 0.0500 M solution of the salt? *Ans. 1.84 g.*

22. What is the normality of a 70.0% aqueous solution of sulfuric acid, for which the specific gravity is 1.610? *Ans. 23.0 N*

23. A solution of sodium carbonate having a volume of 300 ml. contains 4.032 g. of $Na_2CO_3 \cdot 10\ H_2O$. Calculate the normality of this solution. *Ans. 0.0940 N*

24. It is desired to prepare 4.00 l. of 3.00 N sulfuric acid. How many ml. of 96.0% acid by weight (specific gravity, 1.84) would be required? *Ans. 333 ml.*

25. How many liters of 1.50% KOH solution by weight (specific gravity, 1.012) can be obtained by diluting 0.500 liter of 30.0% KOH by weight (specific gravity, 1.288)? *Ans.* *12.7 l.*

26. What is the molarity of a solution which is prepared by dissolving 10.0 g. of P_4O_{10} in sufficient water to make 500 ml. of solution? Assume that the product of the reaction of P_4O_{10} with water is H_3PO_4 (orthophosphoric acid). Would it make a difference in the answer if the product of the reaction were HPO_3 (metaphosphoric acid)? Explain. *Ans.* *0.281 M*

27. Equal volumes of 1.40 N HNO_3 and 0.70 N KOH are mixed. What is the normality of the resulting solution with regard to each of its solutes?

Ans. *0.35 N in KNO_3 and 0.35 N in HNO_3*

28. A standard solution of $Ba(OH)_2$ has a molarity of 0.1055. What volume of 0.211 M nitric acid would be required in the neutralization of 10.5 ml. of the $Ba(OH)_2$ solution? *Ans.* *10.5 ml.*

29. Calculate the gram-equivalent weight of each of the reactants in the following reactions:

(a) $HCl + NaOH \rightarrow NaCl + H_2O$ *Ans.* *HCl, 36.5 g.; NaOH, 40.0 g.*

(b) $2\ LiOH + H_2SO_4 \rightarrow Li_2SO_4 + 2\ H_2O$

Ans. *LiOH, 23.9 g.; H_2SO_4, 49.0 g.*

(c) $Ba(OH)_2 + 2\ HClO_4 \rightarrow Ba(ClO_4)_2 + 2\ H_2O$

Ans. *$Ba(OH)_2$, 85.7 g.; $HClO_4$, 100.5 g.*

(d) $NaOH + NaH_2PO_4 \rightarrow Na_2HPO_4 + H_2O$

Ans. *NaOH, 40.0 g.; NaH_2PO_4, 120.0 g.*

(e) $AgNO_3 + KI \rightarrow \underline{AgI} + KNO_3$ *Ans.* *$AgNO_3$, 169.9 g.; KI, 166.0 g.*

(f) $Na_2SO_4 + BaCl_2 \rightarrow \underline{BaSO_4} + 2\ NaCl$

Ans. *Na_2SO_4, 71.0 g.; $BaCl_2$, 104.1 g.*

(g) $KOH + H_2SO_3 \rightarrow KHSO_3 + H_2O$ *Ans.* *KOH, 56.1 g.; H_2SO_3, 82.0 g.*

(h) $2\ Al(OH)_3 + 3\ H_2SO_4 \rightarrow Al_2(SO_4)_3 + 6\ H_2O$

Ans. *$Al(OH)_3$, 26.0 g.; H_2SO_4, 49.0 g.*

30. Calculate the normality of each of the following solutions:

(a) 10 gram-equivalent weights of NaOH in 5.0 liters of solution.

Ans. *2.0 N*

(b) 0.50 gram-equivalent weight of H_2SO_4 in 0.75 liter of solution.

Ans. *0.67 N*

(c) 1.5 milligram-equivalent weights of $CaCl_2$ in 10 ml. of solution.

Ans. *0.15 N*

(d) 35.0 milligram-equivalent weights of K_2SO_4 in 75 ml. of solution.

Ans. *0.47 N*

31. (a) Calculate the weight of pure H_2SO_4 required in the preparation of 800 ml. of 1.50 N acid. (b) What would be the molarity of this solution?

Ans. *(a) 58.8 g. (b) 0.75 M*

32. Equal volumes of 0.50 M NaOH and 0.40 M HCl are mixed. Calculate the molarity of the resulting solution with regard to each of its solutes.

Ans. *0.05 M in NaOH; 0.20 M in NaCl*

33. What volume of a 0.50 M solution of hydrobromic acid would be required to neutralize completely 1.00 liter of 0.75 M calcium hydroxide? *Ans. 3.0 l.*

34. Calculate the volume of 0.10 N hydrochloric acid necessary to precipitate the silver contained in 50.0 ml. of 0.050 N $AgNO_3$. ($Ag^+ + Cl^- \rightarrow AgCl$)

Ans. 25 ml.

35. What volume of 0.100 N HCl would be required in the precipitation of the silver in 0.100 g. of 98.0% purity $AgNO_3$? *Ans. 5.77 ml.*

36. A mixture of NaCl and KBr weighing 0.80 g. was dissolved in water and then the halides were precipitated as silver salts, weighing together 1.51 g. Calculate the composition of the original mixture. *Ans. 0.28 g. of NaCl; 0.52 g. of KBr*

37. A standard acid solution has a normality of 1.40. What volume of 0.800 N base would be required in the complete neutralization of 30.0 ml. of the acid?

Ans. 52.5 ml.

38. What volume of 0.500 N HCl would be required in a complete reaction with 1.00 g. of sodium hydrogen carbonate? ($NaHCO_3 + HCl \rightarrow NaCl + CO_2 + H_2O$)

Ans. 23.8 ml.

39. A solution of sulfuric acid contains 5.64 mg. of H_2SO_4 per ml. of solution. What is the normality of the solution? *Ans. 0.115 N*

40. How much water must be added to 200 g. of 65.0% HNO_3 (specific gravity, 1.40) to form a 0.200 N solution of the acid? *Ans. 10.2 l.*

41. The sulfate in 50.0 ml. of dilute sulfuric acid was precipitated using an excess of barium chloride. The weight of $BaSO_4$ formed was 0.950 g. Calculate the normality of the sulfuric acid solution. *Ans. 0.163 N*

42. A 1.50 g. sample of an acid, H_2X, required 12.0 ml. of KOH solution for neutralization of all the hydrogen ion. Exactly 14.2 ml. of this same KOH solution was found to neutralize 10.0 ml. of 1.50 N H_2SO_4. Calculate the molecular weight of H_2X. *Ans. 237*

43. How would you prepare a 2.50 molal aqueous solution of glycerine ($C_3H_8O_3$)? What would be the freezing point of this solution?

Ans. Dissolve 230 g. of glycerine in 1000 g. of water; −4.65° C.

44. A sample of an organic compound (nonelectrolyte) weighing 1.350 g. lowered the freezing point of 10.00 g. of benzene by 2.56°. The K_f of benzene is 5.12°. Calculate the molecular weight of the organic compound. *Ans. 270*

45. Twelve grams of a nonelectrolyte were dissolved in 60.0 g. of water. The solution freezes at −1.88° C. Calculate the molecular weight of the substance.

Ans. 198

46. What would be the approximate freezing point of a 0.30 molal aqueous solution of sodium bromide? *Ans. −1.1° C.*

47. Which of the following compounds would serve most effectively as "antifreeze" agents when equal weights are employed: alcohol, C_2H_5OH; glycerine, $C_3H_8O_3$; or glucose, $C_6H_{12}O_6$? *Ans. Alcohol*

48. What would be the boiling point, at 760 mm., of a solution containing 180.0 g. of sucrose ($C_{12}H_{22}O_{11}$) in 500.0 g. of water? *Ans. 100.5°*

49. Calculate the boiling point elevation of 100 g. of water containing 0.100 mole of NaCl, 0.200/mole of Na_2SO_4, and 0.300/mole of $MgCl_2$, assuming complete dissociation of these electrolytes. (K_b for water is 0.512°.) *Ans. 8.70°*

50. If 68.40 g. of sugar ($C_{12}H_{22}O_{11}$) is dissolved in 500.0 g. of water, what is (a) the freezing point of the solution and (b) the boiling point of the solution at 760 mm. pressure? (K_f for water is 1.86° and K_b for water is 0.512°.)

Ans. (*a*) *−0.74°;* (*b*) *100.2°*

51. How many grams of methyl alcohol, CH_3OH, must be added to a 10.00 liter volume of water to prevent freezing at −10.00°? How many grams of ethylene glycol, $C_2H_4(OH)_2$, would be required?

Ans. *1,720 g. of* CH_3OH*; 3,340 g. of* $C_2H_4(OH)_2$

52. If 15.0 g. of the nonelectrolyte $C_6H_4Br_2$ is dissolved in 150 g. of benzene, what is (a) the freezing point of the solution and (b) the boiling point of the solution at 760 mm.? (For benzene, the freezing point is 5.48°, the boiling point is 80.1°, K_f is 5.12°, and K_b is 2.53°.) *Ans.* (*a*) *3.31°;* (*b*) *81.2°*

53. A solution which is 15.0% by weight contains 200 g. of solute per liter of solution. The molecular weight of the solute is 50.0. For each mole of solute, 2 N electrons are involved in the reaction in which the solution is to be utilized (where N is Avogadro's number). Calculate (a) the density, (b) the molarity, (c) the molality, and (d) the normality of the solution.

Ans. (*a*) *1.33 g./ml.;* (*b*) *4.00 molar;* (*c*) *3.53 molal;* (*d*) *8.00 normal*

REFERENCE

"Gram-Equivalent Weights," W. B. Meldrum, *J. Chem. Educ.*, 32 (1) 48 (1955).

CHAPTER TWELVE

Solutions of Electrolytes

12.1 Electrolytes and Nonelectrolytes

Substances that give aqueous solutions which conduct an electric current are known as **electrolytes.** The process of conducting an electric current through a solution, which results in the decomposition of the electrolyte or the solvent, is called electrolysis. Most electrolytes are acids, bases, or salts. Aqueous solutions of substances such as sugar and alcohol do not conduct an electric current. Substances that give nonconducting solutions are called **nonelectrolytes.**

The classification of substances as electrolytes and nonelectrolytes may be carried out experimentally by setting up a simple electrolytic cell as shown in Fig. 12–1.

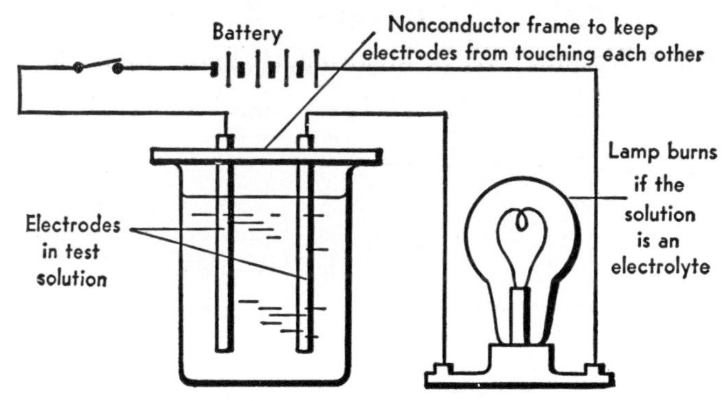

Fig. 12–1 Apparatus for determining the conductivity of solutions.

The terminals of a storage battery or a 110 volt circuit (preferably direct current) are connected through an electric lamp to two electrodes in a beaker. When the beaker is filled with pure water, only a very slight current flows through the circuit, not even enough to cause the electric lamp to emit light. If, however, hydrochloric acid, sodium hydroxide, or sodium chloride is placed in the beaker, the lamp will glow brightly. When an aqueous solution of sugar, alcohol, or glycerine is tested, the lamp does not glow.

12.2 Strong and Weak Electrolytes

If the beaker in Fig. 12–1 is filled with a 0.1 N solution of hydrochloric acid, the lamp in the electrolytic circuit will glow brightly, showing that the solution is a good conductor of electricity. The same is true of 0.1 N solutions of nitric and sulfuric acids, as well as bases such as potassium, sodium, and barium hydroxides. Most salts behave in a similar fashion. Substances whose aqueous solutions are good conductors of electricity are known as **strong electrolytes.** When a 0.1 N solution of acetic acid or ammonium hydroxide is placed in the beaker, it is found that the lamp glows much less brightly than it does with acids like hydrochloric or bases like sodium hydroxide. Substances whose aqueous solutions are poor conductors of electricity are called **weak electrolytes.**

12.3 Theory of Electrolytes

Arrhenius, a Swedish chemist, in 1887 first successfully explained electrolytic conduction, together with certain unique properties of acids, bases, and salts. His theory explained why acids, bases, and salts (electrolytes) dissolved in water affect the vapor pressure, boiling point, freezing point, and osmotic pressure of water more than do nonelectrolytes. Although Arrhenius' theory has since been modified in the light of our present knowledge of atomic structure and chemical bonding, the modern theory of electrolytes embodies most of the principal postulates of the Arrhenius theory.

According to the modern theory, a water solution of an electrolyte contains independent electrically charged positive and negative ions. We may define an **ion** as an atom or group of atoms carrying one or more electrical charges. The positively charged ions migrate toward the negative electrode during electrolysis and are called **cations.** The negatively charged ions migrate toward the positive electrode during electrolytic conduction and are spoken of as **anions.** The movement of the ions toward the electrode of opposite charge during electrolysis accounts for electrolytic conduction. The total number of positive charges on the ions in solution is just equal to the total number of negative charges on the ions. The solutions of electrolytes will therefore be electrically neutral. A water solution of a nonelectrolyte (a compound that does not conduct an electric current) does not contain ions.

The migration of ions during electrolytic conduction can be demonstrated in a striking manner by the following experiment. A U-tube (Fig. 12–2) is partially filled with a solution of potassium nitrate, which is colorless, and which has been acidified with a few drops of sulfuric acid. Then a solution of copper (II) permanganate is carefully introduced into the bottom of the U-tube so as to prevent mixing of the two solutions. When the electrical circuit is closed, the blue copper (II) ions (Cu^{++}) begin to migrate through the colorless potassium nitrate toward the negative electrode, and the purple permanganate ions (MnO_4^-) begin to migrate toward the positive electrode. This ex-

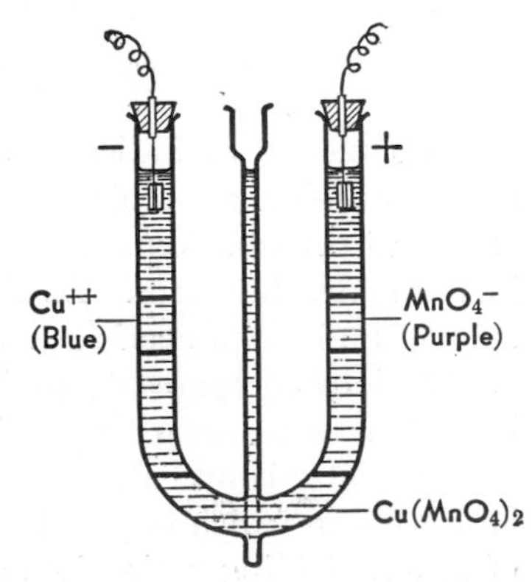

Fig. 12–2 Ions travel toward the electrodes.

periment shows that the electric current is carried by the ions, and that the ions of opposite charge exist independently in the solution.

12.4 Extent of Ionization of Electrolytes

A salt is composed of ions that break away from their crystal lattice when dissolved in water. For example, sodium chloride consists of sodium ions and chloride ions held together in the crystal by strong electrostatic forces. These ions separate when sodium chloride dissolves and become distributed in the solution.

$$\underset{\text{(crystalline)}}{\overset{+}{\text{Na}}\overset{-}{\text{Cl}}} \xrightarrow{H_2O} Na^+ + Cl^-$$

The ions in the crystal lattice of certain metal hydroxides, such as sodium hydroxide, also separate when dissolved in water.

$$\underset{\text{(crystalline)}}{\overset{+}{\text{Na}}\overset{-}{\text{OH}}} \xrightarrow{H_2O} Na^+ + OH^-$$

However, certain covalent substances form ions by reacting with water; i.e., they ionize when brought into contact with water. Hydrogen chloride, which contains polar covalent molecules, ionizes according to the equation

$$HCl + H_2O \rightarrow H_3O^+ + Cl^-$$

According to the theory of electrolytes, if the solution is a good conductor of electricity, the solute consists entirely or principally of ions and if the solution is a poor conductor, the solute consists principally of molecules. Strong electrolytes such as hydrochloric, nitric, and sulfuric acids are virtually completely ionized in dilute aqueous solutions. Most salts and soluble metal hydroxides are also strong electrolytes. Only a small fraction of the molecules of a weak electrolyte undergo, at any one time, ionization in water. The partial ionization of acetic acid, a weak electrolyte, is expressed by the following equation

$$CH_3COOH + H_2O \rightleftharpoons H_3O^+ + CH_3COO^-$$

The double arrow indicates that a definite equilibrium exists between the ions and the un-ionized molecules of acetic acid. A 0.1 M solution of acetic acid is only 1.34 per cent ionized at 25° C. This means that 98.66 per cent of the acid is in the molecular form. As the solution is diluted, the relative number of molecules of un-ionized acetic acid decreases and the relative number of hydronium and acetate ions compared to un-ionized acetic acid increases; i.e., the percentage of ionization increases with dilution.

Pure water is an extremely poor conductor of electricity, indicating very slight ionization in which one molecule of water gives up a proton to another molecule of water, yielding hydronium and hydroxide ions.

$$H_2O + H_2O \rightleftharpoons H_3O^+ + OH^-$$

12.5 Properties of Ions

The chemical properties of an ion are quite different from those of the electrically neutral atom or molecule. Sodium ions and chloride ions are colorless, nonpoisonous, and inert toward water (though they can form unstable hydrated ions of the type described in Section 12.7). Metallic sodium, however, is a silvery-white substance which reacts violently with water, forming hydrogen gas and a solution of the strong base, sodium hydroxide; molecular chlorine, a poisonous greenish-yellow gas, reacts with water forming hypochlorous and hydrochloric acids.

The difference in properties between ions and neutral atoms or molecules is due to differences in electronic structures. Ions have more or fewer orbital electrons than the neutral atoms or molecules from which they are formed. The outer electron shell of the sodium atom contains one electron. When this electron is lost to another atom, such as chlorine, a positive sodium ion with the stable configuration of an inert gas results. Similarly, a neutral chlorine atom with seven electrons in its outside shell assumes the stable electron configuration of a rare gas by gaining an electron to become a negative ion (Section 4.2).

12.6 The Effect of Electrolytes on the Colligative Properties of Solutions

In Chapter 11, we learned that the effect of nonelectrolytes on the vapor pressure, boiling point, freezing point, and osmotic pressure of water is dependent only upon the number, and not on the kind, of molecules present. One mole of any nonelectrolyte in solution in 1000 g. of water produces the same lowering of the freezing point, 1.86° C, as one mole of any other nonelectrolyte because one mole of any nonelectrolyte contains the same number of molecules (6.023×10^{23}). However, the molal lowering of the freezing point produced by electrolytes is much greater than for nonelectrolytes. The water in a solution which contains one mole of sodium chloride dissolved in 1000 g. of water freezes at $-3.37°$. This lowering of the freezing point of water is $3.37 \div 1.86 = 1.81$ times the molal depression for a nonelectrolyte (Section 12.11). This means that one mole of an electrolyte produces more than 6.023×10^{23} solute particles. Acids, bases, and salts behave in this fashion when placed in solution.

12.7 Mechanism of Dissolution of Ionic Compounds

Ionic compounds are ionized in the solid state. Since the ions in a crystal of an ionic compound cannot move from their crystal lattice positions due to strong electrostatic forces of attraction, the ions are said to be associated. Crystalline ionic compounds do not conduct an electric current although they are 100 per cent ionized. When the ionic solid melts, the forces which hold the ions in their lattice positions are overcome, and the ions become able to move about. Liquids composed of ions, such as molten sodium chloride, conduct an electric current when placed in an electrolytic cell.

The process of dissolution of ionic compounds in water is essentially one of separation of the ions. Water reduces the strong electrostatic forces between the ions and thereby brings about their separation. Let us consider the dissolution of potassium chloride in water. The hydrogen (positive) side of the polar water molecule is strongly attracted to the negative chloride ion, and the oxygen (negative) side of the water molecule is strongly attracted to the positive potassium ion. We may picture the water molecules as surrounding individual K^+ and Cl^- ions at the surface of the crystal and penetrating between them, thereby reducing the strong interionic forces of attraction which bind them together in the crystal and permitting them to move off into the water as hydrated ions (Fig. 12–3). Several

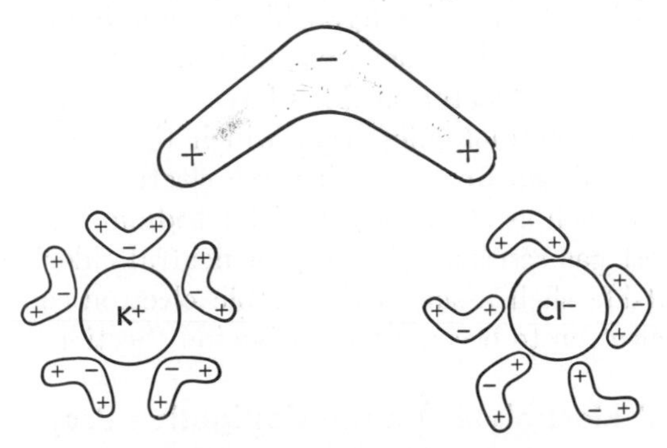

Fig. 12–3 At the top is a symbol for a polarized water molecule. Below is shown how water molecules are thought to be attracted to positive and negative ions.

water molecules become associated with each ion in solution as a result of this **ion-dipole electrostatic attraction.** The increase in the size of the ions brought about by hydration leads to greater effective distances between oppositely charged ions and a reduction in interionic attraction. In addition, water is a good insulator (it has a high dielectric constant) which further reduces the electrostatic attraction between the ions.

Ionic compounds usually dissolve only in polar solvents in which the polar solvent molecules can solvate and insulate the ions in a manner similar to that described for the dissolution of potassium chloride in water. In general, the higher the dielectric constant of the solvent, the greater is the solubility of an ionic compound. This phenomenon is strikingly illustrated in the data of Table 12·1, as regards the

TABLE 12·1 The Solubility of Sodium Chloride and the Dielectric Constant of the Solvent

Solvent	*Solubility of sodium chloride in grams per 100 g. of solvent* (25°)	*Dielectric constant of the solvent*
Water, H_2O	36.12	80.0
Methyl alcohol, CH_3OH	1.3	33.1
Carbon tetrachloride, CCl_4	0.00	2.2

solubility of sodium chloride in water, methyl alcohol, and carbon tetrachloride. Ionic substances in general do not dissolve appreciably in nonpolar solvents, such as benzene or carbon tetrachloride, because the nonpolar solvent molecules are not strongly attracted to ions, and nonpolar solvents have low dielectric constants.

12.8 Solubility of Salts

The solubility of an ionic compound in water is determined for the most part by (1) the magnitude of the crystal forces and (2) the energy of hydration of the ions. A soluble salt is one for which the attraction of the ions for water molecules is greater than the attraction of the oppositely charged ions for each other within the crystal, or one for which the energy of hydration is greater than the crystal lattice energy. On the other hand, a slightly soluble salt is characterized by strong crystal forces and slight tendency of the ions to hydrate.

In any attempt to predict the solubility of a salt, one must take into account the properties of ions that determine the magnitude of the crystal forces and the energy of hydration of the ions. Such predictions become quite involved as can readily be seen from a consideration of the following generalizations.

1. *Solubility and Ionic Size.* Both crystal forces and energy of hydration increase with decrease in ionic size, but at different rates. Thus it is difficult to find any consistent relationship between ionic radii and solubility of ionic salts. For example, note the solubilities of the alkali metal chlorides (Table 12·2).

TABLE 12·2 Solubility of Alkali Chlorides in Grams per 100 g. of Water at 0°

	LiCl	*NaCl*	*KCl*	*RbCl*	*CsCl*
Radius of M^+, Å	0.60	0.95	1.33	1.48	1.69
Solubility	67	35.7	27.6	77.0	161.4

2. *Solubility and Size of Ionic Charge.* With increasing ionic charge, the crystal forces increase much more rapidly than the energy of hydration of the ions. Thus solubility of ionic salts decreases very sharply as the ionic charge increases. Examples are given in Table 12·3.

TABLE 12·3 Solubility versus Ionic Charge—Interionic Distances Relatively Constant

Ionic charge	+1, −1	+2, −1	+2, −2	+3, −2
Compound	LiF	MgF_2	MgO	Al_2O_3
Interionic distance, Å	1.96	2.01	2.05	1.90
Solubility, moles/liter	4.6×10^{-2}	1.7×10^{-3}	1.5×10^{-4}	insoluble

3. *Solubility and Electronic Structure of the Cation.* The crystal forces and energy of hydration are both greater for cations with 18 electrons in the outer shell than for those with 8. The sodium ion has 8 electrons and the silver ion 18 electrons, respectively, in their outer shells. The solubility in grams per 100 grams of water of NaF is 4.0, while that of AgF is 182.0. On the other hand, NaCl has a solubility of 35.7, while that of AgCl is 8.9×10^{-5} g. per 100 g. of water. It is obvious, as indicated by these examples, that it is difficult to predict the solubility of a metallic compound on the basis of the electronic structure of its cation.

Knowledge of the solubilities of metallic compounds is nevertheless very important and useful to the student and chemist. Memorization of the solubility of individual compounds is difficult, laborious, and unnecessary. A simple and worthwhile method of acquiring knowledge of solubilities is to learn the generalizations given in the following section.

12.9 Generalizations on the Solubilities of Common Metallic Compounds

It should be remembered that these generalizations are for the simple compounds of the more common metals, there being many exceptions when the less common metals and complex compounds are considered.

1. Most nitrates and acetates are soluble in water; silver acetate, chromium (II) acetate, and mercury (I) acetate are slightly soluble; bismuth acetate hydrolyzes to bismuthyl acetate, $BiOC_2H_3O_2$, insoluble in water.
2. All chlorates are water soluble; potassium chlorate is slightly soluble.
3. All chlorides are soluble except those of mercury (I), silver, lead, and copper (I) ions; lead chloride is soluble in hot water.
4. All sulfates, except those of strontium, barium, and lead are soluble; calcium sulfate and silver sulfate are slightly soluble.
5. Carbonates, phosphates, borates, arsenates, and arsenites, except those of ammonium and the alkali metals, are insoluble.
6. The sulfides of ammonium and the alkali metals are soluble and other sulfides are insoluble; the alkaline earth metal sulfides are hydrolyzed in water.
7. The hydroxides of sodium, potassium, ammonium, barium, and strontium are soluble and other hydroxides are insoluble; calcium hydroxide is slightly soluble.

12.10 Mechanism of Dissolution and Ionization of Molecular Substances

We saw in Chapter 4 that a hydrogen atom combines with a chlorine atom with the formation of a covalent bond.

$$\mathrm{H\cdot} \quad + \quad \mathrm{{}^{\times}\overset{\times\times}{\underset{\times\times}{Cl}}{}^{\times}_{\times}} \quad \rightarrow \quad \mathrm{H{}^{\times}_{\bullet}\overset{\times\times}{\underset{\times\times}{Cl}}{}^{\times}_{\times}}$$

However, the electron pair involved in the covalent bond is not shared equally between the hydrogen and chlorine atoms. The chlorine atom attracts the electrons more strongly than does the hydrogen due to the greater electronegativity of the chlorine. The hydrogen chloride bond is therefore somewhat polar, with the hydrogen considered as being positive and the chlorine negative. Since dry hydrogen chloride in the liquid state does not conduct an electric current, we conclude that no ions are present. But in aqueous solution, ions are formed because hydrogen chloride reacts with water. The aqueous solution that results conducts electricity and possesses acidic properties. Since no ionization of HCl occurs in such nonpolar solvents as benzene, the polar water molecules must play an important role in bringing about ionization.

The ionization of hydrogen chloride in water may be represented by the following equation in which electronic formulas are employed to help elucidate the mechanism:

$$\begin{matrix} \begin{matrix}\mathrm{H}{:}\ddot{\mathrm{O}}{:} \\ \mathrm{H}\end{matrix} & + & \mathrm{H}{:}\underset{\cdot\cdot}{\ddot{\mathrm{Cl}}}{:} & \rightarrow & \left[\begin{matrix}\mathrm{H}{:}\ddot{\mathrm{O}}{:}\mathrm{H} \\ \mathrm{H}\end{matrix}\right]^{+} & + & \left[{:}\underset{\cdot\cdot}{\ddot{\mathrm{Cl}}}{:}\right]^{-} \\ \overset{+\qquad -}{\longrightarrow} & & \overset{+\qquad -}{\longrightarrow} & & & & \\ \text{Polar molecule} & & \text{Polar molecule} & & \text{Positive ion} & & \text{Negative ion} \end{matrix}$$

The polar water molecule removes a proton from the polar hydrogen chloride molecule, forming the hydronium ion (H_3O^+) and the chloride ion (Cl^-). Note that the pair of electrons that bonded the hydrogen and chlorine together in the HCl molecule remains with the chlorine, making it a chloride ion. Either of the two unshared pairs of electrons on the water molecule can be shared with the proton, and the proton may pass quite readily from one molecule of water to another. It has been shown by X-ray analysis that crystalline perchloric acid monohydrate ($HClO_4 \cdot H_2O$) is actually ionic and that the two ions are H_3O^+ and ClO_4^-. Both the hydronium ions and chloride ions resulting from the ionization of hydrogen chloride in water are undoubtedly hydrated in solution as are all other ions. All molecular acids are polar substances and ionize in solution in the same manner as does hydrogen chloride.

Many substances which are composed of molecules dissolve in water as hydrated molecules rather than as hydrated ions. In most instances, however, a fraction of the hydrated molecules undergo ionization. For example, ammonia (NH_3), which is a polar molecule, dissolves extensively in water as hydrated ammonia molecules. Ionization takes place to a slight degree under ordinary conditions.

$$\begin{matrix}\mathrm{H} \\ \mathrm{H}{:}\ddot{\mathrm{N}}{:} \\ \mathrm{H}\end{matrix} \; + \; \begin{matrix}\mathrm{H}{:}\ddot{\mathrm{O}}{:} \\ \mathrm{H}\end{matrix} \; \rightleftarrows \; \left[\begin{matrix}\mathrm{H} \\ \mathrm{H}{:}\ddot{\mathrm{N}}{:}\mathrm{H} \\ \mathrm{H}\end{matrix}\right]^{+} \; + \; \left[{:}\underset{\cdot\cdot}{\ddot{\mathrm{O}}}{:}\mathrm{H}\right]^{-}$$

A proton is transferred from a water molecule to an ammonia molecule forming ammonium ions and hydroxide ions. Because the OH^- holds the proton more strongly than NH_3, the reaction proceeds only to the extent of 1.34 per cent in a 0.1 M solution of the gas at 25° C. This small degree of ionization classifies ammonia as a weak base.

Weak acids such as acetic (CH_3COOH), nitrous (HNO_2), and hydrocyanic

(HCN) are also soluble in water through the hydration process, but, at any one time, only a small fraction of their hydrated polar molecules undergo ionization.

$$CH_3COOH + H_2O \rightleftharpoons H_3O^+ + CH_3COO^-$$
$$HNO_2 + H_2O \rightleftharpoons H_3O^+ + NO_2^-$$
$$HCN + H_2O \rightleftharpoons H_3O^+ + CN^-$$

Certain nonpolar inorganic compounds readily dissolve in water by forming hydrated molecules. Among these compounds are the halides and cyanides of mercury, cadmium, and zinc. Molecules of these compounds have no dipole moments even though the bonds are of the polar covalent type. Their centers of positive and negative electric charge coincide because of a high degree of molecular symmetry, as in Cl—Hg—Cl. There is, however, a net positive electric charge on the mercury atom and net negative charges on the chlorine atoms of $HgCl_2$. Water dipoles are attracted to these points of electric charge concentration and the molecule becomes hydrated. A small fraction of the bonds between mercury and chlorine break with the formation of a few hydrated mercury (II) ions and hydrated chloride ions. Compounds of this type are classed as weak electrolytes.

Ionization, then, may be defined as a reaction between a solute and solvent which results in the formation of ions. Sodium chloride is ionic in the solid state and dissolution in water merely brings about a separation of the ions. Pure hydrogen chloride is molecular and reaction with water results in the formation of ions.

12.11 Ion Activities

In 1923 Peter J. W. Debye and Erich Hückel accepted the idea that strong electrolytes are completely dissociated or ionized in aqueous solution and proposed a theory to explain the *apparent* incomplete dissociation or ionization of strong electrolytes. If a strong electrolyte, such as sodium chloride, is completely dissociated in aqueous solution, it should produce twice the lowering of the freezing point of water and twice the elevation of the boiling point as that caused by an equal molal concentration of a nonelectrolyte, since it gives two ions per mole in solution. A mole of sodium chloride lowers the freezing point of water only 1.81 times as much as a nonelectrolyte would, instead of twice as much. A similar discrepancy occurs in the boiling point elevation. Debye and Hückel accounted for these discrepancies between calculated and observed values for the colligative properties of solutions of electrolytes by the following theory.

Although the forces of interionic attraction in aqueous solution are very greatly reduced by hydration of the ions and the insulating action of the polar solvent, they are not completely absent. The **residual interionic forces of attraction** prevent the ions from behaving as totally independent particles in so far as the colligative properties of the solution or their function as carriers of the electric current are concerned (Fig. 12–4). Thus the **activities** of the ions as independent units or their "effective concentrations" are less than indicated by their actual concentrations. The more dilute the solution, the greater the separation of oppositely charged ions and the less the residual interionic attraction. Thus, in extremely

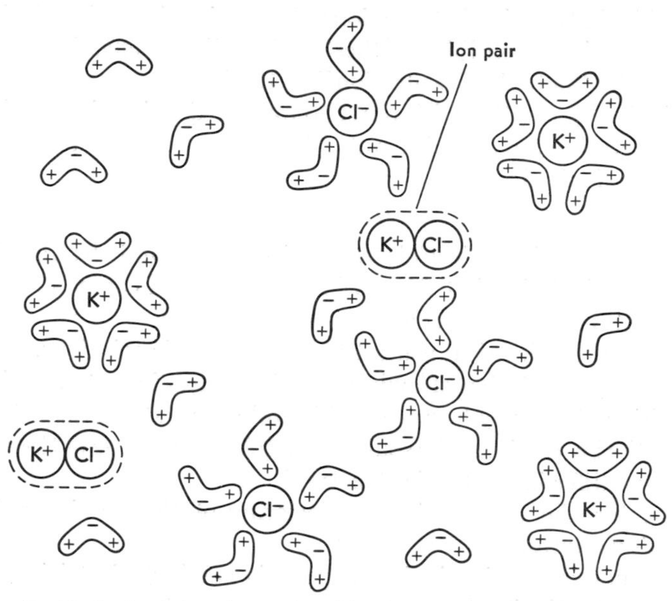

Fig. 12–4 A solution of potassium chloride in water is thought to consist of a mixture as indicated in this diagram.

dilute solutions the effective concentrations of the ions (activities) are essentially equal to the actual concentrations.

The factor by which the actual ion concentration must be multiplied to obtain the activity of the ion is called the **activity coefficient.**

$$\text{activity} = f \times \text{concentration}$$

The activity coefficient (f) approaches unity with increasing dilution. For a 0.100 molal solution of sodium chloride, the activity coefficient has a value of 0.778 at 25.0° C., and the activity of the ions is 0.0778 molal.

$$a = f \times \text{concentration}$$
$$a = 0.778 \times 0.100 = 0.0778 \text{ molal}$$

In solutions of weak electrolytes the concentrations of the ions are small, and the interionic forces are so slight that the activities of the ions are essentially equal to their concentrations.

12.12 Summary of the Modern Theory of Electrolytes

The modern concepts of electrolytes may be summarized as follows:

(1) Ionic compounds are completely ionized in the solid state and in solution.

(2) In aqueous solution the ions of an electrolyte are hydrated, and the electrostatic forces of attraction between ions of opposite charge are so reduced that the charged ions move about as independent particles except for a slight residual attraction between them.

(3) The residual attraction between ions of opposite charge in solution decreases upon dilution. It is responsible for the "activity" or "effective concentration" being less than the "actual concentration" of the ions.

(4) Acids ionize by reacting with water to form hydronium ions and acid anions.

(5) Weak electrolytes react with water to only a very limited extent and are thus only slightly ionized.

QUESTIONS

1. Define the following: electrolyte, nonelectrolyte, and electrolysis.
2. Electrolytes include what three principal classes of compounds?
3. Distinguish between strong and weak electrolytes.
4. Account for the electrical neutrality of electrolytic solutions.
5. Describe why a solution of hydrogen chloride gas in water conducts an electric current, although pure hydrogen chloride and pure water are covalent materials.
6. How do the properties of the sodium ion differ from those of the sodium atom? How do the two differ in electronic structure?
7. Account for the abnormal molal lowering of the freezing point of water produced by electrolytes.
8. Why do not crystalline ionic compounds conduct electricity even though they are 100 per cent ionized?
9. Describe the process of solution of ionic compounds in water.
10. Why do not ionic compounds dissolve in such solvents as benzene or carbon tetrachloride?
11. Relate the solubility of an ionic compound in water to (1) the magnitude of the crystal forces and (2) the energy of hydration of the ions.
12. Account for the fact that dry liquid hydrogen chloride is a nonconductor of electricity whereas the same substance in aqueous solution is a good conductor.
13. If sodium chloride is completely dissociated in aqueous solution, why does it not give twice the molal depression of the freezing point of water for nonelectrolytes?

PROBLEMS

1. Acetic acid, CH_3COOH, is ionized to the extent 1.34 per cent in a 0.1000 M solution of the acid and to the extent of 4.15 per cent in a 0.01000 M solution. Calculate the molar concentration of the molecular acid and that of each of the ions in (a) 0.1000 M solution, and (b) 0.01000 M solution.

Ans. (*a*) 9.87×10^{-2} *M*; 1.34×10^{-3} *M*; 1.34×10^{-3} *M*.
(*b*) 9.59×10^{-3} *M*; 4.15×10^{-4} *M*; 4.15×10^{-4} *M*.

2. The activity coefficient for the ions in 0.050 molal NaBr is 0.824 at 25.0° C. Calculate the activities of these ions. *Ans.* *0.041 molal*

3. The activity of the ions in a 0.20 molal solution of $LiNO_3$ at 25.0° C. is 0.15 molal. Calculate the activity coefficient for the ions. *Ans.* *0.75*

REFERENCE

"The Present State of the Electrolyte Problem," C. A. Kraus, *J. Chem. Educ.*, **35 (7) 324 (1958).**

CHAPTER THIRTEEN

Colloid Chemistry

In our study of solutions in Chapter 11 we learned that they are characterized by their homogeneity, absence of settling, and the molecular or ionic state of subdivision of their components. We considered the molecules or ions of the solute to be uniformly scattered, or dispersed, throughout the solvent. We are now concerned with dispersions of particles somewhat larger than simple molecules and ions, yet not large enough to be seen under an ordinary microscope.

13.1 Colloidal Matter

When powdered starch is heated with water, a mixture is obtained which is not homogeneous, yet the particles of insoluble starch do not settle out but remain in suspension indefinitely. Such a system is called a **colloidal dispersion;** the finely divided starch is called the **dispersed phase,** and the water is called the **dispersion medium.**

The term **colloid** was first used in 1861 by Thomas Graham to classify substances which usually exist in an amorphous or gelatinous condition, such as starch and gelatin. Hence the name "colloid," from the Greek word "kolla," meaning glue, and "eidos," meaning like. It is now known, however, that the properties characterized as colloidal are not peculiar to a special class of substances but that any substance may be obtained in the colloidal form if suitable means are employed. The sizes of many single large molecules, such as synthetic polymers and proteins, place them in the category of colloids.

Colloidal matter is not limited to dispersions of solid particles in liquid media; a gas or solid may be the dispersion medium, and the dispersed phase may be a gas, a liquid, or a solid. A classification of colloidal systems is given in Table 13·1. A gas dispersed in another gas is not a colloidal system because the particles are of molecular dimensions. The most important colloidal systems are those involving a solid dispersed in a liquid, and such systems are called **colloidal suspensions** or **sols.**

13.2 Size of Colloidal Particles

Usually, from a thousand to a billion atoms are present in a colloidal particle. It is customary to express the dimensions of colloidal particles in terms of the **millimicron** ($m\mu$), which is one-millionth of a millimeter or 10^{-7} cm. Many colloidal particles have at least one dimension between 1 $m\mu$ and 200 $m\mu$.

TABLE 13·1 Colloidal Systems

Dispersed phase	*Dispersion medium*	*Examples*	*Common name*
Solid	Gas	Smoke, dust	Solid aerosol
Solid	Liquid	Starch suspension, some inks, paints, milk of magnesia	Sol
Solid	Solid	Colored gems, some alloys	Solid sol
Liquid	Gas	Clouds, fogs, mists, sprays	Liquid aerosol
Liquid	Liquid	Milk, mayonnaise, butter	Emulsion
Liquid	Solid	Jellies, gels, opal (SiO_2 and H_2O), pearl ($CaCO_3$ and H_2O)	Solid emulsion
Gas	Liquid	Foams, whipped cream, beaten egg whites	Foam
Gas	Solid	Pumice stone, floating soaps	

Colloidal particles are usually aggregates of hundreds, or even thousands, of molecules. However, some colloids consist of single, well-defined molecules, with constant molecular weight and definite molecular shape, permitting them to be packed together in a crystalline array. The viruses are one kind of giant molecule with molecular weights ranging from several hundred thousand up to billions. Some diseases, such as the common cold, poliomyelitis, and measles, are caused by viruses. Virus molecules have the remarkable power of causing other molecules identical with themselves to be formed. A disease such as poliomyelitis results from the formation of a large number of virus molecules from a few of these molecules when they are in the right environment in the human body. Tobacco mosaic virus has a molecular weight of about 40,000,000; proteins and synthetic polymers have weights in the range of a few thousand to many million.

The **electron microscope** has made it possible to see and photograph virus molecules, which are too small to be seen with a microscope using ordinary visible light. Beams of electrons are used in place of beams of light in the electron microscope. Its magnifying power is about 200,000 as compared with about 2000 for the ordinary light microscope.

13.3 Preparation of Colloidal Systems

The preparation of a colloidal system consists of producing particles of colloidal dimensions and distributing these particles through the dispersion medium. Particles of colloidal size are formed either by **dispersion methods,** i.e., by the subdivision of larger particles or masses, or by **condensation methods,** i.e., by growth from smaller units, such as molecules or ions.

(1) Dispersion may be accomplished by grinding in special mills designed for this purpose, called colloid mills. Paint pigments are reduced to colloidal size by this method. Colloidal systems are sometimes formed by grinding a solid substance in contact with a liquid.

Some solid substances, when brought into contact with water, disperse spontaneously to form colloidal systems. Gelatin, glue, and starch behave in this manner, and are said to undergo **peptization.** The particles are already of colloidal size and the water disperses these particles to form a colloidal system.

Atomizers have been developed which produce colloidal dispersions by a spraying process. Powdered milk of colloidal particle size is produced by dehydrating milk spray.

(2) Condensation methods involve the formation of colloidal particles by causing smaller particles to aggregate. If the particles grow beyond the colloidal range, no colloidal system will result and larger aggregates, that we usually call **precipitates,** will form.

Condensation methods usually employ chemical reactions. A dark red colloidal suspension of iron (III) hydroxide may be prepared by mixing a concentrated solution of iron (III) chloride with hot water.

$$Fe^{+++} + (3\ Cl^-) + 6\ H_2O \rightarrow Fe(OH)_3 + 3\ H_3O^+ + (3\ Cl^-)$$

A colloidal suspension of arsenic (III) sulfide is produced by the reaction of hydrogen sulfide with arsenic (III) oxide dissolved in water.

$$As_2O_3 + 3\ H_2S \rightarrow As_2S_3 + 3\ H_2O$$

The formation of a colloidal gold sol is accomplished by the reduction of a very dilute solution of gold chloride by such reducing agents as formaldehyde, tin (II) chloride, or iron (II) sulfate ($Au^{+++} + 3\ e^- \rightarrow Au$). Some gold sols prepared by Faraday in 1857 are still perfectly clear after 100 years.

Colloidal metals are often prepared by the condensation of vapors, which are produced by striking an electric arc between two wires of the metal. When the arc is under a liquid, the vapor condenses to particles of colloidal size (Fig. 13–1).

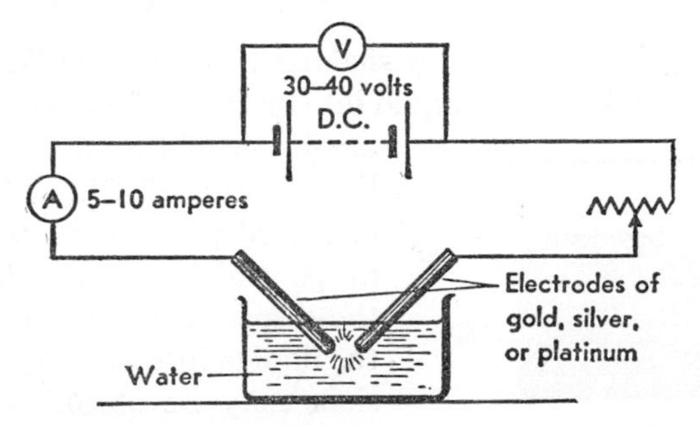

Fig. 13–1 Diagram of Bredig arc for preparing metallic dispersions in water.

Metals below hydrogen in the Activity Series, such as copper, silver, and gold, may be dispersed by forming the arc under water; metals above hydrogen are dispersed by the same process in liquids other than water.

The formation of synthetic polymers and proteins from smaller molecules is described in later chapters (Organic Chemistry and Biochemistry).

13.4 Lyophilic and Lyophobic Colloidal Systems

The most important colloidal dispersions in liquids may be divided into two classes: lyophilic and lyophobic colloids. If the liquid is water, the terms are hydrophilic and hydrophobic. When hot water is added to such substances as starch, gelatin, glue, and agar, the particles of solid take up large quantities of water and form colloidal systems. No special method of preparation is necessary, and the spontaneous dispersion is called peptization, as mentioned in Section 13.3. These **hydrophilic** colloids appear to possess an attraction for water ("water-loving"); the dispersed particles carry a variable electrical charge or none at all; they have high viscosities; they readily form gels; they are coagulated only by electrolytes in high concentrations; and they are reversible, which means that after coagulation, they may be dispersed again by adding water. Gums, resins, and shellacs form colloidal systems which behave in a similar fashion except that the liquid used is some solvent other than water. **Lyophilic** colloids are sometimes called **emulsoids.**

If the dispersed phase has little or no affinity for the dispersion liquid, then the system is called a **lyophobic** ("solvent-hating") colloid or a **suspensoid.** Colloids of this type are, for the most part, elements or compounds of an inorganic character. Their dispersed particles are either all positively or all negatively charged; their viscosities are low, only slightly greater than that of the liquid; they never form gels; they are readily coagulated by added electrolytes; and they are irreversible; i.e., when the liquid is removed, they cannot be dispersed again by addition of the liquid. This group includes such suspensoids as finely divided metals, metallic hydroxides, and metallic sulfides.

13.5 Emulsions

An **emulsion** may be prepared by shaking together two liquids which are immiscible. Agitation breaks up one liquid into droplets of colloidal dimensions which are dispersed through the mass of the other liquid (Fig. 13–2). The droplets of the dispersed phase tend to coalesce, forming drops which are too large to remain in the dispersed condition, and separation of the liquids into two layers follows. Emulsions may be stabilized by the addition of emulsifying agents. These substances may decrease the surface tension of the two liquids and thereby reduce the tendency of the tiny droplets to coalesce and form drops, or they may form protecting layers or films around the droplets. The addition of a little soap will stabilize an emulsion of kerosene in water. The

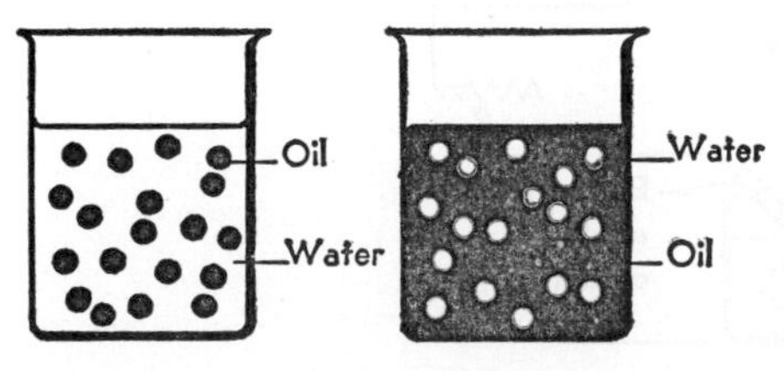

Fig. 13–2 In an emulsion one liquid is dispersed in another liquid with which it will not mix.

cleansing action of soap depends largely upon its action as an emulsifying agent in forming stable emulsions of oils and greases in water.

Milk is an emulsion of droplets of butterfat in water, with casein acting as the emulsifying agent. Mayonnaise is an emulsion of olive oil in vinegar, with egg yolk serving as the emulsifying agent.

13.6 Detergents and Their Cleansing Action

Although the term "detergent" means cleansing agent and includes soap, it is now commonly used to refer to soap substitutes. Soaps are made by boiling natural fats and oils with strong bases such as sodium or potassium hydroxide. When animal fat is treated with sodium hydroxide, glycerol and sodium salts of the fatty acids (palmitic, oleic, and stearic) are formed. Sodium stearate has the formula $C_{17}H_{35}COONa$. The cleansing action of soap depends in part upon its ability to change readily from a solid gel to a dilute colloidal suspension. The dispersed particles of soap adsorb fine particles of dirt and form a protective film about them. In this way the dirt particles are held in suspension in the water and are washed away. Soap also acts as an emulsifying agent in forming stable emulsions of oils and greases in water.

A large number of detergents or soap substitutes are in common use. Each of these compounds contains a hydrocarbon chain or ring structure group which is electrically nonpolar, such as $C_{12}H_{25}$—, or $C_{12}H_{25} \cdot C_6H_4$—; and an electrically polar group, such as a sulfate, —OSO_3Na, or a sulfonate, —SO_3Na. Whereas soaps form insoluble calcium and magnesium compounds in hard water, these detergents give soluble products. Among the detergents with familiar commercial names are Tide, Dreft, Vel, Cheer, and Drene.

The cleansing action of soaps and detergents can be explained in terms of the structures of the molecules involved. The molecules of both soaps and synthetic detergents consist of long hydrocarbon chains attached to a polar group.

$$CH_3(CH_2)_{15}CH_2CO\overset{-}{O}\overset{+}{Na} \qquad CH_3(CH_2)_{10}CH_2OS\overset{-}{O_3}\overset{+}{Na}$$

Sodium stearate — Sodium lauryl sulfate

The hydrocarbon end of such a molecule (hydrophobic) is attracted by the dirt, oil, or grease particles and the polar group (hydrophilic) is attracted by the water (Fig. 13–3). The result is an orientation of the molecules of the cleansing agent at the interface between the dirt particles and the water in such a way that the surface or **interfacial tension** is lowered. This enables the dirt particles to become suspended in the solution as colloidal particles, in which form they are readily washed away. Substances which lower the surface tension of liquids are sometimes called **wetting agents.**

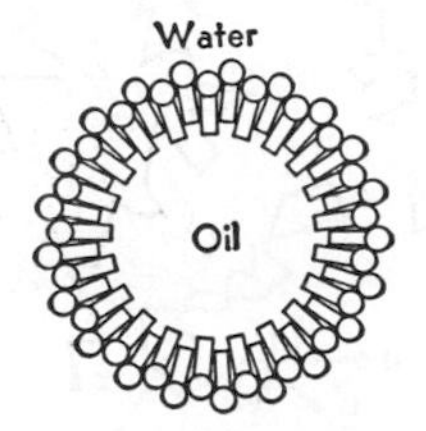

Fig. 13–3 Emulsion of oil in water with negative ions of the soap oriented at the interface between oil particle and water. The hydrocarbon end of the ion is in oil, and the carboxyl end in water.

13.7 The Tyndall Effect

When a beam of light enters a dark room, the path of the beam is readily seen because dust particles, many of which are of colloidal size, reflect the light

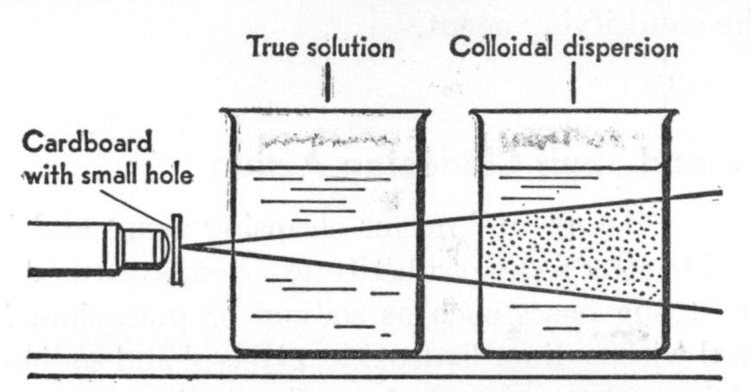

Fig. 13–4 The particles in the colloidal dispersion, or sol, are large enough to reflect light from the lamp at the left.

to the eye. The same phenomenon can be observed if an intense beam of light is passed through a colloidal suspension (Fig. 13–4). The dispersed particles reflect the light to the eye even though they are too small to be seen with the aid of the most powerful microscope. This phenomenon is called the **Tyndall effect,** after the English physicist who first explained it. It should be emphasized that we do not actually see the particles suspended in the liquid; we are only made aware of their presence by their ability to scatter the light that falls upon them. The particles of the solute of a solution of simple molecules are too small to scatter light to an appreciable extent; hence, colloidal solutions may be identified by the Tyndall effect.

Peter J. W. Debye developed the technique of light scattering into a method for determining shapes and molecular weights of polymer molecules in solution.

13.8 The Brownian Movement

When an intense beam of light is passed through a colloidal suspension in a darkened space and the suspension is examined by a powerful microscope against a black background and at right angles to the beam of light, the Tyndall effect is greatly magnified. This arrangement of microscope and light is known as the **ultramicroscope.**

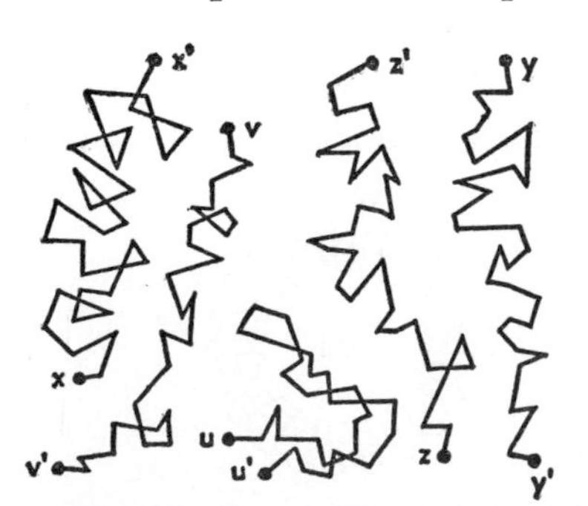

Fig. 13–5 A diagram showing how particles labeled u, v, x, y, and z may move due to unequal molecular bombardment.

Colloidal particles, seen in the ultramicroscope as tiny bright flashes of light, appear in a state of irregular, rapid, dancing motion (Fig. 13–5). This motion is called the **Brownian movement** after the botanist Robert Brown, who first observed it in 1828. He could not explain it, but now we know that the colloidal particles are small enough that bombardment by molecules of the dispersion medium gives them an irregular motion. Any particle in suspension will be bombarded on all sides by moving molecules of the dispersion medium. For large particles, the bombardment force is not sufficient to impart motion, especially inasmuch as bombardment on one side of the particle is likely to be counter-balanced by an equal force on the opposite side. For the small particles of colloidal size, however, the force of bombardment is sufficient in comparison to the mass of the particle to impart momentum, and the probability of equal and simultaneous bombardments on opposite sides of the particle is slight. Hence, the visible motion results. The Brownian movement explains the absence of settling of the dispersed particles in colloidal systems, even though these particles may be more dense than the medium in which they are dispersed. The kinetic-molecular theory of matter received one of its earliest confirmations as a result of studies of the Brownian movement.

13.9 Electrical Properties of Colloidal Particles

One of the most important properties of dispersed colloidal particles is that they are usually electrically charged. When an iron (III) hydroxide sol is placed in an electrolytic cell (Fig. 13–6), the dispersed particles move to the negative electrode. Because opposite charges of electricity attract, this is good evidence that the iron (III) hydroxide particles are positively charged. At the cathode, the charged particles are discharged and the colloidal dispersion coagulates as a precipitate. All particles in any one colloidal system have the same charge. The similar charges on the particles help keep them dispersed because like charges repel each other. Most hydroxides of metals have positive charges, while most sulfides of metals and the metals themselves form negatively charged colloidal dispersions.

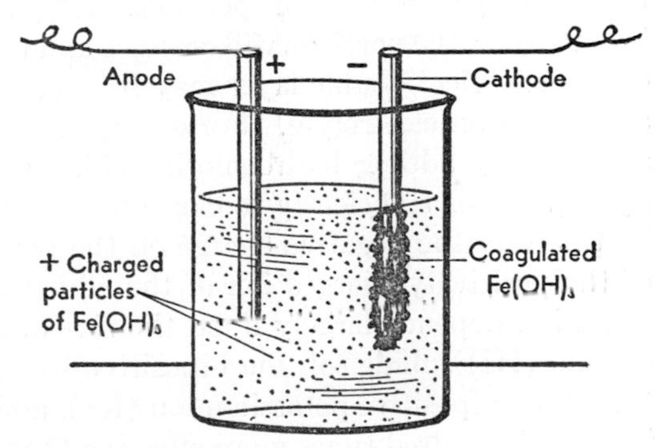

Fig. 13–6 Colloidal iron (III) hydroxide is coagulated in an electrolytic cell.

The charges on colloidal particles result from the adsorption of ions which exist in the dispersion medium. If the colloidal particles preferentially adsorb positive ions, they acquire a positive charge. Thus iron (III) hydroxide particles become positively charged because of a preferential adsorption of iron (III) ions (Fe^{+++}), when $FeCl_3$ hydrolyzes in hot water. Arsenic (III) sulfide (As_2S_3) particles preferentially adsorb sulfide ions ($S^{=}$), resulting from the ionization of H_2S, and become negatively charged.

The hydrogen ions from the ionized form of hydrogen sulfide, called **counter ions,** remain a short distance away from the sulfide ions adsorbed on the particles of As_2S_3. Hence, an **electrical double layer** is set up between the particles with their primarily adsorbed negative sulfide ions and the surrounding solution containing the positive hydrogen ions. An arsenic (II) sulfide particle has a negatively charged surface, whereas the surrounding liquid is positive with respect to the particle. The existence of this electrical double layer is responsible for the stability of the colloidal dispersion. Particles of like charge, even upon close approach, will not collide and coalesce but will repel one another (Fig. 13–7).

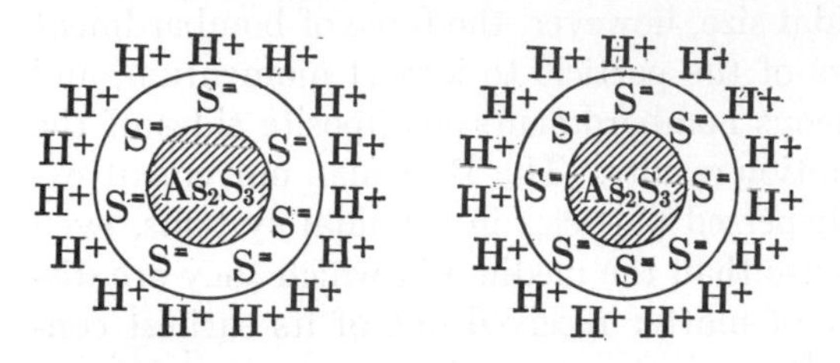

Fig. 13–7 Particles in arsenic (III) sulfide sol. The particles are negatively charged due to adsorbed sulfide ions; the surrounding solution contains positive hydrogen ions.

The study of the migration of colloidal particles in an electric field, **electrophoresis,** is a powerful tool for investigating colloidal electrolytes such as proteins.

13.10 Precipitation of Colloidal Dispersions

We saw in the preceding section that the electrical double layer is responsible for the stability of colloidal dispersions. If by some means this electrical double layer is destroyed, the particles will coalesce and form larger aggregates. The destruction of the electrical double layer may be accomplished by the addition of a sufficient amount of an electrolyte. For example, the arsenic (III) sulfide sol is readily coagulated by adding hydrochloric acid. This increases the concentration of the hydrogen ions sufficiently to cause the reaction, $2\ H^+ + S^= \rightarrow H_2S$, to take place. In this way the negative charge on the particles is neutralized by the adsorption of the positively charged ion of the added electrolyte. The **flocculating power** of an ion depends largely upon the size of its charge. In the flocculation of the arsenic (III) sulfide sol, the bipositive barium ion (Ba^{++}) is much more effective than the unipositive potassium ion (K^+), and the tripositive aluminum ion (Al^{+++}) is several hundred times more effective than the potassium ion.

In washing a finely divided precipitate, the electrolyte which has caused flocculation may be removed in the wash water, and sometimes the precipitate will again pass into colloidal solution by peptization. Peptization may be prevented by adding an electrolyte to the wash water so that when the original flocculating ion is dissolved, it is replaced by an ion of the electrolyte in the wash water. Because ammonium nitrate decomposes when heated and therefore can readily be removed later, this salt is often added to the water used in washing sulfide precipitates.

Colloidal clay or silt particles in a river are negatively charged by the adsorption of negative hydroxide ions. When the river water reaches the salty ocean water, the negatively charged particles are neutralized by the positive sodium and magnesium ions of the sea water, and these clay and silt particles precipitate. Enough precipitate accumulates during thousands of years to form deltas at the mouths of rivers.

The smoke and dust particles from chimneys of furnaces are often colloidally dispersed and electrically charged. A process for precipitating flue dusts was developed by Cottrell, an American chemist, to prevent or lessen the "smoke nuisance" in industrial centers. In this process the charged particles are attracted to highly charged electrodes, where upon discharge they are deposited as dust (Fig. 13–8). The process is also important in the recovery of many valuable products that would otherwise escape from the flues of smelters, furnaces, and kilns.

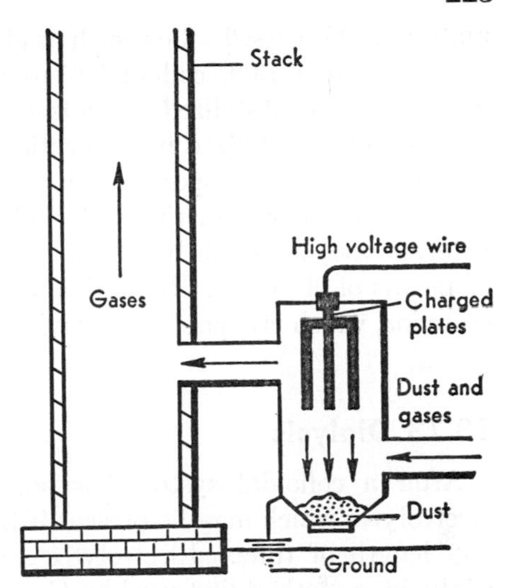

Fig. 13–8 The principle of a Cottrell precipitator. Both positively and negatively charged particles are precipitated by the electrically charged plates over which dust and gases must pass to reach the smokestack.

13.11 Protective Colloids

The coagulation of the dispersed phase in some colloidal systems may be prevented by the presence of another colloid. The second colloid forms a protecting film around the dispersed particles and prevents them from coalescing. Gelatin, dextrin, and gum arabic are the most familiar and widely used **protective colloids.** The gelatin on photographic plates and film maintains the colloidal dispersion of the silver halides by serving as a protective colloid. Gum arabic is used in the stabilization of certain inks.

13.12 Surface Phenomena

One of the properties of any surface is its specific ability to hold other substances to itself. This phenomenon is called **adsorption.** The atoms, molecules, or ions which compose a surface differ from those in the interior of a body of matter in that they are surrounded only on one side by like particles that possess equal and similar cohesive forces. The particles within the body, however, are surrounded on all sides by particles having equal attractive forces. The surface particles, therefore, have a certain amount of attractive force which is not satisfied. These unsatisfied forces are called residual valence forces and they are largely responsible for adsorption.

When matter is subdivided to the extent that its particles become colloidal in dimensions, there is a tremendous increase in the surface exposed to the surrounding medium. A cube 1 cm. along each edge has a surface of 6 cm^2. If this cube is subdivided until the particles are within the colloidal range of 10 mμ on an edge, the total surface area becomes 6,000,000 cm^2. Because colloidal particles have a very large surface area for a given volume of material, they are good adsorbers. In fact, colloidal chemistry is largely the chemistry of surface effects. Hence, the principles of colloid chemistry apply to films, like those of soap bubbles, and to filaments, both of which have a very large surface area for a given volume of material. Dispersed solids, such as charcoal, adsorb vast quantities of gas. As we saw in Section 13.9, colloidal dispersions of arsenic (III) sulfide and iron (III) hydroxide are stabilized by adsorption of ions from solution. Furthermore, emulsions are stabilized by adsorption of an emulsifying agent upon the surface of the droplets of the dispersed phase (Section 13.5).

One of the newer methods of studying surfaces of metals is with the **field ion microscope,** in which beams of positive ions are used instead of beams of light or beams of electrons. Individual atoms have been viewed with the field ion microscope, which is capable of resolving distances smaller than 3 Å.

13.13 Dialysis

After a colloidal system has been prepared, it is often necessary to remove electrolytes which may be present if the colloidal dispersion is to remain stable for any length of time. Electrolytes may be removed from colloidal solutions by **dialysis,** a method first used by Graham in 1861. This process involves the separation of the colloidal system from the solvent by a membrane which permits solutions of electrolytes to pass through but retains the colloidal particles (Fig. 13–9). In practice, cellophane, collodion, animal bladders, and parchment are used as dialyzing membranes.

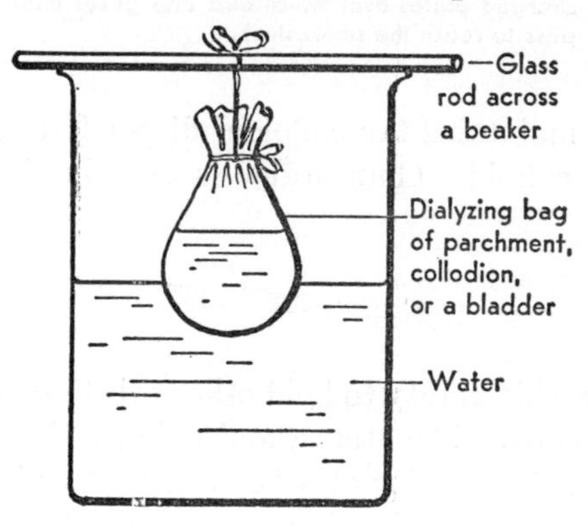

Fig. 13–9 Colloidal particles will not diffuse through a dialyzing membrane.

Ordinary filter paper is permeable to colloidal particles as well as to true solutions and thus cannot be used for filtration of colloidal solutions. However, an ultrafilter will retain colloidal particles. This type of filter is a membrane of suitable pore size fitted to a support in such a manner that the colloidal solution to be filtered may be subjected to high pressures. **Ultrafiltration** is more rapid than dialysis, and colloidal particles of different sizes may be separated from each other by this means if membranes of suitable pore size are employed.

13.14 Gels

Under certain conditions, colloidal systems which exhibit lyophilic behavior coagulate in a manner such that the whole mass, including the liquid, sets to an extremely viscous gelatinous body, known as a gel. For example, a hot aqueous "solution" of gelatin sets to a **gel** upon cooling. Because the formation of a gel is accompanied by the taking up of water or some other solvent, the gel is said to be hydrated or solvated. Apparently the fibers of the dispersed substance form a complex three-dimensional network, the interstices of which are filled with the liquid medium or a dilute solution of the dispersed phase.

A carbohydrate known as "pectin" is a gel-forming hydrophilic substance of fruit juices which is important in jelly making. Silica gel, a colloidal dispersion of hydrated silicon dioxide, is formed when dilute hydrochloric acid is added to a dilute solution of sodium silicate. "Canned heat" is a gel made by mixing alcohol and a saturated aqueous solution of calcium acetate. The wall of the living cell is colloidal in character, and within the cell there is a jellylike dispersion. In fact, all living tissue is colloidal, and the various life processes — nutrition, digestion, secretion — are largely those concerned with the chemistry of the colloidal state. The concentration of low grade ores by flotation processes (Section 33.5) is an important industrial application of colloid chemistry.

QUESTIONS

1. Identify the dispersed phase and the dispersion medium in each of the following colloidal systems: starch suspension, smoke, fog, pearl, whipped cream, floating soap, jelly, milk, and ruby.
2. What is the structure of a gel?
3. How do colloidal "solutions" differ from true solutions with regard to dispersed particle size, homogeneity, and the Tyndall effect?
4. Distinguish between dispersion methods and condensation methods for preparing colloidal systems.
5. Identify each of the following colloidal systems as hydrophilic or hydrophobic: a gold sol, a starch suspension, a jelly, clay suspended in water, and an arsenic (III) sulfide sol.
6. What is meant by "reversible" and "irreversible" colloidal systems?
7. Explain the phenomenon of Brownian movement. What is its relationship to the stability of the dispersed particles of a colloidal system?
8. How can it be demonstrated that colloidal particles are electrically charged? How do the particles acquire charges? How are these charges important to the stability of a colloidal system?
9. Explain the formation of deltas.
10. Explain the cleansing action of soap.
11. What is the function of a protective colloid?
12. Why are colloidal dispersions good adsorbing agents?
13. Explain the purification of colloidal systems by means of dialysis.
14. Why cannot colloidal systems be separated from electrolytes by filtration?

PROBLEM

1. Calculate (a) the surface area of a cube for which each side is 1 cm. long. Then calculate the total surface area if the cube is subdivided into cubes (b) 0.1 cm. along each edge, (c) 0.01 cm. along each edge, (d) 0.001 cm. along each edge, and (e) 10 mμ along each edge.

Ans. (*a*) *6 cm.*^{2}; (*b*) *60 cm.*^{2}; (*c*) *600 cm.*^{2}; (*d*) *6000 cm.*^{2}; (*e*) *6,000,000 cm.*^{2} (Notice that, although the total volume remains the same, the surface area increases as the particle size becomes smaller).

REFERENCES

"Symposium on the Teaching of Colloid Chemistry," *J. Chem. Educ.*, **26** (1) 18–31 (1949).

"Organic Synthetic Detergents," C. P. Neidig and A. B. Hersberger, *Chem. Eng. News*, **30** (35) 3610 (1952).

"Waste Gases," W. A. Schmidt, *Chem. Eng. News*, **27** (45) 3272 (1949).

"The History of Colloid Science," E. A. Hauser, *J. Chem. Educ.*, **32** (1) 2 (1955).

"Syndets and Surfactants," F. D. Snell and C. T. Snell, *J. Chem. Educ.*, **35** (6) 271 (1958).

"Atoms Visualized," E. W. Müller, *Sci. American*, June, 1957; p. 113.

"The Field Ion Microscope," E. W. Müller, *Am. Scientist*, **49**, 88 (1961).

"Poliomyelitis Virus," F. L. Schaffer, *J. Chem. Educ.*, **36** (9) 469 (1959).

"How Giant Molecules are Measured," Peter Debye, *Sci. American*, Sept. 1957; p. 90.

"The Teaching of Colloid and Surface Chemistry," *J. Chem. Educ.*, **39** (4) 166–195 (1962).

CHAPTER FOURTEEN

Oxidation-Reduction Reactions

The term "oxidation" was originally applied only to reactions involving the reaction of oxygen with another element or with a compound. Likewise, the word "reduction" was used to indicate removal of oxygen from a compound. The terms "oxidation" and "reduction" are now used in a much broader sense and are applied to a great many reactions that do not involve oxygen. For example, carbon burns in fluorine in a reaction which closely resembles the union of carbon with oxygen.

$$2\ C + O_2 \rightarrow 2\ CO$$
$$C + 2\ F_2 \rightarrow CF_4$$

Hydrogen burns in fluorine and chlorine as well as in oxygen.

$$2\ H_2 + O_2 \rightarrow 2\ H_2O$$
$$H_2 + F_2 \rightarrow 2\ HF$$
$$H_2 + Cl_2 \rightarrow 2\ HCl$$

Because of the similarity of these reactions, they are all examples of the important class of reactions referred to as **oxidation-reduction** reactions.

14.1 Oxidation-Reduction and Changes in Oxidation Numbers

In Chapter 4, we discussed the concept of oxidation number. Table 14·1 lists the various oxidation numbers exhibited by some of the elements. **Oxidation can be defined as an increase in the positive oxidation number of an atom or ion. Reduction is a decrease in the positive oxidation number of an atom or ion.** Hydrogen is oxidized by chlorine according to the equation

$$\overset{0}{H_2} + \overset{0}{Cl_2} \rightarrow 2\ \overset{+1\ -1}{HCl}$$

The oxidation number of each hydrogen atom is increased from 0 to +1; hydrogen is oxidized. The oxidation number of each chlorine atom is reduced from 0 to −1; chlorine is reduced. Since chlorine is responsible for the increase in oxidation number of the hydrogen, chlorine is called the oxidizing agent. **Oxidizing agents are substances which increase the oxidation number of elements.** Hydrogen causes the decrease in the oxidation number of the chlorine so hydrogen is called the reducing agent. **Reducing agents are substances which decrease the oxidation number of elements.** Oxidation and reduction always occur simul-

TABLE 14·1 Oxidation Numbers of Some of the More Common Elements

+1	+2	+3	+4	+5	+6	+7	−1	−2	−3	−4
K	Ba	Al	Sn	N	S	Cl	H	O	N	C
Na	Sr	Mn	Pb	P	Mn	I	F	S	P	Si
H	Ca	Cr	Mn	As	Cr	Mn	Cl			
Cu	Mg	Fe	S	Sb			Br			
Ag	Mn	Sb	C	Bi			I			
Hg	Zn	Bi	Si	Cl						
Cl	Cr	As		Br						
Br	Fe	N		I						
I	Cd	P								
	Co	Cl								
	Ni	Br								
	Sn									
	Pb									
	Cu									
	Hg									

taneously and the total increase in units of positive oxidation number exactly equals the total decrease in units of positive oxidation number in the balanced equation. Thus two hydrogen atoms increase two units in positive oxidation number and two chlorine atoms decrease two units in positive oxidation number in the above reaction. Oxidation-reduction reactions are often conveniently referred to as "redox" reactions.

14.2 The Balancing of Redox Equations by the Change in Oxidation Number Method

The fact that oxidation and reduction always occur together and to the same extent makes it possible to use the changes in oxidation number in balancing redox equations. In other words, proportions of the reactants and products in the balanced redox equation must be such that the total increase in units of positive oxidation number must equal the total decrease in units of positive oxidation number.

Various types of oxidation-reduction reactions have been selected to illustrate the balancing of equations by the change in oxidation number method.

EXAMPLE 1. Let us consider the reaction of antimony and chlorine to form antimony (III) chloride. First write the reactants and products of the reaction.

$$Sb + Cl_2 \rightarrow SbCl_3$$

Indicate the oxidation number of each atom in the reaction (see Sections 4.9 and 4.11).

$$\overset{0}{Sb} + \overset{0}{Cl_2} \rightarrow \overset{+3}{Sb}\overset{-1}{Cl_3}$$

Designate the changes in oxidation number that occur during the reaction. Use an ascending arrow (↑) to denote an increase in positive oxidation number and a descending arrow (↓) to denote a decrease in positive oxidation number.

$$\overset{0}{Sb} \rightarrow \overset{+3}{Sb} \uparrow 3$$

$$\overset{0}{Cl_2} \rightarrow 2\ \overset{-1}{Cl} \downarrow 2$$

To balance the equation we must select the proper number of antimony and chlorine atoms so that the total increase in units of oxidation number will equal the total decrease. If we use two atoms of antimony and three molecules (six atoms) of chlorine, then there will be both an increase and a decrease of six units of positive oxidation number.

$$\overset{0}{Sb} \rightarrow \overset{+3}{Sb} \uparrow \qquad 3 \times 2 = 6$$

$$\overset{0}{Cl_2} \rightarrow 2\ \overset{-1}{Cl} \downarrow \quad 2 \times 3 = 6$$

Our final equation then becomes

$$2\ Sb + 3\ Cl_2 \rightarrow 2\ SbCl_3$$

EXAMPLE 2. The chloride ion is oxidized by the permanganate ion in acid solution to give the manganese (II) ion, molecular chlorine, and water.

$$MnO_4^- + Cl^- + H^+ \rightarrow Mn^{++} + Cl_2 + H_2O$$

Upon assignment of oxidation numbers, it becomes evident that manganese is reduced from +7 to +2 and chlorine is oxidized from −1 to 0.

$$\overset{+7}{Mn}O_4^- + Cl^- + H^+ \rightarrow Mn^{++} + \overset{0}{Cl_2} + H_2O$$

$$2\ Cl^- \rightarrow \overset{0}{Cl_2} \uparrow \qquad 2 \times 5 = 10$$

$$\overset{+7}{Mn} \rightarrow Mn^{++} \downarrow \quad 5 \times 2 = 10$$

Ten chloride ions will increase by ten units of oxidation number in going to five chlorine molecules (ten chlorine atoms). Two manganese atoms will decrease by ten units of oxidation number.

$$2\ MnO_4^- + 10\ Cl^- + ?\ H^+ \rightarrow 2\ Mn^{++} + 5\ Cl_2 + ?\ H_2O$$

To complete the balancing of this ionic equation, we may now balance the ion charges on both sides of the equation. On the right side of the equation, the only charged particles are the two Mn^{++} with a total ionic charge of +4. The algebraic sum of the charges on the left must also be equal to +4. Excluding the H^+ for the moment, the total charge on the left is −12, ($2\ MnO_4^- + 10\ Cl^-$). Sixteen H^+ are necessary to give an algebraic sum of +4, (−2 − 10 + 16 = +4). The sixteen hydrogen ions are enough to produce 8 molecules of water.

$$2\ MnO_4^- + 10\ Cl^- + 16\ H^+ \rightarrow 2\ Mn^{++} + 5\ Cl_2 + 8\ H_2O$$

The correctness of the balancing of the equation is checked by noting that there are 8 oxygen atoms on each side of the equation.

EXAMPLE 3. Very active reducing agents such as zinc reduce dilute nitric acid to nitrous oxide (N_2O) or ammonium ion. Write the reactants and products of the reaction, and assign oxidation numbers to the atoms that undergo a change in oxidation number.

$$\overset{0}{Zn} + \overset{+5}{N}O_3^- + H^+ \rightarrow Zn^{++} + \overset{-3}{N}H_4^+ + H_2O$$

Balance the equation with regard to the atoms that change in oxidation number.

$$\overset{0}{Zn} \rightarrow Zn^{++} \uparrow \quad 2 \times 4 = 8$$

$$\overset{+5}{N} \rightarrow \overset{-3}{N} \downarrow \quad 8 \times 1 = 8$$

$$4\ Zn + NO_3^- + ?\ H^+ \rightarrow 4\ Zn^{++} + NH_4^+ + ?\ H_2O$$

Balance the ion charges to find the number of H^+ required.

$$\underset{-1}{NO_3^-} + \underset{+10}{?\ H^+} \rightarrow \underset{+8}{4\ Zn^{++}} + \underset{+1}{NH_4^+}$$

$$-1 \quad +10 = \quad +8 \quad +1$$

$$4\ Zn + NO_3^- + 10\ H^+ \rightarrow 4\ Zn^{++} + NH_4^+ + ?\ H_2O$$

Of the 10 hydrogen atoms on the left, 4 are found in the NH_4^+ on the right. Thus 6 hydrogen atoms are left to form 3 molecules of water on the right.

$$4\ Zn + NO_3^- + 10\ H^+ \rightarrow 4\ Zn^{++} + NH_4^+ + 3\ H_2O$$

As a check on the correctness of the balancing of the equation, there are found to be 3 oxygen atoms on each side of the equation

EXAMPLE 4. The chromite ion, $Cr(OH)_4^-$, is oxidized by hydrogen peroxide in basic solution to the chromate ion, $CrO_4^=$. Upon assigning oxidation numbers, remember that each oxygen atom in H_2O_2 is −1.

$$\overset{+3}{Cr}(OH)_4^- + H_2\overset{-1}{O_2} + OH^- \rightarrow \overset{+6}{Cr}O_4^= + H_2O$$

$$\overset{+3}{Cr} \rightarrow \overset{+6}{Cr} \uparrow \quad 3 \times 2 = 6$$

$$\overset{-1}{O_2} \rightarrow 2\ \overset{-2}{O} \downarrow \quad 2 \times 3 = 6$$

$$2\ Cr(OH)_4^- + 3\ H_2O_2 + ?\ OH^- \rightarrow 2\ CrO_4^= + ?\ H_2O$$

Balancing with regard to ion charges, we have

$$2\ Cr(OH)_4^- + ?\ OH^- \rightarrow 2\ CrO_4^=$$

$$-2 \quad -2 \quad = \quad -4$$

$$2\ Cr(OH)_4^- + 3\ H_2O_2 + 2\ OH^- \rightarrow 2\ CrO_4^= + ?\ H_2O$$

A total of 16 hydrogen atoms on the left will produce 8 molecules of water on the right.

$$2\,Cr(OH)_4^- + 3\,H_2O_2 + 2\,OH^- \rightarrow 2\,CrO_4^= + 8\,H_2O$$

There are 16 atoms of oxygen on each side of the balanced equation.

EXAMPLE 5. Hydrogen iodide is active enough to reduce concentrated sulfuric acid to hydrogen sulfide.

$$H_2\overset{+6}{S}O_4 + H\overset{-1}{I} \rightarrow H_2\overset{-2}{S} + H_2O + \overset{0}{I_2}$$

$$2\,\overset{-1}{I} \rightarrow \overset{0}{I_2}\uparrow \quad 2 \times 4 = 8$$

$$\overset{+6}{S} \rightarrow \overset{-2}{S}\downarrow \quad 8 \times 1 = 8$$

$$H_2SO_4 + 8\,HI \rightarrow H_2S + ?\,H_2O + 4\,I_2$$

Of the ten hydrogen atoms on the left, two are needed for the one molecule of H_2S on the right, and eight remain to produce four molecules of water.

$$H_2SO_4 + 8\,HI \rightarrow H_2S \times 4\,H_2O + 4\,I_2$$

There are then 4 atoms of oxygen on each side of the balanced equation.

14.3 Balancing Redox Equations by the Ion-Electron Method

In the ion-electron method of balancing oxidation-reduction equations, the redox reaction is broken down into half-reactions, one half representing the oxidation step and the other half the reduction step.

EXAMPLE 1. Iron (II) is oxidized to iron (III) by chlorine.

$$Fe^{++} + Cl_2 \rightarrow Fe^{+++} + Cl^-$$

The oxidation half-reaction involves

$$Fe^{++} \rightarrow Fe^{+++}$$

To balance this half-reaction in terms of ion charges and electrons, it is necessary to add one electron to the right side of the equation.

$$Fe^{++} \rightarrow Fe^{+++} + e^-$$
$$+2 \quad = \quad +3 \quad -1$$

To balance the reduction half-reaction, it is necessary to add two electrons to the left side of the equation.

$$Cl_2 + 2\,e^- \rightarrow 2\,Cl^-$$
$$-2 \quad = \quad -2$$

In the oxidation half-reaction one electron is lost, while in the reduction half-reaction two electrons are gained. To balance the electrons the oxidation half-reaction must be multiplied by two.

$$2\,Fe^{++} \rightarrow 2\,Fe^{+++} + 2\,e^-$$

Upon adding the balanced half-reactions, the two electrons on either side of the equation cancel, and the balanced equation is obtained.

$$\begin{array}{r} 2\ Fe^{++} \rightarrow 2\ Fe^{+++} + 2\ e^- \\ Cl_2 + 2\ e^- \rightarrow 2\ Cl^- \\ \hline 2\ Fe^{++} + Cl_2 \rightarrow 2\ Fe^{+++} + 2\ Cl^- \end{array}$$

EXAMPLE 2. The dichromate ion will oxidize iron (II) to iron (III) in acid solution.

$$Cr_2O_7^= + H^+ + Fe^{++} \rightarrow Cr^{+++} + Fe^{+++} + H_2O$$

The oxidation half-reaction is balanced as shown in Example 1.

$$Fe^{++} \rightarrow Fe^{+++} + e^-$$

The reduction half-reaction is

$$Cr_2O_7^= + ?\ H^+ \rightarrow 2\ Cr^{+++} + ?\ H_2O$$

By inspection, the 7 atoms of oxygen from the $Cr_2O_7^=$ ion require 14 H^+ ions to produce 7 molecules of water.

$$Cr_2O_7^= + 14\ H^+ \rightarrow 2\ Cr^{+++} + 7\ H_2O$$

To balance this reduction half-reaction in terms of ion charges and electrons, it is necessary to add 6 electrons to the left side of the equation.

$$Cr_2O_7^= + 14\ H^+ + 6\ e^- \rightarrow 2\ Cr^{+++} + 7\ H_2O$$
$$-2 \quad +14 \quad -6 \quad = \quad +6$$

In order that both half-reactions involve the same number of electrons, the oxidation half-reaction must be multiplied by six.

$$6\ Fe^{++} \rightarrow 6\ Fe^{+++} + 6\ e^-$$

Upon adding the balanced half-reactions, the six electrons on either side of the equation will cancel and we have

$$\begin{array}{r} 6\ Fe^{++} \rightarrow 6\ Fe^{+++} + 6\ e^- \\ Cr_2O_7^= + 14\ H^+ + 6\ e^- \rightarrow 2\ Cr^{+++} + 7\ H_2O \\ \hline Cr_2O_7^= + 14\ H^+ + 6\ Fe^{++} \rightarrow 2\ Cr^{+++} + 6\ Fe^{+++} + 7\ H_2O \end{array}$$

EXAMPLE 3. Hydrogen peroxide in acidic solution oxidizes Fe^{++} to Fe^{+++}. The oxidation half-reaction is

$$Fe^{++} \rightarrow Fe^{+++} + e^-$$

The reduction half-reaction involves the reduction of H_2O_2 to H_2O in acid solution.

$$H_2O_2 + ?\ H^+ \rightarrow ?\ H_2O$$

By inspection, it is seen that there is sufficient oxygen in one molecule of H_2O_2 to form two molecules of water. This will require two hydrogen ions.

$$H_2O_2 + 2\ H^+ \rightarrow 2\ H_2O$$

Two electrons are required to balance the positive charges on the two hydrogen ions.

$$H_2O_2 + 2\ H^+ + 2\ e^- \rightarrow 2\ H_2O$$

In order that both half-reactions involve the same number of electrons, the oxidation half-reaction must be multiplied by two.

$$2\ Fe^{++} \rightarrow 2\ Fe^{+++} + 2\ e^-$$

Now let us add the two half-reactions.

$$\begin{array}{r} 2\ Fe^{++} \rightarrow 2\ Fe^{+++} + 2\ e^- \\ H_2O_2 + 2\ H^+ + 2\ e^- \rightarrow 2\ H_2O \\ \hline H_2O_2 + 2\ H^+ + 2\ Fe^{++} \rightarrow 2\ H_2O + 2\ Fe^{+++} \end{array}$$

14.4 Some Half-Reactions

When redox equations are to be balanced by the ion-electron method, it is necessary that the proper half-reactions be selected. The following half-reactions should be studied carefully, for they are very frequently encountered in the balancing of redox equations. The products listed are the *major products* under the conditions given, but in many cases are not the sole products.

$H_2O_2 + 2\ H^+ + 2\ e^- \rightarrow 2\ H_2O$ — Hydrogen peroxide as an oxidizing agent in acid solution.

$H_2O_2 \rightarrow O_2 + 2\ H^+ + 2\ e^-$ — Hydrogen peroxide as a reducing agent in acid solution.

$MnO_4^- + 8\ H^+ + 5\ e^- \rightarrow Mn^{++} + 4\ H_2O$ — Permanganate ion as an oxidizing agent in acid solution.

$MnO_4^- + 2\ H_2O + 3\ e^- \rightarrow \underline{MnO_2} + 4\ OH^-$ — Permanganate ion as an oxidizing agent in neutral or basic solution.

$Cr_2O_7^{=} + 14\ H^+ + 6\ e^- \rightarrow 2\ Cr^{+++} + 7\ H_2O$ — Dichromate ion as an oxidizing agent in acid solution.

$NO_3^- + 2\ H^+ + e^- \rightarrow NO_2 + H_2O$ — Concentrated nitric acid as an oxidizing agent toward less active metals such as Cu, Ag, and Pb.

$NO_3^- + 4\ H^+ + 3\ e^- \rightarrow NO + 2\ H_2O$ — Dilute nitric acid as an oxidizing agent toward less active metals.

$2\ NO_3^- + 10\ H^+ + 8\ e^- \rightarrow N_2O + 5\ H_2O$ — Dilute nitric acid as an oxidizing agent toward moderately active metals such as Zn and Fe.

$H_2SO_4 + 2\ H^+ + 2\ e^- \rightarrow SO_2 + 2\ H_2O$ — Concentrated sulfuric acid as an oxidizing agent toward HBr, C, and Cu.

$H_2SO_4 + 6\ H^+ + 6\ e^- \rightarrow S + 4\ H_2O$ — Concentrated sulfuric acid as an oxidizing agent toward H_2S.

$H_2SO_4 + 8\ H^+ + 8\ e^- \rightarrow H_2S + 4\ H_2O$ — Concentrated sulfuric acid as an oxidizing agent toward HI.

$NO_2^- + 2\,H^+ + e^- \rightarrow NO + H_2O$	Nitrous acid as an oxidizing agent.
$NO_2^- + H_2O \rightarrow NO_3^- + 2\,H^+ + 2\,e^-$	Nitrous acid as a reducing agent.
$HClO + H^+ + 2\,e^- \rightarrow Cl^- + H_2O$	Hypochlorous acid as an oxidizing agent.
$X_2 + 2\,e^- \rightarrow 2\,X^-$	The halogens F_2, Cl_2, Br_2, and I_2 as oxidizing agents.
$O_2 + 4\,H^+ + 4\,e^- \rightarrow 2\,H_2O$	Oxygen as an oxidizing agent in acid solution.
$2\,H^+ + 2\,e^- \rightarrow H_2$	The hydrogen ion as an oxidizing agent.
$H_2 \rightarrow 2\,H^+ + 2\,e^-$	Molecular hydrogen as a reducing agent in aqueous solution.
$M \rightarrow M^{+n} + n\,e^-$	Metals as reducing agents.
$M^{+n} + n\,e^- \rightarrow M$	Metal ions as oxidizing agents.

14.5 Gram-Equivalent Weights of Oxidizing and Reducing Agents

In Section 11.16 the working definition of gram-equivalent weight was stated as follows: The gram-equivalent weight of a substance taking part in a given reaction is the number of grams of the substance associated with the transfer of N electrons or protons or with the neutralization of N negative or positive charges, where N is Avogadro's number, 6.023×10^{23}. A redox reaction between inorganic ions always involves a transfer of electrons from the substance oxidized to the substance reduced. If the half-reactions for a redox reaction are written, the deduction of the gram-equivalent weights of the oxidizing and reducing agents is readily made. The weight of the substance yielding that quantity of the ion which gains or loses N electrons is the gram-equivalent weight.

For example, when potassium permanganate ($KMnO_4$) is used as an oxidizing agent in acid solution, the half-reaction is

$$MnO_4^- + 8\,H^+ + 5\,e^- \rightarrow Mn^{++} + 4\,H_2O$$

One mole of $KMnO_4$ yields one mole of permanganate ion, MnO_4^-, and, as indicated by the equation for the half-reaction, each mole of MnO_4^- requires 5 N electrons in being reduced to Mn^{++}. One mole of $KMnO_4$ constitutes 5 gram-equivalent weights, and the gram-equivalent weight is 158.04/5, or 31.61 g.

When iron (II) sulfate, $FeSO_4$, reacts with potassium permanganate in dilute sulfuric acid solution, Fe^{++} is oxidized to Fe^{+++} according to the equation

$$5\,Fe^{++} + MnO_4^- + 8\,H^+ \rightarrow 5\,Fe^{+++} + Mn^{++} + 4\,H_2O$$

The oxidation half-reaction is

$$Fe^{++} \rightarrow Fe^{+++} + e^-$$

One mole of $FeSO_4$ yields 1 mole of Fe^{++} which, as shown by the oxidation half-reaction, loses N electrons. Therefore, 1 mole, or 151.91 g., of $FeSO_4$ is 1 gram-equivalent weight.

14.6 Normal Solutions of Oxidizing and Reducing Agents

A one-normal solution of an oxidizing or reducing agent contains one gram-equivalent weight of the agent in a liter of solution. One ml. of a one-normal solution of an oxidizing or reducing agent contains one milligram-equivalent weight of the agent. Because one gram-equivalent weight of an oxidizing agent reacts exactly with one gram-equivalent weight of a reducing agent, redox titrations may be conducted in the same way as described for acids and bases (Section 11.19) if a suitable method of determining the equivalence point is available.

Suppose we calculate the volume of 0.100 N $KMnO_4$ required in the oxidation of the Fe^{++} in 200 ml. of 0.050 N $FeSO_4$.

Solution:

200 ml. of 0.050 N $FeSO_4$ contain 200 ml. $\times$ 0.050 mg.-equiv. wt./ml. = 10.0 mg.-equiv. wts. of Fe^{++}. Thus, 10.0 mg.-equivalent weights of $KMnO_4$ will be required to oxidize the 10.0 mg.-equivalent weights of Fe^{++}.

Each ml. of 0.100 N $KMnO_4$ solution contains 0.100 mg.-equivalent weight of $KMnO_4$. The number of ml. of 0.100 N $KMnO_4$ solution that will contain 10.0 mg.-equivalent weights of $KMnO_4$ is

$$\frac{10.0 \text{ mg.-equivalent weights}}{0.100 \text{ mg.-equiv. wt./ml.}} = 100.0 \text{ ml. of } KMnO_4$$

QUESTIONS

1. Give the oxidation number of each of the elements contained in the following substances: NaCl, Na_2O, Na_2S, Na_3N, K_2SO_4, $Ca_3(PO_4)_2$, H_2CO_3, H_2SO_3, Na_2O_2, CO_2, $SiCl_4$, FeS, $KMnO_4$, Na_2CrO_4, CuI.

2. Define "oxidation" and "reduction" in terms of change of oxidation number.

3. What are "oxidizing agents" and "reducing agents"?

4. Balance the following redox equations by the "change of oxidation number" and/or "the ion-electron method":

(a) $Cu + H^+ + NO_3^- \rightarrow Cu^{++} + NO_2\uparrow + H_2O$
(b) $Cu + H^+ + NO_3^- \rightarrow Cu^{++} + NO\uparrow + H_2O$
(c) $Zn + H^+ + NO_3^- \rightarrow Zn^{++} + N_2\uparrow + H_2O$
(d) $Zn + H^+ + NO_3^- \rightarrow Zn^{++} + N_2O\uparrow + H_2O$
(e) $MnO_4^- + H_2S + H^+ \rightarrow Mn^{++} + \underline{S} + H_2O$
(f) $MnO_4^- + S^= + H_2O \rightarrow \underline{MnO_2} + \underline{S} + OH^-$
(g) $MnO_4^- + NO_2^- + H_2O \rightarrow \underline{MnO_2} + NO_3^- + OH^-$
(h) $H_2SO_4 + HBr \rightarrow SO_2\uparrow + Br_2\uparrow + H_2O$
(i) $H_2SO_4 + HI \rightarrow H_2S + I_2 + H_2O$
(j) $NO_3^- + I_2 + H^+ \rightarrow IO_3^- + NO_2\uparrow + H_2O$

(k) $CuS + H^+ + NO_3^- \rightarrow Cu^{++} + S + NO\uparrow + H_2O$
(l) $H_2O_2 + MnO_4^- + H^+ \rightarrow Mn^{++} + H_2O + O_2\uparrow$
(m) $NO_3^- + Zn + OH^- + H_2O \rightarrow NH_3\uparrow + Zn(OH)_4^{=}$
(n) $ZnS + O_2 \rightarrow ZnO + SO_2$
(o) $Al + H^+ \rightarrow Al^{+++} + H_2\uparrow$
(p) $Br_2 + CO_3^{=} \rightarrow Br^- + BrO_3^- + CO_2\uparrow$
(q) $HBrO \rightarrow H^+ + Br^- + O_2\uparrow$
(r) $Br_2 + SO_2 + H_2O \rightarrow H^+ + Br^- + SO_4^{=}$
(s) $ClO_3^- + H_2O + I_2 \rightarrow IO_3^- + Cl^- + H^+$
(t) $HClO_3 \rightarrow HClO_4 + ClO_2 + H_2O$
(u) $OH^- + Cl_2 \rightarrow ClO_3^- + Cl^- + H_2O$
(v) $MnO_4^{=} + Cl_2 \rightarrow MnO_4^- + Cl^-$
(w) $MnO_4^{=} + H_2O \rightarrow MnO_4^- + OH^- + \underline{MnO_2}$
(x) $NH_3 + O_2 \rightarrow NO + H_2O$
(y) $OH^- + NO_2 \rightarrow NO_3^- + NO_2^- + H_2O$
(z) $C + HNO_3 \rightarrow NO_2\uparrow + H_2O + CO_2\uparrow$

5. Complete and balance the following equations. When the reaction occurs in acidic solution, H^+ and/or H_2O may be added on either side of the equation, as necessary, to balance the equation properly; when the reaction occurs in basic solution, OH^- and/or H_2O may be added, as necessary, on either side of the equation. Sometimes, no indication of the acidity of the solution is given below if neither H^+ nor OH^- is necessary as a reactant or product.

(a) $PbO_2 + Cl^- \rightarrow Pb^{++} + Cl_2$ (acidic solution)
(b) $NO_3^- + Zn \rightarrow NH_4^+ + Zn^{++}$ (acidic solution)
(c) $CN^- + MnO_4^- \rightarrow CNO^- + MnO_2$ (basic solution)
(d) $Fe^{++} + MnO_4^- \rightarrow Fe^{+++} + Mn^{++}$ (acidic solution)
(e) $CH_2O + [Ag(NH_3)_2]^+ \rightarrow Ag + HCO_2^- + NH_3$ (basic solution)
(f) $H_2S + I_2 \rightarrow S + I^-$ (acidic solution)
(g) $I_2 + H_3AsO_3 \rightarrow I^- + H_3AsO_4$ (acidic solution)
(h) $CN^- + [Fe(CN)_6]^{\equiv} \rightarrow CNO^- + [Fe(CN)_6]^{\equiv}$ (basic solution)
(i) $S_2O_3^{=} + I_2 \rightarrow S_4O_6^{=} + I^-$
(j) $C_2H_4 + MnO_4^- \rightarrow Mn^{++} + CO_2$ (acidic solution)
(k) $CrO_4^{=} + HSnO_2^- \rightarrow HSnO_3^- + CrO_2^-$ (basic solution)
(l) $MnO_2 + Cl^- \rightarrow Mn^{++} + Cl_2$ (acidic solution)
(m) $Ag + NO_3^- \rightarrow Ag^+ + NO$ (acidic solution)
(n) $Fe^{++} + Cr_2O_7^{=} \rightarrow Fe^{+++} + Cr^{+++}$ (acidic solution)
(o) $CrO_2^- + H_2O_2 \rightarrow CrO_4^{=}$ (basic solution)
(p) $Mn^{++} + Br_2 \rightarrow MnO_2 + Br^-$ (basic solution)
(q) $Br_2 \rightarrow BrO_3^- + Br^-$ (basic solution)
(r) $Sn^{++} + HgCl_2 + Cl^- \rightarrow SnCl_6^{=} + Hg_2Cl_2$
(s) $Cr_2O_7^{=} + I^- \rightarrow Cr^{+++} + I_2$ (acidic solution)
(t) $Ag^+ + AsH_3 \rightarrow Ag + H_3AsO_3$ (acidic solution)
(u) $MnO_2 + H_2C_2O_4 \rightarrow Mn^{++} + CO_2$ (acidic solution)
(v) $H_2O_2 + ClO_2 \rightarrow ClO_2^- + O_2$ (basic solution)
(w) $Fe^{+++} + I^- \rightarrow Fe^{++} + I_2$

(x) $BrO_3^- + AsO_3^{\equiv} \rightarrow Br^- + AsO_4^{\equiv}$
(y) $Hg_2Cl_2 + NH_3 \rightarrow Hg + HgNH_2Cl + NH_4^+ + Cl^-$
(z) $S_2O_3^= + H_2O_2 \rightarrow S_4O_6^=$ (acidic solution)

PROBLEMS

1. Calculate the equivalent weight of the oxidizing and reducing agent in the following reactions of Question 4: (b), (e), (f), (l), and (w).

Ans. (b) NO_3^-, *20.67;* *Cu, 31.77* (e) MnO_4^-, *23.79;* H_2S, *17.04* (f) MnO_4^-, *39.65;* $S^=$, *16.03* (l) MnO_4^-, *23.79;* H_2O_2, *17.01* (w) $MnO_4^= \rightarrow MnO_2$, *59.47;* $MnO_4^= \rightarrow MnO_4^-$, *118.94*

2. What weight of $KMnO_4$ is required to oxidize 5.32 g. of $FeSO_4$ in a solution acidified with sulfuric acid?

$$5\ Fe^{++} + MnO_4^- + 8\ H^+ \rightarrow 5\ Fe^{+++} + Mn^{++} + 4\ H_2O$$

Ans. 1.11 g.

3. How many grams of $FeCl_2$ will be oxidized by 50.0 ml. of 0.100 N $K_2Cr_2O_7$ in HCl solution?

$$Fe^{++} + Cr_2O_7^= + H^+ \rightarrow Fe^{+++} + Cr^{+++} + H_2O \text{ (unbalanced)}$$

Ans. 0.634 g.

4. How many ml. of a 0.100 N iodide solution would be required in the reduction of the copper in a 210 mg. sample of $CuSO_4$?

$$2\ Cu^{++} + 4\ I^- \rightarrow 2\ CuI + I_2$$

Ans. 26.3 ml.

5. What weight of aluminum would be necessary to reduce all the silver in 100 ml. of a 1.50 N solution of $AgNO_3$?

$$3\ Ag^+ + Al \rightarrow 3\ Ag + Al^{+3}$$

Ans. 1.35 g.

6. A 10 ml. solution of 0.100 N $Na_2S_2O_3$ was used in the titration of 12.5 ml. of an iodine solution. Calculate the normality of the iodine solution.

$$2\ S_2O_3^= + I_2 \rightarrow S_4O_6^= + 2\ I^-$$

Ans. 0.080 N

7. A standard solution of oxalic acid contains 0.750 g. of $H_2C_2O_4 \cdot 2\ H_2O$ in 22.40 ml. of solution. In the titration of this oxalic acid solution, 20.00 ml. of a potassium permanganate solution were required. Calculate the normality of the potassium permanganate solution.

$$H_2C_2O_4 + MnO_4^- + H^+ \rightarrow Mn^{++} + H_2O + CO_2 \quad \text{(unbalanced)}$$

Ans. 0.601 N

8. The chlorine content of a solution of chlorine water is to be determined. A 25.0 ml. sample (sp. gr. = 1.02) of this chlorine water is treated with an excess of potassium iodide. To titrate the liberated iodine, 22.0 ml. of 0.100 N $Na_2S_2O_3$

are required. Calculate the percentage of chlorine by weight in the chlorine water. (Chlorine water is a solution of free chlorine in water.)

$$Cl_2 + 2\ I^- \rightarrow 2\ Cl^- + I_2$$

Ans. *0.306 %*

9. State for each of the following whether the initial substance is an oxidizing agent or a reducing agent and make the requested conversion.

(a) 0.3 mole of HBr to equivalent weights of HBr (product is Br_2).

(b) 10 equivalent weights of $KMnO_4$ to moles of $KMnO_4$ (product is Mn^{++}).

(c) 10 milliequivalent weights of HNO_3 to milligrams of HNO_3 (product is NO).

Ans. *(a) 0.3 eq. wts.,* *(b) 2 moles,* *(c) 210 mg.*

10. How many milligrams of potassium permanganate are needed to oxidize completely 2.0 grams of iron (II) ammonium sulfate 6-hydrate, $Fe(NH_4)_2(SO_4)_2 \cdot 6\ H_2O$, in acid solution. The iron is oxidized from the +2 oxidation number to +3; the permanganate ion is reduced from MnO_4^- to Mn^{++}.

Ans. *170 mg.*

11. A solution of $NaMnO_4$ on the laboratory shelf is labeled as being 0.050 M. What would its normality be if it were used in the following reactions? (Complete and balance the equation before making the calculation.)

(a) $Sn^{++} + MnO_4^- \rightarrow Sn^{++++} + Mn^{++}$ (acid solution)

(b) $Ga(s) + MnO_4^- \rightarrow MnO_2(s) + Ga(OH)_3(s)$

(c) $Fe(OH)_2(s) + MnO_4^- \rightarrow Fe(OH)_3(s) + MnO_4^{=}$ (basic solution)

Note: (s) refers to solid crystals.

Ans. *(a) 0.250 N,* *(b) 0.150 N,* *(c) 0.050 N*

12. If O_2 is reduced to H_2O while KI is oxidized to I_2, how many ml. of O_2 gas (S.T.P.) are required to oxidize 3.60 g. of KI in solution?

Ans. *121 ml.*

REFERENCES

"Redox Revisited," K. L. Lockwood, *J. Chem. Educ.*, **38** (6) 326 (1961).

"Oxidation Number in Auto-Redox Reactions," L. P. Eblin, *J. Chem. Educ.*, **28** (4) 221 (1951).

CHAPTER FIFTEEN

The Relationship of the Periodic Classification to the Properties of the Elements

In Chapter 3, it was pointed out that, though each element is different from every other element, similarities in electron structures make possible arrangements that aid greatly in correlating the study of properties and compounds of the elements. The most widely used arrangement is the Periodic Table. In Chapter 3, we considered the relationship between the electron structure and the position of the element in the Periodic Table. We shall now consider in more detail the characteristics which are important in determining the properties of the elements.

15.1 Variation of Properties within Periods and Groups of the Periodic Table

The properties of the elements are determined largely by their atomic structures. As was pointed out in Chapter 3, differences in chemical properties are caused primarily by differences in three characteristics: (1) the magnitude of the nuclear charge and the number of electrons in the shells surrounding the nucleus, both of which are equal to the atomic number, (2) the number of shells of electrons and the number of electrons in these shells, particularly in the valence shells, and (3) the distances of the electrons in the various shells from each other and from the nucleus.

1. *Variation in Atomic Radii.* (See Table on inside back cover.) In general, from left to right across the periods, each succeeding element has a smaller atomic radius than the element preceding it. The atomic radii of the rare gases at the ends of the periods, however, are larger than those of the elements of next lower atomic number; in the free state, the rare gases have completed outer shells.

Each succeeding element across the table has a nuclear charge of one more and has one more orbital electron than the preceding element, though the number of shells is constant in each period. In general, the larger the nuclear charge and number of orbital electrons, the larger will be the force of electrostatic attraction between the nucleus and orbital electrons. This, in theory, causes the gradation in atomic radii across the period.

Atomic radii are based upon interatomic distances in the solid state. In general, strong chemical bonds hold atoms close together in the solid state. However, with the rare gases, such as argon, only weak van der Waals forces hold the atoms together in the crystal lattice. This results in abnormally large interatomic distances and atomic radii for these elements.

The gradation from highly metallic sodium to highly nonmetallic chlorine in the third period shown in Table 15·1 is explainable in terms of the smaller size of each

TABLE 15·1

	Na	*Mg*	*Al*	*Si*	*P*	*S*	*Cl*	*A*
Atomic radius, Å	1.86	1.60	1.48	1.17	1.08	1.06	0.97	1.91
Nuclear charge	+11	+12	+13	+14	+15	+16	+17	+18
Electronic structure	2,8,1	2,8,2	2,8,3	2,8,4	2,8,5	2,8,6	2,8,7	2,8,8

succeeding element in the series. The tendency for each succeeding element to become less metallic results from the fact that the valence electrons are less readily lost as their distance from the positive nucleus becomes less, and the attraction for additional electrons from other atoms becomes greater.

Down the groups, succeeding elements have increasing atomic radii, corresponding to larger numbers of electron shells as shown in Table 15·2. These ele-

TABLE 15·2

	Atomic Radius, Å	*Nuclear Charge*	*Electronic Structure*
Li	1.50	+3	2,1
Na	1.86	+11	2,8,1
K	2.27	+19	2,8,8,1
Rb	2.43	+37	2,8,18,8,1
Cs	2.62	+55	2,8,18,18,8,1
Fr	2.7	+87	2,8,18,32,18,8,1

ments become more metallic (lose valence electrons more readily) as their size and weight increase. This results from the fact that the valence electrons are held less strongly with additional intervening electron shells even though the charge on the nucleus is greater with each succeeding element down a group. Francium is the most active metal of Group IA and radium of Group IIA. Even though Groups IVA, VA, VIA, and VIIA are headed by the nonmetals carbon, nitrogen, oxygen, and fluorine respectively, this same trend toward metallicity down the groups is generally noted. Lead, bismuth, polonium, and astatine all exhibit metallic properties, at least to some degree.

2. *Variations in ionic radii.* The radius of a positive ion is less than that of its parent atom. The disappearance of the outermost shell of electrons as the positive ion is formed results in a smaller radius for the system. Thus the radius of the sodium atom (2,8,1) is 1.86 Å, whereas that of the sodium ion, Na^+ (2,8,0) is 0.95 Å. Not only does the outer electron shell of the sodium atom disappear as the sodium ion is formed, but also the radii of the two remaining electron shells decrease because of an increase in "effective" nuclear charge as the valence electron is removed, giving rise to a greater average attraction of the nucleus per remaining electron. Down the groups of the Periodic Table, positive ions of succeeding elements have larger radii corresponding to larger numbers of electron shells (Table 15·3).

TABLE 15·3

Ion	*Radius, Å*	*Nuclear Charge*	*Electronic Structure*
Li^+	0.60	+3	2,0
Na^+	0.95	+11	2,8,0
K^+	1.33	+19	2,8,8,0
Rb^+	1.48	+37	2,8,18,8,0
Cs^+	1.69	+55	2,8,18,18,8,0

A simple negative ion is formed by the addition of one or more electrons to the valence shell of an atom. This results in a greater force of repulsion among the orbital electrons and a decrease in the "effective" nuclear charge per electron. Both effects operate in the same direction to cause the radius of a negative ion to be greater than that of the parent atom. For example, the chlorine atom (2,8,7) has a radius of 0.99 Å, whereas that of the chloride ion (2,8,8) is 1.81 Å, i.e., nearly twice as large. Down the groups negative ions of succeeding elements have more electron shells, greater nuclear charge, and larger radii (Table 15·4).

TABLE 15·4

Ion	*Radius, Å*	*Nuclear Charge*	*Electronic Structure*
F^-	1.36	+9	2,8
Cl^-	1.81	+17	2,8,8
Br^-	1.95	+35	2,8,18,8
I^-	2.16	+53	2,8,18,18,8

Ions which have the same number of electrons, such as those in the series Na^+, Mg^{++}, Al^{+++}, and Si^{++++}, and those in the series P^{-3}, $S^{=}$, and Cl^- are termed **isoelectronic.** The greater the nuclear charge, the smaller the ionic radius in a series of isoelectronic ions. This trend is illustrated in Table 15·5 for the ions of the

TABLE 15·5

Ion	*Na^+*	*Mg^{++}*	*Al^{+3}*	*Si^{+4}*	*P^{-3}*	*$S^{=}$*	*Cl^-*	*Ar*
Radius, Å	0.95	0.65	0.50	0.41	2.12	1.84	1.81	1.91
Nuclear charge	+11	+12	+13	+14	+15	+16	+17	+18
Electronic structure	2,8,0	2,8,0	2,8,0	2,8,0	2,8,8	2,8,8	2,8,8	2,8,8

elements of the third period. As we shall see later, many of the properties of ions can best be explained in terms of their sizes and charges.

3. *Variation in ionization potentials.* The amount of energy required to remove the most loosely bound electron from an atom is called its **ionization potential** or, more precisely, its **first ionization potential.** This change may be represented by the equation

$$X + \text{energy} \rightarrow X^+ + e^-$$

In general, the greater the nuclear charge of atoms with the same number of electron shells, the greater the ionization potential (Table 15·6). This is true because

TABLE 15·6

	Li	*Be*	*B*	*C*	*N*	*O*	*F*	*Ne*
Ionization potential (in volts)	5.39	9.32	8.30	11.26	14.54	13.61	17.42	21.60
Nuclear charge	+3	+4	+5	+6	+7	+8	+9	+10
Electronic structure	2,1	2,2	2,3	2,4	2,5	2,6	2,7	2,8

the greater the nuclear charge, the greater the attraction of the nucleus for electrons. In general, therefore, succeeding elements across the periods have larger ionization potentials.

Fig. 15–1 shows the relationships between first ionization potentials and atomic numbers of several elements. The values of the first ionization potentials are provided in Table 15·7, page 244. Note that the ionization potential of boron is less

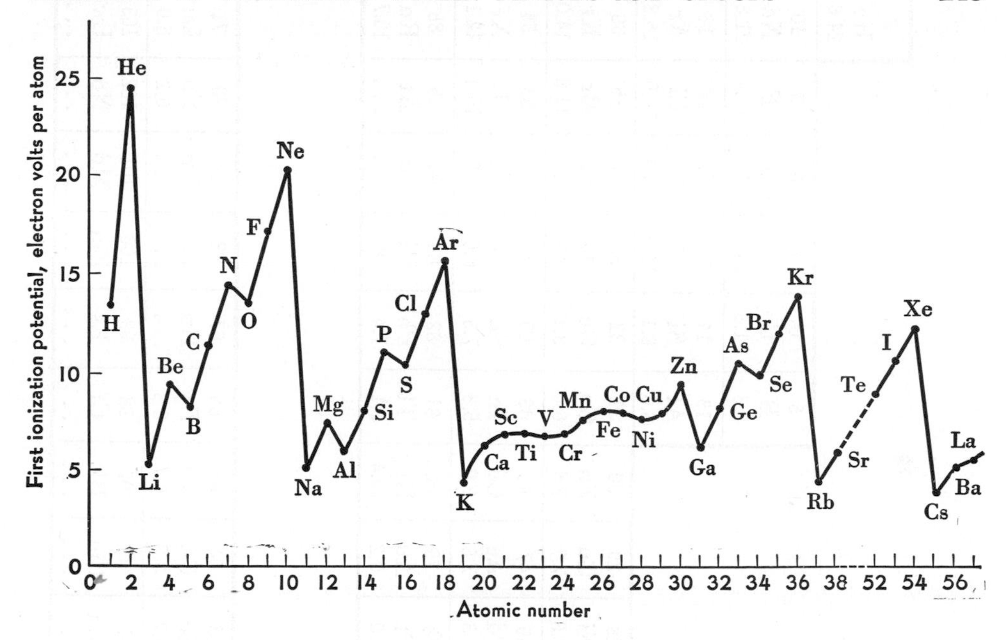

Fig. 15–1 A graphic illustration of the periodic relationships between first ionization potentials and atomic numbers.

than that of beryllium. This is explained in terms of the relative attraction by the positive nucleus of an atom for electrons of different subshells. On the average, an *s* electron will be attracted to the nucleus more tightly than a *p* electron of the same principal shell, a *p* electron more closely than a *d* electron, and so on. This means that an *s* electron will be harder to remove from an atom than a *p* electron, a *p* electron harder to remove than a *d* electron, and a *d* electron harder to remove than an *f* electron, and the ionization potentials will decrease in this order. The electron removed during the ionization of beryllium ($1s^2$, $2s^2$) is an *s* electron whereas a *p* electron is removed during the ionization of boron ($1s^2$, $2s^2$, $2p^1$), and this results in a lower ionization potential for boron even though its nuclear charge is greater by one unit. The ionization potential of nitrogen is abnormally high and that for oxygen slightly lower because of the stability associated with the half-filled $2p$ subshell in nitrogen (Section 3.16).

The values given in Fig. 15–1 and Tables 15·6 and 15·7 are for the removal of one electron and are therefore first ionization potentials. The energy required to remove a second electron is called the **second ionization potential.** Third, fourth, etc., ionization potentials may be defined in a similar fashion.

Metallic elements have small ionization potentials and nonmetals large ones. This means that the metals form positive ions readily by the loss of valence electrons and that the nonmetals do not tend to form positive ions during chemical changes.

The attractive force exerted by the positive nucleus on the valence electrons is partially counterbalanced by the repulsive forces of electrons in inner shells. The

TABLE 15·7 First Ionization Potentials of Some of the Elements

Potentials are given in electron volts per atom.

1 **H** 13.6																	2 **He** 24.6
3 **Li** 5.4	4 **Be** 9.3											5 **B** 8.3	6 **C** 11.3	7 **N** 14.5	8 **O** 13.6	9 **F** 17.4	10 **Ne** 21.6
11 **Na** 5.1	12 **Mg** 7.6											13 **Al** 6.0	14 **Si** 8.1	15 **P** 11.0	16 **S** 10.4	17 **Cl** 13.0	18 **Ar** 15.8
19 **K** 4.3	20 **Ca** 6.1	21 **Sc** 6.6	22 **Ti** 6.8	23 **V** 6.7	24 **Cr** 6.8	25 **Mn** 7.4	26 **Fe** 7.9	27 **Co** 7.9	28 **Ni** 7.6	29 **Cu** 7.7	30 **Zn** 9.4	31 **Ga** 6.0	32 **Ge** 8.1	33 **As** 10	34 **Se** 9.8	35 **Br** 11.8	36 **Kr** 14.0
37 **Rb** 4.2	38 **Sr** 5.7	39 **Y** 6.6	40 **Zr** 7.0	41 **Nb** 6.8	42 **Mo** 7.2	43 **Tc** . . .	44 **Ru** 7.5	45 **Rh** 7.7	46 **Pd** 8.3	47 **Ag** 7.6	48 **Cd** 9.0	49 **In** 5.8	50 **Sn** 7.3	51 **Sb** 8.6	52 **Te** 9.0	53 **I** 10.4	54 **Xe** 12.1
55 **Cs** 3.9	56 **Ba** 5.2	[57-71] *	72 **Hf** 5.5	73 **Ta** 6	74 **W** 8.0	75 **Re** 7.9	76 **Os** 8.7	77 **Ir** 9.2	78 **Pt** 9.0	79 **Au** 9.2	80 **Hg** 10.4	81 **Tl** 6.1	82 **Pb** 7.4	83 **Bi** 8	84 **Po** . . .	85 **At** . . .	86 **Rn** 10.7
87 **Fr** . . .	88 **Ra** 5.3	[89-103] †															

* LANTHANIDE SERIES	57 **La** 5.6	58 **Ce** 6.9	59 **Pr** 5.8	60 **Nd** 6.3	61 **Pm** . . .	62 **Sm** 5.6	63 **Eu** 5.7	64 **Gd** 6.2	65 **Tb** 6.7	66 **Dy** 6.8	67 **Ho** . . .	68 **Er** . . .	69 **Tm** . . .	70 **Yb** 6.2	71 **Lu** 5.0
† ACTINIDE SERIES	89 **Ac** . . .	90 **Th** . . .	91 **Pa** . . .	92 **U** 4	93 **Np** . . .	94 **Pu** . . .	95 **Am** . . .	96 **Cm** . . .	97 **Bk** . . .	98 **Cf** . . .	99 **Es** . . .	100 **Fm** . . .	101 **Md** . . .	102 **No** . . .	103 **Lw** . . .

electron to be removed from an atom is thus shielded from the nucleus by these inner shells. This shielding, and the increasing distance of the outer electron from the nucleus, is the apparent explanation of the fact that down the groups succeeding elements have smaller ionization potentials. Members of a group as a rule have the same outer electronic configuration, and the same number of valence electrons (Table 15·8).

TABLE 15·8

Element	*Ionization Potential*	*Nuclear Charge*	*Electronic Structure*
Li	5.39	+3	2,1
Na	5.14	+11	2,8,1
K	4.34	+19	2,8,8,1
Rb	4.18	+37	2,8,18,8,1
Cs	3.89	+55	2,8,18,18,8,1

The size of the ionization potential is to some degree a measure of the chemical activity of a metal, i.e., its tendency to form positive ions by losing valence electrons. In general, the smaller the ionization potential the more active the metal. With the possible exception of francium, cesium has the smallest ionization potential and is the most active metal.

4. *Variation in electron affinities.* Just as the ionization potential is a measure of the energy required to remove an electron from an atom to form a positive ion, another quantity, the **electron affinity,** is a measure of the energy released when an extra electron is added to an atom to form a negative ion. The change is expressed by the equation

$$X + e^- \rightarrow X^- + \text{energy}$$

Metal atoms have little tendency to form negative ions by gaining extra electrons; thus their electron affinities are very small. Nonmetallic elements, on the other hand, have large electron affinities and, as a result, are good oxidizing agents. Unexpectedly, chlorine has a greater electron affinity (87 kcal. per mole or 3.75 electron volts per atom) than fluorine (84 kcal. per mole or 3.6 electron volts per atom) (Table 15·9, page 246). However, fluorine is a better oxidizing agent than chlorine, even though its electron affinity is less, because the F_2 molecule is more easily broken into single atoms.

In general, across the periods of the Periodic Table, succeeding elements have higher electron affinities, as nonmetallic character increases. In general, succeeding elements down the groups have smaller electron affinities as metallic character becomes more pronounced.

5. *Variation in electronegativities.* The term **electronegativity** was defined in Section 4.6 as a measure of the attraction of an atom for the electrons in its outer

TABLE 15·9 Electron Affinities for the Elements of Group VIIA, in Electron Volts per Atom

Element	*Electron affinity, electron volts/atom*	*Electronic structure*
F	3.63	2, 7
Cl	3.78	2, 8, 7
Br	3.54	2, 8, 18, 7
I	3.24	2, 8, 18, 18, 7

shell. Values for the electronegativities of many of the elements are provided in Table 4·2 in Chapter 4. The electronegativity of an atom is related in a general way to both its ionization potential and electron affinity. In fact, it has been suggested by R. S. Mulliken, a chemical physicist, that the average of the ionization potential and the electron affinity of an atom should be a suitable measure of its electronegativity. The most electronegative elements are found toward the end of the periods; they are the elements with large ionization potentials and large electron affinities, i.e., the nonmetals. The most electropositive elements, those with low electronegativities (small ionization potentials and nearly zero electron affinities) are found at the beginning of the periods. These are the alkali metals and alkaline earth metals. The elements near the middle of the periods have electronegativities which are intermediate in value. As we go down a group, succeeding elements are less electronegative (See Table 4·2).

When the difference between the electronegativities of the two atoms involved in a bond is large, the bond is likely to be ionic in character. Such is the case with LiF, NaCl, K_2O, Li_3N, and CsBr, where the electronegativity difference is 2 or more. Bonds between atoms with small differences in electronegativities are primarily covalent in character. This is the case with CO_2, CCl_4, I_2O_5, NI_3, ICl, NO, and BN. It follows that elements at the extreme left of the table form ionic bonds with those at the extreme right of the table, whereas elements close together in the table form covalent bonds with one another.

6. *Variation in strength as oxidizing and reducing agents.* Oxidizing agents are characterized by their tendency to take up electrons and go into lower oxidation states. The nonmetals at the extreme right of the Periodic Table, with their relatively high ionization potentials, electron affinities, and electronegativities, tend to act as oxidizing agents when they combine with other substances. Reducing agents tend to give up electrons and go into higher oxidation states when they enter into chemical reactions. The reducing power is highest with the metals at the beginning of the periods, where the ionization potentials, electron affinities, and electronegativities are low. In general, the reducing strength of the elements is progressively lower as we pass across the periods and higher as we go down the

groups. Thus francium should be the strongest reducing agent and fluorine the strongest oxidizing agent of all the elements.

7. *Variation in the ionization of hydroxyl compounds.* Hydroxyl compounds of elements at the beginning of the periods consist of metal ions and hydroxide ions, and thus show basic character. Examples are given below.

$$Na(OH) \rightarrow Na^{+} + OH^{-}$$
$$Ca(OH)_2 \rightarrow Ca^{++} + 2\ OH^{-}$$

The basic character of elements which form large positive ions of low charge is particularly pronounced. On the other hand, hydroxyl compounds of elements which form small positive ions and are found at the ends of the periods ionize as acids in water. This is the case with hydroxyl compounds of chlorine and nitrogen.

$$HOCl \rightarrow H^{+} + OCl^{-}$$
$$HONO_2 \rightarrow H^{+} + ONO_2^{-}$$

These properties can be postulated as arising because of the different electronegativities of the various elements. In general, an element, E, can be thought of as being associated with one or more hydroxyl groups in a hydroxyl compound:

$$E \overset{a}{\Big(} :\ddot{\underset{\cdot\cdot}{O}}: \overset{b}{\Big(} H$$

If E has a relatively low electronegativity, its attraction for electrons is low, little tendency exists for it to form a strong covalent bond with the oxygen atom, and the bond between the element and oxygen tends to be weaker than that between oxygen and hydrogen. Hence, the bond at *a* tends to be ionic, hydroxyl ions are released to the solution, and the material behaves as a base. Large size and small charge are factors operating in the direction of low electronegativity, characteristics of the more metallic elements.

If, on the other hand, the element E has a relatively high electronegativity, it attracts the electrons which are available for sharing between it and the oxygen atom rather tightly, giving rise to a relatively strong bond between the element E and the oxygen atom. The oxygen-hydrogen bond is thereby weakened through the displacement of electrons toward the element E, the bond at *b* is ionic releasing hydrogen ions to the solution, and the material behaves as an acid. Small size and large charge operate in the direction of high electronegativity, characteristics of the more nonmetallic elements.

The hydroxides of the elements near the heavy diagonal line separating the metals from the nonmetals in the Periodic Table are usually **amphoteric.** This means that they act as acids toward strong bases and as bases toward strong acids. The amphoterism of aluminum hydroxide is reflected in its solubility in both strong acids and strong bases.

$$Al(OH)_3 + OH^{-} \rightarrow Al(OH)_4^{-}$$
$$Al(OH)_3 + 3\ H^{+} \rightarrow Al^{+++} + 3\ H_2O$$

15.2 Uses of the Periodic Table

The systematic arrangement of the elements found in the Periodic Table has several applications. Most important of these are (1) for the classification of the elements, (2) for the prediction of undiscovered elements and their properties, and (3) for the stimulation of research.

1. *Classification of the elements.* The classification of elements with similar properties into groups simplifies their study. If, for example, one has learned the properties of sodium of Periodic Group IA, one will also know many of the properties of lithium, potassium, rubidium, cesium, and francium. Sodium is an active metal that reacts vigorously with water giving hydrogen gas and forming sodium hydroxide, a strong base. The other alkali metals listed above react with water in a similar fashion. Chlorine of Group VIIA reacts vigorously with sodium forming sodium chloride, a salt. Fluorine, bromine, and iodine of the same group also form salts with sodium.

The fact that elements within a group have similar properties should not be overemphasized, however, because, as has been shown earlier in the chapter, there is a gradation in properties of the elements down the groups so that certain of these properties may be quite different. For example, lithium reacts with water more slowly than does sodium, whereas potassium, rubidium, and cesium react much more vigorously. Chlorine forms a series of oxyacids HClO, $HClO_2$, $HClO_3$, and $HClO_4$, and the corresponding sodium salts, NaClO, $NaClO_2$, $NaClO_3$, and $NaClO_4$. On the other hand, no oxyacids or oxysalts of fluorine have been prepared, a difference in properties which is related to the fact that fluorine is more electronegative than oxygen whereas chlorine and the other elements of Group VIIA are less electronegative than oxygen (see Table 4·2). Nitrogen, the first member of Group VA, is entirely nonmetallic in character whereas bismuth, the last member of this group, is mostly metallic in its properties.

Periodicity as regards valence electrons is reflected in periodicity of oxidation states (Table 15·10). Hydrogen, lithium, and sodium have one valence electron each, and each shows an oxidation number of +1 when this electron is transferred to another atom in the formation of chemical bonds. Carbon and silicon atoms with four valence electrons may form four polar covalent bonds in which the shared electron pairs are shifted away (+4 oxidation number) or towards (−4

TABLE 15·10 Periodicity of Oxidation States

+1 H							0 He
+1 Li	+2 Be	+3 B	+4, −4 C	+5, −3 N	−2 O	−1 F	0 Ne
+1 Na	+2 Mg	+3 Al	+4, −4 Si	+5, −3 P	−2 S	−1 Cl	0 Ar

oxidation number) the carbon or silicon atom. Fluorine and chlorine atoms, each with seven valence electrons, assume completed octets by the addition of one electron giving them −1 oxidation numbers. It should be noted, however, that the Periodic Table emphasizes at most only the maximum and minimum oxidation number, even though many of the elements exhibit additional intermediate oxidation numbers. For example, nitrogen of Group VA forms N_2O_5 with oxidation number +5 because it has five valence electrons, the same number as that of the group, and it forms NH_3 with oxidation number −3 because it lacks three electrons for a complete outer shell. In addition, however, it exhibits oxidation numbers of +4 in NO_2, +3 in N_2O_3, +2 in NO, +1 in N_2O, zero in N_2, −1 in NH_2OH, and −2 in N_2H_4. Furthermore, the number of the group often reflects a relatively minor oxidation number of an element. Thus, copper of Group IB forms a large and important series of compounds in which it is divalent (oxidation number +2), whereas its monovalent compounds (oxidation number +1) are relatively few in number.

2. *Prediction of undiscovered elements.* A very remarkable use of the Periodic Table was made by Mendeleev. His table included only sixty-two elements, the number known at that time. In order that related elements might fall in the same group, he left gaps in his table and predicted that elements would be discovered later to fill these vacant places. He predicted the existence and properties of six elements corresponding to vacant places in his table. These elements have since been discovered; they are scandium, gallium, germanium, technetium, rhenium, and polonium, and they all have properties similar to those predicted by Mendeleev.

A comparison of the properties predicted by Mendeleev for germanium, which he called eka-silicon, and those determined experimentally for the element is given below:

Predicted Properties for Eka-silicon (1871)	*Observed Properties of Germanium (discovered in 1886)*
Atomic weight, 72	Atomic weight, 72.60
Specific gravity, 5.5	Specific gravity, 5.36
A gray colored metal	A grayish-white metal
Valence of 4 toward oxygen	Valence of 4 toward oxygen
EsO_2, a white solid of sp. gr. 4.7, and high m.p.	GeO_2, a white solid of sp. gr. 4.70, m.p. 1100° C
$EsCl_4$, a volatile liquid, b.p. below 100°, and sp. gr. 1.9	$GeCl_4$, a volatile liquid, b.p. 83°, and sp. gr. 1.88
Es will be acted upon by acids only slightly, and not at all by alkalies, like NaOH	Ge does not react with HCl or NaOH, but dissolves in concentrated HNO_3

3. *Stimulation of research.* The Periodic Table has stimulated chemists and physicists to do extensive research. Forty-one elements have been discovered since Mendeleev's original periodic classification of the elements. Before Moseley's work and the assignment of atomic numbers to the elements, much research was

done to establish accurately the atomic weights in order that the elements might be placed in their proper positions in the table. For example, the element indium was thought to have a valence of two, and because its equivalent weight had been found to be about 38, its atomic weight was thought to be about 2×38, or 76. According to the Periodic Table, however, an atomic weight of 76 would place indium between arsenic (74.9) and selenium (79.0) where it obviously did not belong. There was, however, a vacant place in the table, at that time, between cadmium (112.4) and tin (118.7). The general properties of indium were such that it fitted in this Group III position much better than between arsenic and selenium, which are in Groups V and VI, respectively. Later investigations showed indium to have a valence of three instead of two. This meant that its atomic weight would be 3×38, or about 114, instead of 2×38, or 76. Consequently, indium was placed in its logical position in the Periodic Table.

QUESTIONS

1. State the Periodic Law. How can the Periodic Law be accounted for by use of the theory of atomic structure?

2. Account for the positions of argon, cobalt, tellurium, and thorium in the Periodic Table in view of the fact that their positions are not in keeping with their atomic weights.

3. Give the meaning of the following terms as applied to the Periodic Table: period, group, short period, and long period.

4. From its position in the Periodic Table predict the maximum positive oxidation state to be expected for each of the following: gallium, germanium, cesium, astatine, technetium, and vanadium.

5. Why is the radius of a positive ion less than that of its parent atom?

6. Account for the decrease in radius in the following series of isoelectronic ions: Na^{+}, Mg^{++}, Al^{+++}, and Si^{++++}.

7. Relate metallicity to ionization potential, electron affinity, and electronegativity.

8. Why do negative ions have larger radii than their parent atoms?

9. What is the principal similarity between elements in different subgroups of a given group?

10. From their positions in the Periodic Table predict which will be (a) more electronegative, carbon or nitrogen; (b) more electropositive, magnesium or calcium; (c) more metallic, germanium or arsenic; (d) more nonmetallic, iodine or bromine; (e) the stronger reducing agent, lithium or boron; (f) the stronger oxidizing agent, sulfur or chlorine; (g) the larger in atomic radius, potassium or calcium; (h) the larger in positive ionic radius, sodium or cesium; (i) the larger in negative ionic radius, fluorine or chlorine; (j) the more acidic, the hydroxide of aluminum or that of silicon.

11. (a) State which should have the higher ionization potential, and explain why: (1) sodium or magnesium; (2) magnesium or calcium; (3) beryllium or boron; (4) phosphorus or sulfur.

(b) Which should be more basic, $Be(OH)_2$ or $Mg(OH)_2$? Why?

(c) Which should be more acidic, NaOH or HOCl? Why?

(d) Which should be more acidic, HOCl or HOI? Why?

(e) Which should have the higher electron affinity, chlorine or bromine? Why?

(f) Which should be more electronegative, oxygen or phosphorus? Why?

12. Summarize several important uses of the Periodic Table.

CHAPTER SIXTEEN

Chemical Equilibrium

We have frequently employed the general principle of equilibrium in the preceding chapters. **A condition of equilibrium is reached in a system when two opposing changes occur simultaneously at the same rate.** Most of our examples of equilibrium have been systems involving physical changes rather than chemical changes. For example, we have defined the vapor pressure of a liquid (Section 9.2) as the pressure exerted by a vapor in equilibrium with its liquid at a given temperature. The two opposing changes in this case are the evaporation of the liquid and the condensation of the vapor. An example of a chemical equilibrium was given in Section 6.6; this equilibrium involved the reduction of steam by hot iron.

$$3\ Fe + 4\ H_2O \rightleftharpoons Fe_3O_4 + 4\ H_2$$

In this case, the two opposing changes are chemical reactions. At equilibrium these two chemical changes in opposite directions occur at the same rate.

The equilibrium state of a given reversible reaction varies with the conditions under which the reaction takes place. A knowledge of the effect of a change in conditions upon an equilibrium is very important because by proper selection of conditions it is possible to control the relative amounts of the substances which are present at equilibrium. The conditions which influence chemical equilibria are very important both in the laboratory and in industrial practice. For example, although it had been known for many years that nitrogen and hydrogen react to form ammonia ($N_2 + 3\ H_2 \rightleftharpoons 2\ NH_3$), it was only comparatively recently that the industrial manufacture of ammonia by means of this reaction was achieved through an understanding of the factors which influence this equilibrium.

A clear understanding of the subject of chemical equilibrium is possible only after the subject of reaction rate and the factors which influence it has been studied.

16.1 Collision Theory of the Reaction Rate

The rate of a chemical reaction may be defined as the number of moles of a substance which disappear or are formed in the reaction per unit volume in a unit of time. The rates of reactions vary greatly. Reactions involving ions proceed very rapidly. When solutions of sodium hydroxide and hydrochloric acid are mixed, neutralization occurs nearly instantaneously, and involves the union of hydronium ions and hydroxide ions with the formation of water ($H_3O^+ + OH^- \rightarrow 2\ H_2O$). Reactions involving molecules are slower than those involving ions. The reaction between hydrogen and oxygen is extremely slow at room temperature, but when a mixture of the gases is heated to 500°, the reaction to form steam proceeds at a much faster rate. When a mixture of hydrogen and oxygen is ignited, the reaction takes place explosively.

Before two or more molecules (or ions) can react, they must collide with one another. In slow reactions only a few of the billions of collisions that occur between molecules result in reaction. The only collisions which are effective are those involving molecules possessing an energy content higher than a certain minimum value, which is called **energy of activation** (Fig. 16–1). This minimum value is

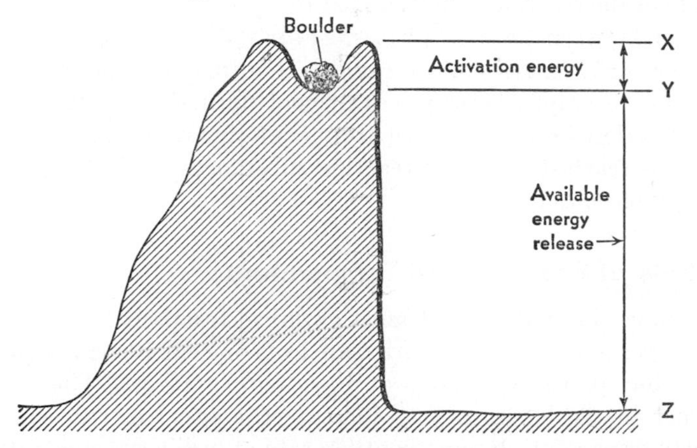

Fig. 16–1 A graphic illustration, by analogy, of activation energy in relationship to available energy release. The boulder potentially can release the amount of energy created by its falling the distance from height Y to height Z. However, an amount of energy must be put into the system (the activation energy) sufficient to lift the boulder over the barrier through the distance Y to X before the boulder can fall to Z. The activation energy is regained as the boulder falls through the distance X to Y, and the additional energy is then released in the continued fall from Y to Z. The *net* energy released is that provided by the fall from Y to Z.

far above the average energy content of the molecules in the case of slow reactions. The kinetic energies of a large fraction of the molecules in a system are close to an average value. However, a few of the molecules, the fast moving ones, have relatively high kinetic energies while the slow moving ones have relatively low energies. The collisions between the fast moving molecules are most apt to be effective ones. In very fast reactions the fraction of molecules in the system possessing the necessary energy of activation is large, and most collisions between the molecules result in reaction. Reactions involving ions are rapid because the ions have a large attraction for each other and no additional energy is required to cause them to react. Practically every collision between ions which tend to combine is an effective one.

Any factor which changes the number of effective collisions per unit time will obviously alter the rate of the reaction. A number of factors affect reaction rates.

16.2 The Rate of Reaction and the Nature of the Reacting Substances

Different reactions involving different substances have different reaction rates under the same conditions. Calcium and sodium both react with water at ordinary temperatures, calcium at a moderate rate and sodium so rapidly that the reaction is of almost explosive violence. Sodium, an active metal, reacts much more rapidly with chlorine than does iron, a moderately active metal. We noted in the preceding section that ionic substances react nearly instantaneously whereas molecular substances usually react much more slowly. It is evident then that the rate of reaction is influenced by the nature of the substances participating in the reaction.

16.3 The Rate of Reaction and the State of Subdivision

In a reaction between substances in different physical states such as a solid and a gas, the rate of the reaction is determined to a great extent by the size of the surface of contact between the two phases. Finely divided solids, because of their more extensive surfaces, react more rapidly than massive specimens of the same substances. For example, large pieces of coal burn slowly, smaller pieces more rapidly, and powdered coal may burn at an explosive rate. The limit of the effect of subdivision is reached when the reacting substances are in the gaseous state or in solution as molecules or ions.

16.4 The Rate of Reaction and Temperature

It is a common observation that most chemical reactions are accelerated by increases in temperature. The oxidation of iron or coal is very slow at ordinary temperatures but proceeds rapidly at high temperatures. The student uses a Bunsen burner in the laboratory to increase the speed of reactions which may proceed slowly or even at an imperceptible rate at ordinary temperatures. It is a familiar fact that foods cook faster at higher temperatures than at lower ones. The same increase in temperature affects the speed of many reactions to about the same extent. In many cases, the rate of a reaction in a homogeneous system is approximately doubled by an increase in temperature of only 10° (Fig. 16–2).

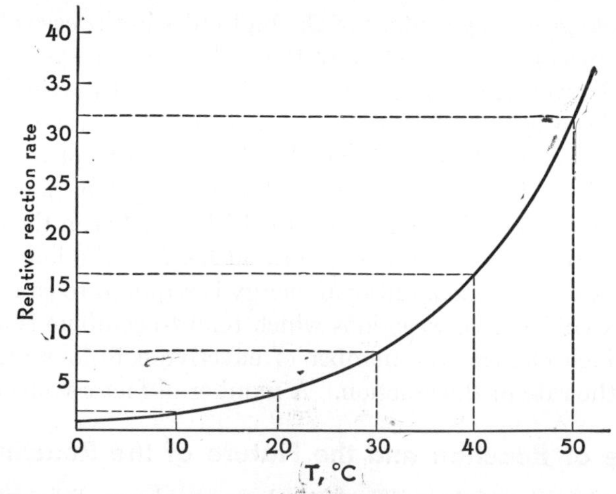

Fig. 16–2 The effect of temperature upon reaction rate, shown graphically. The rate of reaction is often approximately doubled for each ten degree rise in temperature.

The increase in the rate of reactions with increase in temperature is easily explained in terms of the kinetic-molecular theory. As the temperature of the system is raised, the average velocity of the molecules becomes greater and more collisions between molecules per unit time result. In addition, as the temperature rises, more molecules gain the minimum energy necessary for reaction to take place when they collide. In other words, at higher temperatures a greater fraction of the molecules acquire sufficient energy to break the bonds that hold the atoms or radicals together, thus making possible other combinations of the same particles. For many reactions, then, it appears that a rise in temperature of 10° doubles the rate of reaction because this change in temperature doubles the number of "activated" molecules, i.e., those which possess the necessary energy of activation.

16.5 The Rate of Reaction and Catalysis

Many reactions can be accelerated or retarded by the presence of small amounts of substances which are not themselves permanently used up by the reaction. Such substances are called **catalysts** (Section 5.3). Catalysts may be divided into two general classes: (1) contact catalysts and (2) those which form intermediate substances which in turn react and regenerate the catalyst.

Contact catalysts act by furnishing a surface at which the reacting molecules are adsorbed and concentrated. Adsorption of molecules on the surface of the catalyst effectively reduces the energy necessary for activation and more collisions are therefore effective. In addition, the increase in concentration resulting from adsorption results in more collisions per unit time, thus increasing the velocity of the reaction. Hydrogen and oxygen react practically not at all at ordinary temperatures, but metallic platinum has the power to adsorb these gases, particularly hydrogen, so that they will react with each other. Vanadium (V) oxide is extensively used in the "contact process" for the manufacture of sulfuric acid. In this process, the vanadium (V) oxide greatly accelerates the oxidation of sulfur dioxide to sulfur trioxide by oxygen of the air (Section 23.6).

Many catalysts act as "carriers" by the formation of an intermediate substance which decomposes during the overall reaction. Nitric oxide, NO, serves as such a catalyst in the "lead-chamber process" for the manufacture of sulfuric acid (Section 23.6). The reaction

$$2\ SO_2 + O_2 \rightarrow 2\ SO_3$$

is slow, while the reactions

$$2\ NO + O_2 \rightarrow 2\ NO_2$$

and

$$SO_2 + NO_2 \rightarrow SO_3 + NO$$

are fast. The NO formed in the latter reaction combines with more oxygen to produce NO_2. In this way the nitric oxide serves as a carrier for oxygen in the oxidation of sulfur dioxide to sulfur trioxide, the anhydride of sulfuric acid. A small amount of nitric oxide suffices for the manufacture of an almost unlimited quantity of sulfuric acid.

Many reactions of organic compounds are catalyzed by enzymes, which are complex substances produced by living organisms. For example, the production of alcohol from sugars by fermentation is catalyzed by the enzyme zymase which is produced by yeast cells. The many chemical reactions that take place in living organisms, called metabolic processes, are catalyzed by various enzymes. It has been estimated that there may be as many as thirty thousand different enzymes in the body of man, each of which is a protein constructed in such a way as to make it effective as a catalyst for a specific chemical reaction useful to the organism.

16.6 The Rate of Reaction and Concentration

At a fixed temperature and in the absence of a catalyst, the rate of a given reaction depends mainly upon the concentrations of the reacting substances. Many familiar facts might be cited which illustrate this principle. For example, substances burn much more rapidly in pure oxygen than they do in air, in which only about 20 per cent of the molecules are oxygen.

The increase in reaction rate that accompanies an increase in concentration of reacting substances is readily explained in terms of the kinetic-molecular theory. By increasing the concentration of all or any of the reacting substances, the chances for collision between molecules are increased due to the presence of a greater number of molecules per unit volume. More collisions per unit time means a greater reaction rate. Because a mole of any molecular substance always consists of the same number of molecules, it is evident that the concentration of a substance, when expressed in moles per liter, provides a direct measure of the number of molecules per unit space. For this reason concentrations are expressed in moles per liter when the effect of concentration upon reaction rate is being considered.

The quantitative relationship between reaction rate and concentration for a reaction in which one molecule of each reactant appears in the equation (coefficients of 1) was established experimentally by Guldberg and Waage in 1867: **The rate of the reaction is directly proportional to the concentration of each of the reacting substances.** This generalization is referred to as the **law of mass action.**

For a reaction of the type $A \rightarrow B + C$, such as $PCl_5 \rightarrow PCl_3 + Cl_2$, the rate of reaction, R, is directly proportional to the concentration of A.

This relationship between reaction rate and concentration of the reactant may be expressed in the form of an equation as follows:

$$R = k[A] \qquad R = k[PCl_5]$$

The reaction rate is represented by R, and the brackets mean "molar concentration of"; for example, $[PCl_5]$ means "molar concentration of PCl_5." The proportionality constant, k, is called the "rate constant." The value of k remains the same as long as temperature of the system does not change. If the temperature is raised, the reaction rate becomes greater and the value of k increases substantially. The value of k is equal to the rate of the reaction when the molar concentration of the reactant A is unity. When the concentration of A is doubled, the rate of reaction will double because there will be twice as many molecules to undergo decomposition per unit volume in a unit of time.

For a reaction of the type A + B → C, such as $H_2 + I_2 \rightarrow 2\,HI$, the rate equation can be expressed as follows:

$$R = k[A][B] \qquad R = k[H_2][I_2]$$

It must be realized that R and k each have different values for different reactions and, of course, are not the same for the reactions $PCl_5 \rightarrow PCl_3 + Cl_2$ and $H_2 + I_2 \rightarrow 2\,HI$.

In a reaction between the two reactants A and B, doubling the concentration of either one of them doubles the number of total molecular collisions and in turn doubles the number of effective collisions between molecules A and B. Thus, if the concentration of A is doubled (and that of B is left the same), the rate of reaction is doubled. Doubling the concentration of both A and B quadruples the number of collisions and the rate of reaction becomes four times as great (Fig. 16–3). If the initial concentrations of both A and B are trebled, then the reaction proceeds nine times as fast.

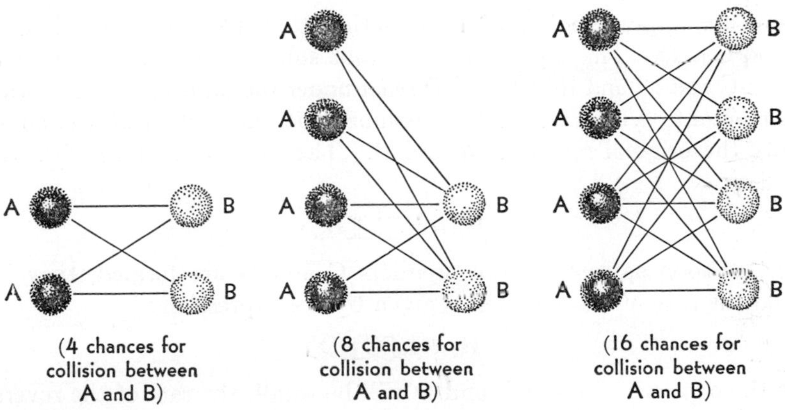

Fig. 16–3 A schematic representation of the effect of concentration on the number of possible collisions and, hence, the rate of reaction.

When more than one molecule of a reactant appears in the equation for a reaction, such as 2 A → B + C, the reaction rate is found by experiment to be proportional to the molar concentration of the reactant raised to the power that is equal to the number of molecules of the reactant appearing in the equation. Hence, for the reaction 2 A → B + C, such as $2\,HI \rightarrow H_2 + I_2$, the reaction rate is proportional to the square of the molar concentration of A:

$$R = k[A]^2 \qquad R = k[HI]^2$$

The fact that the rate of decomposition of HI is proportional to the square rather than the first power of its concentration seems less surprising if the equation is written $HI + HI \rightarrow H_2 + I_2$. We may suppose that this reaction can occur only when one molecule of HI collides with a second molecule of it, and hence we have $R = k[HI][HI] = k[HI]^2$.

For the reaction A + 2 B → C, it follows that the reaction rate is proportional to the molar concentration of A multiplied by the square of the molar concentration of B:

$$R = k[A][B]^2$$

In a general case where n molecules of A react with m molecules of B, such as n A + m B → reaction products, we have

$$R = k[A]^n[B]^m$$

16.7 The Law of Chemical Equilibrium

Whenever the products of a chemical reaction are capable of reacting to form the reactants, then the reaction must remain more or less incomplete. Two reactions are taking place simultaneously, the one tending to offset the other. As a consequence, such reactions do not go to completion and a state of equilibrium is attained. Most chemical reactions possess the quality of reversibility and do not go to completion.

Suppose we apply the law of mass action to a reversible reaction, such as A + B and C + D. This equation states that substances A and B react to form substances C and D, and that C and D react under the same conditions forming the original reactants A and B. Let us assume that the system at the outset contains only the original reactants A and B. The rate of reaction of A with B is expressed as

$$R_1 = k_1[A][B]$$

However, as soon as some of the products C and D are formed, they begin to react, and the rate of this reaction is given by the expression

$$R_2 = k_2[C][D]$$

Because the concentrations of C and D will be small, the rate of the reverse reaction, R_2, will be low at first. But, as the reaction between A and B proceeds, the concentrations of C and D increase and, likewise, the rate of the reverse reaction, R_2, increases. Meanwhile the concentrations of A and B are becoming less and less, so that the rate of the forward reaction, R_1, falls off. Consequently, the two reaction rates approach each other and finally become equal — a condition of dynamic equilibrium in which the opposing reactions are in full operation. Thus at equilibrium, $R_2 = R_1$ and we may write

$$k_2[C][D] = k_1[A][B]$$

or

$$\frac{[C][D]}{[A][B]} = \frac{k_1}{k_2}$$

Because k_1 and k_2 are constants, the ratio k_1/k_2 is also constant, and the expression may be written

$$\frac{[C][D]}{[A][B]} = K.$$

K_e is called the equilibrium constant for the reversible reaction $A + B \rightleftharpoons C + D$. Just as k_1 and k_2 are proportionality constants specific for each reaction at a definite temperature, K_e is likewise a constant specific to this system in equilibrium at a given temperature. The values for the molar concentrations in the above mathematical expression are always those which are found in the system **when it is in a state of equilibrium.**

It is important to note that at equilibrium the rates of reaction, R_1 and R_2, are equal but the molar concentrations of the reactants and products in the equilibrium mixture are usually not equal.

A general equation for chemical equilibria may be written as follows:

$$n\,A + m\,B + \cdots \rightleftharpoons x\,C + y\,D + \cdots$$

By applying the law of mass action to this reversible reaction, we may write

$$\frac{[C]^x[D]^y\ldots}{[A]^n[B]^m\ldots} = K_e$$

This is a mathematical expression of the law of chemical equilibrium which may be stated as follows: **When a reversible reaction has attained equilibrium at a given temperature, the product of the molar concentrations of the substances to the right of the equation, divided by the product of the molar concentrations of the substances to the left, each concentration raised to the power equal to the number of molecules of each substance appearing in the equation, is a constant.**

The equilibrium constant expression given above is valid even if the reactions take place in steps, with rates involving powers of the reactant concentrations different from the coefficients appearing in the balanced equation. In fact, the validity of the equilibrium constant expression is a consequence of the laws of thermodynamics (of physical chemistry) and is not dependent upon the reaction-rate arguments which were presented above.

The meaning of the mathematical expression of the law of chemical equilibrium is that, regardless of how the individual concentrations might be varied, the composition of the system with regard to its various components will always adjust itself so that, when a condition of equilibrium is attained, the quotient $[C]^x[D]^y\ldots/[A]^n[B]^m\ldots$ will have the value K_e. When a mixture of A, B, C, and D is prepared in such proportions that the ratio $[C]^x[D]^y\ldots$ to $[A]^n[B]^m\ldots$ is not equal to K_e, then the system cannot be in a condition of equilibrium, and its composition will change in such a direction that equilibrium will be established. If the ratio is less than K_e, the rate of reaction of A with B will be greater than that of C with D, so that A and B will be used up faster than they are formed until the ratio becomes equal to K_e; conversely, if the ratio is greater than K_e, the rate of reaction of C with D will be greater than that of A with B until the ratio becomes equal to K_e.

The size of an equilibrium constant is a measure of the completeness of a reversible reaction. A large value for K_e indicates that equilibrium is attained only after the reactants A and B have been largely converted into the products C and D.

When K_e is very small — much less than unity — equilibrium is attained when only a small proportion of A and B have been converted to C and D.

The following equations and equilibrium constant expressions will illustrate the law of chemical equilibrium.

$$PCl_5 \rightleftharpoons PCl_3 + Cl_2 \qquad \frac{[PCl_3][Cl_2]}{[PCl_5]} = K_e$$

$$N_2 + 3\,H_2 \rightleftharpoons 2\,NH_3 \qquad \frac{[NH_3]^2}{[N_2][H_2]^3} = K_e$$

16.8 The Determination of Equilibrium Constants

As one example of the determination of equilibrium constants let us consider the reversible reaction $H_2 + I_2 \rightleftharpoons 2\,HI$. For a given mixture of H_2, I_2, and HI at 400°, it was found by analysis that $[H_2] = 0.221$, $[I_2] = 0.221$, and $[HI] = 1.563$, when the system had attained equilibrium. Substituting these values in the expression for the equilibrium constant for this system, we find

$$K_e = \frac{[HI]^2}{[H_2][I_2]} = \frac{(1.563)^2}{(0.221)(0.221)} = 50.0$$

Hence, the equilibrium constant for the system has the value 50.0. If we start with just HI at any molar concentration, or with any mixture of H_2 and I_2, or with any mixture of H_2, I_2, and HI and bring the temperature of the system to 400°, and hold it there until equilibrium is established, the molar concentrations of the three substances will be such that the quotient $[HI]^2/[H_2][I_2]$ will be equal to 50.0.

16.9 The Effect of Changing the Concentration upon an Equilibrium

The equilibrium existing in a chemical system may be shifted by increasing the rate of the forward or the reverse reaction. For the reversible reaction

$$A + B \rightleftharpoons C + D$$

when the system is in equilibrium and an additional quantity of A is added, the rate of the forward reaction is increased because the concentration of the reacting molecules is increased. This means that the rate of the forward reaction will momentarily be greater than that of the reverse reaction; the system, then, is temporarily out of equilibrium. However, as the concentrations of C and D increase, the rate of the reverse reaction increases, whereas the decrease in the concentrations of A and B causes the rate of the forward reaction to decrease. The rates of the two reactions thereby soon become equal again and a new state of equilibrium is attained in which the molar concentrations of A, B, C, and D have changed; however, the ratio [C][D] to [A][B] is again equal to the original value of K_e. The equilibrium is said to have been shifted to the right. In the second state of equilibrium, the substances C and D are present in greater concentration than originally, B is present in smaller concentration than originally, and A is present in greater concentration than before the addition of excess A. By increasing the concentration of B, the equilibrium can be shifted to the right in similar fashion. Increasing the concentration of either C or D, or both, will have the effect of shifting the equilibrium to the left.

The equilibrium may also be shifted to the right by the removal of either C or D, or both. This causes a reduction in the reaction rate of the reverse reaction and thus the forward reaction proceeds faster than the reverse reaction until the reaction rates again become equal as a new condition of equilibrium is attained.

As an example of the effect of a change in concentration upon a system in equilibrium, let us consider the equilibrium $H_2 + I_2 \rightleftharpoons 2\,HI$, for which K_e was found to be 50.0 at 400° in the preceding section. If enough H_2 were introduced into the system to double its concentration, the rate of reaction of H_2 with I_2 to form HI would increase. When equilibrium is again reached, $[H_2] = 0.374$, $[I_2] = 0.153$, and $[HI] = 1.692$. Substituting these new values in the expression for the equilibrium constant for this system, we find

$$\frac{[HI]^2}{[H_2][I_2]} = \frac{(1.692)^2}{(0.374)(0.153)} = 50.0 = K_e$$

Hence, by doubling the concentration of H_2, we have caused the formation of more HI, and have used up about one-third of the I_2 present at the first equilibrium.

The effect of a change in concentration upon a system in equilibrium is an important application of the **principle of Le Châtelier,** which may be stated as follows: **If a stress, such as a change in concentration, pressure, or temperature, is applied to a system in equilibrium, the equilibrium is shifted in a way that tends to undo the effect of the stress.**

16.10 Effect of Change in Pressure on Equilibrium

Changes in pressure affect systems in equilibrium measurably only when gases are involved, and in such cases only when the chemical reaction involves a change in the total number of molecules in the system. As the pressure on a gaseous system is increased, the substances comprising the gas undergo compression and their concentration in moles per liter and the total number of molecules per unit volume increase. Thus, the chemical reaction that will reduce the total number of molecules per unit of volume will be the one favored by an increase in pressure.

Consider the effect of an increase in pressure upon the system in which one molecule of nitrogen and three molecules of hydrogen interact and form two molecules of ammonia.

$$N_2 + 3\,H_2 \rightleftharpoons 2\,NH_3$$

The formation of ammonia will decrease the total number of molecules of the system by 50 per cent, thus reducing the total pressure exerted by the system. In terms of Le Châtelier's principle then, the system tends to undo the effect of the stress of an increase in pressure on the system by the formation of ammonia which results in a lower pressure exerted by the system. On the other hand, lowering the pressure on the system will favor decomposition of ammonia into hydrogen and nitrogen.

One molecule of hydrogen interacts with one molecule of iodine with the formation of two molecules of hydrogen iodide.

$$H_2 + I_2 \rightleftharpoons 2\ HI$$

Because there is no change in the total number of molecules in the system during reaction, a change in pressure does not favor either formation or decomposition of hydrogen iodide at temperatures high enough for all the materials to be present in the gaseous state.

Whenever a gaseous substance is involved in a system in equilibrium, the pressure or partial pressure of the gas can be substituted for the concentration because the concentration of a gas at constant temperature varies directly as the pressure. Thus for the system $H_2(g) + I_2(g) \rightleftharpoons 2\ HI(g)$, we may write

$$\frac{p_{HI}^2}{p_{H_2}p_{I_2}} = K_e$$

16.11 Effect of Change in Temperature on Equilibrium

All chemical changes involve either the evolution of energy or the absorption of energy. In every system in equilibrium, an endothermic and an exothermic reaction are taking place simultaneously. The endothermic reaction is favored by an increase in temperature, the exothermic reaction by a decrease in temperature.

In the reaction between gaseous hydrogen and gaseous iodine, heat is evolved.

$$H_2(g) + I_2(g) \rightleftharpoons 2\ HI(g) + \text{heat}$$

Lowering the temperature of the system favors the formation of hydrogen iodide while raising the temperature favors the decomposition of hydrogen iodide. Thus, raising the temperature of the system will decrease the value of the equilibrium constant since the molar concentration of HI will be decreased while the molar concentrations of H_2 and I_2 will be increased. The value of the equilibrium constant

$$\frac{[HI]^2}{[H_2][I_2]} = K_e$$

decreases from 67.5 at 357° to 50.0 at 400°.

The effect of temperature changes upon systems in equilibrium may be summarized by the statement: **When the temperature of a system in equilibrium is raised, the equilibrium is displaced in such a way that heat is absorbed.** This generalization is known as **van't Hoff's law,** which is a special case of Le Châtelier's principle. It is important to remember that the effect of changing the temperature is to change the value of the equilibrium constant.

The equation for the formation of ammonia from hydrogen and nitrogen,

$$N_2 + 3\ H_2 \rightleftharpoons 2\ NH_3 + 21{,}800\ \text{cal.}$$

indicates that the equilibrium can be shifted to the right in favor of the formation of ammonia by lowering the temperature. However, it must be remembered that, because of the rapid lowering of reaction rates with decreasing temperature, equilibrium is attained more slowly the lower the temperature. In the commercial production of ammonia from nitrogen and hydrogen, it has been found that it is not feasible to use temperatures much lower than 500°, because at such temperatures, even in the presence of a catalyst, the reaction proceeds too slowly.

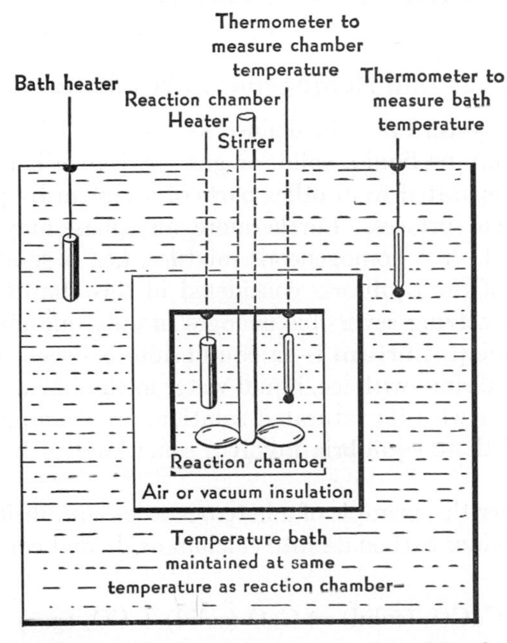

Fig. 16–4 A laboratory calorimeter. *From Principles of Chemistry, by Hiller and Herber. Copyright, 1960. McGraw-Hill Book Company, Inc. Used by permission.*

A **calorimeter** is used to measure the heat change which occurs during a chemical reaction (Fig. 16–4). In the simplest form of calorimeter, the reaction is allowed to take place in a reaction vessel which is immersed in a liquid within an insulated container. The change of temperature in the liquid, caused by release or absorption of heat by the reaction, is measured with a sensitive thermometer.

16.12 Effect of a Catalyst on Equilibrium

Porous iron is used as a catalyst in the production of ammonia from nitrogen and hydrogen to increase the rate of reaction of these two elements.

$$N_2 + 3\ H_2 \xrightarrow{Fe} 2\ NH_3$$

However, this same catalyst serves equally well to increase the rate of decomposition of ammonia into its constituent elements, the reverse of the formation reaction.

$$2\ NH_3 \xrightarrow{Fe} N_2 + 3\ H_2$$

Thus the net effect of iron in the reversible reaction

$$N_2 + 3\,H_2 \rightleftharpoons 2\,NH_3$$

is to cause equilibrium to be reached more rapidly. The **catalyst has no effect** on the value of the equilibrium constant. It merely increases the rate of both the forward and the reverse reactions to the same extent.

16.13 Heterogeneous and Homogeneous Equilibria

A **homogeneous system** may be defined as one in which only a single phase is present. A phase may be liquid, solid, or gas. A **phase** is a homogeneous part of a system that is separated from other parts of a system by physical boundaries in the nature of visible surfaces. Furthermore, any phase may be composed of an element, a compound, or a homogeneous mixture, i.e., a solution of elements or compounds. Most of the equilibria considered in this chapter have been homogeneous equilibria involving reversible changes in only one phase, the gas phase.

A **heterogeneous equilibrium** is an equilibrium between two or more phases. Liquid water in equilibrium with ice, liquid water in equilibrium with water vapor, and a solid in contact with its saturated solution, are examples of heterogeneous equilibria. Each of these equilibria involves some kind of boundary surface between two phases.

Suppose we consider the example of a heterogeneous equilibrium provided by the decomposition of calcium carbonate into calcium oxide and carbon dioxide according to the equation

$$CaCO_3 \text{ (solid)} \rightleftharpoons CaO \text{ (solid)} + CO_2 \text{ (gas)}$$

Let us write the expression for the equilibrium constant for this reversible reaction.

$$\frac{[CaO][CO_2]}{[CaCO_3]} = K_e$$

Now the concentration of a solid substance is proportional to its density, and hence remains constant as long as the temperature is not changed. It follows that the concentrations of whatever solid substances are involved in the equilibrium, since they are constant, may be included in the value of the equilibrium constant, and need not appear at all in the expression for the equilibrium constant. We may write, therefore, the following:

$$[CO_2] = \frac{[CaCO_3]}{[CaO]} \times K_e$$

Now, we have on the right-hand side of the equation only constant terms. These can be combined into a single constant, K.

$$[CO_2] = K$$

The equilibrium constant in terms of partial pressures is written

$$p_{CO_2} = K_p$$

This equation means that, at a given temperature, there is only one pressure at which carbon dioxide gas can be in equilibrium with the two solids, $CaCO_3$ and CaO. Suppose a sample of $CaCO_3$ is placed in a cylinder with a movable piston, as shown in Fig. 16–5, and that the temperature of the system is raised to 900°. Under these conditions calcium carbonate will continue to decompose into calcium oxide and carbon dioxide until there is sufficient carbon dioxide present in the system to exert a pressure of 790 mm., if the piston is held stationary.

$$p_{CO_2} = K_p = 790 \text{ mm. (at } 900°)$$

At this pressure, equilibrium will have been attained; $CaCO_3$ will be decomposing into CaO and CO_2 at the same rate that CaO CO_2 are reacting to produce $CaCO_3$. If one should try to increase the pressure by pushing the piston down and thus compressing the gas, additional carbon dioxide would combine with calcium oxide to form calcium carbonate, and the pressure would soon become equal to 790 mm. again. If, on the other hand, the pressure on the system were decreased by raising the piston, just enough calcium carbonate would decompose to bring the pressure exerted by the carbon dioxide back to its original value of 790 mm.

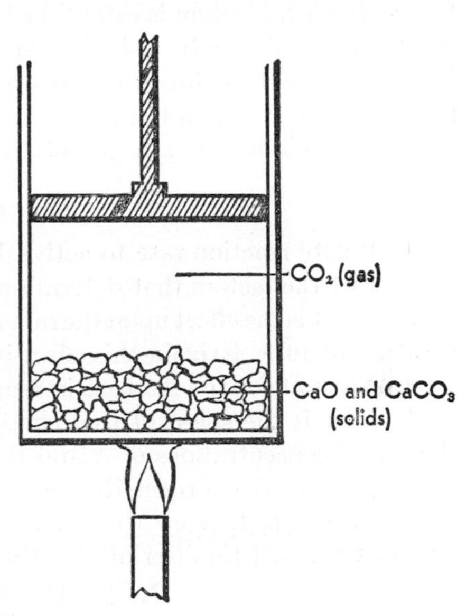

Fig. 16–5 The thermal decomposition of calcium carbonate in a closed system is an example of a heterogeneous equilibrium.

In the commercial production of quicklime, CaO, from limestone, the carbon dioxide is continuously removed as fast as it is formed by means of a stream of air; this causes the equilibrium to shift continually to the right.

16.14 The Distribution Law and Extraction

An important example of heterogeneous equilibria is the distribution of a solute between two immiscible solvents which are in contact but separated by a phase boundary. For example, iodine is soluble in both water and carbon tetrachloride. If an aqueous solution of iodine is shaken vigorously with a sufficient quantity of carbon tetrachloride, the greater part of the iodine will leave the water and go into the carbon tetrachloride. After shaking is stopped, the carbon tetrachloride, colored violet by the iodine, settles to the bottom of the container. The equilibrium between the iodine in the water and in the carbon tetrachloride may be represented by the equation

$$I_2 \text{ (in } H_2O \text{ phase)} \rightleftharpoons I_2 \text{ (in } CCl_4 \text{ phase)}$$

Applying the law of mass action to the system in equilibrium we have

$$\frac{[I_2(CCl_4)]}{[I_2(H_2O)]} = K_e$$

The equilibrium constant for systems of this type is called the **distribution ratio** and it has the value of 85 for this particular system. In other words, the molar concentration of iodine in the carbon tetrachloride is 85 times that in the aqueous layer when equilibrium is established. Thus most of the iodine in a water solution can be removed even by a single treatment with carbon tetrachloride. This process is known as **extraction.** If the aqueous layer is extracted a second time with a fresh portion of carbon tetrachloride, the concentration of iodine in the water solution can be reduced to a negligibly small value.

QUESTIONS

1. Relate reaction rate to activation energy.
2. List the factors that determine the rate of a reaction.
3. What is the effect upon the rate of many reactions caused by an increase in temperature of 10°? Explain this effect in terms of the collision theory of reaction rate.
4. Account for the increase in reaction rate brought about by contact catalysts.
5. How is the speed of the reaction $A + B \rightarrow C + D$ affected by quadrupling the initial concentrations of A and B?
6. Characterize a reversible reaction and give an example of one.
7. Using the Law of Mass Action, derive the mathematical expression of the Law of Chemical Equilibrium for the following reversible reactions:

$$N_2 + 3\ H_2 \rightleftharpoons 2\ NH_3$$
$$CH_4 + Cl_2 \rightleftharpoons CH_3Cl + HCl$$
$$N_2 + O_2 \rightleftharpoons 2\ NO$$
$$2\ SO_2 + O_2 \rightleftharpoons 2\ SO_3\ (g)$$
$$2\ H_2 + O_2 \rightleftharpoons 2\ H_2O\ (g)$$
$$CO_2 + H_2 \rightleftharpoons CO + H_2O\ (g)$$
$$NH_4Cl\ (s) \rightleftharpoons NH_3 + HCl$$
$$BaSO_3\ (s) \rightleftharpoons BaO\ (s) + SO_2$$
$$2\ Pb(NO_3)_2\ (s) \rightleftharpoons 2\ PbO\ (s) + 4\ NO_2 + O_2$$
$$4\ NH_3 + 5\ O_2 \rightleftharpoons 4\ NO + 6\ H_2O\ (g)$$

8. Write the mathematical expression of the Law of Chemical Equilibrium for the reversible reaction

$$2\ CO + O_2 \rightleftharpoons 2\ CO_2 + \text{heat}$$

What will happen to the concentration of CO_2 in the system if it is at equilibrium, and (a) more oxygen is added? (b) CO is removed? (c) the pressure on the system is increased?

9. State Le Châtelier's principle as applied to chemical equilibria.
10. When do changes in pressure affect systems in equilibrium?
11. How will an increase in temperature affect the following equilibria?

$$N_2 + 3\ H_2 \rightleftharpoons 2\ NH_3 + \text{heat}$$
$$H_2O_{liquid} + \text{heat} \rightleftharpoons H_2O_{vapor}$$
$$N_2 + O_2 + \text{heat} \rightleftharpoons 2\ NO$$
$$3\ O_2 + \text{heat} \rightleftharpoons 2\ O_3$$
$$CaCO_3 + \text{heat} \rightleftharpoons CaO + CO_2$$

12. What is the effect of a catalyst upon the equilibrium constant of a system? Of what value is a catalyst upon a system that attains equilibrium?

PROBLEMS

1. Nitrogen reacts with hydrogen to give ammonia according to the equation: $N_2 + 3\ H_2 \rightleftharpoons 2\ NH_3$. An equilibrium mixture of the above substances at 400° C was found to contain 0.60 mole of nitrogen, 0.40 mole of hydrogen, and 0.14 mole of ammonia in a liter. Calculate the equilibrium constant for the system.

Ans. *0.51*

2. The equilibrium constant for the reaction $CO + H_2O \rightleftharpoons CO_2 + H_2$ is 5.0 at a given temperature. Upon analysis an equilibrium mixture of the above substances at the given temperature was found to contain 0.50 mole of CO, 0.25 mole of water vapor, and 0.90 mole of H_2 in a liter. How many moles of CO_2 were there in the equilibrium mixture?

Ans. *0.69*

3. If the rate of a reaction doubles for every ten degree rise in temperature, how much faster would the reaction proceed at 100° than at 20°?

Ans. *256 times faster*

4. The equilibrium constant for the gaseous reaction $H_2 + I_2 \rightleftharpoons 2\ HI$ is 50.2 at 448° C. Calculate the number of moles of HI that are in equilibrium with 5.28 moles of H_2 and 15.23 grams of iodine at this temperature.

Ans. *3.99*

5. At about 990° C., K_e for the reaction

$$H_2(g) + CO_2(g) \rightleftharpoons H_2O(g) + CO(g)$$

is 1.6. Calculate the concentration of each component in the final equilibrium system obtained from adding 0.50 mole H_2, 1.0 mole CO_2, 1.5 moles H_2O and 2.0 moles CO to a 5.00 liter reactor at 990° C.

Ans. *0.17 M H_2; 0.27 M CO_2; 0.23 M H_2O; 0.33 M CO*

6. Ethanol and acetic acid interact to form ethyl acetate and water, according to the following equation:

$$C_2H_5OH + CH_3COOH \rightleftharpoons CH_3COOC_2H_5 + H_2O$$

When one mole each of the alcohol (C_2H_5OH) and the acid (CH_3COOH) are allowed to react, equilibrium is established when one-third of a mole each of the reactants remain. Calculate K_e.

Ans. *4*

7. Consider the gas phase reaction

$$N_2O_4(g) \rightleftharpoons 2\ NO_2(g)$$

At a given temperature, K_e for this reaction is 1.1×10^{-5}. If 0.50 mole of N_2O_4 is dissolved in 500 ml. of chloroform and the above reaction allowed to come to equilibrium, (a) what will be the NO_2 concentration, and (b) what will be the % dissociation of the original N_2O_4?

Ans. *(a) 3.4×10^{-3} mole/l.; (b) 0.17%*

8. At 25° C., the partial pressures in an equilibrium mixture of N_2O_4 and NO_2 are: $p_{N_2O_4} = 0.70$ atmosphere; $p_{NO_2} = 0.30$ atmosphere. Calculate the partial pressures of these two gases when they are in equilibrium at 20.0 atmospheres and 25° C.

Ans. *$p_{N_2O_4} = 18.5$ atm.; $p_{NO_2} = 1.5$ atm.*

9. The equilibrium pressure of carbon dioxide over calcium carbonate at various temperatures is as follows:

Temp., °C.	p_{CO_2}, *mm.*
600	10
800	180
840	320
880	580
896	760
910	1000

Plot the pressure as a function of temperature.

10. Consider the equilibrium reaction

$$PCl_3(g) + Cl_2(g) \rightleftharpoons PCl_5(g)$$

At equilibrium, the following quantities of the substances are present in a volume of 6.00 liters: 0.21 mole of PCl_3, 62.5 g. of Cl_2, and 0.050 mole of PCl_5. Calculate K_e for the system. *Ans. 1.6*

11. In an experiment, a sample of $NaClO_3$ was 90% decomposed in 20 minutes. How long would it have taken, had the sample been heated 20° higher in temperature? *Ans. 5 min.*

CHAPTER SEVENTEEN

The Halogens

The elements of Group VIIA of the Periodic Table are known as the **halogens.** They are fluorine, chlorine, bromine, iodine, and astatine. Astatine, the fifth halogen, was discovered as recently as 1940. Salts of these elements (excepting astatine) are common in nature. As a group they are called halogens, which means "salt formers." Their binary compounds as a group are called **halides.**

17.1 Discovery of the Halogens

Although the compounds of fluorine are fairly common and have been known for a long time, a practical method of preparing the element was not discovered until 1886. The difficulties associated with the isolation of fluorine are related to the fact that it is the most electronegative of the elements, i.e., it is very difficult to remove an electron from the fluoride ion, F^-, to form elementary fluorine. Moissan first isolated fluorine in 1886 as a product of the electrolysis of anhydrous liquid hydrogen fluoride, HF, containing some potassium hydrogen fluoride, KHF_2. The name **fluorine** comes from the Latin word "fluo," meaning "to flow," because the most common fluorine compound, calcium fluoride, CaF_2, is widely used as a flux.

Chlorine was first prepared by Scheele in 1774, as one product of the reaction of hydrochloric acid with manganese dioxide, MnO_2. He thought that the greenish-yellow gas which was formed was a compound. Because it was produced by the action of an oxidizing agent he considered it to be an oxide of hydrochloric acid. Sir Humphry Davy in 1810 tried to decompose the gas, but without success, and finally concluded it was an element. He suggested that the gas be named **chlorine,** which comes from a Greek word meaning "greenish-yellow."

While investigating the mother liquor left after sodium chloride had crystallized from the saline waters of Montpellier, France, Balard in 1826 obtained bromine. He observed it to be a dark reddish-brown liquid with an intensely irritating and unpleasant odor. He named it **bromine,** from the Greek word "bromos," meaning "stench." He thought it to be an element and showed it to be related to chlorine and iodine.

Iodine was discovered in 1811 by Courtois, a French manufacturer of saltpeter. He prepared it by treating the ashes of seaweed with hot sulfuric acid. During the reaction, violet colored vapors formed; these condensed when cooled to form brilliant crystalline plates. In 1814 Gay-Lussac showed the new substance to be an element which he named **iodine,** from the Greek word "ioeides," meaning "violet."

Most of our knowledge of the element astatine has come from a study of one of its isotopes (mass number 211). It was first obtained in 1940 by Corson, Mackenzie, and Segre, who prepared it by bombarding bismuth with alpha particles in the 60-inch cyclotron at the University of California, Berkeley.

$$^{209}_{83}\text{Bi} + ^{4}_{2}\text{He} \rightarrow ^{211}_{85}\text{At} + 2\ ^{1}_{0}\text{n}$$

Astatine may exist in nature as a short-lived intermediate in a nuclear decay chain, but too little of the element is present from this source at a given time to permit its study. The name **astatine** comes from the Greek word for "unstable." One of the vacant places in the original Mendeleev Periodic Table was left for the discovery of element 85, and the name **eka-iodine** was suggested for it, pending its discovery and characterization.

17.2 Occurrence of the Halogens

The halogens never occur free in nature because of their great chemical activity. Chlorine is the most abundant of the halogens, and although fluorine, bromine, and iodine are less common, they are reasonably available. The principal occurrences of the halogens are given in Table 17·1.

TABLE 17·1 Occurrences of the Halogens

Fluorine:	CaF_2, **fluorite** or **fluorspar**
	$Ca_{10}F_2(PO_4)_6$, **fluorapatite**
	Na_3AlF_6, **cryolite**
	Sea water (small amounts)
	Teeth, bones, blood (small amounts)
Chlorine:	Sea water (2.8 per cent NaCl; other chlorides 0.8 per cent)
	Great Salt Lake in Utah (23 per cent NaCl)
	Salt beds (NaCl, $MgCl_2$, $CaCl_2$)
	Gastric juice (0.2 to 0.4 per cent HCl)
Bromine:	Sea water (NaBr, KBr, $MgBr_2$, $CaBr_2$)
	Natural brines
	Salt deposits
Iodine:	Sea water (very small amounts)
	$NaIO_3$ in Chilean nitrate deposits
	Oil well brines of California
	Thyroid gland in human body

17.3 Preparation and Production of the Halogens

The salts in which the halogens (except iodine) exist in an oxidation state of −1 constitute the best sources for the preparation and production of these elements. Various methods of oxidizing the halide ions to the elementary halogens (zero oxidation state) may be employed. The general oxidation half-reaction may be written

$$2\ X^- \rightleftharpoons X_2 + 2\ e^- \quad (X = \text{halogen})$$

The ease of oxidation of the halide ions increases in the order F^-, Cl^-, Br^-, I^-, At^-; the fluoride ion is the most difficult to oxidize and the astatide ion the easiest. The electron removed during oxidation is closest to the nucleus in F^- and farthest from it in At^-. There are enough differences among the methods applicable to the preparation of the free halogens to warrant separate discussions of these methods.

1. *Fluorine.* It is very difficult to prepare fluorine because it is the most highly electronegative element known and it reacts with water, the solvent for most redox reactions, quite violently. It is necessary to resort to electrolytic oxidation (Fig. 17–1) in a nonaqueous electrolyte to oxidize the fluoride ion to fluorine. The electrolyte commonly used is a mixture of potassium hydrogen fluoride, KHF_2, and

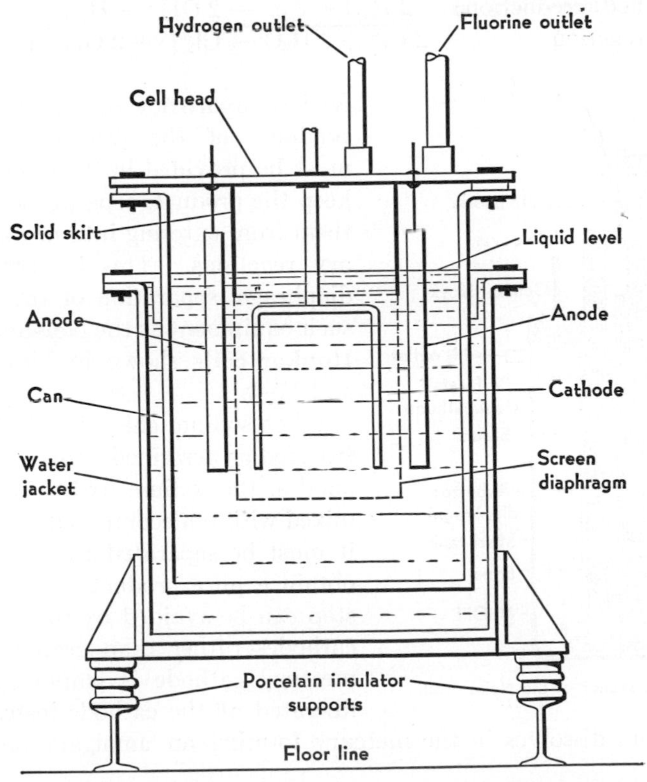

Fig. 17–1 A cross-sectional view of a commercial fluorine cell. *The Harshaw Chemical Company*

40 per cent anhydrous hydrogen fluoride by weight. When electrolysis of the fused electrolyte (melting point 72°) begins, HF is decomposed to form fluorine gas at the anode and hydrogen at the cathode.

$$2\ HF + \text{electrical energy} \rightarrow H_2\uparrow + F_2\uparrow$$

The two gases are kept separate by a barrier and are drawn from the cell continuously. Anhydrous hydrogen fluoride is added to the cell, either continuously or intermittently, to regenerate the electrolyte. The cell commonly used is made of low-grade carbon steel, while the anodes are of carbon and the cathodes of steel. A steel gas barrier surrounds the cathodes and extends below the surface of the electrolyte to keep the products of electrolysis separate.

After purification, fluorine gas is compressed in special steel cylinders at 400 pounds pressure. The purchase price of fluorine (1962) is \$3 to \$15 per pound, depending upon the quantity purchased.

2. *Chlorine.* The bulk of the commercial chlorine is produced by the electrolytic oxidation of chloride ion in aqueous sodium chloride solutions. The half cell reactions are given by the equations

(Anodic oxidation)	$2\ Cl^- \rightarrow Cl_2\uparrow + 2\ e^-$
(Cathodic reduction)	$2\ H_2O + 2\ e^- \rightarrow 2\ OH^- + H_2\uparrow$
Net reaction	$2\ Cl^- + 2\ H_2O \rightarrow Cl_2\uparrow + 2\ OH^- + H_2\uparrow$

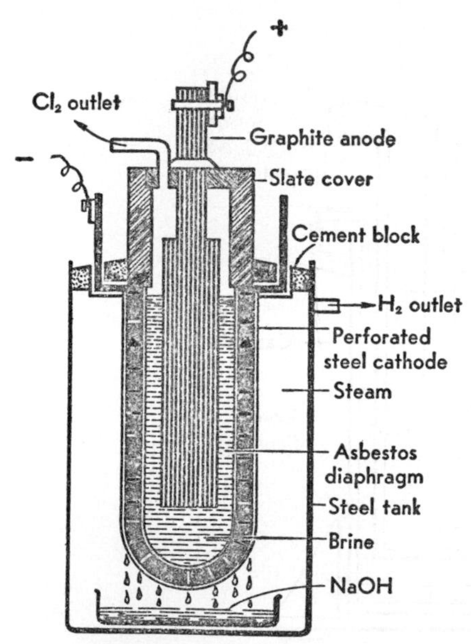

Fig. 17–2 Cross section of the Nelson cell.

Sodium hydroxide and hydrogen are by-products of the process. Some device must be provided in the electrolytic cell to keep the products separate so as to prevent them from entering into unwanted secondary reactions. This is accomplished by diaphragm separation of the electrodes in such equipment as the **Nelson, Vorce,** and **Hooker cells** shown in Figs. 17–2, 17–3, and 17–4.

When sodium chloride solutions are electrolyzed as described above, using graphite anodes, the sodium hydroxide produced is mixed with undecomposed salt, from which it must be separated by crystallization to obtain a pure product. This troublesome step can be avoided by the use of mercury cathodes rather than graphite. When a mercury cathode is employed, sodium is liberated at the cathode instead of hydrogen; the sodium dissolves in the mercury forming an amalgam (an alloy with mercury).

$$\text{(cathodic reduction)}\quad Na^+ + e^- \rightarrow Na\ \text{(amalgam)}$$

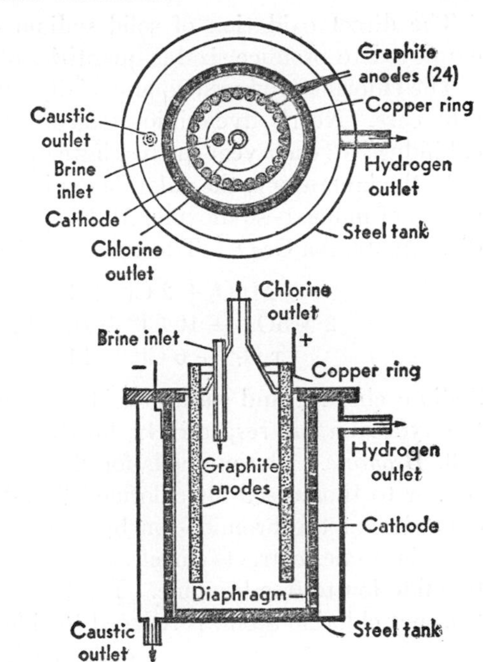

Fig. 17–3 Horizontal and vertical sections of the Vorce cell.

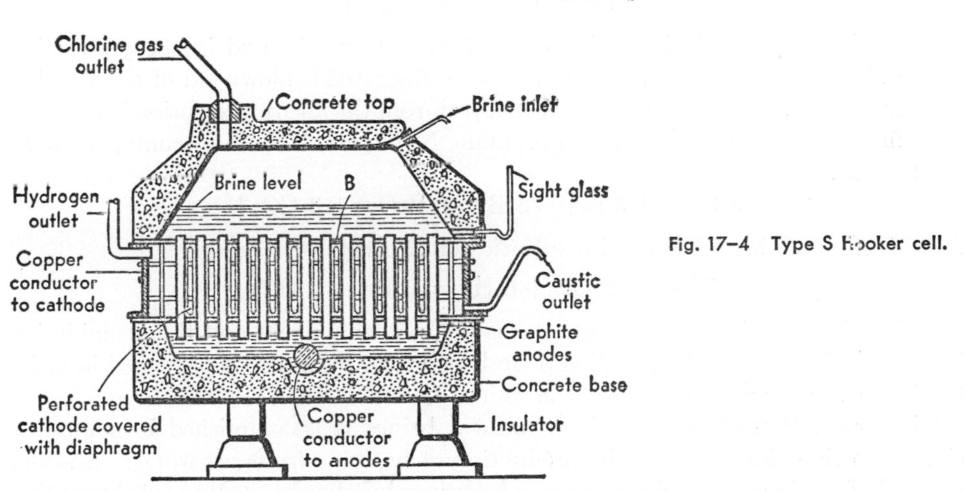

Fig. 17–4 Type S Hooker cell.

The sodium amalgam is then brought in contact with pure water, with which the sodium reacts forming hydrogen and a pure solution of sodium hydroxide.

$$2\ Na\ (amalgam) + 2\ H_2O \rightarrow H_2 \uparrow + 2\ Na^+ + 2\ OH^-$$

Chlorine is a by-product in the production of metals such as sodium, calcium, and magnesium by the electrolytic decomposition of their fused chlorides. For example, when fused sodium chloride is electrolyzed, sodium and chlorine are formed.

$$2\ NaCl\ (fused) + electrical\ energy \rightarrow 2\ Na + Cl_2 \uparrow$$

The direct oxidation of solid sodium chloride by means of nitric acid is also employed to produce sizable quantities of chlorine.

The chlorine produced commercially is liquefied and stored in steel cylinders and tank cars. Nearly five million tons of chlorine are manufactured for use by chemical industries each year in the United States.

In the laboratory, the chloride ion is oxidized to free chlorine in acid solution by means of manganese dioxide, MnO_2, potassium permanganate, $KMnO_4$, or sodium dichromate, $Na_2Cr_2O_7$. The equations for these reactions follow.

$$MnO_2 + 2\ Cl^- + 4\ H^+ \rightarrow Mn^{++} + Cl_2 \uparrow + 2\ H_2O$$
$$2\ MnO_4^- + 10\ Cl^- + 16\ H^+ \rightarrow 2\ Mn^{++} + 5\ Cl_2 \uparrow + 8\ H_2O$$
$$Cr_2O_7^= + 6\ Cl^- + 14\ H^+ \rightarrow 2\ Cr^{+++} + 3\ Cl_2 \uparrow + 7\ H_2O$$

Sodium chloride and sulfuric acid are usually used to supply the chloride ion and the hydrogen ion, respectively, for the above reactions.

3. *Bromine.* The methods for the laboratory scale preparation of bromine are similar to those used for chlorine. In addition, bromine may be prepared by the oxidation of the bromide ion by chlorine. Chlorine, being more electronegative than bromine, attracts an electron from the bromide ion, thereby ozidizing the bromide ion to free bromine. The free chlorine, through the addition of one electron per chlorine atom, is reduced to chloride ion.

$$2\ Br^- + Cl_2 \rightleftharpoons Br_2 + 2\ Cl^-$$

Oxidation of bromide ions with elementary chlorine is used in the production of bromine from sea water. The bromine thus liberated is blown out of the solution by means of air. The bromine is then stripped from the air by adsorption in aqueous sodium carbonate, in which sodium bromide, NaBr, and sodium bromate, $NaBrO_3$, are formed.

$$3\ CO_3^= + 3\ Br_2 \rightarrow 5\ Br^- + BrO_3^- + 3\ CO_2 \uparrow$$

Acidification of this solution with sulfuric acid liberates the bromine.

$$5\ Br^- + BrO_3^- + 6\ H^+ \rightleftharpoons 3\ Br_2 + 3\ H_2O$$

In this redox reaction, the bromate ion is the oxidizing agent and the bromide ion is the reducing agent. One million pounds of sea water must be processed in order to obtain 70 pounds of elementary bromine.

The production of bromine from natural brines is accomplished in a manner similar to that described for the production of bromine from sea water. Another method of producing bromine from natural brines involves electrolysis of the mother liquors remaining after most of the sodium chloride has been removed by crystallization. Because the bromide ion, Br^-, loses an electron (is oxidized) more readily than the chloride ion, Cl^-, the voltage of the electrolytic cell can be kept low enough to oxidize the bromide ion but not the chloride ion.

4. *Iodine.* Chlorine is often employed for liberating iodine from iodides in a manner similar to that described for the preparation of bromine.

$$2\ I^- + Cl_2 \rightarrow \underline{I_2} + 2\ Cl^-$$

Most of the iodine appears as a solid precipitate, which can be separated from the solution by filtration. Care must be taken to avoid the use of an excess of chlorine in this process; otherwise unwanted secondary reactions occur with the formation of iodine chloride, ICl, and iodic acid, HIO_3. Considerable iodine is obtained from iodides concentrated in kelp and other sea plants, and from oil field brines.

Iodine occurs in the form of sodium iodate, $NaIO_3$, in crude Chile saltpeter, $NaNO_3$. The iodine may be liberated from the iodate by reducing it with sodium hydrogen sulfite in accordance with the equation

$$2\ IO_3^- + 5\ HSO_3^- \rightarrow 3\ HSO_4^- + 2\ SO_4^= + H_2O + \underline{I_2}$$

17.4 General Properties of the Halogens

It is a remarkable fact that the halogens fall in the same order of arrangement when any one property is chosen in making the arrangement. A study of Table 17·2, which lists some of their more important properties, will illustrate this point.

TABLE 17·2 Properties of the Halogens

	Fluorine	*Chlorine*	*Bromine*	*Iodine*	*Astatine*
Atomic number	9	17	35	53	85
Atomic weight	18.998	35.453	79.909	126.904	(210)
Electronic structure	2,7	2,8,7	2,8,18,7	2,8,18,18,7	2,8,18,32,18,7
Radius of X^-, Å	1.36	1.81	1.95	2.16	...
Covalent bond radius, Å	0.68	0.97	1.13	1.35	...
Physical state	gas	gas	liquid	solid	solid
Melting point, °C	−218	−101	−7.3	114	...
Boiling point, °C	−188	−34.1	58.78	184	...
Density, g./cm.^{3}	1.108 (liq.)	1.557 (liq.)	3.119 (liq.)	4.93 (sol.)	...
Color	Pale yellow	Greenish-yellow	Reddish-brown	Black (s) violet (g)	...
Electronegativity	4.0	3.0	2.8	2.4	...
Heat of vaporization, cal./mole	1,510	4,878	7,340	11,140	...

The valence shells of the atoms of the halogens each contain seven electrons. They each tend to gain one more electron and become stable univalent negative ions. The large values of their electronegativities indicate the ease with which halide ions are formed from halogen atoms. The tendency to form halide ions and to complete an octet by sharing electrons in covalent linkages decreases as the size of the halogen atom increases because of a resultant reduction in attraction for electrons. This is reflected in a decrease in electronegativity. The halogens are oxidizing agents, with fluorine being the strongest and astatine the weakest in this respect. Each of the halogens is diatomic; this gives each atom an eighth electron through sharing of electron pairs (Fig. 17–5).

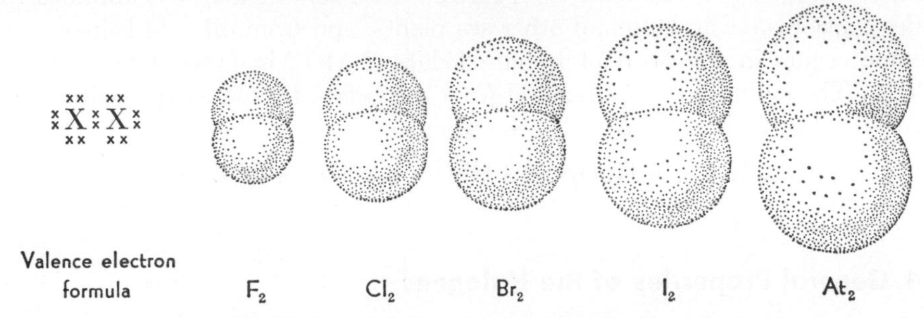

Fig. 17–5 Each halogen forms a diatomic molecule.

For the most part, the chemical properties of the halogens differ in degree rather than in kind. For example, each reacts with hydrogen according to the equation $H_2 + X_2 \rightarrow 2\,HX$; but the heat of formation of HX (Table 18·1) increases in the order HF, HCl, HBr, HI, indicating a **corresponding decrease in the energy evolved** as the hydrogen halides are formed from the free elements (see Section 5.8). The halogens have such high ionization potentials that the formation of positive ions would be highly unlikely, except possibly with iodine and astatine. On the other hand, positive oxidation states resulting from the sharing of electrons with elements more electronegative in character are quite common for the halogens except fluorine, the most electronegative of all the elements. Oxidation states of +1, +3, +5, and +7, and sometimes other oxidation states, are shown when the halogens share electrons with oxygen in their oxides, oxyacids, and oxysalts (Chapter 19).

The halogens oxidize a variety of metals, nonmetals, and ions, including the halide ions. Of course, a free halogen will oxidize only those halide ions which are formed from less electronegative halogens. Thus fluorine will oxidize chloride, bromide, iodide, and astatide ions, whereas chlorine will oxidize only bromide, iodide, and astatide ions.

17.5 Physical Properties of the Halogens

As the atomic structures of the halogens become more complex with increasing atomic weight, there is a gradation in each physical property (Table 17·2). For example, fluorine is a pale yellow gas of low density; chlorine is a greenish-yellow gas and 1.892 times as dense as fluorine gas; bromine is a deep reddish-brown liquid and is three times as dense as water; iodine is a grayish-black crystalline solid with a metallic appearance; and astatine is a solid with properties which indicate that it is somewhat metallic in character.

Liquid bromine has a high vapor pressure and the reddish vapor can easily be seen in a bottle partly filled with the liquid. Iodine crystals have a high vapor pressure, and when heated gently these crystals change into a beautiful deep-purple vapor without melting; the vapor condenses readily upon cooling. This sublimation process (Section 9.13) is used in the purification of iodine.

Bromine dissolves in alcohol, ether, chloroform, carbon tetrachloride, and carbon disulfide, forming solutions that vary in color from yellow to reddish brown, depending upon the concentration.

Iodine dissolves only slightly in water, giving brown solutions. However, it is quite soluble in alcohol, in ether, and in aqueous solutions of iodides, with which it forms brown solutions. The solvents in which iodine combines with the solvent molecules (**solvation**) are the ones which give brown solutions. In chloroform, carbon disulfide, and many hydrocarbons, iodine forms violet solutions. Here the iodine is present in the molecular state (I_2), and the violet color is like that of iodine in the vapor state, where it is also molecular. Solutions of hydrogen iodide, potassium iodide, or other iodides dissolve iodine very readily. Here the iodine and iodide ion combine reversibly, forming the complex ion I_3^-.

$$I^- + I_2 \rightleftharpoons I_3^-$$

The negative iodide ion, when close to a large iodine molecule, whose outer electrons are far from the positive nucleus, disturbs these electronic arrangements enough to induce a dipole within the molecule. An attraction then exists between the negative iodide ion and the positive end of the polar iodine molecule. Compounds containing the complexes I_5^-, Br_3^-, and Cl_3^- have also been reported.

17.6 Chemical Properties of Fluorine

The extreme reactivity of fluorine gas as an oxidizing agent is demonstrated by the fact that immediately upon contact with many substances, it ignites them. When a stream of the gas flows onto the surface of water it actually causes the water to burn. Wood and asbestos rapidly ignite and burn when held in a stream of fluorine. Heated glass will burn in fluorine, giving off smoke which looks much like that from wood. Most hot metals burn vigorously in fluorine. However, fluorine can be handled at ordinary or moderately elevated temperatures in containers made of metals such as copper, iron, magnesium, nickel, and Monel. An adherent film of the metal fluoride appears to protect these metal surfaces from further attack.

Fluorine readily displaces chlorine and other halogens from the solid metal halides. It reacts immediately with water in several simultaneous reactions which involve the formation of O_2, OF_2, H_2O_2, O_3, and HF. Fluorine and hydrogen react explosively at room temperature.

Fluorine, as a result of its high electronegativity, has very recently been reported to react even with the rare gas *xenon* to form **xenon tetrafluoride** — the first reported combination of xenon with another single element (see Section 24.7).

17.7 Chemical Properties of Chlorine

Chlorine is less active as an oxidizing agent than fluorine because of its lower electronegativity; this is a reflection of the larger size of its atoms.

1. *Action with hydrogen.* Chlorine may be mixed safely with hydrogen in the dark, the reaction then being imperceptibly slow. However, when the mixture is exposed to light, the reaction is explosive.

$$H_2 + Cl_2 \rightarrow 2\ HCl + 44{,}126\ \text{cal.}$$

Chemical reactions of this type, which are caused to proceed more rapidly by the effect of light, are called **photochemical reactions.** The absorption of a quantum of light energy by a chlorine molecule causes it to break up into chlorine atoms.

$$Cl_2 + \text{light energy} \rightarrow 2\ Cl^*$$

The energy-rich, or activated, chlorine atoms then react with hydrogen molecules to form hydrogen chloride molecules and activated hydrogen atoms.

$$Cl^* + H_2 \rightarrow HCl + H^*$$

Then these activated hydrogen atoms react with chlorine molecules to form hydrogen chloride molecules and activated chlorine atoms.

$$H^* + Cl_2 \rightarrow HCl + Cl^*$$

The new activated chlorine atoms then react in the same fashion as those originally produced by light, and thus a chain of reactions producing hydrogen chloride is set up. The chain reaction may continue until thousands of hydrogen chloride molecules have been formed. It may stop, however, when two chlorine atoms combine to form a chlorine molecule after they have become deactivated by colliding with the walls of the container, or in some other way.

2. *Action with metals.* Chlorine is less active toward metals than fluorine, and higher temperatures are generally required in its oxidation of metals. Powdered antimony ignites in chlorine to form antimony (III) chloride, $SbCl_3$ (Fig. 17–6). Moist chlorine will attack such inactive metals as gold and platinum when they are heated. Apparently, perfectly dry chlorine does not react appreciably with them, or with such metals as iron and lead. For this reason, dry liquid chlorine may be stored and shipped in steel cylinders and tank cars. A trace of moisture, however, causes chlorine to corrode iron containers.

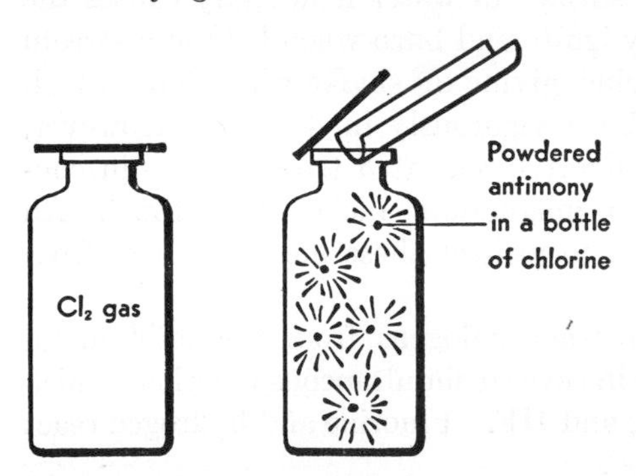

Fig. 17–6 Antimony burns brightly in chlorine gas, producing antimony trichloride.

3. *Action with nonmetals.* Chlorine reacts with many of the nonmetals, forming covalent molecular compounds. For example, it combines with sulfur to give "sulfur monochloride," a liquid used in the vulcanization of rubber.

$$2\ S + Cl_2 \rightarrow S_2Cl_2$$

When the chlorine is in excess, sulfur is oxidized to the dichloride.

$$S + Cl_2 \rightarrow SCl_2$$

Chlorine oxidizes phosphorus to the trichloride, PCl_3, when a limited supply of the halogen is employed. When an excess of chlorine is used, the pentachloride, PCl_5, is formed.

$$2\ P + 3\ Cl_2 \rightarrow 2\ PCl_3$$
$$2\ P + 5\ Cl_2 \rightarrow 2\ PCl_5$$

4. *Action with compounds.* The tendency of chlorine to react with hydrogen is so great that it will remove hydrogen from certain of its compounds. For example, turpentine, $C_{10}H_{16}$, bursts into flame when it is placed in a cylinder of chlorine gas.

$$C_{10}H_{16} + 8\ Cl_2 \rightarrow 16\ HCl + 10\ C$$

The carbon is displaced by the chlorine. A stepwise substitution of hydrogen by chlorine takes place when methane, CH_4, reacts with chlorine.

$$CH_4 + Cl_2 \rightarrow CH_3Cl + HCl$$
$$CH_3Cl + Cl_2 \rightarrow CH_2Cl_2 + HCl$$
$$CH_2Cl_2 + Cl_2 \rightarrow CHCl_3 + HCl$$

A mixture of products is formed.

When chlorine is dissolved in water, an **auto-oxidation-reduction reaction** takes place.

$$Cl_2 + H_2O \rightleftharpoons H^+ + Cl^- + HClO$$

One of the chlorine atoms of Cl_2 is oxidized to the +1 state in hypochlorous acid, HClO, while the other atom of chlorine is reduced to the −1 state in the chloride ion, Cl^-. The reaction between chlorine and water is incomplete, as is indicated by the equation. Thus chlorine water is a mixture of water, chlorine, the ions of hydrochloric acid, and molecules of hypochlorous acid. The solution gives off oxygen in sunlight, as the light-sensitive hypochlorous acid decomposes.

$$2\ HClO \rightarrow 2\ H^+ + 2\ Cl^- + O_2 \uparrow$$

This reaction removes HClO from the equilibrium mixture, $Cl_2 + H_2O \rightleftharpoons H^+ + Cl^- + HClO$, causing the reaction to the right to go slowly to completion. For this reason chlorine water is usually stored in colored bottles which do not permit the passage of light.

17.8 Chemical Properties of Bromine

The chemical properties of bromine are very similar to those of chlorine, as one would expect, but its atoms are larger, have a lower electronegativity, and gain electrons less readily. Thus bromine is a weaker oxidizing agent than chlorine. The reactivity of bromine toward hydrogen, the nonmetals, the metals, and methane is less vigorous than that of chlorine. This lower reactivity is reflected in the evolution of less heat in the formation of bromides as compared to chlorides. Bromine reacts with water to form hydrobromic acid and hypobromous acid; the reaction is less extensive than that between chlorine and water.

$$Br_2 + H_2O \rightleftharpoons H^+ + Br^- + HBrO$$

Hypobromous acid decomposes in sunlight according to the equation

$$2\ HBrO \rightarrow 2\ H^+ + 2\ Br^- + O_2\uparrow$$

17.9 Chemical Properties of Iodine

Considering only the naturally occurring halogens, the iodine atom has the least attraction for an additional electron. This is due to its large radius and greater number of electron shells. Thus iodine is the weakest oxidizing agent of the four halogens and the iodide ion is the most easily oxidized of the four halides.

$$2\ I^- \rightarrow I_2 + 2\ e^-$$

Iodine combines with many of the metals but with the liberation of much less heat than the other halogens; with some metals, heating is required before reaction occurs. Although iodine does not oxidize the other halide ions, it will remove electrons from certain other nonmetal ions such as sulfide ions, $S^=$.

$$S^= + I_2 \rightarrow \underline{S} + 2\ I^-$$

Iodine shows slight activity with water compared with the other halogens.

A very sensitive qualitative test for elementary iodine depends upon the formation of a deep blue color when even trace quantities react with starch.

The trend in the groups in the Periodic Table is from nonmetallic to metallic character down the groups. In line with this trend, iodine is the most metallic of the naturally occurring halogens. Accordingly, chemists have tried to prepare compounds of iodine in which it plays the role of a "true" metal. The preparation of several compounds of tripositive iodine, such as the acetate, $I(C_2H_3O_2)_3$, the phosphate, IPO_4, the nitrate, $I(NO_3)_3$, and the perchlorate, $I(ClO_4)_3 \cdot 2\ H_2O$, has been successful. In these compounds, iodine is acting in the capacity of a trivalent metal. As might be expected, these compounds are readily hydrolyzed by water.

17.10 Properties of Astatine

As would be expected, astatine, the fifth halogen, is a solid with properties which indicate that it is more metallic than iodine. The solid is volatile and is soluble in such solvents as carbon disulfide and carbon tetrachloride. Elementary astatine is the weakest oxidizing agent of the halogens and the astatide ion, At^-, is the strongest reducing agent of the family. In addition to the negative ion, At^-, it forms at least two positive ions. Extensive research on the chemical properties of astatine is being conducted.

17.11 Physiological Action of the Halogens

Fluorine is very corrosive to tissue and produces severe burns. The fluoride ion is highly toxic when taken internally in considerable amounts. An excess of fluoride ion in the drinking water of young children produces mottling (a discoloration) of the teeth. On the other hand, a concentration of approximately one part per million of fluoride ion in the drinking water inhibits the development of caries in the teeth of children. According to reports by the American Dental Association and the U. S. Public Health Service, more than forty-nine million people, by 1962, were drinking fluoridated water in the United States — seven million persons, naturally fluoridated water in concentrations of at least one part per million and 42,182,000 persons, water to which the fluoride has been added artificially. The formulations of some toothpastes include tin (II) fluoride.

Chlorine is a dangerous poison which was used in World War I as a war gas. Small quantities of chlorine in the air produce headaches and bronchial colds; larger quantities soon cause death. Many halogen-containing compounds designed to produce physiological effects in chemical warfare have been prepared.

Bromine causes severe and painful burns and sores which are slow to heal. Its vapor is very irritating to the mucous membranes of the eyes, nose, and throat.

Iodine in alcoholic solution with potassium iodide (**tincture of iodine**) is used extensively as an antiseptic. In the form of iodide salts, it is essential in small amounts in the diet for the proper functioning of the thyroid glands. It is important in growth and metabolism. Iodine deficiency may lead to the development of goiter.

17.12 Uses of the Halogens

Fluorine gas has been used in the fluorination of organic compounds since the early work of Moissan in 1886. Such reactions are usually difficult to control, however, and less vigorous fluorinating agents such as antimony trifluoride, SbF_3, and cobalt trifluoride, CoF_3, are more generally employed for this purpose than is elementary fluorine. The **fluorocarbon** compounds thus produced from hydrocarbons are quite stable and nonflammable. They are used as lubricants, refrigerants, coolants, hydraulic liquids, plastics, and insecticides. Freon-12, which is CCl_2F_2, is widely used as a refrigerant; CCl_3F is used as an insecticide; and teflon is a plastic composed of C_2F_4 units. One of the most important uses of fluorine gas is in the production of uranium hexafluoride, UF_6, which is used in separating the isotopes of uranium by the gaseous diffusion process in connection with the production of atomic energy. Another use is in the making of sulfur hexafluoride, SF_6, a stable gas with high dielectric and insulating capacities for high voltage. During World War II, the Germans used fluorine in the manufacture of chlorine trifluoride, ClF_3, a liquid incendiary. This compound is also of value in the fluorination of other compounds.

Large quantities of the chlorine produced for commercial purposes are used in bleaching wood pulp and cotton cloth. The hypochlorous acid which is formed when chlorine reacts with water bleaches by oxidizing colored substances to colorless compounds. Most community water supplies are treated with small amounts of chlorine to kill bacteria. Large quantities of chlorine are used in chlorinating hydrocarbons (replacing hydrogen with chlorine) to produce such compounds as carbon tetrachloride (CCl_4), chloroform ($CHCl_3$), and para-dichlorobenzene (dichlorocide).

The principal use of bromine is in the manufacture of ethylene dibromide, $C_2H_4Br_2$, a constituent of antiknock gasoline along with lead tetraethyl, $Pb(C_2H_5)_4$. When the gaseous fuel in an internal combustion motor explodes with extreme rapidity, "knocking" occurs with a great loss in efficiency. Lead tetraethyl apparently functions as a negative catalyst in the combustion of the fuel, causing the rate of combustion to be decreased, and a corresponding increase in the efficiency of the motor. The ethylene dibromide is added to convert the lead from lead tetraethyl to lead bromide. This compound escapes from the motor, thus preventing the accumulation of lead in the motor.

Further application of bromine is found in the production of certain organic dyes, in the preparation of light-sensitive silver bromide for use in making photographic film, and in the manufacture of the bromides of sodium and potassium which are used in medicine as sedatives and soporifics.

Mention has already been made of the use of iodine in medicine as "tincture of iodine," and the physiological essentiality of this element. Iodoform, CHI_3, is used as an antiseptic in the dressing of wounds. Iodized table salt contains about 0.023 per cent potassium iodide. Silver iodide is used in photographic films.

17.13 Interhalogen Compounds

The compounds formed by the union of two different halogens are called **interhalogen compounds.** Molecules of these compounds consist of an atom of the heavier halogen bonded to an odd number of atoms of the lighter halogen. Examples of interhalogen compounds are given in Table 17·3.

TABLE 17·3 Interhalogen Compounds

IBr	BrCl	ClF
ICl	BrF	ClF_3
ICl_3	BrF_3	
IF_5	BrF_5	
IF_7		

Because the smaller halogen atoms are grouped about the larger, the number of smaller atoms per molecule increases as the radius ratio, $R_{larger}/R_{smaller}$, increases. Thus iodine forms a heptafluoride, bromine merely the pentafluoride, and chlorine the trifluoride. Most of these compounds are unstable and extremely reactive chemically. The reactions of the interhalogen compounds are similar to those of the component halogens.

The **polyhalides** of the alkali metals such as KI_3, $KICl_2$, $KICl_4$, $CsIBr_2$, and $CsClBr_2$ are closely related to the interhalogen compounds.

Typical structures of the interhalogens and polyhalides are shown in Fig. 17–7.

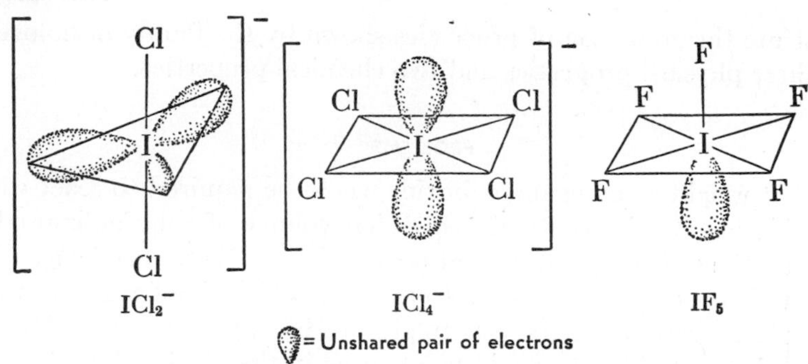

Fig. 17–7 Structures of ICl_2^- (linear), ICl_4^- (square planar), and IF_5 (square base pyramidal). Each shaded lobe indicates an unshared pair of electrons.

QUESTIONS

1. What is the meaning of the term "halogen"? What are the binary compounds of the halogens called?
2. Arrange the halogens in order of increasing (a) atomic radii, (b) ionic radii, (c) electronegativity, (d) boiling points, (e) oxidizing activity, and (f) intensity of color.
3. Why is it difficult to prepare elementary fluorine? How is its preparation accomplished?
4. Why must the chlorine and sodium hydroxide resulting from the electrolysis of brine be kept separate in the manufacture of chlorine? How is this done?
5. Write equations for the interaction of hydrochloric acid and (a) MnO_2, (b) $KMnO_4$, and (c) $Na_2Cr_2O_7$.
6. Describe the chemistry of the extraction of bromine from sea water.
7. Write equations showing the action of chlorine upon a metal, hydrogen, water, sulfur, and phosphorus.
8. Why are the water supplies of many communities fluoridated?
9. What is "tincture of iodine"? What is the physiological action of iodine?
10. Discuss reasons for the differences in oxidizing power for the halogens.
11. What product is formed when phosphorus is burned in a limited supply of chlorine? in an excess of chlorine?
12. Show by means of oxidation state changes that the reaction of chlorine with water is one of auto-oxidation-reduction.
13. Describe the commercial production of iodine from sodium iodate.
14. What are fluorocarbons? List some general uses of these compounds.
15. A solution of iodine in carbon disulfide is violet while an aqueous solution of this element is brown. Explain.
16. Why is an iodide added in the preparation of the tincture of iodine?
17. Why is it necessary to prepare fluorine by the electrolytic method?
18. If chlorine, iodine, a chloride, an iodide, and a starch suspension were available to you, how would you demonstrate the relative activity of chlorine and iodine?

19. Illustrate the gradation of properties shown by the family of halogens with regard to three physical properties and two chemical properties.

PROBLEMS

1. (a) What weight of manganese dioxide would be required to react with 40 g. of sodium chloride in acid solution? (b) What volume of chlorine is produced at standard conditions of temperature and pressure? *Ans.* (*a*) *30 g.;* (*b*) *7.7 l.*

2. What weight of chlorine results from the electrolysis of 0.500 ton of fused sodium chloride, assuming the process to give a 94.0% yield? *Ans. 569 lb.*

3. What volume of chlorine would be required in the combustion of 50 liters of hydrogen? What volume of hydrogen chloride would be produced? *Ans. 50 l.; 100 l.*

4. How much S_2Cl_2 could be produced from 150 l. of chlorine, measured at 7.00 atm. and 25.0°, if the reaction gives a yield of 89.0% *Ans. 5,160 g.*

5. Calculate the densities of gaseous fluorine, chlorine, bromine, and iodine at 0.50 atm. and 200°.
Ans. F_2, *0.490 g./l.;* Cl_2, *0.914 g./l.;* Br_2, *2.06 g./l.;* I_2, *3.27 g./l.*

6. What volume of chlorine measured at 20.0° and 730 mm. would be required to displace 200 g. of bromine from a solution of sodium bromide? *Ans. 31.3 l.*

7. How many grams of iodine can be prepared from 500 g. of sodium iodate by reduction with sodium hydrogen sulfite? *Ans. 323 g.*

8. An electrolytic cell consumes 100 kg. of sodium chloride while it is producing 57 kg. of chlorine. What is the percentage yield? *Ans. 94%*

REFERENCES

"Humphry Davy and the Elementary Nature of Chlorine," R. Siegfried, *J. Chem. Educ.*, **36** (11) 568 (1959).

"Chlorine," (Staff) *Chem. Eng. News*, **29** (5) 363 (1951).

"The Halogen Family," M. E. Weeks, *Discovery of the Elements*, Sixth Edition, Publ. by the Journal of Chemical Education, Easton, Pa., 1956; Chapter 27, pp. 729–777.

"Fluorine — An Important Material for Postwar Development," S. C. Ogburn, Jr., *J. Chem. Educ.*, **24** (7) 314 (1947).

"Recent Advances in Fluorine Chemistry," G. C. Finger, *J. Chem. Educ.*, **28** (1) 49 (1951).

"Fluorine," E. M. Ott, *Chem. Eng. News*, **31** (16) 1626 (1953).

"Organic Fluorine Chemicals," E. T. McBee and C. W. Roberts, *J. Chem. Educ.*, **32** (1) 13 (1955).

CHAPTER EIGHTEEN

The Hydrogen Halides

The binary compounds which contain only hydrogen and one of the halogens are called **hydrogen halides.** These compounds have the general formula HX in which X represents the halogen. At ordinary temperatures, molecules of hydrogen fluoride polymerize through hydrogen bonding into complex units which may be represented by the formula $(HF)_x$.

18.1 Preparation of the Hydrogen Halides

Various methods are used for the preparation of the hydrogen halides.

1. *By direct union.* One method of preparing the hydrogen halides is by the direct union of their constituent elements according to the equation

$$H_2 + X_2 \rightarrow 2\ HX$$

The heats of formation of hydrogen halides are given in Table 18·1. Note that the rapid increase in the heats of formation of these compounds with increasing atomic weight of the halogen indicates a **corresponding decrease in the quantities of energy released** during the formation of the compounds (see Section 5.8). The difficulty of producing elementary fluorine and its relatively high cost make this method of preparing hydrogen fluoride impractical. On the other hand, hydrogen and chlorine are not expensive and one commercial method of producing hydrogen chloride involves the combustion of hydrogen with chlorine in burners specially designed for this purpose. Both hydrogen and chlorine are made available for the production of hydrogen chloride as products of the electrolysis of brine (Section 17.3). The reaction of bromine with hydrogen is much less vigorous than that with either chlorine or fluorine. In fact, for the reaction between hydrogen and bromine to proceed appreciably, the mixture must be heated to about 200° C in contact with a catalyst such as platinum or hot carbon. High temperatures cause hydrogen bromide to decompose so the reaction is a reversible one that readily reaches equilibrium.

$$H_2 + Br_2 \rightleftharpoons 2\ HBr$$

The reaction may be forced nearly to completion by using an excess of hydrogen. The excess hydrogen may then be removed by liquefying the hydrogen bromide and pumping away the gaseous hydrogen.

The direct union of hydrogen and iodine is unsatisfactory for the preparation of hydrogen iodide because the reaction is slow, and never complete. Heat decomposes hydrogen iodide; this means that the reaction is readily reversible and the equilibrium yield of HI is low.

$$H_2 + I_2 \rightleftharpoons 2\ HI$$

This reaction does not become self-sustaining as do the similar reactions of the other halogens.

2. *By the action of concentrated sulfuric acid upon a metallic halide.* The most convenient method of producing hydrogen fluoride and hydrogen chloride is based upon the reaction of concentrated sulfuric acid upon a halide of a metal, according to the general equation

$$2\ MX + H_2SO_4 \rightarrow M_2SO_4 + 2\ HX\uparrow$$

Hydrogen fluoride is usually prepared by heating a mixture of the mineral fluorite, CaF_2, and concentrated sulfuric acid in a lead or platinum retort.

$$CaF_2 + H_2SO_4 \rightarrow CaSO_4 + 2\ HF\uparrow$$

The hydrogen fluoride is evolved as a gas and is immediately absorbed in water, forming hydrofluoric acid. This acid acts upon glass, and for this reason is stored in bottles made of lead, wax, or certain plastics such as polyethylene.

Hydrogen chloride is prepared, both in the laboratory and on a commercial scale, by the action of concentrated sulfuric acid upon sodium chloride, the most plentiful and least costly of the chlorides.

$$NaCl + H_2SO_4 \rightarrow NaHSO_4 + HCl\uparrow$$

At slightly elevated temperatures the reaction goes to completion because hydrogen chloride is insoluble in the reaction mixture. The by-product, $NaHSO_4$, is an example of a **hydrogen salt** and is known as sodium hydrogen sulfate, sodium acid sulfate, or sodium bisulfate. It still contains acidic hydrogen that can be used in preparing more hydrogen chloride. Consequently, by adding more sodium chloride, and heating the mixture to a higher temperature, the following reaction takes place:

$$NaCl + NaHSO_4 \rightarrow Na_2SO_4 + HCl\uparrow$$

The hydrogen chloride thus produced is absorbed in water and marketed as hydrochloric acid.

In the preparation of hydrogen bromide and hydrogen iodide, this method gives rise to undesirable by-products. Hydrogen bromide prepared in this way is impure with bromine and sulfur dioxide because of the oxidation of a portion of the hydrogen bromide by the hot, concentrated sulfuric acid.

$$NaBr + H_2SO_4 \rightarrow NaHSO_4 + HBr\uparrow$$
$$H_2SO_4 + 2\ HBr \rightarrow 2\ H_2O + SO_2\uparrow + Br_2\uparrow$$

The relative ease of oxidation of the halide ions was discussed in Chapter 17. Concentrated sulfuric acid does not oxidize either the fluoride or chloride ions. However, the bromide ion, which is larger and more easily oxidized, loses an electron by reacting with sulfuric acid and becomes free bromine. This means that hydrogen bromide is a stronger reducing agent than hydrogen fluoride or hydrogen chloride; the two latter compounds do not reduce concentrated sulfuric acid. If phosphoric acid, which is not a good oxidizing agent, is used as the nonvolatile acid in place of sulfuric, this secondary reaction is avoided and nearly pure hydrogen bromide is obtained.

As would be predicted, hydrogen iodide is a still stronger reducing agent than hydrogen bromide. Consequently, the hydrogen iodide produced by the reaction of concentrated sulfuric acid upon sodium iodide reduces sulfuric acid to the hydrogen sulfide stage.

$$NaI + H_2SO_4 \rightarrow NaHSO_4 + HI \uparrow$$
$$8\ HI + H_2SO_4 \rightarrow H_2S \uparrow + 4\ I_2 + 4\ H_2O$$

Gaseous hydrogen iodide produced by this method is colored violet by iodine vapor.

3. *By the hydrolysis of nonmetallic halides.* Another method of producing hydrogen halides is by the hydrolysis (reaction with water) of the covalent halides of the nonmetals. Typical of this class of compounds are PCl_3, PBr_3, PI_3, and SCl_4. The halides of this group generally react with water to form two acids; quite often the reaction is a vigorous one. Usually hydrolysis of a nonmetal halide yields the hydrogen halide and an oxyacid of the nonmetal. The hydrolysis of phosphorus trichloride is written

$$PCl_3 + 3\ H_2O \rightarrow H_3PO_3 + 3\ HCl \uparrow$$

The hydrolysis of sulfur tetrachloride yields hydrogen chloride and sulfurous acid, H_2SO_3.

$$SCl_4 + 3\ H_2O \rightarrow H_2SO_3 + 4\ HCl \uparrow$$

These methods are unimportant for the preparation of hydrogen chloride. However, the preparation of hydrogen bromide and hydrogen iodide by the hydrolysis of phosphorus (III) bromide and phosphorus (III) iodide, respectively, is quite commonly employed.

$$PBr_3 + 3\ H_2O \rightarrow H_3PO_3 + 3\ HBr \uparrow$$
$$PI_3 + 3\ H_2O \rightarrow H_3PO_3 + 3\ HI \uparrow$$

The PBr_3 and PI_3 are prepared by the direct union of phosphorus with bromine and iodine, respectively.

4. *The halogenation of hydrocarbons.* When fluorine, chlorine, or bromine (but not iodine) is allowed to react with a saturated hydrocarbon, one product of the reaction is the corresponding hydrogen halide. A catalyst is usually required, and the hydrogen halide is often a by-product of a reaction used to produce a desired halogenated hydrocarbon. For example, hydrogen chloride is a by-product of the manufacture of ethyl chloride (C_2H_5Cl) from ethane (C_2H_6).

$$C_2H_6 + Cl_2 \rightarrow C_2H_5Cl + HCl \uparrow$$

Large quantities of hydrogen chloride are produced commercially by such reactions.

5. *Other methods.* Pure anhydrous hydrogen fluoride can be obtained by heating potassium hydrogen fluoride.

$$KHF_2 \rightarrow KF + HF \uparrow$$

Other methods of producing hydrogen bromide and hydrogen iodide in aqueous solution as the corresponding acids involve the reduction of the elementary halogen by means of hydrogen sulfide or sulfurous acid. These methods are illustrated by the following equations:

$$Br_2 + H_2S \rightarrow 2\ H^+ + 2\ Br^- + \underline{S}$$

$$Br_2 + H_2SO_3 + H_2O \rightarrow \underbrace{2\ H^+ + 2\ Br^-}_{\text{Hydrobromic acid}} + \underbrace{2\ H^+ + SO_4^{=}}_{\text{Sulfuric acid}}$$

$$I_2 + H_2S \rightarrow 2\ H^+ + 2\ I^- + \underline{S}$$

$$I_2 + H_2SO_3 + H_2O \rightarrow 2\ H^+ + 2\ I^- + 2\ H^+ + SO_4^{=}$$

18.2 General Properties of the Hydrogen Halides

HF, HCl, HBr, and HI are colorless gases with sharp, penetrating odors. Their constituent atoms are linked together by polar covalent bonds. The polarity of these molecules is a function of the electronegativity of the halogen atom; it is greatest for HF and least for HI. Some of the more important physical properties are given in Table 18·1.

TABLE 18·1 Some Properties of the Hydrogen Halides

	HF	*HCl*	*HBr*	*HI*
Molecular weight	20.006	36.461	80.917	127.91
Melting point, °C	−83.1	−114.2	−86.8	−50.8
Boiling point, °C	19.9	−85.1	−66.7	−35.36
Solubility in water, g./100 g. of water	∞ (0°)	82.3 (0°)	221 (0°)	234 (10°)
Heat of formation cal./mole	−64,200	−22,063	−8,660	+6,200
Constant boiling solutions: composition, per cent	35.35	20.24	47	57
boiling point, °C	120	110	126	127

All the hydrogen halides decompose into their constituent elements when heated sufficiently. Hydrogen iodide is most easily decomposed while hydrogen chloride and hydrogen fluoride show only slight dissociation at 1000° C. The stability of these gases decreases, then, as the formula weight increases.

The hydrogen halides fume in moist air and all are very soluble in water. With the exception of hydrogen fluoride, the hydrogen halides are strong electrolytes; they ionize completely in dilute aqueous solution. The ionization of hydrogen chloride is given by the equation $HCl \rightarrow H^+ + Cl^-$. As the concentration of these acids in water is greatly increased, the molecular form (HX) appears and escapes from solution as such. All the hydrogen halides form constant boiling solutions with water (Table 18·1).

The anhydrous hydrogen halides are rather inactive chemically and do not attack dry metals at ordinary temperatures. Neither do they conduct electricity in the liquid state; this fact indicates that they are molecular rather than ionic compounds.

18.3 The Hydrohalic Acids

Aqueous solutions of the hydrogen halides are called **hydrofluoric acid, hydrochloric acid, hydrobromic acid,** and **hydriodic acid.**

1. *Properties dependent upon hydrogen ion.* Hydrofluoric acid is a weak acid, but the other hydrohalic acids are very strong. All of them react with the metals above hydrogen in the activity series, halide salts and hydrogen being formed. Their reaction with zinc is given by the equation

$$Zn + 2\,H^+ + (2\,X^-) \rightarrow Zn^{++} + (2\,X^-) + H_2\uparrow$$

Note that the hydrogen ion acts as an oxidizing agent. Zinc is oxidized from 0 to +2 and hydrogen is reduced from +1 to 0. The hydrohalic acids neutralize aqueous bases, forming salts and water. Their reaction with sodium hydroxide is given by the equation

$$\underbrace{(Na^+) + OH^-}_{\text{Base}} + \underbrace{H^+ + (X^-)}_{\text{Acid}} \rightarrow \underbrace{(Na^+) + (X^-)}_{\text{Salt}} + \underbrace{H_2O}_{\text{Water}}$$

2. *Properties dependent upon halide ion.* The halide ion of the hydrohalic acids can serve as a reducing agent or as a precipitating agent, as illustrated by the following reactions.

As reducing agent:

$$(2\,H^+) + 2\,Br^- + Cl_2 \rightleftharpoons (2\,H^+) + 2\,Cl^- + Br_2$$
$$14\,H^+ + 6\,Cl^- + Cr_2O_7^{=} \rightleftharpoons 2\,Cr^{+++} + 3\,Cl_2 + 7\,H_2O$$

As precipitating agent:

$$Ag^+ + (NO_3^-) + (H^+) + Cl^- \rightleftharpoons \underline{AgCl} + (H^+) + (NO_3^-)$$

18.4 Unique Properties of Hydrogen Fluoride and Hydrofluoric Acid

Hydrogen fluoride is unique among the hydrogen halides in that its molecules are associated. Furthermore, hydrofluoric acid is weak while the other hydrohalic acids are strong, and it attacks glass whereas the others do not.

1. *The association of hydrogen fluoride molecules — hydrogen bonding.* Pure hydrogen fluoride differs from the other hydrogen halides because of the tendency of its molecules to associate through hydrogen bonding. In the solid state hydrogen fluoride exists as zigzag chains of molecules which extend the entire length of the crystal.

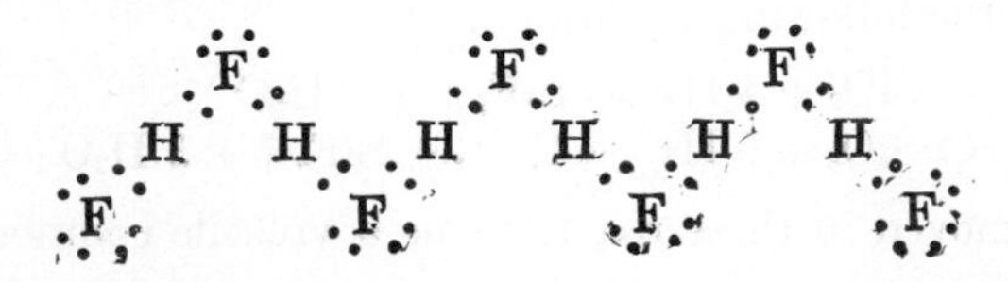

Vapor density measurements show hydrogen fluoride gas to be a mixture of $(HF)_2$ and $(HF)_3$ at 26° C while at 88° C the vapor density corresponds to the formula HF. **The hydrogen atom may be attracted simultaneously to two atoms of high electronegativity, instead of only one, and thereby act as a bond between the two.** The **hydrogen bond** is primarily electrostatic in character; it cannot be covalent because hydrogen has only a single 1*s* orbital and is therefore incapable of forming more than one covalent bond.

Hydrogen bonds exist only between highly electronegative atoms such as fluorine, oxygen, chlorine, and nitrogen. Examples are FHF, OHF, NHF, OHO, NHO, NHN, and OHCl. The strength of hydrogen bonds is about 5 to 10 per cent of that of ordinary covalent bonds. The abnormally high boiling point of hydrogen fluoride, compared to that of each of the other hydrogen halides, results from the fact that hydrogen bonds must be broken to vaporize hydrogen fluoride, and that the associated molecules of the vapor have abnormally high molecular weights.

The tendency to form hydrogen bonds causes many metal fluorides to form hydrogen difluoride salts such as $NaHF_2$ and KHF_2. The hydrogen difluoride ion has the structure

$$\left[\underset{\times\times}{\overset{\times\times}{{}^{\times}_{\times}F^{\times}_{\times}}} \; H \; \underset{\times\times}{\overset{\times\times}{{}^{\times}_{\times}F^{\times}_{\times}}} \right]^-$$

2. *The ionization of hydrofluoric acid.* Hydrofluoric acid is weak whereas the other hydrohalic acids are strong. In order for ionization to occur, the bond in H–X must be broken and then hydration of the resultant ions must take place. The H–F bond is about twice as difficult to break as is the H–I bond, and the strengths of the H–Br and H–Cl lie between those of the other two. The greater strength of the H–F bond as compared to that of the H–I is considered to result from the smaller interatomic distance in HF (HF, 1.0 Å; HI, 1.7 Å). The ionization of hydrogen fluoride in dilute solution may be written as follows:

$$HF \rightleftharpoons H^+ + F^-$$

However, a second ion is formed due to hydrogen bonding; it is the hydrogen difluoride ion.

$$F^- + HF \rightleftharpoons HF_2^-$$

In very concentrated solutions of hydrofluoric acid, the degree of ionization rises sharply. This behavior is opposite to that observed for all other weak electrolytes; and results from an increase in the concentration of the dimer, H_2F_2, which is a stronger acid than the monomer, HF.

$$H_2F_2 \rightleftharpoons H^+ + HF_2^-$$

3. *The action of hydrofluoric acid on glass.* The most characteristic behavior of hydrofluoric acid is its action on sand, which is silicon dioxide, and glass, which is a mixture of silicates. The reaction of hydrofluoric acid with sand and with calcium silicate is given by the following equations:

$$SiO_2 + 4\ HF \rightleftharpoons SiF_4\uparrow + 2\ H_2O$$
$$CaSiO_3 + 6\ HF \rightarrow CaF_2 + SiF_4\uparrow + 3\ H_2O$$

The silicon is removed in these reactions as a volatile compound, silicon tetra-

Fig. 18–1 Hydrofluoric acid is stored and shipped in either wax or plastic bottles. *General Chemical Co.*

fluoride. When one mole of SiF_4 is formed from the elements, the amount of energy released, 361 kcal., is exceedingly high. This large release of energy provides the driving force for the conversion of silicon-oxygen compounds to silicon tetrafluoride by the action of hydrofluoric acid. For example, in the reaction $SiO_2 + 4\ HF \rightleftharpoons SiF_4 + 2\ H_2O$, energy to the extent of 80 kcal. is released, and the escape of the gaseous SiF_4 helps drive the reaction to completion. Glass objects such as electric light bulbs are "frosted" or "etched" by hydrofluoric acid. Hydrofluoric acid cannot be stored in glass containers, so wax and certain plastic vessels are used to contain it (Fig. 18–1). Thermometers, burets, and other glassware may be marked by use of this acid. In order that a restricted area may be etched, the glass is first covered with paraffin, and then, by the use of a sharp-pointed instrument, a part of the paraffin is removed from the glass (Fig. 18–2). Extreme care should be taken in handling hydrofluoric acid for it is very corrosive to the skin and causes painful, slow-healing burns.

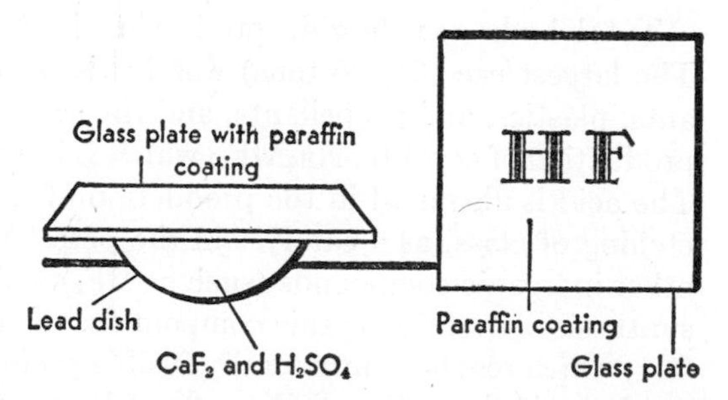

Fig. 18–2 A laboratory demonstration of etching glass with hydrogen fluoride.

18.5 The Metal Halides

All metals form halides, but the variations in character among the halides are striking. The halides of the alkali metals and heavier alkaline earth metals, almost all the metal fluorides, and some halides of the transition metals in their lower oxidation states (e.g., Fe^{++}, Mn^{++}, Cr^{++}) are predominantly ionic or saltlike in character. These halides tend to have high electrical conductivities in the fused state and high boiling points. Those which dissolve appreciably in water undergo little or no hydrolysis.

On the other hand, the halides of metals with large charge-to-size ratios are likely to be predominantly covalent in character because of the attraction by the metal for the electrons in the outer shell of the halide ion. Aluminum chloride, $AlCl_3$, tin (IV) chloride, $SnCl_4$, and titanium (IV) chloride, $TiCl_4$, are typical of this group of halides. These covalent halides are characterized by volatility, by solubility in nonpolar solvents, by lack of electrical conductivity when pure in the fused state, and by extensive hydrolysis in water.

As might be expected, there are metal halides intermediate in character between the ionic and covalent ones. For example, iron (III) chloride, $FeCl_3$, is volatile, is readily hydrolyzed, but is a good conductor of electricity in the fused state.

The anhydrous halides of metals may be prepared by direct union of their constituents. On the other hand, hydrated halo salts are obtained by the action of the hydrohalic acids on metals above hydrogen in the activity series, and by the action of these acids on most oxides, hydroxides, and carbonates of the metals. Several slightly soluble metal halides may be prepared by ionic combination. For example, when solutions containing silver nitrate and sodium chloride are mixed, silver chloride precipitates as a curdy white solid.

$$Ag^+ + (NO_3^-) + (Na^+) + Cl^- \rightarrow \underline{AgCl} + (Na^+) + (NO_3^-)$$

or simply

$$Ag^+ + Cl^- \rightarrow \underline{AgCl}$$

Other slightly soluble halides include AgBr, AgI, $PbCl_2$, $PbBr_2$, PbI_2, CuCl, CuI, CuBr, TlCl, Hg_2Cl_2, CaF_2, and BaF_2. It is a striking fact that the solubilities of the fluorides differ so markedly from those of the other halides. For example, silver fluoride is readily soluble in water whereas the other silver halides are only slightly soluble. On the other hand, calcium and barium fluorides are insoluble while the other halides of these metals are freely soluble in water.

18.6 Uses of the Hydrohalic Acids and Halides

Total hydrogen fluoride production in 1961 was approximately 160,000 tons. The largest use (64,000 tons) was in the production of fluorocarbons for refrigerants, plastics, and propellants, and the second largest use (53,000 tons) was in the production of cryolite, Na_3AlF_6, which is important in the metallurgy of aluminum. The acid is also used in the production of UF_6 in the atomic energy program, the etching of glass, as a catalyst in the petroleum industry and in the production of other inorganic compounds (such as BF_3) which serve as catalysts in the industrial synthesis of certain organic compounds. The mineral fluorspar, CaF_2, is used as a flux, which reacts to form easily fusible products with various substances that cannot be melted readily. Sodium fluoride is used as an insecticide, as a flux, and as a fungicide on wood.

Hydrochloric acid is the most extensively used acid in industry, next to sulfuric. Its uses are numerous and varied. It is used in the manufacture of a number of metal chlorides, dyes, glue, glucose, and various other chemicals. A considerable amount is also used in removing oxide coatings from iron or steel which is to be galvanized, tinned, or enameled.

The amount of hydrobromic and hydriodic acid used is insignificant compared to the amount of hydrocloric acid used. Hydrobromic acid is used in analytical chemistry and in the synthesis of certain organic compounds. Silver bromide is used in photographic film, and the bromides of sodium and potassium are used in medicine as sedatives and soporifics (sleep-inducing drugs). Concentrated hydriodic acid is used in analytical chemistry and as a solvent. Silver iodide is used in photographic film.

QUESTIONS

1. Why is the direct union of constituent elements an unsatisfactory method for producing hydrogen fluoride? hydrogen iodide?
2. Why cannot pure HBr and HI be prepared by the action of concentrated sulfuric acid upon metal bromides and iodides, respectively? Write the equations involved.
3. Compare HI, HBr, HCl, and HF with regard to their strengths as reducing agents.
4. Identify the oxidizing agent and reducing agent in the following equation: $I_2 + H_2S \rightarrow 2\ H^+ + 2\ I^- + S$.
5. Contrast the chemical activity of anhydrous hydrogen chloride with that of hydrochloric acid.
6. List the unique properties of hydrogen fluoride and hydrofluoric acid.
7. Describe the hydrogen bond. Between what kind of atoms are these bonds formed?
8. Describe the chemistry of the etching of glass, including equations.
9. Contrast the properties of ionic and covalent binary metal halides. Give typical examples of each of these classes of halides.
10. Write equations for the reaction of hydrochloric acid with Ca, CaO, $Ca(OH)_2$, and $CaCO_3$.
11. How would you separate a mixture of sodium chloride and silver chloride?
12. Show by an equation that the hydrogen ion acts as an oxidizing agent toward metals above hydrogen in the activity series.

PROBLEMS

1. What weight of calcium fluoride would be required in the production of 2.0 kilograms of hydrogen fluoride? *Ans. 3.9 kg.*
2. What weight of hydrogen chloride would be required in the preparation of 300 g. of constant boiling hydrochloric acid which is 20.24 per cent HCl by weight? What weight of methane would have to be burned in chlorine ($CH_4 + 4\ Cl_2 \rightarrow CCl_4 + 4\ HCl$) to give this quantity of HCl? *Ans. 60.7 g.; 6.65 g.*

3. Calculate the molarity, normality, and molality of constant boiling hydrochloric acid, specific gravity 1.10 and 20.24 per cent HCl.

Ans. *6.16 M; 6.16 N; 6.95 m.*

4. What weight of calcium carbonate can be converted to calcium chloride by 3 liters of 4 M hydrochloric acid? *Ans.* *600 g.*

5. What weight of HBr can be prepared from the hydrolysis of 500 g. of phosphorus (III) bromide? *Ans.* *448 g.*

6. What volume of HCl gas measured at 100° and 1.0 atm. can be prepared from 300 g. of sodium chloride? *Ans.* *157 l.*

7. Compare the rates of diffusion of HCl, HBr, and HI with that of HF.

Ans. *HCl diffuses 0.741 times as fast as HF; HBr, 0.497 times as fast as HF; HI, 0.396 times as fast as HF.*

8. Calculate the quantity of sodium chloride which must react with sulfuric acid to produce sufficient hydrogen chloride to make 70 ml. of 40% hydrochloric acid solution (sp. gr., 1.2). *Ans.* *54 g.*

9. What volume of hydrochloric acid (40.0% by weight; sp. gr., 1.20) would be required to dissolve 200 g. of magnesium?

Ans. *1,250 ml.* (*Note that only three significant figures are justified by the data given; hence, the calculated answer of 1,249 ml. must be rounded off to 1,250 ml.*).

REFERENCES

"The Halogen Fluorides," H. S. Booth and J. T. Pinkston, Jr., *Chem. Rev.*, **41** (3) 421 (1947).

"New Sources of Fluorine," (Staff) *Chem. Eng.*, Dec. 12, 1960; p. 79.

"Changes Keynote Hydrogen Fluoride Market," (Staff) *Chem. Eng. News*, Jan. 29, 1962, Part 1; p. 30.

CHAPTER NINETEEN

The Oxygen Compounds of the Halogens

Although the halogens tend to gain an eighth electron for their outer shells by taking electrons from certain other elements, thus becoming negative halide ions, X^-, they also quite frequently complete their outer shells by sharing electrons with other atoms. For example, electrons are shared in X_2, HX, PX_3, and SnX_4. The halogens also share electrons with oxygen in the formation of oxyacids and oxysalts, in which the halogens assume positive oxidation states. The oxygen compounds of the halogens are noted for their strength as oxidizing agents.

19.1 Binary Halogen-Oxygen Compounds

The halogens do not combine directly with oxygen. However, binary halogen-oxygen compounds can be prepared by indirect methods. Because oxygen is more electronegative than chlorine, bromine, and iodine, it is proper to call their oxygen derivatives oxides. On the other hand, the fluorine compounds with oxygen are called fluorides because fluorine is the more electronegative element. The known binary halogen-oxygen compounds are listed in Table 19·1. These compounds are characteristically reactive and unstable toward heat.

Table 19·1 Binary Halogen-Oxygen Compounds

Fluorine	*Chlorine*	*Bromine*	*Iodine*
OF_2	Cl_2O	Br_2O	I_2O_4
O_2F_2	ClO_2	Br_3O_8	I_4O_9
	Cl_2O_6	BrO_2	I_2O_5
	Cl_2O_7		

1. *Fluorides of oxygen.* Only two oxygen-fluorine compounds are known. They are **oxygen difluoride,** OF_2, a colorless gas, and **oxygen monofluoride,** O_2F_2, a red liquid. Only the difluoride is of sufficient importance for consideration here.

The bonding in OF_2 is essentially covalent and the oxidation states for oxygen and fluorine are +2 and −1, respectively. Oxygen difluoride is prepared by the reaction of elementary fluorine with a solution of sodium hydroxide.

$$2\ F_2 + (2\ Na^+) + 2\ OH^- \rightarrow (2\ Na^+) + 2\ F^- + OF_2\uparrow + H_2O$$

To avoid a secondary reaction between the OF_2 and the sodium hydroxide, the two must be separated immediately. Oxygen difluoride is relatively stable and, as might be expected, it is a powerful oxidizing agent. It reacts with most metals and nonmetals forming a mixture of fluoride and oxide: e.g.,

$$2\ Ca + OF_2 \rightarrow CaO + CaF_2$$
$$2\ H_2 + OF_2 \rightarrow H_2O + 2\ HF$$

Although oxygen difluoride dissolves appreciably in water, it is apparently not the anhydride of an acid because the resulting solutions are not acidic.

2. *Oxides of chlorine.* **Chlorine monoxide,** Cl_2O, is a yellowish-red gas which is apt to decompose explosively. This compound is best prepared by passing chlorine over freshly precipitated, dried mercury (II) oxide.

$$2\ Cl_2 + 2\ HgO \rightarrow HgCl_2 \cdot HgO + Cl_2O\uparrow$$

Chlorine monoxide is an active oxidizing agent and it dissolves in water giving hypochlorous acid, HClO.

Chlorine dioxide, ClO_2, is a yellow gas that is violently explosive when pure. It can be safely handled, however, when diluted with carbon dioxide or air. The chlorine dioxide molecule is thought to contain a three-electron bond coupled with an electron-pair bond (Section 5.18); its valence electronic structure is given below.

$$\underset{\times\times}{\overset{\times\times}{\vdots O \vdots}}\underset{\times\times}{Cl}\overset{\times\times\times}{\underset{\times\times}{\ }}\overset{\times\times}{O}\vdots$$

Although there are several methods available for the preparation of chlorine dioxide, a convenient commercial one involves the reaction of sodium chlorite with chlorine diluted with air.

$$2\ NaClO_2 + Cl_2 \rightarrow 2\ NaCl + 2\ ClO_2\uparrow$$

Chlorine dioxide has developed recently into an important commercial chemical. It is used in the purification of water, as a germicidal agent, and as a bleaching agent for materials composed of cellulose.

Chlorine heptoxide, Cl_2O_7, is a colorless, oily liquid obtained by dehydrating perchloric acid with P_4O_{10} at −10° and then distilling the product at 85°.

$$HClO_4 + P_4O_{10} \rightarrow 2\ Cl_2O_7 + 4\ HPO_3$$

Although Cl_2O_7 is more stable than Cl_2O or ClO_2, it explodes when heated excessively or subjected to a shock, and sometimes even at room temperature.

Great care must be exercised with the oxides of chlorine. They are treacherous. unpredictable, and violent in their tendencies to decompose explosively.

19.2 The Oxyacids of the Halogens and Their Salts

There is no definite evidence for the existence of oxyfluorine acids or oxyfluorine salts. Although oxyacids of the other halogens and their salts are well known, a complete series is known only for chlorine. The oxyacids, including their formulas and the oxidation states of the halogen in them, are given in Table 19·2. The method of nomenclature for these acids and their salts was discussed in Section 4.12.

TABLE 19·2 Oxyacids of the Halogens

Oxidation States	*Oxyacids of Chlorine*	*Oxyacids of Bromine*	*Oxyacids of Iodine*
+1	$HClO$	$HBrO$	HIO
+3	$HClO_2$	$HBrO_2$	
+5	$HClO_3$	$HBrO_3$	HIO_3
+7	$HClO_4$		HIO_4 H_5IO_6

The oxygen compounds of chlorine, bromine, and iodine differ sufficiently to make generalizations concerning them impossible. However, trends in properties of the oxychlorine acids and salts are well established (Table 19·3), and these trends hold, in a general way, for the analogous bromine and iodine compounds.

TABLE 19·3 Trends in Properties of the Oxyacids of Chlorine and Their Sodium Salts

Oxidation State	*Acid*	*Thermal Stability and Acid Strength*	*Oxidizing Power*	*Salt*	*Thermal Stability*	*Oxidizing Power and Anion Base Strength*
+1	$HClO$	increase ↓	increases ↑	$NaClO$	increases ↓	increase ↑
+3	$HClO_2$			$NaClO_2$		
+5	$HClO_3$			$NaClO_3$		
+7	$HClO_4$			$NaClO_4$		

Thermal stability increases greatly →
Oxidizing power increases greatly ←

The greater the oxygen content in members of a series of oxygen compounds (oxyacids or their salts) of one of the halogens, the greater is their stability toward decomposition by heat. The acids decompose at much lower temperatures than do their salts. These rules apply generally to the oxygen compounds of sulfur, nitrogen, and phosphorus, as well as to those of the halogens.

The activity of the oxyacids of the halogens as oxidizing agents is related inversely to the number of oxygen atoms in the molecule, i.e., the activity is greatest for the HXO acids and least for the HXO_4 acids. Note that the oxidizing strength is greatest for the acids of lowest thermal stability.

In a series of oxyacids of any element, the acidic strength, as measured in terms of extent of ionization in aqueous solution, is greater, the larger the number of oxygen atoms in the molecule. Phosphoric acid is stronger than phosphorous acid, sulfuric is stronger than sulfurous, perchloric is stronger than chloric, and so on.

The electronic formulas for the oxyacids of chlorine are given below.

```
                         xx                 xx                    xx
                        xOx                xOx                   xOx
   xx oo           xx   oo            xx   oo             xx     oo   xx
H:O:Cl:         H:O:Cl:            H:O:Cl:              H:O:Cl:O:
   xx oo           xx   oo            xx   oo             xx     oo   xx
                                          xOx                   xOx
                                           xx                    xx
Hypochlorous acid  Chlorous acid     Chloric acid        Perchloric acid
```

In all four acids the hydrogen is attached to the chlorine atom through an oxygen atom. The hydrogen is linked to the oxygen by a polar covalent bond and the oxygen atoms are attached to the central chlorine atom by bonds that are esentially covalent in character. The oxidation state of the chlorine is dependent upon the number of its electrons that it shares with oxygen atoms. Chlorine shares one of its electrons with oxygen in HClO, three in $HClO_2$, five in $HClO_3$, and seven in $HClO_4$. Thus the corresponding oxidation states exhibited by chlorine are +1, +3, +5, and +7, respectively. The oxidation states are positive because oxygen is more electronegative than chlorine. As the positive oxidation state of chlorine increases, the bonding electrons are shifted away from the hydrogen atom, and the tendency for the molecule to lose a proton to water and thereby form hydronium ions in solution increases (see Section 15.1, part 7). This accounts for the positive correlation of strength of the oxyacids as acids with the number of oxygen atoms in the molecule. It follows that the tendency of an oxyhalogen anion to accept protons increases as the oxygen content of the anion decreases. As we shall see in Section 21.6, this tendency of a negative ion to accept protons is a measure of basic strength.

The oxyacids of chlorine are more acidic than the corresponding oxyacids of bromine; and those of bromine are more acidic than the corresponding ones of iodine. This can be accounted for by the decrease in electronegativity with increasing size of the halogen and the resultant decreases in the tendency for the oxyacid to lose a proton to water.

19.3 Hypohalous Acids and Hypohalites

Because of their thermal instabilities, the **hypohalous acids** (HXO) have not been obtained in the pure condition but are known only in aqueous solution. The hypohalous acids are all weak, with the acid strength decreasing with increasing size of the halogen atom. Thus, HClO is a stronger acid than HBrO, which in turn is stronger than HIO (Section 19.2). Because the hypohalous acids are weak, the hypohalite ions readily hydrolyze by accepting protons from water; the solutions of alkali metal hypohalites are basic due to an excess of hydroxide ions.

$$\underset{\text{Hypohalite ion}}{XO^-} + H_2O \rightleftharpoons \underset{\text{Hypohalous acid}}{HXO} + OH^-$$

Aqueous solutions of the hypohalous acids are prepared by hydrolysis of the free halogens according to the general equation

$$X_2 + H_2O \rightleftharpoons H^+ + X^- + HOX$$

This method yields a mixture of the hypohalous acid and the hydrohalic acid. The extent to which the reaction proceeds to the right decreases in the series chlorine, bromine, iodine. The equilibrium may be shifted to the right by the addition of a base, such as NaOH, which neutralizes the acids which are formed. The net reaction may then be represented by the equation

$$X_2 + (2\ Na^+) + 2\ OH^- \rightarrow (Na^+) + X^- + (Na^+) + XO^- + H_2O$$

For these products to be formed, the alkali must be cold and dilute. The hypohalites are unstable at elevated temperatures and undergo auto-oxidation-reduction to form halides and halates.

$$3\ XO^- \rightarrow \underset{\text{Halide}}{2\ X^-} + \underset{\text{Halate}}{XO_3^-}$$

Sodium hypochlorite is produced commercially by the electrolysis of cold, dilute aqueous sodium chloride solutions under conditions where the sodium hydroxide and chlorine can mix. The consecutive and net reactions may be written as follows:

$$2\ Cl^- + 2\ H_2O + \text{electrical energy} \rightarrow 2\ OH^- + Cl_2 + H_2\uparrow$$
$$Cl_2 + 2\ OH^- \rightarrow Cl^- + ClO^- + H_2O$$
$$Cl^- + H_2O + \text{electrical energy} \xrightarrow[\text{dil.}]{\text{cold,}} ClO^- + H_2\uparrow$$

In commercial practice the reaction is not carried to completion, so the solution of sodium hypochlorite produced is impure with some sodium chloride. This solution is sold under a variety of trade names for use as a bleaching agent and an antiseptic. Hypochlorite owes its bleaching action to its ability to oxidize certain colored substances to colorless compounds. It is without effect upon printer's ink because it does not oxidize carbon, which is the coloring matter of the ink.

Bleaching powder, $CaCl(ClO)$, is prepared by passing chlorine gas over slaked lime, $Ca(OH)_2$, according to the equation

$$(Ca^{++}) + 2\ OH^- + Cl_2 \rightarrow (Ca^{++}) + Cl^- + ClO^- + H_2O$$

Bleaching powder has been used for a long time as a bleaching agent and as a source of chlorine and hypochlorous acid.

Calcium hypochlorite, $Ca(ClO)_2$, called "high-test hypochlorite" (H.T.H.), is made from calcium chloride and sodium hypochlorite according to the equation

$$CaCl_2 + 2\ NaClO \rightarrow Ca(ClO)_2 + 2\ NaCl$$

Calcium hypochlorite is more soluble, more stable, and more effective as a disinfectant and bleaching agent than bleaching powder because it contains a higher percentage of the hypochlorite ion.

19.4 Halous Acids and Halites

None of the **halous acids,** HXO_2, can be isolated in pure form, and of the halites, only the chlorites are well-characterized compounds.

Chlorous acid, $HClO_2$, has no true anhydride. However, chlorine dioxide, ClO_2, plays the role of a **double anhydride** in that it gives two oxyacid anions of chlorine when it reacts with alkalies. The reaction is one of auto-oxidation-reduction.

$$2\ ClO_2 + 2\ OH^- \rightarrow \underset{\substack{\text{Chlorite}\\ \text{ion}}}{ClO_2^-} + \underset{\substack{\text{Chlorate}\\ \text{ion}}}{ClO_3^-} + H_2O$$

Chlorine dioxide is not a true anhydride, however, because the chlorine has an oxidation state different from that exhibited in either chlorite or chlorate. An aqueous solution of chlorous acid may be prepared by the action of sulfuric acid upon a suspension of barium chlorite.

$$Ba(ClO_2)_2 + (2\ H^+) + SO_4^= \rightarrow \underline{BaSO_4} + (2\ H^+) + 2\ ClO_2^-$$

The insoluble barium sulfate may be removed from the solution of chlorous acid by filtering. Attempts to isolate pure chlorous acid result in its decomposition into chlorine dioxide, and chloric and hydrochloric acids.

As mentioned above, **chlorites** may be prepared by the reaction of chlorine dioxide with alkalies. Other methods are given by the following equations:

$$H_2O_2 + 2\ OH^- + 2\ ClO_2 \rightarrow 2\ ClO_2^- + O_2\uparrow + 2\ H_2O$$
$$Na_2O_2 + 2\ ClO_2 \rightarrow 2\ NaClO_2 + O_2\uparrow$$

The heavy metal chlorites are explosively unstable and have been studied as detonators. The chlorites are excellent bleaching agents for cellulosic fibers because they bleach without attacking and degrading them.

19.5 Halic Acids and Halates

Although **chloric acid,** $HClO_3$, and **bromic acid,** $HBrO_3$, are obtainable in solution, they decompose when attempts are made to isolate them. However, **iodic acid,** HIO_3, can be obtained in the form of stable colorless crystals which melt with decomposition at 110°.

Solutions of chloric acid and bromic acid are readily obtained by the reaction of their barium salts with sulfuric acid.

$$Ba^{++} + 2\ XO_3^- + (2\ H^+) + SO_4^= \rightarrow \underline{BaSO_4} + (2\ H^+) + 2\ XO_3^-$$

The barium sulfate is removed by filtration. Iodic acid is easily prepared by oxidizing elementary iodine with concentrated nitric acid according to the equation

$$I_2 + 8\ H^+ + 10\ NO_3^- \rightarrow 2\ IO_3^- + 10\ NO_2\uparrow + 4\ H_2O$$

All the halic acids are strong acids and very active oxidizing agents. Chloric acid is quite unstable in the molecular form ($HClO_3$), and decomposes rapidly when heated.

$$3\ HClO_3 \rightarrow HClO_4 + 2\ ClO_2\uparrow + H_2O$$

The halogens react with hot solutions of alkalies giving mixtures of **halates** and **halides.**

$$3\ X_2 + 6\ OH^- \rightarrow XO_3^- + 5\ X^- + 3\ H_2O$$

The halate may be separated from the halide by fractional crystallization. The halates are produced commercially by the electrolysis of hot, concentrated halide solutions in the absence of a diaphragm that is used in the cell when chlorine is the desired product. The hydroxide and halogen which are first formed are thus permitted to react as electrolysis proceeds. The net reaction, analogous to that for the preparation of the hypohalites in cold, dilute solution (Section 19.3), may be expressed as follows:

$$X^- + 3\ H_2O + \text{electrical energy} \xrightarrow[\text{conc.}]{\text{hot,}} XO_3^- + 3\ H_2\uparrow$$

The halates of sodium, potassium, calcium, and barium may be manufactured in this way (Fig. 19–1).

The water solubility of the halates decreases with increasing weight of the halogen. Most chlorates are water soluble, bromates are generally much less soluble, and many iodates are insoluble in water. All halates decompose when heated. Potassium chlorate yields potassium chloride and oxygen at high temperatures.

$$2\ KClO_3 \rightarrow 2\ KCl + 3\ O_2\uparrow$$

At moderate temperatures potassium perchlorate and potassium chloride are formed.

$$4\ KClO_3 \rightarrow 3\ KClO_4 + KCl$$

Thermal decompositions of bromates and iodates may take place in a number of ways. In some cases, the metal oxides and the free halogens are formed.

The structure of the chlorate ion is shown in Figure 19–2 on page 302.

Potassium chlorate is used in the manufacture of matches and fireworks. Bromates and iodates are used as oxidizing agents in analytical chemistry.

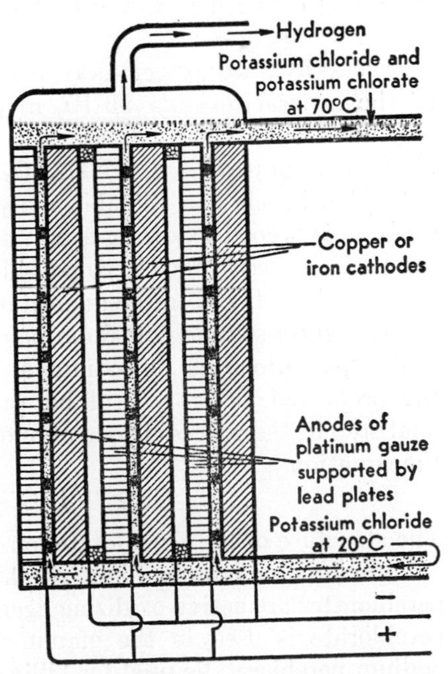

Fig. 19–1 Cell for the production of chlorates or perchlorates.

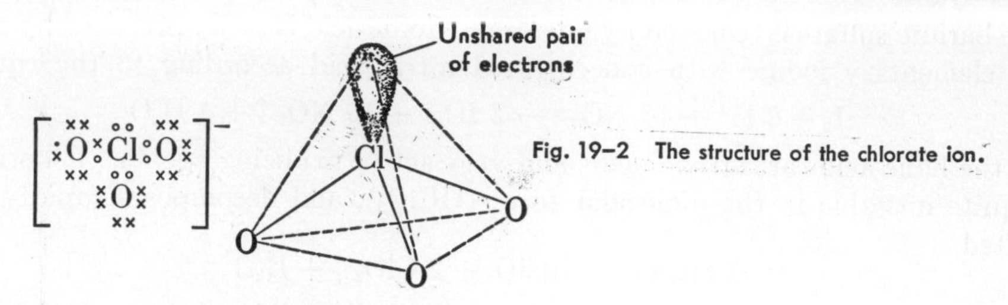

Fig. 19–2 The structure of the chlorate ion.

19.6 Perhalic Acids and Perhalates

Perhalic acids and perhalates of chlorine and iodine are well characterized while those of bromine are not known.

1. *Perchloric acid and its salts.* **Perchloric acid** ($HClO_4$) may be obtained by treating a perchlorate, such as potassium perchlorate, with sulfuric acid.

$$KClO_4 + H_2SO_4 \rightarrow KHSO_4 + HClO_4$$

The perchloric acid is distilled from the reaction mixture under reduced pressure. The acid explodes if its temperature is raised above 92°, whereas it boils below this temperature under reduced pressure with little decomposition. Aqueous solutions of perchloric acid up to concentrations of about 60 per cent are quite stable thermally. The acid is unstable and unsafe to use and handle in concentrations above 60 per cent. It is a powerful oxidizing agent and serious explosions may occur when concentrated solutions of it are heated with substances which are easily oxidized. However, it is a very weak oxidizing agent when cold and dilute.

Several hydrates of perchloric acid are known. They are crystalline compounds of the general formula $HClO_4 \cdot nH_2O$. The monohydrate is called hydronium perchlorate, H_3OClO_4, because of the similarity of its crystal structure with that of ammonium perchlorate, NH_4ClO_4.

Perchloric acid is a valuable analytical reagent because it is the strongest of all acids, it is a good oxidizing agent, and perchlorates are quite soluble in the acid. This acid is used in the electropolishing of metals and alloys such as nickel, copper, brass, and steel, and in the quantitative determination of potassium with which it forms slightly soluble potassium perchlorate.

The **perchlorates** of sodium and potassium are produced commercially by the prolonged electrolysis of hot solutions of their chlorides (Fig. 19–1). The final step in the process is one of anodic oxidation of the chlorate ion according to the equation

$$ClO_3^- + H_2O \rightarrow ClO_4^- + 2\ H^+ + 2\ e^-$$

The structure of the perchlorate ion is shown in Figure 19–3.

Potassium and ammonium perchlorates are slightly soluble in water. The perchlorates are active oxidizing agents but less so than the chlorates. Potassium perchlorate is used in the manufacture of matches, fireworks, and explosives. Sodium perchlorate is used for killing weeds. Anhydrous barium perchlorate and magnesium perchlorate are excellent drying agents.

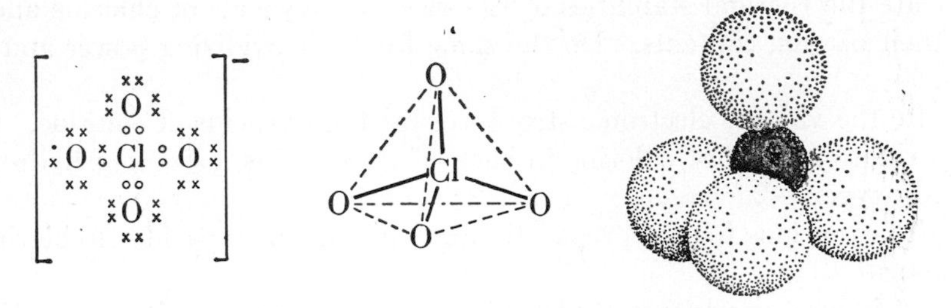

Fig. 19–3 The structure of the perchlorate ion.

2. *Perbromic acid and perbromates.* All attempts to prepare **perbromic acid,** $HBrO_4$, and its salts have failed. This is unexpected and puzzling in view of the fact that analogous compounds of both chlorine and iodine are known. No logical reason for the nonexistence of these compounds has been proposed, and it may well be that they will be prepared if the correct approach can be found. This is quite possible in view of the fact that methods of preparing oxides of bromine have been discovered only recently.

3. *Periodic acids and their salts.* A series of periodic acids is known, either as the acids themselves or in the form of their salts. Most important of these are **metaperiodic** acid, HIO_4, and **paraperiodic** acid, H_5IO_6. The larger size of the iodine atom permits it to surround itself with six oxygen atoms, whereas the smaller chlorine can accommodate no more than four. The periodic acids are strong acids and active oxidizing agents. The oxidizing properties of HIO_4 make it useful in numerous analytical methods.

Sodium metaperiodate, $NaIO_4$, may be prepared by the oxidation of sodium iodate, $NaIO_3$, in a hot alkaline solution with chlorine. Periodates may also be prepared by the electrolytic oxidation of iodates, in analogy to the preparation of perchlorates. The free acid H_5IO_6 may be obtained as a white solid by evaporating a filtered solution resulting from the reaction of barium periodate with sulfuric acid. Salts of paraperiodic acids such as $Na_2H_3IO_6$, $Na_3H_2IO_6$, and Ag_5IO_6, have been prepared (Fig. 19–4).

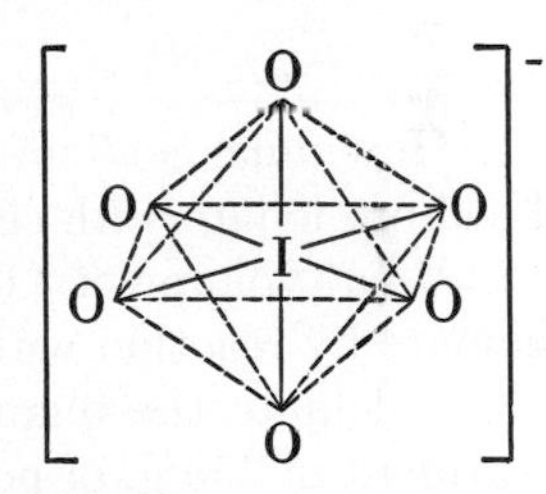

Fig. 19–4 Diagram showing the octahedral structure of the paraperiodate ion, IO_6^{-5}.

QUESTIONS

1. Write the formulas for five compounds in which chlorine is linked by covalent bonds; by ionic bonds.
2. Why is OF_2 called oxygen difluoride rather than fluorine oxide?
3. Show by suitable equations that chlorine monoxide and chlorine heptoxide are acid anhydrides.
4. Write the formulas and names for all the oxyacids of chlorine and the corresponding calcium salts.

5. Relate the thermal stabilities of the series of oxyacids of chlorine and their salts to their oxygen contents. Do the same for their oxidizing power and acidic strength.

6. Write the valence electronic structures for the oxyacids of chlorine. Calculate the oxidation state of chlorine in each of these acids, assuming hydrogen to be +1 and oxygen −2.

7. Write equations for the preparation of each of the oxyacids of chlorine and its sodium salt.

8. What is the composition of bleaching powder and how is it prepared?

9. Explain the basic character of aqueous sodium hypochlorite.

10. Why is chlorine dioxide not considered to be a true acid anhydride?

11. Why is perchloric acid distilled only under reduced pressure?

12. Why does not chlorine form a paraperchloric acid analogous to paraperiodic acid?

13. Predict the products in each of the following cases:
   (a) Oxygen difluoride, OF_2, is brought in contact with powdered aluminum.
   (b) A solution of hypochlorous acid is heated.
   (c) Potassium sulfite is treated with potassium periodate in dilute sulfuric acid solution.

14. Why is $HClO_2$ a stronger acid than $HClO$?

15. Why is $HClO_3$ a stronger acid than $HBrO_3$?

16. List as many products as you can which can be obtained by the electrolysis of aqueous halide solutions. Explain the general procedure involved in the production of each of the substances listed.

PROBLEMS

1. How much sodium metaperiodate can be prepared by the oxidation of 100 g. of sodium iodate with chlorine in hot sodium hydroxide solution? *Ans. 108 g.*

2. What volume of 3.00 M bromic acid could be prepared from 150 g. of barium bromate by reaction with sulfuric acid? *Ans. 255 ml.*

3. Calculate the quantity of perchloric acid which can be prepared from the treatment of 350 g. of potassium perchlorate with sulfuric acid. *Ans. 254 g.*

CHAPTER TWENTY

Electrochemistry

Electrochemistry is that field of chemistry which deals with chemical changes produced by an electric current and with the production of electricity by chemical reactions. In **electrolytic cells,** electrical energy is used to bring about desired chemical changes. In **voltaic cells,** chemical reactions are used to supply electrical energy.

Much of our precise quantitative knowledge concerning the energy changes involved in chemical reactions has come from the study of electrochemistry because the quantity of electrical energy produced or consumed during electrochemical changes can be measured very accurately. Furthermore, an understanding of the reactions which take place at the electrodes of electrochemical cells throws much light upon the process of oxidation and reduction and the chemical activity of many substances.

Many electrochemical processes are important in science and industry. The use of electrical energy in the commercial production of hydrogen, oxygen, ozone, hydrogen peroxide, chlorine, sodium hydroxide, and the oxygen compounds of the halogens has been noted in previous chapters. Other technical applications of electrochemistry include production of many other chemicals, electrorefining of metals, electroplating of metals and alloys, and the production of metal articles by electrodeposition.

20.1 The Conduction of Electricity

A current of electricity consists of a movement of electrically charged particles. These charged particles may be electrons or ions (positive or negative). An electric current in a metal conductor consists of a movement of electrons without any obvious chemical changes taking place in the metal and with no parallel movement of the atoms composing the metal. This type of conduction of electricity is called **metallic conduction.**

Certain compounds, when fused or in aqueous solution, conduct an electric current when placed in an electrolytic cell (Fig. 20–1). An electric generator or battery is connected to two electrodes by metallic wires. The electrodes, which are good conductors, dip into the liquid which conducts the current. Electrons are pumped into one of the electrodes and withdrawn from the other electrode by the battery or generator. The electrode into which the electrons are pumped

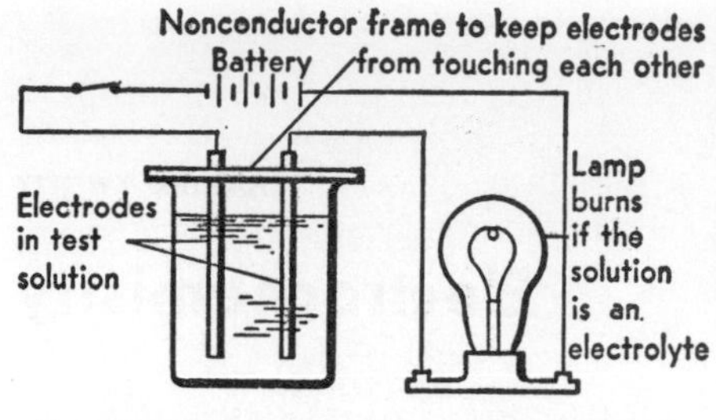

Fig. 20–1 Apparatus for determining the conductivity of solutions.

becomes negatively charged, and the electrode from which electrons are withdrawn becomes positively charged. The positive ions (cations) in the electrolytic liquid are attracted by the negatively charged cathode and move toward it, and the negative ions (anions) are attracted by the positively charged anode and move toward it. This sort of motion of the ions in a liquid is known as **ionic or electrolytic conduction.** The electrolytic liquid may be a molten salt such as fused sodium chloride or an electrolytic solution such as an aqueous solution of hydrochloric acid.

20.2 The Electrolysis of Molten Sodium Chloride

A consideration of the reactions which take place at the electrodes will explain the way in which the electric current passes between the electrodes and the liquid.

Fused sodium chloride consists of equal numbers of positive sodium ions and negative chloride ions which can move about with considerable freedom. Sodium ions are attracted to the cathode where they combine with electrons on the cathode to form sodium atoms, i.e., metallic sodium. The electrode reaction, referred to as a **half-reaction,** may be represented for the cathode by the equation

$$Na^+ + e^- \rightarrow Na$$

The sodium decreases in oxidation state from +1 to 0. This is a reduction reaction sometimes referred to as cathodic reduction. **The cathode is the electrode at which electrons enter the electrolytic liquid, causing reduction.** Chloride ions give up one electron each to the anode and become chlorine atoms, which combine to form molecules of chlorine gas. The anode half-reaction is

$$2\ Cl^- \rightarrow Cl_2 + 2\ e^-$$

The chlorine is oxidized from −1 to 0, and the reaction is known as anodic oxidation. **The anode is the electrode through which electrons are withdrawn from the electrolytic liquid, causing oxidation.**

The net reaction for the electrolytic decomposition of the fused sodium chloride is the sum of the two electrode half-reactions. To balance the equation, the cathode reaction must be multiplied by two.

$$\begin{array}{r} 2\ Na^+ + 2\ e^- \rightarrow 2\ Na \qquad\quad \\ 2\ Cl^- \rightarrow Cl_2 + 2\ e^- \\ \hline 2\ Na^+ + 2\ Cl^- \rightarrow 2\ Na + Cl_2 \quad \end{array}$$

or

$$2\ NaCl \rightarrow 2\ Na + Cl_2$$

The production of an oxidation-reduction reaction by a direct current of electricity is known as electrolysis.

20.3 The Electrolysis of Aqueous Hydrochloric Acid

Let us consider what happens at the electrodes of an electrolytic cell when an aqueous solution of fairly concentrated hydrochloric acid is electrolyzed. The positive hydrogen ions of the hydrochloric acid are attracted to and reduced at the cathode by accepting electrons from it.

$$\text{(cathodic reduction)} \quad 2\,H^+ + 2\,e^- \rightarrow H_2$$

The negative chloride ions lose electrons to the anode and thus are oxidized to chlorine gas.

$$\text{(anodic oxidation)} \quad 2\,Cl^- \rightarrow Cl_2 + 2\,e^-$$

The over-all cell reaction may be obtained by adding the electrode reactions.

$$\begin{array}{r} 2\,H^+ + 2\,e^- \rightarrow H_2 \\ 2\,Cl^- \rightarrow Cl_2 + 2\,e^- \\ \hline 2\,H^+ + 2\,Cl^- \rightarrow H_2 + Cl_2 \end{array}$$

20.4 The Electrolysis of Aqueous Sodium Chloride

Suppose we consider the electrode reactions which take place during the electrolysis of an aqueous solution of sodium chloride (Fig. 20–2). If the difference in

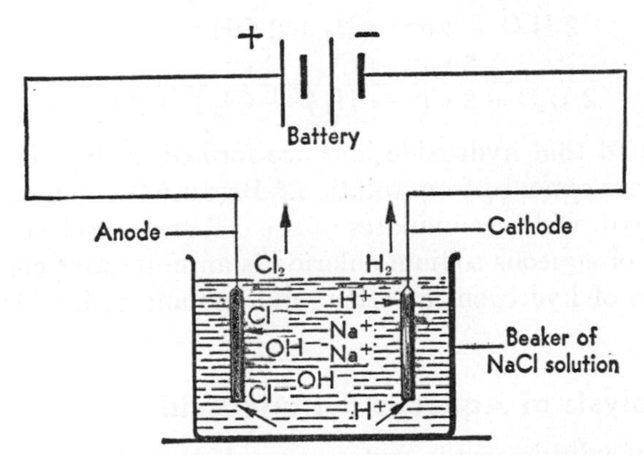

Fig. 20–2 Electric current is carried through the solution by ions. The ions may lose or gain electrons at the electrodes to become atoms. Chlorine atoms pair off at the anode and escape as chlorine molecules; hydrogen atoms unite at the cathode and escape as molecular hydrogen.

potential between the anode and cathode is sufficiently great and the solution is fairly concentrated, hydrogen is evolved at the cathode and chlorine is formed at the anode. In order to account for these products it becomes necessary to consider the hydrogen ion and hydroxide ion formed by the slight ionization of water ($H_2O \rightleftharpoons H^+ + OH^-$), as well as the sodium and chloride ions from the salt. The possible reduction reactions at the cathode are

$$Na^+ + e^- \rightarrow Na$$
$$2\,H^+ + 2\,e^- \rightarrow H_2$$

The hydrogen ion is more easily reduced than the sodium ion, so hydrogen gas is formed at the cathode. The net reaction at the cathode may be obtained by adding the reactions for the ionization of water and the cathodic reduction of the hydrogen ion.

$$\begin{array}{r} 2\ H_2O \rightleftharpoons 2\ H^+ + 2\ OH^- \\ 2\ H^+ + 2\ e^- \rightarrow H_2 \\ \hline 2\ H_2O + 2\ e^- \rightarrow H_2\uparrow + 2\ OH^- \end{array}$$

Hydroxide ions form in the vicinity of the cathode and begin to migrate toward the anode. The possible anodic oxidation reactions are

$$2\ Cl^- \rightarrow Cl_2 + 2\ e^-$$
$$4\ OH^- \rightarrow O_2 + 2\ H_2O + 4\ e^-$$

The chloride ion is not as easily oxidized as the hydroxide ion, but in a concentrated sodium chloride solution, chlorine is formed at the anode because of the much greater concentration of chloride ion than hydroxide ion. If the chloride ion concentration is low, some oxygen may be formed in addition to the chlorine. Little chlorine is produced when the solution of sodium chloride is very dilute.

The net reaction for the electrolysis of aqueous sodium chloride can be obtained by adding the electrode reactions.

$$\begin{array}{r} 2\ H_2O + 2\ e^- \rightarrow H_2 + 2\ OH^- \\ 2\ Cl^- \rightarrow Cl_2 + 2\ e^- \\ \hline 2\ H_2O + 2\ Cl^- \rightarrow H_2\uparrow + Cl_2\uparrow + 2\ OH^- \end{array}$$

It should be noted that hydroxide ions are formed during the electrolysis and that chloride ions are removed from solution. Because the sodium ions remain unchanged, sodium hydroxide accumulates in the cell as electrolysis proceeds.

The electrolysis of aqueous sodium chloride is an important commercial process for the production of hydrogen, chlorine, and sodium hydroxide (Section 17.3).

20.5 The Electrolysis of Aqueous Sulfuric Acid

The ionization of sulfuric acid in water proceeds stepwise as follows.

$$H_2SO_4 \rightarrow H^+ + HSO_4^-$$
$$HSO_4^- \rightleftharpoons H^+ + SO_4^=$$

In dilute solution the anion furnished by the sulfuric acid is principally the sulfate ion. Upon electrolysis, the possible choices for the anode reaction are oxidation of the sulfate ion or oxidation of water, and the decision must be made as to which of these two processes actually occurs.

$$SO_4^= \rightarrow SO_4 + 2\ e^-$$
$$2\ H_2O \rightarrow O_2\uparrow + 4\ H^+ + 4\ e^-$$

The latter electrode reaction is the net reaction of the ionization of water and the oxidation of the hydroxide ion.

$$
\begin{array}{l}
4\ H_2O \rightleftharpoons 4\ H^+ + 4\ OH^- \\
4\ OH^- \rightarrow O_2 + 2\ H_2O + 4\ e^- \\
\hline
2\ H_2O \rightarrow O_2 \uparrow\ + 4\ H^+ + 4\ e^-
\end{array}
$$

Oxygen and hydrogen ions are formed at the anode because the hydroxide ion is more easily oxidized than the sulfate ion; in fact, SO_4 cannot be formed by electrolytic oxidation.

The only possible cathode reaction is

$$2\ H^+ + 2\ e^- \rightarrow H_2$$

The net reaction will be the sum of the anode and cathode reactions after multiplying the cathode reaction by two.

$$
\begin{array}{l}
2\ H_2O \rightarrow O_2 + 4\ H^+ + 4\ e^- \\
4\ H^+ + 4\ e^- \rightarrow 2\ H_2 \\
\hline
2\ H_2O \rightarrow 2\ H_2 \uparrow\ + O_2 \uparrow
\end{array}
$$

Although the hydrogen ion from the sulfuric acid is consumed by cathodic reduction, this same ion is being generated at the anode at the same rate at which it disappears at the cathode. The net result is that water is used up and the sulfuric acid becomes more concentrated as electrolysis proceeds.

20.6 The Preparation of Hydrogen Peroxide by Electrolytic Oxidation

The electrolytic production of hydrogen peroxide is accomplished by the low temperature electrolysis of sulfuric acid solutions which are 45 to 55% H_2SO_4. The HSO_4^- ion is oxidized at the anode with the formation of peroxydisulfuric acid, $H_2S_2O_8$.

$$2\ HSO_4^- \rightarrow H_2S_2O_8 + 2\ e^-$$

Hydrogen gas is formed by reduction of hydrogen ions at the cathode.

$$2\ H^+ + 2\ e^- \rightarrow H_2$$

Subsequent hydrolysis of the $H_2S_2O_8$ results in the formation of hydrogen peroxide.

$$H_2S_2O_8 + 2\ H_2O \rightarrow 2\ H_2SO_4 + H_2O_2$$

The hydrogen peroxide is distilled from the mixture under reduced pressure because it decomposes explosively when distilled at atmospheric pressure. Until largely displaced by the anthraquinone process, this reaction was the basis for the principal industrial method for the production of hydrogen peroxide (Section 10.13).

20.7 Electrolytic Refining of Metals

In the examples of electrolysis that we have considered so far, the electrodes which are employed in the electrolytic cells are composed of relatively inert electrically conducting materials, such as graphite or platinum, which do not undergo reaction under the conditions employed. Whenever a reactive metal is made the anode of an electrolytic cell, the anodic oxidation may involve oxidation of the

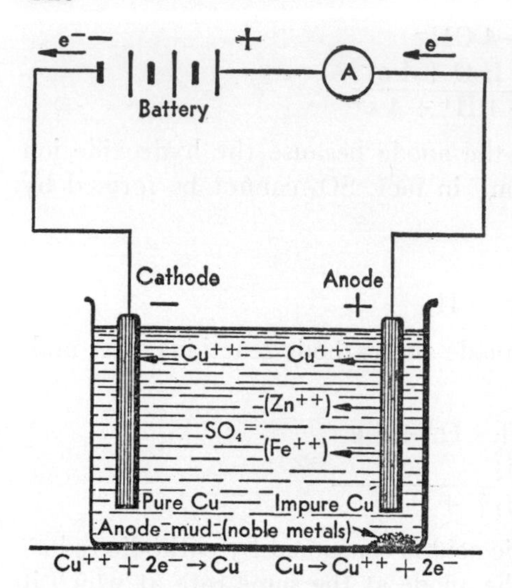

Fig. 20–3 The electrolytic refining of copper.

metal composing the electrode. For example, in the electrolysis of a solution of copper (II) sulfate (Fig. 20–3) with a strip of metallic copper as the anode, the following electrode reaction takes place:

$$Cu \rightarrow Cu^{++} + 2\ e^-$$

The electrode goes into solution as copper (II) ions. The oxidation of the copper takes place more readily than the oxidation of either the sulfate ion from the copper (II) sulfate or the hydroxide ion from the water. The copper (II) ions formed at the anode migrate toward the cathode where they are more readily reduced than the hydrogen ions from the water.

$$Cu^{++} + 2\ e^- \rightarrow Cu$$

Thus copper plates out on the cathode.

This process is made the basis of the electrolytic refining of crude copper by using the impure copper as the anode. The less active impurities, such as gold and silver, do not dissolve (are not oxidized) but fall to the bottom of the cell and form a *mud* from which they are readily recovered. The more active metals, such as zinc and iron, which may be present in the crude copper, are oxidized and go into solution in the electrolyte. If the potential between the electrodes is carefully regulated these metallic ions are not reduced at the cathode. Deposition of the copper in pure form is made either upon a thin sheet of the pure metal which serves as a cathode or upon some other metal from which the deposit may be stripped.

20.8 Faraday's Law of Electrolysis

In 1832–3 Michael Faraday found that the quantity of substances undergoing chemical change at each electrode during electrolysis is directly proportional to the quantity of electricity which passes through the electrolytic cell. Quantity of electricity can be expressed as number of electrons. The quantity of a substance undergoing chemical change at an electrode is related to the number of electrons and can be expressed in terms of the equivalent weight of the substance. Experimental results show that one electron reduces one silver ion while two electrons are required to reduce one copper (II) ion.

$$Ag^+ + 1\ e^- \rightarrow Ag$$
$$Cu^{++} + 2\ e^- \rightarrow Cu$$

One gram-equivalent of silver ion contains 6.023×10^{23} ions. Therefore 6.023×10^{23} electrons are required to reduce one gram-equivalent of silver ions to silver atoms. The weight of silver produced would be one gram-equivalent, 107.870 g., which is the same as the gram-atomic weight, for the silver ion is univalent. Because two electrons are required to reduce one Cu^{++} ion to atomic copper, 6.023×10^{23} electrons would reduce only one-half of a gram-ion weight of copper. However, Cu^{++} being bivalent, one-half of the gram-ionic weight would be the gram-equivalent of this ion, i.e., $63.54/2 = 31.77$ g.

The term **faraday** refers to the quantity of electricity which will reduce one gram-equivalent of a substance at the cathode and oxidize one gram-equivalent at the anode.

$$1 \text{ faraday} = 6.023 \times 10^{23} \text{ electrons} = 96{,}500 \text{ coulombs}$$
$$1 \text{ coulomb} = \text{quantity of electricity involved when a current of 1 ampere flows for 1 second}$$

Faraday's Law may be stated thus: **During electrolysis, 96,500 coulombs (1 faraday) of electricity reduce or oxidize one gram-equivalent of a substance** (Fig. 20–4).

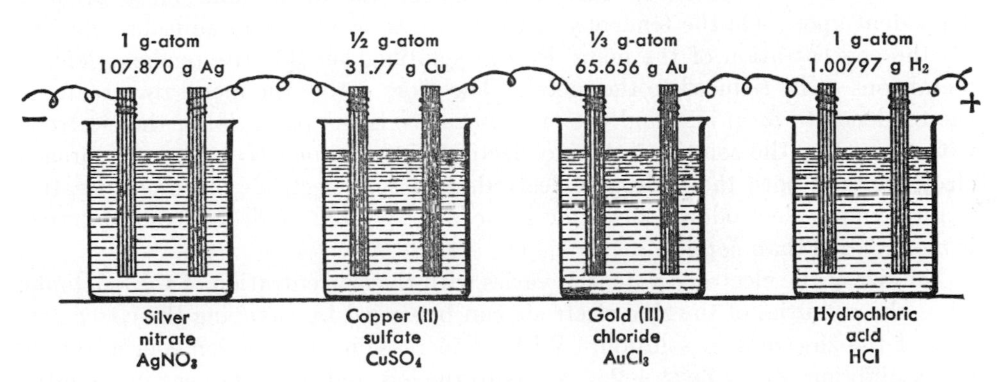

Fig. 20–4 Amounts of various products discharged by one faraday (96,500 coulombs) of electricity.

Let us calculate the weight of copper produced by the cathodic reduction of the Cu^{++} ion upon the passage of 1.600 amperes of current through a solution of copper (II) sulfate for 1 hour.

Solution:

$$\text{amperes} \times \text{seconds} = 1.600 \text{ amp.} \times 60 \text{ min./hr.} \times 60 \text{ sec./min.} = 5760 \text{ coulombs}$$

$$96{,}500 \text{ coulombs will reduce } \frac{63.54 \text{ g.}}{2} = 31.77 \text{ g. of } Cu^{++}$$

$$5760 \text{ coulombs will reduce } 31.77 \text{ g.} \times \frac{5760}{96{,}500} = 1.896 \text{ g. of copper}$$

20.9 Single Electrodes and Electrode Potentials

When a metal such as zinc is placed in water, there is a tendency for the zinc atoms to leave the metal and pass into solution as zinc ions. The change may be expressed by the equation

$$Zn \rightarrow Zn^{++} + 2\ e^-$$

The zinc ions accumulate in the solution and their valence electrons remain behind on the metal. The zinc strip thereby becomes negatively charged and the solution becomes positive. Thus a difference in electrical potential is established between the metal and the solution. On the other hand, the negative charge on the zinc attracts the positive zinc ions and tends to reduce them to the metallic state, according to the equation

$$Zn^{++} + 2\ e^- \rightarrow Zn$$

Also, an increase in the concentration of the zinc ion brought about by the addition of a zinc salt tends to reverse the process. Thus the change is reversible as indicated by double arrows.

$$Zn \rightleftharpoons Zn^{++} + 2\ e^-$$

At equilibrium the potential difference between the metal and the solution is dependent upon: (1) the tendency of the metal to form ions in aqueous solution, (2) the concentration of the metal ions in solution, and (3) the tendency of the metal ions to be reduced to the metal. The more active the metal the greater is the tendency to form ions and the more negative is the potential of the electrode with respect to the solution. A zinc electrode is more negative than a hydrogen electrode, and both the hydrogen electrode and zinc electrode are more negative than a copper electrode because zinc is more active than hydrogen and hydrogen is more active than copper.

The size of the electrode potential varies with the concentration of the reactants. Thus the potential of the zinc electrode can be varied by changing the concentration of the zinc ions in solution. With an increase in the zinc ion concentration, the equilibrium $Zn \rightleftharpoons Zn^{++} + 2\ e^-$ shifts to the left and the difference in potential between the metal and the solution decreases. A decrease in the concentration of zinc ions shifts the equilibrium to the right and the potential difference increases. Because zinc is a solid, its concentration is constant and the size of the electrode does not influence the electrode potential.

20.10 Standard Electrode Potentials

No satisfactory method has been devised for measuring the absolute difference in electrical potential between a metal electrode and a solution of its ions. However, the difference between the potentials of two electrodes can be readily measured. The molar hydrogen electrode, which is described below, has been adopted as a standard electrode with which the potentials of other electrodes are compared.

Single electrodes involving gases can be set up by bubbling the gas around an inert metallic conductor that will conduct electrons but will not itself enter the electrode reaction. For example, the hydrogen electrode can be constructed by bubbling hydrogen gas around a strip of platinum covered with very finely divided platinum and immersed in a solution containing hydrogen ions. Activation of the hydrogen by the platinum results in a tendency of the gas to form hydrogen ions. There is also a tendency for the hydrogen ion to be reduced to hydrogen by acquiring electrons from the electrode. A difference in potential between the electrode and the solution is established in the same way as described for zinc.

$$H_2 \rightleftharpoons 2\ H^+ + 2\ e^-$$

With hydrogen and other gas electrodes, the potential will increase with an increase in the partial pressure of the gas.

The **standard hydrogen electrode** is prepared by bubbling hydrogen gas at a pressure of 1 atm. around platinized platinum immersed in a solution containing hydrogen ions at a concentration of 1 M. We arbitrarily assign the value zero to the potential for the standard hydrogen electrode.

The standard potential of any electrode, then, **is the potential of the electrode measured when the concentration of the ions in the solution is 1 M and the pressure of any gas involved is 1 atmosphere.** Compared with the standard hydrogen electrode potential of 0.00 volt, the standard electrode potential of sodium is 2.71 volts, that of zinc is 0.76 volt, and that of copper is −0.34 volt. The reason for designating the potentials of sodium and zinc as positive and that for copper as negative is given in the next section.

20.11 Measurement of Electrode Potentials

To measure the electrode potential of zinc, for example, an electrochemical cell is set up consisting of a strip of zinc in contact with a 1 M solution of zinc ions as one-half of the cell and a standard hydrogen electrode as the other half (Fig. 20–5, page 314).

The two halves of the cell are connected by a **salt bridge** consisting of a saturated solution of potassium chloride in a gel of agar-agar. This bridge permits ions to migrate through it freely but does not allow the two solutions to mix. The zinc strip and the platinum strip of the hydrogen electrode are connected to a voltmeter by wire. The potential difference of the cell as a whole can now be measured.

Before the circuit is closed, i.e., before the zinc and platinum strips are connected by wire, we have the following electrode half-reactions, each at equilibrium.

$$H_2 \rightleftharpoons 2\ H^+ + 2\ e^-$$
$$Zn \rightleftharpoons Zn^{++} + 2\ e^-$$

Because zinc has a greater tendency to go into solution as ions than does hydrogen, the zinc strip acquires a higher electron density than does the platinum of the hydrogen electrode. Therefore, upon closing the electrical circuit, the greater electron density or electron pressure at the zinc electrode causes electrons to flow to the hydrogen electrode through the wire connecting the two electrodes. As

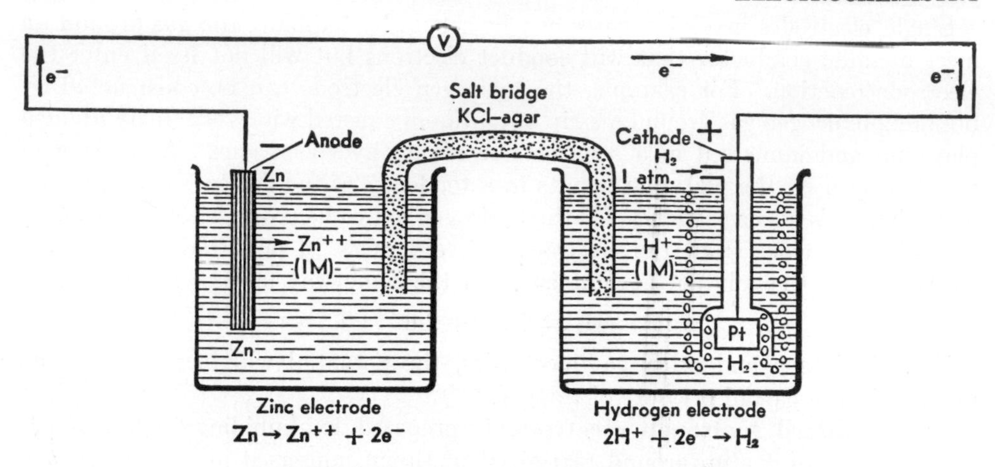

Fig. 20–5 The measurement of electrode potentials.

the electron density increases at the hydrogen electrode, the equilibrium is shifted to the left, causing hydrogen ions to be reduced to free hydrogen.

$$H_2 \leftarrow 2\ H^+ + 2\ e^-$$

At the same time the electron density at the zinc electrode decreases, as the result of the flow of electrons to the hydrogen electrode, and thus the equilibrium at the zinc electrode is shifted to the right, causing more zinc to be oxidized to zinc ions.

$$Zn \rightarrow Zn^{++} + 2\ e^-$$

The difference in potential between the two half cells as measured by a voltmeter is 0.76 volt. The force operating to cause electrons to move from the zinc electrode to the hydrogen electrode is called the **electromotive force** (E.M.F.) and is 0.76 volt. The zinc is the negative electrode because its electron density is higher than that of the hydrogen electrode. However, if we assign the entire electromotive force of the cell to the zinc electrode (the potential of the hydrogen electrode is assumed to be zero), then we may say that the potential of the zinc electrode is 0.76 volt above that of the hydrogen electrode and is positive (+0.76 volt). It should be noted, however, that the assignment of positive or negative signs to the electrode potentials is arbitrary, and some scientists follow the opposite convention.

The over-all reaction that takes place when the zinc-hydrogen cell is operating is one of oxidation and reduction.

(anodic oxidation)	$Zn \rightarrow Zn^{++} + 2\ e^-$
(cathodic reduction)	$2\ H^+ + 2\ e^- \rightarrow H_2$
(cell reaction)	$Zn + 2\ H^+ \rightarrow Zn^{++} + H_2 \uparrow$

This same reaction will take place when zinc metal is immersed in a solution of hydrochloric acid. However, in the cell, the reaction takes place without contact of the reactants. The transfer of electrons involved in the oxidation-reduction reaction has been from the zinc to the hydrogen ions through a wire.

Any cell which generates electric current by an oxidation-reduction reaction is known as a voltaic cell. The cell composed of zinc and hydrogen electrodes as described above may be represented by the convention

$$\mathrm{Zn} \mid \mathrm{Zn^{++}}, \mathrm{M} = 1 \overset{e^-}{\overrightarrow{\;\|\;}} \mathrm{H^+}, \mathrm{M} = 1 \mid \mathrm{H_2(Pt)}, 1 \text{ atm.}$$

The purpose of the salt bridge in the zinc-hydrogen cell is to establish an electrical connection between the solutions of the two electrodes and thereby make a completed circuit. An excess of zinc ions accumulates in the half cell in which zinc goes into solution. Similarly, an excess of anions accumulates in the half cell in which hydrogen ions are being reduced. Migration of ions through the salt bridge compensates for this situation; otherwise the current would soon cease to flow in the external circuit.

20.12 The Electromotive Series of the Elements

By making measurements of the standard electrode potentials of different metals, where the ion concentrations are 1 M, and in the manner described in the preceding section, the relative positions of these metals in the electromotive series (Section 6.9) may be determined. It was shown that zinc has a greater tendency than hydrogen to go into solution and leave electrons on the electrode. The zinc electrode was found to have a standard potential of 0.76 volt. When copper metal in contact with a 1 M solution of copper (II) ions is made the other electrode of a cell containing a standard hydrogen electrode, we find that hydrogen has a greater tendency to form positive ions than does the copper. The formation of hydrogen ions from the hydrogen leaves more electrons on the platinum than are left on the copper when it forms positive ions. Consequently, electrons flow from the hydrogen electrode to the copper electrode where they reduce copper (II) ions.

$$\begin{array}{ll} \text{(anodic oxidation)} & \mathrm{H_2 \rightleftharpoons 2\,H^+ + 2\,e^-} \\ \text{(cathodic reduction)} & \mathrm{Cu^{++} + 2\,e^- \rightleftharpoons Cu} \\ \hline \text{(cell reaction)} & \mathrm{H_2 + Cu^{++} \rightleftharpoons Cu + 2\,H^+} \end{array}$$

The E.M.F. of the cell

$$\mathrm{H_2(Pt)}, 1 \text{ atm.} \mid \mathrm{H^+}, \mathrm{M} = 1 \overset{e^-}{\overrightarrow{\;\|\;}} \mathrm{Cu^{++}}, \mathrm{M} = 1 \mid \mathrm{Cu}$$

as measured by a voltmeter is 0.34 volt. Here the zero potential of the hydrogen electrode is 0.34 volt higher than that of the copper electrode. This makes the potential of the copper electrode −0.34 volt with respect to the hydrogen electrode.

Standard electrode potentials of other metals can be determined in the same manner. When the standard electrode potentials are arranged in order from the most positive to the most negative, we have the electromotive force series (Table 20·1). The table contains the electrode potentials, often referred to as oxidation potentials, of some of the nonmetals as well as the common metals.

TABLE 20·1 Electromotive Series

	Electrode Reaction			Standard Electrode (Oxidation) Potential
	Reduced form		*Oxidized form*	*(volts)*
Potassium	K	$\rightleftharpoons$	$K^+ + e^-$	2.925
Calcium	Ca	$\rightleftharpoons$	$Ca^{++} + 2\ e^-$	2.87
Sodium	Na	$\rightleftharpoons$	$Na^+ + e^-$	2.71
Magnesium	Mg	$\rightleftharpoons$	$Mg^{++} + 2\ e^-$	2.37
Aluminum	Al	$\rightleftharpoons$	$Al^{+++} + 3\ e^-$	1.66
Manganese	Mn	$\rightleftharpoons$	$Mn^{++} + 2\ e^-$	1.18
Zinc	Zn	$\rightleftharpoons$	$Zn^{++} + 2\ e^-$	0.76
Chromium	Cr	$\rightleftharpoons$	$Cr^{+++} + 3\ e^-$	0.74
Iron	Fe	$\rightleftharpoons$	$Fe^{++} + 2\ e^-$	0.44
Cadmium	Cd	$\rightleftharpoons$	$Cd^{++} + 2\ e^-$	0.40
Cobalt	Co	$\rightleftharpoons$	$Co^{++} + 2\ e^-$	0.28
Nickel	Ni	$\rightleftharpoons$	$Ni^{++} + 2\ e^-$	0.25
Tin	Sn	$\rightleftharpoons$	$Sn^{++} + 2\ e^-$	0.14
Lead	Pb	$\rightleftharpoons$	$Pb^{++} + 2\ e^-$	0.13
Hydrogen	H_2	$\rightleftharpoons$	$2\ H^+ + 2\ e^-$	0.00
Copper	Cu	$\rightleftharpoons$	$Cu^{++} + 2\ e^-$	−0.34
Iodine	$2\ I^-$	$\rightleftharpoons$	$I_2 + 2\ e^-$	−0.54
Mercury	Hg	$\rightleftharpoons$	$Hg^{++} + 2\ e^-$	−0.79
Silver	Ag	$\rightleftharpoons$	$Ag^+ + e^-$	−0.80
Bromine	$2\ Br^-$	$\rightleftharpoons$	$Br_2\ (l) + 2\ e^-$	−1.06
Platinum	Pt	$\rightleftharpoons$	$Pt^{++} + 2\ e^-$	−1.2
Oxygen	$2\ H_2O$	$\rightleftharpoons$	$O_2 + 4\ H^+ + 4\ e^-$	−1.23
Chlorine	$2\ Cl^-$	$\rightleftharpoons$	$Cl_2 + 2\ e^-$	−1.36
Gold	Au	$\rightleftharpoons$	$Au^+ + e^-$	−1.68
Fluorine	$2\ F^-$	$\rightleftharpoons$	$F_2 + 2\ e^-$	−2.87

20.13 Uses of the Electromotive Series

The electromotive series of the elements has many uses; some of the more important ones are given below.

(1) The metals with high positive electrode potentials at the top of the series are good reducing agents. They are the metals most easily oxidized by the removal of electrons. They have low electron affinities, low ionization potentials, and low electronegativities.

(2) The elements with negative electrode potentials at the bottom of the series are good oxidizing agents when in the oxidized form, that is, when the metals are in the form of ions and the nonmetals are in the elementary state.

(3) The reduced form of any element will reduce the oxidized form of any element below it in the series. For example, metallic zinc will reduce copper (II) ions according to the equation $Zn + Cu^{++} \rightleftharpoons Cu + Zn^{++}$.

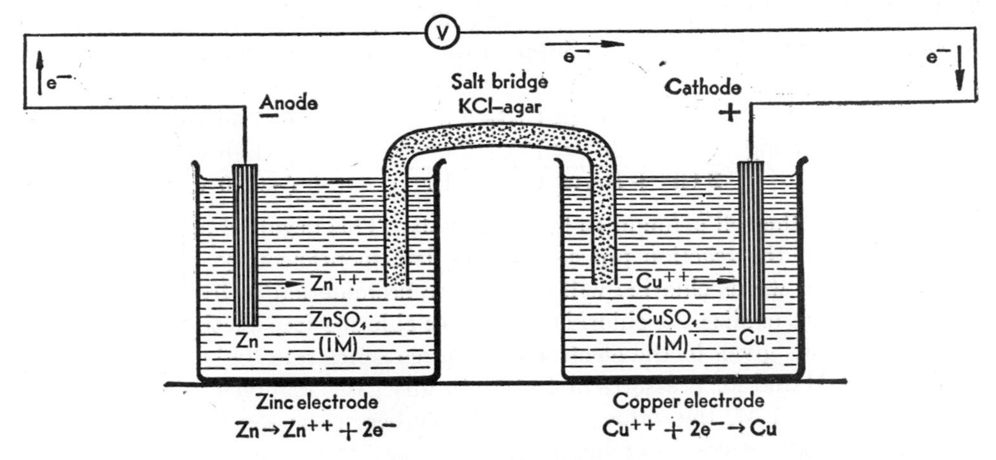

Fig. 20–6 A zinc-copper cell.

For a voltaic cell made up of a standard zinc electrode and a standard copper electrode (Fig. 20–6), the net cell reaction is obtained by subtracting the half-reaction of the copper electrode (the electrode of lower potential, −0.34 volt) from that of the zinc electrode (the electrode of higher potential, 0.76 volt).

$$\begin{array}{ll} & Zn \rightleftharpoons Zn^{++} + 2\,e^- \\ \text{Subtracting} & Cu \rightleftharpoons Cu^{++} + 2\,e^- \\ \hline & Zn - Cu \rightleftharpoons Zn^{++} - Cu^{++} \end{array}$$

$$\text{Transposing} \quad Zn + Cu^{++} \rightleftharpoons Zn^{++} + Cu$$

The electromotive force of the cell is found by subtracting algebraically the potential of the copper electrode from that of the zinc electrode: 0.76 volt − (−0.34 volt) = 1.10 volts.

Suppose we determine the cell reaction and E.M.F. of a cell composed of standard copper (−0.34 volt) and silver (−0.80 volt) electrodes. Because the copper electrode has a higher potential than the silver electrode, the reduced form of copper will reduce the oxidized form of silver, $Cu + 2\,Ag^+ \rightleftharpoons Cu^{++} + 2\,Ag$. To obtain this net cell reaction, we may subtract the half-reactions as follows:

$$\begin{array}{lll} & Cu \rightleftharpoons Cu^{++} + 2\,e^- & (-0.34 \text{ volt}) \\ \text{Subtracting} & 2\,Ag \rightleftharpoons 2\,Ag^+ + 2\,e^- & -\,(-0.80 \text{ volt}) \\ \hline & Cu + 2\,Ag^+ \rightleftharpoons Cu^{++} + 2\,Ag & (0.46 \text{ volt}) \end{array}$$

Hence, the E.M.F. of the cell is 0.46 volt. When the E.M.F. of a cell is found to be positive, then the reaction proceeds spontaneously to the right as written, and the cell delivers current.

Let us calculate the E.M.F. of a cell made up of standard chlorine and bromine electrodes. The half-reactions and standard potentials are given below:

$$\begin{array}{lll} & 2\,Br^- \rightleftharpoons Br_2 + 2\,e^- & (-1.06 \text{ volts}) \\ \text{Subtracting} & 2\,Cl^- \rightleftharpoons Cl_2 + 2\,e^- & -\,(-1.36 \text{ volts}) \\ \hline & 2\,Br^- + Cl_2 \rightleftharpoons Br_2 + 2\,Cl^- & (0.30 \text{ volt}) \end{array}$$

The E.M.F. of the cell is thus found to be 0.30 volt, meaning that the cell reaction proceeds to the right as written. Suppose the half-reactions had been subtracted as follows:

	$2\ Cl^- \rightleftharpoons Cl_2 + 2\ e^-$	(−1.36 volts)
Subtracting	$2\ Br^- \rightleftharpoons Br_2 + 2\ e^-$	− (−1.06 volts)
	$2\ Cl^- + Br_2 \rightleftharpoons Cl_2 + 2\ Br^-$	(−0.30 volt)

The E.M.F. of the cell is found to be −0.30 volt. This negative potential for the cell means that the reaction proceeds to the left spontaneously, but not to the right. In other words chlorine will oxidize the bromide ion to free bromine, but bromine will not oxidize the chloride ion to free chlorine (see Section 17.4).

The potentials given in the electromotive force series refer only to ion concentrations of 1 M and for pressures of 1 atm. for any gases involved. If the concentrations are not 1 M, the values vary and members close together in the series may even change places. Furthermore, the values do not apply to nonaqueous solutions nor to fused salts.

20.14 Electrode Potentials for Other Half-Reactions

In addition to reactions of the elements, there are many other redox reactions which may take place at the electrodes of electrochemical cells. Often the electrode consists of a relatively inactive substance such as graphite or carbon, which undergoes no change itself but merely serves as a carrier of electrons to or from the solution. The standard electrode potentials for some important half-reactions are given in Table 20·2.

TABLE 20·2 Standard Electrode Potentials for Some Important Half-Reactions

Electrode	*Electrode Reaction* (*Reduced form* ⇌ *Oxidized form*)	*Electrode Potential* (*volts*)
Fe, $Fe(OH)_2$, OH^-	$Fe + 2\ OH^- \rightleftharpoons Fe(OH)_2 + 2\ e^-$	0.88
Pb, $PbSO_4$, $SO_4^{=}$	$Pb + SO_4^{=} \rightleftharpoons PbSO_4 + 2\ e^-$	0.36
Pt, Sn^{++}, Sn^{+4}	$Sn^{++} \rightleftharpoons Sn^{+4} + 2\ e^-$	−0.15
Ag, $AgCl$, Cl^-	$Ag + Cl^- \rightleftharpoons AgCl + e^-$	−0.22
Hg, Hg_2Cl_2, Cl^-	$2\ Hg + 2\ Cl^- \rightleftharpoons Hg_2Cl_2 + 2\ e^-$	−0.27
NiO_2, $Ni(OH)_2$, OH^-	$Ni(OH)_2 + 2\ OH^- \rightleftharpoons NiO_2 + 2\ H_2O + 2\ e^-$	−0.49
Pt, Fe^{++}, Fe^{+++}	$Fe^{++} \rightleftharpoons Fe^{+++} + e^-$	−0.77
Pt, Cr^{+++}, $Cr_2O_7^{=}$, H^+	$2\ Cr^{+++} + 7\ H_2O \rightleftharpoons Cr_2O_7^{=} + 14\ H^+ + 6\ e^-$	−1.33
Pt, Mn^{++}, MnO_4^-, H^+	$Mn^{++} + 4\ H_2O \rightleftharpoons MnO_4^- + 8\ H^+ + 5\ e^-$	−1.51
PbO_2, $PbSO_4$, H_2SO_4	$PbSO_4 + 2\ H_2O \rightleftharpoons PbO_2 + SO_4^{=} + 4\ H^+ + 2\ e^-$	−1.69

The standard electrode potential of the Pt, Sn^{++}, Sn^{+4} electrode is that of the inert platinum electrode immersed in a solution which is 1 M with respect to both Sn^{++} and Sn^{+4} ions. Similarly the standard electrode potential of the Pt, Fe^{++}, Fe^{+++} electrode pertains to its potential when the Fe^{++} and Fe^{+++} are both 1 M. The E.M.F. of a cell composed of the two electrodes Pt, Sn^{++}, Sn^{+4} and Pt, Fe^{++}, Fe^{+++} can be calculated as follows:

$$
\begin{array}{lrl}
 & Sn^{++} \rightleftharpoons Sn^{+4} + 2\,e^- & (-0.15\text{ volt}) \\
\text{Subtracting} & 2\,Fe^{++} \rightleftharpoons 2\,Fe^{+++} + 2\,e^- & -\,(-0.77\text{ volt}) \\
\hline
 & Sn^{++} + 2\,Fe^{+++} \rightleftharpoons Sn^{+4} + 2\,Fe^{++} & (0.62\text{ volt})
\end{array}
$$

Thus, the E.M.F. of the cell is 0.62 volt when standard electrodes are used. This means that the reaction will proceed to the right as written and that when solutions containing tin (II) and iron (III) are mixed, the Sn^{++} will reduce the Fe^{+++}.

20.15 Primary Cells

Primary voltaic cells are also referred to as **irreversible cells.** Once the chemicals involved in the production of the current are consumed, further chemical action is not possible because the electrodes and electrolytes are of such a nature that they cannot be restored to their original states by the application of an external electrical potential. The Daniell cell and the "dry" cell are examples of practical primary cells.

1. *The Daniell cell.* The construction of the Daniell cell is shown in Fig. 20–7. Metallic copper is placed in a saturated solution of copper (II) sulfate on the bottom of the cell containing crystals of copper (II) sulfate to keep the solution saturated. A zinc electrode is suspended near the top of the cell in a dilute solution of zinc sulfate, which floats on the more dense solution of copper (II) sulfate. When the two metals are connected by means of a wire, electrons flow through the wire from the more active zinc to the less active copper. The zinc is oxidized and goes into solution as zinc ions, while the copper (II) ions are reduced to metallic copper. This is the same reaction that takes place when metallic zinc becomes plated with copper upon being placed in a solution of copper (II) sulfate.

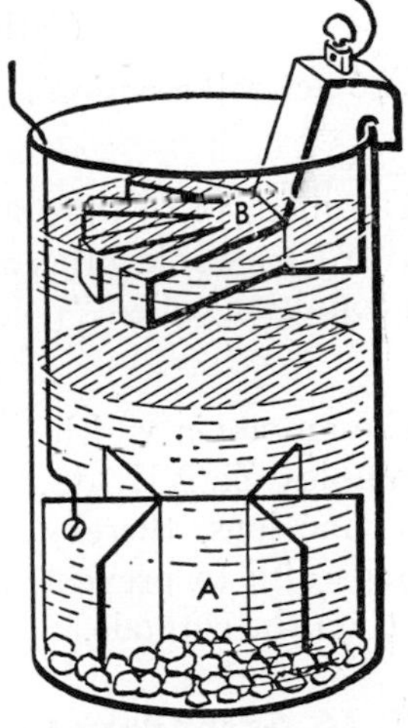

Fig. 20–7 Daniell, or gravity, cell. A, sheet copper surrounded by copper (II) sulfate solution; B, zinc plate surrounded by zinc sulfate solution.

$$
\begin{array}{lr}
\text{(anodic oxidation)} & Zn \rightleftharpoons Zn^{++} + 2\,e^- \\
\text{(cathodic reduction)} & Cu^{++} + 2\,e^- \rightleftharpoons Cu \\
\hline
\text{(cell reaction)} & Zn + Cu^{++} \rightleftharpoons Zn^{++} + Cu
\end{array}
$$

If the zinc ion concentration were increased, the anode reaction would be shifted to the left, resulting in a lower potential for the zinc electrode, and a smaller voltage would be produced by the cell.

A cell similar to the Daniell cell in principle, but based upon cadmium and nickel instead of zinc and copper, is being utilized increasingly in batteries for certain specialized uses.

2. *The dry cell.* The container of the "dry" cell (Fig. 20–8) is made of zinc, which serves also as one of the electrodes. The container is lined with porous paper, which separates the metal from the materials in the center of the cell. A carbon (graphite) rod in the center of the cell acts as the other electrode. The space around the carbon rod contains a moist mixture of ammonium chloride, manganese dioxide, zinc chloride, and some porous, inactive solid such as sawdust. The "dry" cell is sealed with pitch or resin to keep the moisture in. When the "dry" cell delivers a current, the zinc goes into solution as zinc ions and leaves electrons on the zinc cylinder so that it becomes the negative electrode. It is the anode, and oxidation of zinc occurs according to the half-reaction

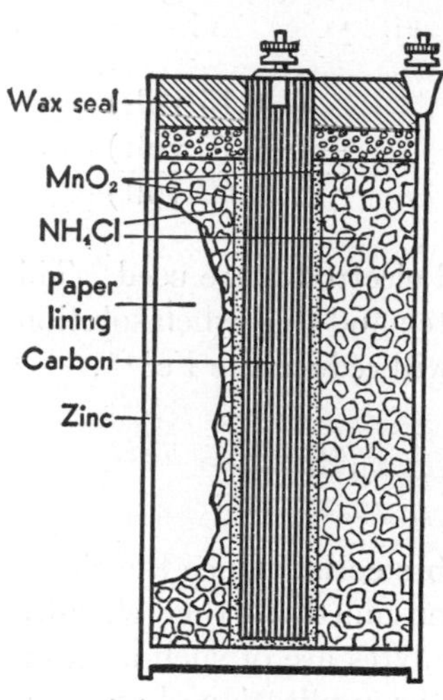

Fig. 20–8 Dry cell.

$$\text{(anode)} \quad Zn \rightarrow Zn^{++} + 2\ e^-$$

The ammonium ion is reduced at the carbon electrode, the cathode.

$$\text{(cathode)} \quad 2\ NH_4^+ + 2\ e^- \rightarrow 2\ NH_3 + 2\ [H]$$

The net cell reaction may be expressed by the equation

$$Zn + 2\ NH_4^+ \rightarrow Zn^{++} + 2\ NH_3 + 2\ [H]$$

The manganese dioxide in the cell oxidizes the hydrogen as it is formed. The hydrogen would otherwise collect on the cathode and stop the action of the cell, a condition called "polarization."

$$2\ [H] + MnO_2 + 2\ H^+ \rightarrow Mn^{++} + 2\ H_2O$$

The ammonia which is formed at the cathode unites with zinc ions forming the complex $Zn(NH_3)_4^{++}$. This reaction prevents an increase in the concentration of zinc ions, thereby keeping the potential of the zinc electrode constant. It helps also to prevent any polarization caused by the accumulation of ammonia gas on the cathode.

20.16 Secondary Cells

In **secondary** or **reversible cells,** the substances which are consumed in producing electricity may be regenerated in their original form by causing a direct current of electricity to flow in the reverse direction of the discharge. This reversal recharges the cell. The lead storage battery and the Edison storage battery are composed of secondary cells.

1. *The lead storage battery* (Fig. 20–9). The electrodes of the lead storage battery consist of two sets of lead plates in the form of grids. The openings of one set

of grids are filled with lead dioxide and the openings of the other with spongy lead. Dilute sulfuric acid serves as the electrolyte. When the battery is delivering a current, the spongy lead is oxidized to lead ion and these plates become negatively charged.

$$\text{(oxidation)} \quad Pb \rightarrow Pb^{++} + 2\ e^-$$

The lead ions formed combine with sulfate ions of the electrolyte and coat the lead electrode with lead sulfate.

$$Pb^{++} + SO_4^{=} \rightarrow \underline{PbSO_4}$$

The net lead electrode reaction is

$$Pb + SO_4^{=} \rightarrow \underline{PbSO_4} + 2\ e^-$$

The negatively charged lead electrode is the anode; it is the electrode at which oxidation occurs.

Electrons flow from the negatively charged lead electrode through the external circuit and enter the lead dioxide electrode. The lead dioxide in the presence of hydrogen ions from the electrolyte is reduced to lead (II) ions.

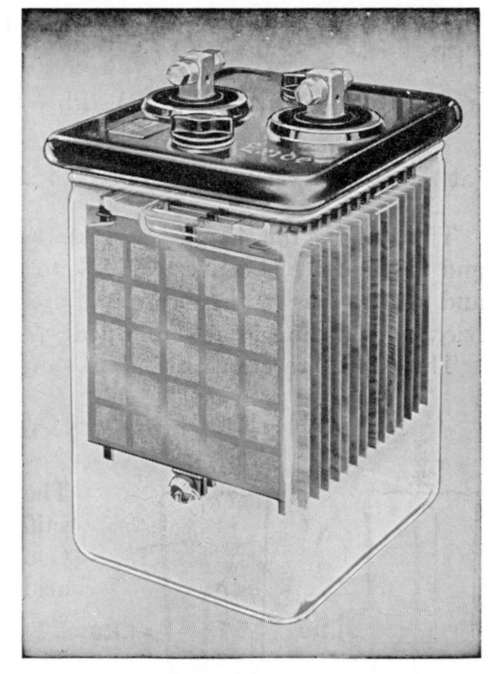

Fig. 20–9 Lead storage cells such as this are used in stationary installations. The plate arrangement is the same as that of the automobile storage battery. *Electric Storage Battery Co.*

$$\text{(reduction)} \quad PbO_2 + 4\ H^+ + 2\ e^- \rightarrow Pb^{++} + 2\ H_2O$$

Again lead ions combine with sulfate ions of the electrolyte and the lead dioxide plate becomes coated with lead sulfate.

$$Pb^{++} + SO_4^{=} \rightarrow \underline{PbSO_4}$$

The net reaction at the positive lead dioxide electrode is

$$\overset{+4}{Pb}O_2 + 4\ H^+ + SO_4^{=} + 2\ e^- \rightarrow \underline{\overset{+2}{Pb}SO_4} + 2\ H_2O$$

The positively charged lead dioxide electrode is the cathode; it is the electrode at which reduction occurs.

The lead storage battery may be recharged by passing electrons through the cell in the reverse direction by applying an external potential. It is thereby made an electrolytic cell during the recharging process. The reactions are just the reverse of those which occur when the cell is operating as a voltaic cell producing a current. Electrons are pumped into the lead electrode making it the cathode, at which reduction of lead ions from the lead sulfate takes place. Electrons are withdrawn from the lead dioxide electrode making it the anode, at which oxidation of lead ions from the lead sulfate takes place.

The charge and discharge at the two plates may be summarized briefly by two equations:

$$\text{(at the lead plate)} \quad Pb + SO_4^{=} \underset{\text{charge}}{\overset{\text{discharge}}{\rightleftharpoons}} \underline{PbSO_4} + 2\ e^-$$

$$\text{(at the lead dioxide plate)} \quad PbO_2 + 4\ H^+ + SO_4^{=} + 2\ e^- \underset{\text{charge}}{\overset{\text{discharge}}{\rightleftharpoons}} \underline{PbSO_4} + 2\ H_2O$$

Thus, during the charging process, the sulfate ion of the electrolyte is regenerated and lead sulfate is converted back to lead at the lead electrode; hydrogen ions and sulfate ions of the electrolyte are regenerated and lead sulfate is converted back to lead dioxide at the lead dioxide electrode.

The net cell reaction of the lead storage battery is given by the equation

$$Pb + PbO_2 + 4\ H^+ + SO_4^{=} \underset{\text{charge}}{\overset{\text{discharge}}{\rightleftharpoons}} 2\ \underline{PbSO_4} + 2\ H_2O$$

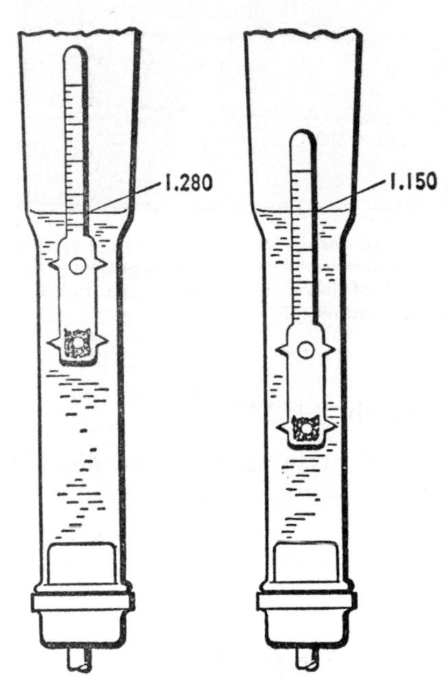

Fig. 20–10 Hydrometers are used for testing the charge of a lead storage battery.

The above equation shows that the amount of sulfuric acid decreases as the cell discharges. Conversely, charging the cell regenerates the acid. Since sulfuric acid is much heavier than water, the condition of a lead storage battery may be tested conveniently by determining the specific gravity of the electrolyte by using a hydrometer (Fig. 20–10). When the specific gravity is 1.25 to 1.30, the battery is charged; when it falls below 1.15 to 1.20, the battery needs charging. As can be calculated from the potentials in Table 20·2, a single, fully charged lead storage cell has a potential of a little over two volts — that is, $0.36 - (-1.69) = 2.05$ v. The potential falls off slowly as the cell is used. A 12-volt automobile battery contains six lead storage cells, whereas a 6-volt battery contains three.

2. *The Edison storage battery.* The Edison battery is another storage battery of practical importance. In the cells of this battery the negative steel plates are packed with finely divided iron and the positive steel plates with hydrated nickel dioxide. The electrolyte is a 21 per cent potassium hydroxide solution containing some lithium hydroxide. When the battery is delivering a current of electricity, oxidation takes place at the anode according to the equation

$$\text{(anode)} \quad Fe + 2\ OH^- \rightarrow \underline{Fe(OH)_2} + 2\ e^-$$

The reduction at the cathode is expressed by the equation

$$\text{(cathode)} \quad NiO_2 + 2\ H_2O + 2\ e^- \rightarrow \underline{Ni(OH)_2} + 2\ OH^-$$

These reactions are reversed while the battery is being charged and the net reaction is as follows:

$$Fe + NiO_2 + 2\,H_2O \underset{\text{charge}}{\overset{\text{discharge}}{\rightleftharpoons}} \underline{Fe(OH)_2} + \underline{Ni(OH)_2}$$

It can be seen from this equation that the electrodes are restored to their original condition on recharging. The electromotive force of each cell in an Edison storage battery, as can be calculated from the potentials in Table 20·2, is about 1.4 volts. This battery is lighter and more durable than the lead storage battery but more costly.

It should be noted that the anode is positive and the cathode negative in an electrolytic cell (see Fig. 20–3, for example), whereas the anode is negative and the cathode positive in a voltaic cell (Fig. 20–6). **For either type of cell, however, oxidation occurs at the anode and reduction at the cathode.**

20.17 The Solar Battery

The interest in turning sunlight directly into electric current arises because the earth receives more energy from sunlight in two days than is stored in all known reserves of fossil fuels. The conventional photoelectric cell, used in electric-eye doors, transforms light into electrical energy (Section 3.1) but delivers as power only about half of one per cent of the total light energy it absorbs. A newer type of photoelectric cell is several times more efficient than the conventional types and is capable of generating electric power from sunlight at the rate of 90 watts per square yard of illuminated surface.

The basic unit of a typical solar battery is a thin wafer of very pure silicon, containing initially no more than one part of impurity per million parts of silicon. The silicon lattice consists of a diamond structure in which each silicon atom is bonded covalently through its four valence electrons to four neighboring silicon atoms at the corners of a regular tetrahedron. For the solar battery, a tiny amount of arsenic is added to the silicon in the body of the silicon wafer. Inasmuch as arsenic has five valence electrons, compared to four for silicon, the addition of arsenic to the tetrahedral silicon crystal lattice creates some excess of free electrons within the lattice in the body of the wafer (commonly referred to as n-type silicon). On the surface of the wafer is placed a thin layer of silicon containing a trace of boron. Inasmuch as boron has only three valence electrons, "holes" (vacant spots for electrons) then exist in the silicon lattice at the surface of the wafer (commonly referred to as p-type silicon). A junction (referred to as a p-n junction) exists between the body of the wafer and the thin surface layer. Electrons diffuse through the junction from the wafer to "holes" in the surface layer; at the same time, "holes," or electron vacancies, move to the body of the wafer. This creates a net positive charge within the body of the wafer, which was neutral prior to the diffusion of electrons out with their negative charges. A net negative charge, from electrons diffusing in, is correspondingly produced in the previously neutral surface layer. Thus, an electrostatic force develops between the two regions, which builds up until the negatively charged region at the surface repels any further diffusion of electrons. A counter force, opposite to the diffusion force, results as the electric field tends to attract the negative electrons back to the positively charged body of the wafer and to attract "holes" to the negatively charged surface of the wafer. When the diffusion of electrons is just balanced by the electric field, equilibrium is established between the two forces and hence also between electrons and "holes." At equilibrium, a net difference in potential exists between the two regions in the wafer.

In the solar battery, one electrical lead is attached to the body of the wafer and one lead to the surface. When the wafer is exposed to sunlight, energy from the sunlight causes electrons to be released from their positions in the lattice near the *p-n* junction, thereby upsetting the equilibrium between electrons and "holes" and causing additional electrons to move across the junction into the body of the wafer. Thus, a sufficient electron pressure (electromotive force) is built up to cause electrons to move through the electrical leads, and a current flows through the wire. The device, thus, is a battery with the positive terminal at the *p*-contact and the negative terminal at the *n*-contact (Fig. 20–11).

In actual practice, a series of such wafers are used side-by-side. The first practical application of a solar battery, still largely in the experimental stage, was in the powering of eight telephones on a rural telephone line in Georgia in 1955. Such cells have, very recently, been used to power communication devices in spacecraft.

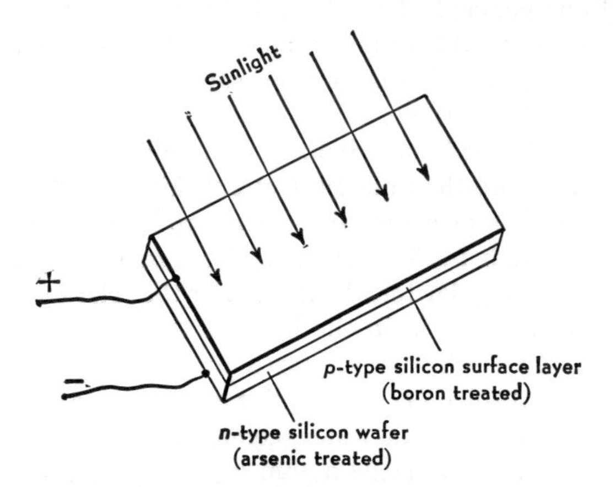

Fig. 20–11 Solar battery cell.

20.18 Fuel Cells

Fuel cells are voltaic cells in which electrode materials, usually in the form of gases, are supplied continuously to a cell and consumed to produce electricity.

A typical fuel cell, currently under development, is that based upon the reaction of hydrogen (the "fuel") and oxygen (the "oxidizer") to form water. At the anode, hydrogen gas is bubbled through a porous carbon electrode, in the surface of which is embedded a catalyst such as fine particles of platinum or palladium.

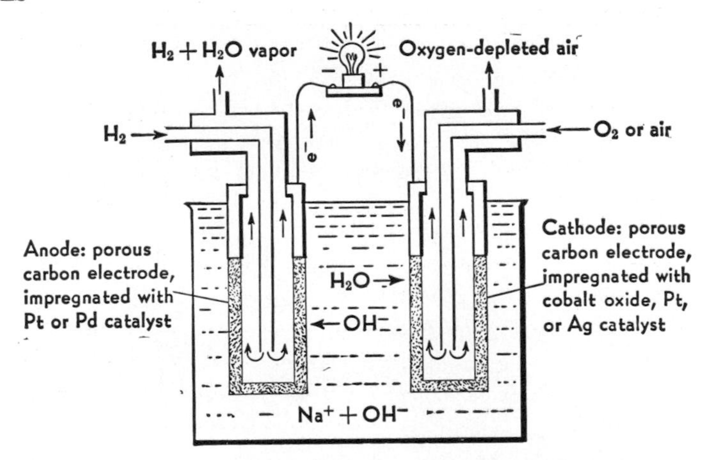

Fig. 20–12 Hydrogen-oxygen fuel cell. *From Scientific American*

At the cathode, oxygen is bubbled through a porous carbon electrode impregnated with cobalt oxide, platinum, or silver as catalyst. The two electrodes are separated by an electrolyte such as a concentrated solution of sodium hydroxide or potassium hydroxide (Fig. 20–12).

As hydrogen diffuses through the anode, it is adsorbed on the electrode surface in the form of hydrogen atoms which react with hydroxyl ions of the electrolyte to form water.

$$H_2 \xrightarrow{\text{catalyst}} 2\,H$$
$$2\,H + 2\,OH^- \rightarrow 2\,H_2O + 2\,e^-$$
$$\text{Net anode reaction: } H_2 + 2\,OH^- \rightarrow 2\,H_2O + 2\,e^-$$

The electrons produced at the anode flow through the external circuit to the cathode. The oxygen, bubbled in at the cathode, is adsorbed on the electrode surface where it is reduced to hydroxyl ions.

$$\text{Cathode reaction: } O_2 + 2\,H_2O + 4\,e^- \rightarrow 4\,OH^-$$

The hydroxyl ions complete the cycle by migrating through the electrolyte from the oxygen electrode (cathode) to the hydrogen electrode (anode). The electrical output of the cell results, as in all voltaic cells, from the flow of electrons through the external circuit from anode to cathode.

The over-all cell reaction is the combination of hydrogen and oxygen to produce water (Fig. 20–13, page 326).

$$\text{(anodic oxidation)} \quad 2\,H_2 + 4\,OH^- \rightarrow 4\,H_2O + 4\,e^-$$
$$\text{(cathodic reduction)} \quad O_2 + 2\,H_2O + 4\,e^- \rightarrow 4\,OH^-$$
$$\text{(cell reaction)} \quad 2\,H_2 + O_2 \rightarrow 2\,H_2O$$

The efficiency of the fuel cell is potentially greater than that of conventional generating equipment, through producing electric current directly from the reac-

Fig. 20–13 A cutaway mock-up of a fuel cell currently under development which will supply electric power for America's two-man Gemini spacecraft. A foot wide and two feet long, this cell will use hydrogen and oxygen to produce electricity and also a pint of pure, drinkable water for each kilowatt-hour operation. *General Electric Co.*

tion of the fuel and oxidizer without going through the inherently wasteful intermediate conversion of chemical energy to heat. Many applications exist for a reliable, low cost fuel cell. A great deal of research effort is being expended in investigating other fuels such as methane and other hydrocarbons, other electrode systems, and high temperature operations.

An interesting possibility for future application of the hydrogen-oxygen fuel cell is as a means of capturing power of the sun. Sunlight can be used, by a recently developed catalytic process, to decompose water into hydrogen and oxygen, which can then be used in fuel cells to produce electric current. It has been suggested, also, that fuel cells might help to cut the cost of nuclear power. Nuclear plants could be operated more nearly at peak capacity if the power generated during periods of low demand were used to electrolyze water into hydrogen and oxygen which would then be used in fuel cells to yield electrical energy during peak demand periods.

QUESTIONS

1. Name the kinds of charged particles which may constitute a current of electricity when they are in motion.
2. Explain the meaning of the terms anode and cathode.
3. Interpret the electrolysis of fused sodium chloride as an oxidation-reduction reaction.
4. Why is the hydrogen ion rather than the sodium ion reduced at the cathode during the electrolysis of aqueous sodium chloride? What is the source of the hydrogen ion?
5. Give the equation for the net reaction in the electrolysis of dilute sulfuric acid.
6. Under what conditions may hydrogen peroxide be formed as a product of the electrolysis of sulfuric acid?
7. Explain the electrolytic purification of copper.
8. State Faraday's Law of Electrolysis. What is a faraday of electricity?
9. What is the importance of Avogadro's number to the electrolytic process?
10. Show by suitable equations that the electrode reaction for the zinc electrode is a reversible one.
11. Define the phrase "standard electrode potential."
12. What is the origin of the value zero for the standard hydrogen electrode?
13. Distinguish between primary and secondary voltaic cells.
14. How was the electromotive series experimentally established?
15. List some uses of the electromotive force series.
16. Describe the construction of the dry cell and give its net reaction.
17. Give equations for the net reactions at the two different kinds of plates in a storage battery.
18. What are the energy conversions which take place during the charging and discharging of a storage battery?
19. Relate the condition of charge of a lead battery to the specific gravity of its electrolyte.
20. Draw a schematic diagram of a Daniell voltaic cell connected so as to supply electric current to an electrolytic cell for the electrolysis of hydrochloric acid. Label the diagram to show (a) which is anode and which is cathode in each cell; (b) direction of electron flow in the external circuit; (c) sign of each electrode of each cell (refer to the last paragraph of Section 20.16); (d) direction of migration of each ion within the electrolyte of each cell; and (e) electrode reactions for each cell.
21. Indicate two ways in which the energy of sunlight may be converted into electrical energy.

PROBLEMS

1. How many grams of copper will be deposited from a solution of copper (II) sulfate by 3.40 faradays of electricity? *Ans. 108 g.*
2. How many grams of nickel will be deposited from a solution of nickel (II) chloride by 24,125 coulombs of electricity? *Ans. 7.34 g.*

3. For a period of 50.0 minutes, an electric current of 2.50 amperes is passed successively through solutions of silver nitrate, copper (II) sulfate, and sulfuric acid. How many grams of silver, copper, and hydrogen are electrolytically produced during the process? *Ans. Ag, 8.38 g.; Cu, 2.47 g.;* H_2*, 0.0783 g.*

4. A current of 12.0 amperes flowed for 120 minutes through water containing a small quantity of sodium hydroxide. How many liters of gas were formed at the cathode at 27.0° and 750 mm. pressure? *Ans. 11.1 l.*

5. How many ampere-hours of electricity are required in the electrolytic refining of 1.00 kg. of copper? *Ans. 844 ampere-hours*

6. How many zinc ions, silver ions, and aluminum ions will be reduced by 6.023×10^{23} electrons in suitable electrolytic cells?

Ans. 3.012×10^{23}; 6.023×10^{23}; 2.008×10^{23}

7. How many coulombs of electricity would be required to reduce 75.000 g. of silver ion from a solution of $Na[Ag(CN)_2]$? *Ans. 67,076*

8. How many grams of copper would be deposited from a solution of copper (II) sulfate by a current of 3.00 amperes flowing for 8.00 hours? *Ans. 28.4 g.*

9. Calculate the E.M.F. for cells made up of the pairs of standard electrodes listed below. Consult Tables 20·1 and 20·2 for the standard electrode potentials. Subtract half-reactions to obtain cell reactions in such a way as to give positive E.M.F. values for each cell. Identify the negative and positive electrodes, and the anode and cathode in each cell. Indicate the direction of the cell reaction in each case.

(a) Mg, Mg^{++} and Cd, Cd^{++} *Ans. 1.97 v.*
(b) Sn, Sn^{++} and Fe, Fe^{++} *Ans. 0.30 v.*
(c) Pt, Cl^-, Cl_2 and Mn, Mn^{++} *Ans. 2.54 v.*
(d) Pt, F^-, F_2 and Pt, Cl^-, Cl_2 *Ans. 1.51 v.*
(e) Pt, Sn^{++}, Sn^{+4} and Al, Al^{+++} *Ans. 1.81 v.*
(f) Pt, Fe^{++}, Fe^{+++} and Pt, Mn^{++}, MnO_4^-, H^+ *Ans. 0.74 v.*

10. For the following cell, calculate the E.M.F. of the cell and write the equation for the cell reaction. $Pb \mid Pb^{++}, M = 1 \parallel Ag^+, M = 1 \mid Ag$. *Ans. 0.93 v.*

11. Write equations for the electrode reactions in each of the following cases and, using potentials from Tables 20·1 and 20·2, calculate:

(a) the E.M.F. of a single lead storage battery cell; the E.M.F. which would be produced by three lead storage cells in series; and the E.M.F. which would be produced by six lead storage cells in series.

Ans. 2.05 v.; 6.15 v.; 12.30 v.

(b) the E.M.F. of a cadmium-nickel battery cell. *Ans. 0.15 v.*

(c) the E.M.F. of an Edison storage battery cell. *Ans. 1.37 v.*

12. A total of 24,125 coulombs of electricity was required in the electrolytic reduction of 25.0 g. of a metal from a solution of its *dipositive* ions. What is the atomic weight of the metal? *Ans. 200*

13. A zinc-copper cell (Daniell cell) has initially 50.0 g. of zinc and 500 ml. of 0.100 M $CuSO_4$. How long can this cell deliver a current of 100 milliamperes?

Ans. 26.8 hours

14. In the production of aluminum electrolytically, oxygen is produced at the

anode. Some of it is used up by reaction with the carbon electrode to produce CO_2. Calculate the volume of CO_2 produced and the volume of O_2 liberated (S.T.P.) for every pound of aluminum produced, assuming that 15% of the total oxygen initially produced reacts with the electrode.

Ans. *42.3 l.* CO_2*; 239.7 l.* O_2

15. Three cells containing Pb^{++} in the following concentrations are connected in series. Cell no. 1 contains 0.100 M Pb^{++}, cell no. 2 contains 0.010 M Pb^{++}, and cell no. 3 contains 1.00 M Pb^{++}. If 0.200 ampere is passed through the circuit for exactly two hours, how much metallic lead would be deposited in each cell?

Ans. Same for each (1.55 g.)

16. The international ampere is that current which under specified conditions deposits 0.001118 g. of silver per second. Taking into account the atomic weight of silver and the number of significant figures justified in your answer, calculate the value of the faraday in coulombs. *Ans. 96,500 coulombs*

17. One liter of 0.2 M $AgNO_3$ has in it two platinum electrodes. A current of one ampere is run through the solution for 9650 seconds. Assuming none of the solution is lost through electrolysis, what is the final concentration of the $AgNO_3$?

Ans. 0.1 M

18. How many electrons must flow through the wires connecting a source of direct current to the electrodes to produce 0.71 g. of chlorine by the electrolysis of melted NaCl? *Ans.* 1.2×10^{22}

REFERENCES

"Electrochemical Conventions," W. F. Luder and A. A. Vernon, *J. Chem. Educ.*, **22** (2) 63 (Feb. 1945).

"Primary Cells — A Brief Historical Sketch," C. J. Brockman, *J. Chem. Educ.*, **4** (6) 770 (1927).

"Fundamentals in Applied Electrochemistry," C. G. Fink, *J. Chem. Educ.*, **25** (4) 219 (1948).

"A Modern Approach to the Teaching of Electrochemistry," A. W. Davidson, *J. Chem. Educ.*, **25** (10) 533 (1948).

"The Solar Battery," G. Raisbeck, *Sci. American*, Dec. 1955, p. 102.

"Fuel Cells," L. G. Austin, *Sci. American*, Oct. 1959, p. 72.

"Fuel Cells — Electrochemical Converters of Chemical to Electrical Energy," J. Weissbart, *J. Chem. Educ.*, **38** (5) 267 (1961).

"Fuel Cells," E. Yeager, *Science*, **134** (3486) 1178 (1961).

CHAPTER TWENTY-ONE

Acids, Bases, and Salts

Acids and bases are among the most important of the numerous classes of chemical compounds. Because these two classes of substances are in effect opposite each other in character and yet related through their ability to neutralize one another, it is convenient and instructive to consider them together.

The subjects of acids and bases have been responsible for much interesting controversy because the terms "acid" and "base" can be defined in a number of ways. It is of interest to review briefly the historical development of the acid-base concept.

21.1 History of the Acid-Base Concept

The first significant characterization of acids and bases was made by Boyle in 1680. He noted that acids dissolve many substances, that they change the color of certain natural dyes from blue to red, and that they lose these characteristic properties after coming in contact with alkalies. In the eighteenth century it was recognized that acids have a sour taste, that they react with limestone with the liberation of a gaseous substance (CO_2), and that neutral substances result from their interaction with alkalies. Lavoisier in 1787 proposed that acids are binary compounds of oxygen and he considered oxygen to be responsible for the acidic properties of this class of substances. The essentiality of oxygen was disproved by Davy in 1811 when he showed that hydrochloric acid contains no oxygen. Davy made a great step forward in the development of the acid-base concept by concluding that hydrogen, rather than oxygen, is the essential constituent of acids. In 1814 Gay-Lussac concluded that acids are substances which can neutralize alkalies and that these two classes of substances can be defined only in terms of each other. The ideas of Davy and Gay-Lussac are fundamentally those of our modern concepts of acids and bases when they are considered from a practical point of view.

21.2 The Classical or Arrhenius Concept of Acids and Bases

Early in his study of elementary chemistry the student learns that **acids** are compounds that yield hydrogen ions, H^+, or hydronium ions, H_3O^+, when dissolved in water, and that **bases** yield hydroxide, OH^-, ions. The process of neutralization is then considered to be the union of hydrogen and hydroxyl ions to form neutral water, $H^+ + OH^- \rightarrow H_2O$. These definitions are the basis for the Arrhenius acid-base concept. Because beginning students in chemistry use water almost exclusively as the solvent for carrying out reactions in solution, the Arrhenius concepts are quite adequate while the student is being introduced to the field of chemistry. However, it is now found convenient to use the terms "acid" and "base" and "acid-base reactions" in many instances in which neither hydrogen ions, hydroxide ions, nor the union of these ions to form water, is involved. Furthermore, many ions and molecules possess basic properties comparable to those of the hydroxide ion, and reactions involving salt formation occur in many solvents other than water and even in the absence of a solvent. This does not mean, however, that the classical concept should be discarded, for with slight modifications, it does more to explain the behavior of aqueous solutions than some of the more complex modern views.

21.3 The Protonic Concept of Acids and Bases

As a result of the work of several chemists, especially Brönsted, the classical acid-base theory has been extended to give a more general concept of acids and bases. According to this view, acids and bases are related by the equation

$$\underset{\text{Acid}}{HA} \rightleftharpoons \underset{\text{Proton}}{H^+} + \underset{\text{Base}}{A^-}$$

From the protonic acid-base point of view, **an acid is any species (molecule or ion) that can give up a proton to another species. A base is any species that can combine with a proton.** Stated simply, an acid is a proton donor, while a base is a proton acceptor. These definitions do not specify a solvent, as do the classical definitions. Furthermore, species which are acids or bases according to this view do not necessarily exhibit the properties which we usually associate with aqueous acids and bases of the classical concept.

In order for an acid to act as a proton donor, a proton acceptor must be present to receive the proton. The proton acceptor in aqueous solution is water.

$$HA + H_2O \rightleftharpoons H_3O^+ + A^-$$

Thus, hydronium ions are formed when the acid HA gives up its proton to a water molecule. Because the water molecule accepts a proton, it is acting as a base. In addition, when the reversible reaction proceeds to the left, the ion A^- acts as a base by accepting a proton from the hydronium ion, an acid. The equilibrium, then, involves two acids and two bases.

$$\underset{\text{Acid}_1}{HA} + \underset{\text{Base}_1}{H_2O} \rightleftharpoons \underset{\text{Acid}_2}{H_3O^+} + \underset{\text{Base}_2}{A^-}$$

Other solvents, as well as water, may act as bases according to the proton acid-base theory. Hydrogen chloride reacts with liquid ammonia forming ammonium ions and chloride ions. Ammonia is the proton acceptor.

$$\underset{\text{Acid}_1}{HCl} + \underset{\text{Base}_1}{NH_3} \rightleftharpoons \underset{\text{Acid}_2}{NH_4^+} + \underset{\text{Base}_2}{Cl^-}$$

In accordance with the definition that acids are proton donors, there may be molecular acids such as HCl, HNO_3, H_2SO_4, CH_3COOH, HCN, H_2S, H_2CO_3, HF, and H_2O; anion acids such as HSO_4^-, HCO_3^-, $H_2PO_4^-$, $HPO_4^{=}$, and HS^-; and cation acids such as H_3O^+, NH_4^+, $Cu(H_2O)_4^{++}$, and $Fe(H_2O)_6^{+++}$.

As in the case of acids, there are molecular bases such as H_2O, NH_3, and CH_3NH_2; anion bases such as OH^-, HS^-, $S^{=}$, HCO_3^-, $CO_3^{=}$, HSO_4^-, $SO_4^{=}$, $HPO_4^{=}$, Cl^-, F^-, NO_3^-, and $PO_4^{\equiv}$; and cation bases such as $Fe(H_2O)_5OH^{++}$ and $Cu(H_2O)_3OH^+$. The most familiar base is the hydroxide ion, OH^-, which accepts protons from acids forming water.

$$HA + OH^- \rightleftharpoons H_2O + A^-$$
$$H_3O^+ + OH^- \rightleftharpoons H_2O + H_2O$$

It follows from this discussion, then, that the proton view enables us to extend our classical concept of acids and bases to include many more species. It also enables us to look upon a large number of apparently unrelated reactions as truly acid-base reactions.

21.4 Amphiprotic Species

From a study of the examples of acids and bases given in the preceding section, it is seen that certain molecules and ions are classed as both acids and bases. **A species that may either gain or lose a proton is said to be amphiprotic.** For example, water may lose a proton to a base, such as NH_3, or gain a proton from an acid, such as HCl.

$$\underset{\text{Acid}}{H_2O} + \underset{\text{Base}}{NH_3} \rightleftharpoons NH_4^+ + OH^-$$
$$\underset{\text{Base}}{H_2O} + \underset{\text{Acid}}{HCl} \rightleftharpoons H_3O^+ + Cl^-$$

The proton-containing negative ions are amphiprotic, as is readily seen from a study of the following equations:

$$\underset{\text{Acid}}{HS^-} + \underset{\text{Base}}{OH^-} \rightleftharpoons S^{=} + H_2O$$
$$\underset{\text{Base}}{HS^-} + \underset{\text{Acid}}{H_3O^+} \rightleftharpoons H_2S + H_2O$$
$$\underset{\text{Acid}}{HCO_3^-} + \underset{\text{Base}}{OH^-} \rightleftharpoons CO_3^{=} + H_2O$$
$$\underset{\text{Base}}{HCO_3^-} + \underset{\text{Acid}}{H_3O^+} \rightleftharpoons H_2CO_3 + H_2O$$

The hydroxides of certain metals are amphiprotic and react either as acids or bases.

$$\underset{\text{Acid}}{Al(H_2O)_3(OH)_3} + \underset{\text{Base}}{OH^-} \rightleftharpoons Al(H_2O)_2(OH)_4^- + H_2O$$
$$\underset{\text{Base}}{Al(H_2O)_3(OH)_3} + \underset{\text{Acid}}{H_3O^+} \rightleftharpoons Al(H_2O)_4(OH)_2^+ + H_2O$$

In the first reaction, one of the water molecules of the hydrated aluminum hydroxide loses a proton to the hydroxide ion. In the second reaction, the aluminum hydroxide receives a proton from the hydronium ion. In both cases the hydrated aluminum hydroxide is dissolved.

21.5 Polyprotic Acids

Acids may be classified in terms of the number of protons per molecule of acid that can be given up in a reaction. Acids such as HCl, HNO_3, and HCN, that contain one ionizable hydrogen atom in one molecule of acid, are called **monoprotic acids.** Their reaction with water is given by the following equations:

$$HCl + H_2O \rightarrow H_3O^+ + Cl^-$$
$$HNO_3 + H_2O \rightarrow H_3O^+ + NO_3^-$$
$$HCN + H_2O \rightleftharpoons H_3O^+ + CN^-$$

Acetic acid, CH_3COOH, is monoprotic because only one of the four hydrogen atoms contained in a single molecule can be given up as a proton in reacting with bases.

$$CH_3COOH + H_2O \rightleftharpoons CH_3COO^- + H_3O^+$$

Diprotic acids contain two ionizable hydrogen atoms in one molecule of the acid; ionization of such acids occurs in two stages. The primary ionization always takes place to a greater extent than the secondary. For example, carbonic acid ionizes as follows:

$$H_2CO_3 + H_2O \rightleftharpoons H_3O^+ + HCO_3^- \quad \text{(primary ionization)}$$
$$HCO_3^- + H_2O \rightleftharpoons H_3O^+ + CO_3^= \quad \text{(secondary ionization)}$$

Triprotic acids such as phosphoric acid ionize in three steps:

$$H_3PO_4 + H_2O \rightleftharpoons H_3O^+ + H_2PO_4^- \quad \text{(primary ionization)}$$
$$H_2PO_4^- + H_2O \rightleftharpoons H_3O^+ + HPO_4^= \quad \text{(secondary ionization)}$$
$$HPO_4^= + H_2O \rightleftharpoons H_3O^+ + PO_4^{-3} \quad \text{(tertiary ionization)}$$

Often the terms monobasic, dibasic, and tribasic are used instead of monoprotic, diprotic, and triprotic.

21.6 The Strength of Acids and Bases

In the fundamental acid-base relationship, $HA \rightleftharpoons H^+ + A^-$, the anion A^- is said to be the **conjugate base** of the acid HA. The strength of an acid is a measure of the tendency of its conjugate base to combine with protons, as compared with that of some other base such as water. For example, the stronger the acid, the greater is the extent of its ionization in water.

$$HCl + H_2O \rightarrow H_3O^+ + Cl^- \quad \text{(complete in dilute solution)}$$
$$HF + H_2O \rightleftharpoons H_3O^+ + F^- \quad \text{(8.5 per cent in 0.1 M solution)}$$
$$CH_3COOH + H_2O \rightleftharpoons H_3O^+ + CH_3COO^- \quad \text{(1.3 per cent in 0.1 M solution)}$$

It follows that strong bases are characterized by high proton affinities. The fluoride ion is a strong base as indicated by the weakness of its conjugate acid, HF; i.e., the fluoride ion holds the proton firmly in the hydrogen fluoride molecule. On the other hand, the chloride ion is such a weak base that HCl readily loses its proton to the water molecule, which is a stronger base. Thus the ionization of HCl is extensive, and the acid is strong. Other weak bases are Br^-, I^-, NO_3^-, ClO_4^-, and HSO_4^-; thus HBr, HI, HNO_3, $HClO_4$, and H_2SO_4 are strong acids; i.e., they are almost 100 per cent ionized in dilute aqueous solution. The acetate ion, CH_3COO^-, is a much stronger base than is the water molecule; it is therefore the conjugate base of a weak acid. Acetic acid is ionized only 1.3 per cent in a 0.1 M solution. Other examples of weak acids are H_2O, HS^-, HCO_3^-, NH_4^+, H_2S, HCN, and H_2SO_3; thus OH^-, $S^=$, $CO_3^=$, NH_3, HS^-, CN^-, and HSO_3^- are strong bases.

According to the proton theory, then, the strongest acids have the weakest conjugate bases and the strongest bases have the weakest conjugate acids.

21.7 The Relative Strengths of Strong Acids and Bases

The strongest acids, such as HCl, HBr, and HI, appear to have about the same strength in water solution, and the same is true of the strongest bases such as $O^=$ and NH_2^-. However, the strength of the bonds between hydrogen and the negative ion in strong acids is different even though their ionization in water does not indicate a difference. When HCl, HBr, and HI, for example, are studied in solvents less strongly basic than water, they are observed to differ markedly in tendency to give up a proton to the solvent. In methyl alcohol, a weaker base than water, the extent of ionization increases in the order HCl, HBr, HI. Apparently the water molecule is such a strong base as compared to the conjugate bases Cl^-, Br^-, and I^- of the strong acids HCl, HBr, and HI, that ionization is nearly complete for all the acids in aqueous solutions. Because water tends to level off any differences in strength among strong acids, the effect is known as the "leveling effect" of water.

To a somewhat lesser extent, water exerts a leveling effect upon the base strength of very strong bases. For example the oxide ion, $O^=$, and the amide ion, NH_2^-, are such strong bases that reaction with water by the removal of protons from the water is complete.

$$O^= + H_2O \rightarrow OH^- + OH^-$$
$$NH_2^- + H_2O \rightarrow NH_3 + OH^-$$

Thus, these bases appear to have the same strength as indicated by their complete reaction with water. The relative strengths of weaker bases may be measured by the extent to which they react with water to yield hydroxide ions. This point is illustrated by the following examples for 0.1 M solutions:

$$CH_3COO^- + H_2O \rightleftharpoons CH_3COOH + OH^- \quad \text{(0.0075 per cent)}$$
$$NH_3 + H_2O \rightleftharpoons NH_4^+ + OH^- \quad \text{(1.34 per cent)}$$
$$CO_3^= + H_2O \rightleftharpoons HCO_3^- + OH^- \quad \text{(3.9 per cent)}$$

21.8 Properties of Acids in Aqueous Solution

The properties which are common to all acids in aqueous solution are those of the hydronium ion, formed when the acid dissolves in water. Although the hydrogen ion is actually hydrated, the symbol H^+ is often used instead of H_3O^+ for the sake of convenience. It is important to remember, however, that H^+ is an abbreviated symbol and that actually the hydrogen ion is always hydrated in water solution. Acids in aqueous solution exhibit the following properties:

(1) They have a sour taste.

(2) They change the color of certain indicators. For example, they change litmus from blue to red, and phenolphthalein from red to colorless.

(3) They react with metals above hydrogen in the electromotive series with the liberation of hydrogen.

$$2\ H^+ + Zn \rightarrow Zn^{++} + H_2 \uparrow$$

(4) They react with oxides and hydroxides of metals, forming salts and water.

$$2\ H^+ + (2\ Cl^-) + FeO \rightarrow Fe^{++} + (2\ Cl^-) + H_2O$$
$$3\ H^+ + (3\ Cl^-) + Fe(OH)_3 \rightarrow Fe^{+++} + (3\ Cl^-) + 3\ H_2O$$

(5) They react with salts of weaker acids, such as carbonates or sulfides, to give a new salt and a new acid.

$$2\ H^+ + (2\ Cl^-) + CaCO_3 \rightarrow H_2CO_3 + Ca^{++} + (2\ Cl^-)$$
$$H_2CO_3 \rightleftharpoons H_2O + CO_2 \uparrow$$
$$2\ H^+ + (2\ Cl^-) + FeS \rightarrow H_2S \uparrow + Fe^{++} + (2\ Cl^-)$$

(6) Their aqueous solutions conduct an electric current because they contain ions; they are electrolytes.

21.9 Formation of Acids

Acids may be formed by one or more of the following methods:

1. *By the direct union of their elements.*

$$H_2 + Cl_2 \rightarrow 2\ HCl$$
$$H_2 + S \rightarrow H_2S$$

2. *By the action of water on oxides of nonmetals.*

$$CO_2 + H_2O \rightarrow H_2CO_3$$
$$SO_3 + H_2O \rightarrow H_2SO_4$$
$$P_4O_{10} + 6\ H_2O \rightarrow 4\ H_3PO_4$$

3. *By heating salts of volatile acids with nonvolatile acids.*

$$NaCl + H_2SO_4 \rightarrow NaHSO_4 + HCl \uparrow$$
$$NaBr + H_3PO_4 \rightarrow NaH_2PO_4 + HBr \uparrow$$

4. *By the action of salts with other acids producing a precipitate.*

$$(H^+) + Cl^- + Ag^+ + (NO_3^-) \rightarrow \underline{AgCl} + (H^+) + (NO_3^-)$$
$$(2\ H^+) + SO_4^{=} + Ba^{++} + (2\ ClO_3^-) \rightarrow \underline{BaSO_4} + (2\ H^+) + (2\ ClO_3^-)$$
$$H^+ + (Cl^-) + (Na^+) + ClO^- \rightarrow \overline{HClO} + (Na^+) + (Cl^-)$$

5. *By hydrolysis.*

$$PBr_3 + 3\ H_2O \rightarrow H_3PO_3 + 3\ HBr$$
$$PCl_5 + 4\ H_2O \rightarrow H_3PO_4 + 5\ HCl$$

6. *By oxidation and reduction.*

$$H_2S + I_2 \rightarrow 2\ H^+ + 2\ I^- + S$$
$$2\ HNO_3 + 2\ SO_2 + H_2O \rightarrow 2\ H_2SO_4 + NO \uparrow + NO_2 \uparrow$$

21.10 Properties of Hydroxide Bases in Aqueous Solution

The most important and characteristic base (proton acceptor) in aqueous solution is the hydroxide ion. In common usage the term base refers to hydroxide base. The hydroxides of the alkali metals (potassium and sodium) are called alkali bases, and those of the alkaline earth metals (barium, strontium, and calcium) are known as alkaline earth bases. The hydroxides of sodium, potassium, and barium are referred to as strong bases because they give a high concentration of hydroxide ions in aqueous solution. The hydroxides of the alkali metals are very soluble in water, those of the alkaline earth metals are moderately soluble, while all of the other metal hydroxides are only sparingly soluble.

The properties which are common to hydroxide bases in aqueous solution are due to the presence of the hydroxide ion.

(1) They have a bitter taste.

(2) They change the colors of certain indicators. For example, they change litmus from red to blue, and phenolphthalein from colorless to red.

(3) They neutralize aqueous acids, forming salts and water.

$$(M^+) + OH^- + H^+ + (A^-) \rightarrow (M^+) + (A^-) + H_2O$$

(4) They give aqueous solutions which conduct an electric current; they are electrolytes.

It must be remembered that the hydroxide ion is not the only proton acceptor but that other anions such as cyanide, acetate, sulfide, and carbonate have a strong affinity for protons and may be looked upon as strong bases, while chloride, bromide, iodide, nitrate, and sulfate ions are weak bases. In addition, ammonia as a neutral molecule has a weak affinity for protons and reacts with water yielding a low concentration of hydroxide ions.

$$NH_3 + H_2O \rightleftharpoons NH_4^+ + OH^-$$

21.11 Formation of Hydroxide Bases

Hydroxide bases may be prepared by one or more of the following methods:

1. *By the action of alkali or alkaline earth metals with water.*

$$2\ K + 2\ H_2O \rightarrow 2\ K^+ + 2\ OH^- + H_2\uparrow$$
$$2\ Na + 2\ H_2O \rightarrow 2\ Na^+ + 2\ OH^- + H_2\uparrow$$
$$Ca + 2\ H_2O \rightarrow Ca^{++} + 2\ OH^- + H_2\uparrow$$

2. *By the action of water on the oxides of metals.*

$$Na_2O + H_2O \rightarrow 2\ Na^+ + 2\ OH^-$$
$$CaO + H_2O \rightarrow Ca^{++} + 2\ OH^-$$

3. *By the action of salts with other bases by which a precipitate results.*

$$(2\ Na^+) + CO_3^{=} + Ca^{++} + (2\ OH^-) \rightarrow \underline{CaCO_3} + (2\ Na^+) + (2\ OH^-)$$

4. *By the electrolytic method.*

$$(2\ Na^+) + 2\ Cl^- + 2\ H_2O \xrightarrow{\text{electrolysis}} (2\ Na^+) + 2\ OH^- + H_2\uparrow + Cl_2\uparrow$$

5. *By dissolving ammonia in water.*

$$NH_3 + H_2O \rightleftharpoons NH_4^+ + OH^-$$

21.12 Acid-Base Neutralization

When aqueous solutions of hydrochloric acid and sodium hydroxide are mixed, a reaction takes place during which the acidic and basic properties disappear and we say that **neutralization** has occurred. The hydrogen ion, which is responsible for the acidic properties, has reacted with the hydroxide ion, which is responsible for the basic properties, producing neutral water. The sodium and chloride ions have undergone no chemical change and appear in the form of sodium chloride upon evaporation of the resultant solution.

$$H^+ + (Cl^-) + (Na^+) + OH^- \rightarrow H_2O + (Na^+) + (Cl^-)$$

Because the only change that takes place is the reaction of the hydrogen and hydroxide ions, the neutralization may be represented simply as

$$H^+ + OH^- \rightarrow H_2O$$

This equation may be used to represent the reaction of any hydroxide base with any acid. The fact that the heat evolved is the same for any completely ionized acid and metal hydroxide is evidence that acid-base neutralizations involve only the hydrogen ion of the acid and the hydroxide ion of the base, and is independent of the acid anion and the base cation.

$$H^+ + (Cl^-) + (Na^+) + OH^- \rightarrow H_2O + (Na^+) + (Cl^-) + 13{,}700\ \text{cal.}$$
$$H^+ + (NO_3^-) + (Na^+) + OH^- \rightarrow H_2O + (Na^+) + (NO_3^-) + 13{,}700\ \text{cal.}$$
$$H^+ + (Cl^-) + (K^+) + OH^- \rightarrow H_2O + (K^+) + (Cl^-) + 13{,}700\ \text{cal.}$$
$$2\ H^+ + (2\ Cl^-) + (Ca^{++}) + 2\ OH^- \rightarrow 2\ H_2O + (Ca^{++}) + (2\ Cl^-) + 27{,}400\ \text{cal.}$$

In each of these reactions the metal ion and the acid anion appear on both sides of the equation, showing that they do not enter the reaction. Accordingly, these ions may be omitted, and the same equation may be written for all the reactions.

$$H^+ + OH^- \rightarrow H_2O + 13{,}700 \text{ cal.}$$

In the event that either the acid or base is not completely ionized, the neutralization reaction may not go to completion, and the heat of neutralization may be less than 13,700 calories. For example, acetic acid, which is weak, does not completely neutralize an equivalent of sodium hydroxide; the reaction does not proceed to completion.

$$CH_3COOH + (Na^+) + OH^- \rightleftharpoons H_2O + (Na^+) + CH_3COO^- + 13{,}400 \text{ cal.}$$

Acid-base neutralization pertains to the reaction which occurs when equivalent quantities of an acid and a base are mixed. This statement does not imply, however, that the resulting solution is always neutral. The nature of the particular acid and base involved in the reaction determines whether or not the resulting solution is neutral. The following equations illustrate some neutralization reactions when equivalents of acid and base are brought together in aqueous solution.

1. *A strong acid plus a strong base gives a neutral solution.*

$$H^+ + Cl^- + (Na^+) + (OH^-) \rightarrow H_2O + (Na^+) + (Cl^-)$$

Both acid and base are completely ionized, the reaction goes to completion, and only un-ionized water and sodium and chloride ions remain as the final products of the reaction.

2. *A strong acid plus a weak base gives an acidic solution.*

$$H^+ + (Cl^-) + NH_3 \rightleftharpoons NH_4^+ + (Cl^-)$$

Because ammonia is a weak base, all the hydrogen ion is not taken up by the ammonia, the reaction does not go to completion, and there is an excess of hydrogen ions in solution when equilibrium is established.

3. *A weak acid plus a strong base gives a basic solution.*

$$HOAc + (Na^+) + OH^- \rightleftharpoons H_2O + (Na^+) + OAc^-$$

Acetic acid is a weak acid. Most of its molecules are not ionized, and their protons are not transferred to hydroxide ions, so there is an excess of hydroxide ions in solution when equilibrium is established.

21.13 The Lewis Concept of Acids and Bases

G. N. Lewis in 1923 proposed a generalized theory in which acids and bases are not restricted to proton donors and proton acceptors, respectively. According to the **Lewis theory, an acid is any species (molecule or ion) which can accept a pair of electrons; a base is any species (molecule or ion) which can donate a pair of electrons.** An acid-base reaction then consists of the donation of a pair of electrons from the base to the acid with the formation of a coordinate bond between the two.

An example of an acid-base reaction that involves a proton transfer is given by the following equation:

$$H_2O + HCl \rightarrow [H_3O]^+ + [Cl]^-$$

Base Acid

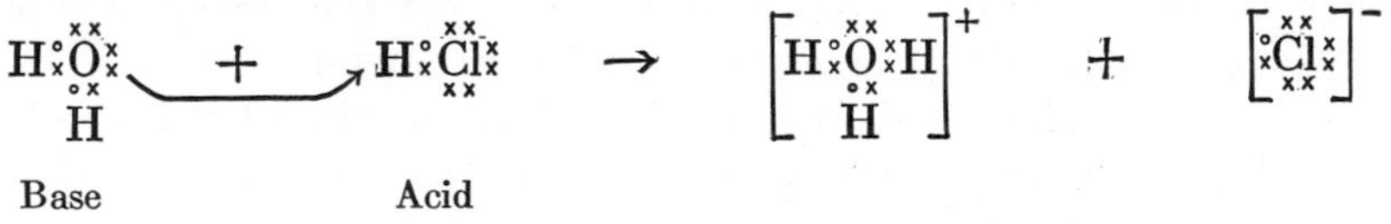

In the above reaction, the oxygen atom of the water molecule donates an electron pair for the formation of a coordinate bond with the hydrogen of the hydrogen chloride molecule, the electron pair acceptor. Hence, water is the Lewis base and hydrogen chloride is the Lewis acid. Note that this acid-base reaction results in the formation of a new coordinate bond and the rupture of an old covalent one.

The following equations serve to show the more general application of the acid-base theory as proposed by Lewis:

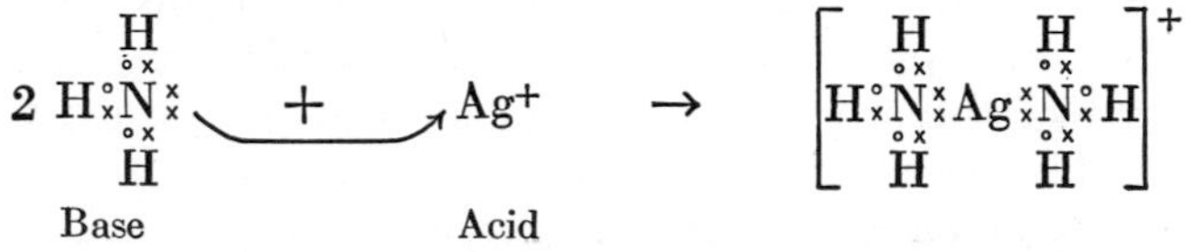

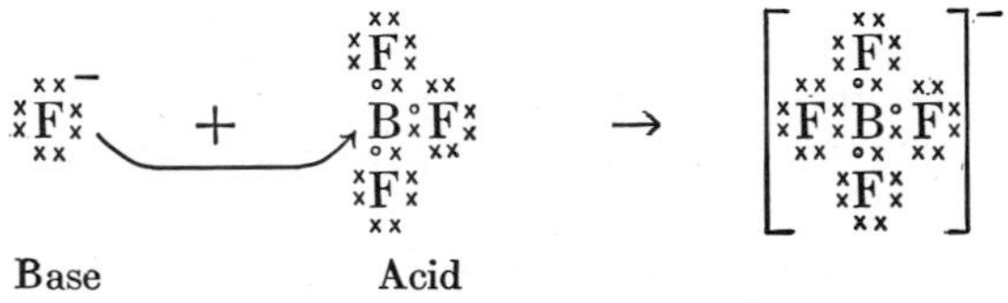

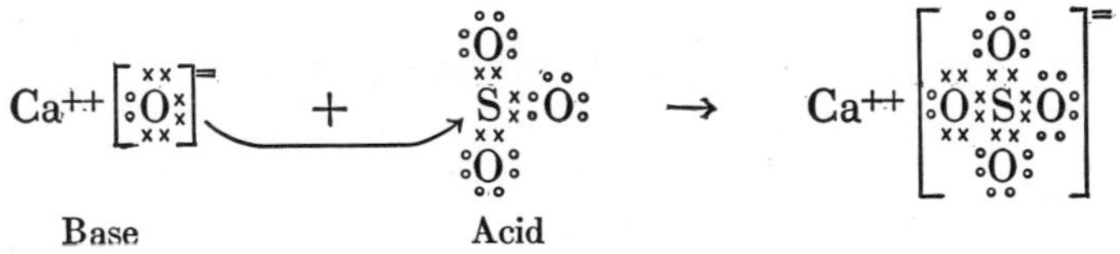

$$2\,NH_3 + Ag^+ \rightarrow [H_3N{:}Ag{:}NH_3]^+$$

Base Acid

$$F^- + BF_3 \rightarrow [BF_4]^-$$

Base Acid

$$Ca^{++}[O]^{=} + SO_3 \rightarrow Ca^{++}[SO_4]^{=}$$

Base Acid

One distinct advantage of the Lewis theory is that it explains the long-recognized basic properties of metal oxides and the acidic properties of nonmetal oxides, as illustrated in the reaction $CaO + SO_3 \rightarrow CaSO_4$, given above.

21.14 Salts

Salts are ionic compounds. Among the positive ions most frequently found in salts are the simple metal ions such as Na^+, K^+, Ca^{++}, and Ba^{++}; solvated metal ions such as $Al(H_2O)_6^{+++}$ and $Ag(NH_3)_2^+$; and solvated hydrogen ions such as NH_4^+ and H_3O^+. The simple negative ions of salts include F^-, Cl^-, Br^-, I^-, $O^=$, $S^=$, P^{-3}, N^{-3}, $C_2^=$, and H^-. Many salts contain polyatomic negative ions such as NO_3^-, $SO_4^=$, PO_4^{-3}, CN^-, and OH^-. Salts are to be regarded simply as compounds made up of positive and negative ions which may be related only indirectly to acid-base reactions. For example, the salt NaCl may be formed by the direct union of sodium metal with elementary chlorine.

Beginners in the study of chemistry quite often get the erroneous impression that all compounds composed of a metal and a nonmetal are salts. However, many such compounds have building units which are not ions but instead may be atoms or molecules; examples are $AlCl_3$, $SnCl_4$, $PbCl_4$, and $GeCl_4$. The bonding is either covalent or polar covalent in such compounds, and the absence of any ions is indicated by the fact that they are nonconductors in the liquid state. In contrast to anhydrous aluminum chloride (a covalent compound), the hexahydrate $Al(H_2O)_6Cl_3$ is a salt composed of $Al(H_2O)_6^{+++}$ and Cl^- ions.

21.15 Normal, Hydrogen, Hydroxy-, and Oxysalts

Salts which contain neither replaceable hydrogen nor hydroxide groups are called **normal salts;** examples are NaCl, K_2SO_4, and $Ca_3(PO_4)_2$.

When only a part of the acidic hydrogen of an acid has been replaced by a metal, the compound is known as a **hydrogen salt;** examples are sodium hydrogen carbonate, $NaHCO_3$ (generally called sodium bicarbonate or baking soda), and sodium dihydrogen phosphate, NaH_2PO_4.

When only a part of the hydroxide groups of an ionic metal hydroxide have been replaced, the compound is known as a **hydroxysalt;** examples are barium hydroxychloride, Ba(OH)Cl, and bismuth dihydroxychloride, $Bi(OH)_2Cl$. Some hydroxysalts readily lose the elements of one or more molecules of water and form **oxysalts.** Thus, bismuth dihydroxychloride breaks down to give the oxychloride, BiOCl, sometimes called bismuthyl chloride.

$$Bi(OH)_2Cl \rightarrow BiOCl + H_2O$$

21.16 Properties of Salts

Salts vary greatly in all of their properties except their ionic character. Salts may taste salty, sour, bitter, astringent, sweet, or be tasteless. Solutions of salts may be acidic, basic, or neutral to acid-base indicators. Fused salts and aqueous solutions of salts conduct an electric current. The reactions of salts are numerous and varied.

21.17 Preparation of Salts

Salts may be prepared by one or more of the following methods:

1. *By the direct union of their elements.*

$$2\ Na + Cl_2 \rightarrow 2\ NaCl$$
$$Fe + S \rightarrow FeS$$

2. *By the reaction of acids with metals, hydroxides of metals, or oxides of metals.*

$$Zn + 2\ H^+ + (SO_4^=) \rightarrow Zn^{++} + (SO_4^=) + H_2 \uparrow$$
$$Ca + 2\ H^+ + (2\ Cl^-) \rightarrow Ca^{++} + (2\ Cl^-) + H_2 \uparrow$$
$$Fe(OH)_3 + 3\ H^+ + (3\ Cl^-) \rightarrow Fe^{+++} + (3\ Cl^-) + 3\ H_2O$$
$$CuO + 2\ H^+ + (SO_4^=) \rightarrow Cu^{++} + (SO_4^=) + H_2O$$

The solid salts, often in the hydrated form, may be obtained by evaporating the solutions to dryness.

3. *By the reaction of acid anhydrides with basic anhydrides.*

$$BaO + SO_3 \rightarrow BaSO_4$$
$$CaO + CO_2 \rightarrow CaCO_3$$

4. *By the reaction of acids with salts.*

$$BaCO_3 + 2\ H^+ + (2\ Cl^-) \rightarrow Ba^{++} + (2\ Cl^-) + H_2O + CO_2 \uparrow$$
$$Ba^{++} + (2\ Cl^-) + (2\ H^+) + SO_4^= \rightarrow \underline{BaSO_4} + (2\ H^+) + (2\ Cl^-)$$

5. *By the reaction of salts with other salts.*

$$Ag^+ + (NO_3^-) + (Na^+) + Cl^- \rightarrow \underline{AgCl} + (Na^+) + (NO_3^-)$$
$$Zn^{++} + (2\ Cl^-) + (2\ Na^+) + S^= \rightarrow \underline{ZnS} + (2\ Na^+) + (2\ Cl^-)$$

QUESTIONS

1. Define the terms "acid" and "base" according to the Arrhenius concept; the protonic concept.

2. Write equations for the reaction of the following acids with water: HCl, HNO_3, $HClO_4$, and NH_4^+. What is the role played by water in these acid-base reactions?

3. Show by suitable equations that the following species are bases: OH^-, NH_3, Cl^-, NO_3^-, and H_2O.

4. What is the conjugate base of each of the following acids: NH_4^+, HCl, HNO_3, $HClO_4$, HOAc, and HCN?

5. Relate the extent of ionization of an acid in aqueous solution to the strength of the acid.

6. List five strong acids and their conjugate weak bases.

7. List five weak acids and their conjugate strong bases.

8. What are amphiprotic substances? Illustrate with suitable equations.

9. Write equations to show the stepwise ionization of the following polyprotic acids: H_2S, H_2CO_3, and H_3PO_4.

10. Write equations to illustrate three typical and characteristic reactions of aqueous acids.

11. Contrast the action of water upon oxides of metals with that of water upon oxides of nonmetals.

12. Distinguish between alkali metal hydroxide bases and alkaline earth metal hydroxide bases.

13. Give four methods of preparing hydroxide bases.

14. Write the equation for the essential reaction between aqueous solutions of acids and bases.

15. Define acid-base neutralization. Does this definition imply that the resulting solution is always neutral?

16. What is the nature of the resulting solution (acidic, basic, or neutral) when equivalent quantities of the following acids and bases are brought together: HNO_3 and KOH; HCl and NH_3; HNO_2 and NaOH; and HOAc and NH_3?

17. Define: a Lewis acid; a Lewis base; acid-base reaction according to the Lewis theory.

18. What is meant by the leveling effect of water on strong acids and strong bases? How can the relative strengths of strong acids be measured?

19. Define the term "salt" and give examples of normal, hydrogen, hydroxy-, and oxysalts.

20. Write equations for four methods of preparing calcium fluoride, CaF_2.

REFERENCES

"Contemporary Acid-Base Theory," W. F. Luder, *J. Chem. Educ.*, **25** (10) 555 (1948).

The Electronic Theory of Acids and Bases, W. F. Luder and S. Zuffanti, John Wiley and Sons, Inc., New York (1946).

Acids, Bases, and the Chemistry of the Covalent Bond, C. A. VanderWerf, Reinhold Publ. Corp., New York (1961).

CHAPTER TWENTY-TWO

The Sulfur Family

The elements sulfur, selenium, tellurium, and polonium follow oxygen in Group VIA of the Periodic Table. These elements comprise what is known as the **sulfur family.** Oxygen, the first member of this periodic group, exhibits properties which set it apart from the other elements of the sulfur family, just as fluorine, the first member of the halogen family, is different in many respects from the other members of its group. Polonium is formed only as a product of radioactive change; it is, itself, highly radioactive. Some properties are given for the elements of the sulfur family, excluding polonium, in Table 22·1. Oxygen is included for the sake of comparison.

TABLE 22·1 Some Properties of the Sulfur Family

	Oxygen	*Sulfur*	*Selenium*	*Tellurium*
Atomic number	8	16	34	52
Atomic weight	15.9994	32.064	78.96	127.60
Electronic structure	2,6	2,8,6	2,8,18,6	2,8,18,18,6
Radius of divalent anion, Å	1.40	1.84	1.98	2.21
Radius of covalent atom, Å	0.60	1.06	1.16	1.44
Physical state	Gas	Solid	Solid	Solid
Color	Colorless	Yellow	Red or gray	Silvery
Melting point, °C	−218.4	112.8, 119.25	217 (gray)	450
Boiling point, °C	−183	444.6	688	1390
Electronegativity	3.5	2.5	2.4	2.1
Heat of formation of hydride (cal./mole)	−57,798	−4,815	+20,500	+36,900
Oxidation states	−2, −1	−2, −1, +2, +4, +6	−2, +4, +6	−2, +4, +6

Each element in this periodic group has six valence electrons. Oxygen, more electronegative than any other element except fluorine, usually exhibits an oxidation state of −2 in its compounds, but the larger and therefore the less electronegative elements of the sulfur family exhibit both negative and positive oxidation states. As the electronegativity decreases with increasing atomic size, the strengths of the elements as oxidizing agents decreases, a property which is reflected very strikingly in the heats of formation of their respective hydrides (Table 22·1).

As would be expected from the change in electronegativity, metallic character within the group increases with increasing atomic size. Oxygen is a typical nonmetal, whereas metallic character begins to become evident with selenium, and polonium is a typical metal.

22.1 Occurrence

1. *Sulfur.* **Sulfur** has been known from very early times simply because it occurs free in nature as a solid. It is referred to in the Bible as brimstone, which means "burning stone." Until recent years about half the world's supply of industrial sulfur was obtained from volcanic regions in Italy and Japan. Since about 1900, Texas and Louisiana have supplied most of the sulfur used in the Americas. Extensive deposits of sulfur have recently been found and developed in Mexico. Minerals containing sulfur in the combined form are numerous and widely distributed and many of the metallic sulfides serve as valuable sources of the element. Sulfides of iron, zinc, lead, and copper and sulfates of calcium, barium, copper, and magnesium are common and abundant. Sulfur is also a constituent of proteins and is therefore found in animal and vegetable matter.

2. *Selenium.* **Selenium** was discovered by Berzelius in 1817 in the red slime he had collected at the bottom of a lead chamber of a sulfuric acid plant in Sweden. The name of the element comes from the Greek and means "moon." It is found in nature associated with sulfur in both the free and the combined states. A usual commercial source of the element is the flue dust of pyrite (FeS_2) burners.

3. *Tellurium.* **Tellurium** was discovered by von Reichenstein in 1782. He extracted this metallic-appearing element from a gold ore and at first thought it to be antimony. The name tellurium means "the earth." It occurs in nature as the free element and in the combined state in small amounts. It is frequently found combined with gold, lead, and silver as tellurides. It is usually obtained from the anode mud (Section 20.7) when copper and lead are purified electrolytically.

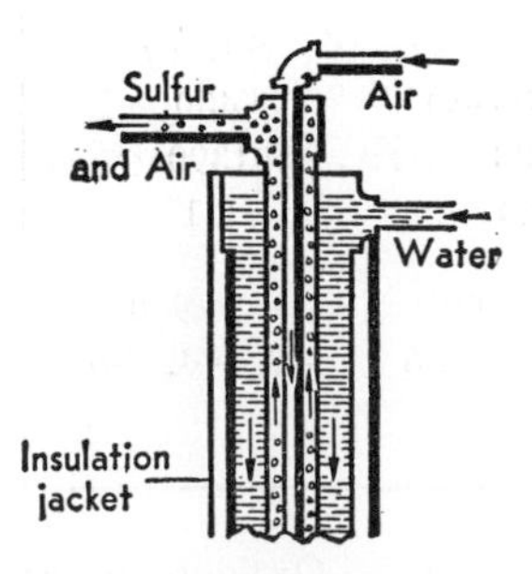

Fig. 22–1 Diagram showing Frasch method of mining sulfur.

22.2 Extraction of Sulfur

Sulfur is obtained by the **Frasch process** from the tremendous underground deposits in Texas and Louisiana (Fig. 22–1). Superheated water (170° and 100 pounds per square inch pressure) is forced down the next to the outermost of three concentric pipes to the deposit of sulfur located several hundred feet below the surface. The hot water melts the sulfur, and then compressed air is forced down the innermost pipe. The liquid sulfur mixed with air forms an emulsion that is less dense than water, and this mixture readily flows up through the third pipe. The emulsified sulfur is conveyed to large settling vats where it solidifies upon cooling (Fig. 22–2). Sulfur produced by this method is remarkably pure, 99.5 to 99.9 per cent, and for most of its uses requires no purification.

Fig. 22–2 Stockpile of sulfur ready for shipment. Huge vats a quarter of a mile long hold over 2,000,000 tons. The sulfur is broken up by blasting and loaded into cars by cranes. *Texas Gulf Sulfur Co.*

Recently, strip mining methods have been started in the mining of large sulfur deposits in Poland near the surface of the ground.

22.3 Allotropic Modifications

All members of the sulfur family exist in allotropic forms (Section 5.14).

1. *Sulfur.* Native sulfur is a yellow solid which forms crystals that belong to the orthorhombic system; it is usually called **rhombic sulfur** (Fig. 22–3). This form of sulfur is insoluble in water, but soluble in carbon disulfide (CS_2), giving solutions from which well-formed crystals separate when it is allowed to evaporate slowly. When heated to 112.8°, crystals of rhombic sulfur melt and form a straw-

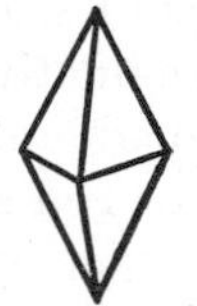

Fig. 22–3 Rhombic crystals of yellow sulfur.

colored liquid, known as **lambda-sulfur.** When this liquid crystallizes, long, transparent needles of **monoclinic sulfur** are formed (Fig. 22-4). This crystalline modification of sulfur, the stable form of sulfur above 96°, melts at 119.25° and is soluble in carbon disulfide. Upon standing at room temperature, it gradually changes to the rhombic form. Rhombic sulfur, monoclinic sulfur, and the straw-colored liquid all contain S_8 molecules in which the atoms form an eight-membered, puckered ring (Fig. 22–5). Each atom of sulfur is linked to each of its two neighbors in the ring by single electron-pair bonds; each atom thus has a completed octet of electrons.

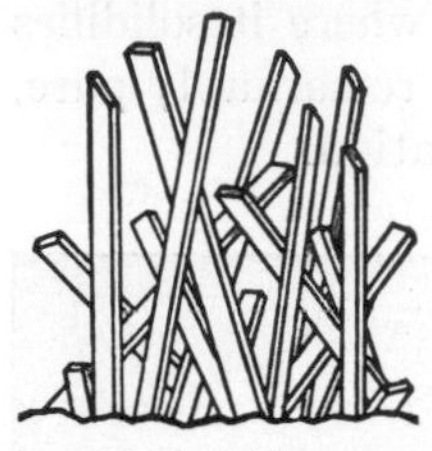

Fig. 22–4 Monoclinic sulfur.

The straw-colored liquid form of sulfur is quite mobile, i.e., its viscosity is low, because its S_8 molecules are essentially spherical in shape and offer relatively little resistance to motion past one another. As the temperature is raised, the S_8 rings of the yellow mobile sulfur rupture; long chains of sulfur atoms (Fig. 22–5) are formed and become entangled with one another, causing an increase in the viscosity of the liquid. The liquid gradually darkens in color and becomes so viscous that finally (at about 230°) it will not pour from its container. The unpaired electrons at the ends of the chains of sulfur atoms are responsible for the dark red color. This liquid form of the element is known as **mu-sulfur.** When it is cooled rapidly, a rubberlike amorphous mass, insoluble in carbon disulfide, results. This form of the element is known as **plastic sulfur,** and it is a supercooled liquid. Upon standing for some time at room temperature, plastic sulfur, like all of the other forms, changes to the rhombic form.

Fig. 22–5 Perspective drawings of an S_8 molecule (left) and a sulfur chain (right).

Sulfur boils at 444.6° and forms a vapor consisting of S_2, S_6, and S_8 molecules; at about 1000° the vapor density corresponds to the formula S_2.

2. *Selenium.* Several allotropic forms of selenium are known. **Metallic** or **gray selenium** belongs to the hexagonal crystal system. It contains parallel "zigzag" chains of selenium atoms. It is the stable form at room temperature. Its electrical conductivity is greatly increased by exposure to light, a property which is used to advantage in certain photoelectric cells.

Monoclinic or **red selenium** exists in two forms, one of which consists of Se_8 molecules of the same puckered ring type characteristic of crystalline sulfur. Like sulfur, the red form of selenium is soluble in carbon disulfide. Black and red forms of amorphous selenium are also known.

3. *Tellurium.* Elementary tellurium commonly exists as a brittle, silvery-white, metallic solid. Its crystals belong to the hexagonal-rhombohedral system. An amorphous variety is also known.

22.4 Chemical Properties

Because of the change from typical nonmetallic character with oxygen to essentially metallic character with tellurium, the chemical properties of the sulfur family are not readily treated systematically. The small size of the oxygen atom is responsible in part for its great reactivity as an oxidizing agent, and chemically speaking it is somewhat more like the halogens than like sulfur, selenium, and tellurium.

1. *Sulfur.* Elementary sulfur is quite reactive, even at ordinary temperatures, although generally less so than oxygen. Many of the metals will react with solid sulfur upon coming in contact with it at room temperature. Mercury has been shown to combine with sulfur at temperatures as low as −180°. Only the rare gases and the elements iodine, nitrogen, tellurium, gold, platinum, and palladium do not combine directly with elementary sulfur.

Elementary sulfur acts as an oxidizing agent toward hydrogen, forming **hydrogen sulfide,** H_2S; toward carbon at elevated temperatures, forming **carbon disulfide,** CS_2; and toward iron when heated, forming **iron (II) sulfide.**

$$H_2 + S \rightarrow H_2S$$
$$C + 2\,S \rightarrow CS_2$$
$$Fe + S \rightarrow FeS$$

Binary compounds in which sulfur is combined with an element more electropositive than itself are called **sulfides.** The sulfur has an oxidation state of −2 in such compounds. Sulfides are analogous to the corresponding oxides, but the properties of these two varieties of compounds are often quite different.

Sulfur acts as a reducing agent toward the nonmetals such as oxygen and the halogens, which are more electronegative than sulfur. When sulfur is ignited in the air, it burns with a blue flame, forming **sulfur dioxide** and a little **sulfur trioxide.**

$$S + O_2 \rightarrow SO_2$$
$$2\,SO_2 + O_2 \rightarrow 2\,SO_3$$

As we shall see in the next chapter, the oxidation of sulfur is important in the production of **sulfurous acid,** H_2SO_3, and **sulfuric acid,** H_2SO_4. Sulfur in moist air is slowly oxidized to sulfuric acid.

$$2\,S + 2\,H_2O + 3\,O_2 \rightarrow 4\,H^+ + 2\,SO_4^{=}$$

Sulfur reduces chlorine in a series of reactions, the products of which depend upon the temperature and relative quantities of the reactants.

$2\,S + Cl_2 \rightarrow S_2Cl_2$, "sulfur monochloride" (a misnomer)
$S_2Cl_2 + Cl_2 \rightleftharpoons 2\,SCl_2$, sulfur dichloride
$SCl_2 + Cl_2 \rightleftharpoons SCl_4$, sulfur tetrachloride

Both S_2Cl_2 and SCl_2 are important in the production of rubber. Sulfur monochloride is an excellent solvent for sulfur, iodine, certain metallic halides, and many organic compounds. The valence electronic structure of S_2Cl_2 is

```
  ××  ×× ××  ××
 ×Cl×S×S×Cl×
 ×  ×  ×  ×  ×
  ××  ×× ××  ××
```

Only one bromide of sulfur is known; it is the "monobromide," S_2Br_2, a garnet-red liquid. Sulfur forms a series of fluorides which includes the hexafluoride, SF_6, a very stable gaseous compound (Section 17.12). In SF_6, the fluorine atoms are arranged around the sulfur atom at the corners of a regular octahedron (Fig. 22–6), and the bonding is highly covalent in character. There are twelve bonding electrons in the valence shell of sulfur in SF_6 rather than the usual eight. The existence of a shell of twelve electrons is not unusual and is shown also in such other materials as PF_6^- and perhaps XeF_4. Sulfur attains its maximum oxidation state of +6 only with fluorine in its binary compounds with the halogens because of the small size of the fluorine atom compared to that of the atoms of the other halogens.

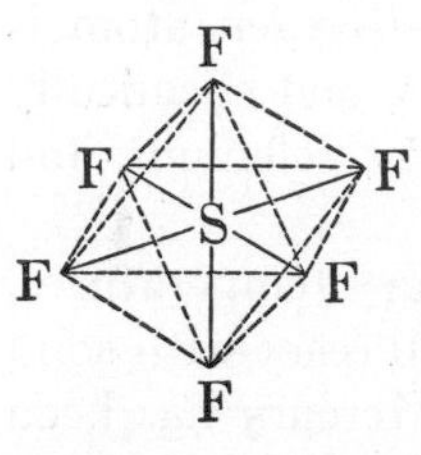

Fig. 22–6 The octahedral configuration of SF_6.

Sulfur reduces strong oxidizing agents such as concentrated nitric acid and hot, concentrated sulfuric acid. The equations are

$$S + 6\,H^+ + 6\,NO_3^- \rightarrow 2\,H^+ + \underset{\text{Sulfuric acid}}{SO_4^=} + 2\,H_2O + 6\,NO_2\uparrow$$

$$S + 2\,H_2SO_4 \rightarrow 3\,SO_2\uparrow + 2\,H_2O$$

2. *Selenium.* Selenium is both a weaker oxidizing agent and weaker reducing agent than sulfur. Elementary selenium burns in oxygen to form the **dioxide,** SeO_2, a solid. **Selenium monochloride,** Se_2Cl_2, and the **dichloride,** $SeCl_2$, are known. Selenides of several metals have been prepared by the direct union of the elements. Hydrogen selenide is discussed in a later section, and the oxides and oxyacids of selenium are considered in the next chapter. **Selenium compounds are extremely poisonous.**

3. *Tellurium.* The chemical properties of tellurium are, in general, similar to those of sulfur and selenium, the differences being those which would be predicted from its position in the Periodic Table.

22.5 Uses of the Elements of the Sulfur Family

1. *Sulfur.* In recent years, approximately 7 million tons of sulfur have been used each year in the chemical industries. The largest single use is in the production of tremendous quantities of sulfuric acid, the most important acid of commerce. Sulfur is burned to the dioxide, which is used in bleaching straw and wool. Sulfur is used in producing carbon disulfide, a valuable organic solvent. Elementary sulfur is used in the vulcanization of rubber and in the production of lime-sulfur

sprays for controlling plant diseases. Much sulfur is also used in producing gunpowder, sulfites, thiosulfates, fertilizers, and medicinals.

2. *Selenium.* Selenium and its compounds have a number of important uses. Its use in the "electric eye" has already been mentioned. The addition of a little selenium to ordinary glass offsets the green color which such glass usually has due to the presence of iron (II) silicate. If selenium is added in larger amounts, it colors the glass red; glass so colored is widely used in making lights for danger signals, and in coloring glazes and enamels for ceramics. Sodium selenide is used as the source of the element when it is to be incorporated in glass because selenium is volatile at the temperatures employed. In the electronics industries, selenium of high purity is used as an efficient rectifier for alternating current. Selenium is also used in the production of certain stainless steels and special copper alloys.

3. *Tellurium.* This element is used to some extent in coloring glass blue, brown, or red. It is used to increase the hardness of lead in battery plates and type metal. Traces of tellurium in stainless steel increase its machinability, and give cast iron a hard, wear-resistant surface.

THE HYDRIDES OF THE SULFUR FAMILY

Each member of Group VIA of the Periodic Table forms a hydride. The strength of these hydrides as acids and their reducing powers increase, whereas their thermal stabilities decrease in the order H_2O, H_2S, H_2Se, H_2Te, H_2Po.

22.6 Preparation of the Hydrides

Hydrogen sulfide occurs dissolved in the water of sulfur springs and in the gases issuing from volcanoes. It is a product of the decay of animal matter in the absence of air. The offensive odor of spoiled eggs is responsible for the name "rotten-egg gas" that is sometimes applied to hydrogen sulfide.

Large quantities of hydrogen sulfide are produced at petroleum refineries. Controlled combustion of hydrogen sulfide produces sulfur and water vapor. In this way, approximately one thousand tons of sulfur are recovered at oil refineries each day. This process resulted from attempts to decrease air pollution in such industrial areas as that at Los Angeles, California. The production of hydrogen sulfide by the direct union of its elements is unsatisfactory because the reaction is reversible and, as it is usually carried out not more than two per cent of the elements remain combined.

$$H_2 + S \rightleftharpoons H_2S + 4{,}815 \text{ cal.}$$

Hydrogen sulfide is usually prepared by bringing together iron (II) sulfide and a dilute acid.

$$FeS + 2\,H^+ \rightarrow Fe^{++} + H_2S \uparrow$$

Many other sulfides may be substituted for FeS in the above reaction. When an aqueous solution of hydrogen sulfide is desired, it may be prepared conveniently by the hydrolysis of the organic sulfur-containing compound, **thioacetamide,** CH_3CSNH_2. The equation for the hydrolysis is

$$CH_3CSNH_2 + 2\ H_2O \rightarrow CH_3COO^- + NH_4^+ + H_2S \uparrow$$

Heating accelerates the hydrolysis considerably.

Hydrogen selenide, H_2Se, can be formed by heating a mixture of hydrogen and selenium in a sealed tube, or by treating a metallic selenide with a dilute acid.

$$H_2 + Se \rightleftharpoons H_2Se$$

$$FeSe + 2\ H^+ \rightarrow Fe^{++} + H_2Se \uparrow$$

Hydrogen telluride can be prepared by the action of dilute acids on certain metallic tellurides.

22.7 Physical Properties of the Hydrides

The hydrides of sulfur, selenium, tellurium, and polonium are all colorless gases with offensive odors. They are toxic and great care must be exercised in handling them. Hydrogen sulfide is nearly as toxic as hydrogen cyanide (prussic acid), which is used in lethal chambers in some states for capital punishment. Small amounts of H_2S gas in the air cause headaches while larger amounts cause paralysis in the nerve centers of the heart and lungs which results in fainting and death. Hydrogen selenide is still more toxic than hydrogen sulfide.

Liquid hydrogen sulfide freezes at $-82.9°$ and boils at $-61.8°$. The gas is slightly more dense than air and its molar solubility in water is 0.1 at 18°.

The boiling points of H_2S ($-61.8°$) and H_2Se ($-42°$) are much lower than that of water (100°), indicating that the effect of molecular association through hydrogen bonding decreases greatly in the series H_2O, H_2S, H_2Se. Of the three hydrides, hydrogen bonding is pronounced only in the case of water with its highly electronegative oxygen atom.

22.8 Chemical Properties of the Hydrides

The hydrides of the elements of the sulfur family decompose into their constituent elements when heated. Hydrogen sulfide burns in air forming water and sulfur dioxide. The equation for the combustion of hydrogen sulfide is

$$2\ H_2S + 3\ O_2 \rightarrow 2\ H_2O + 2\ SO_2$$

When hydrogen sulfide is ignited in a limited supply of air or when a burning jet of the gas is impinged upon a cold surface, free sulfur is deposited.

$$2\ H_2S + O_2 \rightarrow 2\ H_2O + 2\ S$$

Hydrogen selenide and hydrogen telluride readily react with air but yield free selenium and tellurium rather than the oxides.

Most of the more reactive metals will displace hydrogen from hydrogen sulfide. Thus, lead sulfide is formed by the action of hydrogen sulfide upon metallic lead, according to the equation

$$Pb + H_2S \rightarrow PbS + H_2$$

Hydrogen sulfide will cause metallic silver to tarnish, black silver sulfide being formed. Hence, silver tableware tarnishes when it is used with eggs and other foods containing certain sulfur compounds.

$$4\ Ag + 2\ H_2S + O_2 \rightarrow 2\ Ag_2S + 2\ H_2O$$

The sulfur in hydrogen sulfide readily gives up electrons; thus hydrogen sulfide is an active reducing agent. In acidic solutions, it reduces Fe^{+++} to Fe^{++}, Br_2 to Br^-, MnO_4^- to Mn^{++}, $Cr_2O_7^=$ to Cr^{+++}, and HNO_3 to NO_2. The sulfur of the H_2S is usually oxidized to elementary sulfur, unless a large excess of the oxidizing agent is present, in which case the sulfide may be oxidized to SO_2 or $SO_4^=$. In the presence of moisture, hydrogen sulfide reduces sulfur dioxide to sulfur.

$$2\ H_2S + SO_2 \rightarrow 2\ H_2O + 3\ S$$

The deposits of sulfur in volcanic regions may be the result of this reaction because both H_2S and SO_2 are constituents of volcanic gases.

22.9 The Hydrides in Aqueous Solution

Aqueous solutions of the hydrides of the sulfur family are known as **hydrosulfuric acid, hydroselenic acid,** and **hydrotelluric acid.** These acids are weak and diprotic, i.e., they ionize in two stages. Hydrogen sulfide, for example, yields hydrosulfide ions, HS^-, in the first stage and sulfide ions, $S^=$, in the second.

$$H_2S \rightleftharpoons H^+ + HS^-$$
$$HS^- \rightleftharpoons H^+ + S^=$$

When a solution of hydrogen sulfide is exposed to the air for a length of time sulfur precipitates as the result of oxidation of the sulfide ion.

$$4\ H^+ + 2\ S^= + O_2 \rightarrow 2\ H_2O + 2\ \underline{S}$$

Hydrogen selenide is about 1000 times as strong an acid as hydrogen sulfide. The trend is in the same direction as noted for the hydrogen halides (Section 21.7), i.e., acidic strength increases with increasing size of the negative atom.

22.10 Sulfides, Selenides, and Tellurides

Because the hydroacids of sulfur, selenium, and tellurium are diprotic, two series of salts are possible. For example, both **normal sulfides** such as Na_2S, and **hydrosulfides** such as NaHS, are known.

Sodium hydrosulfide may be made by passing hydrogen sulfide into a solution of sodium hydroxide.

$$H_2S + (Na^+) + OH^- \rightleftharpoons (Na^+) + (HS^-) + H_2O$$

By adding an equivalent amount of sodium hydroxide to a solution of sodium hydrosulfide, normal **sodium sulfide,** Na_2S, is formed.

$$(Na^+) + OH^- + (Na^+) + HS^- \rightleftharpoons (2\ Na^+) + S^= + H_2O$$

Many normal metal sulfides are prepared by the direct union of sulfur with the metal; the following equations serve to illustrate this method:

$$Fe + S \rightarrow FeS$$
$$2\ Al + 3\ S \rightarrow Al_2S_3$$

Hydrogen sulfide is important in analytical work because the metal sulfides show a wide variation in solubility. Because of this wide variation, it is possible to divide the metallic ions into analytical groups, the members of which form sulfides of similar solubilities. For example, certain metal sulfides such as CuS, PbS, and CdS are insoluble in dilute, nonoxidizing acids. Other metal sulfides such as FeS, MnS, and ZnS are insoluble in water but soluble in dilute acids. Still other metal sulfides are soluble in water; these include BaS, CaS, Na_2S, and K_2S. By separating the metallic ions into groups by making use of the similarities and differences in the solubilities of their sulfides, the problems of the analytical chemistry of the metallic ions are greatly simplified.

The selenides and tellurides of a number of metals are also known.

Because of the strong tendency of the sulfide ion and the hydrosulfide ion to act as proton acceptors, as indicated by the weakness of hydrogen sulfide as an acid, aqueous solutions of soluble sulfides and hydrosulfides are basic.

$$S^{=} + H_2O \rightleftharpoons HS^- + OH^-$$
$$HS^- + H_2O \rightleftharpoons H_2S + OH^-$$

Because H_2Se and H_2Te are stronger acids than H_2S, their soluble normal and hydrogen salts are less extensively hydrolyzed than those of hydrogen sulfide.

The presence of sulfide or hydrosulfide ions in solution may be detected by the following test: The solution is acidified with acetic acid and then a piece of filter paper saturated with lead acetate is held above it. When the solution is warmed, it gives off hydrogen sulfide, which reacts with the lead acetate forming black lead sulfide. The equations are

$$S^{=} + 2\ CH_3COOH \rightarrow H_2S\uparrow + CH_3COO^-$$
$$Pb^{++} + H_2S \rightarrow \underline{PbS} + 2\ H^+$$

22.11 Polysulfides, Polyselenides, and Polytellurides

When elementary sulfur is added to a solution of a soluble metal sulfide, it dissolves by forming **polysulfides.** The elementary sulfur combines with the sulfide ion and forms complex polysulfide ions which may be formulated as $S_n^{=}$, in which n = 2 to 5. **Disulfide ions,** $S_2^{=}$, are analogous to peroxide ions in structure (Section 10.15). The sulfur atoms of these complex ions are linked together through shared electron pairs. The valence electronic structures of $S_2^{=}$ and $S_5^{=}$ and the structural formula of H_2S_5 are given below.

$$\left[\,\overset{\times\times\ \times\times}{\underset{\times\times\ \times\times}{{}^{\times}_{\times}S{}^{\times}_{\times}S{}^{\times}_{\times}}}\,\right]^{=} \qquad \left[\,\overset{\times\times\ \times\times\ \times\times\ \times\times\ \times\times}{\underset{\times\times\ \times\times\ \times\times\ \times\times\ \times\times}{{}^{\times}_{\times}S{}^{\times}_{\times}S{}^{\times}_{\times}S{}^{\times}_{\times}S{}^{\times}_{\times}S{}^{\times}_{\times}}}\,\right]^{=} \qquad H{-}S{-}S{-}S{-}S{-}S{-}H$$

The polysulfide ions, like the peroxide ion, are oxidizing agents. For example, tin (II) sulfide is oxidized to the thiostannate ion by the disulfide ion.

$$SnS + S_2^{=} \rightarrow SnS_3^{=}$$

When solutions containing polysulfide ions are acidified, free sulfur in a white, very finely divided form (milk of sulfur) and hydrogen sulfide are produced.

$$S_2^{=} + 2\ H^+ \rightarrow H_2S \uparrow + \underline{S}$$

Although both elementary selenium and tellurium dissolve in selenide and telluride solutions, respectively, no selenium or tellurium analogues of hydrogen peroxide are known.

QUESTIONS

1. List the elements in Group VIA of the Periodic Table in order of increasing (a) atomic number, (b) melting point, (c) electronegativity, (d) strength as oxidizing agents, and (e) heat of hydride formation.
2. Give two properties of oxygen which set it apart from the other members of Group VIA.
3. Explain, with the aid of a diagram, the Frasch process for extracting sulfur from underground deposits of the element.
4. What are the allotropic forms of solid sulfur and how may they be produced?
5. What is the molecular structure of sulfur in the liquid, solid, and gaseous states?
6. Account for the viscosity and color of mu-sulfur.
7. Write equations for the reaction of sulfur with H_2, C, Fe, O_2, Cl_2, and HNO_3.
8. How may hydrogen sulfide be prepared conveniently in the laboratory?
9. Account for the fact that hydrogen sulfide is a gas at ordinary temperatures whereas water, which has a smaller formula weight, is a liquid.
10. Why are solutions of sulfides and hydrosulfides alkaline? Write equations.
11. Write equations for the reaction of hydrogen sulfide with acidic solutions containing Fe^{+++}, MnO_4^-, Br_2, and $Cr_2O_7^{=}$.
12. What are the principal commercial uses of sulfur? of selenium? of tellurium?
13. What property of selenium makes it useful in photoelectric cells?
14. How is hydrogen sulfide used in analytical chemistry?

PROBLEMS

1. Calculate the volume of hydrogen sulfide at S.T.P. obtainable from 150 g. of 94.8 per cent pure iron (II) sulfide (FeS) by acidification with hydrochloric acid.
Ans. 36.3 l.
2. What volume of sulfur dioxide (S.T.P.) would be formed by the complete combustion of 75.0 g. of hydrogen sulfide? What weight of steam would be formed?
Ans. 49.3 l.; 39.6 g.

3. What would be the density of sulfur vapor in grams per liter (measured at S.T.P.) if 65.0 per cent of the molecules were S_8 and 35.0 per cent were S_2?

Ans. *8.44 g./l.*

4. Calculate the percentage of sulfur in the compounds FeS, Al_2S_3, $CaSO_4$, and H_2S_2. *Ans.* *36.5%; 64.0%; 23.6%; 97.0%*

REFERENCES

"Plastic and Allotropic Forms of Sulfur," H. F. Schaefer and G. D. Palmer, *J. Chem. Educ.*, **17** (10) 473 (1940).

Noxious Gases (including Hydrogen Sulfide), (American Chemical Society Monograph No. 35), Y. Henderson and H. W. Haggard, Reinhold Publ. Corp., New York (1943).

"Sulfur," M. E. Weeks, *Discovery of the Elements*, Sixth Edition, Publ. by the Journal of Chemical Education, Easton, Pa., 1956; pp. 52–58.

"Tellurium and Selenium," M. E. Weeks, *Discovery of the Elements*, Sixth Edition, Publ. by the Journal of Chemical Education, Easton, Pa., 1956; Chapter 11.

"Tellurium," A. Nussbaum, *American Scientist*, **50,** 312 (1962).

CHAPTER TWENTY-THREE

Oxygen Compounds of the Sulfur Family

Sulfur, selenium, and tellurium form a variety of oxides and oxyacids. Such compounds are especially numerous in the case of sulfur.

A list of the oxides of sulfur, selenium, and tellurium is given in Table 23·1.

TABLE 23·1 Oxides of the Sulfur Family

Sulfur	*Selenium*	*Tellurium*	*Name*
SO	...	TeO	monoxide
S_2O_3	...	...	sesquioxide
SO_2	SeO_2	TeO_2	dioxide
SO_3	SeO_3	TeO_3	trioxide
S_2O_7	...	...	heptoxide
SO_4(?)	...	...	tetroxide

We shall consider only the more important of these oxides, namely the dioxides and trioxides, and their corresponding acids and other derivatives.

23.1 Sulfur Dioxide

1. *Physical properties.* The odor of burning sulfur is that of **sulfur dioxide,** SO_2. It is a colorless gas, 2.26 times as heavy as air, and very soluble in water (80 volumes of gas to 1 volume of water at S.T.P.). It is readily condensed to the liquid which boils at $-10°$, and freezes to a white solid which melts at $-75.5°$. Liquid sulfur dioxide is stored and shipped in steel cylinders and tank cars. However, it cannot be shipped in this way unless it is quite dry because moisture, even in trace amounts, causes it to corrode the steel of its container.

2. *Occurrence and preparation.* Sulfur dioxide occurs in volcanic gases, and in the atmosphere near industries where it is formed by the combustion of coal containing sulfur compounds.

For commercial purposes, sulfur dioxide is produced by burning free sulfur and by roasting (heating in air) certain sulfide ores, such as ZnS, FeS_2, Cu_2S. The roasting of sulfide ores to oxidize the sulfur to the dioxide and to form the oxide of the metal is the first step in the metallurgy of these metals (Section 33.5). The quantity of sulfur involved in such operations exceeds the total annual production from Texas and Louisiana.

Sulfur dioxide may be prepared conveniently in the laboratory by the action of sulfuric acid upon either sodium sulfite or sodium hydrogen sulfite. The sulfuric acid furnishes the hydrogen ions for the reactions. Sulfurous acid is first formed, but it then decomposes into sulfur dioxide and water.

$$2\,H^+ + SO_3^{=} \rightarrow H_2SO_3 \rightarrow H_2O + SO_2\uparrow$$
$$H^+ + HSO_3^- \rightarrow H_2SO_3 \rightarrow H_2O + SO_2\uparrow$$

Many reducing agents react with hot concentrated sulfuric acid with the formation of sulfur dioxide. Three examples are given below:

$$Cu + 2\,H_2SO_4 \rightarrow CuSO_4 + SO_2\uparrow + 2\,H_2O$$
$$C + 2\,H_2SO_4 \rightarrow CO_2\uparrow + 2\,SO_2\uparrow + 2\,H_2O$$
$$S + 2\,H_2SO_4 \rightarrow 3\,SO_2\uparrow + 2\,H_2O$$

3. *The structure of the sulfur dioxide molecule and resonance.* The valence electronic formula of the sulfur dioxide molecule may be written in two ways:

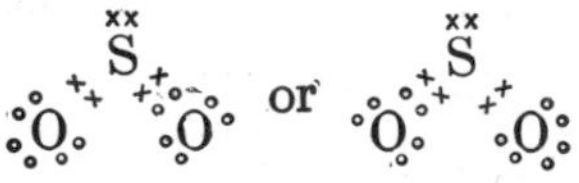

S / O O (A) or S / O O (B)

A B

In any one molecule of sulfur dioxide there are two possible positions for the double bond, as shown in structures A and B above. The two structures are equivalent. When two (or more) reasonable electronic structures can be written for a compound, we say that the "real" electronic structure (often called **resonance hybrid**) is identical to neither, but is intermediate in character between the two. It has been shown experimentally that the two sulfur-oxygen bonds in SO_2 are not different, but have the same length and strength and are intermediate in character between a single and double bond. Furthermore, the SO_2 molecule is more stable than would be predicted for either structure A or B. The concept is called **resonance.** A homely analogy of resonance, that has been suggested by others, is a mule, which is a hybrid of a jackass and a horse. Just as the characteristics of a mule are fixed, so the properties of a resonance hybrid are fixed, with no oscillation between the contributing electronic structures.

4. *Spatial arrangements in simple molecules and ions.* As shown above, the sulfur dioxide molecule is angular rather than linear. The following rules are useful in evaluating the arrangement in space of the atoms in certain simple molecules and ions: (1) A molecule or ion of the type AX_2 is linear if the central atom has no unshared electron pairs, and angular if the central atom has one or more

unshared pairs. Thus CO_2 and CS_2 have linear structures while H_2O and NO_2^- are angular.

(2) A molecule or ion of the type AX_3 is planar if the central atom has no unshared electron pairs, and pyramidal if the central atom has one or more unshared pairs. Thus, BF_3 and $CO_3^=$ are planar, while NH_3 and $SO_3^=$ are pyramidal.

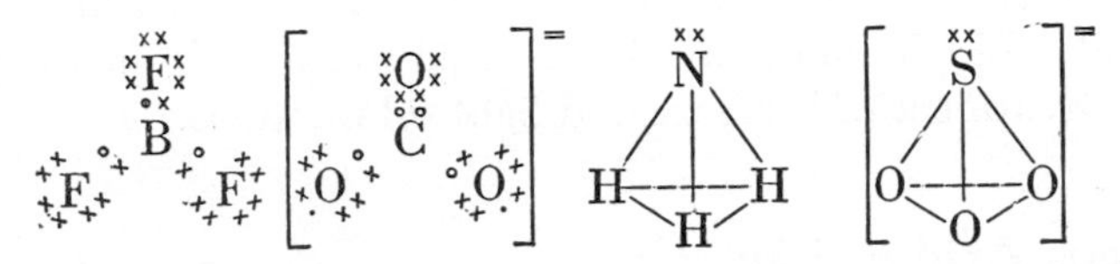

5. *Solvent properties of liquid sulfur dioxide.* Liquid sulfur dioxide is a good solvent for a wide variety of substances, including many salts, and it is used as a medium for carrying out certain types of reactions. Its electrical conductivity is about twice that of water, and it has been suggested that it undergoes auto-ionization to a small degree, according to the equation

$$SO_2 + SO_2 \rightleftharpoons SO^{++} + SO_3^=$$

The auto-ionization of SO_2 resembles that of water and that of liquid ammonia.

$$H_2O + H_2O \rightleftharpoons H_3O^+ + OH^-$$
$$NH_3 + NH_3 \rightleftharpoons NH_4^+ + NH_2^-$$

The polar character of the SO_2 molecule is responsible, at least in part, for its ability to dissolve ionic compounds, giving solutions of high electrical conductivity.

6. *Reactions of sulfur dioxide.* Sulfur dioxide is slowly oxidized by oxygen of the air to sulfur trioxide, according to the equation

$$2\ SO_2 + O_2 \rightleftharpoons 2\ SO_3$$

This oxidation is much faster in the presence of suitable catalysts, and the reaction is one step in the production of sulfuric acid (Section 23.6).

Sulfur dioxide reacts with phosphorus pentachloride, PCl_5, to form **thionyl chloride,** $SOCl_2$ (Fig. 23–1a), and **phosphorus oxychloride,** $POCl_3$.

$$SO_2 + PCl_5 \rightarrow SOCl_2 + POCl_3$$

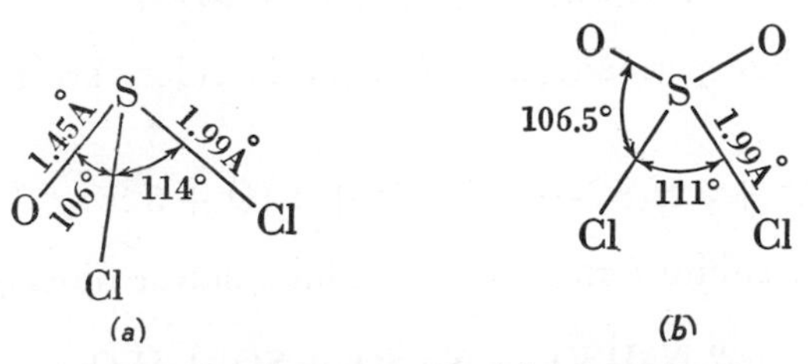

Fig. 23–1 (a) Thionyl chloride; (b) sulfuryl chloride.

Sulfur dioxide combines with chlorine when the mixture is exposed to sunlight; **sulfuryl chloride,** SO_2Cl_2, is formed (Fig. 23–1b).

$$SO_2 + Cl_2 \rightarrow SO_2Cl_2$$

The reaction of sulfur dioxide with water is considered in Section 23.2.

7. *Uses of sulfur dioxide.* Sulfur dioxide is used in the bleaching of such materials as straw, paper, silk, and wool. It is used as a bleaching agent for certain fruits and as a preservative for dried fruits to prevent fermentation and the growth of molds. Tremendous quantities of sulfur dioxide are used in the manufacture of sulfuric acid. Liquid sulfur dioxide is used extensively in the petroleum industry for the treatment of kerosene and light oil fractions.

23.2 Sulfurous Acid and Sulfites

When sulfur dioxide dissolves in water, it gives a weakly acidic solution of **sulfurous acid.**

$$H_2O + SO_2 \rightleftharpoons H_2SO_3$$

Sulfurous acid is unstable and cannot be isolated in the anhydrous condition; all of the sulfur dioxide may be expelled from solution by boiling. Like other diprotic acids, sulfurous acid ionizes in two steps.

$$H_2SO_3 \rightleftharpoons H^+ + HSO_3^-$$
$$HSO_3^- \rightleftharpoons H^+ + SO_3^=$$

The ionization is slight in both stages, but it is much less in the secondary stage than in the primary.

Both normal and hydrogen salts are formed by sulfurous acid. When in excess it reacts with sodium hydroxide and forms the hydrogen sulfite.

$$(Na^+) + OH^- + H_2SO_3 \rightarrow (Na^+) + HSO_3^- + H_2O$$

The addition of another mole of sodium hydroxide gives the normal sulfite.

$$(Na^+) + OH^- + (Na^+) + HSO_3^- \rightarrow (2\ Na^+) + SO_3^= + H_2O$$

Sulfurous acid acts as a reducing agent toward strong oxidizing agents. Oxygen of the air oxidizes it to the more stable sulfuric acid.

$$2\ H_2SO_3 + O_2 \rightarrow 4\ H^+ + 2\ SO_4^=$$

Solutions of potassium permanganate (purple in color) are rapidly bleached by sulfurous acid.

$$2\ MnO_4^- + 5\ H_2SO_3 \rightarrow 2\ Mn^{++} + 4\ H^+ + 5\ SO_4^= + 3\ H_2O$$

Sodium hydrogen sulfite forms sodium sulfite, sulfur dioxide, and water when heated.

$$2\ NaHSO_3 \rightarrow Na_2SO_3 + SO_2 + H_2O$$

When solid sodium sulfite is heated to high temperatures, auto oxidation-reduction occurs, with the formation of sodium sulfide and sodium sulfate.

$$4\ \overset{+4}{Na_2SO_3} \rightarrow \overset{-2}{Na_2S} + 3\ \overset{+6}{Na_2SO_4}$$

Solutions of sulfites are very susceptible to air oxidation, as is sulfurous acid, and sulfates are formed. Thus solutions of sulfites always contain sulfates after standing in contact with the air.

23.3 Uses of Sulfurous Acid and Sulfites

Sulfurous acid is used as a bleaching agent, a preservative, and an antiseptic. It bleaches by forming colorless compounds, many of which are relatively unstable. The reactions involve either reduction by the sulfurous acid or the formation of addition compounds with sulfur dioxide. These colorless compounds are often decomposed by light so that straw hats and paper which have been bleached by sulfurous acid turn yellow in sunlight.

Calcium hydrogen sulfite (or bisulfite), $Ca(HSO_3)_2$, is used extensively in the manufacture of paper from wood. The chips of wood are digested in a solution of $Ca(HSO_3)_2$ under pressure at 177° for several hours to dissolve **lignin,** a substance that cements the fibers of cellulose together in the wood. This treatment also bleaches the wood, leaving the white wood pulp used in the manufacture of paper.

23.4 The Dioxides of Selenium and Tellurium and Their Derivatives

1. *Selenium dioxide.* This compound is a white crystalline solid composed of SeO_2 units polymerized into long chains. It may be prepared by burning selenium in oxygen or by dissolving the element in concentrated nitric acid and evaporating the solution to dryness. When heated under atmospheric pressure, selenium dioxide sublimes, giving long white needles. It mixes with water in all proportions. In contrast to sulfurous acid, **selenous acid,** H_2SeO_3, is stable, and is obtained as large transparent prisms when a concentrated solution of the dioxide is evaporated. Selenous acid is a much weaker reducing agent and a much stronger oxidizing agent than sulfurous acid. **Selenites** and **hydrogen selenites,** such as K_2SeO_3 and $KHSeO_3$, respectively, are known.

2. *Tellurium dioxide.* The oxide can be prepared by burning tellurium in air or by oxidizing the element by dissolving it in nitric acid. Like SeO_2, tellurium dioxide can be obtained as a sublimate of long white needles. Tellurium dioxide is practically insoluble in water, but dissolves readily in alkali hydroxide solutions forming tellurites, from which **tellurous acid** may be precipitated by the addition of a strong acid.

$$TeO_2 + 2\ OH^- \rightleftharpoons TeO_3^= + H_2O$$
$$TeO_3^= + 2\ H^+ \rightleftharpoons \underline{H_2TeO_3}$$

Tellurous acid is weaker than sulfurous and selenous acids and it is somewhat amphiprotic in character, a reflection of the metallic nature of tellurium.

23.5 Sulfur Trioxide

1. *Preparation.* When sulfur burns in air, small amounts of **sulfur trioxide** are formed in addition to sulfur dioxide. When sulfur dioxide and oxygen are heated together, a small amount of the trioxide is formed according to the equation

$$2\,SO_2 + O_2 \rightleftharpoons 2\,SO_3 + 46{,}980 \text{ cal.}$$

If the temperature of the system is raised to about 400° the conversion to SO_3 is practically complete, but at this temperature the time required to attain equilibrium is too great to be feasible. It has been found that certain catalysts, such as finely divided platinum or vanadium pentoxide, greatly decrease the time required for equilibrium to be reached. The higher the temperature, the more the equilibrium shifts to the left. This is an application of van't Hoff's law (Section 16.11).

2. *Structure.* Sulfur trioxide in the vapor state is **monomeric,** i.e., its molecules are single SO_3 units, with the sulfur atom at the center and the oxygen atoms at the corners of an equilateral triangle (see rule 2, under item 4, Section 23.1). Because the sulfur-oxygen bond distance is less than that for a single bond, resonance structures involving double bonds (two pairs of electrons) and single bonds (one pair of electrons) are written for the sulfur trioxide molecule.

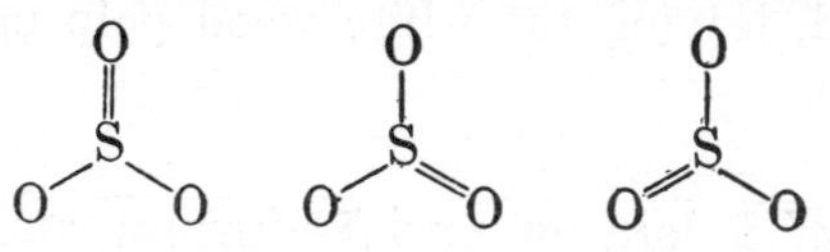

Liquid sulfur trioxide is thought to consist of an equilibrium mixture of monomers and **trimers** $(SO_3)_3$. The trimeric polymer has been found to contain six-membered rings.

O_2
S
O O
O_2S SO_2
O

There are apparently three distinct solid forms of sulfur trioxide. One modification is icelike in appearance and has as building units the trimeric molecular units. A second form is an asbestoslike solid in which SO_3 units are joined to each other in long chains which extend the length of the crystal. In the third form, SO_3 chains are joined together to give a layerlike arrangement.

3. *Properties.* Liquid sulfur trioxide boils at 43° and freezes at 17° to the icelike solid form. When a trace of moisture is added to liquid sulfur trioxide, it changes to the asbestoslike solid form.

Liquid sulfur trioxide fumes in moist air and dissolves in water in a highly exothermic reaction which results in the formation of sulfuric acid, H_2SO_4. With a limited amount of water, the molecular acid is formed according to the equation

$$SO_3 + H_2O \rightarrow H_2SO_4 + 40{,}500 \text{ cal.}$$

Sulfur trioxide dissolves readily in concentrated sulfuric acid and forms **pyrosulfuric acid,** $H_2S_2O_7$, also known as "fuming sulfuric acid" or "oleum."

$$H_2SO_4 + SO_3 \rightarrow H_2S_2O_7$$

At elevated temperatures, 900° or higher, sulfur trioxide decomposes into the dioxide and oxygen.

$$2\ SO_3 + \text{heat} \rightleftharpoons 2\ SO_2 + O_2$$

The trioxide reacts with many oxides and hydroxides in acid-base reactions (of the Lewis type) with the formation of sulfates.

$$\underset{\text{Base}}{BaO} + \underset{\text{Acid}}{SO_3} \rightarrow \underset{\text{Salt}}{BaSO_4}$$

SULFURIC ACID

Sulfuric acid was known to the later alchemists. In the 15th century Valentine and Glauber made it by distilling certain metallic sulfates with sand, particularly iron (II) sulfate, $FeSO_4 \cdot 7\ H_2O$.

$$FeSO_4 \cdot 7\ H_2O + SiO_2 \rightarrow FeSiO_3 + H_2SO_4 + 6\ H_2O$$

The common name for $FeSO_4 \cdot 7\ H_2O$ is **green vitriol,** and the sulfuric acid obtained as the distillate from it is an oily liquid, which was called "oil of vitriol."

The amount of sulfuric acid used in the industries exceeds that of any other manufactured compound. Its importance is so great that the amount of it produced from year to year is a fairly accurate index of industrial prosperity.

23.6 Manufacture of Sulfuric Acid

This most important and widely used commercial acid is produced by two methods.

1. *The contact process for sulfuric acid.* The chemistry of the **contact process** for the manufacture of sulfuric acid is very simple. Usually nearly pure sulfur is burned in air, giving sulfur dioxide.

$$S + O_2 \rightarrow SO_2$$

The sulfur dioxide is oxidized by means of air in the presence of a suitable catalyst, the trioxide being formed.

$$2\ SO_2 + O_2 \rightarrow 2\ SO_3$$

Finely divided platinum was originally used as the "contact" catalyst. This substance has been replaced to a considerable extent by vanadium (V) oxide (V_2O_5), which is more resistant to poisoning (inactivation by impurities) and is much less expensive than platinum. Although the oxidation of the dioxide to the trioxide is exothermic and thus favored by low temperatures, the reaction is too slow to be commercially feasible at low temperatures; and the oxidation step is carried out at about 400°. A yield of about 98 per cent is obtained at this temperature.

Because sulfur trioxide vapor mixed with air does not dissolve readily in water, in spite of the vigorous reaction of the compound with water, it is first absorbed in concentrated sulfuric acid, pyrosulfuric acid being formed.

$$H_2SO_4 + SO_3 \rightarrow H_2S_2O_7$$

The addition of water to one mole of pyrosulfuric acid gives two moles of sulfuric acid.

$$H_2S_2O_7 + H_2O \rightarrow 2\ H_2SO_4$$

A diagram of the "contact process" is given in Fig. 23–2. Since the sulfur dioxide used in this process must be quite pure (to avoid poisoning of the catalyst), the contact process gives pure acid, which may be highly concentrated. Most of the sulfuric acid used today is produced by the contact process.

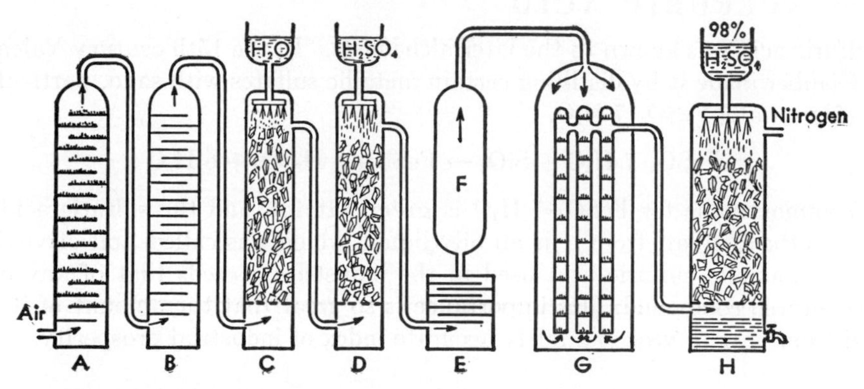

Fig. 23–2 A diagram of the contact process. A is the pyrite burner; B is a dust chamber; C is the scrubber filled with quartz pebbles over which water drips; in D, also containing loose quartz, concentrated sulfuric acid dries the gases; E is the purifier to remove arsenic; F is the heater; G is the contact tower, the temperature being regulated by the flow of gas over the contact chambers in G; in H the SO_3 is dissolved in strong sulfuric acid.

2. *The lead-chamber process for sulfuric acid.* This process received its name from the fact that the reactions involved are carried out in large lead-lined chambers. The chemistry of the chamber process differs from that of the contact process principally with regard to the mode of oxidation of the sulfur dioxide to the trioxide.

Sulfur dioxide is obtained by burning sulfur or roasting sulfide ores (Section 23.1). With reference to Fig. 23–3, sulfur dioxide is produced when an excess of air is passed through the burners, B. Gaseous nitric acid and sulfur dioxide are introduced at the bottom of the Glover tower where some sulfuric acid is formed by direct oxidation.

$$3\ SO_2 + 2\ HNO_3 + 2\ H_2O \rightarrow 3\ H_2SO_4 + 2\ NO$$

Sulfur dioxide (which was not oxidized in the previous step), nitric oxide, nitrogen dioxide, steam, and excess air enter the chambers, CC. Although the reactions

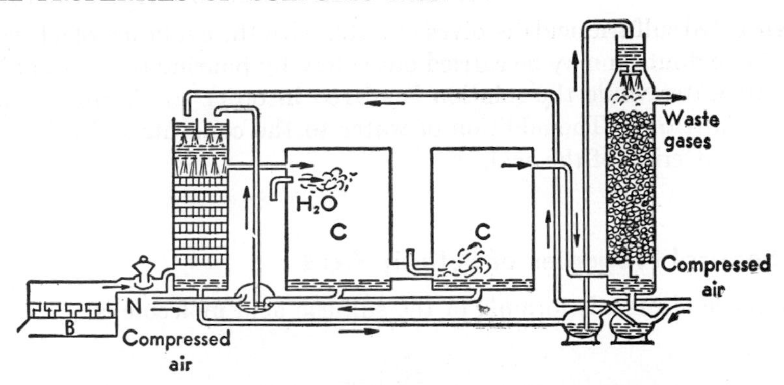

Fig. 23–3 Diagram of the lead-chamber process, showing two chambers. Acid may be withdrawn from the bottom of the chambers or from the Glover tower.

in the lead chambers are quite complicated and not well understood, the net changes can be represented by the following equations:

$$2\,NO + O_2 \rightarrow 2\,NO_2 \quad (1)$$
$$SO_2 + NO_2 \rightarrow SO_3 + NO \quad (2)$$
$$SO_3 + H_2O \rightarrow H_2SO_4 \quad (3)$$

The nitric oxide (and some nitrogen dioxide) which is recovered at the end of the process is returned to the Glover tower where it is again available for use as an "oxygen-carrier." It acts as catalyst in that it combines with oxygen of the air in reaction (1) and is regenerated again after delivering the oxygen to the sulfur dioxide in reaction (2). During the process some of the oxides of nitrogen are lost mechanically, and thus a fresh supply must be furnished continually.

The acid from the chamber process contains 60 to 70 per cent sulfuric acid. For many purposes, a more concentrated acid is desirable. Sufficient water can be removed by heating in lead pans to give an acid of 77 per cent concentration. The dilute sulfuric acid forms a protective coating of lead sulfate which is converted to soluble lead hydrogen sulfate when the concentration of the acid reaches 77 per cent. By further concentration in vessels of silica or duriron (an alloy of Fe and Si), 93 per cent sulfuric acid may be obtained.

In contrast to the relatively pure acid produced by the contact process, that from the chamber process is impure, containing lead salts as well as impurities from the original sulfide ore.

23.7 Physical Properties of Sulfuric Acid

Pure sulfuric acid (or **hydrogen sulfate**) is a colorless, oily liquid. It freezes at 10.5°. It fumes when heated, due to decomposition of a small portion of the acid into water and sulfur trioxide. More sulfur trioxide is lost than water until a concentration of 98.33 per cent acid is reached. The acid of this concentration boils at 338° without further change in concentration.

Concentrated sulfuric acid dissolves in water with the evolution of a large amount of heat. The dilution may be carried out safely by pouring the concentrated acid slowly into water while the solution is stirred in order to distribute the heat of dilution. **Caution.** The addition of water to the concentrated acid may cause dangerous spattering of the acid.

23.8 Chemical Properties of Sulfuric Acid

The valence electronic formula of the sulfuric acid molecule is:

$$\begin{array}{c} \circ\circ \\ {}^{\circ}_{\circ}\mathrm{O}^{\circ}_{\circ} \\ \circ\circ\ \times\times\ \circ\circ \\ {}^{\circ}_{\circ}\mathrm{O}^{\times}_{\times}\mathrm{S}^{\circ}_{\times}\mathrm{O}^{\circ}_{\times}\mathrm{H} \\ \circ\circ\ \circ\times\ \circ\circ \\ {}^{\circ}_{\circ}\mathrm{O}^{\circ}_{\circ} \\ \circ\times \\ \mathrm{H} \end{array}$$

The sulfur atom in the H_2SO_4 molecule is surrounded tetrahedrally by four oxygen atoms. The hydrogen atoms form hydrogen bonds between these tetrahedra, binding them together and making the boiling point of the liquid high.

The large heat of dilution of sulfuric acid is caused by hydrate and hydronium ion formation. The hydrates $H_2SO_4 \cdot H_2O$, $H_2SO_4 \cdot 2\ H_2O$, and $H_2SO_4 \cdot 4\ H_2O$ are known. The acid ionizes in two stages as follows:

$$H_2SO_4 \rightarrow H^+ + HSO_4^-$$
$$HSO_4^- \rightleftharpoons H^+ + SO_4^=$$

In dilute solution sulfuric acid undergoes almost complete primary ionization. The secondary ionization is less complete.

The strong affinity of concentrated sulfuric acid for water makes it a good dehydrating agent. Gases which do not react with the acid may be dried by being passed through it. So great is the affinity of concentrated sulfuric acid for water that it will remove hydrogen and oxygen as water from many compounds containing these elements. Organic substances containing hydrogen and oxygen in the proportion of two to one, such as cane sugar, $C_{12}H_{22}O_{11}$, and cellulose, $(C_6H_{10}O_5)_x$, are charred by concentrated sulfuric acid.

$$C_{12}H_{22}O_{11} \rightarrow 12\ C + 11\ H_2O$$

Sulfuric acid acts as an oxidizing agent, particularly when concentrated and heated. Depending upon the strength of the reducing agent with which it acts, its concentration, the temperature, and other factors, sulfuric acid may undergo reduction to SO_2, HSO_3^-, $SO_3^=$, S, H_2S, or $S^=$. Its oxidizing action towards hydrogen bromide and hydrogen iodide was noted in Section 18.1, and towards metals and carbon in Section 23.1. The displacement of volatile acids from their salts by means of concentrated sulfuric acid has been mentioned in Section 21.9. Aqueous solutions of sulfuric acid exhibit the characteristic properties of strong acids.

23.9 Sulfates

Being a diprotic acid, sulfuric acid forms both **normal sulfates,** such as Na_2SO_4, and **hydrogen sulfates,** such as $NaHSO_4$.

The normal sulfates of barium, strontium, calcium, and lead are only slightly soluble in water. These salts occur in nature as the minerals barite, $BaSO_4$; celestite, $SrSO_4$; gypsum, $CaSO_4 \cdot 2\ H_2O$; and anglesite, $PbSO_4$. They can be prepared in the laboratory by ionic combination. For example, the addition of barium chloride to a solution containing sulfate ions causes the precipitation of white barium sulfate.

$$Ba^{++} + SO_4^{=} \rightarrow \underline{BaSO_4}$$

This reaction is the basis of a qualitative test for the sulfate ion.

Among the important soluble sulfates are **Glauber's salt,** $Na_2SO_4 \cdot 10\ H_2O$; **Epsom salt,** $MgSO_4 \cdot 7\ H_2O$; **blue vitriol,** $CuSO_4 \cdot 5\ H_2O$; **green vitriol,** $FeSO_4 \cdot 7\ H_2O$; and **white vitriol,** $ZnSO_4 \cdot 7\ H_2O$.

23.10 Uses of Sulfuric Acid

Over 18,000,000 tons of sulfuric acid are produced and used each year in the various chemical industries of the United States. The major uses are in the production of ammonium sulfate and soluble phosphate fertilizers; in the refining of petroleum to remove impurities from such products as gasoline and kerosene; in the pickling of steel to clean its surface of iron rust before coating it with tin, zinc, or enamel; in the production of dyes, drugs, and disinfectants from coal tar; in the electrometallurgy of certain metals as the electrolyte or in the production of sulfates of metals to be used as electrolytes; in the manufacture of other chemicals, such as hydrochloric and nitric acids, and the sulfates of metals; and for such miscellaneous uses as in the manufacture of textiles, paints, pigments, plastics, explosives, and lead storage batteries.

23.11 Selenic and Telluric Acids

Selenium trioxide is a white solid that is extremely hygroscopic. No method for the synthesis of the pure compound has been devised. Attempts to prepare it by the dehydration of **selenic acid,** H_2SeO_4, result in decomposition to H_2SeO_3 and O_2. Selenic acid is a white solid that may be prepared by oxidizing selenous acid by chloric acid, by hydrogen peroxide, by chlorine, or by the action of bromine on a suspension of silver selenite.

$$Ag_2SeO_3 + Br_2 + H_2O \rightarrow 2\ AgBr + 2\ H^+ + SeO_4^{=}$$

Selenic acid is similar in properties to sulfuric acid, except that it is a stronger oxidizing agent. When heated, the concentrated acid dissolves gold, forming gold (III) selenate, $Au_2(SeO_4)_3$, and selenium dioxide:

$$2\ Au + 6\ H_2SeO_4 \rightarrow Au_2(SeO_4)_3 + 6\ H_2O + 3\ SeO_2$$

Tellurium trioxide, TeO_3, is prepared by heating **telluric acid,** H_6TeO_6, to a moderate temperature. It is an orange solid similar in appearance to telluric acid. It is insoluble in water, dilute alkalies, and acids but dissolves in strong alkalies with the formation of tellurates. Telluric acid is made by oxidizing elementary tellurium with a mixture of nitric acid and chromic acid. The formula of ordinary telluric acid is H_6TeO_6 rather than H_2TeO_4. It is more fully "hydrated" than sulfuric and selenic acid. This is attributed to the larger radius of tellurium. Telluric acid is very weakly acidic. Salts of telluric acid, such as $MHTeO_4$, M_2TeO_4, and $M_2H_4TeO_6$, are known.

OTHER ACIDS OF SULFUR

In addition to the acids of sulfur which have been discussed, there are several others of commercial importance. These are described in the following sections.

23.12 Thiosulfuric Acid

It was pointed out in Section 23.2 that sulfites are slowly oxidized to sulfates by oxygen. Sulfur plays a role similar to that of oxygen by transforming sulfites to thiosulfates. For example, when a mixture of sulfur and a solution of sodium sulfite is boiled, **sodium thiosulfate,** $Na_2S_2O_3$, is formed.

$$(2\ Na^+) + SO_3^= + S \rightarrow (2\ Na^+) + S_2O_3^=$$

Crystals of the **pentahydrate,** $Na_2S_2O_3 \cdot 5\ H_2O$, separate when the solution is evaporated.

When a solution of sodium thiosulfate is acidified, unstable **thiosulfuric acid,** $H_2S_2O_3$, is formed.

$$(2\ Na^+) + S_2O_3^= + 2\ H^+ + (2\ Cl^-) \rightarrow H_2S_2O_3 + (2\ Na^+) + (2\ Cl^-)$$

The acid decomposes immediately into sulfurous acid and sulfur, which appears either as a precipitate or in colloidal suspension.

$$H_2S_2O_3 \rightarrow H_2SO_3 + S$$

The valence electronic structure of the thiosulfate ion is compared to that of the sulfate ion to show that one of the oxygen atoms of the sulfate is replaced by the sulfur atom.

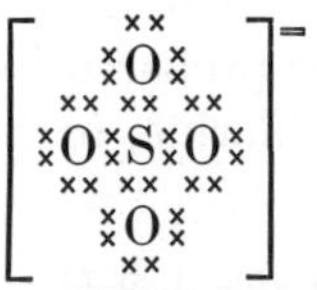

```
     xx      ]=          xx      ]=
    xOx                 xOx
  xx xx xx            xx xx xx
 xOxSxOx             xOxSxOx
  xx xx xx            xx xx xx
    xOx                 xSx
     xx                  xx
  Sulfate            Thiosulfate
```

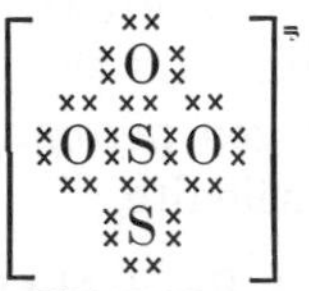

Sodium thiosulfate, also known as "hypo," is used in the photographic process as a fixing solution to dissolve from the plate or film any silver halides which have not been reduced to metallic silver by the developer.

$$AgX + 2\ S_2O_3^= \rightleftharpoons Ag(S_2O_3)_2^{-3} + X^- \quad (X = \text{halogen})$$

Standard solutions (solutions of known concentration) of sodium thiosulfate are used in the quantitative determination of elementary iodine. The reaction involved is given by the equation

$$2\ S_2O_3^{=} + I_2 \rightarrow S_4O_6^{=} + 2\ I^-$$

The thiosulfate ion is oxidized by the iodine to the **tetrathionate ion** ($S_4O_6^{=}$). The sulfur atoms in $S_2O_3^{=}$ have an "average" oxidation state of +2, whereas in $S_4O_6^{=}$ it is +2.5. Therefore, the average oxidation state of sulfur increases by 0.5 unit during the reaction.

Sodium thiosulfate is used in the bleaching industry (Fig. 23–4) and in paper-

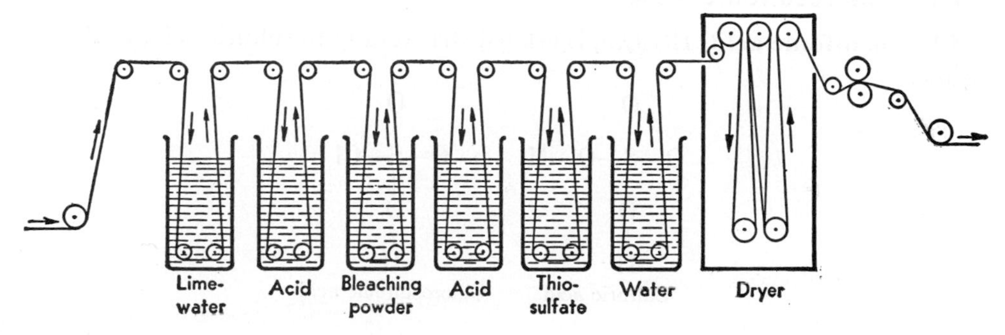

Fig. 23–4 Diagram of a machine for bleaching fabrics.

making to remove excess chlorine by reducing it to the chloride ion. Failure to remove the excess chlorine results in damage to the materials which are being bleached. In this application, sodium thiosulfate is called an "antichlor."

23.13 Peroxymonosulfuric Acid and Peroxydisulfuric Acid

These acids have the formulas H_2SO_5 and $H_2S_2O_8$, respectively. Both acids may be considered as derivatives of hydrogen peroxide. One of the hydrogen atoms of hydrogen peroxide has been replaced by the HSO_3 group in the case of peroxymonosulfuric acid. Both hydrogen atoms of hydrogen peroxide have been replaced by HSO_3 groups in peroxydisulfuric acid. The valence electronic formulas of these acids are given below:

```
      xx                      xx       xx
     xOx                     xOx      xOx
  xx  xx xx  xx           xx  xx  xx  xx  xx  xx
H:O:S:O:O:H             H:O:S:O:O:S:O:H
  xx  xx xx  xx           xx  xx  xx  xx  xx  xx
     xOx                     xOx      xOx
      xx                      xx       xx
```

Peroxymonosulfuric acid — Peroxydisulfuric acid

Peroxydisulfuric acid is produced commercially by the anodic oxidation of hydrogen sulfate ions in 45–55 per cent sulfuric acid at a low temperature (see Section 20.6).

$$2\ HSO_4^- \rightarrow H_2S_2O_8 + 2\ e^-$$

Electrolysis of potassium hydrogen sulfate gives potassium peroxydisulfate ($K_2S_2O_8$) in solution. Treatment of this salt at low temperatures with concentrated sulfuric acid produces peroxymonosulfuric acid, commonly called Caro's acid. This acid is also produced by the reaction of sulfur trioxide with hydrogen peroxide.

$$H_2O_2 + SO_3 \rightarrow H_2SO_5$$

The peroxysulfuric acids and their salts are useful as strong oxidizing agents.

23.14 Chlorosulfonic Acid

Chlorosulfonic acid, HSO_3Cl, is related structurally to sulfuric acid, as shown below:

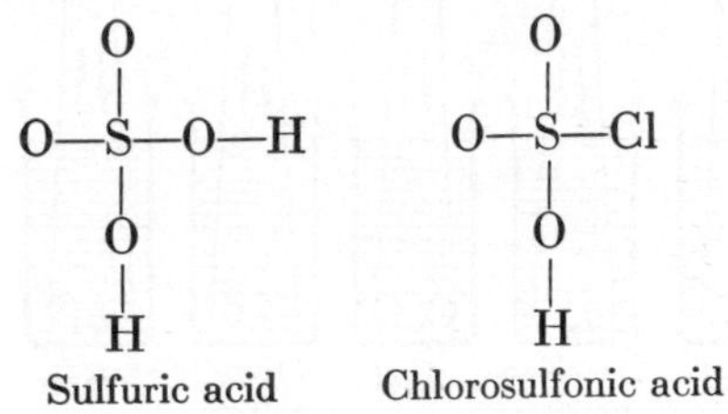

Sulfuric acid Chlorosulfonic acid

Chlorosulfonic acid is prepared by the direct reaction of dry hydrogen chloride with sulfur trioxide or fuming sulfuric acid

$$HCl + SO_3 \rightarrow HSO_3Cl$$

or by the reaction of phosphorus trichloride or pentachloride with fuming sulfuric acid. It is a colorless liquid, which fumes in moist air, and reacts vigorously with water forming sulfuric and hydrochloric acids. It is used to introduce the sulfonate group, HSO_3^-, into many organic compounds.

23.15 Sulfamic Acid

Sulfamic acid, HSO_3NH_2, is also closely related to sulfuric acid, one of the OH groups being replaced by NH_2. It may be made by treating hydroxylammonium sulfate with sulfur dioxide, according to the equation

$$(NH_3OH)_2SO_4 + 2\ SO_2 \rightarrow 2\ HSO_3NH_2 + H_2SO_4$$

Sulfamic acid is a colorless, crystalline, nonhygroscopic solid. It is of some importance in the titration of bases (Section 11.19), for it is one of the few strong monoprotic inorganic acids which can be weighed out without special precautions. Its ammonium salt, $NH_4SO_3NH_2$, is used as a flame-proofing agent and a weed killer, while the acid itself is used in dyeing, in the tanning of hides, and in electroplating.

23.16 Polythionic Acids

The four **polythionic acids,** $H_2S_2O_6$, $H_2S_3O_6$, $H_2S_4O_6$, and $H_2S_5O_6$, consist of two sulfonic groups, HSO_3—, with 0, 1, 2, and 3 sulfur atoms, respectively, between them. Although the acids themselves have not been isolated, corresponding salts (thionates) of all of them have been prepared (Fig. 23–5).

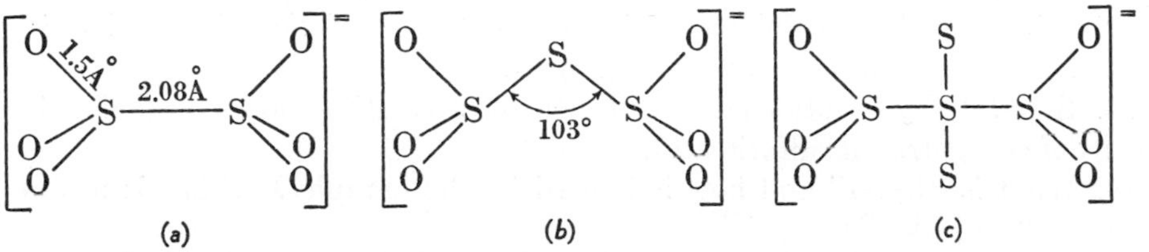

Fig. 23–5 (a) Dithionate; (b) trithionate ion; (c) pentathionate ion.

The salt $Na_2S_2O_4$ has been called at various times **sodium hydrosulfite, hyposulfite,** and **dithionite.** The structural formula of the dithionite ion is

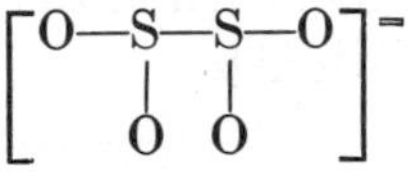

$$\left[\begin{array}{cccc} O- & S- & S- & O \\ & | & | & \\ & O & O & \end{array}\right]^{=}$$

Sodium dithionite is made by reducing sodium hydrogen sulfite with zinc. Dithionites are powerful reducing agents and the sodium salt is industrially important as a bleach for dyes.

QUESTIONS

1. How is sulfur dioxide produced commercially and what are its uses?
2. Write equations for the reaction of carbon and of copper with hot, concentrated sulfuric acid.
3. What is one disadvantage of using sulfur dioxide as a refrigerant?
4. What single chemical test could be used to distinguish sulfides, polysulfides, sulfites, and sulfates from one another?
5. Write equations showing the action of sulfurous acid as a reducing agent.
6. Why do solutions of sulfites usually contain sulfate ions?
7. How would you make sodium sulfite in the laboratory?
8. Interpret the following reaction in terms of an acid-base relationship according to the Lewis theory:

$$CaO + SO_3 \rightarrow CaSO_4$$

9. What is the formula for pyrosulfuric acid and how is this acid formed?
10. Write the equations for the contact process for the manufacture of sulfuric acid. What does the term "contact" signify in this process?
11. What is meant by catalyst poisoning?
12. How did the "lead-chamber" process for sulfuric acid get its name?

13. The essential difference between the contact and chamber processes lies in the method of oxidizing the sulfur dioxide. Explain.

14. Compare the acid ordinarily obtained by the two processes for the manufacture of sulfuric acid with regard to purity and concentration.

15. How may concentrated sulfuric acid be diluted safely?

16. Show by equations the dehydrating action of sulfuric acid upon cane sugar and upon cellulose.

17. What are the possible reduction products of sulfuric acid? What is the oxidation state of sulfur in each of these products?

18. Illustrate by equations the displacement of volatile acids from their salts by means of concentrated sulfuric acid.

19. What is "hypo" and how is it used in photography? What is meant by the term "antichlor"?

20. Account for the formation of sulfur in a solution of sodium thiosulfate in contact with air (air contains carbon dioxide, the anhydride of carbonic acid).

21. Show by writing formulas that the peroxysulfuric acids are derivatives of hydrogen peroxide.

22. Write the electronic formula of each of the following: $S^{=}$, H_2S_2, SO_2, H_2SO_3, SO_3, Na_2SO_4, $H_2S_2O_7$, H_2SO_5, and $H_2S_2O_8$.

PROBLEMS

1. A volume of 12.40 ml. of a 0.1102 N standard sodium thiosulfate solution is required to titrate a 25.00 ml. sample of a solution containing iodine. What is the iodine concentration in the solution? *Ans. 0.55 N*

2. How much sulfuric acid can be prepared from one ton of sulfur by the contact process, assuming a 98% yield? *Ans. 3 tons*

3. What volume of oxygen measured at 27.0° and 750 mm. would be required to burn 750 g. of sulfur to sulfur dioxide? *Ans. 584 l.*

4. What volume of a 0.100 M sodium sulfate solution would be required to precipitate the Ba^{++} in a solution containing 135 g. of $BaCl_2$? How much $BaSO_4$ is formed in the reaction? *Ans. 6.48 l.; 151 g.*

REFERENCES

"Sulfuric Acid Index Follows Industrial Activity," C. C. Concannon and F. M. Hoffheims, *Chem. Eng. News*, **26** (15) 1072 (April, 1948).

Manufacture of Sulfuric Acid, (American Chemical Society Monograph No. 144), edited by W. W. Duecker and J. R. West, Reinhold Publ. Corp., New York (1959).

"Chemistry of Solutions in Liquid Sulfur Dioxide," P. J. Elving and J. M. Markowitz, *J. Chem. Educ.*, **37** (2) 75 (1960).

CHAPTER TWENTY-FOUR

The Atmosphere and the Rare Gases

THE ATMOSPHERE

24.1 The Composition of the Atmosphere

The **atmosphere** is the mixture of gaseous substances which surrounds the earth. For the most part, the atmosphere consists of uncombined elements. A limited portion of the atmosphere is called "air," although the two terms are often used interchangeably. Nitrogen, oxygen, and the rare gases are present in the atmosphere in almost constant proportion. The per cent of carbon dioxide in the air varies somewhat and that of dust and water vapor is widely variable. There are also traces of hydrogen, ammonia, hydrogen sulfide, oxides of nitrogen, sulfur dioxide, and other gases. The average composition of dry air at sea level is given in Table 24·1.

TABLE 24·1 Composition of the Atmosphere

Component	*Per Cent by Volume*	*Component*	*Per Cent by Volume*
Nitrogen	78.03	Neon	0.0012
Oxygen	20.99	Helium	0.0005
Argon	0.94	Krypton	0.0001
Carbon dioxide	0.035–0.04	Ozone	0.00006
Hydrogen	0.01	Xenon	0.000009

The percentage composition of dry air does not vary much with location on the earth's surface or with altitude. However, the density of air, as reflected in pressure, varies greatly with altitude. The average pressure at sea level and 45° latitude is 760 mm., at 15,000 feet it is about 400 mm., at 10 miles it is about 40 mm., and at 30 miles is only about 0.1 mm.

24.2 Liquid Air

1. *Preparation.* Before air is liquefied it must be freed of moisture and carbon dioxide because these substances change to the solid state when cooled and thus clog the pipes of the liquid-air machine (Fig. 24–1). The air is compressed to about 100 atmospheres and cooled to remove the heat produced by compression. The air is then compressed to about 200 atmospheres and again cooled by a mixture of salt and ice. The cold compressed air is then passed into the liquefier in which it escapes through a valve and expands to a pressure of about 20 atmospheres. This expansion is accompanied by the absorption of heat from the compressed air in the small inner coil of the liquefier. As the process continues, each quantity of air that escapes from the valve is colder than that which preceded it, and finally the air becomes a liquid.

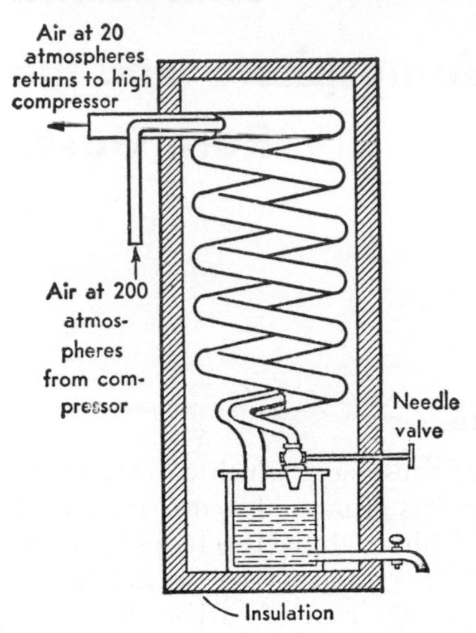

Fig. 24–1 A liquefier of a liquid-air machine.

2. *Properties.* Liquid air is a mobile liquid with a faint blue color. It evaporates rapidly in an open container with the absorption of a large quantity of heat. To reduce the rate of evaporation, liquid air is stored in Dewar flasks. These flasks (Fig. 24–2) have the space between the inner and outer walls evacuated. Heat is not transmitted through a vacuum and without heat the liquid air cannot evaporate. The Dewar flasks are frequently silvered on the walls of the evacuated space for the purpose of reflecting heat waves which fall upon them. "Thermos" bottles are constructed on the principles described for Dewar flasks.

Because liquid air is a mixture, it has no definite boiling point. Oxygen boils at −183.0 and nitrogen at −195.8° (Fig. 24–3). Commercial supplies of nitrogen, oxygen, and argon are obtained by the fractional distillation of liquid air. The low temperature of liquid air is of great practical value in scientific research work that must be carried out at low temperatures. Liquid air is also used as a source of liquid oxygen in rocket and jet-propelled planes and missiles.

The extremely low temperature of liquid air makes it useful in demonstrating how the properties of various materials change at very low temperatures.

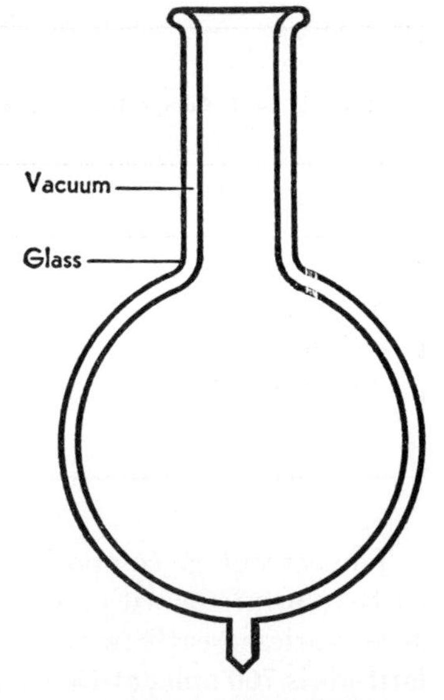

Fig. 24–2 Dewar flask.

It will cause mercury to freeze and become so hard that a mercury hammer head can be made by pouring liquid air over mercury held in a small box. Rubber immersed in liquid air loses its elastic properties and becomes hard and brittle so that it shatters like glass when struck a sharp blow. A bell made of lead and cooled in liquid air will ring like one made of brass. All metals become very good conductors of electricity when cooled to the temperature of liquid air.

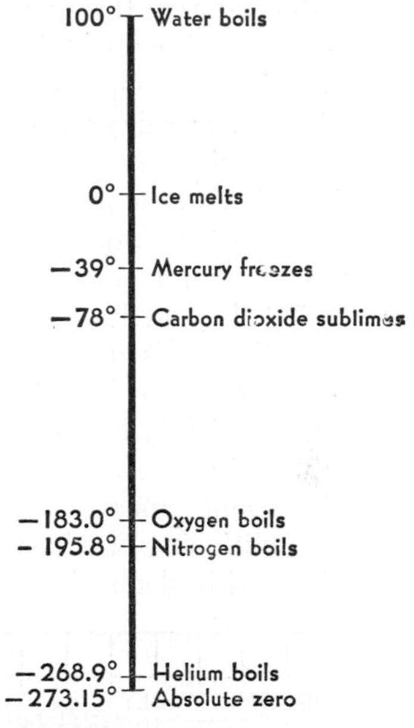

Fig. 24–3 Comparative temperature chart.

24.3 Humidity

The **absolute humidity** of the atmosphere is defined as the mass of water vapor present in a unit volume. We noted in Section 24.1 that the content of water vapor in the air is quite variable. The air over large bodies of water tends to become saturated with water vapor. The ratio (expressed in per cent) of the amount of water vapor present in any volume of air at a given temperature to the amount needed to saturate the same volume at that temperature is known as **relative humidity.** Because the partial pressure of the water vapor in the air is directly proportional to the amount of water vapor in a given volume of air, the ratio of the partial pressure of the water vapor in the air to the saturation partial pressure may be used in calculating the relative humidity. Saturated air has a relative humidity of 100 per cent. The following problem illustrates how the relative humidity of the air is calculated. In a sample of air the partial pressure of the water vapor is 12.8 mm. at 22°. The saturation vapor pressure of water is 19.8 mm. at 22°. Calculate the relative humidity of the air. The relative humidity is

$$\frac{12.8 \text{ mm.}}{19.8 \text{ mm.}} \times 100 = 64.6 \text{ per cent}$$

What will be the relative humidity if the sample of air is heated to 28°? The saturation vapor pressure of water at 28° is 28.3 mm. The relative humidity at 28° is therefore

$$\frac{12.8 \text{ mm.}}{28.3 \text{ mm.}} \times 100 = 45.2 \text{ per cent}$$

If this same sample of air is cooled to 15°, at which temperature the saturation vapor pressure of water is 12.8 mm., the air becomes saturated and the relative humidity is 100 per cent.

The temperature at which a sample of air has a relative humidity of 100 per cent is called the **dew point.** If the temperature of the air is lowered below its dew point, the excess water will separate out as dew or fog; if the air saturated with water vapor is cooled below 0° C, then the excess water will form snow or frost. It should be noted that relative humidity is dependent upon the partial pressure of the water vapor in the air and the temperature.

Our personal comfort is closely related to the relative humidity of the air. Evaporation of perspiration from the surface of our bodies is a cooling process. On a hot summer day when the air is nearly saturated with water vapor, evaporation of perspiration is extremely slow and we suffer discomfort. If the relative humidity is low, the perspiration evaporates rapidly and we feel more comfortable even though the temperature is just as high.

Dust in the air consists of solid particles of various substances which are so small that they settle very slowly. About 1000 tons of dust settle on a city of the size of Indianapolis in one year. The dust particles serve as nuclei for the condensation of water vapor into droplets in the formation of clouds. When the droplets become sufficiently large, they fall as rain or snow. Were there no dust particles, water would condense upon the surfaces of all objects as a liquid film whenever the air became supersaturated.

Air conditioning provides homes, trains, theaters, hotels, and many other public buildings with clean air of optimum temperature and humidity. The recom-

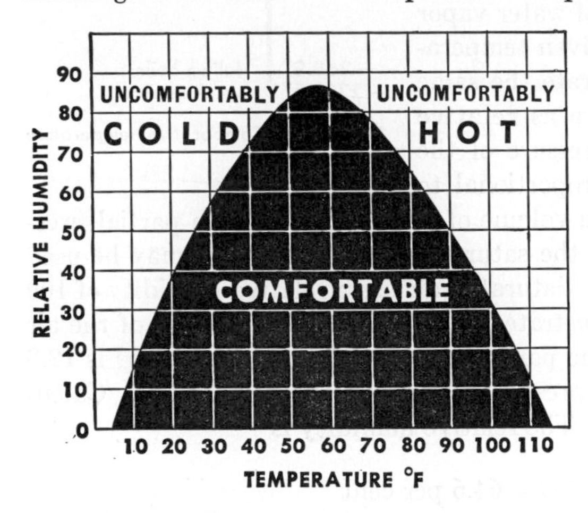

Fig. 24–4 Assuming he wears suitable but not uncommon types of clothing, a person will be comfortable if the temperature and humidity are adjusted to values within the black area.

mended temperature range is 65° F to 75° F and the relative humidity range is 40 per cent to 60 per cent (Fig. 24–4). In hot weather, the air must be cooled and its humidity must be lowered, while in cold weather the air must be warmed and its humidity raised.

THE RARE GASES

24.4 Discovery

The story of the discovery of the rare gases is interesting. In 1894, the British chemist Lord Rayleigh observed that a liter of nitrogen which he had prepared by removing the oxygen, carbon dioxide, and water vapor from air weighed 1.2572 grams, while a liter of nitrogen prepared from ammonia weighed only 1.2506 grams under the same conditions. This discrepancy caused Rayleigh to suspect the presence of a previously undiscovered element in the atmosphere. By passing nitrogen obtained from the air over red-hot magnesium ($3\ Mg + N_2 \rightarrow Mg_3N_2$), he found a small amount of residual gas which he could not cause to combine with any other element. Rayleigh and Ramsay found that the residual gas showed a spectrum never before observed for any gas. In 1894 these scientists announced the discovery of the first rare gas, which they called **argon,** meaning "the lazy one." It was later found that this residual gas contained the rare gases helium, neon, krypton, and xenon, as well as argon.

Helium was first discovered in the atmosphere which surrounds the sun. In 1868 the French astronomer Janssen went to India to study a total eclipse of the sun using a spectroscope. He observed among other bright lines one new yellow line, which caused Frankland and Lockyer to conclude that the sun contained a previously undiscovered element. They called this new element **helium,** from the Greek word "helios," meaning "the sun." All attempts to find this element on the earth were unsuccessful until 1895, when Ramsay showed that the gas given off when the uranium mineral cleveite is heated has a spectrum identical with that of helium.

In 1898 Ramsay and Travers isolated **neon** (meaning "the new element") by the fractional distillation of impure liquid oxygen. Shortly thereafter they showed the less volatile fractions from liquid air to contain two other new elements, **krypton** ("the hidden element") and **xenon** ("the stranger").

In 1900 Friedrich Ernst Dorn discovered that one of the disintegration products of radium is a gas, similar in chemical properties to the rare gases. At first this gas was called radium emanation, but later its name was changed to **radon.**

24.5 Production of the Rare Gases

Helium is produced from certain natural gases, which sometimes contain as much as 2 to 5 per cent of the element. The condensable components of the gas are liquefied in a liquid-air machine, leaving helium in the gaseous condition. The United States has most of the world's commercial supply of this element in its helium-bearing gas fields.

Argon, neon, krypton, and xenon are produced by the fractional distillation of liquid air. Radon gas is collected from radium salts.

24.6 Physical Properties of the Rare Gases

The principal properties of the rare or noble gases are given in Table 24·2.

The boiling points and melting points of the rare gases are extremely low in comparison to those of other substances of comparable atomic or molecular weights. The reason for this is that no strong chemical bonds, but only weak van der Waals forces, operate to hold the atoms together in the liquid and solid states. Van der

TABLE 24·2 Properties of the Rare Gases

	Helium	*Neon*	*Argon*	*Krypton*	*Xenon*	*Radon*
Atomic number	2	10	18	36	54	86
Electrons in outer shell	2	8	8	8	8	8
Atomic weight	4.0	20.18	39.95	83.8	131.3	222
Atomic radius, Å	0.93	1.60	1.91	2.0	2.2	...
Melting point, °C	−269.7*	−248.6	−189.3	−157.2	−111.9	−71
Boiling point, °C	−268.9	−245.9	−186	−153.2	−108.1	−62
Critical temperature, °C	−267.9	−228.7	−122.3	−63.8	−16.6	105
Critical pressure, atms.	2.26	26.9	48.3	54.3	57.6	62.4

* at 10.3 atmospheres of pressure

Waals forces become quite effective only when molecular motion is very slight, as it is at very low temperatures, so as to permit close approach of neighboring atoms.

24.7 Chemical Properties of the Rare Gases

The elements of Group 0 were formerly called the "inert gases" because until recently it was thought that they were chemically inert. Many unsuccessful attempts were made to cause these elements to combine with other elements by treatment with oxidizing and reducing agents. The stability of the rare gas type of structure has been mentioned frequently in the preceding chapters. The two electrons of helium represent a completed shell, while a complement of eight electrons in the outer shell of each of the other rare gases gives them a stable configuration. Many elements form stable ions which have rare gas structures. These include the elements of high electron affinities (the halogens) which immediately precede the rare gases in the Periodic Table, and the elements of low ionization potentials (the alkali metals) which immediately follow them.

Until very recently, the rare gases were assumed to undergo practically no chemical changes at room temperatures and pressures. However, almost from the time these elements were first discovered, chemists have tried to force them to enter into chemical combination by using unusual conditions. These efforts have been successful to a limited extent.

Helium has been forced to combine with certain other elements by using the large energies obtainable in electrical discharge tubes. Examples of species thus formed are He_2^+, with a three-electron bond between the two nuclei, and such combinations with hydrogen as HeH^+ and HeH_2^+. These combinations are not stable and have only momentary existence. On the other hand, comparatively stable helides of certain metals have been reported. These include $HgHe_{10}$,

Pt_3He, FeHe, etc. "Compounds" of this type may be alloys in which the small helium atoms occupy the holes in the crystal lattice of the metal (Section 33.13).

A strong dipole, such as the water molecule, may polarize a rare gas atom so that it acts as a dipole itself and thereby attracts the original dipole. The larger the rare gas atom, the greater is the susceptibility toward dipole induction. Thus, hydrates of argon, krypton, xenon, and radon have been prepared. These compounds have formulas such as $Ar{\cdot}xH_2O$, $Kr{\cdot}xH_2O$, and $Xe{\cdot}xH_2O$ where x is 1 to 6, but equal to 6 only with the rare gases of largest radii. These compounds are crystalline solids which form when water and the rare gases are brought together at low temperatures and high pressures.

The fact that the rare gases have higher ionization potentials than those of any of the other elements in their respective horizontal rows of the Periodic Table (see Fig. 15–1 and Table 15·7) has encouraged the widely held concept of the chemical inertness of these gases. However, if the ionization potentials of the larger rare gases are compared with the ionization potentials of other elements, it is apparent that these values are of the order of magnitude of those of certain other elements and indeed are even smaller than the ionization potentials for a few elements. In June, 1962, Neil Bartlett reported the preparation of a yellow compound of xenon to which he ascribed the formula $Xe[PtF_6]$. This discovery led a group of chemists to think that perhaps xenon might be oxidized by a highly electronegative element such as fluorine, and in September, 1962, they reported the preparation of **xenon tetrafluoride, XeF_4. This was the first report of a stable compound of a rare gas with another single element.** The compound was made by the surprisingly simple procedure of mixing xenon gas and fluorine gas at 400° C for one hour and cooling to −78°. The material is reported to have the form of colorless crystals (see Fig. 24–5, page 378) which melt at about 90° and which are stable at room temperature, showing no evidence of reaction or decomposition after six weeks' storage in glass vessels.

Shortly after reporting the preparation of xenon tetrafluoride, the same group of chemists reported the existence of still another fluoride of xenon, XeF_2, two oxyfluorides, $XeOF_3$ and $XeOF_4$, and possibly a stable fluoride of radon.

As this significant work is checked, research in this new field will undoubtedly progress rapidly. The achievement not only opens the door to an exciting new area of research; it also provides a lesson that we should always keep our minds open to new possibilities and not blindly accept preconceived or entrenched ideas that may not be correct.

24.8 Uses of Rare Gases

1. *Helium.* This gas is used for filling observation balloons and other lighter-than-air craft, particularly by the U.S. Navy. The fact that helium does not burn makes it safer to use than hydrogen. Although it is twice as dense as hydrogen, helium has a lifting power which is 92.6 per cent of that of hydrogen. This results from the fact that the lifting power of a gas with a density less than that

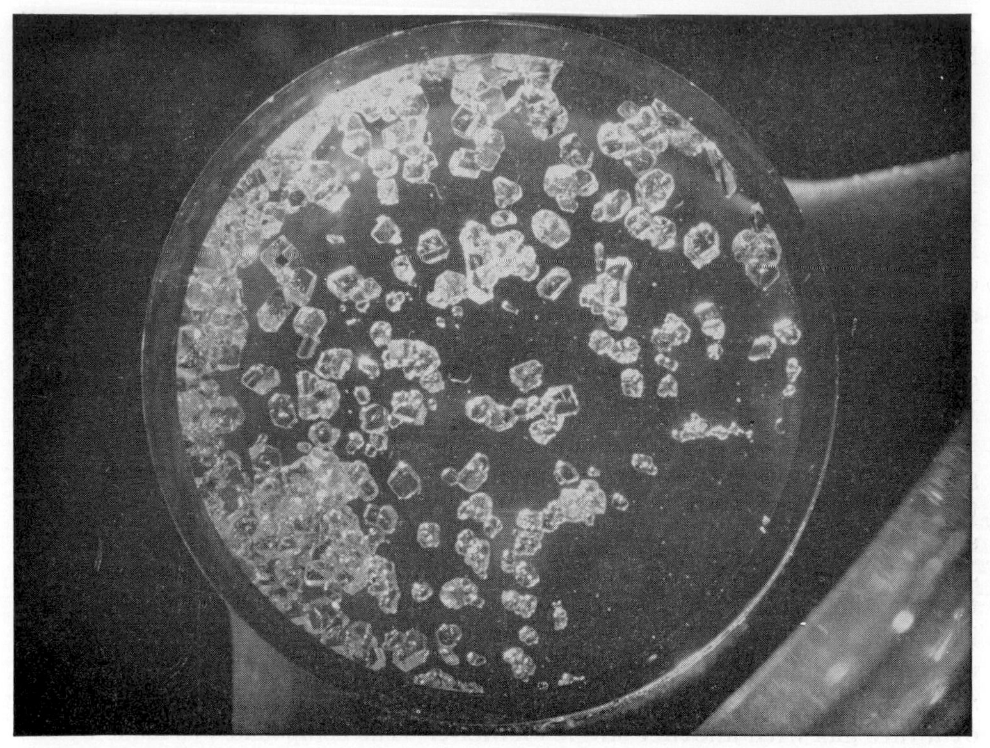

Fig. 24–5 Crystals of xenon tetrafluoride, XeF_4, the first stable compound reported for a rare gas with another single element. The crystals shown are about four times their actual sizes. *Photograph courtesy of Argonne National Laboratory*

of air is determined by the difference between its weight and that of an equal volume of air.

$$\begin{array}{l} 1.293 \text{ g./l. (air)} \\ \underline{0.090 \text{ g./l. (hydrogen)}} \\ 1.203 \text{ g./l. (lifting power)} \end{array} \qquad \begin{array}{l} 1.293 \text{ g./l. (air)} \\ \underline{0.179 \text{ g./l. (helium)}} \\ 1.114 \text{ g./l. (lifting power)} \end{array}$$

$$\frac{1.114 \text{ g./l. (helium)}}{1.203 \text{ g./l. (hydrogen)}} \times 100 = 92.6 \text{ per cent}$$

Because helium is less soluble than nitrogen in the blood stream, mixtures of it with oxygen are used by divers working under high pressures. The use of helium in place of nitrogen reduces the danger of a pathological condition called "bends" which is caused by the formation of bubbles of nitrogen in the blood; this results from the decrease in its solubility at lower pressures.

Mixtures of helium and oxygen are also used in the treatment of certain respiratory diseases such as asthma. The lightness and rapid diffusion of helium decrease the muscular effort involved in breathing.

Helium is used as an inert atmosphere for the melting and welding of easily oxidizable metals and for many chemical processes which are sensitive to air.

Liquid helium is of extremely great value in attaining low temperatures for scientific research.

2. *Neon.* Neon is used in the familiar neon lamps and signs. When an electric current is passed through neon under low pressure, it emits a brilliant orange-red glow. The color of the light given off by a neon tube may be changed by mixing argon and mercury vapor with neon and by using tubes made of glasses of special compositions. Neon lamps cost less to operate than ordinary electric lamps and their light penetrates fog better.

3. *Argon.* This gas is used in gas-filled electric lamps, where its lower heat conductivity and chemical inertness make it preferable to nitrogen for inhibiting volatilization of the tungsten filament and prolonging the life of the lamp. Fluorescent tubes contain a mixture of argon and mercury vapor. Many Geiger-counter tubes are filled with argon.

4. *Krypton and Xenon.* A krypton-xenon photographic flash tube has been developed for taking high speed photographic exposures. An electric discharge through the tube gives a very intense light which lasts only 1/50,000 of a second.

5. *Radon.* This gas is collected in hospitals from radium supplies and it is sealed in small tubes, which are used in the radiotherapy of malignant growths such as cancer.

QUESTIONS

1. Name some "accidental" components of the air in the community in which you live.
2. What evidence can you cite to show that air is a mixture rather than a compound?
3. What physical principles are employed in the liquefaction of air?
4. Describe the construction of Dewar flasks.
5. Relate personal comfort to relative humidity on hot summer days and cold winter days.
6. What is meant by the "dew point" of air?
7. How was the discovery of argon related to its chemical inertness?
8. Give a brief account of the discovery of helium.
9. Relate the chemical inactivity of the rare gases to their electronic structures.
10. Discuss the uses of the rare gases in terms of their properties.

PROBLEMS

1. The partial pressure of water vapor in a sample of air is 11.2 mm. at 20.0° C. The vapor pressure of water at 20.0° is 17.5 mm. Calculate the relative humidity of the air. What will be the relative humidity if the sample of air is heated to 26.1° C? At 26.1° C the vapor pressure of water is 25.4 mm.
Ans. 64.0%; 44.1%

2. Calculate the lifting power of 4000 liters of helium at standard conditions. The density of air is 1.293 g./l. and that of helium is 0.179 g./1. *Ans. 4,456 g.*

REFERENCES

Argon, Helium, and the Rare Gases, Edited by G. A. Cook, Interscience Publishers, New York (1961); Volume I — History, Occurrence, and Properties; Volume II — Production, Analytical Determination, and Uses.

"Xenon Tetrafluoride," H. H. Claasen, H. Selig, and J. G. Malm, *J. Am. Chem. Soc.*, **84**, 3593 (1962).

"'Inert' Xenon Reacts with Fluorine," (Staff) *Chem. Eng. News*, October 8, 1962; p. 39.

"Fluorine Compounds of Xenon and Radon," C. L. Chernick, et al., *Science*, **138** (3537) 136 (October 12, 1962).

CHAPTER TWENTY-FIVE

Nitrogen, Ammonia, and Rocket Propellants

The elements of Periodic Group VA are known as the **nitrogen family.** Nitrogen is the first member of the family, which also includes phosphorus, arsenic, antimony, and bismuth. Nitrogen and phosphorus are among our most important and useful nonmetals. There is a regular gradation with increasing atomic weight in the nitrogen family from the characteristics of a true nonmetal with nitrogen to those of an almost true metal with bismuth. As has been noted with fluorine and oxygen, which are the lightest members of their families of the Periodic Table, some of the properties of nitrogen are anomalous, while more regular trends are found in the series phosphorus, arsenic, antimony, and bismuth (discussed in later chapters of this book).

The chemistry of nitrogen is sufficiently important and interesting to warrant its study apart from the other members of the family.

25.1 History and Occurrence of Nitrogen

Nitrogen was first recognized as an element by the Scotch botanist Rutherford in 1772. He demonstrated that this gas does not support either life or combustion. Lavoisier named it "azote," meaning "lifeless," by which name it is known in France today. The name **nitrogen** comes from "niter," which is a nitrogen-containing compound, KNO_3, also known as saltpeter.

Nitrogen comprises 78 per cent of the atmosphere by volume and 75 per cent by weight. It has been estimated that there are more than 20 million tons of nitrogen over every square mile of the earth's surface. Natural gas also contains some free nitrogen. The most important mineral sources of nitrogen in compound form are the **saltpeter** (KNO_3) and **Chile saltpeter** ($NaNO_3$) deposits in South America (mainly Chile). Nitrogen is an essential element of the proteins of all plants and animals. An important source of nitrogen compounds is the coal that is used in the production of coke and illuminating gas.

25.2 Preparation

On an industrial scale, nitrogen is obtained by the fractional distillation of liquid air. Nitrogen prepared in this way contains a small amount of oxygen and the rare gases, particularly argon.

Pure or chemical nitrogen is prepared by heating a solution of ammonium nitrite, which decomposes as follows:

$$NH_4NO_2 \rightarrow 2\ H_2O + N_2$$

Usually a mixture of sodium nitrite and ammonium chloride is used to furnish the ions of ammonium nitrite because ammonium nitrite is so unstable that it cannot be stored. The equation for the reaction may be written

$$NH_4^+ + (Cl^-) + (Na^+) + NO_2^- \rightarrow (Na^+) + (Cl^-) + 2\ H_2O + N_2 \uparrow$$

Nitrogen may also be prepared by the oxidation of ammonia. One such method involves passing ammonia gas over red-hot copper oxide.

$$2\ NH_3 + 3\ CuO \rightarrow 3\ H_2O + N_2 + 3\ Cu$$

A convenient laboratory method of obtaining atmospheric nitrogen (nitrogen plus the rare gases) is to burn phosphorus in air which is confined over water (Fig. 25–1). The P_4O_{10} which is formed dissolves in the water, and the residual gas is mainly nitrogen.

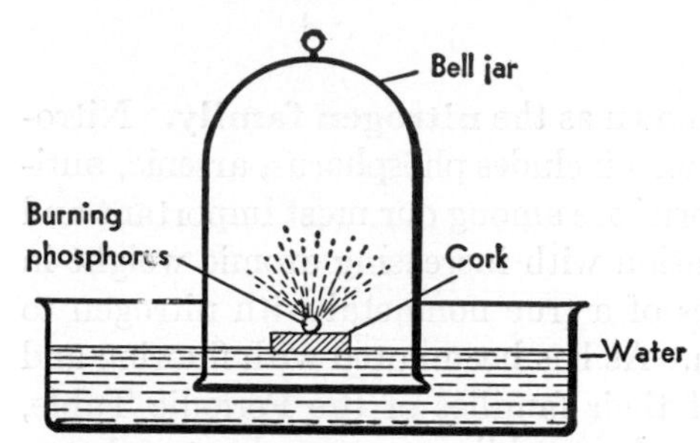

Fig. 25–1 Laboratory preparation of atmospheric nitrogen.

25.3 Properties of Nitrogen

1. *Physical properties.* Under ordinary conditions nitrogen is a colorless, odorless, and tasteless gas. It boils at −195.8° under one atmosphere of pressure, and its freezing point is −210.0°. Its density under standard conditions is 1.2506 g./l.; it is slightly less dense than air, for air contains the heavier molecules of oxygen as well as those of nitrogen. Under standard conditions, 100 ml. of water dissolves 2.4 ml. of nitrogen.

2. *Chemical properties.* The nitrogen atom has five electrons in its outermost shell. The diatomic molecule, N_2, consists of two atoms bonded together by three pairs of electrons, as shown in the structure

$$:N:::N:$$

The triple bond between the atoms is very strong. An evidence of this is the fact that 171,000 calories of energy are absorbed when one mole of the element is decomposed into its atoms. The nitrogen molecule is the most stable diatomic molecule known. The lack of chemical reactivity of nitrogen under ordinary conditions also reflects the stability of its molecular structure. When heated with certain active metals, nitrogen forms **ionic nitrides** which contain the nitride ion, N^{-3}. Examples are Li_3N, Ca_3N_2, and Mg_3N_2. At high temperatures nitrogen combines with hydrogen, forming ammonia, NH_3, and with oxygen, forming nitric oxide, NO.

Although the reactions of nitrogen take place at high temperatures, this does not mean that the triple bond has to be broken before nitrogen reacts. Instead, the preliminary step in its reactions may involve union with activated molecules which have become active by the elevation of one or more bonding electrons to higher energy levels. This may be followed by the breaking of the double bond (N═N) or single bond (N—N) which remains, because these are far less stable than the original N≡N triple bond.

Most nitrogen compounds are formed from ammonia, nitric acid, or one of the oxides of nitrogen rather than directly from the element. For the most part, nitrogen compounds are unstable and revert readily to the element; this is due to the high heat of formation of the triple bond of the nitrogen molecule.

Nitrogen is a highly electronegative element, its electronegativity being exceeded only by those of oxygen and fluorine (see Section 4.6). As seen in Table 25·1, nitrogen assumes every integral oxidation state from −3 to +5.

TABLE 25·1 Oxidation States of Nitrogen

Oxidation state	*Formula*	*Name*
−3	NH_3	Ammonia
−3	NH_4^+	Ammonium ion
−2	$N_2H_4(H_2N\text{–}NH_2)$	Hydrazine
−1	NH_2OH	Hydroxylamine
0	N_2	Nitrogen
+1	N_2O	Nitrous oxide or dinitrogen (mon)oxide
+2	NO	Nitric oxide or nitrogen oxide
+3	N_2O_3	Nitrogen trioxide or dinitrogen trioxide
+3	HNO_2	Nitrous acid
+4	NO_2	Nitrogen dioxide
+4	N_2O_4	Nitrogen tetroxide or dinitrogen tetroxide
+5	N_2O_5	Nitrogen pentoxide or dinitrogen pentoxide
+5	HNO_3	Nitric acid

25.4 Uses of Elementary Nitrogen

Large quantities of elementary nitrogen are used in the various processes for "fixing atmospheric nitrogen," i.e., bringing about the combination of nitrogen with other elements. These processes are discussed later. Several uses of nitrogen are based on its inactivity. Frequently, when a chemical process requires an inert atmosphere, nitrogen is used. Nitrogen was formerly widely used to fill electric light bulbs to inhibit vaporization of the filament but now has been displaced to a large extent by argon, which is even more inert. In thermometers designed for measuring temperatures above 350° C, nitrogen is used to fill the space above the mercury and thus to reduce the evaporation of the mercury (boiling point 357°). Such mercury thermometers can be used for measuring temperatures as high as 500°. Certain canned foods such as coffee and hydrogenated vegetable oils (Crisco and Spry) retain their flavor and color much better if the "air space" in the can is filled with nitrogen instead of air.

AMMONIA

Ammonia was known to the early chemists but was first prepared in the pure state in 1774 by Priestley. He obtained ammonia by heating sal ammoniac, NH_4Cl, with slaked lime, $Ca(OH)_2$, and he called the gas "alkaline air." Berthollet showed in 1785 that ammonia is a compound of hydrogen and nitrogen. It is the most important of the compounds containing only these two elements.

Ammonia, NH_3, is produced in nature when any nitrogen-containing organic material is decomposed in the absence of air. The decomposition may be brought about by the action of heat or of bacteria which produce decay. The odor of ammonia is prevalent in stables and is frequently detected in sewage where decay is taking place.

25.5 Preparation of Ammonia

1. *A laboratory method.* Ammonia is usually prepared in the laboratory by heating an ammonium salt with sodium hydroxide or slaked lime. For example, the reaction of NH_4Cl with NaOH is given by the equation

$$NH_4^+ + (Cl^-) + (Na^+) + OH^- \rightarrow NH_3\uparrow + H_2O + (Na^+) + (Cl^-)$$

The gaseous ammonia which is evolved may be collected by the downward displacement of air from an inverted bottle.

Ammonia is also formed by the hydrolysis of ionic nitrides. Examples are given by the following equations:

$$Mg_3N_2 + 6\ H_2O \rightarrow 3\ Mg(OH)_2 + 2\ NH_3\uparrow$$
$$Li_3N + 3\ H_2O \rightarrow 3\ Li^+ + 3\ OH^- + NH_3\uparrow$$

2. *From coal.* Soft coal contains about one per cent combined nitrogen. About one fifth of this nitrogen is liberated as ammonia when the coal is heated in the absence of air (destructive distillation). The ammonia gas which comes off is mixed with a variety of substances. It is dissolved in water, and when the resulting solution is treated with lime, pure ammonia is produced and is absorbed in sulfuric or hydrochloric acid to form ammonium sulfate or ammonium chloride. One ton of coal yields, on the average, enough ammonia to produce 20 pounds of

ammonium sulfate. In recent years, nearly a million tons of ammonium sulfate have been produced annually by this method. The ammonium sulfate is a valuable fertilizer.

3. *By the Haber process.* Ammonia is produced on a commercial scale by the direct union of its elements by the Haber process.

$$N_2 + 3\ H_2 \rightleftharpoons 2\ NH_3 + 22{,}080 \text{ cal.}$$

Note that the reaction is exothermic and reversible, so that the yield of ammonia becomes less and less as the temperature of the system is raised. However, at low temperatures the reaction is too slow to be of practical value. Because four volumes of the reactants (1 of N_2 and 3 of H_2) give two volumes of the product (NH_3), high pressure causes an increase in the yield of ammonia at any given temperature. It would seem, then, that the process should be carried out at the lowest temperature and highest pressure practicable. Because the reaction rate at low temperatures is too low for the process to be of any value, the need for a catalyst is apparent. Of the many catalysts which have been tried, the most efficient is a mixture of iron oxide and potassium aluminate. A yield of 15 per cent is obtained by employing a pressure of 200 atmospheres, and a temperature of 500°. In the similar Claude process, a yield of 40 per cent is attained using a pressure of about 1000 atmospheres at the same temperature.

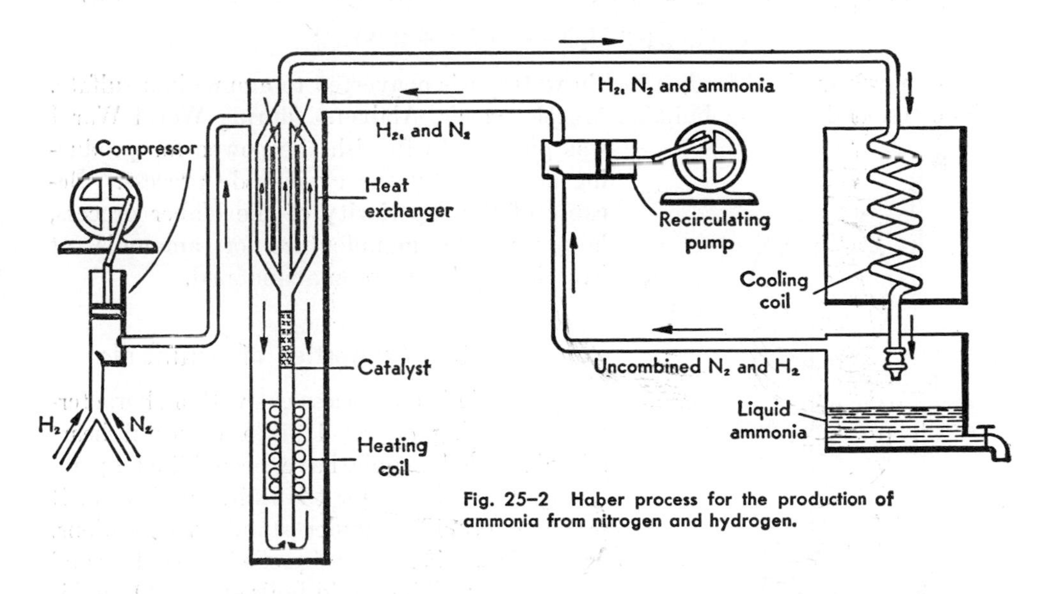

Fig. 25–2 Haber process for the production of ammonia from nitrogen and hydrogen.

The hydrogen and nitrogen which are used in the Haber process (Fig. 25–2) must be very pure to avoid "poisoning" of the catalyst. The nitrogen for the process is obtained from liquid air and much of the hydrogen is obtained from "water gas" (Section 6.2). The mixture of hydrogen and nitrogen is compressed, heated, and then passed over the catalyst. The ammonia is removed by liquefaction and the residual hydrogen and nitrogen are recycled through the catalyst chamber.

Fritz Haber, a German chemist, received the 1918 Nobel award in chemistry for his success in developing the direct synthesis of ammonia on a commercial scale.

4. *By the cyanamide process.* Another process for the fixation of atmospheric nitrogen in the form of ammonia is the **cyanamide process** of Frank and Caro (1895). The steps in the process are as follows:

(a) Calcium carbide is formed by heating lime and coke in an electric furnace.

$$CaO + 3\ C \rightarrow CaC_2 + CO$$

(b) Nitrogen, obtained from liquid air, is passed over crushed calcium carbide mixed with some calcium chloride or fluoride and heated to 1100°. This produces **calcium cyanamide,** $CaCN_2$, and carbon; the mixture is dark gray in color and is called **nitrolime.**

$$CaC_2 + N_2 \rightarrow CaCN_2 + C$$

Calcium cyanamide may be used directly as a fertilizer, but it is more satisfactory to convert it into ammonium salts for this use.

(c) The calcium cyanamide is agitated with cold water to hydrolyze any unchanged calcium carbide ($CaC_2 + 2\ H_2O \rightarrow Ca(OH)_2 + C_2H_2$), and then it is treated with steam under pressure in an autoclave to hydrolyze the cyanamide.

$$CaCN_2 + 3\ H_2O \rightarrow CaCO_3 + 2\ NH_3 \uparrow$$

The ammonia evolved is absorbed in water or is converted to ammonium sulfate.

The tremendous dam built at Muscle Shoals, Alabama, during World War I was planned to furnish the power for producing ammonia by the cyanamide process. Because of the superiority of the Haber process, however, the manufacture of ammonia at Muscle Shoals was soon abandoned.

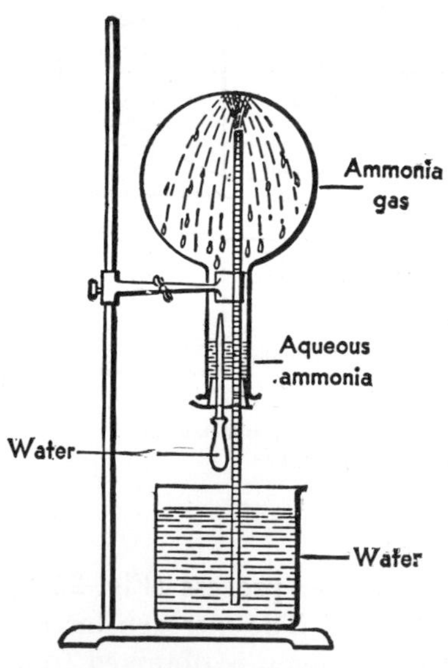

Fig. 25–3 Ammonia fountain, based upon the immense solubility of ammonia in water.

25.6 Physical Properties of Ammonia

Ammonia is a colorless gas with a characteristic, irritating odor. It is a powerful heart stimulant and people have been killed by inhaling it. It is lighter than air, one liter of it weighing 0.7710 g. under standard conditions. Ammonia gas is readily liquefied by cooling and compressing. The liquid boils at −33.43° and is colorless. The solid is white and crystalline; it melts at −77.76°. The heat of vaporization of liquid ammonia (328.3 calories per gram) is higher than that of any other liquid except water, so ammonia is valuable as a refrigerant. Ammonia is quite soluble in water, alcohol, and ether. One liter of water at 0° dissolves 1185 liters of the gas; consequently, a small quantity of water introduced into a flask of the gas produces a fountain (Fig. 25–3). All of the gas may be expelled from its aqueous solutions by boiling.

25.7 Chemical Properties of Ammonia

Ammonia is a chemically active compound in which the three hydrogen atoms are linked to the nitrogen atom by covalent bonds. This leaves the nitrogen atom with one unshared pair of electrons.

$$\begin{array}{c} H \\ {\scriptstyle \circ\times} \\ H \overset{\circ}{\underset{\times}{}} N \overset{\times}{\underset{\times}{}} \\ {\scriptstyle \circ\times} \\ H \end{array}$$

Ammonia

The ammonia molecule is pyramidal in shape (rule 2, under item 4, Section 23.1). This structure may be regarded as a tetrahedron with the unshared pair of electrons occupying one tetrahedral position.

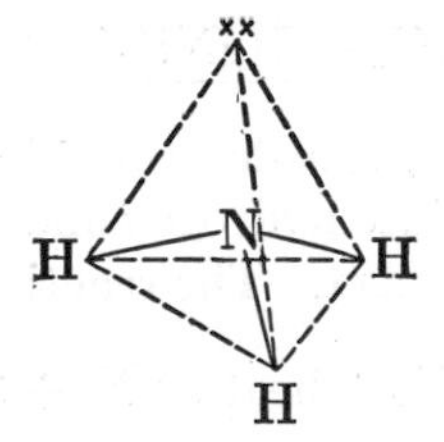

The ammonia molecule is highly polar, a property which is responsible in part for its physical and chemical behavior.

In comparison with the corresponding hydrides of the other members of the nitrogen family, ammonia is the most highly associated in the liquid state, the most stable toward decomposition by heat, and the most strongly basic.

The unshared electron pair of the ammonia molecule can readily be shared by an atom or ion that has an incomplete outer shell, with the formation of a coordinate bond. The chemical properties of ammonia may be outlined as follows:

(1) Ammonia is a base in that it readily accepts protons and acts as an electron pair donor. When ammonia dissolves in water, part of it reacts, forming ammonium and hydroxide ions.

$$\begin{array}{c} H \\ {\scriptstyle \circ\times} \\ H \overset{\circ}{\underset{\times}{}} N \overset{\times}{\underset{\times}{}} \\ {\scriptstyle \circ\times} \\ H \end{array} + \begin{array}{c} {\scriptstyle \times\times} \\ H \overset{\circ}{\underset{\times}{}} O \overset{\times}{\underset{\times}{}} \\ {\scriptstyle \circ\times} \\ H \end{array} \rightleftarrows \left[\begin{array}{c} H \\ {\scriptstyle \circ\times} \\ H \overset{\circ}{\underset{\times}{}} N \overset{\times}{\underset{\times}{}} H \\ {\scriptstyle \circ\times} \\ H \end{array}\right]^{+} + \left[\begin{array}{c} {\scriptstyle \times\times} \\ \overset{\circ}{\underset{\times}{}} O \overset{\circ}{\underset{\times}{}} H \\ {\scriptstyle \times\times} \end{array}\right]^{-}$$

The reaction is reversible and the equilibrium lies far to the left so that ionization is only slight. **Aqueous ammonia** is, therefore, only weakly basic.

Ammonia accepts protons from acids and hydronium ions, as shown by the equations

$$NH_3 + HCl \rightleftharpoons NH_4^+ + Cl^-$$
$$NH_3 + H_3O^+ \rightleftharpoons NH_4^+ + H_2O$$

The ammonium ion (NH_4^+) is similar in properties to the potassium ion, and its salts are called ammonium salts.

Gaseous ammonia and gaseous hydrogen chloride react and form a cloud of very small crystals of ammonium chloride. This reaction is used in forming smoke screens; it also accounts largely for the white deposit found on windowpanes and glassware in chemical laboratories.

Ammonia forms **ammines** by sharing electrons with certain metallic ions, just as water forms hydrates (see Chapter 34).

$$Cu^{++} + 4\ {}^{\times}_{\times}NH_3 \rightarrow Cu({}^{\times}_{\times}NH_3)_4^{++} \quad \text{(tetraamminecopper (II) ion)}$$
$$Ag^+ + 2\ {}^{\times}_{\times}NH_3 \rightarrow Ag({}^{\times}_{\times}NH_3)_2^+ \quad \text{(diamminesilver ion)}$$

(2) Certain compounds undergo **ammonolysis** in the presence of ammonia. This process is analogous to hydrolysis. The equation for the ammonolysis of mercury (II) chloride is

$$HgCl_2 + 2\ NH_3 \rightarrow \underline{HgNH_2Cl} + NH_4^+ + Cl^-$$

$HgNH_2Cl$ is called **mercury (II) amido chloride.**

(3) Ammonia is decomposed into hydrogen and nitrogen at red heat; the action of electric sparks has the same effect. The reaction is reversible.

$$2\ NH_3 + \text{heat} \rightleftharpoons N_2 + 3\ H_2$$

(4) Hot ammonia is an active reducing agent and reduces the oxides of certain metals, such as copper (II) oxide.

$$2\ NH_3 + 3\ CuO \rightarrow N_2 + 3\ Cu + 3\ H_2O$$

Ammonia also exhibits its properties as a reducing agent when it burns in oxygen, forming water vapor and nitrogen.

$$4\ NH_3 + 3\ O_2 \rightarrow 2\ N_2 + 6\ H_2O$$

A mixture of ammonia and air in contact with platinum at 700° forms nitric oxide.

$$4\ NH_3 + 5\ O_2 \rightarrow 4\ NO + 6\ H_2O$$

This reaction is one step in the production of nitric acid from ammonia (Section 26.2).

(5) Ammonia forms nitrides by acting upon certain metals at high temperatures.

$$2\ NH_3 + 3\ Mg \rightarrow Mg_3N_2 + 3\ H_2$$
$$2\ NH_3 + 6\ Li \rightarrow 2\ Li_3N + 3\ H_2$$

25.8 Liquid Ammonia as a Solvent

In the early part of the 20th century, E. C. Franklin (Fig. 25–4), professor of chemistry at Stanford University, conducted extensive research on liquid ammonia as a solvent for electrolytes. Of the various solvents which have been studied, liquid ammonia most closely resembles water. It dissolves many electrolytes readily and the solutions so formed are good conductors of electricity. The waterlike character of liquid ammonia is due to association of ammonia molecules through hydrogen bonding. However, because the NHN bond of ammonia is weaker than the OHO bond of water, the properties which depend upon association are less pronounced with ammonia than with water. Ammonia is a poorer solvent for electrolytes than water because its dielectric constant is lower than that of water. This means that ammonia does not insulate oppositely charged ions in solution as well as does water (Section 12.7).

Fig. 25–4 E. C. Franklin, pioneer in the use of liquid ammonia. *Boyé*

The various types of reactions which occur in water also take place in liquid ammonia. Like water, pure ammonia is a very poor conductor of electricity, but it does ionize slightly in accordance with the equation

$$2\ NH_3 \rightleftharpoons NH_4^+ + NH_2^-$$

Note the similarity to the ionization of water.

$$2\ H_2O \rightleftharpoons H_3O^+ + OH^-$$

Liquid ammonia possesses the ability to dissolve the more electropositive metals such as Na, K, Ba, and Ca. The free metals can be recovered by evaporation of the solvent. If the solutions are concentrated, they exhibit a bronze color and conduct electricity like a pure metal. When dilute, they are bright blue and conduct electricity like aqueous solutions of salts. It appears that when a metal such as sodium dissolves in liquid ammonia, it becomes a positive ion by losing its valence electron.

$$Na \rightleftharpoons Na^+ + e^-$$

The ammonia molecules then solvate these ions and electrons reversibly according to the equations

$$Na^+ + x\ NH_3 \rightleftharpoons Na(NH_3)_x^+$$
$$e^- + y\ NH_3 \rightleftharpoons e^-(NH_3)_y$$

The "ammoniated electron" is responsible for the color and the strong reducing properties shown by solutions of metals in liquid ammonia. Such solutions are abundant sources of free electrons which may be taken up readily by reducible ions or compounds. In fact, liquid ammonia solutions of sodium are used widely in both organic and inorganic reductions.

If metal-liquid ammonia solutions are allowed to stand, hydrogen is slowly liberated according to the equation (in the case of sodium)

$$2\ Na + 2\ NH_3 \rightarrow 2\ Na^+ + \underset{\text{Sodium amide}}{2\ NH_2^-} + H_2$$

However, metallic iron catalyzes the reaction so that it takes place quite rapidly.

The **amide ion** (NH_2^-) in the liquid ammonia system is analogous to the OH^- ion in the water system. The amide ion is a base in liquid ammonia, and the ammonium ion (NH_4^+) is an acid, analogous to the hydronium ion (H_3O^+) in the water system. In aqueous solutions, neutralization involves the formation of the water (the solvent).

$$H_3O^+ + OH^- \rightarrow 2\ H_2O$$

Neutralization reactions in liquid ammonia result in the formation of ammonia (the solvent).

$$NH_4^+ + NH_2^- \rightarrow 2\ NH_3$$

In aqueous solution:

$$H_3O^+ + (Cl^-) + (Na^+) + OH^- \rightarrow (Na^+) + (Cl^-) + 2\ H_2O$$

In liquid ammonia:

$$NH_4^+ + (Cl^-) + (Na^+) + NH_2^- \rightarrow (Na^+) + (Cl^-) + 2\ NH_3$$

Metathetical (double decomposition) reactions very often proceed in an entirely different direction in liquid ammonia than in water because solubility relationships are not always the same in the two solvents. For example, silver chloride is soluble in ammonia, but not in water, whereas barium chloride is insoluble in liquid ammonia, but soluble in water. The reaction between silver nitrate and barium chloride in water is

$$2\ Ag^+ + (2\ NO_3^-) + (Ba^{++}) + 2\ Cl^- \rightarrow 2\ \underline{AgCl} + (Ba^{++}) + (2\ NO_3^-)$$

The reaction in liquid ammonia differs from that in water, as shown by the equation

$$(2\ Ag^+) + 2\ Cl^- + Ba^{++} + (2\ NO_3^-) \rightarrow \underline{BaCl_2} + (2\ Ag^+) + (2\ NO_3^-)$$

Ammonia combines with the proton with the formation of a stronger bond than does water, and hence many ammonium salts are quite stable, whereas most of the corresponding hydronium compounds are unstable and exist in solution only, or at low temperature. The fact that hydronium ions give up protons to ammonia molecules shows that the bond between the proton and ammonia is stronger than that between the proton and water. The equation for the reaction is

$$NH_3 + H_3O^+ \rightleftharpoons NH_4^+ + H_2O$$

25.9 Uses of Ammonia

About three fourths of the ammonia produced in the United States is used in fertilizers, either as the compound itself or as ammonium salts such as the sulfate and nitrate. The practice of the direct application of anhydrous ammonia and of solutions of ammonium compounds to the soil is rapidly increasing. Large quantities of ammonia are used in the production of nitric acid, urea, and other nitrogen compounds. Ammonia is the most common refrigerant used in the production of ice and for the maintenance of low temperatures in refrigerating plants. "Household ammonia" is an aqueous solution of ammonia. It is used to remove the carbonate hardness from hard water and thus save soap in cleansing and washing in the home.

OTHER COMPOUNDS OF NITROGEN AND HYDROGEN

25.10 Hydrazine

When ammonia is oxidized by sodium hypochlorite in the presence of sodium hydroxide and gelatin or glue, **hydrazine** (N_2H_4) is produced. The reactions involved may be described by the following equations:

$$NH_3 + OCl^- \rightarrow NH_2Cl + OH^-$$
$$NH_2Cl + NH_3 + OH^- \rightarrow N_2H_4 + Cl^- + H_2O$$

Chloramine, NH_2Cl, is an intermediate in the process. A large excess of ammonia is used and the reactants are thoroughly mixed at low temperatures.

Their structural formulas show that hydrazine may be regarded as the nitrogen analogue of hydrogen peroxide.

```
   H H                  •• xx
H:N:N:H              H:O:O:H
  •• xx                 •• xx
```

Hydrazine Hydrogen peroxide

Anhydrous hydrazine is thermally stable but very reactive toward many reagents. It burns in air and reacts vigorously with the halogens. Aqueous hydrazine is weakly alkaline and forms two series of salts, as shown by the following equations:

$$N_2H_4 + H_2O \rightleftharpoons N_2H_5^+ + OH^-$$
$$N_2H_4 + HCl \rightleftharpoons N_2H_5^+ + Cl^-$$
$$N_2H_4 + 2\ HCl \rightleftharpoons N_2H_6^{++} + 2\ Cl^-$$

Anhydrous hydrazine is readily oxidized to free nitrogen and water by hydrogen peroxide.

$$N_2H_4 + 2\ H_2O_2 \rightarrow N_2\uparrow + 4\ H_2O$$

Because the products of the reaction between these two liquids are both gaseous at the temperature of the reaction and the reaction is highly exothermic, it is accompanied by a tremendous increase in volume and so have been used in the propulsion of rockets.

25.11 Hydrazoic Acid

When hydrazine is reduced by nitrous acid, a colorless liquid, **hydrazoic acid** (HN_3), is formed.

$$N_2H_4 + HNO_2 \rightarrow HN_3 + 2\ H_2O$$

Hydrazoic acid detonates violently when subjected to shock. It is a weak acid and it reacts with both oxidizing and reducing agents. Its salts are called **azides;** like the acid, they are unstable. Lead azide, $Pb(N_3)_2$, is used as a detonator for military explosives. The structure of hydrazoic acid is best represented by

$$\mathrm{H{:}\ddot{N}{::}N{::}\ddot{N}{:}}$$

The three nitrogen atoms of the azide ion (N_3^-) lie in a straight line.

25.12 Hydroxylamine

Hydroxylamine, NH_2OH, may be considered to be a derivative of ammonia in which an OH group has replaced one hydrogen atom of ammonia. The electronic formula of hydroxylamine is

$$\begin{array}{c}\mathrm{H{:}\ddot{N}{:}\ddot{O}{:}H}\\ \mathrm{H}\end{array}$$

As a solvent, hydroxylamine exhibits waterlike character. The pure substance is an unstable white solid that undergoes thermal decomposition about 15° to ammonia, water, and a mixture of nitrogen and nitrous oxide. The decomposition can be explosive at elevated temperatures. Aqueous solutions of hydroxylamine are more stable. They are weakly basic, their basic strength being somewhat less than that of solutions of ammonia. Hydroxylamine is usually prepared and handled as a **hydroxylammonium salt,** such as the chloride, $NH_3OH^+Cl^-$.

These salts are ordinarily prepared by the reduction of the nitrite ion, either electrolytically or by means of sulfur dioxide (or alkali metal hydrogen sulfite). The industrial production of hydroxylammonium salts involves treatment of primary nitroparaffins with mineral acids. Hydroxylamine is an active reducing agent.

ROCKET PROPELLANTS

25.13 Meanings of Terms

Rocket propellants contain an **oxidant** (oxidizing substance) and a **fuel** (reducing substance). Usually, the term "fuel" is used to mean the reducing component; occasionally, the term is alternatively used to indicate the propellant as a whole. If the oxidant and the fuel are two separate materials which are mixed during the burning process, the propellant is referred to as a **bipropellant** or a **bifuel.** If the oxidant and fuel are in close association or are parts of the same molecule, the propellant is referred to as a **monopropellant** or **monofuel.**

Propellants are classified in terms of **liquid propellants** and **solid propellants.** In motors using liquid bipropellants, the oxidant and fuel are carried in separate tanks from which both are pumped and injected into the combustion chamber in fine streams. A prime problem is the high temperature of about 2500–3500° K and also the high rate of transfer of energy from burning gases to the walls of the chamber. The flame temperature is high compared to the melting point of the thin-walled casing of the rocket. However, the problem exists for a very short period of time during the combustion process. Overheating the casing is also avoided by circulating the fuel through a honeycombed wall of the reaction chamber and around the throat of the exit nozzle. In motors using solid propellants, the combustion takes place in a cavity extending through the entire length of the charge, from the center out, toward the thin inner wall of the casing. Ideally, the flame does not touch the casing until essentially all of the propellant has been consumed. Thus, the charge, itself, solves part of the insulation problem. The solid fuel motor in flight carries no mechanical pumps or valves which might stick or leak, and the propellant has less chance of getting into places not intended than would a liquid.

25.14 Selection of Materials as Oxidants and Fuels

The commonly accepted criterion of propellant performance is **specific impulse.** Specific impulse is the number of pounds of thrust, or force, developed per second for each pound of propellant and is listed in seconds. Several typical propellants and the specific impulse of each are listed in Table 25·2 on page 394.

A high energy fuel must have a high heat of combustion, low vapor pressure, good thermal stability, high density, and a high flame speed. In addition, it must have the physical properties necessary to insure safe handling during manufacture, shipping, and storage. The heat of combustion is the net energy resulting from breaking chemical bonds and making new bonds to form different molecular arrangements.

The requirements for high energy fuels are satisfied only in molecules of low molecular weight. Hence, the choice of elements as fuel constituents is quite limited and includes principally the elements up to about silicon in the Periodic Table.

H							He
Li	Be	B	C	N	O	F	Ne
Na	Mg	Al	Si				

Most common rocket systems have used carbon, hydrogen, oxygen, and nitrogen as fuel constituents.

TABLE 25·2 Some Typical Rocket Propellants

Oxidant	*Fuel*	*Theoretical Specific Impulse (in Seconds)*
	LIQUID BIPROPELLANTS	
Hydrogen peroxide; Nitric acid (fuming); Dinitrogen tetroxide	Alcohols, petroleum fuels, hydrazine hydrate	250–300
Oxygen (liq.)	Ethanol (92.5%)	287
	Kerosene	300
	Ammonia (liq.)	294
	Hydrazine	313
	Hydrogen (liq.)	391
Chlorine trifluoride	Kerosene	294
	Hydrazine	258
Fluorine (liq.)	Ammonia (liq.)	357
	Hydrazine	363
	Hydrogen (liq.)	410
	LIQUID MONOPROPELLANTS	
	Hydrogen peroxide (90%)	147
	Ethylene oxide	180
	Hydrazine	196
	Propyl nitrate	173
	Nitromethane	220
	SOLID PROPELLANTS	
Cordite (colloidally dispersed nitrocellulose in nitroglycerine)		190–235
Perchlorates	Organic polymers	180–245

Liquid hydrogen liberates a large amount of energy for a given weight when oxidized and for this reason is an important fuel in the space program of the United States. Its low boiling point and low liquid density, however, constitute rather serious disadvantages for a high energy fuel. Materials used as fuels, therefore, are often compounds in which hydrogen is combined with another light element to yield a denser material of higher boiling point than hydrogen, itself.

The high thermal stability of the nitrogen molecule is one of the reasons why nitrogen-containing substances are often used in fuels.

$$2\ N = N_2 + 171\ \text{kcal.}$$

When monopropellants are used, they must be chosen carefully because of their sensitivity. Decomposition, once started through friction, electric discharge, or impact, is often self-sustaining and may change from steady burning into detonation. In general, the useful monopropellants have lower specific impulses than bifuels, because in bifuels it is possible to keep the two components physically separated until ready to mix for combustion. With monofuels, a delicate balance must be met in which the materials must have a sufficiently high burning rate to allow them to ignite without undue difficulty but not so high that they will be too easily detonated. One of the early monopropellants was hydrogen peroxide, which can also be used as the oxidant in bifuel systems. Its use as a monofuel depends upon catalytic decomposition:

$$2\ H_2O_2 = 2\ H_2O + O_2 + 48.0\ \text{kcal.}$$

Organic nitrates and other nitrogen compounds are also used as monofuels (Table 25·2).

The period of combustion for a rocket propellant is usually not more than two to three minutes and is often much shorter. During the brief period of burning, the rate at which power is generated is extremely high. The average rate of fuel consumption in flight may exceed a half-ton per second, which is equivalent, in the case of a propellant using oxygen as the oxidant and kerosene as the fuel, to six million B.T.U. per second, or about nine million horsepower.

Motors utilizing liquid propellants are very expensive because of the necessary equipment for pumping and mixing the liquids. Many rockets, such as the huge Atlas, use liquid oxygen as the oxidant. The low boiling temperature of oxygen (−183° C) is difficult to maintain in the rocket because of the undesirable weight of extra insulation. A sufficient temperature rise to create a hazardous situation may occur within seven or eight hours after the rocket is fueled. Delays, therefore, necessitate removing the liquid oxygen and proceeding with a tedious task of washing, drying, and checking the engine for contamination before refueling. Such procedures are costly in time, money, manpower, and material. However, at the present stage of propellant development, liquid propellants are generally more powerful and permit better guidance and control than do solid propellants.

Solid fuel boosters, by comparison, have the major advantages of ease in handling, low cost, and reliability, because of their relatively simple design. They are self-contained. They can be held for long periods of time on the launching pad without hazard. Solid fuel boosters can be reloaded and checked in a short time. There is no evaporation of fuel. The latest types of solid rocket propellants contain a crystalline oxidant, such as ammonium nitrate or ammonium perchlorate, constituting about 80–90% of their weight, and a solid fuel containing a large proportion of combined hydrogen for the other 10–20% of the total weight. The mixture is cemented together in order to gain more mechanical strength and greater flexibility than obtained by merely compressing the materials together.

The Minuteman, the Cajun, and the Polaris (Fig. 25–5, page 396) are United States rockets using reliable solid fuel boosters.

The technique of "staging" — ejecting each stage as it is burned out — is often used to remove useless weight. The Saturn vehicle, for example, is a three-stage liquid propellant rocket of 1.5 million pounds thrust, designed to put 7-ton payloads into orbit. Some of the recent rockets have had initial liquid stages with later stages consisting of clusters of solid motors. Plans are being developed to use a cluster of eight liquid fuel engines of 1.5 million pounds thrust each for the first stage of the Nova space rocket, being designed for the primary purpose of landing a man on the moon. The third stage of the Nova is to use solid propellants.

Fig. 25–5 The Polaris, the nation's first solid fuel ballistic missile fired from a submarine. *U.S. Navy Photograph*

It is possible that large solid fuel boosters may be developed with specific impulse comparable to that now available with liquid fuel and combining the reliability and economy of solid fuel boosters with the ease of control attainable with liquid fuel engines.

Nuclear power for rocket engines, a possibility for the not-too-distant future, will provide propellants which are several orders of magnitude more powerful than present propellants.

QUESTIONS

1. How is "atmospheric nitrogen" prepared? pure nitrogen?
2. Relate the inactivity of molecular nitrogen (N_2) to its thermal stability.
3. What is the oxidation state of nitrogen in each of the following: N_2, NH_4^+, $NaNO_2$, N_2H_4, NH_2OH, NO_2, N_2O_4, NH_4NO_3, and N_2O?
4. In what ways may atmospheric nitrogen be "fixed"?
5. Explain the effects of temperature, pressure, and a catalyst upon the direct synthesis of ammonia.
6. Write the equations for producing ammonia by the Cyanamide Process.
7. What compounds act as acids in liquid ammonia? as bases? What is the essential reaction involved in neutralizations in liquid ammonia?
8. Write electronic structures for N_2, NH_3, NH_4^+, N_2H_4, HN_3, and NH_2OH.
9. Account for the solubility of electrolytes in liquid ammonia.
10. What are the necessary properties for a high energy rocket fuel?
11. Compare liquid rocket fuels and solid rocket fuels with respect to the advantages and disadvantages of each.

12. Given the following energy data and making use of other important factors, evaluate the various substances in the reactions as possible fuel constituents. Consider forward and reverse reactions in your evaluation.

$$2\ N = N_2 + 171\ kcal.$$
$$2\ H_2O_2 = 2\ H_2O + O_2 + 48.0\ kcal.$$
$$2\ C + O_2 = 2\ CO + 52.84\ kcal.$$
$$2\ CO + O_2 = 2\ CO_2 + 135.3\ kcal.$$
$$CO + H_2O\ (g) = CO_2 + H_2 + 9.83\ kcal.$$
$$2\ H_2 + O_2 = 2\ H_2O + 136.0\ kcal.$$
$$N_2 + 3\ H_2 = 2\ NH_3 + 22.1\ kcal.$$
$$N_2H_4 + H_2O_2 = N_2 + 4\ H_2O\ (g) + 198.4\ kcal.$$

PROBLEMS

1. What volume of ammonia, collected at 25° and 740 mm., would be produced by the treatment of 100 g. of ammonium chloride with 100 ml. of 0.15 M sodium hydroxide? *Ans. 38 l.*

2. What volume of 0.430 M HCl is required to react with 36.2 l. of ammonia, measured at 1.30 atm. and 73.0°? *Ans. 3.86 l.*

3. What weight of magnesium nitride could be formed from the action of ammonia on 75.0 g. of magnesium? *Ans. 114 g.*

4. What volume of ammonia, measured at 750 mm. and 245° K, is required for the production of 300 g. of hydrazine, if a 75.0% yield is obtained? *Ans. 509 l.*

REFERENCES

"Chemistry of Hydrazine," L. F. Audrieth and P. H. Mohr, *Chem. Eng. News*, **26** (49) 3746 (1948).
"Liquid Ammonia as a Solvent," W. C. Fernelius and W. C. Johnson, *J. Chem. Educ.*, **5** (6) 664; (7) 828 (1928).
"Hydrazine," L. P. Lessing, *Sci. American*, July, 1953; p. 30.
"New Fuels," C. H. Johnson, *Proc. Chem. Soc. (London)*, August, 1959; p. 212.
"Solid and Liquid Propellants," (Staff) *Science*, **134**, 317 (1961) — Aug. 4, 1961.
"Solid Propellants," A. O. Dekker, *J. Chem. Educ.*, **37** (11) 597 (1960).
"Chemical Rocket Propulsion Systems," F. J. Hendel, *Chem. Eng.*, March 6, 1961; p. 99.
"Advanced Rocket Propulsion," F. J. Hendel, *Chem. Eng.*, April 3, 1961; p. 131.
"Exotic Rocket Propulsion Systems," F. J. Hendel, *Chem. Eng.*, July 24, 1961; p. 135.
"Liquid Propellants," (Staff) *Chem. Eng. News*, May 21, 1962; p. 27.

CHAPTER TWENTY-SIX

Oxygen Compounds of Nitrogen

Nitrogen forms a series of oxides and oxyacids. Nitric acid is the most important of these compounds and all the others may be obtained from it; for these reasons nitric acid is considered first.

OXYACIDS OF NITROGEN

26.1 Nitric Acid

Nitric acid, HNO_3, was known to the alchemists of the eighth century as aqua fortis (meaning "strong water"). It was prepared from KNO_3 and was used in the separation of gold and silver; it will dissolve the silver from alloys rich in silver, leaving the gold. Traces of nitric acid occur in the atmosphere after thunderstorms, and its salts are widely distributed in nature. Chile saltpeter ($NaNO_3$) is found in tremendous deposits (2 by 200 miles, and to a thickness of up to 5 feet) in the desert region near the boundary of Chile and Peru. Bengal saltpeter (KNO_3) is found in India and other countries of the Orient.

26.2 Preparation of Nitric Acid

1. *From nitrates.* Nitric acid was formerly produced commercially by heating a mixture of sodium nitrate and concentrated sulfuric acid.

$$NaNO_3 + H_2SO_4 \rightleftharpoons NaHSO_4 + HNO_3 \uparrow$$

At ordinary temperatures the reaction is reversible, and equilibrium is soon established. Because nitric acid boils at 86° while sulfuric acid boils at 338° ($NaNO_3$ and $NaHSO_4$ are nonvolatile), the nitric acid is readily removed from the reaction mixture by gentle heating. Consequently, the equilibrium is shifted to the right and the reaction goes to completion. The preparation of nitric acid on a laboratory scale involves the use of a glass retort of the type shown in Fig. 26–1. On a commercial scale, the retort is made of iron and the condenser tubes of glass, quartz, or duriron.

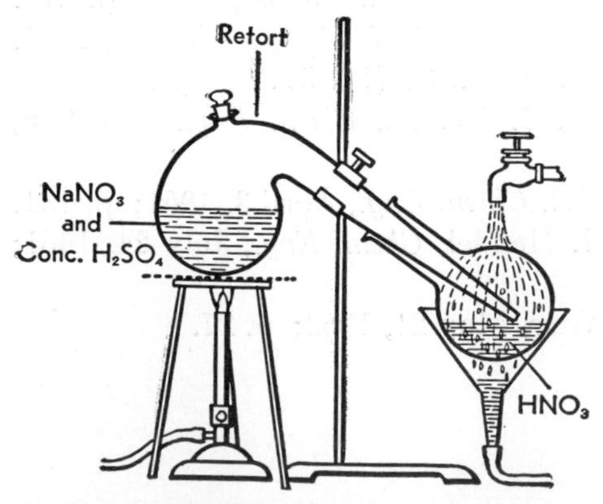

Fig. 26–1 Laboratory production of nitric acid.

2. *From ammonia.* The **Ostwald Process** for producing nitric acid consists of the oxidation of ammonia to nitric oxide (NO); the oxidation of nitric oxide to nitrogen dioxide (NO_2); and finally the conversion of nitrogen dioxide to nitric acid. Ammonia is mixed with 10 times its volume of air, the mixture is first heated to 600°, and then it is brought in contact with platinum gauze which acts as a catalyst. The reaction which results is exothermic and raises the temperature of the system to about 1000°.

$$4\ NH_3 + 5\ O_2 \rightarrow 4\ NO + 6\ H_2O + 216{,}240 \text{ cal.}$$

Additional air is admitted to the reaction chamber to cool the mixture and oxidize the nitric oxide to nitrogen dioxide.

$$2\ NO + O_2 \rightarrow 2\ NO_2 + 27{,}000 \text{ cal.}$$

The nitrogen dioxide, excess oxygen, and the unreacted nitrogen from the air are passed through a spray of water in an absorption tower where nitric acid and nitric oxide are formed.

$$3\ NO_2 + H_2O \rightarrow 2\ H^+ + 2\ NO_3^- + NO$$

The nitric oxide is combined with more oxygen and returned to the absorption tower. The nitric acid is drawn off and concentrated. Most of our nitric acid is now produced by this process although some is still made from nitrates and a small quantity is made by a newly developed process which produces nitric oxide directly from the elements.

3. *From nitric oxide produced directly from the elements.* Nitric oxide was formerly produced by the direct union of the elements at the very high temperature of the electric arc. This is the basis of the Arc Process for the production of nitric acid from the air.

$$N_2 + O_2 + 43{,}200 \text{ calories} \rightleftharpoons 2\ NO$$

The reaction is reversible and the union of the elements is endothermic; thus formation of NO is favored by high temperatures. However, even at 3000°, the equilibrium mixture contains only five per cent nitric oxide. The high cost of electricity for the electric arc and the low yield of nitric oxide caused abandonment of this process.

Recently, a highly promising process for making nitric oxide from air heated to 2100° has been developed. Air is passed through a preheating chamber and mixed with hot fuel gases to bring it to a temperature of 2100°. At this temperature, nitrogen and oxygen in air combine directly to form nitric oxide at a rapid rate, with a little over two per cent of the equilibrium mixture being nitric oxide. The gas is then cooled rapidly to 300° or below in a quick chilling chamber. The function of each chamber is reversed whenever the temperature of the quick chilling chamber rises to 300°. The rapid cooling brings the nitric oxide to thermal stability before appreciable decomposition to N_2 and O_2 can take place; whereas if nitric oxide is allowed to cool gradually, it decomposes completely to the elements. The chilling process is exceptionally efficient inasmuch as the gas flows at a rate of 360 inches per second and is cooled from 2100° to 300° while passing through a pebble chilling bed only 18 inches thick. The nitric oxide is oxidized to nitrogen dioxide as it cools in the large volume of air. The gas is concentrated by passing it over beds of silica gel which absorb nitrogen dioxide. The nitrogen dioxide is then driven off the silica gel by heating and is allowed to react with water to produce nitric acid.

The raw materials for the process are air and water. Cost of fuel gas and requirements for labor are not large. The process, which shows promise of being competitive with the Ostwald Process, has been utilized in at least one plant capable of producing 40 tons of nitric acid per day.

26.3 Physical Properties of Nitric Acid

Pure nitric acid is a colorless liquid that boils at 86°, has a density of 1.50 g./ml., and freezes to a white solid at −42°. It fumes in moist air, forming a cloud of very small droplets of aqueous nitric acid. An aqueous solution containing 68 per cent of the acid has a constant boiling point of 120.5° at one atmosphere of pressure. This is the concentrated acid of commerce; it has a specific gravity of 1.4048 at 20°.

26.4 Chemical Properties of Nitric Acid

The nitric acid molecule may be represented by the following electronic formula:

$$\begin{array}{c} \overset{\times\times}{\,\text{H}{:}\underset{\times\times}{\text{O}}{:}\text{N}{:}\underset{\times\times}{\text{O}}{:}} \\ {:}\text{O}{:} \end{array}$$

Pure nitric acid is unstable; it decomposes, upon being heated, to produce a mixture of nitrogen oxides, of which nitrogen dioxide is predominant:

$$4\ HNO_3 \rightarrow 4\ NO_2 + 2\ H_2O + O_2$$

In aqueous solution nitric acid is stable and exhibits (a) the properties of a strong acid, and (b) the properties of a strong oxidizing agent.

When brought in contact with the skin, concentrated nitric acid causes painful burns. If nitric acid is accidentally spilled on the skin, it should be washed off immediately with copious quantities of water. If the skin has been burned by the acid, a paste of sodium hydrogen carbonate (baking soda) should be applied.

26.5 Nitric Acid as an Oxidizing Agent

1. *Action with metals.* The products formed when nitric acid reacts with a metal depend upon (a) the concentration of the acid, (b) the activity of the metal, and (c) the temperature. A mixture of oxides and other reduction products is usually produced, but the less active metals, such as copper, silver, and lead, reduce dilute nitric acid primarily to nitric oxide. The reaction with copper is given by the equation

$$3\ Cu + 8\ H^+ + 2\ NO_3^- \rightarrow 3\ Cu^{++} + 2\ NO\uparrow + 4\ H_2O$$

With concentrated nitric acid, nitrogen dioxide is formed predominantly.

$$Cu + 4\ H^+ + 2\ NO_3^- \rightarrow Cu^{++} + 2\ NO_2 \uparrow + 2\ H_2O$$

The more active metals, such as zinc and iron, reduce dilute nitric acid to nitrous oxide (N_2O). With zinc, we have

$$4\ Zn + 10\ H^+ + 2\ NO_3^- \rightarrow 4\ Zn^{++} + N_2O \uparrow + 5\ H_2O$$

When the acid is very dilute, nitrogen or ammonium ions may be formed.

$$5\ Zn + 12\ H^+ + 2\ NO_3^- \rightarrow 5\ Zn^{++} + N_2 \uparrow + 6\ H_2O$$
$$4\ Zn + 10\ H^+ + NO_3^- \rightarrow 4\ Zn^{++} + NH_4^+ + 3\ H_2O$$

In concentrated nitric acid, zinc, as well as copper, produces nitric oxide and nitrogen dioxide. The nitrate salts of these metals separate as crystals when the solutions resulting from the above reactions are evaporated.

The action of nitric acid on a metal rarely produces hydrogen in more than small amounts.

It is seen, then, that it is difficult to predict with certainty what the reduction products of nitric acid will be and that frequently mixtures of compounds are obtained.

2. *Action with nonmetals.* Nonmetallic elements, such as sulfur, carbon, iodine, and phosphorus, are oxidized by concentrated nitric acid to their oxygen acids (or acid anhydrides), and NO_2 is formed.

$$S + 6\ HNO_3 \rightarrow H_2SO_4 + 6\ NO_2 \uparrow + 2\ H_2O$$
$$C + 4\ HNO_3 \rightarrow CO_2 + 4\ NO_2 \uparrow + 2\ H_2O$$

3. *Action of nitric acid on inorganic compounds.* Many compounds are oxidized by nitric acid. Hydrochloric acid is readily oxidized by concentrated nitric acid to chlorine and chlorine dioxide. A mixture of nitric and hydrochloric acids reacts vigorously with metals. It is particularly useful in dissolving gold and platinum and other metals which lie below hydrogen in the Electromotive Series. A mixture of three parts of concentrated hydrochloric acid and one part concentrated nitric acid is called **aqua regia** (meaning "royal water"). The action of aqua regia on gold may be represented, in a somewhat simplified form, by the following equation:

$$Au + 4\ HCl + 3\ HNO_3 \rightarrow HAuCl_4 + 3\ NO_2 \uparrow + 3\ H_2O$$

Dilute nitric acid oxidizes hydrogen sulfide to elementary sulfur and water.

$$3\ H_2S + 2\ H^+ + 2\ NO_3^- \rightarrow 3\ S + 2\ NO \uparrow + 4\ H_2O$$

Sulfur dioxide is oxidized to sulfuric acid by nitric acid.

$$3\ SO_2 + 2\ NO_3^- + 2\ H_2O \rightarrow 4\ H^+ + 3\ SO_4^{=} + 2\ NO \uparrow$$

4. *Action of nitric acid on organic compounds.* A mixture of concentrated nitric acid and concentrated sulfuric acid acts upon ordinary glycerin with the formation of **nitroglycerin.**

$$\underset{\text{Glycerin}}{C_3H_5(OH)_3} + 3\ HNO_3 \rightarrow \underset{\text{Nitroglycerin}}{C_3H_5(NO_3)_3} + 3\ H_2O$$

The sulfuric acid, by combining with the water which is formed, prevents the dilution of the nitric acid. The product is a liquid which may be transformed quickly into gaseous products, mostly carbon dioxide, nitrogen, and steam. Nitroglycerin is used in the manufacture of explosives such as dynamite, in which the liquid is taken up by a porous material such as infusorial earth or wood pulp. Nitroglycerin is also widely used as a drug for some heart ailments.

Guncotton is a cellulose nitrate which is made by nitrating cotton (cellulose) with nitric acid in the presence of sulfuric acid.

Trinitrotoluene (TNT), a valuable explosive, is produced by nitrating toluene; three NO_2 groups replace three hydrogen atoms of toluene in the reaction

$$\underset{\text{Toluene}}{CH_3C_6H_5} + 3\ HNO_3 \rightarrow \underset{\text{TNT}}{CH_3C_6H_2(NO_2)_3} + 3\ H_2O$$

26.6 Uses of Nitric Acid

Nitric acid is used extensively in the laboratory and in the chemical industries as a strong acid and principally as an active oxidizing agent. It is used in the manufacture of explosives, dyes, plastics, and drugs. Salts of nitric acid (nitrates) are valuable as fertilizers. **Black gunpowder** is a mixture of potassium nitrate, sulfur, and charcoal. **Ammonal,** an explosive, is a mixture of ammonium nitrate and aluminum powder.

26.7 Nitrates

The nitrate ion has a planar structure (see rule 2, under item 4, Section 23.1), with each bond between nitrogen and oxygen being a single-bond-double-bond hybrid. The three resonance structures are given below:

```
[   :O:   ]-   [   :Ö:   ]-   [   :Ö:   ]-
[   ::    ]    [    x•   ]    [    x•   ]
[    N    ]    [    N    ]    [    N    ]
[ :Ö:  :Ö:]    [ Ö:  :Ö: ]    [ :Ö:  Ö  ]
```

The salts of nitric acid may be prepared by treating metals or their oxides or hydroxides with nitric acid. All normal nitrates are soluble in water, and the oxynitrates, such as those of bismuth and mercury, are soluble in nitric acid. All nitrates decompose when heated. When sodium or potassium nitrate is heated, a nitrite is formed and oxygen is evolved.

$$2\ NaNO_3 \rightarrow 2\ NaNO_2 + O_2$$

A nitrate of a heavy metal produces the oxide of the metal when heated. With copper (II) nitrate, the equation is

$$2\ Cu(NO_3)_2 \rightarrow 2\ CuO + 4\ NO_2 + O_2$$

Ammonium nitrate produces nitrous oxide, N_2O, when heated (see Section 26.10).

26.8 Nitrous Acid and Nitrites

Nitrous acid (HNO_2) is obtained in solution (pale blue in color) when an acid, such as sulfuric, is added to a cold solution of a nitrite.

$$(2\ Na^+) + 2\ NO_2^- + 2\ H^+ + (SO_4^=) \rightarrow 2\ HNO_2 + (2\ Na^+) + (SO_4^=)$$

Nitrous acid is very unstable and is known only in solution. It changes slowly at room temperature (rapidly when heated) into nitric acid and nitric oxide.

$$3\ HNO_2 \rightarrow H^+ + NO_3^- + 2\ NO\uparrow + H_2O$$

Nitrous acid is a weak acid; i.e., it ionizes only slightly in solution. However, it acts as an active oxidizing agent toward strong reducing agents. On the other hand, it is oxidized to nitric acid by active oxidizing agents.

Sodium nitrite is the most important salt of nitrous acid. It is usually made by reducing the nitrate with lead.

$$NaNO_3 + Pb \rightarrow NaNO_2 + PbO$$

The nitrites are much more stable than the acid, and like the nitrates, they are soluble in water ($AgNO_2$ is sparingly soluble). The two resonance structures to the nitrite ion are

$$\left[\begin{matrix} \overset{\times}{\underset{\times}{}}N\overset{\times}{\underset{\times}{}}:\ddot{\underset{\cdot\cdot}{O}} \\ \overset{\times\circ}{} \\ :\ddot{\underset{\cdot\cdot}{O}}: \end{matrix}\right]^- \quad \text{and} \quad \left[\begin{matrix} \overset{\times}{\underset{\times}{}}N\overset{\times}{\underset{\circ}{}}\ddot{\underset{\circ\circ}{O}}: \\ \overset{\times\times}{\underset{\circ\circ}{}} \\ :\ddot{O}: \end{matrix}\right]^-$$

26.9 Hyponitrous Acid and Hyponitrites

Hyponitrous acid, $H_2N_2O_2$, is a white crystalline solid with the following electronic formula:

$$\begin{matrix} H\overset{\times}{\underset{\times}{}}\overset{++}{O}{}^{+}_{\circ} & & {}^{\circ}_{+}\overset{\circ\circ}{O}\overset{\times}{\underset{\times}{}}H \\ & N\underset{\circ\circ}{}::\underset{\times\times}{N} & \end{matrix}$$

It is very unstable and upon standing, either in the dry state or in solution, it breaks down into nitrous oxide and water according to the equation

$$H_2N_2O_2 \rightarrow H_2O + N_2O$$

The decomposition is explosive when the acid is heated. The reverse reaction is not possible; that is, the acid cannot be formed by dissolving N_2O in water even when high pressures are employed. The acid is weak and its salts are extensively hydrolyzed in aqueous solution. **Hyponitrites,** such as $Na_2N_2O_2$, may be prepared by the reduction of nitrites or nitrates with sodium amalgam (an alloy of sodium and mercury). The free acid is prepared by allowing the silver salt, $Ag_2N_2O_2$, to react with hydrogen chloride in ether and evaporating the resulting ethereal solution.

$$Ag_2N_2O_2 + 2\ HCl \rightarrow 2\ \underline{AgCl} + H_2N_2O_2$$

OXIDES OF NITROGEN

26.10 Nitrous Oxide

When ammonium nitrate is heated, **nitrous oxide** (N_2O) is formed.

$$NH_4NO_3 \rightarrow N_2O + 2\ H_2O$$

This is an oxidation-reduction reaction in which the nitrogen in the ammonium ion is oxidized by the nitrogen in the nitrate ion. **Caution!** If ammonium nitrate is heated too strongly, an explosion may occur.

Nitrous oxide is a colorless gas possessing a slight, pleasing odor and a sweet taste. When inhaled, it produces a feeling of exhilaration that is often accompanied by boisterous laughter. For this reason, it is commonly called **laughing gas.** Nitrous oxide is used as an anesthetic for minor operations. The nitrous oxide molecule has a resonance structure involving the following:

$$\overset{\times\times}{\text{:N}}\!::\!\overset{\times\times}{\text{N}}\!:\!\overset{\times\times}{\text{O}}\!: \quad \text{and} \quad \text{:N}\!:::\!\text{N}\!:\!\overset{\times\times}{\underset{\times\times}{\text{O}}}\!:$$

Nitrous oxide resembles oxygen in its behavior as an oxidizing agent with combustible substances. It decomposes when heated and forms nitrogen and oxygen.

$$2\ N_2O \rightarrow 2\ N_2 + O_2$$

Because one-third of the gas liberated is oxygen, nitrous oxide supports combustion better than air. A glowing splint will burst into flame when thrust into a bottle of this gas.

26.11 Nitric Oxide

Nitric oxide (NO) is prepared in various ways. When copper is treated with dilute nitric acid (33 per cent, specific gravity 1.2) nitric oxide is formed as the chief reduction product of the nitric acid.

$$3\ Cu + 8\ H^+ + 2\ NO_3^- \rightarrow 3\ Cu^{++} + 2\ NO \uparrow + 4\ H_2O$$

Prepared in this way, the nitric oxide is usually mixed with other oxides of nitrogen. Pure nitric oxide may be obtained by reducing nitric acid with iron (II) sulfate in dilute sulfuric acid solution.

$$3\ Fe^{++} + NO_3^- + 4\ H^+ \rightarrow 3\ Fe^{+++} + NO \uparrow + 2\ H_2O$$

Methods of production of nitric oxide on a commercial scale by the Ostwald Process, in which ammonia is oxidized in the presence of platinum, and by the direct union of the elements at very high temperatures were discussed in Section 26.2. Nitric oxide is formed in the air by lightning during thunderstorms (Fig.

Fig. 26–2 Some atmospheric nitrogen is "fixed" during a thunderstorm. *General Electric Co.*

26–2). It has been estimated that as a result of electrical phenomena 40,000,000 tons of nitrogen are fixed annually.

Nitric oxide is a colorless gas, which is only slightly soluble in water. It is the most stable thermally of the oxides of nitrogen. Two resonance forms are written for nitric oxide, as follows:

$$:\dot{N}::\dot{O}: \quad \text{and} \quad :\ddot{N}::\dot{O}:$$

Note that these forms contain an unpaired electron which makes the substance paramagnetic.

Nitric oxide will act as an oxidizing agent and give up its oxygen or it will act as a reducing agent and take up more oxygen, as shown in the following equations:

$$P_4 + 6\ NO \rightarrow P_4O_6 + 3\ N_2$$
$$2\ NO + O_2 \rightarrow 2\ NO_2$$

Nitric oxide combines with the iron (II) ion (Fe^{++}) to form a brown complex ion ($FeNO^{++}$), a reaction which is used in the detection of nitrites and nitrates.

26.12 Nitrogen Trioxide

When a mixture of one part of nitric oxide and one part of nitrogen dioxide is cooled, it becomes a blue liquid at −21°. This liquid contains a compound of the formula N_2O_3. When it is warmed, it forms the brown equilibrium mixture of NO and NO_2.

$$N_2O_3 \rightleftharpoons NO + NO_2$$

Nitrogen trioxide is the anhydride of nitrous acid. The electronic structure of N_2O_3 is:

$$\begin{array}{ccccc} :\dot{O}: & & :\ddot{O}: & & :O: \\ & N & & N & \\ & \text{xx} & & \text{xx} & \end{array}$$

26.13 Nitrogen Dioxide and Nitrogen Tetroxide

Nitrogen dioxide is prepared in the laboratory (1) by heating the nitrate of a heavy metal:

$$2\ Pb(NO_3)_2 \rightarrow 2\ PbO + 4\ NO_2 + O_2$$

or (2) by the action of concentrated nitric acid upon copper metal:

$$Cu + 4\ H^+ + 2\ NO_3^- \rightarrow Cu^{++} + 2\ NO_2\uparrow + 2\ H_2O$$

Nitrogen dioxide is prepared commercially by exposing nitric oxide to the air.

$$2\ NO + O_2 \rightarrow 2\ NO_2$$

At 140° nitrogen dioxide has a deep brown color and a density corresponding to the formula NO_2. At low temperatures the color almost entirely disappears and the density corresponds to the formula N_2O_4. At ordinary temperatures an equilibrium exists between the colored and the colorless compounds.

$$2\ NO_2 \rightleftharpoons N_2O_4$$

Nitrogen dioxide contains an odd number of electrons and therefore an unpaired electron. The resonance forms are

$$\times N \begin{matrix} \overset{\circ\circ}{:O:} \\ \overset{\circ\circ}{:O:} \end{matrix} \quad \text{and} \quad \overset{\times}{\underset{\times}{}}N \begin{matrix} \overset{\circ\circ}{:O:} \\ \overset{\circ\circ}{:O:} \end{matrix} \quad \text{and} \quad \overset{\times}{\underset{\times}{}}N \begin{matrix} \overset{\circ\circ}{:O:} \\ \overset{\circ\circ}{:O:} \end{matrix}$$

The unpaired electron accounts for the fact that NO_2 is paramagnetic and highly colored. Two molecules of NO_2 share their unpaired electrons with each other when they combine to form N_2O_4; the tetroxide is not paramagnetic.

$$O_2N \overset{\circ}{\underset{\times}{}} NO_2$$

When nitrogen dioxide is dissolved in cold water, a mixture of nitric and nitrous acids is formed.

$$2\ NO_2 + H_2O \rightarrow H^+ + NO_3^- + HNO_2$$

26.14 Nitrogen Pentoxide

This compound is a white solid which is formed by the dehydrating action of phosphorus (V) oxide upon pure nitric acid.

$$P_4O_{10} + 4\ HNO_3 \rightarrow 4\ HPO_3 + 2\ N_2O_5$$

Nitrogen pentoxide decomposes above 30°.

$$2\ N_2O_5 \rightarrow 4\ NO_2 + O_2$$

It is the anhydride of nitric acid, reacting as shown by the following equation:

$$N_2O_5 + H_2O \rightarrow 2\ HNO_3$$

The electronic structure of N_2O_5 in the gaseous state is

$$\begin{array}{ccccc} :\ddot{O}: & & \ddot{O} & & :\ddot{O}: \\ & N & & N & \\ & \times\times & & \times\times & \\ & :\ddot{O}: & & :\ddot{O}: & \end{array}$$

26.15 The Cycle of Nitrogen in Nature

Nitrogen is an essential constituent of all plants and animals. It is present principally in the proteins, which are complex organic materials containing carbon, hydrogen, and oxygen as well as nitrogen. Plants obtain the nitrogen necessary for their growth through their roots as nitrogen compounds, mainly in the form of ammonium and nitrate salts. Certain legumes such as clover, alfalfa, peas, and beans are able to obtain nitrogen indirectly from the air by means of nitrogen-fixing bacteria, which are found in the modules on their roots (Fig. 26–3). These bacteria convert atmospheric nitrogen into nitrites and nitrates which are assimilated by the "host" plant in the form of proteins. Generally, the bacteria fix more nitrogen in the form of soluble compounds than is used by the plant itself. When legumes die, much of the combined nitrogen remains in the soil and is available for use by nonleguminous plants.

Fig. 26–3 Nodules of nitrogen-fixing organisms on clover roots. *Wisconsin Agricultural Experiment Station*

As was mentioned in Section 26.11, tremendous quantities of nitrogen are fixed as nitric oxide by electrical phenomena in the atmosphere. The nitric oxide is oxidized to nitrogen dioxide by oxygen of the air, and the reaction of the dioxide with water forms nitrous and nitric acids. These acids are carried to the soil by rain where they react with oxides and carbonates of metals to form nitrites and nitrates, respectively. Certain soil bacteria oxidize the nitrites to nitrates, a process called "nitrification." Certain other kinds of bacteria change ammonia into nitrites. There are also denitrifying bacteria which decompose nitrates and other nitrogen compounds, thereby returning free nitrogen to the air.

Animals obtain their nitrogenous compounds by feeding on plants and other animals. The decay of both plant and animal matter returns nitrogen to the soil in the form of nitrates, and ammonia or free nitrogen is produced. Thus we see that nitrogen passes through a cycle (Fig. 26–4) which is of fundamental importance to all plants and animals.

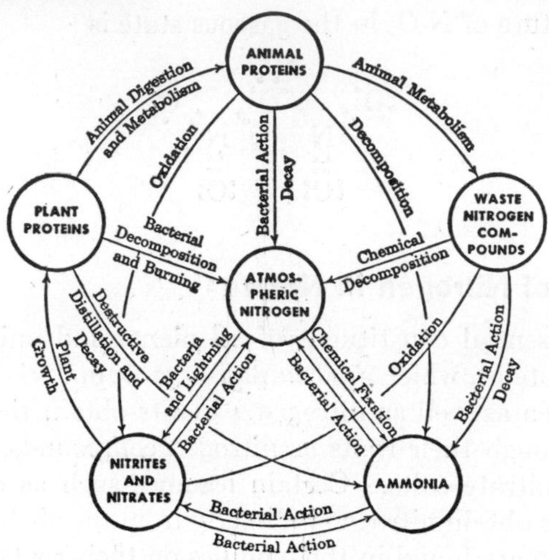

Fig. 26–4 Nitrogen cycle in nature.

OTHER COMPOUNDS OF NITROGEN

26.16 Nitrogen Trihalides

Nitrogen forms binary trihalides such as NF_3 and NCl_3. The pure tribromide and triiodide are not known, but ammoniates of the type $NBr_3 \cdot 6\,NH_3$ and $NI_3 \cdot NH_3$ have been described.

Nitrogen trifluoride, NF_3, is a gas which was first prepared by the electrolysis of fused ammonium hydrogen fluoride (NH_4HF_2) in a copper cell. Unlike the unstable trichloride and triiodide, nitrogen trifluoride is relatively stable; it does not decompose on heating or sparking.

When a solution of ammonium chloride is treated with chlorine for a long while, a yellow oily liquid, NCl_3, is produced. This substance explodes with great violence when heated above its boiling point or exposed to ultraviolet radiation. This does not mean that the N—Cl bond is a weak bond, but the N≡N triple bond is so strong by comparison that NCL_3 is unstable, and it decomposes to form N_2 and Cl_2. In fact, the remarkable stability of elementary nitrogen, N≡N, is responsible for the explosive properties of many nitrogen compounds.

Nitrogen triiodide l-ammoniate, $NI_3 \cdot NH_3$, is a highly explosive solid which, when dry, detonates at the slightest touch.

26.17 Nitrosyl Compounds

Several compounds containing the NO group are known. Certain of these compounds are derived directly or indirectly from nitric oxide and are referred to as **nitrosyl compounds.** Examples are NOX (X = F, Cl, Br); $NOHSO_4$; $NONO_3$; and $NOClO_4$. The NO group in certain of these compounds is present as a positive ion, NO^+, resulting from the loss of an electron by the nitric oxide molecule. The nitrosyl cation is thought to have the following structure:

$$[\overset{\times}{\underset{\times}{}}N\overset{\times\times\times}{\underset{\times\times\times}{}}O\overset{\times}{\underset{\times}{}}]^+$$

The nitrosyl halides, NOX, are prepared by various methods, one of which is the direct union of nitric oxide with the respective halogen, as shown by the equation

$$2\ NO + X_2 \rightarrow 2\ NOX$$

NOF is a colorless gas, NOCl an orange-yellow gas, and NOBr a red gas. The nitrosyl halides are polar covalent compounds.

Nitrosyl sulfuric acid, $NOHSO_4$, is an intermediate in the chamber process for the manufacture of sulfuric acid.

QUESTIONS

1. Outline the chemistry of the production of nitric acid from ammonia.
2. List the possible reduction products of nitric acid. What factors determine which product will be formed when nitric acid is reduced?
3. Write equations for the reaction of concentrated HNO_3 with each of the following: Cu, S, C, $C_3H_5(OH)_3$, and SO_2.
4. What substances are formed when black gunpowder burns?
5. Write equations for the preparation of each of the oxides of nitrogen.
6. Write equations for the preparation of nitrous acid starting with sodium nitrate.
7. Describe the fixation of nitrogen by the Arc Process.
8. What is the anhydride of nitrous acid? of nitric acid?
9. Describe the nitrogen cycle in nature.
10. Write electronic formulas for HNO_3, NO_3^-, HNO_2, $H_2N_2O_2$, N_2O, NO, NO_2, N_2O_3, N_2O_5, NCl_3, and NOCl.

PROBLEMS

1. What quantity of nitric acid could be prepared by the Ostwald Process from 5000 l. of ammonia, measured at 5.00 atm. and 275°, if a 93.0% yield is obtained based upon the original quantity of ammonia? *Ans. 39.8 kg.*
2. What volume of 0.100 M HNO_3 would be required to neutralize 25.0 g. of sodium hydroxide? *Ans. 6.25 l.*
3. What volume of nitrous oxide, measured at 25.0° and 730 mm., can be prepared from 325 g. of ammonium nitrate? *Ans. 178 l.*
4. What weight of oxygen is formed by the decomposition of 34.0 l. of N_2O at 75.0° and 740 mm.? *Ans. 18.6 g.*

REFERENCES

"Industrial and Military Explosives," R. W. Cairns, *J. Chem. Educ.*, **19** (3) 109 (1942).

"High Temperatures: Chemistry," Farrington Daniels, *Sci. American*, Sept., 1954; p. 109 (describes production of nitric oxide directly from air).

"Symposium on Recent Advances in the Chemistry of Inorganic Nitrogen Compounds," *J. Chem. Educ.*, **34** (11) 537–561 (1957).

CHAPTER TWENTY-SEVEN

Phosphorus and Its Compounds

Phosphorus is the second element of the nitrogen family. Nitrogen, the first element of this family, was considered in Chapters 25 and 26. Although the chemistry of phosphorus closely resembles that of nitrogen in many respects, there are marked differences between the two elements and their compounds. Phosphorus is less nonmetallic than nitrogen chiefly because the phosphorus atom is larger than the nitrogen atom and because phosphorus is less electronegative (2.1) than nitrogen (3.0). Nitrogen is quite inert except at elevated temperatures, whereas phosphorus (the white modification) is very active at even low temperatures. The union of nitrogen with oxygen is an endothermic reaction, whereas phosphorus burns readily in air with the evolution of considerable heat. Nitric acid and nitrous acid are relatively strong oxidizing agents, but phosphoric acid and phosphorous acid are very weak oxidizing agents. Furthermore, phosphine (PH_3) is a much stronger reducing agent than ammonia (NH_3). On the other hand, both of these elements are nonmetals, the atoms of each have five electrons in their outer shells, they have the same oxidation states, and many of their compounds have similar formulas.

27.1 History and Occurrence of Phosphorus

Phosphorus was discovered in 1669 by the German alchemist Brand while searching for the philosopher's stone (a substance that was supposed to transmute baser metals into gold). He heated a mixture of evaporated urine (which contains combined phosphorus), sand, and charcoal in a retort and distilled out a substance that had the property of glowing in the dark. This substance was later recognized as an element by Lavoisier and was named **phosphorus** (from the Greek, meaning "light bearer"). The term **phosphorescence** is derived from this phenomenon; the phosphorescence of phosphorus is the result of slow oxidation.

Because of its activity towards oxygen, phosphorus does not occur free in nature, but it is abundant and widely distributed in the form of phosphates. The most important of the naturally occurring phosphates are those of calcium. These compounds include **phosphorite,** $Ca_3(PO_4)_2$, and the apatites: **hydroxyapatite,** $Ca_{10}(OH)_2(PO_4)_6$; **fluorapatite,** $Ca_{10}F_2(PO_4)_6$; and **chlorapatite,** $Ca_{10}Cl_2(PO_4)_6$. The naturally occurring apatites are always mixtures of two or more of the above apatites. These minerals, of fossil origin, make up a large part of the phosphate rock deposits found in Florida, Tennessee, Idaho, Montana, Utah, Wyoming, Ontario, Algeria, and Tunis.

Phosphorus is essential to both plants and animals. Bones, teeth, and nerve and muscle tissue contain combined phosphorus. The nucleoproteins (found in the nucleus of every cell) contain phosphorus. Phosphorus compounds are also important in the metabolism of sugar. Such foods as eggs, beans, peas, and milk furnish phosphorus for our body requirements. Plants obtain phosphorus from the soil in the form of soluble phosphates. Soils which have become deficient in phosphorus may be enriched by the addition of soluble phosphates.

27.2 Preparation of Phosphorus

Phosphorus is produced commercially by heating calcium phosphate with sand and coke in an electric furnace (Fig. 27–1).

$$2\ Ca_3(PO_4)_2 + 6\ SiO_2 + 10\ C \rightarrow 6\ CaSiO_3 + 10\ CO\uparrow + P_4\uparrow$$

The phosphorus distills off and is condensed to the solid state or burned to P_4O_{10} from which other compounds of phosphorus may be manufactured. The calcium silicate, along with any calcium fluoride or ferrophosphorus, melts and collects at the bottom of the furnace where it is drawn off as a slag. The elementary phosphorus is shipped in tank cars to the plants where it is to be made into phosphoric acid and phosphates. In this way the cost of the freight on the oxygen and water used in the manufacture of phosphorus compounds is avoided. The profits of chemical industries often depend on such considerations.

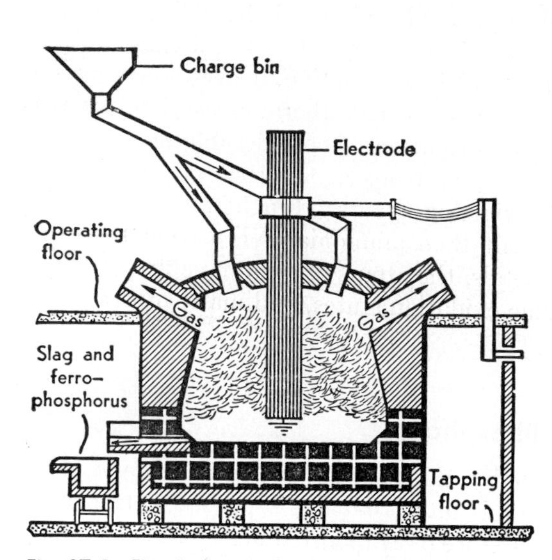

Fig. 27–1 Electric furnace for production of phosphorus and ferrophosphorus.

27.3 Physical Properties of Phosphorus

Phosphorus exists in several allotropic modifications, of which only two are of general interest and importance; these are **white phosphorus** and **red phosphorus.**

As prepared by the method described in the previous section, phosphorus is a white, translucent, soft, waxlike solid. When exposed to light, white phosphorus slowly turns yellow, due to the formation of a superficial coating of red phosphorus. For this reason, white phosphorus is frequently called **yellow phosphorus.**

White phosphorus is very soluble in carbon disulfide and less so in ether, chloroform, and other organic solvents. It is very nearly insoluble in water, 0.0033 g. dissolving in one liter of ice water. White phosphorus melts at 44.2° and boils at 280°. Vapor density measurements show that just above the boiling point the vapor of phosphorus is composed of molecules which have the formula P_4. The four phosphorus atoms are arranged at the corners of a regular tetrahedron and each atom is covalently bonded to the three other atoms of the molecule. At very high temperatures phosphorus gas consists of P_2 molecules; these are assumed to have the structure $\overset{\times}{\underset{\times}{}}P\overset{\times\circ}{\underset{\times\circ}{\times\circ}}P\overset{\circ}{\underset{\circ}{}}$, which is similar to that of the N_2 molecule. The P_4 molecule exists in solid white phosphorus, and in solutions of phosphorus, as well as in phosphorus vapor. In red phosphorus the atoms are bonded together in larger aggregates. White phosphorus is very poisonous; a dose of about 0.15 g. produces acute pains, convulsions, and may even result in death. Necrosis ("decay") of the bones of the jaw and nose is caused by continued breathing of small amounts of the fumes of phosphorus. In very small doses phosphorus stimulates the nervous system.

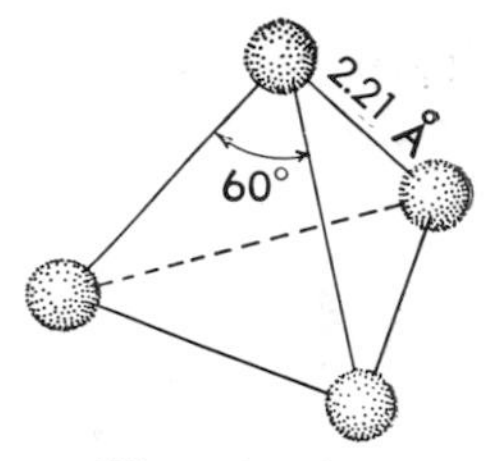

White phosphorus

Red phosphorus is made by heating the white modification in a retort between 230° and 300°, with air excluded.

$$\text{P (white)} \rightleftharpoons \text{P (red)} + 4{,}400 \text{ cal.}$$

This change is catalyzed by a trace of iodine. Because the change from white to red phosphorus is exothermic, the heat of combustion of red phosphorus is less than that of the white form. Red phosphorus sublimes when heated, forming a vapor identical to that from the white variety. The red modification is insoluble in the solvents which dissolve white phosphorus. Red phosphorus is not poisonous.

27.4 Chemical Properties of Phosphorus

The most important chemical property of phosphorus is its chemical activity towards oxygen. Slow oxidation of white phosphorus at room temperature causes a rise in temperature and spontaneous combustion results when the ignition temperature (35–45°) is reached. Because of the readiness with which white phosphorus ignites, it must be stored under water. Burns caused by phosphorus are very painful and slow to heal, so that it should never be handled with the fingers. When moist phosphorus is allowed to oxidize slowly in air, a faint light is emitted (phosphorescence) and ozone, phosphoric acid, and phosphorous acid are formed. When phosphorus is burned in an excess of air or in oxygen, phosphorus (V) oxide, P_4O_{10}, is formed. In moist air, the cloud of solid phosphorus (V) oxide from burning phosphorus forms a fog of minute droplets of phosphoric acid. Burning phosphorus has been used in the production of smoke screens and for incendiary purposes in warfare.

Phosphorus combines with the halogens exothermically. When heated, it combines with sulfur and many of the metals. Concentrated nitric acid oxidizes phosphorus to orthophosphoric acid.

Red phosphorus is less active than the white form; it does not ignite in air until it is heated to about 250°. However, the products of the reactions of red phosphorus are the same as those of the white modification.

27.5 Uses of Phosphorus

Formerly white phosphorus was used in the manufacture of matches. Because it is poisonous and the workers who were exposed to the fumes suffered from necrosis of the bones, it has been replaced, in the heads of "strike anywhere" matches, by tetraphosphorus trisulfide (P_4S_3). Figure 27–2 shows the composition of this

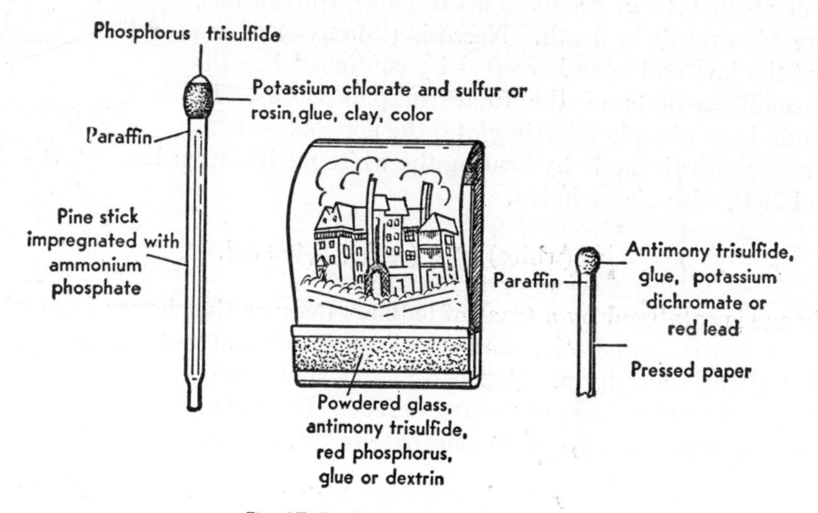

Fig. 27–2 Modern forms of matches.

type of match and also that of the safety match. The wood of the "strike anywhere" match is impregnated with ammonium phosphate to prevent the lower part of the stick from burning too fast and also to keep it from glowing after the flame has been extinguished. The head of the match contains a combustible mixture of potassium chlorate and sulfur or rosin, which is tipped with tetraphosphorus trisulfide. Friction ignites the sulfide of the tip, which in turn ignites the head, and then the wood is ignited.

The head of a safety match contains no phosphorus but some other combustible substance, usually antimony (III) sulfide (Sb_2S_3), mixed with an oxidizing agent such as potassium dichromate ($K_2Cr_2O_7$), and held in place with glue. The prepared surface on the side of the box or on the "book" consists of red phosphorus and powdered glass mixed with glue. The head of the safety match ignites when it is struck upon the prepared surface, but it is not easily ignited by friction alone.

Large quantities of phosphorus are converted into acids and salts to be used in fertilizers and in the chemical industries. Other uses include the manufacture of special alloys such as ferrophosphorus and phosphorbronze. Considerable quantities are used in making fireworks, bombs (Fig. 27–3), and rat poisons.

Fig. 27–3 Explosion of a small phosphorus bomb. What compound is formed when the phosphorus burns in air? *War Department, Chemical Corps*

27.6 Phosphine

Phosphorus forms a series of hydrides, the most important of which is **phosphine,** PH_3, a gaseous compound which is analogous to ammonia in formula and structure. Unlike ammonia, phosphine cannot be made by the direct union of the elements, but it is prepared by heating white phosphorus in a concentrated solution of sodium hydroxide (Fig. 27–4, page 416).

$$(3\ Na^+) + 3\ OH^- + P_4 + 3\ H_2O \rightarrow (3\ Na^+) + \underset{\text{Sodium hypophosphite}}{3\ H_2PO_2^-} + PH_3 \uparrow$$

Since phosphine obtained in this way is spontaneously inflammable, the air in the flask is first removed by flushing the flask with nitrogen or illuminating gas. As the bubbles of phosphine escape into the air, they ignite, forming a fog of phosphoric acid which rises in the form of smoke rings.

$$PH_3 + 2\ O_2 \rightarrow H_3PO_4$$

Pure phosphine is not spontaneously combustible in air, but when produced by this method, it contains some P_2H_4, which ignites on coming in contact with the air.

Phosphine can also be prepared by the hydrolysis of phosphides of certain metals.

$$Ca_3P_2 + 6\ H_2O \rightarrow 3\ Ca(OH)_2 + 2\ PH_3 \uparrow$$

Phosphides of several of the metals may be prepared by reducing the corresponding phosphates with carbon.

$$Ca_3(PO_4)_2 + 8\ C \rightarrow Ca_3P_2 + 8\ CO$$

Phosphine is a colorless, very poisonous gas, which has an odor like that of decaying fish. It is easily decomposed by heat ($4\ PH_3 \rightarrow P_4 + 6\ H_2$). Like ammonia, phosphine unites with the hydrogen halides with the formation of the corresponding **phosphonium compounds,** PH_4Cl, PH_4Br, and PH_4I. Unlike the ammonium halides, however, the phosphonium compounds do not give the phosphonium ion, PH_4^+, in solution, but phosphine escapes and the hydrogen halide remains in solution as the hydrohalic acid. Phosphine is only very slightly soluble in water and is a much weaker base than ammonia.

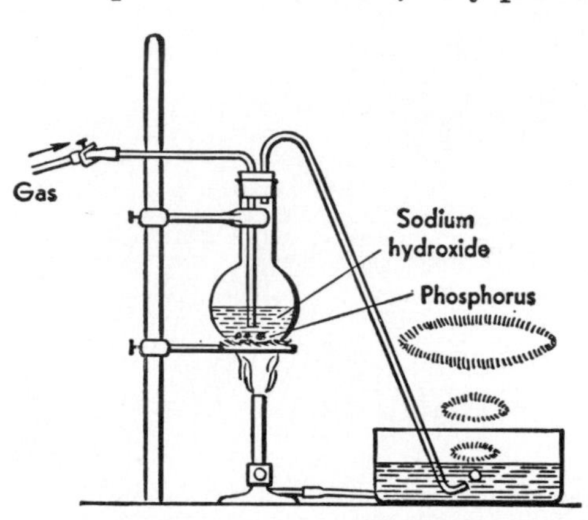

Fig. 27–4 Production of phosphine.

27.7 Halides of Phosphorus

Phosphorus unites directly with all of the halogens, forming trihalides (PX_3) and pentahalides (PX_5); only the penta-iodide is not known. These are much more stable than the corresponding compounds of nitrogen.

It is interesting that only nitrogen of the nitrogen family elements cannot form pentahalides. This can be explained in terms of the availability of orbitals for bond formation. The orbitals in the valence shell of a nitrogen atom and the number of electrons in each is given by the subshell notation $2s^22p^12p^12p^1$. In forming NF_3, for example, each of the three $2p$ electrons is shared with a fluorine atom. The $2s^2$ orbital and electrons are not involved in bond formation in NF_3. However, nitrogen cannot form a pentafluoride because five orbitals would be required, and no more than four are available in the second principal electron shell. With phosphorus, on the other hand, in which the valence shell is the third principal electron shell, $3d$ orbitals are presumably available for bond formation, and pentahalides of phosphorus are possible. In PF_3, for example, the valence electron distribution in the five bonding orbitals of phosphorus is $3s^13p^13p^13p^13d^1$. Each fluorine atom furnishes one electron to each of these five orbitals; the valence orbitals of phosphorus then contain two electrons each, $3s^23p^23p^23p^23d^2$.

The trichloride (PCl_3) and the pentachloride (PCl_5) are the most important halides of phosphorus. **Phosphorus trichloride** is prepared by passing dry chlorine over molten phosphorus ($P_4 + 6\ Cl_2 \rightarrow 4\ PCl_3$). It is a colorless liquid which boils at 76° and freezes at −92°. The PCl_3 molecule is pyramidal.

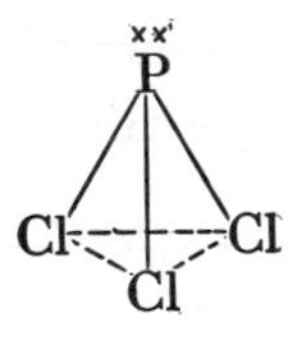

Phosphorus trichloride is irreversibly hydrolyzed by water with the formation of phosphorous acid and hydrogen chloride.

$$PCl_3 + 3\ H_2O \rightarrow H_3PO_3 + 3\ HCl \uparrow$$

Because of hydrolysis, all of the halides of phosphorus fume in moist air, much as concentrated hydrochloric acid does.

Phosphorus pentachloride is prepared by oxidizing the trichloride with an excess of chlorine ($PCl_3 + Cl_2 \rightarrow PCl_5$). The pentachloride is a straw-colored solid, which sublimes when heated in air, and dissociates reversibly into the trichloride and chlorine ($PCl_5 \rightleftharpoons PCl_3 + Cl_2$).

In the vapor and liquid states, the structure of PCl_5 is that of a triangular bipyramid.

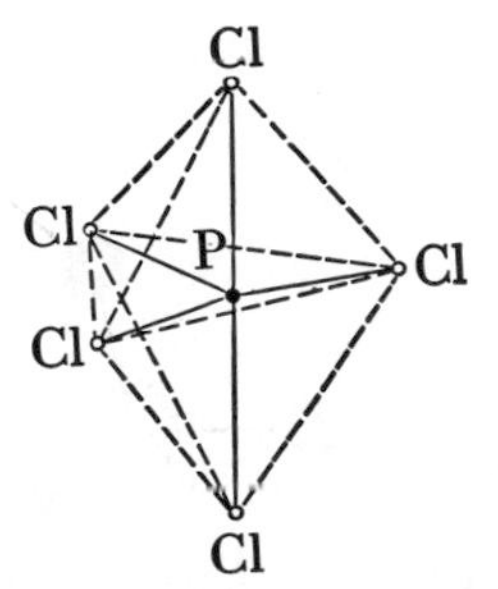

X-ray studies show solid phosphorus pentachloride to have an ionic structure, $[PCl_4]^+[PCl_6]^-$, in which the cation has a tetrahedral structure and the anion an octahedral one. The structure is the same when PCl_5 is in solution in solvents of high dielectric constant. Phosphorus pentachloride undergoes partial hydrolysis when treated with a limited amount of cold water, forming phosphorus (V) oxychloride, $POCl_3$, and hydrogen chloride.

$$PCl_5 + H_2O \rightarrow POCl_3 + 2\ HCl \uparrow$$

When an excess of water is employed, the hydrolysis of the pentachloride is complete, and orthophosphoric acid is formed.

$$PCl_5 + 4\ H_2O \rightarrow H_3PO_4 + 5\ HCl \uparrow$$

27.8 Phosphorus (V) Oxyhalides

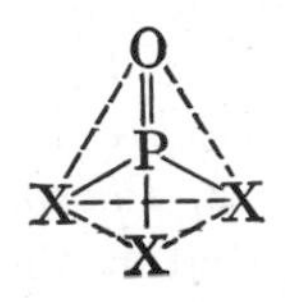

Compounds of the type POX_3 are called **phosphorus (V) oxyhalides** or **phosphoryl halides.** Their molecules have tetrahedral structures. The chloride and bromide are readily obtained by the action of the pentahalide upon phosphorus (V) oxide.

$$P_4O_{10} + 6\ PX_5 \rightarrow 10\ POX_3$$

Partial hydrolysis of a phosphorus pentahalide produces the corresponding oxyhalide.

$$PX_5 + H_2O \rightarrow POX_3 + 2\ HX \uparrow$$

The iodide, POI_3, apparently does not exist. These compounds, especially $POCl_3$, are used in replacing OH groups in organic compounds with halogens. They hydrolyze to give the orthophosphoric acid and HX.

$$POX_3 + 3\ H_2O \rightarrow H_3PO_4 + 3\ HX \uparrow$$

27.9 Oxides of Phosphorus

Phosphorus forms several oxides, three of which are well defined. The formulas of these three oxides are P_4O_6, P_8O_{16}, and P_4O_{10}. The oxidation states of phosphorus in these compounds correspond to those of nitrogen in N_2O_3, N_2O_4, and N_2O_5, respectively. The structures of P_4O_6 and P_4O_{10} are given below.

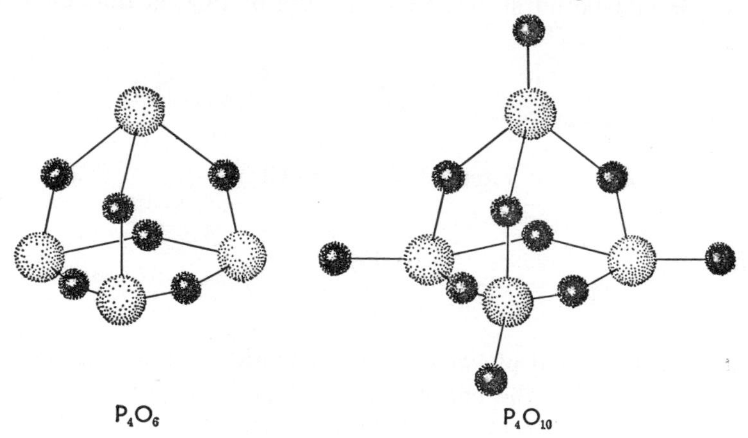

The combustion of phosphorus in air generally produces a mixture of P_4O_6 and P_4O_{10}. However, it is virtually impossible to get much of the lower oxide by the burning of phosphorus, even in a limited supply of air.

1. *Phosphorus (III) oxide, P_4O_6.* This compound is often formulated as P_2O_3 and called phosphorus trioxide, but vapor density measurements have shown that the formula is actually P_4O_6. Phosphorus (III) oxide is a white crystalline solid which melts at 23.8° and boils at 175.3°. When the vapor of this oxide is heated to 448°, it decomposes forming red phosphorus and P_8O_{16}. Phosphorus (III) oxide has a garliclike odor and its vapor is very poisonous. It oxidizes slowly in air and takes fire when heated to 70°, forming P_4O_{10}. Phosphorus (III) oxide dissolves slowly in cold water with the formation of phosphorous acid, H_3PO_3.

2. *Phosphorus (V) oxide, P_4O_{10}.* This oxide of phosphorus is frequently formulated as P_2O_5 and called phosphorus pentoxide. It is a white flocculent powder

which melts at 420°. Its heat of formation is very high, and for this reason it is quite stable and a very poor oxidizing agent. With a limited amount of water it forms metaphosphoric acid, HPO_3.

$$P_4O_{10} + 2\ H_2O \rightarrow 4\ HPO_3$$

When more water is added, the metaphosphoric acid slowly changes to orthophosphoric acid, H_3PO_4. The net reaction is given by the equation

$$P_4O_{10} + 6\ H_2O \rightarrow 4\ H_3PO_4$$

When P_4O_{10} is dropped into water, it reacts with a hissing sound, and much heat is liberated. Because of its great affinity for water, phosphorus (V) oxide is used extensively for drying gases and for removing water from many compounds.

ACIDS OF PHOSPHORUS

The important oxygen acids of phosphorus are: orthophosphoric acid, H_3PO_4; pyrophosphoric (diphosphoric) acid, $H_4P_2O_7$; triphosphoric acid, $H_5P_3O_{10}$; metaphosphoric acid, $(HPO_3)_x$; phosphorous acid, H_3PO_3; and hypophosphorous acid, H_3PO_2.

27.10 Orthophosphoric Acid

The various phosphoric acids all have the same anhydride, P_4O_{10}, and each acid represents a different degree of hydration of this oxide, but not a different oxidation state of phosphorus, which is +5 in every case. These acids are stable toward reducing agents.

One commercial method of preparing **orthophosphoric acid** (commonly called **phosphoric acid**) is the treatment of calcium phosphate with concentrated sulfuric acid.

$$Ca_3(PO_4)_2 + 3\ H_2SO_4 \rightarrow 2\ H_3PO_4 + 3\ CaSO_4$$

The product is diluted with water and the calcium sulfate removed by filtration. This method gives a dilute acid which is impure with calcium dihydrogen phosphate, $Ca(H_2PO_4)_2$, and certain fluorine compounds which are formed from the fluorapatite usually associated with rock phosphate.

Pure orthophosphoric acid is manufactured by oxidizing phosphorus from the electric furnace (Section 27.2) to P_4O_{10} and dissolving the product in water.

The pure acid forms colorless, deliquescent crystals that melt at 42.4°. A common commercial form of the acid contains 82 per cent H_3PO_4 and is known as "syrupy phosphoric acid." The electronic structure of orthophosphoric acid is

```
        H
        ••
       :O:
    ••  ox  oo
  H:O:P:O:H
    ••  xx  oo
       :O:
        ••
```

Large quantities of crude orthophosphoric acid are used in the manufacture of fertilizers. The acid is also used in medicine as an astringent, as an antipyretic, and as a stimulant.

27.11 Salts of Orthophosphoric Acid

Because orthophosphoric acid is a triprotic acid, it forms three series of salts corresponding to the three stages of ionization.

$$H_3PO_4 \rightleftharpoons H^+ + H_2PO_4^- \quad \text{(primary ionization)}$$
$$H_2PO_4^- \rightleftharpoons H^+ + HPO_4^= \quad \text{(secondary ionization)}$$
$$HPO_4^= \rightleftharpoons H^+ + PO_4^{-3} \quad \text{(tertiary ionization)}$$

The sodium salts and their names are given below:

NaH_2PO_4	Primary sodium (ortho)phosphate or Sodium dihydrogen phosphate
Na_2HPO_4	Secondary sodium (ortho)phosphate or Disodium hydrogen phosphate
Na_3PO_4	Tertiary sodium (ortho)phosphate or Trisodium phosphate

Sodium dihydrogen phosphate forms aqueous solutions that are weakly acidic by hydrolysis, as shown by the equation

$$H_2PO_4^- + H_2O \rightleftharpoons HPO_4^= + H_3O^+$$

Disodium hydrogen phosphate solutions are alkaline because the monohydrogen phosphate ion is a stronger proton acceptor than donor.

$$HPO_4^= + H_2O \rightleftharpoons H_2PO_4^- + OH^-$$

Trisodium phosphate solutions are strongly alkaline by hydrolysis.

$$PO_4^{-3} + H_2O \rightleftharpoons HPO_4^= + OH^-$$

The hydrogen and ammonium phosphate salts are decomposed by heating, with volatile products such as water and ammonia being given off. Several examples are given below:

$$xNaH_2PO_4 \rightarrow (NaPO_3)_x + xH_2O$$
$$2\ Na_2HPO_4 \rightarrow Na_4P_2O_7 + H_2O$$
$$xNaNH_4HPO_4 \rightarrow (NaPO_3)_x + xNH_3 + xH_2O$$
$$2\ MgNH_4PO_4 \rightarrow Mg_2P_2O_7 + 2\ NH_3 + H_2O$$

Sodium dihydrogen phosphate is used as a boiler compound (to prevent the formation of boiler scale) and in certain baking powders; disodium hydrogen phosphate as a boiler compound and in the weighting of silk; and trisodium phosphate as a water softener, boiler compound, and detergent. **Calcium dihydrogen phosphate,** $Ca(H_2PO_4)_2$, is used as a fertilizer and as a constituent of baking powders. **Calcium monohydrogen phosphate,** $CaHPO_4$, is used as a mineral animal food, and as a polishing agent in tooth pastes.

Phosphorus in the form *of soluble orthophosphates* is *essential to plant growth.* Tricalcium phosphate is too insoluble to furnish an adequate supply of phosphorus to plants. Calcium dihydrogen phosphate, however, is soluble in water and therefore suitable for use as a fertilizer. This compound is prepared commercially by treating tricalcium phosphate with sulfuric acid.

$$Ca_3(PO_4)_2 + 2\ H_2SO_4 + 4\ H_2O \rightarrow Ca(H_2PO_4)_2 + 2(CaSO_4 \cdot 2\ H_2O)$$

The mixture of calcium dihydrogen phosphate and gypsum, $CaSO_4 \cdot 2\ H_2O$, is sold as **superphosphate of lime.** A product containing a higher percentage of phosphorus, **triple superphosphate of lime,** is manufactured by treating pulverized tricalcium phosphate with orthophosphoric acid.

$$Ca_3(PO_4)_2 + 4\ H_3PO_4 \rightarrow 3\ Ca(H_2PO_4)_2$$

The direct use of $Ca_3(PO_4)_2$ and $CaHPO_4$ as phosphate fertilizers depends upon the weathering process which changes them slowly into the soluble dihydrogen phosphate.

The mixed phosphate **magnesium ammonium phosphate,** $MgNH_4PO_4$, is a white, insoluble compound which is very useful in the detection and quantitative determination of both magnesium ion and orthophosphates.

$$Mg^{++} + NH_4^{+} + HPO_4^{=} \rightarrow \underline{MgNH_4PO_4} + H^{+}$$

27.12 Pyrophosphoric Acid

Pyrophosphoric acid, $H_4P_2O_7$, may be prepared by heating the ortho acid to 250°. The equation for the reaction is

$$2\ H_3PO_4 \rightleftharpoons H_4P_2O_7 + H_2O$$

This reaction involves the elimination of a molecule of water from two molecules of orthophosphoric acid, as shown by the equation

$$\begin{array}{ccccccccc}
 & \mathrm{H} & & \mathrm{H} & & \mathrm{H} & & \mathrm{H} & \\
 & | & & | & & | & & | & \\
 & \mathrm{O} & & \mathrm{O} & & \mathrm{O} & & \mathrm{O} & \\
 & | & & | & & | & & | & \\
\mathrm{H{-}O{-}} & \mathrm{P} & \mathrm{{-}O{-}}\boxed{\mathrm{H\ \ H{-}O}}\mathrm{{-}} & \mathrm{P} & \mathrm{{-}O{-}H} \rightarrow \mathrm{H{-}O{-}} & \mathrm{P} & \mathrm{{-}O{-}} & \mathrm{P} & \mathrm{{-}O{-}H} + H_2O \\
 & \downarrow & & \downarrow & & \downarrow & & \downarrow & \\
 & \mathrm{O} & & \mathrm{O} & & \mathrm{O} & & \mathrm{O} &
\end{array}$$

In the above formulas the straight line between two symbols represents a covalent bond (shared pair of electrons), and the arrow designates a coordinate bond in which the phosphorus furnishes both electrons of the shared pair. These abbreviations are often used in chemical formulas, especially when the molecules represented are rather complex. Pyrophosphoric acid is a white crystalline solid which melts at 61°. When it is dissolved in water, it gradually hydrolyzes to the ortho acid. Among the salts of pyrophosphoric acid that have been prepared are **tetrasodium pyrophosphate,** $Na_4P_2O_7$, **trisodium monohydrogen pyrophosphate,**

$Na_3HP_2O_7$, and **disodium dihydrogen pyrophosphate,** $Na_2H_2P_2O_7$. Normal pyrophosphates are prepared by heating monohydrogen orthophosphates.

$$2\ Na_2HPO_4 \rightarrow Na_4P_2O_7 + H_2O$$
$$2\ CaHPO_4 \rightarrow Ca_2P_2O_7 + H_2O$$

Tetrasodium pyrophosphate is used as a water softener; in this application it sequesters (binds in complex ions) the magnesium and part of the calcium ions in hard water and prevents these cations from forming insoluble compounds with soap.

27.13 Triphosphoric Acid

Triphosphoric acid, $H_5P_3O_{10}$, is formed by the elimination of two molecules of water from three molecules of orthophosphoric acid, as shown below.

```
 H            H         H          H     H     H
 |            |         |          |     |     |
 O            O         O          O     O     O
 |            |         |          |     |     |
O←P– O[–H  H–O]–P–[OH  H–]O–P→O  →  O←P–O–P–O–P→O  +  2 H2O
 |            ↓         |          |     ↓     |
 O            O         O          O     O     O
 |                      |          |           |
 H                      H          H           H
```

The sodium salt of triphosphoric acid, $Na_5P_3O_{10}$, is used as a water softener. It may be prepared by fusing together suitable quantities of sodium pyro- and metaphosphates.

$$Na_4P_2O_7 + NaPO_3 \rightarrow Na_5P_3O_{10}$$

Polyphosphate linkages of the type found in pyrophosphates and triphosphates are of great biochemical importance. The energy required for the contraction of muscles results from hydrolysis of "energy-rich" P—O—P bonds of a complex organic polyphosphate existing in muscle tissue, and known as adenosine triphosphate. The enzyme-catalyzed hydrolysis is slow but involves the release of 10 kilocalories of energy per mole of adenosine triphosphate. The equation for the reaction is given below (R represents the complex organic portion of the molecule):

```
    O     O     O                        O     O              O
    ↑     ↑     ↑                        ↑     ↑              ↑
R–O–P–O–P–O–P–OH + H2O → R–O–P–O–P–OH + HO–P–OH
    |     |     |                        |     |              |
    OH    OH    OH                       OH    OH             OH
 Adenosine triphosphate            Adenosine diphosphate   Phosphoric acid
```

27.14 Metaphosphoric Acid and Its Salts

The elimination of a molecule of water from a single molecule of orthophosphoric acid gives **metaphosphoric acid,** HPO_3.

$$H_3PO_4 \rightarrow HPO_3 + H_2O$$

Metaphosphoric acid is usually manufactured by heating orthophosphoric acid above 400°. It solidifies from the liquid as a glassy product called "glacial" phosphoric acid.

In metaphosphoric acid, oxygen bridges are formed between adjacent phosphorus atoms to build up rings and chains, in which there are four oxygen atoms linked to every phosphorus atom. By combining with each other, the HPO_3 molecules polymerize into multiple units which may be represented by the formula $(HPO_3)_x$. The acid dissolves readily in water, in which it slowly changes into orthophosphoric acid.

Sodium metaphosphate is made by heating sodium dihydrogen orthophosphate.

$$xNaH_2PO_4 \rightarrow (NaPO_3)_x + xH_2O$$

If the product is heated to about 700° and then cooled rapidly, a water soluble, **glassy polymetaphosphate** is formed. This is a long-chain polymer which is best formulated as $(NaPO_3)_x$ although it has been called "sodium hexametaphosphate" because it was once thought to have the composition $(NaPO_3)_6$. The metaphosphates form soluble complexes with the calcium ion and reduce its concentration to such a low value that it cannot be precipitated by soaps. For this reason the sodium polymetaphosphates are used as water softeners.

27.15 Phosphorous Acid and Its Salts

Phosphorous acid, H_3PO_3, can be prepared by the action of water upon P_4O_6, PCl_3, PBr_3, or PI_3. Pure phosphorous acid is most readily obtained by hydrolyzing phosphorus trichloride.

$$PCl_3 + 3\ H_2O \rightarrow H_3PO_3 + 3\ HCl \uparrow$$

The resulting solution is evaporated to expel the hydrogen chloride, and white crystals of phosphorous acid appear upon cooling the solution. The crystals are deliquescent, very soluble in water, and have an odor like that of garlic. The solid melts at 70.1°, and decomposes at about 200° by an auto-oxidation-reduction reaction into phosphine and orthophosphoric acid.

$$4\ H_3PO_3 \rightarrow PH_3 + 3\ H_3PO_4$$

The electronic structure of phosphorous acid is given below.

```
         H
    ..   •x   ..
  H:O:P:O:H
    ..   xx   ..
         :O:
          ..
```

Phosphorous acid and its salts are active reducing agents because they are readily oxidized to phosphoric acid and phosphates, respectively. Phosphorous acid reduces the silver ion to free silver, mercury (II) salts to the mercury (I) stage, and sulfurous acid to sulfur.

Phosphorous acid forms only two series of salts, such as **sodium dihydrogen phosphite,** NaH_2PO_3, and **disodium hydrogen phosphite,** Na_2HPO_3. The third atom of hydrogen cannot be replaced by a cation. The nonacidic character of the third hydrogen atom is due to its direct linkage to the phosphorus atom rather than to an oxygen atom.

27.16 Hypophosphorous Acid and Its Salts

The solution remaining from the preparation of phosphine from white phosphorus and sodium hydroxide contains sodium hypophosphite, NaH_2PO_2 (Section 27.6). The corresponding barium salt may be obtained by replacing sodium hydroxide with barium hydroxide in the preparation of phosphine. When barium hypophosphite is treated with sulfuric acid, barium sulfate precipitates and **hypophosphorous acid,** H_3PO_2, is formed in solution.

$$Ba^{++} + 2\ H_2PO_2^- + 2\ H^+ + SO_4^= \rightarrow \underline{BaSO_4} + 2\ H_3PO_2$$

The acid is weak and monoprotic, forming only one series of salts. The two nonacidic hydrogen atoms are linked directly to the phosphorus atom.

$$\begin{array}{c} \mathrm{H} \\ \mathrm{H:\ddot{O}:\ddot{P}:\ddot{O}:} \\ \mathrm{H} \end{array}$$

Hypophosphorous acid and its salts are strong reducing agents.

27.17 The Sulfides of Phosphorus

Four phosphorus sulfides have been prepared and characterized. They are P_4S_3, P_4S_5, P_4S_7, and P_4S_{10}. Of these compounds, only P_4S_{10} has an oxygen analogue, it being P_4O_{10}. All the sulfides of phosphorus are yellow solids which are prepared by the direct union of the elements or from **tetraphosphorus trisulfide,** P_4S_3. The latter compound, also called **phosphorus sesquisulfide,** is a component of "strike anywhere" matches. **Phosphorus (V) sulfide,** P_4S_{10}, is readily hydrolyzed by water to orthophosphoric acid and hydrogen sulfide.

$$P_4S_{10} + 16\ H_2O \rightarrow 4\ H_3PO_4 + 10\ H_2S$$

The sulfides of phosphorus are used in replacing the oxygen of certain organic oxy compounds with sulfur.

QUESTIONS

1. Contrast the chemical properties of elementary phosphorus and nitrogen; of phosphoric acid and nitric acid; and of phosphine and ammonia.
2. Calculate the oxidation state of phosphorus in each of the following: PH_3, H_3PO_2, H_3PO_3, H_3PO_4, $H_4P_2O_7$, and PH_4I.
3. Write electronic formulas for each of the compounds given in Question 2.
4. Contrast the properties of white and red phosphorus.

5. Write equations for the preparation and hydrolysis of calcium phosphide. Compare the hydrolysis of metallic phosphides to that of metallic nitrides.

6. Relate $H_5P_3O_{10}$, $H_4P_2O_7$, H_3PO_4, and HPO_3 to P_4O_{10} in terms of extent of hydration of the latter compound.

7. Name each of the following compounds: K_2HPO_4, $FePO_4$, NaH_2PO_2, $(NaPO_3)_x$, $Na_4P_2O_7$, $Ca(H_2PO_4)_2$, and Na_2HPO_3.

8. Write equations for each of the following preparations: (a) P_4 from $Ca_3(PO_4)_2$, (b) P_4O_{10} from P_4, (c) H_3PO_4 from P_4O_{10}, (d) Na_2HPO_4 from H_3PO_4, and (e) $Na_4P_2O_7$ from Na_2HPO_4.

9. Write equations showing the stepwise ionization of phosphoric acid.

10. Write equations showing the hydrolysis of PO_4^{-3}, $HPO_4^{=}$, and $H_2PO_4^{-}$.

11. Write equations to show the action of heat upon NaH_2PO_4, $NaNH_4HPO_4$, and $MgNH_4PO_4$.

12. How may the phosphorus in insoluble tricalcium phosphate be made available for plant nutrition?

13. Explain the action of sodium polymetaphosphates as water softeners.

14. Show that the decomposition of phosphorous acid by heat involves auto-oxidation-reduction.

15. Why does phosphorous acid form only two series of salts although its molecule contains three hydrogen atoms?

16. Write equations for the preparation of hypophosphorous acid, starting with white phosphorus.

17. Explain the difference in spelling in the name of the element, phosphorus, and the name of H_3PO_3, phosphorous acid.

PROBLEMS

1. How much phosphorus can be prepared from 3 tons of calcium orthophosphate in the electric furnace process, if a yield of 89% is obtained? *Ans. 0.5 ton*

2. What volume of phosphine, measured at 24.0° and 732 mm., can be prepared by heating 135 g. of white phosphorus in a concentrated solution of NaOH? What weight of orthophosphoric acid can be formed by the combustion of the phosphine? *Ans. 27.7 l.; 107 g.*

3. What is the normality of an orthophosphoric acid solution, 25.0 ml. of which is neutralized by 43.5 ml. of 0.104 N sodium hydroxide? *Ans. 0.181 N*

REFERENCES

"Matches," A. C. Moffett, *J. Chem. Educ.*, **6** (7, 8) 1359 (July, Aug. 1929).

"Industrial Uses of Phosphates," Paul Logue, *J. Chem. Educ.*, **23** (11) 529 (Nov. 1946).

"Phosphates for Agriculture," a Symposium on, *Ind. and Eng. Chem.*, **41** (7) 1314–1337 (July 1949).

"Phosphorus Sulfides," John C. Pernert and J. Howard Brown, *Chem. Eng. News*, **27** (30) 2143 (July 25, 1949).

CHAPTER TWENTY-EIGHT

Carbon and Its Inorganic Compounds

CARBON

Carbon is the first member of Group IVA of the Periodic Table; the other members of this group are silicon, germanium, tin, and lead. Carbon and silicon are predominantly nonmetallic in character whereas germanium, tin, and lead are metallic elements. Each of these elements has four valence electrons and each exhibits a maximum oxidation state of +4; these elements also show an oxidation state of +2.

28.1 Chemical Bonding of Carbon

Atoms which have four electrons in the outer shell usually form compounds by sharing electrons rather than by complete transfer from one atom to another. Carbon, with four electrons in the outer shell and needing four more to fill the shell, nearly always combines with other atoms by sharing electrons.

An isolated carbon atom in its normal state has the valence-electron configuration $2s^2 2p^1 2p^1 2p^0$ (see Section 3.17). Its valence-electron configuration when carbon forms four covalent bonds is $2s^1 2p^1 2p^1 2p^1$, that is, one electron has been raised from the $2s$ orbital to the less stable $2p$ orbital. The electron in each of the four orbitals is shared with another atom, making the carbon tetravalent. One might suppose that the carbon atom would form one kind of bond with its $2s$ orbital and three bonds of another kind with its three $2p$ orbitals. This is not the case, however, and the four bonds that it forms are exactly equivalent in such molecules as those of methane, CH_4, and carbon tetrachloride, CCl_4.

```
    H                :Cl:
    xo               ..  x.  ..
  H:C:H           :Cl:C:Cl:
    ox               ..  .x  ..
    H                :Cl:
                       ..
 Methane        Carbon tetrachloride
```

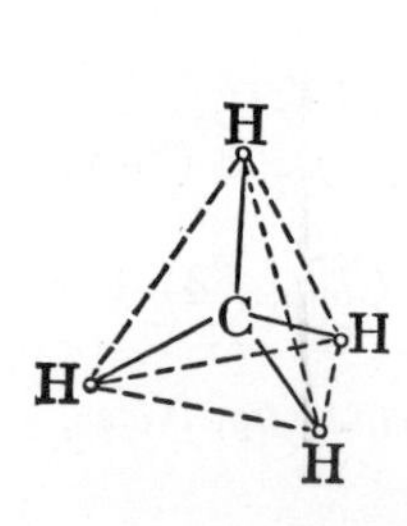

In methane, for example, the nuclei of the hydrogen atoms are exactly the same distance from the nucleus of the carbon atom, which is at the center of a regular tetrahedron with the hydrogen atoms at its corners.

The one $2s$ orbital and the three $2p$ orbitals **hybridize** (combine) to form four orbitals which are exactly equivalent to one another (Fig. 28–1). These hybrid bonds are stronger than either s or p bonds and they are directed toward the corners of a regular tetrahedron whereas s bonds are nondirected and p bonds have angles of the order of 90° between them.

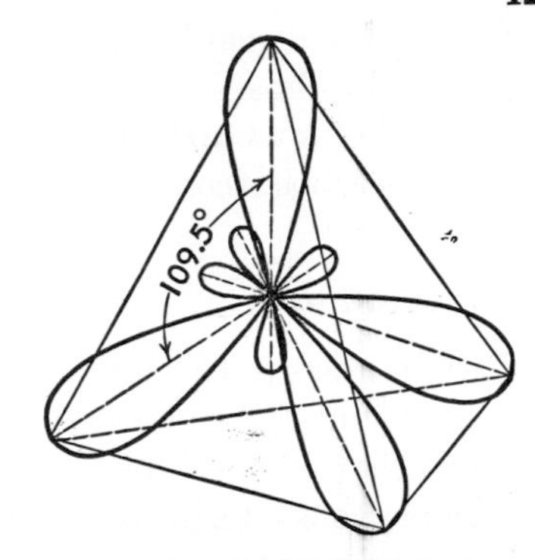

Fig. 28–1 Diagram illustrating the four tetrahedral (sp^3) hybridized orbitals of the carbon atom.

Carbon is one of the elements that combine with both electropositive and electronegative atoms simultaneously. For example, in the chloroform molecule ($CHCl_3$), hydrogen is electropositive and chlorine is electronegative.

```
    ..
   :Cl:
    x.  ..
 H:C:Cl:
    .x  ..
   :Cl:
    ..
```

Chloroform

Carbon atoms also display the unusual ability to form covalent bonds with other carbon atoms and thus form compounds containing chains or rings of carbon atoms. Examples are shown below.

```
   H H H H H H
H:C:C:C:C:C:C:H
   H H H H H H
```

Hexane

```
       H
       C
  H:C     C:H
  H:C     C:H
       C
       H
```

Benzene

Because of these unusual bonding properties, carbon forms a very large number of compounds. Well over a million different compounds of carbon have already been reported and described in the chemical literature. Many of these compounds have been isolated from plant and animal matter, and many more have been synthesized in the laboratory. It is not surprising that the study of the compounds of carbon constitutes a separate branch of chemistry which is called **organic chemistry.**

28.2 Occurrence of Carbon

Carbon is nineteenth among the elements in abundance; it constitutes only about 0.027 per cent of the earth's crust. It is found in the free state in the form of diamond and graphite; and it occurs combined in natural gas, petroleum, coal, plants and animals, limestone, dolomite, coral, sponges, and chalk. Carbon is found in the air as carbon dioxide and in natural waters as carbon dioxide, carbonic acid, and carbonates.

28.3 Diamonds

Carbon exists in two allotropic forms, diamond and graphite. Crystal chemistry has shown that "amorphous" carbon has a crystalline structure precisely the same as that of graphite. Charcoal, coke, and carbon black are microcrystalline or "amorphous" forms of carbon.

Diamonds are found in South Africa, the Belgian Congo, the Gold Coast, Brazil, India, and Australia. Most of the world's supply comes from Africa. The accepted theory is that diamonds are formed when very pure carbon is subjected to a high temperature and very great pressure. This theory follows from the fact that diamonds are found in the conical pipes of extinct volcanoes, where it appears that they were formed when carbon was trapped in the molten lava held at the great heat and pressure of the heart of the volcano when it was active.

Many attempts have been made during the past one hundred years to synthesize diamonds, but apparently none were successful until relatively recently. On December 16, 1954, a group of scientists headed by H. Tracy Hall carried out the successful production of man-made diamonds. Details of the method of synthesis were released in the fall of 1959. Graphite, in FeS as a solvent, was placed in a pressure cell and subjected to a pressure of 95,000 atmospheres at 1650° C for about three minutes. The material, still under pressure, was then cooled to room temperature during an interval of five minutes, after which the pressure was reduced to atmospheric pressure during an 18 minute period. When the cell was broken open, several dozen tiny, transparent diamond crystals were found near the top end of the cell. Hundreds of thousands of carats (one carat = 200 mg.) of man-made industrial diamonds have been produced since the announcement of the first synthesis. Although the cost is somewhat more than that for natural diamonds, the man-made diamonds are considered worth the extra cost because they are superior to natural diamonds for various industrial uses. No man-made, gem-quality diamonds have yet been reported.

Natural diamonds in the "rough" are covered with a deposit of mineral matter and are shaped like pebbles. The natural diamonds are cut by grinding them with diamond dust in such a manner as to obtain the maximum reflection of light from the interior. The great brilliance of diamonds is due to a high index of refraction of light and to the manner in which facets (little faces) are cut. The largest diamond so far discovered was the Cullinan diamond, found at Kimberley, South Africa, in 1905. It weighed about 1.6 pounds, but was later cut into smaller gems.

Diamond is very brittle, and it is the hardest substance known; this means that it is not scratched by any other substance (with the possible exception of boron carbide, B_4C). It is a good conductor of heat but not of electricity. The specific gravity of diamond averages about 3.5. Diamonds burn when heated in air or oxygen. In 1814 Davy proved that carbon dioxide is the only product of combustion except a trace of ash. When heated to 1000° in the absence of air, diamond changes to graphite. Diamond is inert to all chemicals at ordinary temperatures.

A diamond crystal belongs to the cubic system, with each atom covalently bonded to four others located at the corners of a regular tetrahedron (Fig. 28–2). These covalent bonds bind all of the atoms in the diamond crystal into a single giant molecule. The important physical properties of the diamond are related to its structure. Because the carbon-carbon bonds are very strong and they extend throughout the crystal in its three dimensions, the crystal is very hard, and has a high melting point (probably the highest of all elements). The diamond is a non conductor of electricity because all of its electrons are used in bond formation, and there are no mobile electrons in the crystal.

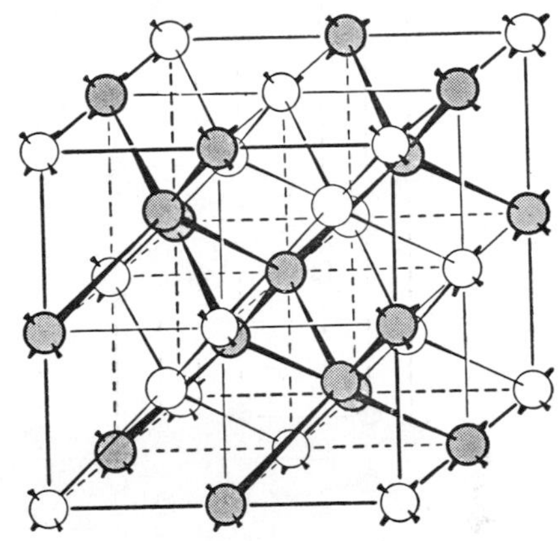

Fig. 28–2 The crystal structure of diamond. Notice in the diagram that the atom shared by all eight cubes is bonded to the center atom of four of the cubes. Bonds in these four cubes are shown heavier and the atoms darker for distinction.

28.4 Graphite

Graphite, which is also known as "plumbago," or "black lead," is distinctly different in crystalline form and physical properties from diamond. It is a soft, grayish-black solid which crystallizes in hexagonal plates that have a metallic luster and conduct electricity. The name "graphite" comes from the Greek meaning "to write" because it is used for this purpose. Graphite has a specific gravity of 2.2, it melts at 3527° (under pressure), and it is inert to most chemical reagents. The internal energy of graphite is less than that of diamond. This means that graphite is the more stable of the two crystalline forms. More energy is released in the combustion of diamond, therefore, than in the combustion of graphite.

$$\text{C (diamond)} + O_2 \rightarrow CO_2 + 94{,}505 \text{ calories}$$
$$\text{C (graphite)} + O_2 \rightarrow CO_2 + 94{,}052 \text{ calories}$$

The softness and electrical conductivity of graphite are in accord with its structure (Fig. 28–3, page 430). The crystal consists of layers of atoms, each of which has three carbon atoms as its near neighbors. Each carbon atom is bonded to two others by single covalent bonds, and to the third by a double bond. This arrangement completes the octet of each atom. The double bonds are not fixed but move around in such a manner (resonate) as to give each bond some double bond character. These covalent bonds bind the atoms very tightly together into layers of hexagons. However, the forces holding the layers on one another are weak and thus the layers can be separated easily. The flaky, soft character of graphite shows this binding to be weak. The loosely held electrons of the mobile double bonds

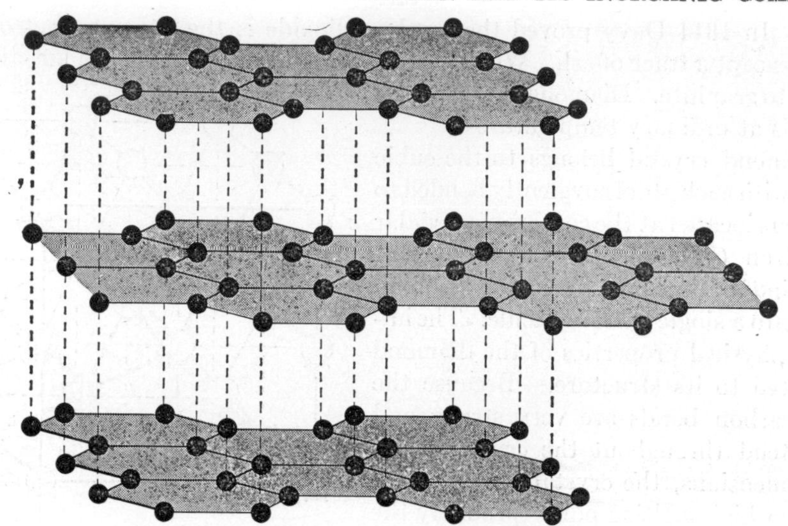

Fig. 28–3 The crystal structure of graphite.

within the layers of carbon atoms are responsible for the electrical conductivity and color of graphite.

28.5 Preparation and Uses of Graphite

Natural graphite is mined in Mexico, Madagascar, Ceylon, and Canada. The United States leads in the production of synthetic graphite. A mixture of amorphous carbon and a little sand and iron oxide (as catalysts) is heated in an electric furnace for 24 to 30 hours at a temperature of about 3500°. The carbon vapor condenses in the form of graphite. The Acheson process, which is used extensively at Niagara Falls, New York, uses petroleum coke or granular anthracite coal as the source of carbon.

Because of its resistance to heat and chemical action, its high vaporization temperature, and its ability to conduct electricity, graphite is used in making electrodes and crucibles. It is also used in the manufacture of stove polish, paints, commutator brushes, and "lead" pencils. Suspensions of colloidal graphite in water (aqua-dag) or in oil (oil-dag) provide excellent lubricants for many purposes.

28.6 Coal

Large quantities of coal have been formed in nature by a process called "carbonization" of vegetable matter (Fig. 28–4). This process is essentially the slow decomposition of vegetable matter (chiefly cellulose, a compound containing carbon, hydrogen, and oxygen) under high pressure and without much heating, but in the presence of water and in the absence of air. This decomposition results in the loss of a large proportion of the hydrogen in the form of volatile hydrocarbons, such as methane (CH_4), and of the oxygen in the form of carbon dioxide (CO_2). The residue becomes richer in carbon and poorer in hydrogen, oxygen,

Fig. 28–4 From a study of the fossils in coal, it is often possible to reconstruct the vegetation that was subsequently carbonized. This is a photograph of a reconstructed forest that grew 300 million years ago. *Chicago Natural History Museum*

nitrogen, and water. During the progressive stages of carbonization the several varieties of coal (peat, lignite, bituminous, and anthracite) are formed. The average free carbon content of peat is 11 per cent; lignite, 22 per cent; bituminous, 60 per cent; and anthracite, 88 per cent.

28.7 Coke

The residue remaining after coal is heated in the absence of air in by-product coke ovens (Fig. 28–5) is known as coke. This solid product is composed chiefly

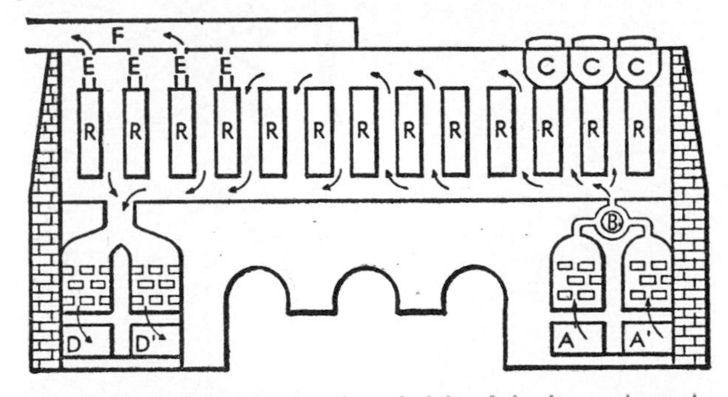

Fig. 28–5 Diagram showing the principle of the by-product coke oven. Fuel gas enters A where it is heated by the checkerwork; in the burner B it comes in contact with air which is heated as it passes through A. The superheated gases obtained in this way pass upward between the retorts RR which are charged with coal through the hoppers, some of which are shown at CC. At the other end the spent gas passes downward through DD, which becomes very hot. At intervals the gas current is reversed, entering at DD and leaving at AA. The volatile products obtained by heating the coal pass upward through flues, some of which are shown at EE, then through the main F to the refining plant.

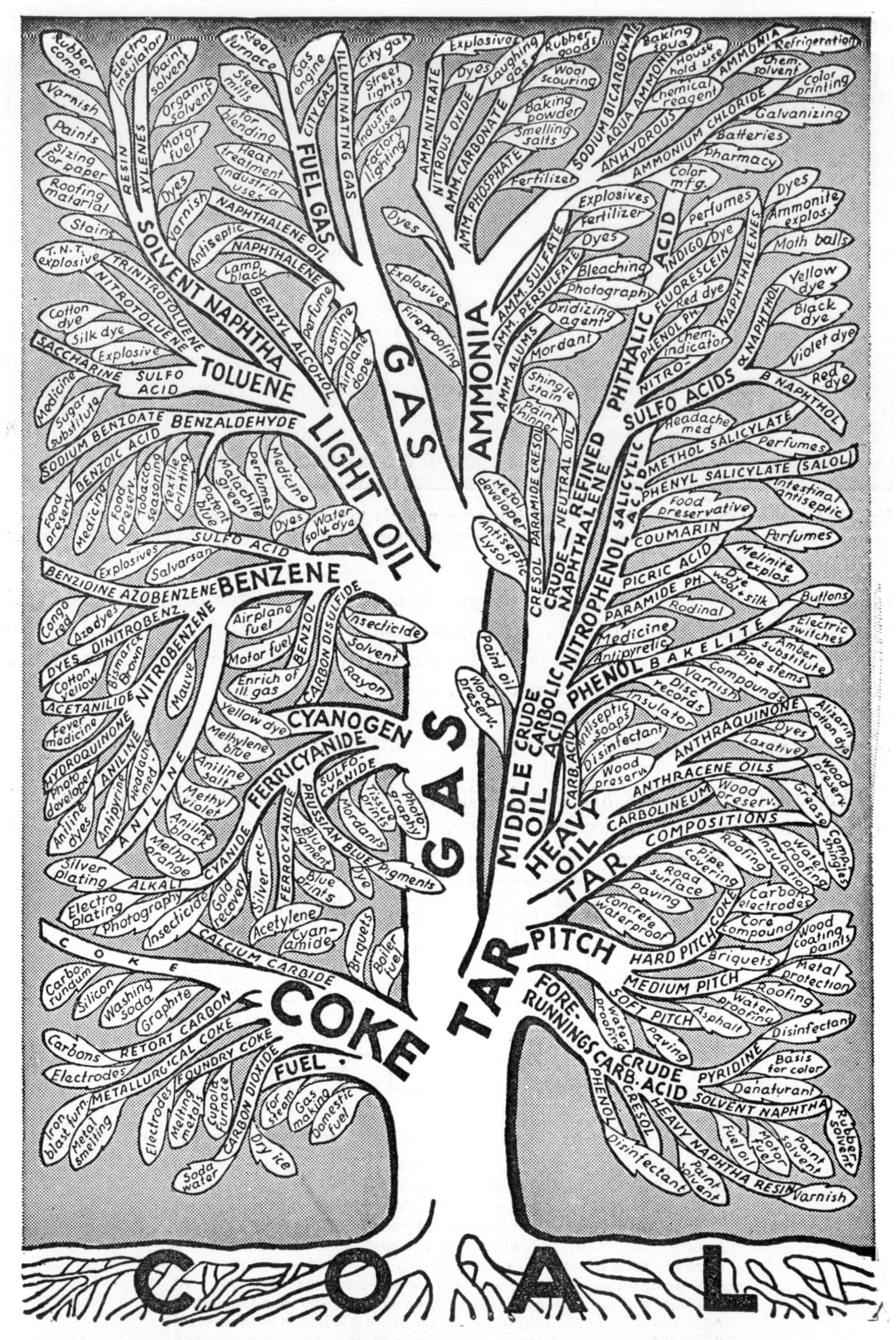

Fig. 28–6 Products obtained by the use of economy in the carbonization of coal. Most of these materials were formerly wasted. *Adapted with permission from The Coal Products Tree, Koppers Construction Co.*

of carbon and ash. The "by-products" of the process are ammonia, illuminating gas, and coal tar. Among the compounds obtained from the coal tar are benzene, toluene, phenol, and naphthalene (Fig. 28–6). Coke is used in large quantities in the reduction of metallic ores, as a smokeless fuel, and in the production of "water gas."

28.8 Charcoal

Wood charcoal is produced by the destructive distillation of wood, i.e., the dry distillation of wood in the absence of air. Among the valuable by-products of the process are wood alcohol (methanol), acetic acid, acetone, and a tarry mixture. The solid product retains the shape of the wood from which it was made, and it is very porous.

Charcoal is used to a limited extent as a fuel. More important is its use as a decolorizing agent for certain liquids such as sugar solutions, alcohol, and petroleum products. This use depends upon the ability of charcoal (and other "amorphous" forms of carbon) to absorb certain substances which are responsible for the discoloration of many liquids that are colorless when pure. Adsorption is a surface phenomenon in which forces existing on the surface of the adsorbing agent attract and hold molecules of the substance being adsorbed. Gases, as well as solids and liquids, may be adsorbed on the surface of the very porous charcoal. One milliliter of finely powdered charcoal may have a total surface as great as 1000 square meters. Charcoal is "activated" by heating it in steam. This treatment increases its adsorptive capacity by breaking down the granules and removing gas already adsorbed. Charcoal is used in removing odoriferous gases from petroleum products and in gas masks to protect the wearer who may be exposed to poisonous gases.

28.9 Bone Black

Bone black is made by the destructive distillation of bones or the refuse from the meat-packing industry. Bone black contains a high percentage of mineral matter and only about 10 per cent carbon. Its chief use is in the sugar industry for the decoloration of crude sugar which is colored yellow or brown by impurities.

28.10 Lampblack and Carbon Black

The soot deposited when oil is burned in a limited supply of air is known as lampblack. The smoky, luminous flame is chilled by contact with a water-cooled cylinder and the deposit of lampblack is scraped from the cylinder. Carbon black is produced by burning natural gas in a limited supply of air (Fig. 28–7). Carbon black is used in the manufacture of automobile tires

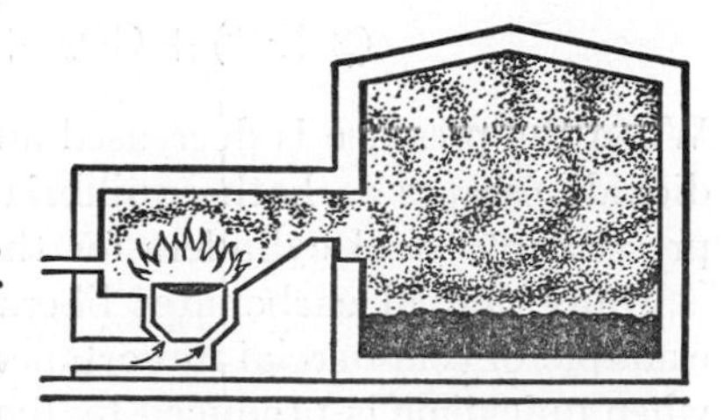

Fig. 28–7 When natural gas burns in a limited supply of air, finely divided carbon (carbon black) is one of the products.

to increase the wear-resistance of the tires and to make a tougher, stronger, and more resilient product. Because of its insolubility and chemical inactivity, carbon black is used in the manufacture of printer's ink, India ink, carbon paper, and typewriter ribbons.

28.11 Chemical Properties of Carbon

Carbon is almost chemically inert toward most reagents at ordinary temperatures. However, graphite is slowly oxidized by a mixture of nitric acid and sodium chlorate, and charcoal is rapidly oxidized by this mixture. The activity of carbon increases rapidly with rising temperatures and at elevated temperatures it is very active. At high temperatures carbon unites with oxygen, forming either carbon monoxide (CO), or carbon dioxide (CO_2); with sulfur, forming carbon disulfide (CS_2); with certain metals, forming carbides, such as iron carbide (Fe_3C); and with fluorine, forming carbon tetrafluoride (CF_4). Hot carbon combines directly with hydrogen in the presence of a suitable catalyst, forming such products as methane (CH_4) and acetylene (C_2H_2) in very low yields.

CARBON DIOXIDE

28.12 Preparation of Carbon Dioxide

When any form of carbon is burned in an excess of oxygen, carbon dioxide is produced ($C + O_2 \rightarrow CO_2$). The same is true of almost all compounds of carbon. The equations for the combustion of methane, CH_4, and ethyl alcohol, C_2H_5OH, are given below.

$$CH_4 + 2\ O_2 \rightarrow CO_2 + 2\ H_2O$$
$$C_2H_5OH + 3\ O_2 \rightarrow 2\ CO_2 + 3\ H_2O$$

Carbon dioxide is produced for commercial use by burning coke in a large excess of air. The carbon dioxide thus formed is not pure, but is mixed with nitrogen and a considerable quantity of excess oxygen. The gaseous mixture is brought in contact with a cold solution of sodium carbonate under pressure which dissolves carbon dioxide but not nitrogen or oxygen. The following reversible reactions take place:

$$CO_2 + H_2O \rightleftharpoons H_2CO_3$$
$$(2\ Na^+) + CO_3^{=} + H_2CO_3 \rightleftharpoons (2\ Na^+) + 2\ HCO_3^-$$

When the pressure is decreased and the temperature is raised, fairly pure carbon dioxide escapes as both equilibria shift to the left. The carbon dioxide is compressed into steel cylinders for the market, and the solution is used over again.

Many normal carbonates liberate carbon dioxide when they are heated. An example of commercial importance is provided by the reaction which takes place when quicklime is produced by lime-burning.

$$CaCO_3 \rightarrow CaO + CO_2$$

In the laboratory, carbon dioxide is produced by the action of acids on carbonates (Fig. 28–8).

$$CaCO_3 + 2\ H^+ \rightarrow Ca^{++} + H_2O + CO_2 \uparrow$$

Carbon dioxide is formed by the decay and fermentation of organic matter. Large quantities of the gas are obtained for commercial purposes as a by-product of the fermentation of sugar (glucose) during the preparation of alcohol and alcoholic beverages. The net reaction is given by the equation

$$C_6H_{12}O_6 \rightarrow 2\ C_2H_5OH + 2\ CO_2 \uparrow$$

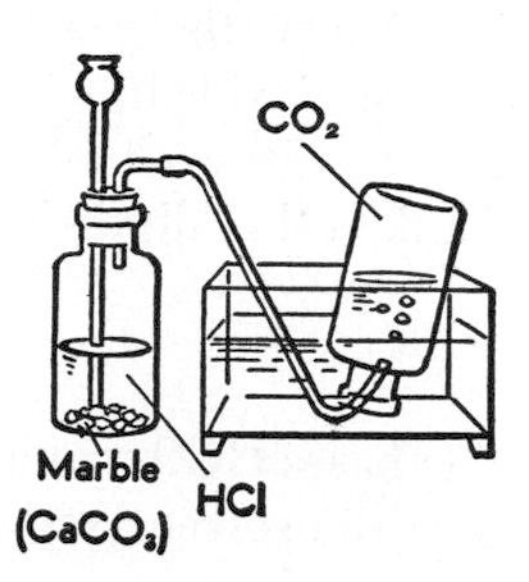

Fig. 28–8 Carbon dioxide generator.

28.13 Physical Properties of Carbon Dioxide

Carbon dioxide is a colorless and odorless gas which is 1.5 times as heavy as air. It has a mildly acid taste due to the formation of carbonic acid in the mouth. One liter of water at 20° dissolves 0.9 liter of carbon dioxide. The gas is readily liquefied by compression because its critical temperature is relatively high (31.1°). When the liquid is allowed to evaporate, it freezes to a snowlike solid at −56.2°. The solid vaporizes without melting (sublimes) because its vapor pressure is 1 atmosphere at −78.5°. This property makes solid carbon dioxide valuable as a refrigerant that is always free from the liquid; for this reason it is called "Dry Ice." Temperatures as low as −77° may be obtained by mixing Dry Ice with a volatile liquid such as ether or chloroform. Such mixtures are commonly used in the laboratory for attaining low temperatures.

28.14 Chemical Properties of Carbon Dioxide

The carbon atom in carbon dioxide completes its outer shell by sharing two pairs of electrons with each oxygen atom $\ddot{\underset{\circ\circ}{O}}{:}{:}C{:}{:}\ddot{\underset{\circ\circ}{O}}$. The double bonds are strong and the molecule is quite stable towards heat. At 2000° the dissociation into carbon monoxide and oxygen is only 1.8 per cent ($2\ CO_2 \rightleftharpoons 2\ CO + O_2$). When the heating is carried out in the presence of carbon, carbon monoxide is formed in good yield ($CO_2 + C \rightarrow 2\ CO$). Burning magnesium reduces carbon dioxide to carbon.

$$CO_2 + 2\ Mg \rightarrow 2\ MgO + C$$

Other active metals, such as potassium and sodium, will reduce carbon dioxide to carbon when the gas is led over the heated metal.

28.15 Carbonic Acid and Carbonates

An aqueous solution of carbon dioxide exhibits the properties of a weak acid. **Carbonic acid** (H_2CO_3) is unstable and has never been isolated as such. The solubility of carbon dioxide in water is in accordance with Henry's Law (Section 11.4) up to a pressure of about four atmospheres. At higher pressures the solubility is greater than we should expect from Henry's Law, probably because of the reaction of the gas to form carbonic acid. When the pressure on a solution of carbon dioxide in water is decreased, effervescence takes place. This phenomenon may be observed when a bottle of a carbonated beverage is opened.

Like other diprotic acids, carbonic acid ionizes in two steps:

$$H_2CO_3 \rightleftharpoons H^+ + HCO_3^-$$
$$HCO_3^- \rightleftharpoons H^+ + CO_3^{=}$$

The bases HCO_3^- and $CO_3^{=}$ both tend to combine with protons more strongly than does the solvent water; thus, carbonic acid and the hydrogen carbonate ion are weak acids.

When a solution of sodium hydroxide is saturated with carbon dioxide, **sodium hydrogen carbonate** is formed.

$$(Na^+) + OH^- + CO_2 \rightarrow (Na^+) + HCO_3^-$$

The compound $NaHCO_3$ is also called sodium bicarbonate or baking soda. Solutions of $NaHCO_3$ are weakly alkaline by hydrolysis.

$$HCO_3^- + H_2O \rightleftharpoons H_2CO_3 + OH^-$$

When an equivalent amount of sodium hydroxide is added to a solution of sodium hydrogen carbonate, **sodium carbonate** (Na_2CO_3) is formed.

$$(Na^+) + HCO_3^- + (Na^+) + OH^- \rightleftharpoons (2\ Na^+) + CO_3^{=} + H_2O$$

Solutions of sodium carbonate are strongly basic due to extensive hydrolysis of the carbonate ion.

$$CO_3^{=} + H_2O \rightleftharpoons HCO_3^- + OH^-$$

The carbonates of the alkali metals and ammonium are soluble in water, but the carbonates of the other metals are almost insoluble. A sensitive test for the presence of carbon dioxide involves the precipitation of calcium carbonate or barium carbonate. For example, a white precipitate is formed when carbon dioxide reacts with clear limewater.

$$Ca^{++} + 2\ OH^- + CO_2 \rightarrow \underline{CaCO_3} + H_2O$$

When an excess of the gas is used, the precipitate dissolves by forming the soluble hydrogen carbonate, $Ca(HCO_3)_2$.

$$CaCO_3 + H_2CO_3 \rightarrow Ca^{++} + 2\ HCO_3^-$$

Natural waters dissolve limestone and other carbonates according to this same reaction.

28.16 Uses of Carbon Dioxide

Large quantities of carbon dioxide are used in the manufacture of **washing soda,** $Na_2CO_3 \cdot 10\ H_2O$, and **baking soda,** $NaHCO_3$, by the Solvay process; in the production of **white lead,** $Pb(OH)_2 \cdot 2\,PbCO_3$, a paint pigment; and in the preparation of carbonated soft drinks.

Carbon dioxide is a valuable fire extinguisher because ordinary combustible substances do not burn in it, it is easily generated, and it is cheap. Air containing as little as 2.5 per cent carbon dioxide will extinguish a burning candle; thus it is suitable for smothering fires.

The familiar "acid and soda" fire extinguisher (Fig. 28–9) contains a solution of sodium hydrogen carbonate and a bottle of sulfuric acid. When the tank is inverted, the acid mixes with the hydrogen carbonate solution and carbon dioxide is liberated.

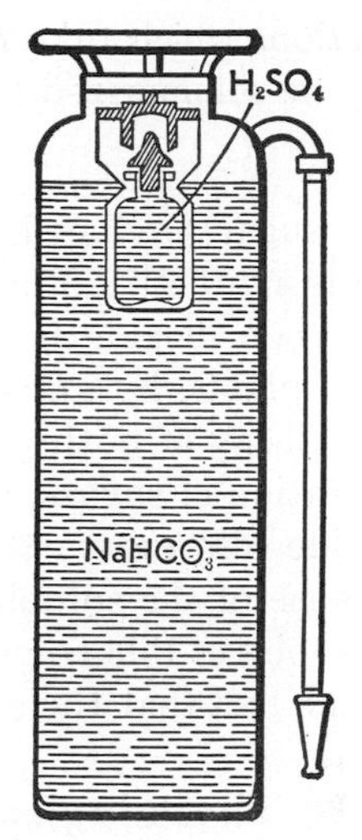

Fig. 28–9 Diagram of acid and soda fire extinguisher.

$$HCO_3^- + H^+ \rightarrow H_2CO_3 \rightarrow H_2O + CO_2 \uparrow$$

The increased pressure which results forces a stream of the solution saturated with carbon dioxide out of the hose with considerable pressure. The carbon dioxide escapes from the solution and dilutes the oxygen of the air surrounding the burning material; the water, of course, helps cool the material.

Fig. 28–10 Carbon dioxide fire extinguisher.

One type of modern carbon dioxide fire extinguisher is essentially a steel tank of liquid carbon dioxide (Fig. 28–10). When the valve is open, the liquid carbon dioxide evaporates and freezes to carbon dioxide "snow." Fires are smothered by a cloud of this "snow."

Solid carbon dioxide which has been compressed into blocks (Dry Ice) is used as a refrigerant for ice cream, meats, and butter. Liquid carbon dioxide has been used to some extent in place of ammonia in mechanical refrigeration plants. Carbon dioxide plays an important role in the baking industry, causing the breads produced to be light and fluffy. Carbon dioxide gas is sometimes used as an "inert" atmosphere for reactions which must be performed in the absence of air.

28.17 The Carbon Dioxide Cycle in Nature

The atmosphere contains about 0.04 per cent by volume of carbon dioxide and thus serves as a huge reservoir of this compound. Green plants absorb carbon dioxide from the air or water, and under the influence of sunlight and chlorophyll (as a catalyst) the carbon dioxide and water become sugar and free oxygen. The reactions which take place during "photosynthesis" are complex, but the process may be summarized by the following equation:

$$6\ CO_2 + 6\ H_2O \rightarrow C_6H_{12}O_6 + 6\ O_2$$

The sugar produced during photosynthesis is glucose, $C_6H_{12}O_6$; from it green plants synthesize other materials such as other sugars, starches, cellulose, and fats.

Carbon dioxide is a product of respiration and is returned to the air by the green plants, by animals, by the organisms (mostly nongreen plants) which produce decay of both plant and animal matter, by the organisms which cause fermentation of sugars, and by the combustion of carbon-containing fuels. Carbon dioxide also enters the air from volcanoes and from other geological processes. Because of the solubility of carbon dioxide in water, oceans and lakes are great reservoirs of this compound. The ocean reservoir is to a great extent responsible for the fact that the carbon dioxide content of the air is almost constant.

28.18 Physiological Action of Carbon Dioxide

Carbon dioxide is not toxic; its harmful effects when it is present in the air in large concentration are due to suffocation, i.e., lack of oxygen. Breathing air which contains an increased percentage of carbon dioxide stimulates the respiratory centers and causes rapid breathing. Use is made of this fact by administering carbon dioxide, mixed with oxygen, in the treatment of conditions in which rapid breathing is desirable.

CARBON MONOXIDE

28.19 Preparation of Carbon Monoxide

A second oxide of carbon, the **monoxide** (CO), is prepared in the laboratory by heating crystals of oxalic acid ($H_2C_2O_4$) with concentrated sulfuric acid; the latter compound dehydrates the oxalic acid.

$$H_2C_2O_4 \rightarrow H_2O + CO_2 + CO$$

The carbon monoxide may be removed from the mixture of gases by passing the mixture through sodium hydroxide, which absorbs the carbon dioxide.

Carbon monoxide is formed when carbon or its compounds are burned in a limited supply of air. The blue flame observed over a coal fire is due to the combustion of carbon monoxide. Carbon dioxide is formed by the combustion of the coal in the lower layers of the fire (Fig. 28–11), but as this gas rises and comes in contact with red-hot coals in the upper layers, it is reduced to carbon monoxide.

$$CO_2 + C \rightarrow 2\ CO$$

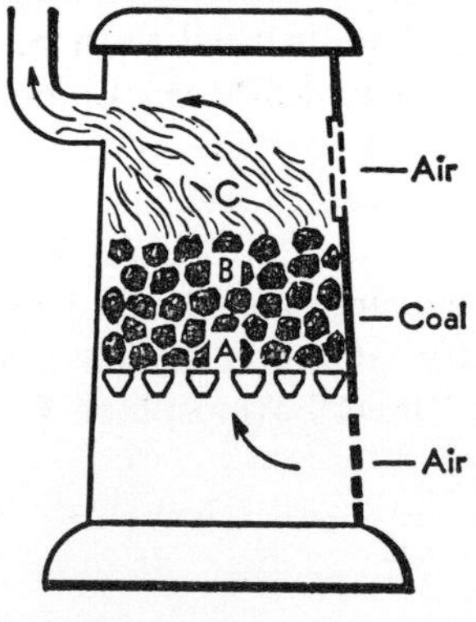

Fig. 28–11 Combustion in a coal stove. Region A (above) is characterized by the reaction $C + O_2 \rightarrow CO_2$; Region B, $CO_2 + C \rightarrow 2\ CO$; Region C, $2\ CO + O_2 \rightarrow 2\ CO_2$

When a limited supply of air is passed through hot coke, a mixture of carbon monoxide and nitrogen, in a ratio of about 1 to 2 by volume, is obtained. This product, called "producer gas," is used as an inexpensive and economical gaseous fuel for certain industrial operations.

When steam is passed through a bed of red-hot coke, a mixture of hydrogen and carbon monoxide, called "water gas," is formed.

$$C + H_2O + 29{,}100 \text{ calories} \rightarrow H_2 + CO$$

Because the reaction is endothermic, the coke soon becomes too cool to reduce the steam. Hence, oxygen and steam are passed together through the coke to keep it heated to red-heat. "Water gas" is used extensively as an industrial fuel and as a source of hydrogen.

28.20 Properties of Carbon Monoxide

Carbon monoxide is a colorless, odorless, and tasteless gas, which is only slightly soluble in water. Liquid carbon monoxide boils at −192° and freezes at −205°.

The atoms in the carbon monoxide molecule are bonded together by three pairs of shared electrons ($\overset{\circ}{\underset{\circ}{}}C\overset{\circ\times\times}{\underset{\circ\times\times}{}}O\overset{\times}{\underset{\times}{}}$). This arrangement of electrons gives a completed shell to each atom. In contrast to the behavior of carbon dioxide, carbon monoxide is an active compound. It readily burns in oxygen forming the dioxide.

$$2\ CO + O_2 \rightarrow 2\ CO_2 + 135{,}272 \text{ cal.}$$

This reaction makes carbon monoxide valuable as a gaseous fuel.

Carbon monoxide will reduce many metallic oxides at high temperatures. Two examples are given below.

$$CuO + CO \rightarrow Cu + CO_2$$
$$FeO + CO \rightarrow Fe + CO_2$$

Therefore, this gas is important as a reducing agent in metallurgical operations.

Carbon monoxide combines with chlorine in the presence of sunlight and charcoal (as a catalyst), forming **carbonyl chloride,** $COCl_2$, which is also called **phosgene** (meaning "produced by light"). The equation is

$$CO + Cl_2 \rightarrow COCl_2$$

Phosgene, a poisonous gas, was used in World War I in gas attacks. It is also used in the manufacture of valuable dyes.

Carbon monoxide combines directly with several metals forming "metallic carbonyls." Examples of this type of compound are **iron carbonyl,** $Fe(CO)_5$; **nickel carbonyl,** $Ni(CO)_4$; and **cobalt carbonyl,** $Co_2(CO)_8$. Nickel carbonyl is important because of its use in the purification of nickel.

28.21 Physiological Action of Carbon Monoxide

Carbon monoxide is a very dangerous poison. It is especially dangerous because it is odorless and tasteless, and therefore it gives no warning of its presence. It combines with the hemoglobin of the blood and forms a compound which is too stable to be broken down by the body processes. In this way carbon monoxide destroys the ability of the blood to carry oxygen and thus makes the oxygen supply of the body inadequate. An anemic condition is produced when small amounts of the gas are breathed over a long period. One volume of carbon monoxide in 800 volumes of air will cause death in about thirty minutes because the carbon monoxide paralyzes the respiratory organs.

The danger of carbon monoxide poisoning is particularly great in the case of the exhaust gas from automobile motors. A small motor idling in a closed single garage may produce sufficient carbon monoxide to cause death within five minutes. Other sources of carbon monoxide poisoning are faulty ventilation of stoves and furnaces, and leaky connections in the gas supply.

Carbon monoxide is not effectively adsorbed by charcoal, so special gas masks are necessary for protection against it. A mixture of CuO, MnO_2, Co_2O_3, and Ag_2O (called "hopcalite") is employed in gas masks to catalyze the oxidation of carbon monoxide to the dioxide at ordinary temperatures.

Small animals, particularly mice and canaries, are quite sensitive to small amounts of carbon monoxide and are used in the detection of this gas in mines. A mixture of iodine pentoxide and sulfuric acid adsorbed on pumice stone turns green in the presence of carbon monoxide. This reaction is a test for the gas.

OTHER COMPOUNDS

28.22 Carbon Disulfide

At the temperature of the electric furnace carbon is oxidized by sulfur to **carbon disulfide** (Fig. 28–12).

$$C + 2\,S \rightarrow CS_2$$

Air must be excluded because the volatile carbon disulfide is highly inflammable, and burns according to the equation

$$CS_2 + 3\,O_2 \rightarrow CO_2 + 2\,SO_2$$

Carbon disulfide is also produced commercially by burning methane in sulfur vapor at about 700° in the presence of silica gel or activated alumina.

Pure carbon disulfide is a colorless liquid which boils at 46.3°. The commercial product is yellow and has a disagreeable odor due to impurities. The liquid is heavy (specific gravity 1.27 to 1.29), has a high index of refraction, and is immiscible with water. The vapor is heavier than air, very poisonous, and highly inflammable.

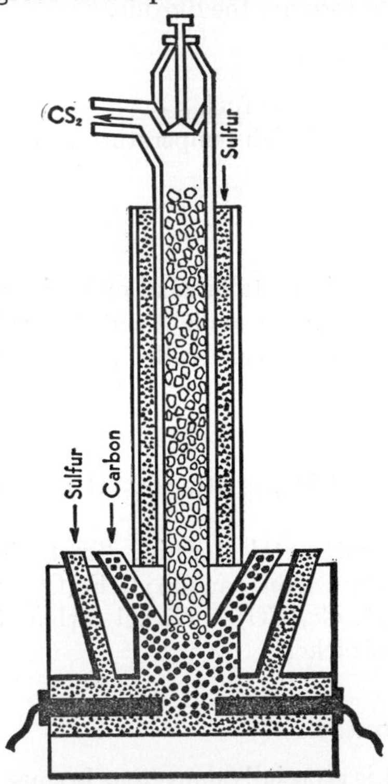

Fig. 28–12 Electric furnace for the manufacture of carbon disulfide.

Large quantities of carbon disulfide are used in making rayon by the viscose process and in the manufacture of cellophane and carbon tetrachloride. It is an excellent solvent for such substances as sulfur, phosphorus, iodine, fats and oils, waxes, resins, and rubber.

28.23 Carbon Tetrachloride

Carbon tetrachloride (CCl_4) is manufactured by passing chlorine into carbon disulfide containing iodine or antimony pentachloride, which act as catalysts.

$$CS_2 + 3\ Cl_2 \rightarrow CCl_4 + S_2Cl_2$$

The carbon tetrachloride (b.p. 76.7°) is readily separated from the higher boiling "sulfur monochloride" (b.p. 138°) by fractional distillation.

Carbon tetrachloride is a colorless, pleasant-smelling liquid, with a specific gravity of 1.58, and a freezing point of −23°. It is an excellent solvent for fats, oils, and greases; therefore it is used in the dry cleaning of various fabrics. Because its vapor is about five times as heavy as air and it does not burn, it makes a good fire extinguisher. "Pyrene" fire extinguishers are filled with carbon tetrachloride. The fact that it is a nonconductor of electricity makes carbon tetrachloride particularly useful in fighting fires involving electrical equipment where water might cause short circuits.

28.24 Calcium Carbide

Calcium carbide (CaC_2) is an important commercial product which is made by heating quicklime with coke in an electric furnace. The equation for the reaction is

$$CaO + 3\ C \rightarrow CaC_2 + CO$$

The product, which is liquid at the temperature of the furnace, is drawn off and solidified by cooling. Calcium carbide is an ionic compound with the structure $Ca^{++}[:C:::C:]^{=}$. It hydrolyzes in water forming acetylene (H—C≡C—H), according to the equation

$$CaC_2 + 2\ H_2O \rightarrow Ca(OH)_2 + C_2H_2\uparrow$$

Acetylene is an important compound that is used in the synthesis of many organic materials such as ethyl alcohol, synthetic fabrics, synthetic rubber, and plastics. It is also used as an illuminant, and as a fuel for cutting and welding metals.

The use of calcium carbide in the cyanamide process for synthetic ammonia was described in Section 25.5.

28.25 Cyanogen

Cyanogen (C_2N_2) is a colorless, very poisonous gas, that burns with a blue flame. The molecule is linear and has the structure N≡C—C≡N. This compound may be prepared by heating a mixture of mercury (II) cyanide and mercury (II) chloride

$$Hg(CN)_2 + HgCl_2 \rightarrow C_2N_2 \uparrow + Hg_2Cl_2$$

or by heating a solution containing copper (II) ions and cyanide ions.

$$2\ Cu^{++} + 6\ CN^- \rightarrow 2\ Cu(CN)_2^- + C_2N_2 \uparrow$$

Cyanogen hydrolyzes in a manner analogous to that of molecular chlorine, as shown by the equation

$$C_2N_2 + H_2O \rightarrow \underset{\text{Hydrogen cyanide}}{HCN} + \underset{\text{Cyanic acid}}{HOCN}$$

28.26 Hydrogen Cyanide

Hydrogen cyanide (HCN) is a gas with an odor like that of bitter almonds. It is formed when a cyanide is treated with an acid.

$$(Na^+) + CN^- + H^+ + (Cl^-) \rightarrow (Na^+) + (Cl^-) + HCN \uparrow$$

The liquid boils at 25.7° and freezes at −13.2°. When hydrogen cyanide is dissolved in water, hydrocyanic acid is formed. This acid is so weak that it will not turn blue litmus red. Its salts, such as sodium cyanide, form solutions which are alkaline by hydrolysis.

Hydrogen cyanide is a very poisonous substance. A dose of about 0.05 g. is fatal to man; moreover, its toxic action is very rapid. It paralyzes the central nervous system and inhibits all tissue respiration by combining with the iron in the respiration enzymes.

Cyanide ions resemble chloride ions. Silver cyanide, like silver chloride, is almost insoluble in water. Cyanide ions form stable complexes with many metals. For example, sodium cyanide is used extensively in the extraction of gold and silver from their ores; these processes involve the formation of complex cyanides.

QUESTIONS

1. In terms of the bonding properties of carbon, account for the fact that it forms such a great number of compounds.
2. Describe the crystal structure of graphite and diamond and relate the physical properties of each to their structures.
3. What experimental evidence shows that diamond contains more internal energy than graphite? How is this fact related to the manufacture of synthetic diamonds?
4. Explain the formation of coal by the carbonization of vegetable matter.
5. What is meant by the "destructive distillation" of coal and what are the products of this process?
6. Why is charcoal such an effective adsorbent?
7. How is carbon dioxide produced, purified, and stored and shipped commercially?

8. Describe the production of Dry Ice. What are the advantages of its use as a refrigerant over "water ice"?

9. Why does not carbon dioxide support the combustion of most combustible substances?

10. How can Na_2CO_3 and $NaHCO_3$ be made from NaOH and CO_2?

11. Describe the construction and use of the "acid and soda" fire extinguisher.

12. Relate photosynthesis and respiration to the carbon dioxide cycle in nature.

13. Compare the heat of combustion of carbon monoxide to that of carbon. Explain.

14. How are "producer gas" and "water gas" manufactured?

15. Write the electronic structures for carbon monoxide and for phosgene.

16. Explain the toxicity of carbon monoxide.

17. How may the presence of carbon monoxide be detected?

18. Write equations for the production of carbon disulfide, carbon tetrachloride, calcium carbide, acetylene, cyanogen, and hydrogen cyanide.

PROBLEMS

1. What volume of CO_2, measured at 0.750 atm. and 25.0°, would be produced by the complete combustion of 35.0 g. of methane? What volume of oxygen is required? *Ans. 71 l.; 142 l.*

2. What weight of $CaCO_3$ would be required to produce 40.0 pounds of quicklime? What volume of CO_2 would be produced during the reaction if measured under standard conditions? *Ans. 71.4 lb.; 72.5 l.*

3. How much $CaCO_3$ would be formed upon the addition of 3.0 l. of CO_2, measured at 25° and 740 mm., to an excess of limewater? *Ans. 12 g.*

4. What volume of oxygen, measured at 730 mm. and 52°, would be required for the complete combustion of 73 g. of CO to CO_2? *Ans. 36 l.*

REFERENCES

"Solid Carbon Dioxide Industry," D. H. Killeffer, *J. Chem. Educ.*, **19** (10) 482 (1942).

"Synthetic Diamonds," P. W. Bridgman, *Sci. American*, Nov., 1955; p. 42.

"Ultrahigh Pressures," H. Tracy Hall, *Sci. American*, Nov., 1959; p. 61.

"The Synthesis of Diamond," H. Tracy Hall, *J. Chem. Educ.*, **38** (10) 484 (1961).

"Carbon — An Old but New Material," P. L. Walker, Jr., *American Scientist*, **50** (2) 259 (June, 1962).

CHAPTER TWENTY-NINE

Boron and Silicon

Although boron and silicon are members of different groups (IIIA and IVA, respectively) of the periodic system, they resemble each other rather closely in chemical behavior. Boron is a **bridge element,** i.e., it is a member of one periodic group with a valence characteristic of that group, yet its chemical properties and compounds are similar to those of the second member of the next group of the periodic system. Both lithium and beryllium, as well as boron, are spoken of as bridge elements because each of them exhibits properties like those of the second member of the next group. Lithium has chemical properties like those of magnesium, and beryllium is similar in properties to aluminum. Furthermore, oxygen is like chlorine, and nitrogen is somewhat similar to sulfur, although the "bridge" relationship with these nonmetals is less pronounced than with the metals noted above. The explanation of this phenomenon lies in the fact that in each case the ratio of the atomic radius to nuclear charge is nearly the same, which means that the outer shell electrons are attracted to the nucleus with about the same force.

A comparison of some of the properties of boron with those of aluminum (the second member of Group IIIA) and with those of silicon (the second member of Group IVA) illustrates that boron is a bridge element. It resembles aluminum in forming compounds in which the elements are trivalent — for example, B_2O_3 and Al_2O_3, $B(OH)_3$ and $Al(OH)_3$, and BCl_3 and $AlCl_3$. However, BCl_3 is more like $SiCl_4$ than $AlCl_3$ in physical and chemical properties. Boron and silicon chlorides have melting and boiling points much lower than those of aluminum chloride. Aluminum chloride hydrolyzes reversibly

$$AlCl_3 + 3\ H_2O \rightleftharpoons \underline{Al(OH)_3} + 3\ H^+ + 3\ Cl^-$$

whereas boron trichloride and silicon tetrachloride hydrolyze almost completely.

$$BCl_3 + 3\ H_2O \rightarrow \underline{B(OH)_3} + 3\ H^+ + 3\ Cl^-$$
$$SiCl_4 + 4\ H_2O \rightarrow \underline{Si(OH)_4} + 4\ H^+ + 4\ Cl^-$$

Boron and silicon are primarily nonmetallic in their chemical properties, but both show some metallic character in the elementary state. Neither occurs free in nature, but both exist as compounds with oxygen. Each forms a number of binary compounds with hydrogen.

BORON

The boron-containing compound "borax" is referred to in early Latin works on chemistry. Borax was employed as a flux in metallurgical processes and later to some extent as a medicine. In 1702 Hormberg prepared boric acid from borax. The element was first prepared in an impure form by Gay-Lussac and Thénard, and also by Davy in 1808, by reducing boric acid with potassium. The name boron is derived from borax, a word of Persian origin.

29.1 Occurrence and Preparation of Boron

Boron occurs in nature combined with oxygen. It constitutes less than 0.001 per cent of the earth's crust, but is widely distributed. It is found as **orthoboric acid,** H_3BO_3, in volcanic regions, and as borates, such as **borax,** $Na_2B_4O_7 \cdot 10\ H_2O$, **kernite,** $Na_2B_4O_7 \cdot 4\ H_2O$, and **colemanite,** $Ca_2B_6O_{11} \cdot 5\ H_2O$, in dry lake regions, especially in the desert areas of southern California.

Boron is usually prepared by reducing the oxide with powdered magnesium. The equation for the reaction is

$$B_2O_3 + 3\ Mg \rightarrow 2\ B + 3\ MgO$$

The magnesium oxide is removed by dissolving it in hydrochloric acid. Prepared in this way, boron is impure and remains as a brown amorphous powder. Pure boron may be obtained by passing a mixture of the trichloride and hydrogen through an electric arc, according to the equation

$$2\ BCl_3 + 3\ H_2 \rightarrow 2\ B + 6\ HCl$$

29.2 Properties of Boron

Crystalline boron is transparent and nearly as hard as diamond. Its brittleness and high electrical resistance classify it as a nonmetallic element. Boron combines with fluorine at room temperature and with chlorine, bromine, oxygen, and sulfur at elevated temperatures. Iodine has no action on it. Boron reacts with carbon at the temperature of the electric arc and forms boron carbide, B_4C, which ranks next to diamond in hardness.

Boron acts as a reducing agent when heated with water, sulfur dioxide, nitric oxide, carbon dioxide, or many other oxides. It is used as a deoxidizing agent in the purification of fused copper before it is cast. It also reduces concentrated nitric or sulfuric acid, in which reactions it is oxidized to boric acid. In most of its chemical properties, boron acts as a nonmetal; its halides are volatile and irreversibly hydrolyzed. However, boron is intermediate in character between nonmetals and metals, as evidenced in part by $B(OH)_3$, which is a weak acid.

29.3 Boron Hydrides

Boron forms a series of volatile hydrides which somewhat resemble the hydrides of carbon and silicon. The simplest and most important of these compounds is

diborane, B_2H_6. No hydride of the formula BH_3 exists. This is unexpected because boron usually exhibits a valence of three. Furthermore, an electronic structure cannot be written for B_2H_6 which would be in keeping with our theory of valence as outlined in Chapter 4, and with the properties of the compound. Fourteen valence electrons (seven electron pairs) would be required for a covalent structure of the type

```
    H  H
    |  |
 H—B—B—H
    |  |
    H  H
```

However, only twelve electrons are available for bond formation. Compounds of this sort are said to be "electron deficient." Recent investigations have shown that two of the six hydrogen atoms of B_2H_6 are different from the other four and that rotation around the B—B linkage is hindered. The proposed structure most in keeping with the properties of diborane is one in which two "hydrogen bridges" bond the two halves of the molecule together:

```
H ∘  ∘ H ∘  ∘ H
  ∘ B ∘   B ∘
H ∘   ∘ H ∘  ∘ H
```

Diborane

Diborane is readily prepared by the action of lithium aluminum hydride upon boron trifluoride in ether solution.

$$4\ BF_3 + 3\ LiAlH_4 \rightarrow 2\ B_2H_6 \uparrow + 3\ LiF + 3\ AlF_3$$

Diborane gas decomposes slowly at room temperature to form higher boron hydrides, such as B_4H_{10}, and hydrogen. Above 300° it rapidly decomposes into boron and hydrogen. It ignites spontaneously in moist air, the products of combustion being boric oxide and water. Diborane reacts violently with chlorine to form the trichloride and hydrogen chloride. It is hydrolyzed by water to orthoboric acid and hydrogen.

$$B_2H_6 + 6\ H_2O \rightarrow 2\ H_3BO_3 + 6\ H_2 \uparrow$$

When an excess of sodium hydride acts upon boron trifluoride, the complex **borohydride,** $NaBH_4$, is formed. The four hydrogen atoms are covalently bonded to the boron atom in the complex anion, $[BH_4]^-$. The structure is

$$Na^+\left[\begin{array}{c} H \\ H:\overset{\cdot\cdot}{\underset{\cdot\cdot}{B}}:H \\ H \end{array}\right]^-$$

Sodium borohydride and other similar complex hydrides, such as **lithium aluminum hydride** ($LiAlH_4$), are very useful reducing agents, particularly toward organic compounds.

29.4 The Boron Halides

As mentioned in Section 29.2, the fluoride, chloride, and bromide of boron can be prepared by direct union of the elements. The fluoride is a colorless gas that hydrolyzes in water to form boric acid and hydrofluoric acid.

$$BF_3 + 3\ H_2O \rightarrow H_3BO_3 + 3\ HF \uparrow$$

The hydrofluoric acid thus formed combines with boron trifluoride and gives **fluoboric acid,** HBF_4.

$$BF_3 + HF \rightarrow H^+ + BF_4^-$$

In this reaction the electron deficient BF_3 molecule acts as a Lewis acid (electron-pair acceptor), and fluorine as a Lewis base (electron-pair donor), as shown by the equation

$$H{:}\ddot{\underset{\cdot\cdot}{F}}{:} + \begin{matrix} F \\ B{:}F \\ F \end{matrix} \Rightarrow H^+ + \left[\begin{matrix} & F & \\ F & B & F \\ & F & \end{matrix} \right]^-$$

Fluoboric acid is a strong acid that has not been isolated in the free condition. It undergoes slow hydrolysis in dilute aqueous solutions at room temperature according to the equation

$$BF_4^- + 3\ H_2O \rightleftharpoons H_3BO_3 + 3\ H^+ + 4\ F^-$$

Crystal structure studies show the fluoborate ion, BF_4^-, to be tetrahedral. The fluoborates are similar to the perchlorates in crystal structures and solubilities. The other halogens do not form stable halo-complexes with boron, probably because they are larger and less electronegative than fluorine.

Boron trichloride is a colorless mobile liquid, the bromide is a viscous liquid, and the iodide is a white crystalline solid. All three compounds are hydrolyzed by water. Boron trifluoride is a valuable catalyst for many reactions of organic substances.

29.5 Oxide and Oxyacids of Boron

Boron takes fire at 700° in oxygen and burns to form **boric oxide,** B_2O_3. Boric oxide finds use in the production of chemical-resistant glass and certain optical glasses. The oxide dissolves in water to form **orthoboric acid,** H_3BO_3.

$$B_2O_3 + 3\ H_2O \rightarrow 2\ H_3BO_3$$

Orthoboric acid is the most common acid of boron and is usually referred to as **boric** or **boracic acid.** It is prepared commercially by heating borax, $Na_2B_4O_7 \cdot 10\ H_2O$, the most common of the borates, with a strong acid such as hydrochloric acid, as shown by the equation

$$B_4O_7^{=} + 2\ H^+ + 5\ H_2O \rightarrow 4\ H_3BO_3$$

When the mixture is cooled, the product crystallizes as colorless, slippery scales. Boric acid dissolves to a small extent in water (6.27% at 25°) and forms a weakly acidic solution. It ionizes according to the equation

$$H_3BO_3 \rightleftharpoons H^+ + H_2BO_3^-$$

Boric acid is used as a mild antiseptic and as a food preservative. The latter use is prohibited in many countries because boric acid is injurious to the health.

At 100° solid H_3BO_3 loses water and forms **metaboric acid,** HBO_2; the latter changes to **tetraboric acid,** $H_2B_4O_7$, at 140° to 160°; at still higher temperatures boric anhydride is formed.

$$H_3BO_3 \rightarrow HBO_2 + H_2O$$
$$4\ HBO_2 \rightarrow H_2B_4O_7 + H_2O$$
$$H_2B_4O_7 \rightarrow 2\ B_2O_3 + H_2O$$

The boron atom in H_3BO_3 is at the center of an equilateral triangle with oxygen atoms at the corners, as shown below.

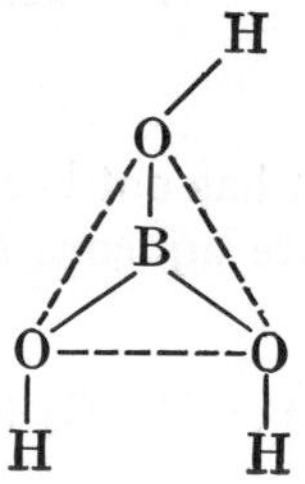

In the solid acid these triangular units are held together by hydrogen bonding. When boric acid is heated, a molecule of water is split out between pairs of adjacent OH groups, and a B—O—B linkage is formed in which two BO_3 triangles share a corner. A structure which has been suggested for the $B_4O_7^=$ portion of borax, $Na_2B_4O_7 \cdot 10\ H_2O$, is represented below.

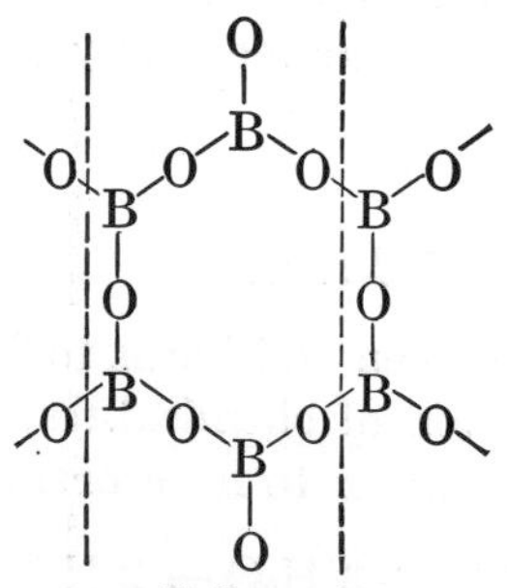

$B_4O_7^=$ unit

29.6 Borates

The most important borate is **borax,** or **sodium tetraborate 10-hydrate,** $Na_2B_4O_7 \cdot 10\ H_2O$. Most of the supply of borax comes directly from dry lakes, such as Searles Lake in California, or is prepared from **kernite,** $Na_2B_4O_7 \cdot 4\ H_2O$.

Aqueous solutions of borax are basic because it is a salt of a strong base and weak acid. The hydrolysis of the tetraborate ion may be represented by the following equation:

$$B_4O_7^{=} + 7\ H_2O \rightleftharpoons 4\ H_3BO_3 + 2\ OH^-$$

Borax is used for softening water and for composing washing compounds, uses which depend upon the alkaline character of its solutions and the insolubility of the borates of calcium and magnesium.

When heated, borax fuses to form a glass which is capable of dissolving fused metal oxides. An example is given by the equation

$$Na_2B_4O_7 + CuO \rightarrow 2\ NaBO_2 + Cu(BO_2)_2$$

The use of borax to remove oxides from metal surfaces in soldering and welding depends upon this property. The mixed salts which are formed when metal oxides dissolve in fused borax are often highly and characteristically colored. These colored salts are used in the identification of metal oxides in borax bead tests. Powdered borax is fused on a loop of platinum wire into a clear bead. When this bead is heated with manganese dioxide, for example, a violet color is imparted to the glass. Borax has many other uses, as in the production of glass with a low coefficient of expansion and high coefficient of refraction, in the manufacture of enamel, and in the sizing of paper.

29.7 Peroxyborates

When a solution of borax is treated with sodium hydroxide and hydrogen peroxide, transparent monoclinic crystals of the composition $NaBO_2 \cdot 3\ H_2O \cdot H_2O_2$ are formed. This substance is used as an antiseptic and bleaching agent under the name "sodium perborate." It is usually considered to be peroxyborate, but erroneously so, because the salt is a **peroxyhydrate.** True **peroxyborates** such as $(KBO_3)_2 \cdot H_2O$ and $(NH_4BO_3)_2 \cdot H_2O$ are known, however, and $NaBO_3$ can be formed by the action of sodium hydroperoxide, $NaHO_2$, on boric acid. These compounds liberate hydrogen peroxide upon hydrolysis, and as a result they are of value as oxidizing and bleaching agents.

29.8 Boron-Nitrogen Compounds

A number of compounds containing boron-nitrogen linkages have been prepared and studied. Two of these are of particular interest, **boron nitride,** BN, and **triborinetriamine,** $B_3N_3H_6$ (also called **borazole** and **borazine**).

Boron nitride is the final product of the thermal decomposition of many boron-nitrogen compounds such as $B(NH_2)_3$ and $BF_3 \cdot NH_3$. It can also be prepared by heating boron with nitrogen or ammonia, or by heating borax with ammonium chloride. Crystalline boron nitride is a white solid which sublimes below 3000°; it melts at this temperature under pressure. It is inert to most reagents but can be decomposed by fusion with alkalies. The crystalline structure of boron nitride is analogous to that of graphite (Section 28.4). In fact, boron nitride has been called "inorganic graphite." The layers of atoms in graphite and boron nitride are made up of analogous hexagonal rings as shown below.

Graphite layer

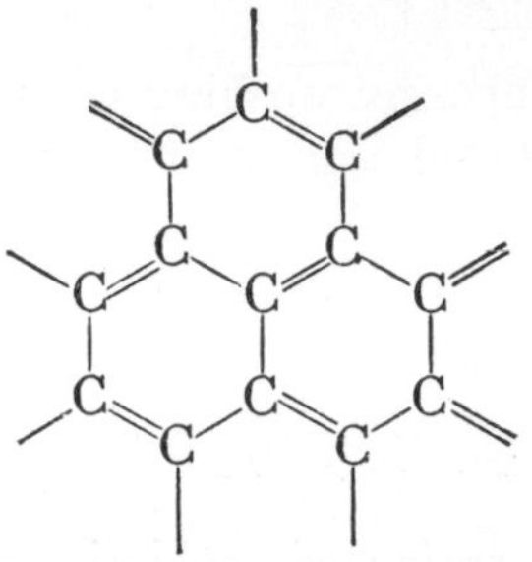

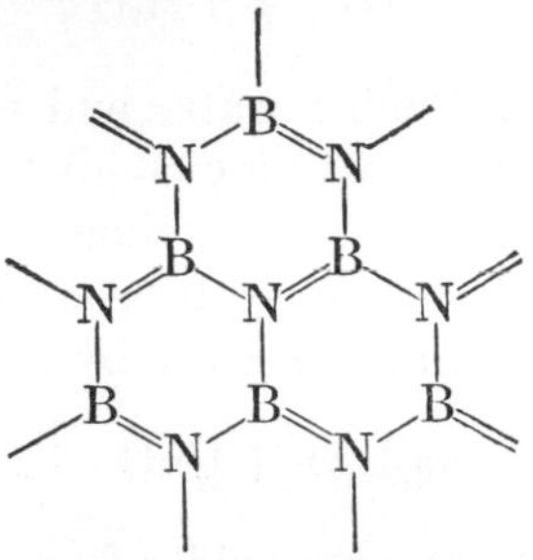

Boron nitride layer

The loosely held electrons of the resonating double bonds in graphite are responsible for its electrical conductivity and shining black color. The fact that boron nitride is a nonconductor and white in color indicates that its double bonds do not resonate. A second crystalline form of boron nitride has recently been synthesized. It has the diamond cubic structure and is very hard.

Borazine, $B_3N_3H_6$, is formed when ammoniates of the boron hydrides, such as $B_2H_6{\cdot}2\ NH_3$, are heated at 180° to 200°; hydrogen is the other product of the reaction. Borazine has been termed "inorganic benzene" because its structure and physical properties are similar to those of benzene. The structures of these two compounds are given below.

Borazine

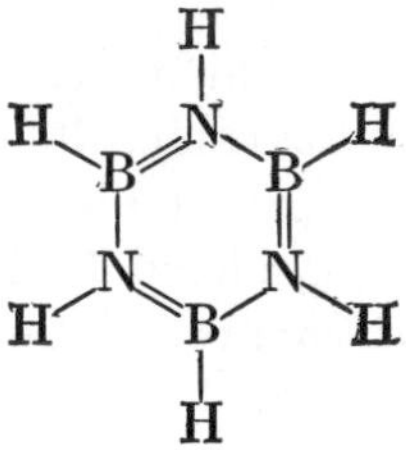

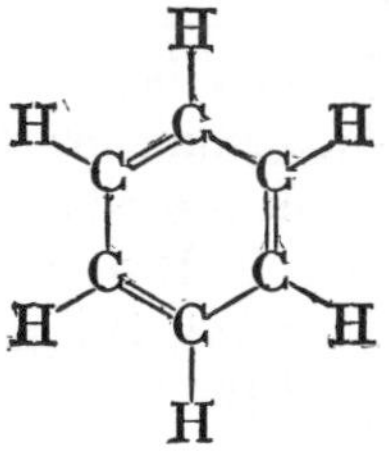

Benzene

Because a boron atom and a nitrogen atom bonded together have the same number of electrons as two carbon atoms and the sizes of these two groups are about the same, it is not surprising that the forms of boron nitride are similar to graphite and diamond, nor that borazine resembles benzene. Groups of this type are called **isosteres.** The concept of **isosterism** has been of particular value in accounting for similarities among the properties of many apparently unrelated structures.

SILICON

The name silicon is derived from the Latin word "silex," meaning flint. It is the second element of Periodic Group IVA, which also contains carbon, germanium, tin, and lead.

Whereas carbon, with its ability to form carbon-carbon bonds, plays the dominant structural role in the animal and vegetable worlds, the compounds of silicon containing Si—O—Si bonds are of prime importance in the mineral world. The earth's crust is made up principally of silicate minerals in which silicon atoms are connected by oxygen atoms in complex structures involving chains, layers, and three-dimensional frameworks.

29.9 Occurrence

The earth's crust is composed almost entirely of silicate minerals and silica. These constitute the bulk of most common rocks (except limestone and dolomite), and of soils, clays, and sands, which are the products of the weathering of rocks. Inorganic building materials such as granite, bricks, cement, mortar, ceramics, and glasses are composed of silicates. Metallic ores and other minerals make up only a very small fraction of the mass of the earth's crust. Silicon comprises nearly one-fourth of the mass of the earth's crust, being second only to oxygen in abundance. Its binary compound with oxygen is called silica, SiO_2. Familiar forms of impure silica are sand and sandstone. Silica also occurs as quartz, amethyst, agate, and flint. Certain aquatic organisms have skeletons rich in silica, and oat hulls are 40 per cent silica. Diatomaceous or Fuller's earth is composed of such siliceous skeletons. This material finds use as a good absorbent and insulator.

Silica is acidic in character and at high temperatures it combines with basic metal oxides forming silicates.

$$CaO + SiO_2 \rightarrow CaSiO_3$$

Most silicate rocks are built up of the common metal cations and complex silicate anions. A great variety of silicates exists in nature. A few of the more important silicates are given in Table 29·1. Most of these silicates have important specific uses, but they are such stable compounds that it is not economically feasible to use them as sources of the metals which they contain.

TABLE 29·1 Some Important Silicate Minerals

Mineral	Formula
Asbestos	$H_4Mg_3Si_2O_9$
Natrolite (a zeolite)	$Na_2(Al_2Si_3O_{10}) \cdot 2\ H_2O$
Garnet	$Ca_3Al_2(SiO_4)_3$
Zircon	$ZrSiO_4$
Mica	$K_2Al_2(AlSi_3O_{10})(OH)_2$
Talc	$Mg_3(Si_4O_{10})(OH)_2$
Kaolin (a clay)	$Al_2Si_2O_5(OH)_4$
Feldspar	$KAlSi_3O_8$
Beryl	$Be_3Al_2Si_6O_{18}$

29.10 Preparation of Silicon

Elementary silicon was first prepared in an impure, amorphous form by Berzelius in 1823 by heating silicon tetrafluoride with potassium. It may be obtained by the action of strong reducing agents at high temperatures upon silicon dioxide. With carbon and magnesium as the reducing agents, the equations are

$$SiO_2 + 2\ C \rightarrow Si + 2\ CO$$
$$SiO_2 + 2\ Mg \rightarrow Si + 2\ MgO$$

A second reaction always accompanies the reduction of silica by magnesium.

$$SiO_2 + 4\ Mg \rightarrow Mg_2Si + 2\ MgO$$

The silicide and the oxide are dissolved in hydrochloric acid, leaving amorphous silicon as a brown powder. An important alloy of iron and silicon, known as ferrosilicon, is produced by the simultaneous reduction of iron (III) oxide and silica with carbon at the high temperature (about 3000°) of the electric furnace.

29.11 Properties and Uses of Silicon

Silicon crystallizes with the diamond structure in which each silicon atom is covalently bonded to four neighboring silicon atoms at the corners of a regular tetrahedron. Thus a single crystal of silicon is a three-dimensional giant molecule. Silicon is hard enough to scratch glass, melts at 1410°, and is a brittle, gray-black, metallic appearing solid.

Silicon is inactive at low temperatures and resists attack by air, water, and acids. It does react, however, with strong oxidizing agents and strong bases. It dissolves in hot sodium or potassium hydroxide solutions forming silicates and hydrogen.

$$Si + 2\ OH^- + H_2O \rightarrow SiO_3^= + 2\ H_2 \uparrow$$

Silicon is attacked by the halogens at high temperatures with the formation of the volatile tetrahalides such as SiF_4, and it burns in air to give the dioxide.

Elementary silicon is used as a deoxidizer in the production of steel, copper, and bronze, and in the manufacture of certain acid resistant alloys such as "duriron" and "tantiron." Highly purified silicon, containing no more than one part impurity per million parts silicon, is used in semiconductor, transistor-type devices such as the solar battery (Section 20.17).

29.12 Silicon Hydrides

Silicon, like carbon of the same periodic group, forms a series of hydrides. This series is quite limited compared to that of carbon and includes SiH_4, Si_2H_6, Si_3H_8, Si_4H_{10}, Si_5H_{12}, and Si_6H_{14}. The chemical behavior of the hydrides of silicon is often decidedly different from that of the hydrocarbons of similar formulas. For example, the silanes are spontaneously combustible in air whereas the hydrocarbons are not.

Acids react with magnesium silicide to form **silane,** SiH_4, analogous in formula to methane, CH_4.

$$Mg_2Si + 4\ H^+ \rightarrow 2\ Mg^{++} + SiH_4 \uparrow$$

A convenient laboratory method for the preparation of silane depends on the reduction of silicon tetrachloride with lithium aluminum hydride in ether solution, according to the equation

$$SiCl_4 + LiAlH_4 \rightarrow SiH_4 \uparrow + LiCl + AlCl_3$$

Silane is a colorless gas, thermally stable at ordinary temperatures, and spontaneously combustible in air. Silicon dioxide and water are its combustion products.

$$SiH_4 + 2\ O_2 \rightarrow SiO_2 + 2\ H_2O$$

Stepwise halogenation of silane is possible, though the reaction is difficult to control. A better method of obtaining partially halogenated silanes involves the use of hydrogen halides in the presence of the corresponding aluminum halide as a catalyst With HBr and $AlBr_3$, the reactions are given by the equations

$$SiH_4 + HBr \rightarrow SiH_3Br + H_2$$
$$SiH_3Br + HBr \rightarrow SiH_2Br_2 + H_2$$
$$SiH_2Br_2 + HBr \rightarrow SiHBr_3 + H_2$$
$$SiHBr_3 + HBr \rightarrow SiBr_4 + H_2$$

The products are monobromo-, dibromo-, tribromo-, and tetrabromo-silane, respectively. Silane is extremely sensitive to alkalies, giving silicates and hydrogen.

$$SiH_4 + 2\ OH^- + H_2O \rightarrow SiO_3^= + 4\ H_2 \uparrow$$

29.13 Silicon Carbide

When a mixture of sand and a large excess of coke is heated in an electric furnace (Fig. 29–1), **silicon carbide,** SiC, is produced according to the equation

$$SiO_2 + 3\ C \rightarrow SiC + 2\ CO$$

Silicon carbide (**Carborundum**) is manufactured in large quantities at Niagara Falls by this process. The product comes from the furnace in the form of blue-black iridescent crystals, nearly as hard as diamonds, and very stable at high temperatures. The crystals are crushed, the particles are screened to uniform size, mixed with a binder of clay or sodium silicate, molded into various shapes such as grinding wheels, and fired. Silicon carbide is used as an abrasive for cutting, grinding, and polishing.

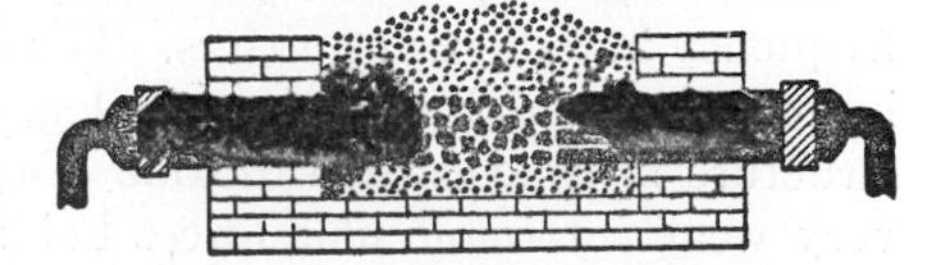

Fig. 29–1 Carborundum furnace.

Silicon carbide exists in three different crystalline forms; yet in each of these, carbon and silicon atoms have alternate positions, and each atom is surrounded tetrahedrally by four others. One crystalline form has the diamond structure. In order to rupture a crystal of silicon carbide, one must break a number of strong covalent bonds. The high decomposition temperature (above 2200°), the extreme hardness, and the chemical inactivity of silicon carbide are in accord with such a structure.

29.14 Silicon Halides

All the tetrahalides of silicon, SiX_4, have been made, and several mixed halides of the type $SiCl_2F_2$ have also been prepared.

Silicon tetrachloride can be prepared by direct chlorination at elevated temperatures or by heating silicon dioxide with chlorine and carbon. The equations are

$$Si + 2\ Cl_2 \rightarrow SiCl_4$$
$$SiO_2 + 2\ C + 2\ Cl_2 \rightarrow SiCl_4 + 2\ CO$$

Silicon tetrachloride is a low boiling (57°), colorless liquid, which fumes strongly in moist air and produces a dense smoke of finely divided silicic acid.

$$SiCl_4 + 4\ H_2O \rightarrow H_4SiO_4 + 4\ HCl \uparrow$$

Smoke screens were produced in World War I by liberating ammonia and silicon tetrachloride at the same time, the density of the smoke being increased by the formation of solid ammonium chloride.

Elementary silicon ignites spontaneously in an atmosphere of fluorine, forming **silicon tetrafluoride,** SiF_4, which is a gas. This compound is very readily prepared by the action of hydrofluoric acid upon silica or a silicate.

$$SiO_2 + 4\ HF \rightarrow SiF_4 \uparrow + 2\ H_2O$$
$$CaSiO_3 + 6\ HF \rightarrow CaF_2 + SiF_4 \uparrow + 3\ H_2O$$

Silicon tetrafluoride hydrolyzes in water and produces **fluosilicic acid** as well as **orthosilicic acid.**

$$3\ SiF_4 + 4\ H_2O \rightarrow \underline{H_4SiO_4} + 4\ H^+ + 2\ SiF_6^{=}$$

Fluosilicic acid is a stronger acid than sulfuric. It is stable only in solution, however, and upon evaporation it decomposes according to the equation

$$H_2SiF_6 \rightarrow 2\ HF \uparrow + SiF_4 \uparrow$$

29.15 Silicon Dioxide (Silica)

The common crystalline form of silicon dioxide is quartz, a hard, brittle, refractory, colorless solid (Fig. 29–2). It is used in many ways — for architectural decorations, semiprecious jewels, optical instruments, and in the control of the frequency in radio transmitters. The contrast in structure and physical properties between silica and its carbon analog, carbon dioxide, is interesting. The unit of structure in solid carbon dioxide (Dry Ice) is the single CO_2 molecule with but very weak intermolecular forces holding the building units at the points of the crystal lattice. The low melting point and volatility of Dry Ice reflect the weak

Fig. 29–2 Crystals of pure quartz. The crystals are hexagonal when formed. Many of the crystals in this photograph have had their original surfaces eroded by washing in river gravels over a long period of time. The structure of quartz and other forms of silica may be described as consisting of SiO_4 tetrahedra bonded together by sharing the oxygen atoms at the corners between two of these tetrahedra. *August E. Miller*

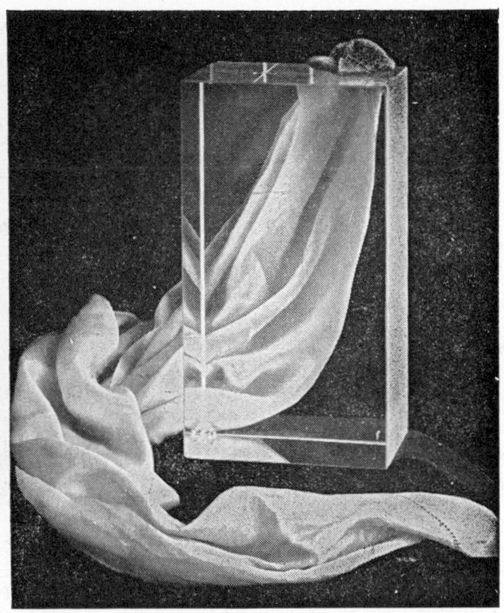

Fig. 29–3 Transparent fused quartz. The block of quartz measures 9 by 5 by 3 inches. Such material is the most transparent substance known. *General Electric Co.*

crystal forces between its building units. Each of the two oxygen atoms is attached to the central carbon atom by double electron-pair bonds. In contrast, a silicon atom in quartz is linked to four oxygen atoms by single bonds directed toward the corners of a regular tetrahedron, and the SiO_4 tetrahedra are bonded together by sharing the oxygen atoms at the corners between two tetrahedra. This structure extends in three dimensions to form a continuous, giant silicon-oxygen network extending out to give a **macromolecule** of silicon dioxide, the quartz crystal. The over-all ratio of silicon to oxygen atoms is one to two, and the simplest formula for the compound is SiO_2, but the formula SiO_2 does not represent a single molecule as does the formula CO_2.

At 1600°, quartz melts to give a viscous liquid with a random internal structure. When the liquid is cooled it does not crystallize readily, but usually undercools and forms a glass, called **silica glass** (Fig. 29–3). The SiO_4 tetrahedra in this glass have the random arrangement characteristic of undercooled liquids and the glass has some very interesting and useful properties. Silica glass is highly transparent to both visible and ultraviolet light and so finds use in the manufacture of mercury vapor lamps, which give radiation rich in the ultraviolet region of the spectrum, and in the production of certain optical instruments used in the ultraviolet region. The coefficient of expansion of this glass is very small, so it is not easily fractured by sudden changes in temperature. It is also insoluble in water and inert towards acids except hydrofluoric.

$$SiO_2 + 4\ HF \rightarrow SiF_4 \uparrow + 2\ H_2O$$

This reaction is used in the quantitative separation of silica from other oxides, both products of the reaction being volatile. Hot alkali hydroxides and fused alkali carbonates convert silica into soluble silicates.

$$SiO_2 + 4\ OH^- \rightarrow SiO_4^{-4} + 2\ H_2O$$
$$SiO_2 + Na_2CO_3 \rightarrow Na_2SiO_3 + CO_2$$

The latter reaction is employed in the conversion of silicate rocks to soluble forms for analysis.

29.16 Silicic Acids

Orthosilicic acid, H_4SiO_4, is an extremely weak acid, and it cannot be formed from its acid anhydride, SiO_2, by hydration due to the fact that silica is very nearly insoluble in water. However, the addition of a strong mineral acid to a solution of an alkali metal silicate results in the formation of orthosilicic acid.

$$SiO_4^{-4} + 4\ H_3O^+ \rightarrow \underline{H_4SiO_4} + 4\ H_2O$$

The orthosilicic acid first appears as a colloidal dispersion and then very shortly precipitates as a gelatinous mass. The addition of the silicate solution to the mineral acid produces orthosilicic acid which remains suspended in the colloidal form. In this form silicic acid adsorbs certain ions so that they cannot be removed by washing with water. It is thought that this is the mechanism by which colloidal silicic acids present in soils retain soluble salts which are essential to plant growth.

The loss of water from orthosilicic acid when it is heated gives silica as the final product of dehydration. Although there is no evidence to support the mechanism, it is thought that the dehydration is stepwise with the formation of **metasilicic acid,** H_2SiO_3, **disilicic acid,** $H_6Si_2O_7$, and **trisilicic acid,** $H_4Si_3O_8$, as intermediates. Salts of these and other polysilicic acids are found among the naturally occurring silicates.

Silica gel is obtained when gelatinous silicic acid is dehydrated until it contains a few per cent of moisture. This gel has an open, porous structure with a large surface area per unit of mass. It has a great tendency to adsorb gases and to catalyze certain chemical reactions involving substances in the gaseous state.

29.17 Natural Silicates

The silicates, as a group, are characterized by the great number of variations in the silicon-oxygen ratio which occur from one silicate to another. In all of them, however, the silicon atoms are to be found at the centers of oxygen tetrahedra, and thus the tetravalency of silicon is maintained. The variation in the silicon-oxygen ratio is the result of the fact that the silicon-oxygen tetrahedra may exist as discrete and independent building units, or they may share corners, edges, and more rarely faces, in a variety of ways. The silicon-oxygen ratio varies with the extent of sharing of oxygen atoms by silicon atoms in the linking together of the tetrahedra.

It is convenient to classify all the silicates whose structures are known in a few groups based upon the manner of linking of the silicon-oxygen tetrahedra.

1. *Single SiO_4 tetrahedra existing as independent groups in the crystal lattice.* Examples are **olivine,** Mg_2SiO_4, **and zircon,** $ZrSiO_4$. The positively charged metallic ions (Mg^{++}, Zr^{+4}) serve to bind together the negative SiO_4 radicals, which have the tetrahedral structure shown below. Note that only the oxygen atoms are shown. A silicon atom is in the middle of each tetrahedron and is not shown.

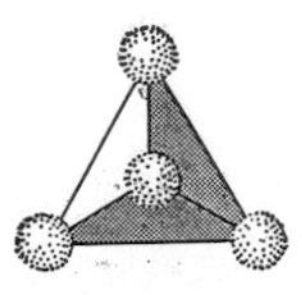

2. *Two SiO_4 tetrahedra sharing one oxygen corner and thus forming Si_2O_7 groups which act as discrete building units.* Examples are **hardystonite,** $Ca_2ZnSi_2O_7$ and **hemimorphite,** $Zn_4(OH)_2Si_2O_7{\cdot}H_2O$. The cations are to be found between the negative Si_2O_7 groups, binding them together. The structure of the $Si_2O_7^{-6}$ anion is

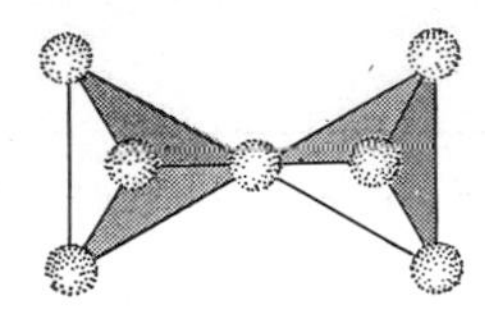

3. *Three tetrahedra sharing corners with each other and forming closed rings.* An example is **benitoite,** $BaTiSi_3O_9$. The Si_3O_9 rings are held together by the positive metallic ions. The ring ions are arranged in sheets with their planes parallel. The structure of the $Si_0O_9^{-6}$ ion is

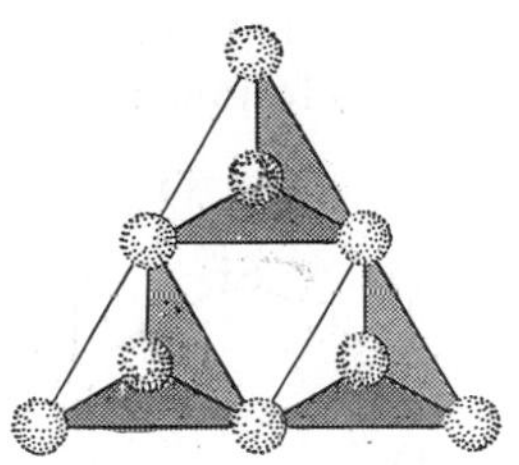

Beryl (emerald) has the formula $Be_3Al_2Si_6O_{18}$ — its structure involves six SiO_4 tetrahedra sharing corners to form a closed ring.

4. *Single silicon-oxygen endless chains formed from SiO_4 tetrahedra, each sharing*

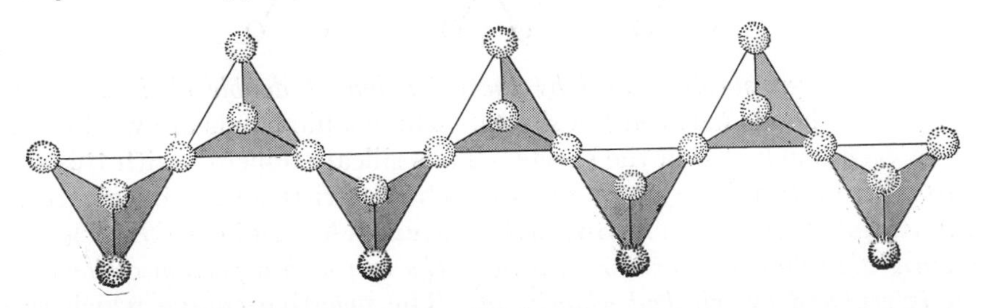

two oxygen atoms. This structure gives a radical composition of SiO_3, although there are no SiO_3 radicals present as independent groups. An example is **diopside,** $CaMg(SiO_3)_2$. The chains are considered to extend the full length of the crystal, and the parallel chains are held together by the metal ions lying between them.

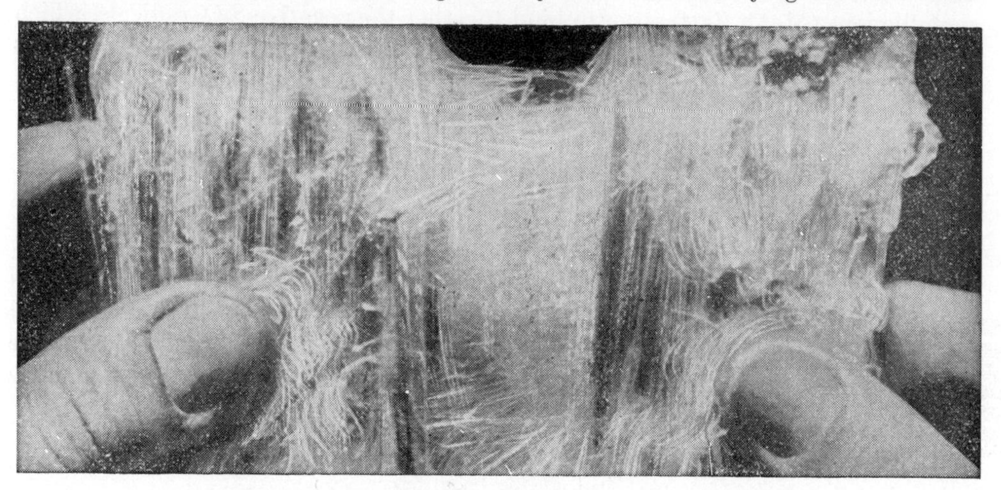

Fig. 29–4 Asbestos, a chain-type silicate mineral. *Johns-Manville Corp.*

5. *Double silicon-oxygen chains.* In the single- and double-chain crystals the metallic ions link the parallel chains together. The fact that these ionic linkages are not as strong as the silicon-oxygen bonds within the chains accounts for the fibrous nature of **asbestos** (Fig. 29–4), a chain type silicate. An example is **tremoline,** $Ca_2Mg_5(Si_4O_{11})_2(OH)_2$. These silicates always contain some hydroxyl groups which are attached to the metal atoms and never to the silicon atoms. The double chains may be represented as follows:

```
           O   O           O   O           O   O
            \ /             \ /             \ /
     O      Si      O       Si      O       Si      O
  \  |    /    \    |     /    \    |     /    \    |  /
   O-Si--O      O--Si----O      O--Si----O      O--Si-O
     |              |               |               |
     O              O               O               O
     |              |               |               |
   O-Si--O      O--Si----O      O--Si----O      O--Si-O
  /  |    \    /    |     \    /    |     \    /    |  \
     O      Si      O       Si      O       Si      O
            / \             / \             / \
           O   O           O   O           O   O
```

6. *Silicon-oxygen sheets formed by the extension of double chains.* The metal ions form ionic bonds between the sheets. These ionic bonds are weaker than the silicon-oxygen bonds within the sheets. Thus silicate minerals with this structure tend to cleave into thin layers, a property characteristic of the micas. Examples are **talc,** $Mg_3Si_4O_{10}(OH)_2$ and **muscovite mica,** $KAl_2(AlSi_3O_{10})(OH,F)_2$.

7. *Three-dimensional silicon-oxygen networks in which a portion of the tetravalent silicon is replaced by trivalent aluminum.* The negative charge which results is

neutralized by a distribution of positive ions throughout the network. Examples are **feldspar,** $K(AlSi_3O_8)$, and the **zeolites,** such as

$$Na_2(Al_2Si_3O_{10})\cdot 2H_2O.$$

29.18 Water Glass

Commercial sodium silicate is manufactured by the reaction of sodium hydroxide or sodium carbonate with silica, usually by fusion.

$$2\ NaOH + SiO_2 \rightarrow Na_2SiO_3 + H_2O$$
$$Na_2CO_3 + SiO_2 \rightarrow Na_2SiO_3 + CO_2\uparrow$$

The glassy product is soluble in water to give a syrupy liquid which is called water glass. It is used in making soaps and washing compounds to provide an alkaline reaction.

$$SiO_3^{=} + 2\ H_2O \rightarrow \underline{H_2SiO_3} + 2\ OH^-$$

The formulation of water glass as Na_2SiO_3 is an oversimplification because it is usually richer in SiO_2 than the formula indicates; i.e., it contains $Na_2Si_3O_7$, $Na_4Si_3O_8$, or other similar substances. Water glass is also used in fireproofing, adhesives, and egg preservation.

29.19 Glass

The common glass used for windowpanes, bottles, dishes, and the like is a mixture of sodium and calcium silicates with an excess of silica. It is made by heating together sand, sodium carbonate or sodium sulfate, and calcium carbonate.

$$Na_2CO_3 + SiO_2 \rightarrow Na_2SiO_3 + CO_2\uparrow$$
$$Na_2SO_4 + SiO_2 \rightarrow Na_2SiO_3 + SO_3\uparrow$$
$$CaCO_3 + SiO_2 \rightarrow CaSiO_3 + CO_2\uparrow$$

After the bubbles of gas have been expelled, a clear viscous melt results. This material is poured into molds or

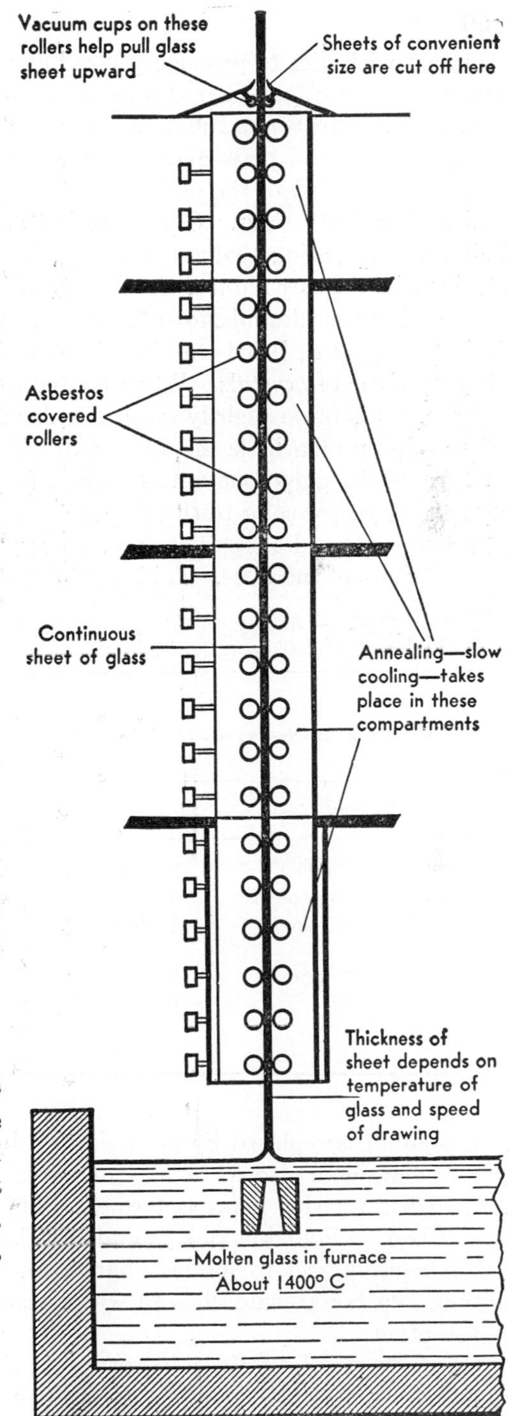

Fig. 29–5 The Pennvernon process. By this method window glass is drawn from the furnace in a continuous sheet. *Pittsburgh Plate Glass Co.*

stamped with dies to produce pressed glassware. Articles such as bottles, flasks, and beakers are formed by taking a lump of the molten glass on a hollow tube, inserting it into a mold and blowing until the outline of the mold is assumed. Window glass and plate glass are drawn from the glass furnaces in broad strips (Fig. 29–5), rolled to the desired thickness, and then ground flat. Plate glass is polished on both sides. Glassware is "annealed" by heating it for a time just below the softening temperature and then cooling it slowly. Annealing avoids strains and thereby reduces the danger of breakage.

Glass is a complex mixture of silicates, and is classified as an undercooled liquid. It is transparent, brittle, and entirely lacking in the ordered internal structure characteristic of crystals. When heated, it does not melt sharply, but gradually softens. It is often slightly green in color due to the presence of iron (II) silicate. The addition of a little manganese dioxide as an oxidizing agent, during manufacture of the glass, converts the iron (II) to iron (III) which imparts the less noticeable yellow color to the glass.

When a colored glass is desired, an appropriate substance is added during the manufacture of the glass. Table 29·2 lists a few of the substances used in coloring glass.

TABLE 29·2 Substances Used in the Production of Color in Glass

Substance	*Color*	*Substance*	*Color*
Iron (II) compounds	Green	Cobalt (II) oxide	Blue
Iron (III) compounds	Yellow	Manganese dioxide	Violet
Uranium compounds	Yellow, green, fluorescence	Calcium fluoride	Milky
		Tin (IV) oxide	Opaque
Colloidal selenium	Ruby	Copper (I) oxide	Red, green, blue
Colloidal gold	Red, purple, blue		

If sodium is replaced by potassium, a higher melting, harder, and less soluble glass is obtained. If part of the calcium is replaced by lead, a glass of high density and high refractive index is formed. This variety of glass is called **flint glass** and it is used in making lenses and cut-glass articles. **Pyrex glass,** very suitable for articles subject to sudden changes in temperature and resistant to chemical action, is a borosilicate glass in which some of the silicon atoms are replaced by boron atoms.

One form of **safety glass,** important in the manufacture of automobiles, consists of a thin layer of plastic held between two pieces of thin plate glass. Adhesion of the glass to the flexible plastic decreases the danger from flying glass and jagged edges when the glass is broken.

Glazes on pottery, and enamels on iron kitchen utensils, sinks, and bathtubs are made of easily fusible glass containing opacifiers such as titanium dioxide and tin (IV) oxide.

29.20 Cement

Portland cement is essentially powdered calcium aluminosilicate which sets to a hard mass when treated with water. It is made by pulverizing a mixture of limestone and clay, and roasting the powder in a rotary kiln heated by gas or powdered coal to a temperature of about 1500° (Fig. 29–6). This treatment yields sintered lumps called "clinker" about the size of small marbles. The clinker is then ground with a little gypsum, $CaSO_4 \cdot 2\ H_2O$, to a very fine powder.

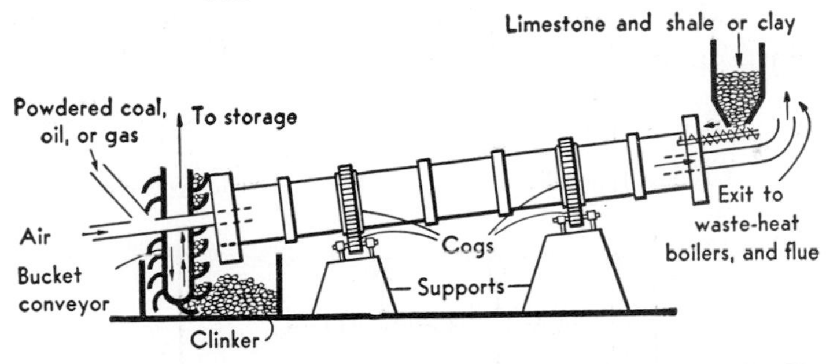

Fig. 29–6 Rotary cement kiln. The upper figure shows the apparatus diagrammatically. The lower figure is a photograph taken from the fuel end of the kiln. The mechanism for removing the clinker is beneath the floor. *Allis-Chalmers Manufacturing Co.*

The reactions taking place during the setting of Portland cement are complex and not completely understood. During the process, calcium aluminate hydrolyzes, forming calcium hydroxide and aluminum hydroxide. These compounds then react with the calcium silicates present, forming calcium aluminosilicate, in the form of interlocking crystals. Portland cement "sets" rapidly (within 24 hours), and then "hardens" slowly, years being required for completing the reactions.

The concrete from which roads, walks, foundations, and floors are constructed, is made by adding water to a mixture of cement, sand, and stone or gravel.

29.21 Silicones

A recent development in the field of silicon chemistry has been the production of polymeric organosilicon compounds containing Si—O—Si linkages. These compounds are known as "silicones," and they may be linear, cyclic, or cross-linked polymers of the types

$$R_3Si{-}O{-}\left[SiR_2{-}O\right]_x{-}SiR_3$$

Linear type silicone

$$(R_2SiO)_3 \text{ ring: } R_2Si{-}O{-}SiR_2{-}O{-}SiR_2{-}O{-}$$

Cyclic type silicone

$$\left[\begin{array}{c} {-}SiR_2{-}O{-}Si(O{-})(O{-})(O{-}){-}O{-}SiR_2{-}O{-} \\ {-}Si(O{-})(O{-}){-}O{-}SiR_2{-}O{-}SiR_2{-}O{-} \end{array}\right]_x$$

Cross-linked type silicone

The R in the formulas represents an organic group such as methyl (CH_3), ethyl (C_2H_5), or phenyl (C_6H_5). The linear and cyclic silicones are produced by hydrolyzing organochlorosilanes of the type R_2SiCl_2, followed by polymerization through the elimination of a molecule of water from two hydroxyl groups of adjacent $R_2Si(OH)_2$ molecules.

$$R_2SiCl_2 + 2\,H_2O \rightarrow R_2Si(OH)_2 + 2\,HCl$$

$$HO{-}SiR_2{-}O\boxed{H + HO}{-}SiR_2{-}OH \rightarrow HO{-}SiR_2{-}O{-}SiR_2{-}OH + H_2O$$

The organosilicon polymers combine to some extent the properties of both hydrocarbons and oxysilicon compounds. They are remarkably stable toward heat and chemical reagents, and they are not wetted by water. Depending upon the extent of polymerization and molecular complexity, the silicones may take the form of oils, greases, rubberlike substances, or resins. They are used as lubricants, hydraulic fluids, for electrical insulators, and as moisture-proofing agents (Fig. 29–7).

Fig. 29–7 Two uses of silicones. In the photograph at the left a drop of ink is put on each of two pieces of cloth. One piece of cloth is untreated and is readily wet by the ink; the other piece of cloth is silicone-treated and water repellent, so that the drop of ink retains its spherical shape and does not soak into the cloth. In the photograph on the right are two electric motors of equal power rating. The smaller motor is silicone-insulated and weighs only 60% as much as the larger motor with ordinary insulation.

A particularly valuable property of silicone oils is their very low temperature coefficient of viscosity. Thus, such oils can be employed as lubricants where there are extreme variations in temperature.

Such materials as paper, wool, glass, silk, and porcelain can be coated with a water-repellent film by simply exposing them for a second or two to the vapor of trimethylchlorosilane, $(CH_3)_3SiCl$. The surface becomes coated with a thin layer of $(CH_3)_2Si$ O groups, which repel water in a manner like that of a hydrocarbon film.

Sales of silicones amount to 70–75 million dollars, annually.

QUESTIONS

1. Lithium, beryllium, and boron are often spoken of as bridge elements. Explain.
2. Compare boron and silicon with respect to atomic size, ionization potential, and electronegativity.
3. List the physical and chemical properties of boron that classify it as a nonmetal.
4. Write equations showing the action of boron as a reducing agent toward H_2O, SO_2, NO, CO_2, and conc. HNO_3.
5. Explain what is meant by the "irreversibility" of the hydrolysis of the halides of boron.
6. Why is B_2H_6 said to be an "electron deficient" compound?
7. Write equations to show the formation of fluoboric acid from boron trifluoride.
8. Why does an aqueous solution of borax turn red litmus blue?
9. Show by equations the relationship of the boric acids to boric oxide.

10. Explain the chemistry of the use of borax as a flux in soldering and welding.

11. Write the structural formula for true sodium peroxyborate, showing that it is derived from hydrogen peroxide.

12. Evaluate the statement, "Silicon is the central element of the inorganic world."

13. How does the following reaction show the acidic character of SiO_2: $CaO + SiO_2 + \Delta \rightarrow CaSiO_3$?

14. By heating a mixture of sand and coke in an electric furnace, either silicon or silicon carbide may be obtained. What determines which will be formed?

15. In terms of molecular and crystal structure, account for the low melting point of Dry Ice (solid CO_2) and the high melting point of SiO_2.

16. How does the internal structure of silica glass differ from that of quartz?

17. What treatment will remove silica from a mixture of nonvolatile oxides?

18. Describe the conversion of silicate rocks to soluble forms for the purpose of analysis.

19. Relate colloidal silicic acid to soil fertility.

20. Account for the existence of the great variety of silicates in terms of the manner of linking of SiO_4 tetrahedra.

21. Show by an equation why a solution of water glass is alkaline to litmus.

22. Give equations for the reactions involved in the production of common window glass.

23. How does the incorporation of the following substances affect the properties of glass: potassium oxide; cobalt (II) oxide; lead (II) oxide; boric oxide; iron (II) oxide; colloidal gold?

REFERENCES

"Manufactured Abrasives," R. R. Ridgway, *Chem. Eng. News*, **1** (11) 858 (1943).

"The Boron Hydrides," B. Siegel and J. L. Mack, *J. Chem. Educ.*, **34** (7) 314 (1957).

"The Development of Borane Fuels," D. R. Martin, *J. Chem. Educ.*, **36** (5) 208 (1959).

"Bonding in Boron Compounds and in Inorganic Polymers," A. B. Burg, *J. Chem. Educ.*, **37** (9) 482 (1960).

"Chemistry of the Silicones," E. G. Rochow, *Sci. American*, Oct., 1948; p. 50.

An Introduction to the Chemistry of the Silicones, E. G. Rochow, John Wiley and Sons, New York, 1951.

"Fluosilicic Acid," E. Colton, *J. Chem. Educ.*, **35** (10) 562 (1958).

"Natural Quartz from the Laboratory," J. F. Corwin, *J. Chem. Educ.*, **37** (1) 11 (1960).

"Glass," F. C. Flint, *J. Chem. Educ.*, **19** (6) 287 (1942).

"Glass Evolution: A Factor in Science," A. Silverman, *J. Chem. Educ.*, **32** (3) 149 (1955).

"Glass," C. H. Greene, *Sci. American*, Jan., 1961; p. 92.

"Inorganic Polymer Chemistry Points Way to High Temperature Plastics," G. Barth-Wehrenalp, *Chem. Eng.*, Oct. 30, 1961; p. 117.

CHAPTER THIRTY

Nuclear Chemistry

The chemical changes (transformations of one form of matter into another) which we have studied thus far have involved changes only in the electronic structures of atomic systems without alteration of their nuclear structures. Another type of transformation of matter, involving changes in atomic nuclei, has become increasingly important during the past twenty years. This branch of science, which is on the borderline between physics and chemistry and is called **nuclear chemistry,** had its beginning with the discovery of radioactivity.

30.1 Natural Radioactivity

In 1896, the French scientist Becquerel discovered that the element uranium emitted very penetrating rays which would affect a photographic plate. The subsequent work of Pierre and Marie Curie (Fig. 30–1) and others led to the discovery that atoms of certain elements, such as uranium and radium, undergo spontaneous disintegration to form atoms of other elements. These spontaneous decompositions of atomic nuclei are called radioactive changes because they are always accompanied by the emission of penetrating radiations. The fact that some elements undergo these transmutations in nature has led to the use of the term **natural radioactivity** in speaking of these phenomena.

Fig. 30–1 Marie Curie, shown here with her daughter Irene, was the first to isolate metallic radium. She and her husband Pierre Curie worked together in discovering this element. *Doubleday and Co.*

When a radioactive element disintegrates spontaneously, high velocity particles are emitted from the nuclei of the radioactive atoms. It has been established that two kinds of particles may be given off from the nucleus: **alpha-particles,** each of which consists of two neutrons and two protons and which are identical with helium nuclei; and **beta-particles,** which are high velocity electrons. In addition to alpha- and beta-particles, natural radioactivity is frequently accompanied by the emission of **gamma-rays.** These rays are electromagnetic waves, like X-rays in character, and more penetrating than alpha- and beta-particles.

The spontaneous disintegration of the radium nucleus may be represented by the following equation:

$$^{226}_{88}Ra \rightarrow ^{222}_{86}Rn + ^{4}_{2}He$$

The loss of an alpha-particle, containing two protons and having a mass of four units, decreases the atomic number from 88 to 86 and the mass number from 226 to 222. The loss of two protons from the nucleus is accompanied by the loss of two planetary electrons, whereby the electrical balance in the atom is retained. The part of the radium atom remaining after the emission of the alpha-particle is an atom of radon. Radon atoms also decompose spontaneously and form atoms of polonium (element 84) by losing one alpha particle.

When a beta-particle is ejected from the nucleus, a neutron in the nucleus evidently decomposes to give a proton and electron according to the equation

$$^{1}_{0}n \rightarrow ^{1}_{1}H + ^{0}_{-1}e$$

The proton remains in the nucleus, but the electron is ejected at high velocity. The formation of a proton in the nucleus as a result of this reaction increases the net positive charge on the nucleus by one unit and thus the atomic number is increased by one unit. The ejection of an electron from the nucleus of an atom causes no appreciable change in the mass of the nucleus because the mass of the electron is relatively very small. This is illustrated by the transformation of an isotope of thorium to one of protactinium, which is accompanied by the emission of an electron from the nucleus.

$$^{232}_{90}Th \rightarrow ^{232}_{91}Pa + ^{0}_{-1}e$$

The emission of either alpha- or beta-particles may be accompanied by gamma radiation. The emission of gamma-rays does not alter the atomic number or the mass number of an atom, because gamma-rays possess neither mass nor charge.

The rates at which the disintegrations of the various radioactive elements take place vary widely. The number of atoms that undergo change per unit of time is a constant fraction of the total number of atoms present. The time required for one-half of the atoms in a sample to disintegrate is called its **half-life.** The half-life of $^{226}_{88}Ra$ is 1590 years, that of $^{222}_{86}Rn$ is 3.82 days, and that of $^{218}_{84}Po$ is 3.0 minutes. Only one-half of a sample of radium will remain unchanged after 1590 years, and at the end of another 1590 years the sample will be reduced to one-fourth its initial mass, and so on.

Shortly after the discovery of natural radioactivity, it was found that the radiations from radium and other radioactive elements were effective in the treatment of cancer. Because the cancerous cells are often more sensitive to radiation than normal cells, radium treatment can be used to kill the cells in cancerous growths with little injury to the normal tissues.

30.2 Radioactive Disintegration Series

All elements with atomic numbers larger than that of bismuth have one or more isotopes which are radioactive. A few elements of low atomic number, such as potassium and rubidium, have naturally occurring isotopes which are radioactive.

The naturally occurring radioisotopes of the heavier elements belong to chains of successive disintegrations or "decays," and all the species in one chain constitute a radioactive family or series. Three of these series include most of the natural radioactive elements of the Periodic Table. They are the **uranium series,** the **actinium series,** and the **thorium series.** Each series is characterized by a parent (first member) of long half-life and a series of decay processes which ultimately lead to a stable end product. With the three natural series, the end products are isotopes of lead: $^{206}_{82}Pb$ in the uranium series, $^{207}_{82}Pb$ in the actinium series, and $^{208}_{82}Pb$ in the thorium series.

Successive transformations in the natural disintegration series take place in a manner which is described by the so-called **displacement laws** originally formulated by Rutherford, Soddy, and Fajans. (1) When an atom emits an alpha-particle, the product is an isotope of an element two places to the left of the parent element in the Periodic Table. (2) When a beta-particle is emitted, the product is an isotope of an element one place to the right of the parent in the Periodic Table.

The steps in the thorium series are given in Table 30·1 as an illustration of one natural radioactive decay series.

TABLE 30·1 The Thorium Series

$$^{232}_{90}Th \xrightarrow[1.39 \times 10_{10}\text{ y.}]{\alpha} {}^{228}_{88}Ra \xrightarrow[6.7\text{ y.}]{\beta} {}^{228}_{89}Ac \xrightarrow[6.13\text{ h.}]{\beta} {}^{228}_{90}Th$$

$$^{228}_{90}Th \xrightarrow[1.90\text{ y.}]{\alpha} {}^{224}_{88}Ra$$

$$^{212}_{82}Pb \xleftarrow[0.16\text{ sec.}]{\overline{\alpha}} {}^{216}_{84}Po \xleftarrow[54.5\text{ sec.}]{\alpha} {}^{220}_{86}Rn \xleftarrow[3.64\text{ d.}]{\alpha} {}^{224}_{88}Ra$$

$$^{212}_{82}Pb \xrightarrow[10.6\text{ sec.}]{\beta} {}^{212}_{83}Bi$$

$$^{212}_{83}Bi \xrightarrow[60.5\text{ min.}]{\beta} {}^{212}_{84}Po$$

$$^{212}_{83}Bi \xrightarrow[60.5\text{ min.}]{\alpha} {}^{208}_{81}Tl \qquad {}^{212}_{84}Po \xrightarrow[3 \times 10^{-7}\text{ sec.}]{\alpha} {}^{208}_{82}Pb$$

$$^{208}_{81}Tl \xrightarrow[3.1\text{ min.}]{\beta} {}^{208}_{82}Pb$$

A fourth radioactive series was discovered during World War II. This series is called the **neptunium series** after its member of longest half-life, and it was discovered through the production of its members by artificial means (Section 30.5). The end product of the series is an isotope of bismuth, $^{209}_{83}Bi$. Both the parent and end product of this chain have been detected in uranium ores in recent years.

The four radioactive series are referred to as the 4 n (or thorium), 4 n + 1 (or neptunium), 4 n + 2 (or uranium), and the 4 n + 3 (or actinium) series. This numerical designation indicates whether the mass numbers of the members of the series are exactly divisible by 4, or by 4 with a remainder of 1, 2, or 3.

30.3 The Age of the Earth

One of the most interesting applications of natural radioactivity has been its use in determining the age of the earth. An estimate of the lower limit of the earth's age can be made by determining the age of various minerals, assuming that the earth must be at least as old as the rocks and minerals in its crust. Several methods using radioactivity have been used for this purpose. One method involves the rate of disintegration in any one of the three naturally occurring radioactive series mentioned in the previous section. For example, one gram of uranium–238 would produce 0.4326 g. of lead–206 and 0.0674 g. of helium, and leave 0.5000 g. of uranium–238 after decaying for 4.5 billion years (its half-life). Thus, by comparing the amount of lead–206 to the amount of uranium–238 in a uranium mineral, the age of the rock containing the uranium mineral can be estimated. Analyses of uranium minerals for lead–206 show the age of the earth's crust to be about 2.6 billion years. It is interesting to note that the age of the universe as calculated from the observed velocity of recession of the nebulae (expanding universe) is 3.8 billion years.

30.4 Artificial Nuclear Changes

Atoms with stable nuclei may be converted to other atoms by means of collisions of their nuclei with high velocity particles. The first nuclear reaction to be artificially produced in the laboratory was carried out by Lord Rutherford in 1919. Using high velocity alpha-particles emanating from a naturally radioactive isotope of radium as projectiles, he bombarded nitrogen atoms (Fig. 30–2) and observed that the following nuclear reaction occurred:

$$^{14}_{7}N + ^{4}_{2}He \rightarrow ^{17}_{8}O + ^{1}_{1}H$$

Thus, two new nuclei are formed, an $^{17}_{8}O$ nucleus and a proton. The $^{17}_{8}O$ nucleus is stable, so that this nuclear reaction does not lead to further radioactive changes. However, many other elements undergo similar nuclear reactions, with the forma-

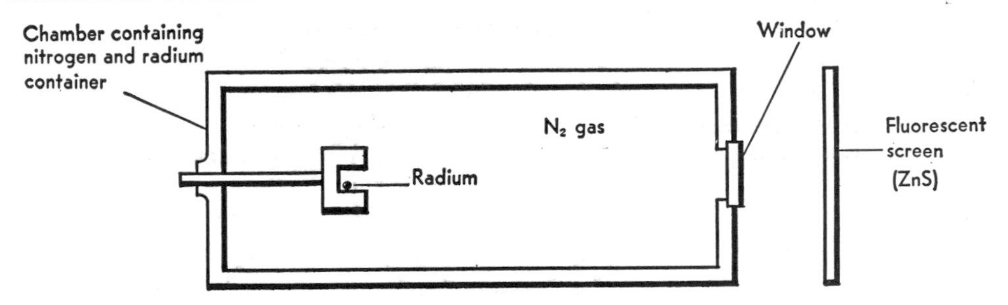

Fig. 30–2 This type of apparatus was used by Rutherford in the transmutation of nitrogen. Alpha-particles from the radium, upon striking the fluorescent screen, produced a flash of light. When the screen was moved beyond the range of alpha-particles, an occasional flash of light was still noted. This was due to the screen being struck by hydrogen nuclei (protons) which were knocked from the nitrogen atom by the alpha-particle "bullets" from radium.

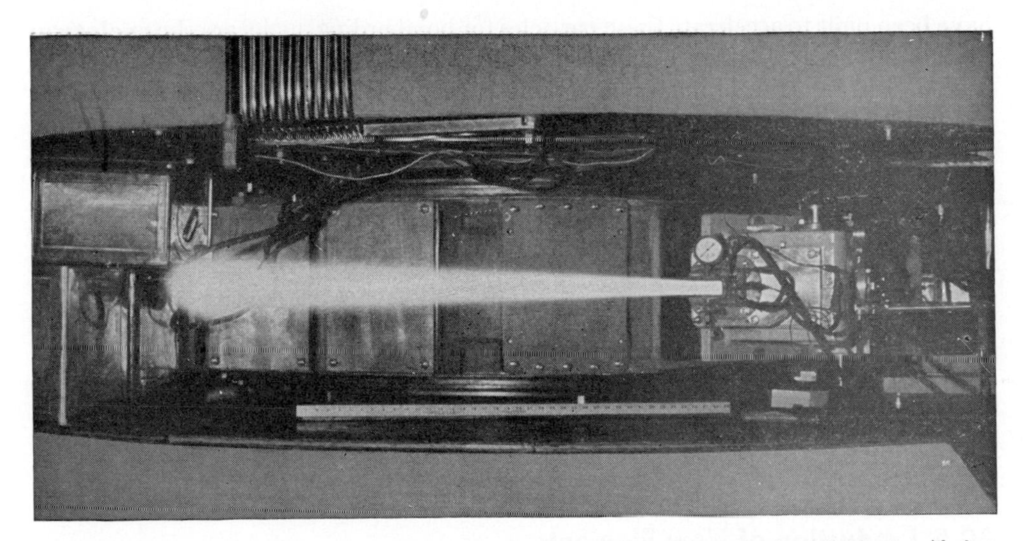

Fig. 30–3 The bright streak is a beam of deuterons from a cyclotron at the University of California. Nuclear reactions take place when deuterons and other atom particles strike the nuclei of atoms. *Rockefeller Foundation*

tion of unstable nuclei, which then undergo radioactive disintegration. An example of artificial radioactivity is given below.

$$^{25}_{12}Mg + ^{4}_{2}He \rightarrow \underset{\text{radioactive}}{^{28}_{13}Al} + ^{1}_{1}H$$

$$^{28}_{13}Al \longrightarrow \underset{\text{stable}}{^{28}_{14}Si} + ^{0}_{-1}e$$

In addition to alpha-particles from natural radioactive elements, high velocity projectiles have been produced in the laboratory. Charged particles such as protons, alpha-particles, and electrons can be accelerated to very high velocities by means of strong magnetic and electrostatic fields. Among the instruments which

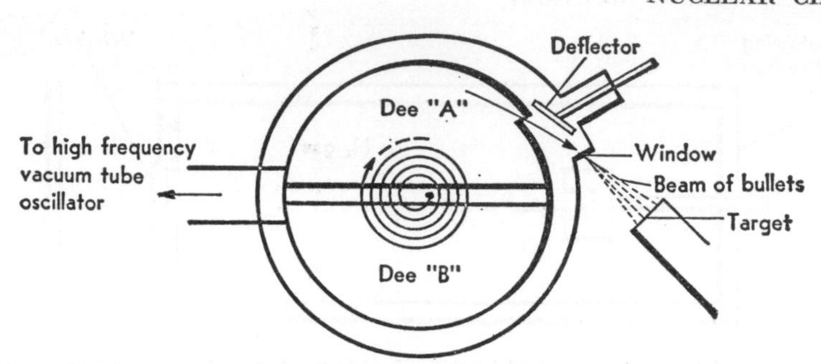

Fig. 30–4 Diagram of the vacuum chamber of a cyclotron. By making the dees, "A" and "B," alternately plus and minus and correctly adjusting the strength of the magnetic field, ionic bullets are caused to follow an ever-widening spiral path until they are finally deflected and pass through the thin metal window to the target. Some cyclotrons have only one dee.

have been built to accelerate these particles for bombarding nuclei are the **cyclotron** (Figs. 30–3 and 30–4), the **betatron,** and the **synchrotron.**

The yield in artificial nuclear reactions is very small because collisions between the projectiles and atomic nuclei are rare. The fact that the nucleus of an atom is very small and that positively charged projectiles such as protons and alpha-particles are repelled by positive nuclei limits the number of direct hits.

An example of a nuclear reaction produced by accelerated projectiles is the transmutation of calcium to scandium by the bombardment of the former with protons.

$$^{44}_{20}\mathrm{Ca} + {}^{1}_{1}\mathrm{H} \rightarrow {}^{44}_{21}\mathrm{Sc} + {}^{1}_{0}\mathrm{n}$$

Deuterons, which are the nuclei of the heavy hydrogen isotope, $^{2}_{1}\mathrm{H}$, have been used to bombard aluminum atoms and cause the following nuclear reaction:

$$^{27}_{13}\mathrm{Al} + {}^{2}_{1}\mathrm{H} \rightarrow {}^{25}_{12}\mathrm{Mg} + {}^{4}_{2}\mathrm{He}$$

30.5 Production of New Elements

Not only have many of the known elements been transmuted one into another by artificial nuclear changes, but recently several new elements have been synthesized in the laboratory. These new elements include element 43, technetium (Tc); element 85, astatine (At); element 87, francium (Fr); and element 61, promethium (Pm).

Prior to 1940, the heaviest known element was uranium, atomic number 92. In 1940, McMillan and Abelson were able to make element 93, neptunium (Np), by bombarding uranium with high velocity deuterons. The nuclear reaction is given by the equation

$$^{238}_{92}\mathrm{U} + {}^{2}_{1}\mathrm{H} \rightarrow \underset{\text{radioactive}}{^{239}_{92}\mathrm{U}} + {}^{1}_{1}\mathrm{H}$$

$$\underset{\text{radioactive}}{^{239}_{92}\mathrm{U}} \longrightarrow {}^{239}_{93}\mathrm{Np} + {}^{0}_{-1}\mathrm{e}$$

Neptunium is also radioactive, with a half-life period of 2.3 days, and converts to plutonium (Pu), atomic number 94.

$$^{239}_{93}Np \rightarrow ^{239}_{94}Pu + ^{0}_{-1}e$$

Elements 95 through 103 have likewise been prepared by artificial means. These elements have been named, in order, americium (Am), curium (Cm), berkelium (Bk), californium (Cf), einsteinium (Es), fermium (Fm), mendelevium (Md), nobelium (No), and lawrencium (Lw), respectively. The elements 93 through 103 are known as the **transuranium elements** and these elements, along with those of atomic numbers 89, 90, 91, and 92, make up a second rare earth series, the **actinide series,** the properties of which are similar to those of the **lanthanide** rare earths.

Typical transmutation reactions by which the transuranium elements have been produced are as follows:

$$^{239}_{94}Pu + ^{1}_{0}n \rightarrow ^{240}_{94}Pu$$

$$^{240}_{94}Pu + ^{1}_{0}n \rightarrow ^{241}_{94}Pu \rightarrow ^{241}_{95}Am + ^{0}_{-1}e$$

$$^{239}_{94}Pu + ^{4}_{2}He \rightarrow ^{242}_{96}Cm + ^{1}_{0}n$$

$$^{241}_{95}Am + ^{4}_{2}He \rightarrow ^{243}_{97}Bk + 2\ ^{1}_{0}n$$

$$^{242}_{96}Cm + ^{4}_{2}He \rightarrow ^{245}_{98}Cf + ^{1}_{0}n$$

$$^{238}_{92}U + 15\ ^{1}_{0}n \rightarrow ^{253}_{99}Es + 7\ ^{0}_{-1}e$$

$$^{239}_{94}Pu + 15\ ^{1}_{0}n \rightarrow ^{254}_{100}Fm + 6\ ^{0}_{-1}e$$

$$^{253}_{99}Es + ^{4}_{2}He \rightarrow ^{256}_{101}Md + ^{1}_{0}n$$

$$^{246}_{96}Cm + ^{12}_{6}C \rightarrow ^{254}_{102}No + 4\ ^{1}_{0}n$$

$$^{250}_{98}Cf + ^{11}_{5}B \rightarrow ^{257}_{103}Lw + 4\ ^{1}_{0}n$$

30.6 The Determination of Atomic Weights with the Mass Spectrograph

We noted in Section 3.8 that most of the elements, as they occur in nature, are mixtures of two or more isotopes, and that different isotopes of the same element contain the same number of protons but different numbers of neutrons. Thus ordinary oxygen is composed of 99.76 per cent $^{16}_{8}O$, 0.04 per cent $^{17}_{8}O$, and 0.2 per cent $^{18}_{8}O$; these isotopes contain 8, 9, and 10 neutrons, respectively. The existence of isotopes was discovered by means of an instrument known as the mass spectrograph which was devised by Aston in England.

The principle upon which the mass spectrograph is based is illustrated by the simple apparatus shown in Fig. 30–5, page 472. The element to be investigated is made to form positively charged gaseous ions by means of an electrical discharge through the gas at low pressure. The positive ions are then accelerated to high velocities by an electrical potential. When these charged particles are passed through a slit and allowed to fall upon a photographic plate, a line is produced upon the

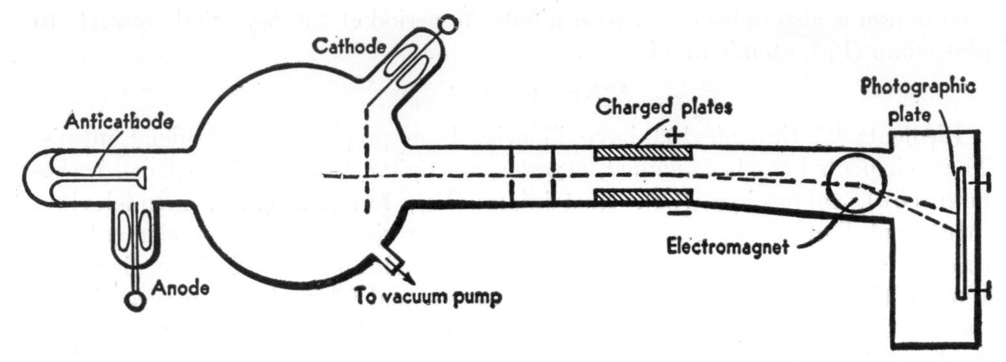

Fig. 30–5 A diagram showing the principles of the mass spectrograph.

plate. By causing the beam of positive ions to pass through electrical and magnetic fields, the ions are deflected from their straight path. Ions of the same mass and charge will be deflected to the same extent, and they will strike the photographic plate in the same place. Ions of different masses will be deflected by different amounts and will produce lines upon the plate according to their masses. The masses of the positive ions can be calculated from the position of the lines, and the relative amounts of each can be obtained from the intensity of the lines.

Atomic masses obtained with the mass spectrograph are now usually reported relative to the isotope ${}^{12}_{6}C = 12$, which is the new standard for atomic weights (see Sections 2.4 and 3.9).

By replacing the photographic plate with separate pockets to collect the ions of different masses, a separation of the isotopes can be accomplished.

30.7 The Structure of the Atomic Nucleus

A tremendous amount of research is being carried on by physicists who are accumulating a great body of information about the composition of nuclei. They are attempting to interpret this information by developing a theory of the structure of the nucleus. It is thought that the heavier nuclei are built of protons and neutrons with intranuclear attractive forces operating between them. The forces may be designated as proton-proton forces, neutron-neutron forces, and proton-neutron forces. These intranuclear forces are different in character from either electrostatic or gravitational forces and they are strong only when the distance between the particles is very small. It appears that the protons and neutrons in the heavier atoms are arranged in nuclear "subdivisions" or energy levels, just as the electrons are grouped together in the energy shells of the atom. It is believed by most theoretical physicists that the nuclear particles are held together by "π-mesons," which are particles with mass intermediate between that of the electron and that of the proton. The positive π-meson has a $+1$ unit charge and the negative π-meson has a -1 unit charge. These particles are primary products of the interaction of cosmic rays and nuclei.

30.8 The Packing Effect

Precision measurements by means of the mass spectrograph have shown that the mass of each isotope is very nearly a whole number. For example, the values of 19.999 and 21.998 for two of the isotopes of neon deviate from whole numbers by only slight amounts. The exact value is called the **atomic mass** and the nearest whole number is called the **mass number.** In view of the fact that isotopic masses are very nearly whole numbers, they are not multiples of 1.00797 (the mass of the hydrogen atom) and 1.0087 (the mass of the neutron). If the helium atom were made from two hydrogen atoms and two neutrons without change of mass, its mass should be 4.0333; however, it is only 4.002. This difference represents a loss in mass of 0.031 unit.

The loss in mass which accompanies the formation of a heavier atom from hydrogen atoms and neutrons is due to the fact that such reactions involve a change of mass into energy; they are strongly exothermic. Einstein, in his theory of relativity, related energy and mass by means of the equation

$$E = mc^2$$

in which E represents energy in ergs, m stands for mass in grams, and c is the velocity of light in cm. per sec. The fact that the velocity of light is very high, 3×10^{10} cm. per sec., and that this term is squared in Einstein's equation, makes it evident that a tremendous quantity of energy results from the destruction of a small quantity of matter.

The changes in mass in all ordinary chemical changes are negligibly small; these changes involve the formation or breakage of chemical bonds. On the other hand, the breakdown of a nucleus into its component protons and neutrons requires very large energies, and the formation of a stable nucleus from protons and neutrons involves the release of large energies. The decrease in mass from that of the neutrons and protons from which the nucleus may be considered to be formed is called the **packing effect.** The greater the loss of mass (packing effect), the more stable the nucleus, i.e., the greater the quantity of energy liberated during the formation of the nucleus. Because this quantity of energy would have to be supplied in order to break the nucleus down completely into protons and neutrons, it is known as the **binding energy** of the nucleus.

30.9 Nuclear Fission

The binding energy per nuclear particle (protons and neutrons) is greatest for the nuclei of elements of mass numbers between 40 and 100, and gradually falls off with increasing and decreasing mass numbers (Fig. 30–6, page 474). Greater stability of elements with mass numbers of intermediate values suggests the possibility of spontaneous splitting of the less stable nuclei of the heavy elements into fragments of approximately half size, and that such nuclear fissions be accompanied by the release of large quantities of energy. Two German scientists, Hahn and Strassman, reported in 1939 that when they bombarded uranium with slow moving

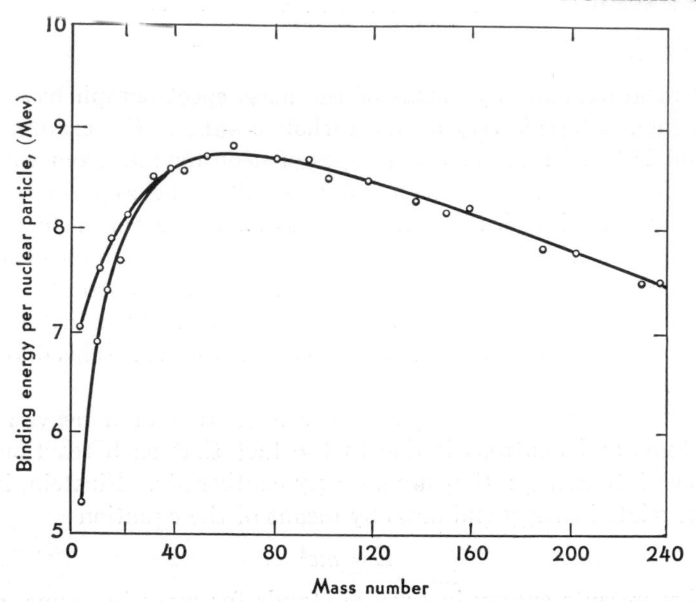

Fig. 30–6 Binding energy curve for the elements. Note the split in the curve for the lighter elements.

neutrons, each uranium atom split into two parts of approximately equal size. Among the fission products identified were barium, krypton, lanthanum, and cerium, the nuclei of all of which are more stable than that of uranium. In the fission of uranium, a low velocity neutron causes the splitting of the uranium isotope of mass number 235 into fission fragments and several neutrons.

$$^{235}_{92}U + ^{1}_{0}n \rightarrow \underset{\text{(isotopes of Ba, Kr, etc.)}}{\text{Fission fragments}} + 2.5\,n + \text{energy}$$

The sum of the atomic numbers of the fission products is 92, the atomic number of the original nucleus. In this type of disintegration a loss of mass occurs which corresponds to the release of a fantastic quantity of energy. A pound of uranium–235 undergoing fission may produce 2.5 million times as much energy as the burning of a pound of coal. A combination of technological development of the use of atomic energy and the availability of large quantities of uranium and other fissionable elements in the earth's crust will undoubtedly make nuclear fission a prime source of energy in the future.

The fission products of a U–235 nucleus include, on the average, 2.5 neutrons as well as the fission fragments. These neutrons may cause the fission of neighboring U–235 atoms, which in turn provide more neutrons for setting up a **chain reaction.** By the use of substances which arrest the reaction by absorbing neutrons, the chain reaction can be controlled to avoid the danger of its getting out of hand. The nuclear-fission chain reaction can thereby be controlled in such a manner that the nuclear energy produced can be used as a source of industrial power.

30.10 The Atomic Bomb

An atomic bomb is composed of several pounds of $^{235}_{92}U$ or $^{239}_{94}Pu$ and an explosive device for compressing the fissionable material quickly into a small volume. In a small chunk of fissionable material the proportion of neutrons which escape through the surface is relatively large so that a chain reaction does not take place. When the small pieces of fissionable material are brought together quickly to form a larger body with a mass larger than the "critical mass," the relative number of escaping neutrons decreases, and the auto-catalytic fission of the nuclei occurs nearly completely. The explosion of an atomic bomb (Fig. 30–7) can release energy greater than that involved in the detonation of a million tons of TNT (trinitrotoluene).

Fig. 30–7 Atomic bomb test at Bikini Lagoon. *United States Army Signal Corps*

As it occurs in nature, uranium consists of a mixture of several isotopes; the most abundant of these is U–238. About one atom in every 140 atoms of uranium is the fissionable U–235 isotope. Because pure U–235 is needed for a chain reaction like that which takes place in the atomic bomb, it became necessary to separate U–235 from U–238 and U–234. This proved to be one of the major tasks in the development of the atomic bomb because there is relatively very little difference in the masses of these isotopes. Electromagnetic methods, based upon the principles of the mass spectrograph, were found to be effective, but the yields were small. The most successful of the several methods tried made use of the separation of $^{235}_{92}UF_6$ from $^{238}_{92}UF_6$ by fractional diffusion of large volumes of gaseous UF_6

at low pressure through porous diffusion barriers of very large areas. This method is based upon the fact that the lighter $^{235}_{92}UF_6$ molecules diffuse through a porous barrier faster than the heavier molecules of $^{238}_{92}UF_6$.

30.11 Nuclear Chain Reactors (Piles)

The control of chain reactions of fissionable materials is achieved in nuclear **chain reactors** or **piles.** By using efficient neutron absorbers such as cadmium, chain propagation can be so controlled that the number of neutrons builds up to a constant level and does not increase to the explosive stage. There are three components in a nuclear chain reactor or pile: (1) the charge material, which includes a fissionable substance such as U–235, Pu–239, or U–233; the charge material is often uranium considerably enriched with regard to U–235; (2) a substance to reduce the velocity of the neutrons, called **a moderator;** graphite, heavy water, and ordinary water have been used; (3) a nonfissionable material such as cadmium or boron steel in the form of control rods to absorb neutrons. A drawing of a nuclear chain reactor is shown in Fig. 30–8. The uranium reactor consists of rods of the fissionable metal inserted in channels in graphite blocks containing cadmium rods so arranged that they may be removed to permit the slow neutrons to strike the fissionable metal. In addition to the fission reaction with U–235 (Section 30.9), the following series of reactions takes place in a uranium nuclear reactor.

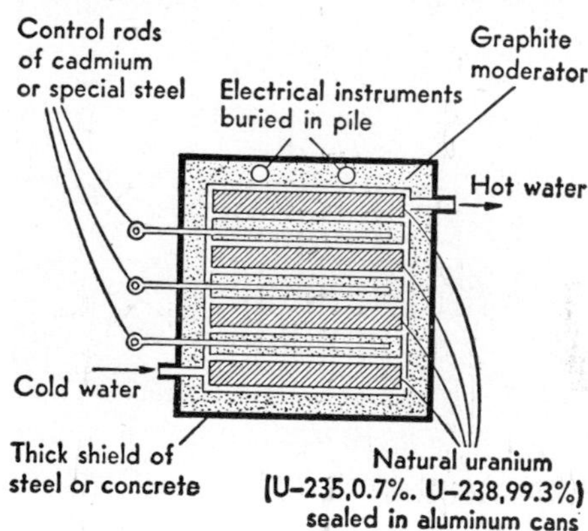

Fig. 30–8 An atomic pile. *Westinghouse Electric Corp.*

$$^{238}_{92}U + ^{1}_{0}n \longrightarrow ^{239}_{92}U$$

$$^{239}_{92}U \xrightarrow{\text{23 min.}} ^{239}_{93}Np + ^{0}_{-1}e$$

$$^{239}_{92}Np \xrightarrow{\text{2.3 days}} ^{239}_{94}Pu + ^{0}_{-1}e$$

Hence, the uranium pile serves as a source of the fissionable isotope $^{239}_{94}Pu$. The energy released by the pile can be utilized as heat to convert water to steam for use in conventional turbines for the production of electrical power.

Reactors of the type described above are now in operation at Oak Ridge, Tenn.; Hanford, Wash.; Brookhaven National Laboratory; and Harwell, England. Heavy water moderators are used in the uranium reactors at Argonne National Laboratory; at Chalk River, Canada; and at Fort de Chatillon, France. Ordinary water is used in a reactor at Los Alamos, New Mexico. The "nuclear fuel" in another reactor at Los Alamos is plutonium; no moderator is present, but a circulating liquid coolant is employed.

A recent development in the field of reactor technology is the **breeder reactor,** by means of which the large quantities of uranium and thorium in the ores of the earth's crust may be used to produce fissionable materials. Such reactors are of much current interest, because of their potential far-reaching effects in the search for new sources of energy in the universe. In contrast to the regular reactor, the breeder reactor is constructed with a blanket of "fertile" material (U–238 or Th–232) surrounding a core of concentrated fissionable material (U–235, Pu–239, or U–233). Extra neutrons arising from the fission of the core material are captured by the blanket of fertile material to form ("breed") more fissionable atoms. Hence, the breeder reactor is designed to produce as much fuel as it consumes.

Breeder reactors are based upon one of two sets of nuclear reactions. One begins with U–238 and the other with Th–232, which are the most abundant isotopes of their respective elements and are present in trace amounts in the various types of granite rock. U–238 produces the fissionable atom $^{239}_{94}Pu$ according to the reactions described on page 476. Th–232 produces the fissionable atom $^{233}_{92}U$ by means of the following reactions.

$$^{232}_{90}Th + ^{1}_{0}n \longrightarrow ^{233}_{90}Th$$

$$^{233}_{90}Th \xrightarrow{23\ min.} ^{233}_{91}Pa + ^{0}_{-1}e$$

$$^{233}_{91}Pa \xrightarrow{27\ days} ^{233}_{92}U + ^{0}_{-1}e$$

Several experimental breeder reactors are in operation in the United States, Great Britain, and Russia.

30.12 Nuclear Fusion and the Hydrogen Bomb

We saw in Section 30.9 that the nuclear binding energy of heavy atoms may be increased by fission into fragments of lower mass numbers, and that such nuclear fissions are accompanied by the liberation of large quantities of energy. The process of converting very light nuclei into heavier nuclei is likewise accompanied by large conversions of mass into energy. Such reactions are known as **nuclear fusions** and are the basis of an intensive research effort to develop a practical thermonuclear reactor. It is supposed that the principal source of energy of the sun is due to the fusion of four hydrogen nuclei into one helium nucleus. The four hydrogen nuclei have a greater mass (0.7 per cent) than the helium nucleus, so the fusion converts matter into energy.

It has been found that a deuteron ($^{2}_{1}H$) and a triton ($^{3}_{1}H$), which are the positive ions of the heavy isotopes of hydrogen, will undergo **fusion** at extremely high temperatures to form a helium nucleus and a neutron.

$$^{2}_{1}H + ^{3}_{1}H \rightarrow ^{4}_{2}He + ^{1}_{0}n$$

This change is accompanied by a conversion of a portion of the mass into energy and is the nuclear reaction of the hydrogen bomb. A fission type of atomic bomb (uranium or plutonium) is exploded inside a charge of deuterium and tritium to provide the temperature of many millions of degrees required for the detonation of the hydrogen bomb.

If the large-scale controlled fusion of heavy isotopes of hydrogen can be perfected, the hydrogen of the oceans will provide an inexhaustible supply of energy for future generations.

30.13 Applications of Nuclear Reactions

1. *Atomic power.* A considerable number of atomic power plants for the experimental production of power are presently in operation. Atomic power for submarines has proved to be feasible. In 1961, the United States launched the world's first nuclear-powered surface ship, the N.S. *Savannah* (Fig. 30–9).

Fig. 30–9 N.S. *Savannah,* the first nuclear-powered merchant ship. This 22,000-ton vessel, nearly 600 feet in length, is powered by a 69-thermal megawatt pressurized water reactor and has a normal cruising speed of 20 knots. The reactor holds 17,000 pounds of uranium oxide fuel capable of operating the ship for $3\frac{1}{2}$ years without replacement. Liquid and solid radioactive wastes are collected in monitor-equipped tanks for disposal into a specially designed barge at port; gaseous wastes are disposed of at sea through a radio mast also containing detection equipment. *Photo courtesy of Babcock and Wilson Co.*

The world demand for power increases about 25 per cent every ten years. If this continues, the world's supply of petroleum and coal may have diminished to critically small quantities by 2000 A.D. Although atomic power, at present, costs more to produce than power from conventional sources, power from atomic energy to supply our homes and factories may be commonplace in the not too distant future. Pound for pound, uranium has at least a million times the energy of oil. As has been described in Sections 30.11 and 30.12, the rocks and oceans potentially provide an inexhaustible supply of energy through appropriate nuclear reactions. We are, indeed, entering an atomic age which promises to give us a life of abundance, insofar as a bountiful supply of energy can make it possible.

2. *Production of radioactive isotopes.* A variety of radioactive isotopes are produced by fission or by neutron bombardment of other elements in the nuclear reactor and by other suitable transmutation reactions. Large quantities of radioactive isotopes are used annually by universities, hospitals, research institutes, and industries in a variety of ways, including such diverse applications as study of the mechanisms by which chemical reactions take place, treatment of cancer, location of flaws in metal objects to be used for structural purposes, study of the digestive and milk-producing processes in the cow, determination of the effects of lubrication additives on engine wear, and study of factors involved in plant growth.

QUESTIONS

1. How do nuclear reactions differ from ordinary chemical changes?
2. Describe the three types of radiation which are emitted from nuclei of naturally radioactive elements.
3. The loss of an alpha-particle by a nucleus causes what change in the atomic number and the mass of the nucleus? What is the change in the atomic number when a beta-particle is emitted?
4. What is the change in the nucleus that gives rise to a beta-particle?
5. Define and illustrate the phrase "half-life period."
6. How may charged particles be accelerated artificially for use in promoting nuclear reactions?
7. Complete the following equations:
   (a) $^{9}_{4}Be + ^{4}_{2}He \rightarrow ^{12}_{6}C +$
   (b) $^{23}_{11}Na + ^{2}_{1}H \rightarrow ^{24}_{11}Na +$
   (c) $^{7}_{3}Li + \qquad \rightarrow 2\ ^{4}_{2}He$
8. Give two reasons why the atomic weights of the elements are not whole numbers.
9. Describe the separation of the isotopes of an element by the mass spectrograph.
10. Explain the term "packing effect." How is the packing effect related to the binding energy of a nucleus?
11. Distinguish between nuclear fission and nuclear fusion. Why are both processes exothermic?
12. How are atomic bombs and hydrogen bombs detonated?
13. Describe the construction and operation of a uranium nuclear reactor.
14. What is meant by the term "breeder reactor"?

REFERENCES

Atomic Energy for Military Purposes, H. D. Smyth, Princeton University Press, Princeton, N.J., 1945.

"The Hydrogen Bomb," L. N. Ridenour, *Sci. American*, March, 1950; p. 11.

"Radiocarbon Dating," E. S. Deevey, Jr., *Sci. American*, Febr., 1952; p. 24.

"Radioactivity and the Age of the Earth," V. J. Linnenbom, *J. Chem. Educ.*, **32** (2) 58 (1955).

"Hot Atom Chemistry," W. F. Libby, *Sci. American*, March, 1950; p. 44.

"Tritium in Nature," W. F. Libby, *Sci. American*, April, 1954; p. 38.

"Ancient Temperatures," (use of isotopes in temperature determinations), C. Emiliani, *Sci. American*, Febr., 1958; p. 54.

"Nuclear Batteries," A. B. Garrett, *J. Chem. Educ.*, **33** (9) 446 (1956).

"Nuclear Rockets," J. J. Newgard and M. Levoy, *Sci. American*, May, 1959; p. 46.

"Atomic Pile Chemistry," J. F. Flagg and E. L. Zebrowski, *Sci. American*, July, 1952; p. 62.

"Reactor Fuel Elements," J. F. Schumar, *Sci. American*, Febr., 1959; p. 37.

"Nuclear Power Plant Core Materials and Fabrication," R. S. Shane, *J. Chem. Educ.*, **35** (10) 534 (1958).
"Breeder Reactors," A. M. Weinberg, *Sci. American*, Jan., 1960; p. 82.
"Discovery of Fission," Otto Hahn, *Sci. American*, Febr., 1958; p. 76.
"Fusion Power," R. F. Post, *Sci. American*, Dec., 1957; p. 73.
"The Uses of Fission Products," P. J. Lovewell, *Sci. American*, June, 1952; p. 19.
"The Fuel Situation," E. Ayres, *Sci. American*, Oct., 1956; p. 43.
"Non-Military Uses of Nuclear Explosives," G. W. Johnson and H. Brown, *Sci. American*, Dec., 1958; p. 29.
"Developments in the Peacetime Uses of Atomic Energy," W. F. Libby, *J. Chem. Educ.*, **36** (12) 627 (1959).
"Particle Accelerators," R. R. Wilson, *Sci. American*, March, 1958; p. 64.
"Birth of the Nuclear Atom," E. N. da C. Andrade, *Sci. American*, Nov., 1956; p. 93.
"The Atomic Nucleus," R. E. Peierls, *Sci. American*, Jan., 1959; p. 75.
"The Structure of the Nucleus," B. H. Flowers, *J. Chem. Educ.*, **37** (12) 610 (1960).
"Elementary Particles," Murray Gell-Mann and E. P. Rosenbaum, *Sci. American*, July, 1957; p. 72.
"The Weak Interactions," S. B. Treiman, *Sci. American*, March, 1959; p. 72.
"Huge Unit Weighs Atomic Nuclei," (Staff) *Chem. Eng. News*, Jan. 25, 1960; p. 49.
"The Newest Synthetic Elements," A. Ghiorso and G. T. Seaborg, *Sci. American*, Dec., 1956; p. 66.
"The First Isolations of the Transuranium Elements — A Historical Survey," J. C. Wallmann, *J. Chem. Educ.*, **36** (7) 340 (1959).
"The Chemistry of the Creation of the Heavy Elements," C. D. Coryell, *J. Chem. Educ.*, **38** (2) 67 (1961).
Symposium on "The New Elements," *J. Chem. Educ.*, **36** (1) 2–44 (1959):
"Technetium and Promethium," G. E. Boyd, p. 3.
"Astatine and Francium," E. K. Hyde, p. 15.
"Neptunium and Plutonium," J. C. Hindman, p. 22.
"Americium and Curium," T. K. Keenan, p. 27.
"Berkelium and Californium," B. B. Cunningham, p. 32.
"The Transcalifornium Elements," (includes elements 99–102), G. T. Seaborg, p. 38.
"Element 103 Created and Identified," (Staff) *Science*, **133**, 1225 (April 21, 1961).
"Breeder Reactors Hold Key to Energy Needs," (Staff) *Chem. Eng. News*, December 3, 1962; p. 21.

CHAPTER THIRTY-ONE

Organic Chemistry

The term "organic" appears to have been used for the first time about 1777 and was applied to those materials occurring in or derived from living organisms. Accordingly such substances as starch, alcohol, and urea were classified as organic, for starch is produced by living plants, alcohol is a product of fermentation caused by microorganisms, and urea is contained in urine. In 1824 the German chemist Wöhler synthesized urea, a white crystalline compound normally found in the urine of mammals. Thousands of other organic compounds have been synthesized since that time. **Organic compounds,** in the modern sense, are the compounds of carbon. Many thousands of carbon compounds which are not found in or derived from living organisms have been produced by chemists, and well over a million organic compounds are already known.

The existence of so many organic compounds is due primarily to the ability of carbon to combine with other carbon atoms, forming chains of different lengths and rings of different sizes (Section 28.1). The elements other than carbon most frequently found in organic compounds are hydrogen, oxygen, nitrogen, sulfur, the halogens, phosphorus, and some of the metals.

Although the number of organic compounds is vast, the study of organic chemistry is greatly simplified by the fact that these compounds can be classified into groups having similar properties. In this chapter and in the following chapter (dealing with biochemistry) we shall discuss a few of these groups.

HYDROCARBONS

31.1 The Hydrocarbons

The simplest organic compounds are those containing only carbon and hydrogen. Such compounds are known as **hydrocarbons;** and some of them are found in nature, where they were derived from plant or animal forms of life.

The simplest hydrocarbon is **methane,** CH_4, a colorless, odorless, and tasteless gas. It occurs in natural gas (Section 31.7) and is used as a fuel. It is also used in the manufacture of carbon black (Section 28.10) by burning it in a limited supply of air.

$$CH_4 + O_2 \rightarrow 2\ H_2O + C$$

Methane is the first member of a series of hydrocarbons having the general formula C_nH_{2n+2}, which is known as the "methane" or "paraffin" series. Some of the members of the series are listed in Table 31·1.

TABLE 31·1 Some Members of the Methane or Paraffin Series

	Formula	*Melting Point °C*	*Boiling Point °C*	*Usual Form*	*Number of Possible Isomers*
Methane	CH_4	−182.5	−161.5	Gas	0
Ethane	C_2H_6	−183.2	−88.6	Gas	0
Propane	C_3H_8	−187.7	−42.1	Gas	0
n-Butane	C_4H_{10}	−138.3	−0.5	Gas	2
n-Pentane	C_5H_{12}	−129.7	36.1	Liquid	3
n-Hexane	C_6H_{14}	−95.3	68.7	Liquid	5
n-Heptane	C_7H_{16}	−90.6	98.4	Liquid	9
n-Octane	C_8H_{18}	−56.8	125.7	Liquid	18
n-Nonane	C_9H_{20}	−53.6	150.8	Liquid	35
n-Decane	$C_{10}H_{22}$	−29.7	174.0	Liquid	75
n-Undecane	$C_{11}H_{24}$	−25.6	195.8	Liquid	159
n-Dodecane	$C_{12}H_{26}$	−9.6	216.3	Liquid	355
n-Tridecane	$C_{13}H_{28}$	−5.4	235.4	Liquid	802
n-Tetradecane	$C_{14}H_{30}$	5.9	253.5	Liquid	1858
n-Octadecane	$C_{18}H_{38}$	28.2	316.1	Solid	60523

The lighter members of the paraffin series are gases, the members of intermediate weight are liquids, and the heavier members are solids. From the formulas of the compounds of this series it becomes evident that each member differs from the preceding one by the increment CH_2. Series of compounds in which each member differs from the one before it by a common increment are called **homologous series.**

The hydrocarbons of this group are not very reactive, thus the name "paraffin" which means "having little affinity." The electronic formulas for methane, ethane, and propane are

$$\begin{array}{ccc} \begin{array}{c} H \\ H:\underset{\cdot\cdot}{\overset{\cdot\cdot}{C}}:H \\ H \end{array} & \begin{array}{c} H\;H \\ H:\underset{\cdot\cdot}{\overset{\cdot\cdot}{C}}:\underset{\cdot\cdot}{\overset{\cdot\cdot}{C}}:H \\ H\;H \end{array} & \begin{array}{c} H\;H\;H \\ H:\underset{\cdot\cdot}{\overset{\cdot\cdot}{C}}:\underset{\cdot\cdot}{\overset{\cdot\cdot}{C}}:\underset{\cdot\cdot}{\overset{\cdot\cdot}{C}}:H \\ H\;H\;H \end{array} \\ \text{Methane} & \text{Ethane} & \text{Propane} \end{array}$$

In the hydrocarbons with molecules heavier than methane, the carbon atoms share electrons to form covalent bonds not only with atoms of hydrogen, but with other carbon atoms as well.

There are two hydrocarbons having the molecular formula C_4H_{10}, and these are known as normal butane and isobutane. The two butanes are **isomers.** They have the same composition but different properties because they differ in the arrangement of the atoms in their molecules. Normal butane is a "straight chain" molecule, and isobutane is a "branched chain" molecule.

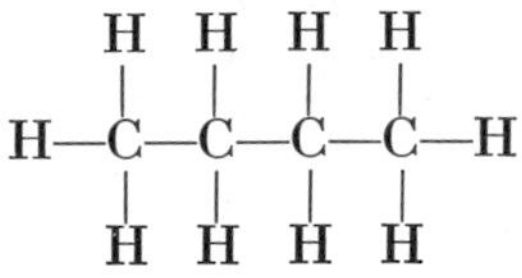

```
   H  H  H  H              H  H  H
   |  |  |  |              |  |  |
H—C—C—C—C—H          H—C—C—C—H
   |  |  |  |              |  |  |
   H  H  H  H              H  |  H
                           H—C—H
                              |
                              H
```

n-Butane 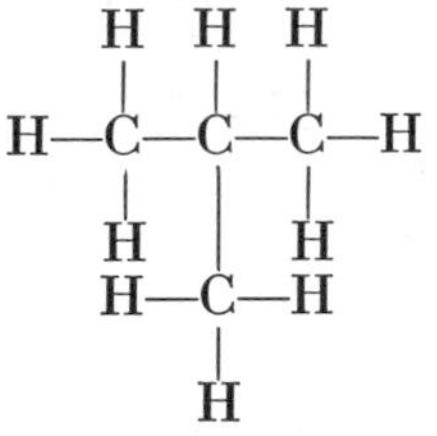   Isobutane

The number of possible isomers increases with molecular weight; the hydrocarbons of large molecular weight have great numbers of isomers (see Table 31·1).

31.2 Unsaturated Hydrocarbons

A second homologous series of hydrocarbons has the general formula C_nH_{2n}. A molecule of any member of this series contains two hydrogen atoms less than are present in a molecule of the methane series having the same number of carbon atoms. These two hydrogen atoms are lacking on adjacent carbon atoms. Each of these two carbon atoms, therefore, has an additional electron available for bond formation, so that four electrons are involved in the bond between them. Thus the electronic formula for ethylene, the first member of the series, is

```
  H  H
  ..  ..
H:C::C:H
```

Ethylene

In writing formulas for members of the ethylene series, the two shared electron pairs are usually represented by two lines.

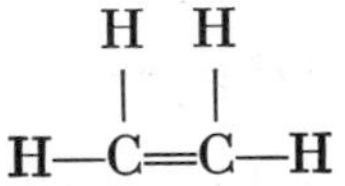

```
   H  H                 H  H  H
   |  |                 |  |  |
H—C═C—H           H—C—C═C—H
                        |
                        H
```

Ethylene 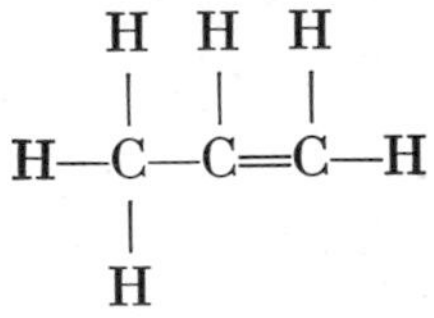   Propylene

Ethylene is a colorless gas with a rather sweet odor. It occurs in natural gas, and is formed when coal or wood is submitted to destructive distillation. The double bond in the ethylene molecule makes it more chemically reactive than the related compound, ethane. Thus ethylene readily combines with two atoms of chlorine, forming ethylene dichloride, $C_2H_4Cl_2$,

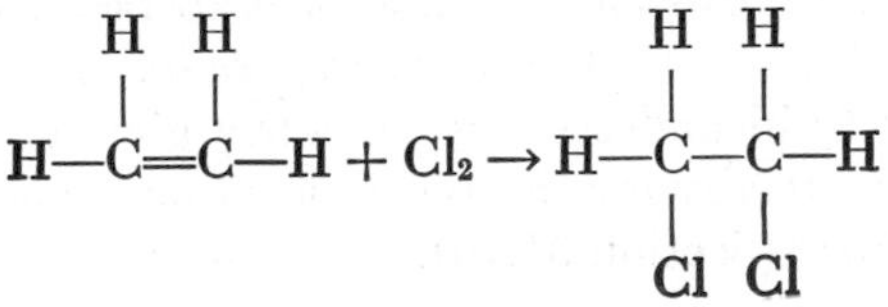

```
   H  H                 H  H
   |  |                 |  |
H—C═C—H + Cl2 → H—C—C—H
                        |  |
                        Cl Cl
```

and under the influence of a catalyst, with two atoms of hydrogen, forming ethane.

$$\begin{array}{ccc} \text{H} & \text{H} & \\ | & | & \\ \text{H—C} & \text{=C—H} & \end{array} + H_2 \rightarrow \begin{array}{cc} \text{H} & \text{H} \\ | & | \\ \text{H—C} & \text{—C—H} \\ | & | \\ \text{H} & \text{H} \end{array}$$

Because ethylene has the ability to *add* chlorine and other atoms, it is called an **unsaturated compound.** On the other hand, ethane reacts with chlorine by *substitution* only, so it is called a **saturated compound.**

$$\begin{array}{cc} \text{H} & \text{H} \\ | & | \\ \text{H—C} & \text{—C—H} \\ | & | \\ \text{H} & \text{H} \end{array} + 2\ Cl_2 \rightarrow \begin{array}{cc} \text{H} & \text{H} \\ | & | \\ \text{H—C} & \text{—C—H} \\ | & | \\ \text{Cl} & \text{Cl} \end{array} + 2\ HCl$$

Ethylene is mixed with oxygen and used as an anesthetic in dentistry and surgery. It has the interesting property of causing green fruits to ripen, and is used commercially for this purpose.

31.3 The Acetylene Series

Acetylene, C_2H_2, is the first member of a homologous series of hydrocarbons containing two carbon atoms joined by the sharing of three electron pairs, i.e., by a triple bond. The general formula for the acetylene series is C_nH_{2n-2}, and the formula for acetylene is represented by

$$H:C:::C:H \qquad \text{or} \qquad H—C{\equiv}C—H$$

Acetylene is a colorless gas with almost no odor, but as ordinarily prepared from calcium carbide, it has a garliclike odor.

$$CaC_2 + 2\ HOH \rightarrow Ca(OH)_2 + C_2H_2 \uparrow$$

Acetylene is more highly unsaturated than ethylene, and adds halogen atoms in two steps. With bromine, the first compound formed is acetylene dibromide, $CHBr{=}CHBr$; with more bromine, acetylene tetrabromide, $CHBr_2CHBr_2$, is formed.

Because pure acetylene may explode when compressed, it is usually held under pressure in solution in acetone.

Acetylene is used in the oxyacetylene torch for cutting and welding metals. At one time acetylene was used to light homes and in lamps for bicycles and automobiles. Acetylene burns with a brilliantly luminous flame. The heat liberated when acetylene burns causes some of it to break down according to the equation $C_2H_2 \rightarrow 2\ C + H_2$. At the temperature of the flame the particles of carbon become heated to incandescence; i.e., they give off a brilliant white light. Acetylene is used commercially for the synthesis of acetic acid, ethyl alcohol, plastics, and synthetic rubber (Section 31.16).

31.4 Benzene and Other Aromatic Hydrocarbons

Benzene, C_6H_6, is an important hydrocarbon. This volatile liquid is the first member of a homologous series in which each member differs from its predecessor by the increment CH_2. Benzene and its homologs have the general formula C_nH_{2n-6}. Prominent among these are toluene, C_7H_8; xylene, C_8H_{10}; and mesitylene, C_9H_{12}. Compounds of this series are spoken of as **aromatic hydrocarbons** because many of them have pleasant odors.

Extensive studies of the structure of benzene have revealed that the compound is unsaturated and that the six carbon atoms are arranged in a planar hexagonal ring, as indicated by the structural formula. Note that one hydrogen atom is bonded to each of the six carbon atoms and that the ring contains three single bonds and three double bonds in alternate positions. Thus the normal tetravalency of carbon is maintained.

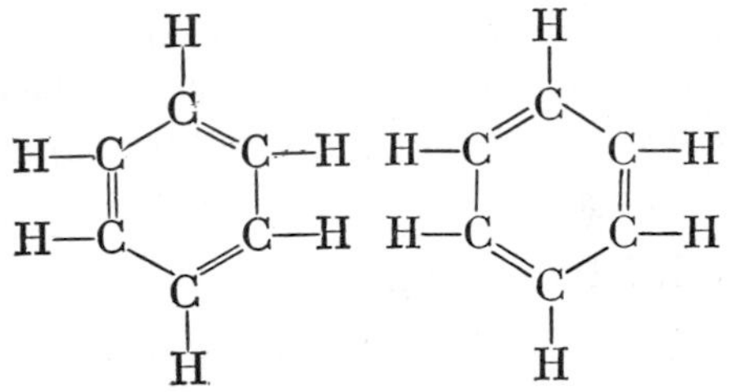

Benzene

Two structures with alternating single and double bonds, as shown in the diagram at the right, can be drawn for benzene. Actually, however, each bond between two carbon atoms is equivalent to each of the others and is intermediate in character (**hybrid**) between a single and a double bond. Whereas each structure is a contributing form, neither alone represents a true picture of the benzene molecule. Only one kind of molecule is present, a **resonance hybrid,** which is intermediate between the two structures shown (see Section 23.1, part 3). Resonance between two or more electronic structures is an important concept in chemistry and can be applied to many compounds.

Replacement of one of the hydrogen atoms of benzene by a methyl group, $-CH_3$, gives toluene, $C_6H_5CH_3$.

There are three xylene isomers, which are derivatives of benzene in which two hydrogen atoms have been replaced by methyl groups, $C_6H_4(CH_3)_2$.

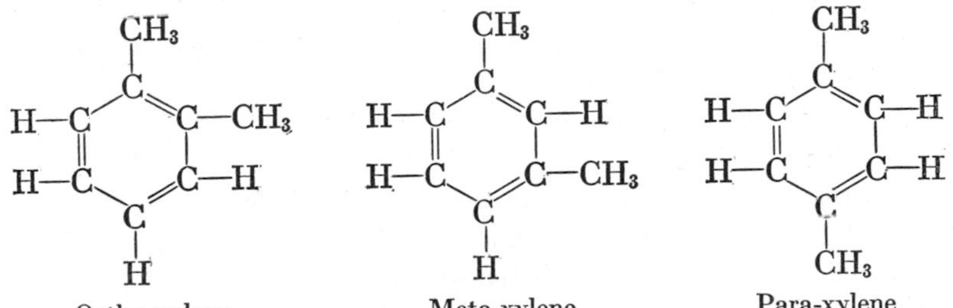

Ortho-xylene

Meta-xylene

Para-xylene

Some of the important aromatic hydrocarbons and their derivatives contain more than one ring. Examples are naphthalene, $C_{10}H_8$, familiarly known in moth balls, and anthracene, $C_{14}H_{10}$.

Naphthalene Anthracene Trinitrotoluene

The aromatic hydrocarbons are obtained by the fractional distillation of coal tar (Section 28.7, Fig. 28–6) and are widely used in the manufacture of dyes, synthetic drugs, explosives, plastics, and many other substances. For example, the important explosive trinitrotoluene (TNT), $C_6H_2(CH_3)(NO_2)_3$, is synthesized from toluene by replacing three hydrogen atoms with nitro groups, —NO_2.

31.5 Petroleum

Two very important sources of hydrocarbons are the natural gas and petroleum deposits found in certain sections of the earth (Fig. 31–1). Large deposits of petroleum (Latin, rock oil) are found in many parts of the world, usually in porous rocks which were originally laid down as sediment at the bottoms of seas. Although many theories have been proposed to account for the origin of petroleum, it is generally believed that it has resulted from the decomposition of the remains of plants and animals which were living in the strata in the geological age when the rocks were formed.

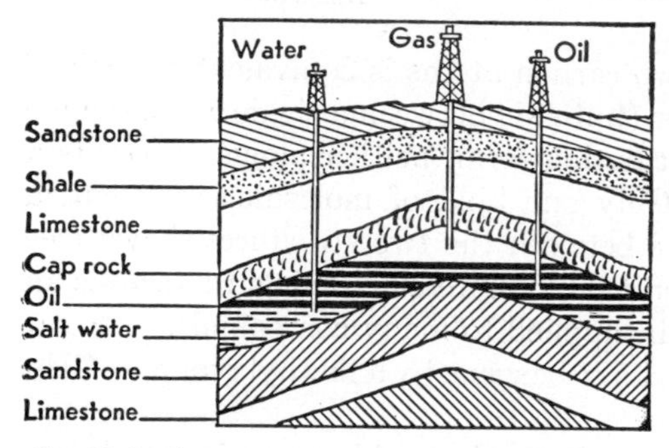

Fig. 31–1 One kind of geological formation containing oil and gas. Gas, oil, or salt water may come from wells drilled in the same "oil-field."

Petroleum is composed chiefly of paraffin hydrocarbons, but may also contain unsaturated hydrocarbons, aromatic hydrocarbons and their derivatives, nitrogen compounds, and sulfur compounds. The main step in the refining of petroleum is its separation by distillation into a number of fractions (fractional distillation, Section 11.6), each one of which is a complex mixture of hydrocarbons and has properties which make it commercially valuable. The composition of each fraction depends upon the temperature range over which it is collected. Some of the more important products obtained from the refining of petroleum, classified according to number of carbon atoms, are listed in Table 31·2.

Before the distillation products of petroleum are ready for use, further purification is usually necessary. For example, objectionable compounds such as those containing sulfur may be removed from gasoline and lubricating oils by extraction with concentrated sulfuric acid. Further purification may be accomplished by distillation at low pressures.

TABLE 31·2 Some Hydrocarbon Products from Petroleum

	Approximate Composition	*Boiling-Point Range*	*Uses*
Petroleum ether	C_4 to C_{10}	35–80°	Solvent
Gasoline	C_4 to C_{13}	40–225°	Motor fuel
Kerosene	C_{10} to C_{16}	175–300°	Fuel, lighting
Lubricating oils	C_{20} up	350° up	Lubrication
Paraffin	C_{23} to C_{29}	50–60° (m.p.)	Candles, waxed paper
Asphalt		Viscous liquids	Paving, roofing
Coke		Solid	Fuel

31.6 Gasoline

Ordinary gasoline is principally a mixture of n-hexane, n-heptane, n-octane, and their isomers. The gasoline obtained by the direct distillation of petroleum constitutes only about 10 per cent of that used in the United States; the bulk of the gasoline used is produced by converting larger and smaller hydrocarbon molecules to molecules of the proper weight and complexity. The decomposition of long chain hydrocarbon molecules into those hydrocarbons present in gasoline is known as "cracking." This is accomplished by heating the less volatile components of petroleum to high temperatures, usually in the presence of catalysts. Chemists have also developed methods for making gasoline by reactions which are, in a sense, the reverse of cracking. The simpler hydrocarbons are caused to combine, forming hydrocarbons containing 6, 7, or 8 carbon atoms. Such reactions are called "polymerization reactions" and they are brought about at high temperatures and varying pressures.

Gasolines are rated upon an arbitrary scale in which iso-octane, once thought to be the ideal fuel for the gasoline engine, is given the rating "100 octane." Gasolines with octane numbers less than 100 are less efficient and those with octane numbers greater than 100 are more efficient than iso-octane. Present-day aviation fuels have an octane rating well over 100. High octane gasolines are usually the result of the blending of **aliphatic** (open chain) and aromatic hydrocarbons and the addition of tetraethyl lead (Section 35.22).

31.7 Natural Gas

Natural gas is usually associated with deposits of petroleum. Its composition varies widely but it consists mainly of methane and ethane, along with smaller quantities of propane, butane, and traces of pentane and hexane. Nearly all natural gas contains nitrogen, and the gas from some wells contains as much as 98 per cent nitrogen. Carbon dioxide is always present, and in some wells it runs as high as 30 per cent. Helium is present in small quantities in certain natural gases, especially in those of Kansas, Oklahoma, and Texas. Natural gas is a very important fuel for heating, cooking, and electric power. It is transported through pipe lines from the gas fields to consumers, sometimes many hundred miles away. Natural gas is also becoming increasingly important as a raw material in the synthesis of various organic compounds.

DERIVATIVES OF THE HYDROCARBONS

31.8 Alcohols

An alcohol is obtained from a hydrocarbon by replacing one or more hydrogen atoms by hydroxyl groups, —OH. Thus methyl alcohol, CH_3OH, is derived from methane, CH_4; and ethyl alcohol, C_2H_5OH, from ethane, C_2H_6. Their structural formulas are

```
     H                 H  H
     |                 |  |
  H—C—OH           H—C—C—OH
     |                 |  |
     H                 H  H
```

Methyl alcohol — Ethyl alcohol

Alcohols differ from bases such as sodium hydroxide and potassium hydroxide in that they do not furnish hydroxide ions in water, nor do they have the other usual properties of bases.

The simplest alcohol, **methyl alcohol** or **methanol,** CH_3OH, is also called **wood alcohol,** because formerly most of it was obtained by the destructive distillation of wood. Most of the methyl alcohol produced today is synthesized from carbon monoxide or carbon dioxide.

$$CO + 2\ H_2 \rightarrow CH_3OH$$
$$CO_2 + 3\ H_2 \rightarrow CH_3OH + H_2O$$

Methyl alcohol is a colorless liquid boiling at about 65°. In odor and taste it is similar to ethyl alcohol, ordinary "grain alcohol." It is very poisonous, however; intoxication, blindness, and death may result when its vapors are breathed in quantities or when the liquid is taken internally.

Methyl alcohol is used in the manufacture of formaldehyde and other organic products; as an antifreeze; as a solvent for resins, gums, and shellac; and as a denaturant for ethyl alcohol.

Ethyl alcohol, C_2H_5OH, is the most important of the alcohols. It is also known as **grain alcohol, ethanol,** or simply as **alcohol.** It has long been prepared from starch, cellulose, and sugars of certain plants by the process of alcoholic fermentation.

$$\underset{\text{Glucose}}{C_6H_{12}O_6} \xrightarrow[\text{yeast}]{\text{enzymes in}} \underset{\text{Ethyl alcohol}}{2\ C_2H_5OH} + 2\ CO_2\uparrow$$

Solutions of alcohol resulting from fermentation contain from 8 to 12 per cent alcohol, but upon fractional distillation 95 per cent alcohol is obtained. Removal of the residual water by distillation over calcium oxide or barium oxide results in the production of **absolute alcohol.**

Large quantities of ethyl alcohol are produced synthetically from both ethylene and acetylene. The synthesis from ethylene is summarized by the equation

$$\begin{array}{ccccccccccc} & & \mathrm{H} & & \mathrm{H} & & & & \mathrm{H} & & \mathrm{H} & & \\ & & | & & | & & & & | & & | & & \\ \mathrm{H} & - & \mathrm{C} & = & \mathrm{C} & - & \mathrm{H} + \mathrm{HOH} \overset{\mathrm{H^+}}{\rightleftharpoons} \mathrm{H} & - & \mathrm{C} & - & \mathrm{C} & - & \mathrm{H} \\ & & & & & & & & | & & | & & \\ & & & & & & & & \mathrm{H} & & \mathrm{OH} & & \end{array}$$

Ethyl alcohol is a colorless liquid with a characteristic and somewhat pleasant odor. It is miscible with water in all proportions. The boiling point of the pure alcohol is 78.37° and it forms a constant boiling mixture with water that contains 95.57 per cent alcohol by weight, boiling point 78.15°. Ethyl alcohol is the least toxic of all the alcohols and is present in all alcoholic beverages.

Of all organic compounds, ethyl alcohol ranks first in quantity and value of production. It is used as a solvent in the preparation of tinctures, essences, extracts, and varnishes. It is used in the preparation of iodoform, ether, medicinals, dyes, perfumes, vinegar, collodion, and solvents for the lacquer industry. It is used as an antifreeze and has been used to some extent as a motor fuel.

Alcohols containing two or more hydroxyl groups can be made. Ethylene glycol, $C_2H_4(OH)_2$, and glycerol, $C_3H_5(OH)_3$, are important examples.

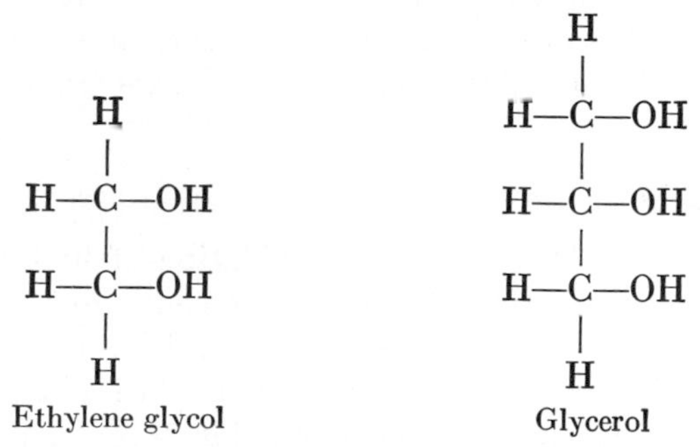

Ethylene glycol   Glycerol

Ethylene glycol is used as a solvent and as an antifreeze in motor cars, and it is sold under the familiar trade name Prestone. Glycerol (also called glycerin) is produced along with soap when fats or oils are digested with alkali (Section 31.15). It is used in lotions, other cosmetics, and in the manufacture of nitroglycerin.

31.9 Phenols

Derivatives of benzene which contain one or more hydroxyl groups attached directly to carbon atoms of the benzene ring are called **phenols.** The hydroxyl group in these compounds is markedly acidic in character, and phenol itself, C_6H_5OH, is commonly known as **carbolic acid.** It is an important constituent of coal tar, and it is produced synthetically from benzene. When pure, phenol is a colorless crystalline substance, melting at 42–43° and boiling at 181.4°. It has a very corrosive action on tissues, and on the skin it causes blisters to form rapidly. If taken internally, phenol causes irritation and necrosis of the mucous membranes. It may also paralyze the central nervous system, causing death. Dilute solutions of phenol are used as a disinfectant. Commercially, it is used in the manufacture of dyes, drugs, photographic developers, explosives, and resins such as Bakelite.

31.10 Ethers

The ethers are compounds obtained by the condensation of alcohols, with the elimination of water. For example, when ethyl alcohol is treated with a limited amount of sulfuric acid and heated to 140°, **diethyl ether** (ordinary ether) is formed in a series of reactions in which the net result is the loss of one molecule of water.

$$\begin{array}{c} \text{H H} \\ | \;\; | \\ \text{H—C—C—O}\boxed{\text{H + HO}}\text{—C—C—H} \\ | \;\; | \\ \text{H H} \end{array} \rightarrow \text{H—C(H)(H)—C(H)(H)—O—C(H)(H)—C(H)(H)—H + HOH}$$

Diethyl ether

The general formula for ethers is R—O—R, in which the hydrocarbon radicals (R) may be the same or different. Diethyl ether is the most important compound of this class. It is a colorless volatile liquid (boiling point 35°), giving a highly inflammable vapor. It has been used since 1846 as an anesthetic. Diethyl ether and other ethers are valuable solvents for gums, fats, waxes, and resins.

31.11 Aldehydes

The alcohols represent the first stage of oxidation of hydrocarbons. Further oxidation leads to the production of compounds containing the group, —CHO, known as **aldehydes.** The general formula for aldehydes is RCHO. When a mixture of methyl alcohol and air is passed through a heated tube containing silver or a mixture of iron powder and molybdenum oxide, formaldehyde is formed.

$$2\,\text{H—}\overset{\text{H}}{\underset{\text{H}}{\text{C}}}\text{—OH} + O_2 \rightarrow 2\,\text{H—}\overset{\text{H}}{\text{C}}\text{=O} + 2\,H_2O$$

Formaldehyde

Formaldehyde, HCHO, is a colorless gas with a pungent and irritating odor; it is very soluble in water. Formaldehyde is sold in an aqueous solution which contains about 37–37.5 per cent of formaldehyde by weight and is known as **formalin.** The solution also contains 7 per cent of methyl alcohol, which is added to inhibit the formation of insoluble polymers of formaldehyde. The extensive use of formaldehyde in the production of resins such as Bakelite has made it very important industrially. Formaldehyde has the property of coagulating proteins, making it useful as a preservative of anatomical specimens and in embalming fluids. It is also used as a disinfectant and as a reducing agent in the production of silver mirrors.

Acetaldehyde, CH_3CHO, is a liquid boiling at 20.2°. It is colorless, water-soluble, and has an odor like that of freshly cut green apples. It is used in the manufacture of aniline dyes, synthetic rubber, and other organic materials.

31.12 Ketones

Ketones resemble aldehydes in certain respects, since both contain the "carbonyl group," $>C{=}O$. In fact, a ketone may be regarded as an aldehyde in which the hydrogen in the aldehyde group is replaced by a hydrocarbon radical. The general structural formula of ketones, in which R may be the same or different, is

$$R{-}\overset{\overset{\displaystyle O}{\|}}{C}{-}R$$

Dimethyl ketone, CH_3COCH_3, commonly called **acetone,** is the simplest and most important member of this series. It is made commercially by the fermentation of corn or molasses, or by the oxidation of petroleum gases. It is also one of the products of the distillation of wood. Acetone is a colorless liquid boiling at 56.5° and possessing a characteristic and pungent odor and sweet taste. Among the uses of acetone are the following: as a solvent for cellulose acetate, cellulose nitrate, acetylene, plastics, and varnishes; as a remover of paints, varnishes, and fingernail polish; and as a solvent in the manufacture of drugs, chemicals, smokeless powder, and the high explosive **cordite.**

31.13 Acids

The carboxyl group, —COOH, is characteristic of many organic acids. The general structural formula for simple organic acids of this kind is

$$R{-}\overset{\overset{\displaystyle O}{\|}}{C}{-}OH$$

In general, the carboxylic acids are weak acids, yet they readily form metallic salts. The monocarboxy derivatives of the paraffins constitute a homologous series of acids known as the "fatty acids" because some of the higher members of the series are obtained from fats.

The simplest carboxylic acid is **formic acid,** HCOOH, which was first obtained in 1670 by the distillation of red ants, and its name was derived from the Latin word "formicus" for ant. It is at least partially responsible for the irritation of ant bites and bee stings.

Acetic acid, CH_3COOH, constitutes 3 to 6 per cent of vinegar, which is produced by allowing cider to undergo alcoholic fermentation and then bringing the liquid into contact with the bacteria called "mother of vinegar." Prepared in this manner vinegar has a light brown color, but if a colorless alcoholic solution is used, a colorless "white wine" vinegar is obtained. The wood distillation industry has for a long time been a source of acetic acid, one ton of wood yielding about 7 gallons of acid. Synthetic methods for the production of acetic acid make use of acetylene or ethyl alcohol as starting material. Pure, anhydrous acetic acid is a liquid boiling at 118.1°. It freezes at 16.6° forming a solid resembling ice in appearance; for this reason the pure acid is usually called **glacial acetic acid.** Acetic acid has a penetrating odor and a sour taste, and it produces painful burns on the skin. It is an excellent solvent for many organic compounds and some inorganic compounds. In addition to its use as a solvent, acetic acid is essential in the production of cellulose acetate and has wide application in the textile and rubber industries.

Oxalic acid is a dicarboxylic acid represented by the formula $(COOH)_2$ or $H_2C_2O_4$. Its molecule consists of two carboxyl groups bonded together.

```
       O   O
       ‖   ‖
   HO—C—C—OH
```

Oxalic acid is a colorless crystalline solid, which is found as a hydrogen salt in sorrel, rhubarb, and other plants to which it imparts a sour taste. Undiluted it is poisonous. It is used to remove rust and iron-ink stains and also to bleach straw hats.

Lactic acid contains a hydroxyl group as well as a carboxyl group, and has the structural formula

```
     H  H  O
     |  |  ‖
  H—C—C—C—OH
     |  |
     H  OH
```

Lactic acid

This acid is produced by the fermentation of milk sugar or glucose by the lactic acid bacillus. It is formed when milk sours and it gives the sour taste to milk.

Benzoic acid, C_6H_5COOH, is a colorless crystalline solid with the structural formula

```
       H   H
       |   |
       C—C      O
      //    \\     ‖
  H—C        C—C—OH
      \     /
       C=C
       |   |
       H   H
```

Benzoic acid

It is a monocarboxylic acid of the aromatic series and occurs in cranberries and coal tar. It is used technically in the form of its sodium salt in the preservation of certain foods, such as tomato ketchup and fruit juices.

31.14 Esters

Esters are the products of reaction of acids with alcohols. For example, the ester ethyl acetate, $CH_3COOCH_2H_5$, is formed when acetic acid reacts with ethyl alcohol.

$$CH_3COOH + C_2H_5OH \rightarrow CH_3COOC_2H_5 + H_2O$$

This reaction is similar to that between acetic acid and sodium hydroxide, whereby the salt sodium acetate, CH_3COONa, is formed.

$$CH_3COOH + NaOH \rightarrow CH_3COONa + H_2O$$

However, esters differ from metallic salts of organic acids in that, generally speaking, esters are volatile liquids with a pleasing odor, they are not ionized, and they are soluble in organic solvents but not in water. The distinctive and attractive odors and flavors of many flowers and fruits are due to the presence of one or more esters. Some common esters are listed in Table 31·3.

TABLE 31·3 Some Common Esters

	Formula	*Odor of*
Butyl acetate	$CH_3COOC_4H_9$	Bananas
Ethyl butyrate	$C_3H_7COOC_2H_5$	Pineapples
Octyl acetate	$CH_3COOC_8H_{17}$	Oranges
Methyl salicylate	$C_6H_4(OH)(COOCH_3)$	Oil of wintergreen
Methyl anthranilate	$C_6H_4(NH_2)(COOCH_3)$	Grapes

Among the most important of the natural esters are fats such as lard, tallow, and butter, and oils such as linseed, cottonseed, and olive. These are made up of esters of such complex acids as palmitic, $C_{15}H_{31}COOH$, stearic, $C_{17}H_{35}COOH$, and oleic, $C_{17}H_{33}COOH$, and the trihydroxyl alcohol, glycerol, $C_3H_5(OH)_3$ (see Section 32.20).

31.15 Soaps

Soaps are made by boiling natural fats and oils with strong bases such as sodium and potassium hydroxide. When animal fat is treated with sodium hydroxide, glycerol and sodium salts of the fatty acids, palmitic, stearic, and oleic acid, are formed. The reaction in the case of glyceryl stearate is given by the equation

$$(C_{17}H_{35}COO)_3C_3H_5 + 3\ NaOH \rightarrow 3\ C_{17}H_{35}COONa + C_3H_5(OH)_3$$

Glyceryl stearate; Sodium stearate; Glycerol

To obtain the soap free from glycerol and water, sodium chloride is added which causes the soap to precipitate or "salt out." The soap, being lighter, collects as a crust on the top where it is removed, partially dried, and pressed into cakes for use. This batch process has been replaced in part by continuous methods of producing soap.

The cleansing action of soap is discussed in Section 13.6, and the action of soaps with hard water, in Section 10.6.

POLYMERS

Polymers are compounds of very high molecular weight which are built up of a large number of simple molecules which have been caused to react with each other. Among the polymers which occur in nature are rubber, cellulose, starch, and proteins (see Chapter 32). Synthetic polymers familiar to all include synthetic rubber, Nylon, rayon, Bakelite, Dacron, and many others.

31.16 Rubber

Natural rubber is obtained mainly from the sap, called latex, of the rubber tree, *Hevea brasiliensis*. The rubber is present in the latex in an emulsified form, but is coagulated upon the addition of an acid. Rubber consists of very long molecules, which are polymers formed by the union of isoprene units, C_5H_8, as shown below:

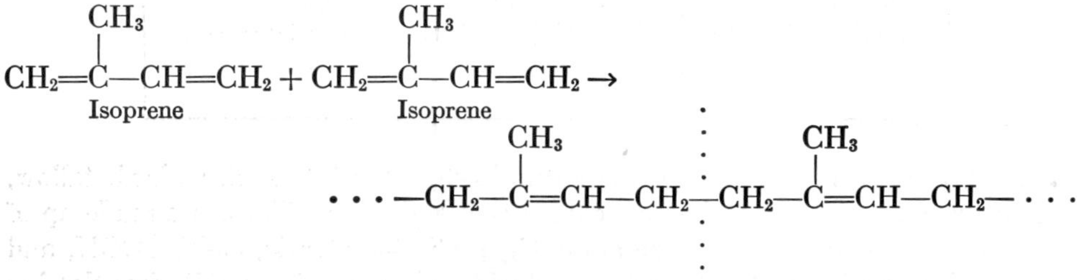

$$\underset{\text{Isoprene}}{CH_2{=}\overset{\overset{\displaystyle CH_3}{|}}{C}{-}CH{=}CH_2} + \underset{\text{Isoprene}}{CH_2{=}\overset{\overset{\displaystyle CH_3}{|}}{C}{-}CH{=}CH_2} \rightarrow$$

$$\cdots{-}CH_2{-}\overset{\overset{\displaystyle CH_3}{|}}{C}{=}CH{-}CH_2{-}\vdots{-}CH_2{-}\overset{\overset{\displaystyle CH_3}{|}}{C}{=}CH{-}CH_2{-}\cdots$$

The number of isoprene units in the rubber molecule is about 2000, giving a molecular weight of approximately 136,000.

Rubber has the undesirable property of becoming sticky when warmed, but the stickiness is eliminated by the process of **vulcanization.** Rubber is vulcanized by heating it with sulfur to about 140°. During the process sulfur atoms add at the double bonds in the linear polymer and form bridges which bind one rubber molecule to another. In this way a linear polymer is converted into a three-dimensional polymer. During vulcanization, fillers are also added to increase the wearing qualities of the rubber and to yield colored products. Among the substances used as fillers are carbon black, zinc oxide, antimony (V) sulfide, barium sulfate, and titanium dioxide.

The materials called "synthetic rubbers" are not identical with natural rubber, although in some respects they resemble it, and in others they are superior. For example, neoprene is a synthetic elastomer with rubberlike properties. It is made from vinylacetylene and hydrogen chloride according to the equations

$$\underset{\text{Vinylacetylene}}{CH_2{=}CH{-}C{\equiv}CH} + HCl \rightarrow \underset{\text{Chloroprene}}{CH_2{=}CH{-}\underset{\displaystyle Cl}{\overset{|}{C}}{=}CH_2}$$

$$n\ CH_2{=}CH{-}\underset{\displaystyle Cl}{\overset{|}{C}}{=}CH_2 \xrightarrow{\text{Polymerization}} \underset{\text{Neoprene}}{\left[{-}CH_2{-}CH{=}\underset{\displaystyle Cl}{\overset{|}{C}}{-}CH_2{-}\right]_n}$$

The repeating unit "chloroprene" is similar to isoprene except for the replacement of a methyl group by a chlorine atom. Neoprene stretches better than natural rubber, resists abrasion well, and is unchanged by such solvents as oil and gasoline. It is used for making gasoline and oil hose, automobile and refrigerator parts, and electrical insulation. Other synthetic elastomers of this type are Buna S (GR—S), Buna N, Butyl (GR—I), and Thiokol A.

31.17 Synthetic Fibers

A "condensation polymer" familiar to everyone is Nylon. Two kinds of molecules take part in the condensation reaction which produces Nylon, each of which contains two like groups. One of the reactants is hexamethylenediamine and the other is adipic acid, which is a dicarboxylic acid. During the condensation the linkage R—NH—CO—R, called the "amide linkage," is formed and a molecule of water is eliminated.

$$\underset{\text{Hexamethylenediamine}}{NH_2{-}(CH_2)_6{-}NH_2} + \underset{\text{Adipic acid}}{HOOC{-}(CH_2)_4{-}COOH} \rightarrow$$
$$NH_2{-}(CH_2)_6{-}NH{-}CO{-}(CH_2)_4{-}COOH + H_2O$$

Because the molecule resulting from the condensation has $-NH_2$ at one end and $-COOH$ at the other, the polymerization can be repeated many times to form a linear polymer of great length. Nylon may be made into fine threads by melting and extruding through a spinneret. The use of Nylon in hosiery and other clothing is well known. It is also used in making bristles for toothbrushes, surgical sutures, strings for tennis rackets, fishing leaders, and many other things.

Dacron is made similarly from terephthalic acid and ethylene glycol.

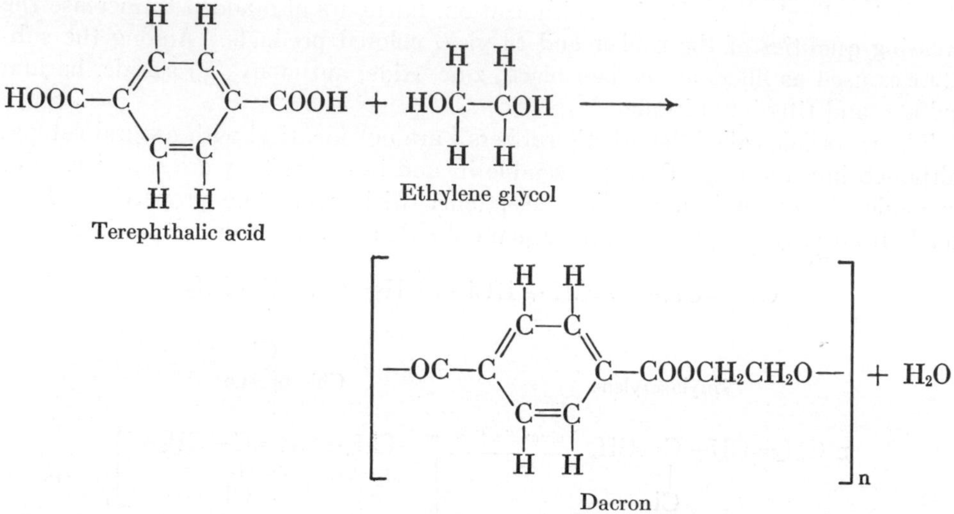

$$
\begin{array}{c}
\text{H H} \\
| \;\; | \\
\text{C—C} \\
\text{HOOC—C} \qquad\quad \text{C—COOH} \\
\text{C=C} \\
| \;\; | \\
\text{H H}
\end{array}
\;+\;
\begin{array}{c}
\text{H H} \\
| \;\; | \\
\text{HOC—COH} \\
| \;\; | \\
\text{H H}
\end{array}
\longrightarrow
$$

Terephthalic acid Ethylene glycol

$$
\left[
\begin{array}{c}
\text{H H} \\
| \;\; | \\
\text{C—C} \\
\text{—OC—C} \qquad\quad \text{C—COOCH}_2\text{CH}_2\text{O—} \\
\text{C=C} \\
| \;\; | \\
\text{H H}
\end{array}
\right]_n + H_2O
$$

Dacron

Typical additional examples of synthetic fibers are Acrilan, Orlon, Dynel, and Kodel.

31.18 Polyethylene

The use of polyethylene in plastic bottles, bags for fruits and vegetables, and in many other items has become commonplace. Polyethylene is a flexible, tough polymer which has high water resistance and excellent electrical insulating properties. Originally, it was made by polymerization of ethylene ($CH_2{=}CH_2$) at high temperatures and pressures using a peroxide catalyst. It is now possible, with a type of catalyst called a Ziegler catalyst, to polymerize the ethylene at atmospheric pressure and at only slightly elevated temperatures.

$$
\underset{\text{Ethylene}}{nCH_2{=}CH_2} \xrightarrow{\text{polymerization}} \underset{\text{Polyethylene}}{\left[\text{—}CH_2CH_2\text{—} \right]_n}
$$

Polypropylene is an analogous polymer which is fast gaining in popularity and usage.

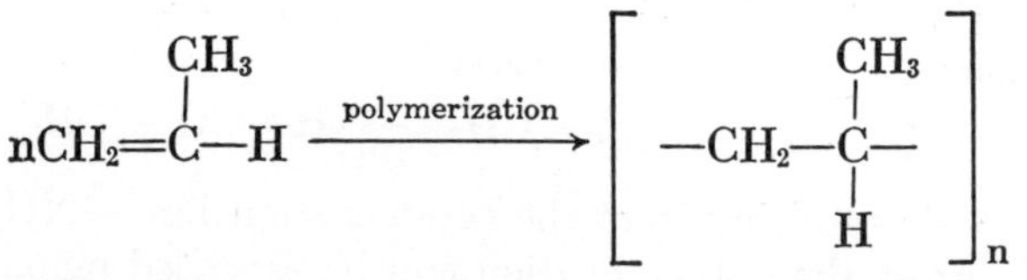

$$
\underset{\text{Propylene}}{nCH_2{=}\overset{\displaystyle CH_3}{\overset{|}{C}}\text{—}H} \xrightarrow{\text{polymerization}} \underset{\text{Polypropylene}}{\left[\text{—}CH_2\text{—}\overset{\displaystyle CH_3}{\overset{|}{\underset{\displaystyle H}{\underset{|}{C}}}}\text{—} \right]_n}
$$

Various derivatives of ethylene, such as vinyl acetate ($CH_2{=}CH\text{—}OOC\text{—}CH_3$), vinyl chloride ($CH_2{=}CHCl$), and tetrafluoroethylene ($CF_2{=}CF_2$), can be similarly polymerized. The polymerization of tetrafluoroethylene produces Teflon, a polymer which is unusually resistant to solvents and acids.

MEDICAL AGENTS

31.19 Chemotherapy

One of the major tasks of the organic chemist has been the synthesis and the determination of the structure of organic compounds of medicinal value. The treatment of disease with chemical substances, called **chemotherapy,** began with the work of Paul Ehrlich (1854–1915). It was known that some organic derivatives of arsenic would kill the microorganisms responsible for certain diseases, but these were toxic to the human body as well as the microorganisms. In attempting to find a compound that would kill the microorganisms but not be harmful to the body, Ehrlich synthesized 606 organo-arsenic compounds before achieving complete success. He found his "606," which is also called Salvarsan and arsphenamine, to be very effective in killing the microorganisms responsible for syphilis, and its greatest use has been in the treatment of this disease. This drug has the formula $[HCl—NH_2—OH—C_6H_3—As]_2—2\ H_2O$.

Since the beginning of the twentieth century there has been continual progress in the synthesis of chemotherapeutic agents. Among these are the sulfa drugs, which will be discussed in the following section.

31.20 Sulfa Drugs

The name **sulfa drugs** is applied to a series of sulfur-containing aromatic compounds which have been used with sensational success in the treatment of certain dread diseases. The parent substance in the series is sulfanilamide, which has the structural formula

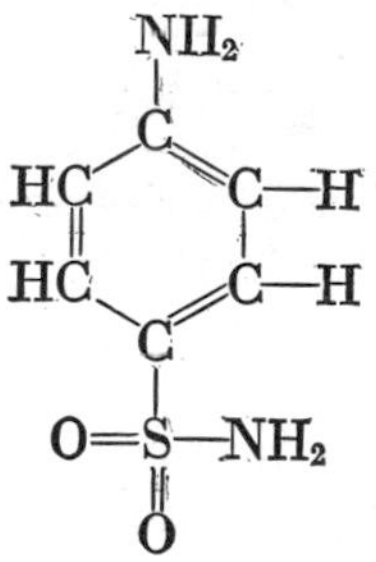

```
        NH2
        |
        C
      /   \\
   HC       C—H
   ||       |
   HC       C—H
      \   //
        C
        |
    O=S—NH2
        ||
        O
```

Sulfanilamide

About 1300 derivatives of sulfanilamide have been synthesized by substituting various radicals for the hydrogens of the $—NH_2$ groups. These include sulfapyridine, sulfathiazole, and sulfadiazine. They have been used in the treatment of blood poisoning, pneumonia, boils, intestinal infections, gonorrhea, meningitis, and a number of other infectious diseases.

31.21 Antibiotics

A great step forward in medical treatment was the discovery that certain soil-inhabiting bacteria and fungi produce complex organic compounds which are very active against a wide variety of pathogenic bacteria. The first of these so-called **antibiotics** to be produced was penicillin, which was discovered in 1928 by Dr. Alexander Fleming, a bacteriologist working in the University of London. It is produced by a mold, *Penicillium notatum*, which is now cultured on a commercial scale in a sterilized broth medium in large tanks. Penicillin is particularly effective in the treatment of pneumonia, gonorrhea, syphilis, meningitis, gas gangrene, wound infections, mastoid infections, and many other infectious diseases. The chemical structure of penicillin has been determined and the compound can now be synthesized in the laboratory. Its structural formula is given as

```
                          CH3
                           |
      O  H  H  S-----------C--CH3
      ‖  |  |  |           |
  R---C--N--C--C--H        |    O
            |  |           |    ‖
            C--N-----------C----C--O--H
            ‖              |
            O              H
```

Penicillin

Various types of penicillin are produced by varying the radical R in the formula.

The tremendous success of penicillin as a medicinal agent has led to the search for other antibiotics produced by living organisms. Several such agents have been prepared. These include streptomycin, aureomycin, neomycin, and chloromycetin. Two of these, chloromycetin and aureomycin, are capable of controlling viral infections.

QUESTIONS

1. What is the property of carbon that makes possible such a large number of organic compounds?
2. What is meant by a homologous series of compounds?
3. Write the structural formulas for the five isomers of hexane.
4. Write the equation for a substitution reaction of ethane; an addition reaction of ethylene.
5. Write the equations for the synthesis of acetylene from limestone and coke.
6. Write structural formulas for ethylbenzene, chlorobenzene, dichloromethane, and orthodibromobenzene.
7. Describe the two conversion processes for producing gasoline synthetically.
8. Write general formulas for and name the types of hydrocarbon derivatives studied in this chapter.
9. What is the difference in the structures of the saturated and unsaturated hydrocarbons?
10. Write the structure of cyclohexane, C_6H_{12}.
11. What is the oxidation state of carbon in each of the following compounds: CH_4, CO_2, CCl_4, CH_3Cl, CH_3OH, CH_3OCH_3, and $HCOOH$?
12. Why is C_2H_5OH soluble in water whereas C_2H_6 is not?
13. What is absolute alcohol and how is it prepared?

14. How do alcohols differ from inorganic hydroxides, and esters from salts?

15. What are the products which may be formed in the stepwise oxidation of methane? of ethyl alcohol?

16. Write structural formulas for propionaldehyde, methylethyl ether, diethylketone, methyl acetate, and propionic acid.

17. Describe the preparation of the soap sodium stearate.

18. What two kinds of hydrocarbon derivatives are represented by lactic acid?

19. What are polymers? List five naturally occurring polymers.

20. Describe the chemistry involved in the vulcanization of rubber.

21. Describe the chemical composition of several synthetic polymers.

REFERENCES

"Some Aspects of Organic Molecules and Their Behavior. I. Electronegativity," Otto Reinmuth, *J. Chem. Educ.*, **34** (6) 272 (1957).

"Organic Chemical Reactions," John D. Roberts, *Sci. American*, Nov., 1957; p. 117.

"Recent Advances in Petroleum Refining," B. H. Shoemaker, E. L. d'Ouville, and R. F. Marschner, *J. Chem. Educ.*, **32** (1) 30 (1955).

"Porphyrins in Petroleum," T. Muniyappan, *J. Chem. Educ.*, **32** (5) 277 (1955).

"The Chemistry of Lubricating Oil Additives," A. Miller, *J. Chem. Educ.*, **33** (7) 308 (1956).

"Hydrocarbons in Petroleum," F. D. Rossini, *J. Chem. Educ.*, **37** (11) 554 (1960).

"Reduction with Complex Metal Hydrides," N. G. Gaylord, *J. Chem. Educ.*, **34** (8) 367 (1957).

"Our Versatile Rubbers," Harry L. Fisher, *J. Chem. Educ.*, **32** (8) 417 (1955).

"Rubber," Harry L. Fisher, *Sci. American*, Nov., 1956; p. 74.

"Molecular Characteristics of Rubber-like Materials," W. P. Schlichter, *J. Chem. Educ.*, **36** (4) 185 (1959).

"New Horizons in Elastic Polymers," Harry L. Fisher, *J. Chem. Educ.*, **37** (7) 369 (1960).

"Fluorocarbons," J. H. Simons, *Sci. American*, Nov., 1949; p. 44.

"Giant Molecules," H. F. Mark, *Sci. American*, Sept., 1957; p. 80.

"How Giant Molecules Are Made," G. Natta, *Sci. American*, Sept., 1957; p. 98.

"Hydrogen Bonding in High Polymers and Inclusion Compounds," M. L. Huggins, *J. Chem. Educ.*, **34** (10) 480 (1957).

"The Geometry of Giant Molecules," C. C. Price, *J. Chem. Educ.*, **36** (4) 160 (1959).

"Contributions of Vinyl Polymerization to Organic Chemistry," F. R. Mayo, *J. Chem. Educ.*, **36** (4) 157 (1959).

"Polyethylene," G. Oster, *Sci. American*, Sept., 1957; p. 139.

"Rational Approaches to Drug Structure," A. Burger, *J. Chem. Educ.*, **33** (8) 362 (1956).

"Symposium: Medicinal Chemistry," *J. Chem. Educ.*, **37** (4) 168–200 (1960).

"New Penicillins," A. H. Rose, *Sci. American*, March, 1961; p. 66.

"Trends in the Fast-Moving World of Synthetic Fibers," (Staff) *Chem. Eng. News*, **Aug. 20, 1962; p. 86.**

CHAPTER THIRTY-TWO

Biochemistry

Biochemistry is the study of the chemical composition and structure of living organisms and the chemical reactions that take place in these organisms. During the past century, biochemistry has developed into an important branch of science. In order to solve problems in biochemistry, workers in the field must be well trained in organic, analytical, and theoretical chemistry because living matter is made up of organic substances of complex composition and structure and the mechanisms of biochemical reactions can be explained only in terms of the principles and laws of chemistry.

Living organisms are composed of water, proteins, carbohydrates, lipids (fats and oils), nucleic acids, porphyrins, inorganic substances, vitamins, enzymes, and hormones. Some of these will be considered briefly in the following sections.

32.1 Water in Living Organisms

From the standpoint of weight, water is the principal constituent of living matter. Most plants and animals contain 60 to 90 per cent of water by weight, the content varying with the kind of organism and with the organ or tissue concerned. For example, bones contain 12 to 15 per cent of water, whereas the water content of the blood is about 80 per cent.

The principal function of water is that of a solvent for both inorganic and organic substances, by which they are transported through the living organism. Foods, when digested, are carried to various parts of the body in aqueous solution. Likewise, many waste products are eliminated from the body as water-soluble substances. The oxygen which we breathe dissolves before it passes through the tissues of the lungs into the blood. Plants extract their supply of nutrients from the soil in the form of aqueous solutions. Food manufactured in the leaves of a plant is transported in solution to the storage places such as roots and seeds.

The large amount of water in the body helps to maintain the average body temperature because of its high heat capacity. A relatively large amount of heat is required to raise the temperature of the body even a few degrees. Thus the body is able to absorb excess heat without the occurrence of an appreciable change in temperature. In addition, the high heat of vaporization of water makes its evaporation from the skin effective in cooling the body.

Plants use water, along with carbon dioxide and nitrogen (or nitrogen compounds), as a raw material in the production of organic molecules. On the other hand, water and carbon dioxide are formed in the animal body as end products of the oxidation of organic matter.

The water of the body fluids such as the blood, lymph, and urine is called free water because it is free to flow. However, much of the water in plant and animal tissues does not flow out when the tissue is cut, indicating that it is somehow bound or immobilized. This is spoken of as bound water. Some of the bound water is held mechanically in a lattice of fibrous molecules and membranes, while other portions of it are chemically bonded to body tissues as water of hydration.

PROTEINS

32.2 Importance of Proteins

Proteins are the most important of all the substances present in plants and animals. They are found in all the cells of living organisms, and the human body contains many thousands of different proteins, each with a special structure that permits it to exhibit a specific function. Certain proteins are enzymes while others are hormones. Proteins also make up the contractile substance of muscle cells as well as the structural framework of animal cells. Because only proteins have the property of reproduction and growth, it seems that only they are true living matter.

32.3 Composition of Proteins

All **proteins** are nitrogenous substances, most of them containing on the average approximately 16 per cent nitrogen, 53 per cent carbon, 6 per cent hydrogen, and 23 per cent oxygen; some of them contain small amounts of other elements such as sulfur, phosphorus, iron, and copper. Proteins may occur as separate molecules of very large molecular weight, ranging from about 10,000 to many millions.

32.4 Amino Acids

When proteins are heated with aqueous acids or bases they undergo hydrolysis, producing compounds called **amino acids.** The amino acids from proteins are carboxylic acids which contain an amino group ($—NH_2$) attached to the carbon atom adjacent to the carboxylic group; that is, they are α-amino acids. The simplest of these α-amino acids is glycine, $H_2N—CH_2—COOH$. The other natural amino acids contain other organic groups, often simply designated as R, in place of one of the hydrogen atoms on the alpha carbon atom, making their general formula $H_2N—CHR—COOH$. For example, R is $—CH_3$ in alanine, $—CH_2OH$ in serine, and $—CH_2—C_6H_5$ in phenylalanine. There are twenty-four different amino acids which have been found to be important constituents of proteins.

32.5 Structure of Proteins

Many scientists have devoted much effort to the problem of the structure of proteins. The basic chemical structure of proteins was determined by the German chemist Emil Fischer between 1900 and 1910. He found that protein molecules consist of long chains of α-amino acids linked together by acid amide bonds, —CO—NH—, which are called **peptide bonds.** When two amino acids are joined together by the formation of an acid amide bond, a molecule called a **dipeptide** is formed. The reaction is similar in principle to that for the formation of Nylon (Section 31.17) and may be represented by the equation

$$\underset{\text{Amino acid}}{H_2NCHR\overset{\overset{\displaystyle O}{\|}}{C}\boxed{OH}} + \underset{\text{Amino acid}}{\boxed{H}\overset{\overset{\displaystyle H}{|}}{N}CHRCOOH} \rightleftarrows \underset{\text{Dipeptide}}{H_2NCHR\overset{\overset{\displaystyle O}{\|}}{C}-\overset{\overset{\displaystyle H}{|}}{N}-CHRCOOH} + H_2O$$

Peptide bond formation can be reversed by the hydrolysis of peptide bonds, as indicated by the equation. The process of forming these peptide bonds can be continued, resulting in the production of a long chain containing many amino acid residues. The result is a **polypeptide** or protein molecule. A protein of the molecular weight 120,000 contains about 1000 amino acid residues, assuming that the average molecular weight of —NHCHRCO— is approximately 120.

Each protein molecule is composed of several different amino acid residues which can be separated as amino acids by hydrolysis of the protein molecule. Protein molecules differ from one another not only in the number and kind of amino acid residues, but also in the order in which the residues are arranged in the polypeptide chains. This means that the number of possible protein structures is extremely great.

Fig. 32–1 Linus Pauling (left) receives the Nobel prize in chemistry for 1954 from the hands of Gustav VI, King of Sweden. *Chemical and Engineering News*

It has been found recently that many fibrous proteins, such as hair and muscle, consist of polypeptide chains with the configuration of a helix, the chains being arranged nearly parallel to one another, and with the axis of the helix lying in the direction of the fiber. The net effect in many fibrous proteins is a structure in which the polypeptide chains are twisted about one another to form ropes or cables. These discoveries have been made through the application of X-ray diffraction techniques; much of the credit for this very important work belongs to Linus Pauling, Professor of Chemistry in the California Institute of Technology, who received the Nobel Award in chemistry for the year 1954 (Fig. 32–1).

32.6 Essentiality of Amino Acids

Proteins are essential constituents of foods. During digestion they are hydrolyzed by the digestive juices into amino acids which are able to pass through the walls of the stomach and intestines into the blood stream. The blood carries the amino acids to the tissues, where they are used as building units for the manufacture of the specific proteins needed by the body. Only eight of the amino acids are essential in the diet of man, for the body is able to synthesize the remaining ones it needs; these are called nonessential amino acids. The principal sources of animal protein are lean meat, cheese, eggs, and milk. The proteins from these sources contain all the essential amino acids.

CARBOHYDRATES

32.7 Introduction

Carbohydrates are polyhydroxy aldehydes and polyhydroxy ketones, or their condensation products. The name is derived from the fact that many sugars have the empirical formula $C_nH_{2n}O_n$, or $C_n(H_2O)_n$, and hence the French applied the name "hydrate of carbon" or carbohydrate. This name has been retained even though it is not descriptive of the nature of these substances.

The most important carbohydrates are sugars, starches, cellulose, and substances related to them. Carbohydrates are among the most abundant constituents of plants and animals, in which they serve many useful functions. They are an important source of energy for animals; they form the supporting tissues of plants and some animals; and plants use them in the manufacture of proteins and lipids. The three important classes of carbohydrates are (1) the monosaccharides, (2) the disaccharides, and (3) the polysaccharides.

32.8 Monosaccharides

Practically all the monosaccharides that occur in nature contain 5 or 6 carbon atoms, and these are known as pentoses and hexoses, respectively. They are colorless, crystalline compounds with a sweet taste. The most important monosaccharides are glucose and fructose. Their formulas are shown below.

```
                              CHO                    CH2OH
                               |                       |
                            H—C—OH                    C=O
                               |                       |
                           HO—C—H                  HO—C—H
                               |                       |
        Glucose             H—C—OH                  H—C—OH            Fructose
(a polyhydroxy aldehyde)       |                       |        (a polyhydroxy ketone)
                            H—C—OH                  H—C—OH
                               |                       |
                             CH2OH                   CH2OH
```

Experimental evidence has shown that these sugars exist mainly in cyclic forms, in which two carbon atoms are linked by an oxygen atom, as shown below.

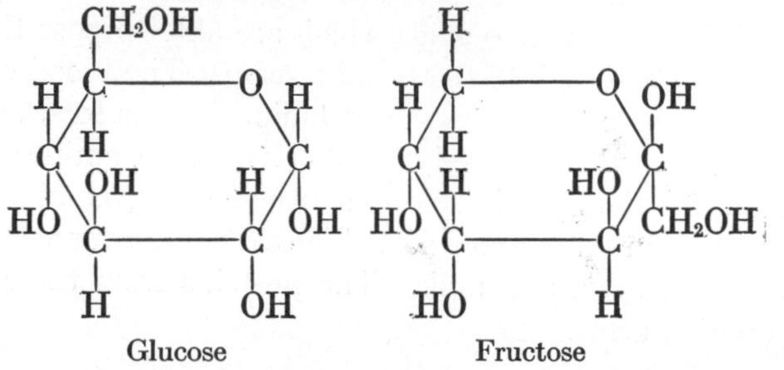

```
      CH2OH                       H
        |                         |
    H   C----------O   H      H   C----------O   OH
      / |           \ /         / |           \ /
     C  H            C         C  H            C
     |\ OH       H  /          |\ H       HO  /
  HO   \|          /| OH    HO   \|          /  CH2OH
        C----------C                C----------C
        |          |                |          |
        H          OH               HO         H
          Glucose                      Fructose
```

Glucose, $C_6H_{12}O_6$, is also known as **dextrose** and **grape sugar.** It occurs in many plants and is found either alone or mixed with fructose in leaves, sap, flowers, honey, and fruits. Ripe grapes often contain up to 30 per cent of glucose. Human blood normally contains about 0.1 per cent of this sugar. Sometimes a solution of glucose is injected directly into the blood stream of patients seriously in need of nourishment, for this sugar is available immediately for this purpose. In cases of sufferers from diabetes the body is unable to assimilate glucose, and this sugar is eliminated through the kidneys. The urine may contain as much as 8 to 10 per cent of glucose in such cases, and its presence there is one symptom of the disease.

Glucose is prepared commercially by the hydrolysis of starch. When corn starch, for example, is heated with water containing a small amount of acid, the changes indicated below occur.

$$\underset{\text{Starch}}{(C_6H_{10}O_5)_x} \xrightarrow[\text{heat}]{H^+,\ H_2O} \text{Dextrins} \xrightarrow[\text{heat}]{H^+,\ H_2O} \underset{\text{Maltose}}{C_{12}H_{22}O_{11}} \xrightarrow[\text{heat}]{H^+,\ H_2O} \underset{\text{Glucose}}{C_6H_{12}O_6}$$

Commercially, the hydrolysis is not carried to completion, so that the corn syrup thus produced is a mixture of glucose, maltose, and dextrins.

Fructose, $C_6H_{12}O_6$, has the same empirical formula as glucose but its structural formula is different as shown above. The two compounds are isomers (Section 31.1). Fructose contains the ketone group, —C═O, while glucose contains the aldehyde group, —CHO. Fructose, also called **levulose** and **fruit sugar,** occurs in fruits and honey. Combined with glucose in the disaccharide known as sucrose, it occurs in sugar cane and sugar beets. It is nearly twice as sweet as sucrose and, in fact, is the sweetest of all the sugars.

Fructose is prepared by the hydrolysis of inulin $(C_6H_{10}O_5)_x$, which is a polysaccharide closely related to starch, and found in dahlia bulbs and in the Jerusalem artichoke. It can also be prepared by the hydrolysis of sucrose.

32.9 Disaccharides

A disaccharide is made up of two monosaccharide molecules, either the same or different, the union of which is accompanied by the elimination of the elements of one molecule of water. For example,

$$\underset{\text{Monosaccharide}}{2\,C_6H_{12}O_6} \rightarrow \underset{\text{Disaccharide}}{C_{12}H_{22}O_{11}} + H_2O$$

The disaccharide **sucrose,** $C_{12}H_{22}O_{11}$, is the most familiar sugar. Cane and sugar beets furnish most of the world's supply of sucrose.

The production of sucrose from sugar cane involves a number of operations. The cane is first shredded and passed through roller mills. Water is then added to the crushed material to extract the sugar. The extracted juice is treated with milk of lime (an aqueous suspension of calcium hydroxide) to neutralize the acid and to precipitate calcium saccharate, leaving the impurities in solution. The calcium saccharate is filtered off, washed, and reconverted to sugar by treatment with carbon dioxide. The juice is then concentrated in closed vessels under reduced pressure to prevent the decomposition and charring of the sugar. The resulting concentrated solution (6 to 8 per cent water) is run into a tank and the sugar is allowed to crystallize. The crystalline product is separated from the mother liquor (molasses) by centrifuging. The sugar is then refined by passing it through a process which resembles that described for processing the raw juice, except that the solution is filtered through charcoal to remove coloring matter and thus to insure a colorless product. Refined sugar is 99.98 per cent pure. Cane sugar and beet sugar are identical when carefully purified.

Because sucrose is converted into a mixture of equal quantities of glucose and fructose by hydrolysis, it must be an anhydride of these two monosaccharides. The structural formula for sucrose is given below.

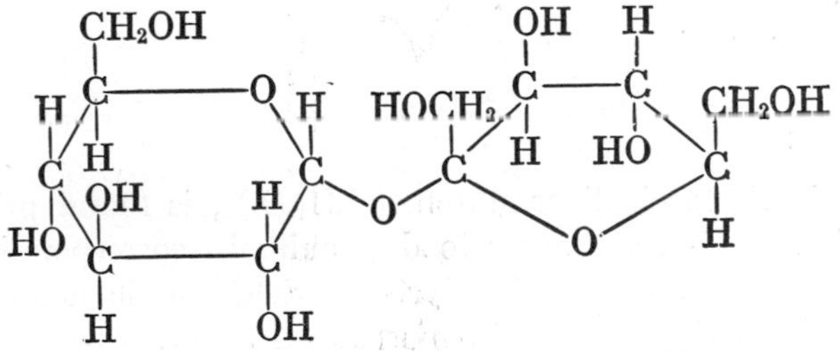

(glucose unit) (fructose unit)

Sucrose

Maltose, or **malt sugar,** $C_{12}H_{22}O_{11}$, is a disaccharide formed by the action of an enzyme called diastase upon starch, or by the partial hydrolysis of starch or dextrins by dilute acids. It is made up of two glucose residues as shown by the formation of two molecules of glucose upon hydrolysis. Maltose is fermentable in the presence of yeast, since yeast produces both maltase, which catalyzes the conversion of maltose to glucose, and zymase, which catalyzes alcoholic fermentation of glucose.

Lactose, or **milk sugar,** $C_{12}H_{22}O_{11}$, occurs in the milk of mammals to the extent of 3 to 5 per cent. Hydrolysis in the presence of either dilute mineral acid or lactase converts lactose to glucose and galactose (an isomer of glucose). Certain microorganisms catalyze the fermentation of lactose to butyric or lactic acid and are in this way responsible for the souring of milk. Lactose is an important ingredient of infant foods.

32.10 Polysaccharides

The polysaccharides are carbohydrates of high molecular weight and consist of monosaccharide units linked through oxygen atoms to form chains of different lengths. They occur in large quantities in plants and animals, either as reserve food materials, such as starches and glycogen, or as skeletal substances, such as cellulose. They are nearly tasteless and are either insoluble in water or form colloidal dispersions in it (Chapter 13). Upon hydrolysis they yield monosaccharides.

32.11 Starch

Starch, $(C_6H_{10}O_5)_x$, is stored by plants in grains, tubers, and fruits, as a food supply for the young plant until it has developed a leaf system of its own and can manufacture its own food. Starch may be hydrolyzed completely to glucose by boiling it with dilute acid, so must consist entirely of glucose residues. Incomplete hydrolysis of starch gives rise to dextrin, which has the same empirical formula as starch $(C_6H_{10}O_5)_x$; the difference is in the value of x, which is smaller for dextrin than for starch. Starches are important commercially as foods, but have other uses as well. The use of starch in the laundry is familiar to everyone, and its use in producing corn syrup has already been mentioned. Large quantities of starch are used in the production of ethyl alcohol by fermentation. Wheat starch is utilized in making paste because it is very adhesive. Starch is also used in sizing cloth and paper.

32.12 Glycogen

Glycogen, animal starch, liver starch, $(C_6H_{10}O_5)_x$, is found principally in the liver and muscles. It is the storage food of animals, corresponding to starch in plants. The breakdown of muscle glycogen yields lactic acid, the enzymatic oxidation of which provides energy for muscular activity.

32.13 Cellulose

Cellulose, $(C_6H_{10}O_5)_x$, has the same empirical formula as starch, and its molecules are made up of many glucose units joined together through oxygen linkages to form long chains. The cellulose chains are arranged in bundles whose long axes are parallel to the axes of the cellulose thread or fiber. Cellulose is widely distributed in nature. It is the chief structural material of the cell walls of plants. Cotton contains about 90 per cent of cellulose, coniferous woods 60 per cent, and cereal straws 35 per cent.

Animals, excepting ruminants (cud-chewing animals, such as the cow), do not digest cellulose because the enzymes of the digestive tract do not hydrolyze it. However, many bacteria attack cellulose, particularly those in the intestinal tract of ruminants. For this reason, these animals are able to utilize cellulose as a food.

32.14 Rayon

Natural silk is a protein, whereas rayon is a carbohydrate which is made from cellulose by three processes. In the **viscose process,** cellulose from wood pulp or cotton is treated with concentrated sodium hydroxide and then with carbon disulfide. This treatment converts it to a viscous yellow liquid (viscose). After an aging period, the viscose is forced through spinnerets into a solution of dilute sulfuric acid and sodium hydrogen sulfate (Fig. 32–2). When the material issuing

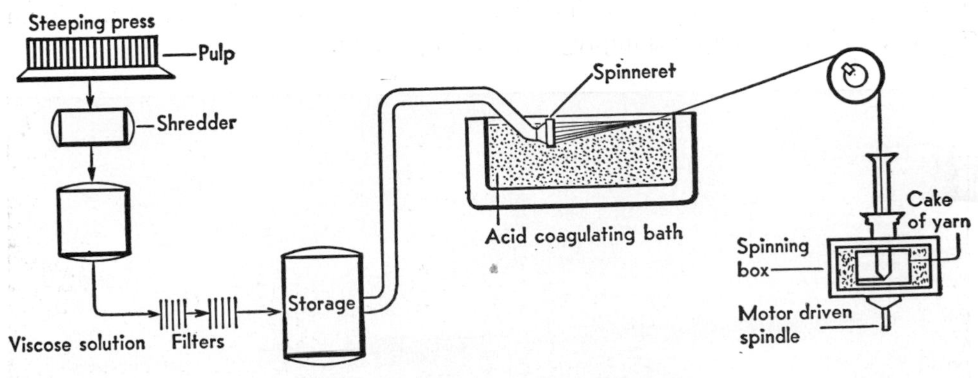

Fig. 32–2 Production of viscose rayon yarn.

from the orifice of the spinnerets comes in contact with the acid solution, it hardens to filaments of regenerated cellulose. Cellophane is made in a similar manner, excepting that the cellulose is precipitated in the form of sheets instead of filaments.

The **cuprammonium process** for making rayon is based upon the fact that cellulose is dissolved by tetraamminecopper (II) hydroxide, $Cu(NH_3)_4(OH)_2$. Upon the acidification of the solution, cellulose is regenerated.

The production of rayon by the **cellulose acetate** method involves treatment of cellulose with glacial acetic acid containing acetic anhydride. The product is first hydrolyzed and then dissolved in acetone. The viscous solution thus obtained is forced through a spinneret into a tube through which a current of warm air is passing. The solvent evaporates and filaments of cellulose acetate are formed. Rayon made by this process is a cellulose ester rather than regenerated cellulose, and it is known by such names as Celanese and Acetate.

32.15 Paper

Cellulose is used in the manufacture of paper, about 300 pounds of which are used per year by the average citizen of the United States. The cellulose used is obtained from wood, cotton rags, cereal straw, and similar materials. To prepare wood for paper-making, wood chips are digested under pressure with calcium hydrogen sulfite which contains sulfur dioxide (Section 23.3). This dissolves the lignin, which holds the cellulose fibers together, and leaves the cellulose as wood pulp. The pulp is then washed with water and bleached to obtain a white product. Much of the water is removed from the refined pulp, which is squeezed between rollers to form a continuous sheet and is dried by passing it over heated rollers (Fig. 32–3). Many substances, such as clay, rosin, dextrin, aluminum silicate, barium sulfate, and dyes or pigments are added to the pulp to produce paper of special properties. For example, rosin and similar materials are used as "sizing" to fill up the spaces between the cellulose fibers; this prevents ink from spreading on the paper and gives it a smooth finish. Glazed papers contain clay or aluminum sulfate, and waxed paper is impregnated with paraffin.

Fig. 32–3 Machine for making book paper. The pulp is distributed evenly over an endless wire screen, then pressed between rollers and dried by a long series of heated cylinders. *Beloit Iron Works*

32.16 Cellulose Esters

The most important esters of cellulose are the acetates and nitrates.

The synthetic fiber known as Celanese consists of cellulose acetate (Section 32.14). This material is used in the manufacture of photographic films, which are much safer than films made from cellulose nitrate (Section 32.17), for they burn slowly and do not form noxious gases. The acetate is used to a considerable extent as a molding plastic for various objects and in making nonshattering glass (Section 29.19).

32.17 Cellulose Nitrates

When cellulose is treated with concentrated nitric acid or with a mixture of concentrated nitric and sulfuric acids at a temperature below 40°, cellulose nitrates (**nitrocellulose**) are formed. The number of hydroxyl groups replaced by nitrate radicals depends upon the nature of the nitrating agent, the time the reactants are in contact, and the temperature of the reaction mixture.

The cellulose nitrates which contain from 13 to 13.3 per cent nitrogen are explosive and are known as **guncotton.** They are used in the manufacture of **smokeless powder** (Fig. 32–4), for when they explode only nitrogen, hydrogen, steam, carbon monoxide, and carbon dioxide are formed, and no smoke is produced. Motion picture films were at one time made of cellulose nitrate and were highly inflammable. Films are now mostly made of the less inflammable cellulose acetate.

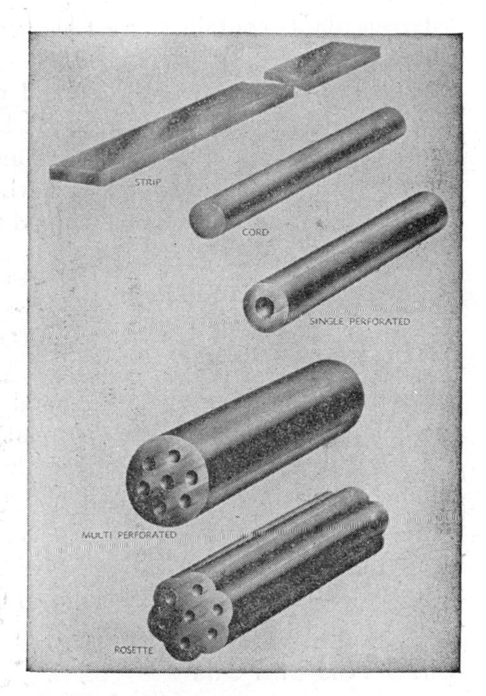

Fig. 32–4 Smokeless powder grains are made in various shapes to control the speed of burning. These grains are highly magnified. *U.S. Department of Defense*

The products of lower nitration are soluble in a mixture of ethyl alcohol and ether and are called **pyroxylin.**

A solution of soluble nitrocellulose in an alcohol-ether mixture is known as **collodion.** When exposed to air the solvent evaporates quickly and leaves a tough deposit of nitrocellulose. Celluloid is made by mixing dried pyroxylin with camphor and coloring matter, and then pressing the mixture into blocks or sheets. Certain lacquers, such as Duco, contain pyroxylin, resin, and pigments dissolved in amyl acetate or other esters. These lacquers are quick-drying and form smooth films upon evaporation of the solvent.

32.18 Photosynthesis

Green plants are able to synthesize their complex organic constituents from carbon dioxide, water, and inorganic salts. On the other hand, animals lack the power of synthesizing organic materials from these simple substances, and they depend upon preformed organic materials supplied in the diet.

Photosynthesis is an oxidation-reduction reaction in which the required energy is supplied by the solar energy which is absorbed by the green coloring matter of the plant. In the reaction, carbohydrates are formed from carbon dioxide and water and molecular oxygen is produced. Because one mole of oxygen is formed for each mole of carbon dioxide and each mole of water consumed, the reaction can be represented by the equation

$$n\,CO_2 + n\,H_2O \xrightarrow{\text{light}} \underset{\text{Carbohydrate}}{(CH_2O)_n} + n\,O_2$$

By providing plants with water labeled with the $^{18}_{8}O$ isotope, it has been found that most of the molecular oxygen released during photosynthesis is derived from the water molecules and not from those of carbon dioxide. It appears that photosynthesis consists in the reduction of carbon dioxide, water serving as the reducing agent.

Green plants contain a green pigment called **chlorophyll,** which absorbs light chiefly from the red portion of the spectrum. The formation of carbohydrate and oxygen from carbon dioxide and water is a highly endothermic reaction, requiring a large supply of energy. It has been found that 120 kcal. of energy are required for the production of each mole of the carbohydrate unit, CH_2O. This same quantity of energy is released when the carbohydrate is completely oxidized to carbon dioxide and water in animal organisms or upon combustion.

LIPIDS

32.19 Introduction

The term **lipid** is used as a general name for a group of substances having all the following characteristics: (a) relationship to the fatty acids as either actual or potential esters, (b) solubility in the fat solvents (e.g., ether, chloroform, benzene), but insolubility in water, and (c) utilizability by living organisms. The criterion of solubility is not absolute, for some lipids are water-soluble and some are not soluble in all the fat solvents. The lipids include such substances as fats, oils, waxes, fatty acids, phospholipids, glycolipids, and sterols.

32.20 Fats and Oils

The fats and oils are fatty acid esters of glycerol. Glycerol is a trihydroxy alcohol, $C_3H_5(OH)_3$, and the term "fatty acid" refers to any organic acid that occurs in a fat. The fats and oils have the general formula shown below.

```
                                                  O     H
                                                  ‖     |
(RCOO)3C3H5     or     RCOOCH2     or        R—C—O—C—H
                           |                            |
                       RCOOCH                     O     |
                           |                      ‖     |
                       RCOOCH2                 R—C—O—C—H
                                                  O     |
                                                  ‖     |
                                               R—C—O—C—H
                                                        |
                                                        H
```

General formula of fats and oils

The R groups in the formula may be the same or different and the fatty acid residue may be saturated or unsaturated. In saturated fatty acid esters of glycerol, most of the acid residues have the general formula $CH_3(CH_2)_nCO—$, where n is always an even number, most frequently 14 or 16. Compounds of this type are solid and are called fats. When the fatty acid residues are predominantly of the unsaturated variety, the esters are liquid and are called oils.

The fatty acid radicals most often found in fats and oils are those of the acids listed below.

Butyric	$CH_3CH_2CH_2COOH$
Lauric	$CH_3(CH_2)_{10}COOH$
Palmitic	$CH_3(CH_2)_{14}COOH$
Stearic	$CH_3(CH_2)_{16}COOH$
Oleic	$CH_3(CH_2)_7CH{=}CH(CH_2)_7COOH$
Linoleic	$CH_3CH_2CH{=}CHCH_2CH{=}CHCH_2CH{=}CH(CH_2)_7COOH$
Ricinoleic	$CH_3(CH_2)_5CHOHCH_2CH{=}CH(CH_2)_7COOH$

Each naturally occurring fat or oil is a mixture of many different esters of glycerol. The more important fats include milk fat, lard, and tallow. Familiar oils are coconut oil, cottonseed oil, linseed oil, and palm oil.

Like other esters, fats and oils undergo hydrolysis; and a fatty acid and glycerol are formed.

$$\underset{\text{Glyceryl palmitate}}{(C_{15}H_{31}COO)_3C_3H_5} + \underset{\text{(in excess)}}{3\ H_2O} \xrightleftharpoons{\text{catalyst, heat}} \underset{\text{Palmitic acid}}{3\ C_{15}H_{31}COOH} + \underset{\text{Glycerol}}{C_3H_5(OH)_3}$$

Fats and oils are hydrolyzed by certain enzymes, which are called **lipases.** During digestion the lipases of gastric and pancreatic juices hydrolyze fats and oils to fatty acids and glycerol. Enzymes known as phosphatases, present in kidney, bone, the intestines, and other animal tissues, hydrolyze the lipids known as phospholipids (Section 32.22).

Fats and oils play two important roles in the diet. Part of these substances is used in the synthesis of certain essential constituents of the tissues, such as phospholipids, and part is used as body fuel, which may be utilized immediately or stored for future use. Fats also serve to some extent to insulate the body against loss of heat and to protect other tissues against injury.

The products of complete oxidation of fats and oils in the body are carbon dioxide and water. However, under certain pathological conditions (for example, diabetes and starvation), normal oxidation is interfered with and substances such as β-hydroxybutyric acid, β-oxybutyric acid, and acetone appear in the urine in abnormally large quantities.

32.21 Waxes

The esters of the fatty acids and alcohols other than glycerol are known as **waxes.** They are widely distributed in plants and animals, where they frequently serve as protective agents. **Spermaceti** is a crystalline wax obtained from sperm oil, and it is mainly cetyl myristate, $C_{13}H_{27}COOC_{16}H_{33}$, and cetyl laurate, $C_{11}H_{23}COOC_{16}H_{33}$. It is used in the manufacture of candles, confectionery, and perfumery. **Beeswax,** from the honeycomb of the bee, is chiefly myricyl palmitate, $C_{15}H_{31}COOC_{31}H_{63}$. **Carnauba wax** is a vegetable wax found as a coating on the leaves of a Brazilian palm. This wax contains myricyl alcohol, $C_{31}H_{63}OH$, cerotic acid, $C_{26}H_{53}COOH$, and myricyl cerotate, $C_{26}H_{53}COOC_{31}H_{63}$. It is a valuable ingredient of polishes because it gives a high luster. It is also used in making candles and in adulterating beeswax.

32.22 Compound Lipids

The compound lipids are esters containing groups in addition to the fatty acid radicals. The **phospholipids,** for example, are fats containing phosphoric acid and nitrogen, while the glycolipids are compounds of fatty acids with a carbohydrate which contains nitrogen but no phosphoric acid.

The phospholipids are present in every cell of plants and animals, and are very abundant in the tissues of the brain, heart, liver, muscle, kidney, and bone marrow. Many of the phospholipids of certain tissues serve as intermediates in the metabolism of fats and oils. The general formulas of two types of phospholipids are given below.

```
CH2OCOR                          CH2OCOR
|                                |
CHOCOR'                          CHOCOR'
|    O                           |    O
|    ||                          |    ||
CH2OPOCH2CHCOR                   CH2OPOCH2CH2N(CH3)3
     |     |                          |        |
     OH    NH2                        OH       OH
```

Cephalin

Lecithin

The **glycolipids** (also called **cerebrosides**) are associated with the phospholipids in the tissues, particularly in the brain. Upon hydrolysis they yield galactose (a sugar), sphingosine, and a fatty acid.

```
                                     COR(CH2)nCH3
                                     |
CH3(CH2)12CH=CH—CHOH—CHNH—CH2O
                                           |
CH2OH—CH—CHOH—CHOH—CHOH—CH
      |____________O______________|
```

Glycolipid

32.23 Sterols and Steroids

The sterols occur widely distributed in nature and are related structurally to the complex organic compound cyclopentanoperhydrophenanthrene, the formula of which is shown below.

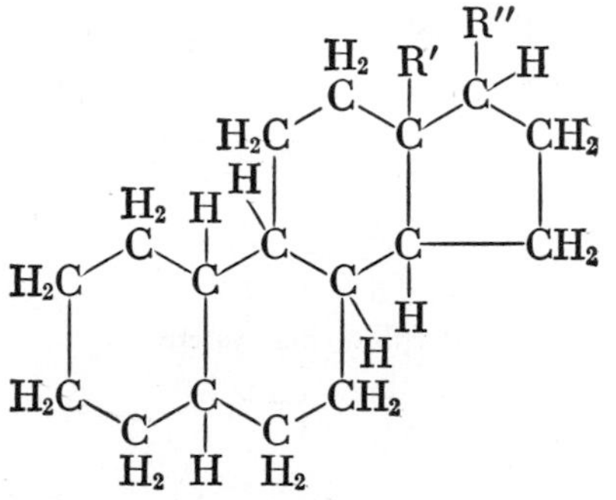

Ring system of sterols and steroids

This group of lipids includes the sterols, steroids, bile acids, certain vitamins, and sex hormones.

The best-known sterol is **cholesterol,** $C_{27}H_{45}OH$, which is found free or as an ester of a fatty acid in almost all tissues, but particularly in the brain, nerves, and suprarenal gland. Physiologically, cholesterol serves as a vehicle for the transfer and oxidation of fatty acids; it is important to the colloidal chemistry of protoplasm; it is valuable in immunological processes; and it is a precursor of the sex hormones.

Human bile is a liquid containing bile salts, inorganic salts, and small quantities of cholesterol, lecithin, and bile pigments. Bile is stored in the gall bladder and secreted into the intestines. The chief function of the bile acids is to aid in the digestion of fats and other lipids by producing fat emulsions and by forming soluble compounds with some of the fatty acids. The bile acids are formed in the body from cholesterol.

The sex hormones are responsible for the development of specific male and female sexual characteristics. They are related in structure to cholesterol.

PORPHYRINS AND THEIR DERIVATIVES

32.24 Introduction

Most of the porphyrins found in nature are present in the form of chlorophyll, the green pigment of plants, and as hemoglobin, the red pigment of blood. In these substances it is the porphyrin portion of the molecule that is responsible for the important biological activity.

The **porphyrins** are intensely colored compounds containing the porphin ring system shown on page 514.

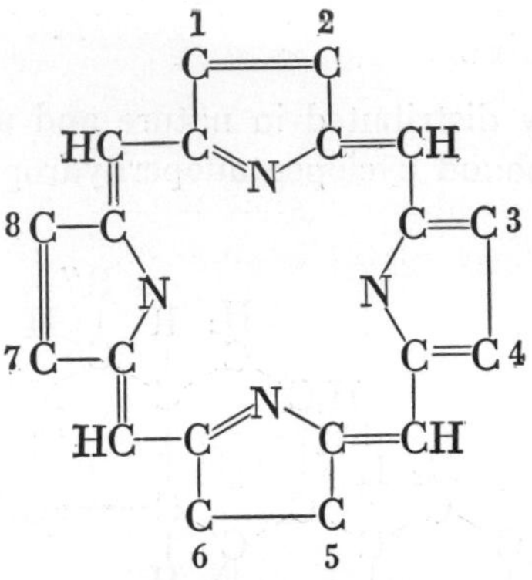

Porphin ring system

32.25 Chlorophyll

The pigment of green plants is a mixture of two closely related porphyrin derivatives which are called chlorophyll-a and chlorophyll-b. The structure of chlorophyll-a is shown below.

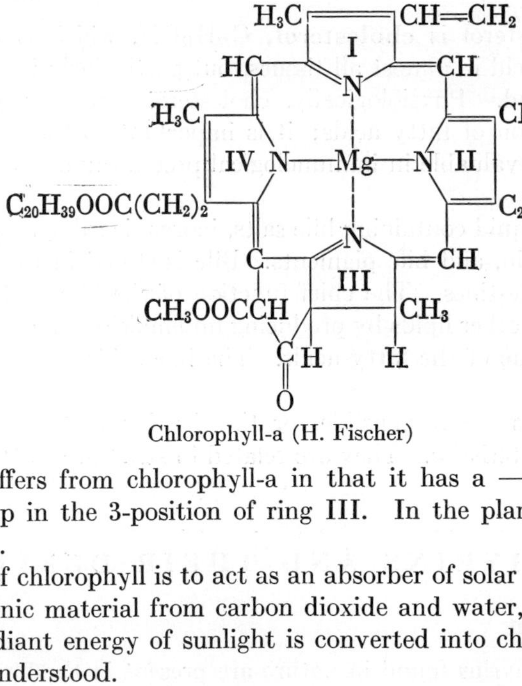

Chlorophyll-a (H. Fischer)

Chlorophyll-b differs from chlorophyll-a in that it has a —CHO group instead of a —CH_3 group in the 3-position of ring III. In the plant, the pigments are bound to protein.

The function of chlorophyll is to act as an absorber of solar energy in the photosynthesis of organic material from carbon dioxide and water, but the mechanism by which the radiant energy of sunlight is converted into chemical energy is not yet completely understood.

32.26 Hemoglobin

The solid content of the red corpuscles of mammals contains on the average 32 per cent of **hemoglobin.** On careful hydrolysis with hydrochloric acid, the protein is cleaved into two fragments: hemin (6 per cent) and globin (94 per cent). Hemoglobin must, therefore, be made up of the protein globin linked to an organic group, which contains all the iron. The chloride ion of hemin is derived from the hydrochloric acid used in the hydrolysis; hemin has the empirical formula $C_{34}H_{32}O_4N_4FeCl$, and is a chloride derived from the parent compound heme, $C_{34}H_{32}O_4N_4FeOH$. The structure of hemin is given below.

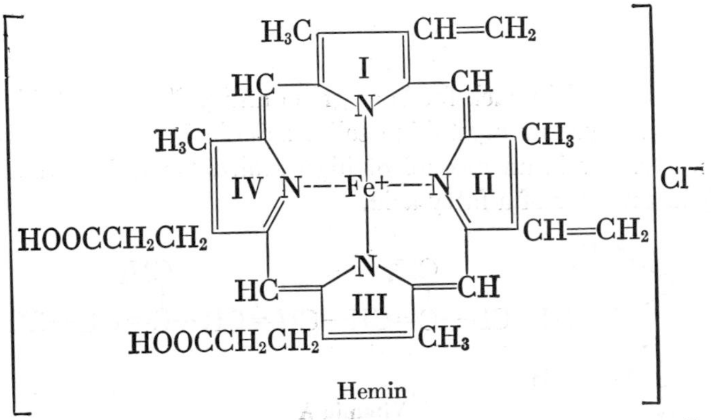

```
                 H3C ┌────────┐ CH=CH2
                     │   I    │
             HC ─────┘   N    └───── CH
             ‖           │           ‖
     H3C ┌───┘           │           └───┐ CH3
         │ IV  N ---- Fe+ ---- N  II     │                  Cl⁻
HOOCCH2CH2 └───┐         │           ┌───┘ CH=CH2
             │           N           │
             HC ═════┐  III   ┌═════ CH
    HOOCCH2CH2 └═════════════┘ CH3
```

Hemin

The principal function of hemoglobin is the transport of oxygen from the lungs to the tissues, where oxygen is consumed in the oxidation of such organic substances as carbohydrates, lipids, and proteins. Hemoglobin, the pigment of blood in the veins, is purplish-red. It combines with oxygen, forming bright-red **oxyhemoglobin,** the pigment of arterial blood. Since one hemoglobin molecule contains 4 atoms of iron (and hence four hemin molecules), and the maximum amount of oxygen carried corresponds to one molecule of oxygen (O_2) per atom of iron, one hemoglobin molecule can carry 4 oxygen molecules. The union of oxygen with hemoglobin is not a reaction that can be spoken of as oxidation, for the iron remains in the +2 oxidation state when oxygen is bound to the hemoglobin molecule. The bond between hemoglobin and oxygen is a very weak one, as indicated by the fact that oxygen is liberated upon subjecting solutions of oxyhemoglobin to low pressure.

Hemoglobin readily combines with carbon monoxide, CO, forming a pinkish-red complex, called **carbon monoxide hemoglobin.** Because this complex is more stable than oxyhemoglobin, oxygen will not replace the carbon monoxide, and blood loses its ability to combine with oxygen.

VITAMINS

32.27 Introduction

The **vitamins** are substances which, in addition to carbohydrates, fats, proteins, and inorganic salts, are essential for the normal nutrition of animals. Most of the vitamins are synthesized in plants or bacteria, but not in the animal body. The fact that the lack of such substances can cause diseases in man was not generally recognized until about 1920. Scurvy, caused by lack of vitamin C, and beriberi, caused by the lack of vitamin B_1, were two of the most important deficiency diseases in the recognition of vitamins. Because vitamin C is destroyed when food containing it is cooked, scurvy was quite common among persons whose diet consisted only of cooked or preserved foods. Beriberi appeared in the Far East with the introduction of rice-polishing machines because the indispensable food substance vitamin B_1 was removed in the rice-polishings.

32.28 Vitamin A

This vitamin is found in such foods as green and yellow vegetables, eggs, milk, and butter. It is a yellow crystalline solid, soluble in fats and oils, but nearly insoluble in water. It is an alcohol of high molecular weight and in the body occurs mainly as an ester of a fatty acid.

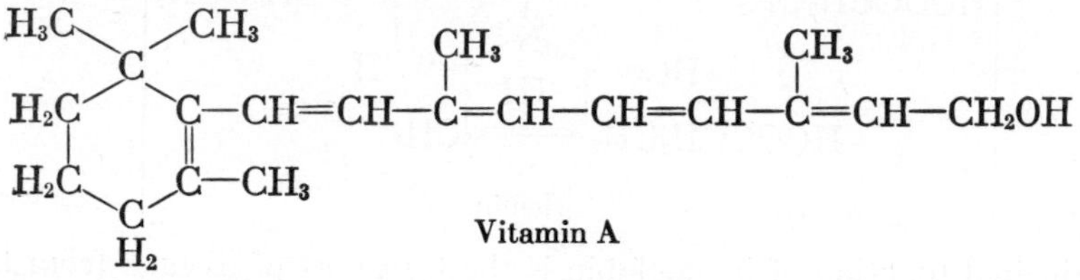

```
H3C   CH3
   \ /
    C          CH3                  CH3
   / \         |                    |
H2C   C—CH=CH—C=CH—CH=CH—C=CH—CH2OH
 |    ||
H2C   C—CH3
   \ /
    C
    H2
```

Vitamin A

One of the first clinical symptoms of deficiency of vitamin A in the diet is night blindness. The eye disease known as xerophthalmia, in which the eyes become hemorrhagic and infected, results from insufficient vitamin A. Vitamin A is also essential for normal growth, and it increases resistance to infections that enter the body by way of the nose and throat.

32.29 The B Vitamins

Before 1920 the B vitamins, which are found in rice bran, yeast, liver, and other materials, were thought to be one substance. It was later found, however, that the vitamin consists of several substances. In order to distinguish them from one another, designations such as B_1, B_2, B_3, etc., are used, with B_1 being assigned to the antiberiberi factor.

Vitamin B_1, or thiamin, is present in rice bran and the germ of other cereals such as wheat, rye, barley, and oats. Meat and vegetables contain less thiamin, but yeast has a high thiamin content. Thiamin exists in the tissues chiefly as a pyrophosphoric acid ester of the alcoholic side chain of the vitamin, as shown below.

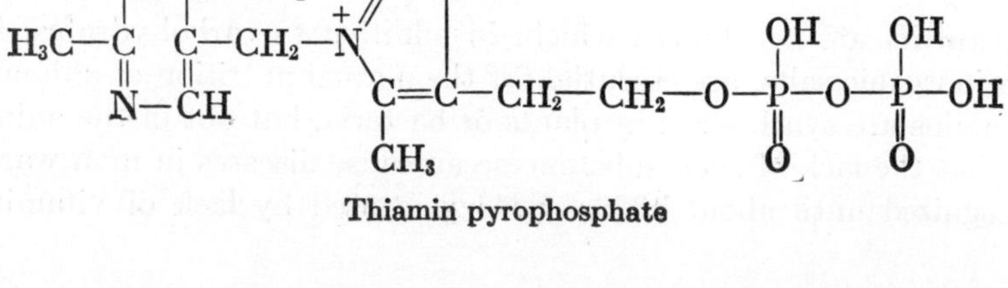

```
                              H
                              |
      N=C—NH2                 C—S
      |  |                 + //  |
  H3C—C  C—CH2—N          |                      OH    OH
      ||  ||             \         |                      |     |
      N—CH                C=C—CH2—CH2—O—P—O—P—OH
                              |                            ||    ||
                              CH3                          O     O
```

Thiamin pyrophosphate

Thiamin deficiency causes polyneuritis in man and many animals, particularly birds. Thiamin pyrophosphate is the enzyme cocarboxylase, which serves a vital function in the oxidation of glucose to carbon dioxide and water. If the diet is thiamin deficient, the energy derived from this oxidation is insufficient for the needs of nerve tissues. The results are loss of appetite, fatigue, fear, nervousness, and depression.

Vitamin B_2, or riboflavin, is a yellow pigment found in liver, yeast, cereal germ, and many other foodstuffs. It plays an important role in the oxidation reactions associated with cell respiration. The structure of riboflavin is shown below.

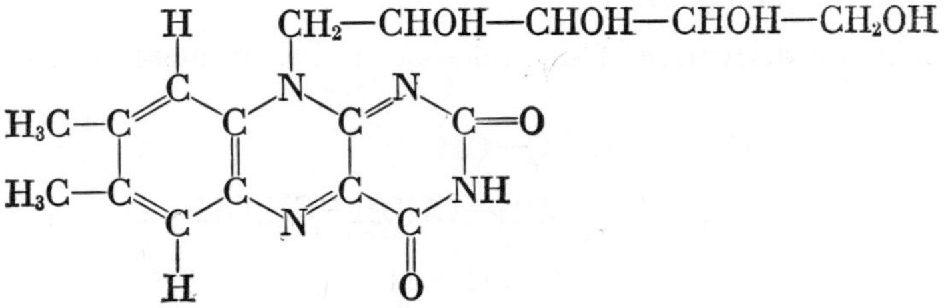

```
          H      CH2—CHOH—CHOH—CHOH—CH2OH
          |       |
          C       N       N
        //  \   /   \   //  \
H3C—C        C        C        C=O
     |       ||       |        |
H3C—C        C        C        NH
        \\  /   \   //  \    /
          C       N        C
          |                ||
          H                O
```

Riboflavin

This vitamin stimulates the growth of young animals and prevents dermatitis and baldness.

Vitamin B_{12} is the substance which prevents the disease known as pernicious anemia, characterized by a decrease in the number of red cells in the blood and by nervous degeneration. This vitamin is a dark-red cobalt complex with the elemental composition $C_{63}H_{90}N_{14}O_{14}PCo$, and it is often called cobalamin. It is a normal component of most diets, so sufferers from pernicious anemia apparently cannot utilize vitamin B_{12}, even though it is present.

Vitamin B_6 (pyridoxine), pyridoxal, and pyridoxamine are substances whose deficiency gives rise to anemia and nervous symptoms in animals. It is not definitely established that these vitamins are essential to man. The structures of the substances of the vitamin B_6 group are given below.

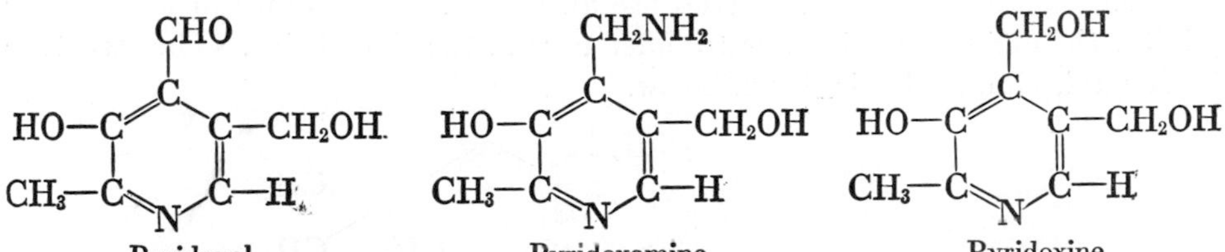

```
        CHO                      CH2NH2                    CH2OH
         |                         |                         |
         C                         C                         C
       //  \                     //  \                     //  \
HO—C         C—CH2OH    HO—C         C—CH2OH    HO—C         C—CH2OH
    |        ||              |        ||              |        ||
CH3—C        C—H        CH3—C        C—H        CH3—C        C—H
      \\   /                  \\   /                  \\   /
        N                       N                       N
    Pyridoxal               Pyridoxamine             Pyridoxine
```

These vitamins are found in liver, milk, eggs, and vegetables, and function in the metabolism of amino acids.

Niacin, or **nicotinic acid,** is a vitamin of the B group that is efficient in the control of pellagra, a disease affecting the mucous membranes, the skin, and nervous system. The structural formula of niacin is given on page 518.

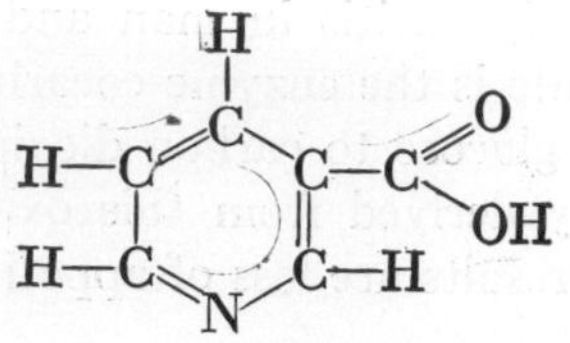

H—C(=C(H)—C(=C—H)—N=C—H)—C(=O)OH

Niacin

It is probable that niacin plays a role in keeping tissue metabolism normal. It can be synthesized in man from the amino acid tryptophan.

32.30 Vitamin C, Ascorbic Acid

This vitamin is a derivative of the monosaccharide furanose, and its structural formula is

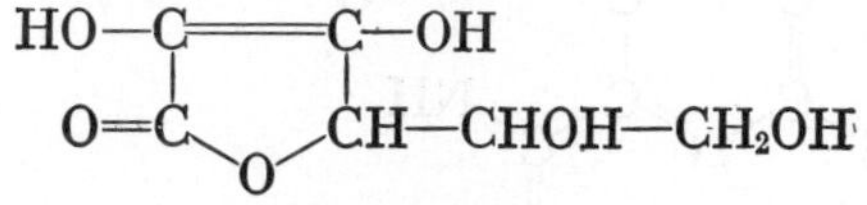

HO—C═C—OH
O═C—O—CH—CHOH—CH_2OH

Ascorbic acid

Vitamin C prevents scurvy, the symptoms of which are hemorrhages in the gums and in the periosteum of the bones. This substance is found in many fruits and vegetables, particularly citrus fruits (lemons, limes, oranges). Because ascorbic acid is destroyed by cooking, scurvy was quite common when cooked food alone was eaten.

32.31 Vitamin D

This is the vitamin which prevents rickets, a severe disease involving the skeleton. The chief symptom of rickets is softness and deformation of the bones in growing children, caused by insufficient calcification.

"Vitamin D" includes materials designated as vitamin D_1, vitamin D_2, vitamin D_3, and vitamin D_4. Vitamin D_1 is a mixture of calciferol and lumisterol; calciferol has antirachitic activity, but lumisterol is inactive. Vitamin D_2 is calciferol and its antirachitic activity is quite similar to that of naturally occurring "vitamin D." Vitamin D_3 occurs naturally in the liver oils of cod, halibut, and tuna fish. Vitamins D_2, D_3, and D_4 are all sterols. They differ in antirachitic activity, the difference being due to differences in the side chains. The structure of calciferol, vitamin D_2, is shown below.

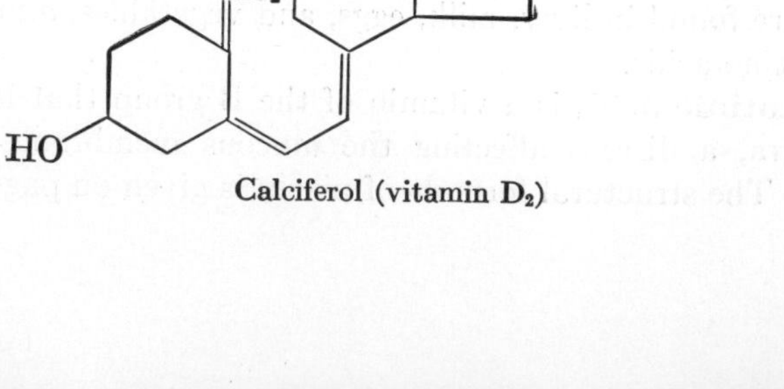

H_3C CH_3 CH_3 CH_3 CH_3 CH_2 HO

Calciferol (vitamin D_2)

32.32 Vitamin E

The specific reproductive (antisterility) factor is designated as vitamin E. It is found in wheat-germ oil, corn-germ oil, and cottonseed oil, in the green leaves of lettuce, spinach, and water cress, and in egg yolks. There are four types of vitamin E — α-, β-, γ-, and δ-tocopherol. The structure of α-tocopherol is shown below.

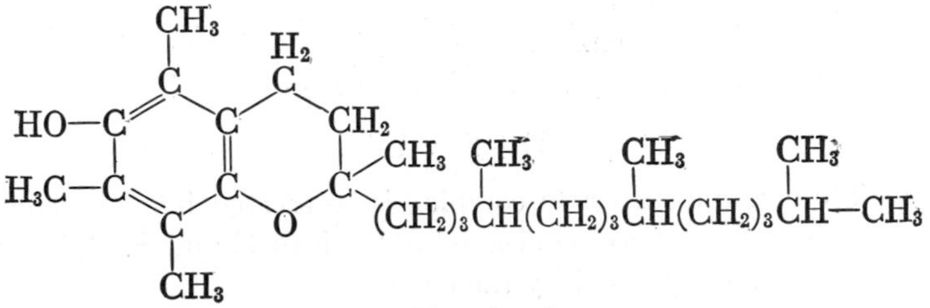

```
            CH3
            |        H2
            C        C
          //  \    /   \
   HO—C        C       CH2
      |        ||       |   CH3   CH3        CH3        CH3
      |        ||       |  /      |          |          |
  H3C—C        C        C
       \\    /   \    /   \
         C         O       (CH2)3CH(CH2)3CH(CH2)3CH—CH3
         |
        CH3
```

α-Tocopherol

32.33 Vitamin K

This vitamin seems to function in the blood-clotting mechanism, and a lack of it causes a tendency to hemorrhage. There are known to be two K vitamins — vitamin K_1 and vitamin K_2. They are found in leafy vegetables, the fat of hog liver, fish meal, and the oils of grains and cereals. The structure of vitamin K_1 is shown below.

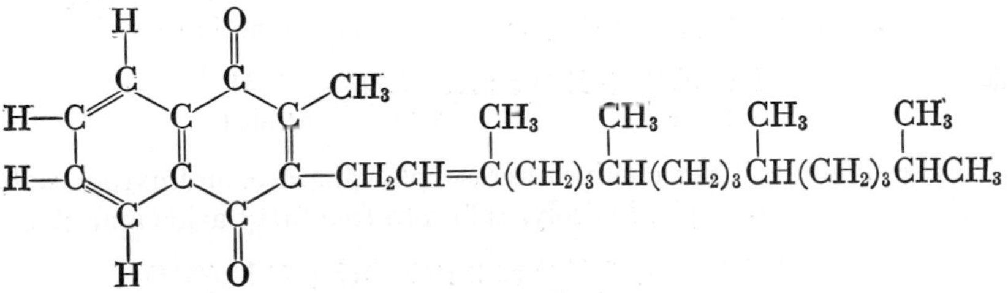

```
       H         O
       |         ||
       C         C
     //  \     /   \    CH3
 H—C       C         C/       CH3    CH3        CH3        CH3
   |       ||        ||        |      |          |          |
 H—C       C         C—CH2CH=C(CH2)3CH(CH2)3CH(CH2)3CHCH3
     \\  /   \     /
       C         C
       |         ||
       H         O
```

Vitamin K_1

ENZYMES

32.34 Introduction

Most of the chemical reactions occurring in living organisms are accelerated by enzymes. The reaction catalyzed by an enzyme would proceed with extreme slowness in the absence of the enzyme. An **enzyme** is a chemical substance of organic nature, elaborated by living organisms, and capable of accelerating a chemical reaction. In other words, an enzyme is a biological catalyst. All the enzymes which have been investigated are proteins. The substances which undergo chemical reactions due to the catalytic action of enzymes are called substrates.

Very small amounts of an enzyme suffice for the reaction of large amounts of substrate. Like all proteins, enzymes are unstable toward acids, alkalis, and heat. Denaturation of the enzyme protein usually causes inactivation of the enzyme.

Many enzymes contain a definite chemical group (coenzyme) which can be separated from the protein portion of the enzyme (apoenzyme). Neither the coenzyme nor apoenzyme shows catalytic activity after separation. Enzymes are, in general, very specific in regard to the reactions which they catalyze, and the apoenzyme is responsible for the substrate specificity of the total enzyme.

It has been shown that the enzyme (E) combines with the substrate (S) forming the enzyme-substrate complex (ES), according to the equation

$$E + S \rightleftharpoons ES$$

The intermediate enzyme-substrate complex is converted into the enzyme E and the reaction product P, or may be cleaved again into E and S. The enzyme catalyzed reaction may be expressed by the equation

$$E + S \rightleftharpoons ES \rightarrow E + P$$

The two chief classes of enzymes are the hydrolases and the enzymes catalyzing oxidation-reduction reactions. These are discussed in the following sections.

32.35 Hydrolases

These are enzymes which catalyze the hydrolysis of food substances in the digestive tract. They include the esterases, the carbohydrases, and the proteinases.

1. *Esterases.* These enzymes catalyze the reversible reaction

$$\underset{\text{Ester}}{RCOOR'} + H_2O \rightleftharpoons \underset{\text{Acid}}{RCOOH} + \underset{\text{Alcohol}}{R'OH}$$

The **esterases** include lipase, choline esterase, phosphatase, and pyrophosphatases. Pancreatic lipase, for example, hydrolyzes fats to free fatty acids and glycerol.

$$\underset{\text{Fat}}{(RCOO)_3C_3H_5} + 3\,H_2O \rightleftharpoons \underset{\text{Fatty acid}}{3\,RCOOH} + \underset{\text{Glycerol}}{C_3H_5(OH)_3}$$

2. *Carbohydrases.* These are enzymes which catalyze the hydrolytic cleavage of the oxygen bonds linking the monosaccharide residues together in di- or polysaccharides. The **carbohydrases** include such enzymes as maltase, lactase, sucrase, diastases, amylases, and cellulase. Sucrase, for example, catalyzes the hydrolysis of sucrose to glucose and fructose.

$$\underset{\text{Sucrose}}{C_{12}H_{22}O_{11}} + H_2O \rightleftharpoons \underset{\text{Glucose}}{C_6H_{12}O_6} + \underset{\text{Fructose}}{C_6H_{12}O_6}$$

3. *Proteinases.* The **proteinases** catalyze the hydrolysis of proteins. They catalyze the hydrolysis of peptide bonds inside the long peptide chains which form protein molecules. The hydrolytic cleavage of a peptide bond is shown by the following equation:

$$R-\overset{\overset{O}{\|}}{C}-\overset{\overset{H}{|}}{N}-R' + H_2O \rightleftharpoons R-COOH + H_2N-R'$$

The most important proteinases involved in digestion are pepsin, trypsin, and chymotrypsin. The clotting of blood is an enzymic reaction catalyzed by the enzyme thrombin. It is a reaction in which the soluble protein fibrinogen is converted into insoluble fibrin, and it is accompanied by the splitting of several peptide bonds with the release of small polypeptides. The clotting of milk is caused by the enzyme rennin of the gastric juice of mammals. The reaction involves the formation of an insoluble compound from casein, which is soluble in solutions which are neutral.

32.36 Enzymes Catalyzing Oxidation-Reduction Reactions

In 1770, Lavoisier showed that animals use oxygen for respiration. In this process, lipids, carbohydrates, and proteins are oxidized with the formation of energy and heat. The mechanisms by which biological oxidations and reductions are carried on have not been completely explained, but during the past 20 years a great deal has been discovered and we now have a rather good picture of the process.

Biological oxidation-reduction reactions are catalyzed by enzymes. The enzymes catalyze the transfer of electrons from the substance being oxidized to the substance being reduced. The most important electron donors in biological systems are the hydrogen atoms of organic molecules. The most important electron acceptor in aerobic organisms is the oxygen molecule. Because the oxidation of organic molecules involves, most frequently, the loss of hydrogen atoms, the reaction is designated as dehydrogenation, and the enzymes which catalyze reactions of this type are called dehydrogenases. The dehydrogenases are not able to transfer hydrogen and electrons directly to molecular oxygen. Instead, certain enzymes, called oxidases, catalyze the reduction of oxygen by hydrogen. Thus two enzymes — a dehydrogenase and an oxidase — are involved in the overall oxidation-reduction reaction. The electrons and hydrogen of the organic substrate are first transferred to the dehydrogenase, which in turn transfers them to the oxidase, and finally to oxygen. In many instances of enzyme catalyzed oxidation-reduction reactions, several electron carriers operate between the dehydrogenase and the oxidase.

QUESTIONS

1. List the principal chemical constituents of living organisms. What are the specific functions of each of these constituents?
2. Explain the way in which water helps to maintain body temperature.
3. What chemical element distinguishes the composition of proteins from that of carbohydrates?
4. What are amino acids?

5. Relate amino acids, with the aid of an equation, to proteins.

6. What was the contribution of Linus Pauling (Nobel Award in chemistry for 1954) to our knowledge of the structure of proteins?

7. What is the literal meaning of the term "carbohydrate," and why was it initially adopted?

8. Write the name and formula for one example each of a monosaccharide, a disaccharide, and a polysaccharide.

9. What is the chemistry involved in the souring of milk?

10. What makes it possible for ruminants to utilize cellulose as food?

11. How do natural silk and rayon differ in composition?

12. Describe the production of rayon by the viscose process.

13. How does "acetate" rayon differ from "viscose" rayon in composition?

14. Outline the steps involved in the manufacture of paper from wood.

15. What are the advantages of photographic film made of cellulose acetate over that made of cellulose nitrate?

16. What is the composition of guncotton and why is it called smokeless powder?

17. Show that the energy we derive from foodstuffs comes initially from the sun.

18. Write the general formula for fats and oils. How do fats and oils differ from each other in composition?

19. Write the equation for the hydrolysis of glyceryl stearate and name the products of the reaction.

20. Relate diabetes to the oxidation of fats and oils in the body.

21. What is the composition and function of human bile?

22. Describe the function of chlorophyll; of hemoglobin.

23. What is the chemistry of carbon monoxide poisoning?

24. What vitamin deficiency is associated with each of the following: night blindness, rickets, beriberi, scurvy, sterility, pernicious anemia, pellagra, and poor blood-clotting?

25. What are enzymes? Relate "coenzyme," "apoenzyme," and "substrate" to "enzyme."

26. What are the three main classes of hydrolytic enzymes?

27. Write the equation for the sucrase catalyzed hydrolysis of sucrose.

28. Enzymes of what class are effective in the cleavage of peptide bonds?

29. What is the function of the enzyme thrombin?

30. What kinds of enzymes are involved in the redox reactions of living organisms?

REFERENCES

"The History of the Discovery of the Amino Acids," H. B. Vickery and C. L. A. Schmidt, *Chemical Reviews*, **9,** 169–318 (1931).

"Emil Fischer's Discovery of the Configuration of Glucose," C. S. Hudson, *J. Chem. Educ.*, **18,** 353 (1941).

"Chemicals from Fats," R. L. Kenyon, D. V. Stingley, and H. P. Young, *Ind. Eng. Chem.*, **42,** 202 (1950).

"Chemical Structure and Biological Activity," A. Burger, *J. Chem. Educ.*, **35** (3) 142 (1958).
"Biochemistry," O. Meyerhof, *Sci. American*, Sept., 1950; p. 62.
"Proteins," Paul Doty, *Sci. American*, Sept., 1957; p. 173.
"Nucleic Acids and Proteins," M. B. Hoagland, *Sci. American*, Dec., 1959; p. 55.
"Structure of Protein Molecules," Linus Pauling, R. B. Corey, and R. Hayward, *Sci. American*, July, 1954; p. 51.
"The Chemical Structure of Proteins," W. H. Stein and S. Moore, *Sci. American*, Feb., 1961; p. 81.
"Cellulose," R. D. Preston, *Sci. American*, Sept., 1957; p. 157.
"Progress in Photosynthesis," E. I. Rabinowitch, *Sci. American*, Nov., 1953; p. 80.
"The Nurture of Creative Science and the Men Who Make It — The Photosynthesis Story," Melvin Calvin, *J. Chem. Educ.*, **35** (9) 428 (1958).
"The Chemical Problem of Spontaneous Generation," S. W. Fox, *J. Chem. Educ.*, **34** (10) 472 (1957).
"Photosynthesis," J. A. Bassham, *J. Chem. Educ.*, **36** (11) 548 (1959).
"New Aspects of Photosynthesis," J. A. Bassham, *J. Chem. Educ.*, **38** (3) 151 (1961).
"Steroids," Louis F. Fieser, *Sci. American*, Jan., 1955; p. 52.
"Some Recent Advances in the Field of Steroids," R. E. Beyler, *J. Chem. Educ.*, **37** (9) 491 (1960).
"The Functioning of Vitamins and Hormones," R. J. Williams, *J. Chem. Educ.*, **36** (11) 538 (1959).
"Enzymes and Metaphor," I. Asimov, *J. Chem. Educ.*, **36** (11) 535 (1959).

PART 2

The Metals

CHAPTER THIRTY-THREE

The Metallic Elements

Many times in the preceding chapters we have had occasion to classify the elements as either metallic or nonmetallic in their properties. Thus far, however, our study has been confined chiefly to the nonmetals and their compounds. Before taking up the study of each of the more important metallic elements and its compounds, a general consideration of the metals as a class of elements will be of value in correlating the study of the individual metals.

The metals may be classified into groups in two distinctly different ways: (1) according to the groups of the Periodic Table, which grouping reflects similarities in electronic structures and gradation in physical and chemical properties, and (2) according to the way in which the metals are associated in their systematic identification, or qualitative analysis. The latter classification depends upon the solubilities of the various salts formed by the metals.

Although our study of the metals will be organized according to the groups of the Periodic Table, it is of interest to see how the metals are classified into analytical groups on the basis of the solubilities of certain of their salts.

33.1 Classification of the Metals into Analytical Groups

Qualitative analysis pertains to the identification of the constituents present in a sample of a substance, a mixture of substances, or a solution. In the qualitative analysis of a solution which may contain any or all of the common metal ions, the first step is that of separating the ions of the metals into several groups, each of which contains ions exhibiting a common chemical property which is the basis of the separation. The separation of the common metal ions into groups as it is usually done is outlined briefly below:

The Metals of Analytical Group I. When dilute hydrochloric acid is added to a solution containing all of the common metal ions (and NH_4^+), mercury (I) chloride, silver chloride, and lead chloride precipitate. The chlorides of all the other common metal ions are soluble in this acid solution and can be separated from those of Group I by filtration or centrifugation.

The Metals of Analytical Group II. After the Group I chlorides have been separated, the solution is made 0.3 molar in hydrochloric acid, and the Group II metals are precipitated as sulfides upon the addition of hydrogen sulfide to the solution. The precipitate formed consists of the sulfides of lead, bismuth, copper, cadmium, mercury (II), arsenic, antimony, and tin.

The Metals of Analytical Group III. After the Group II sulfides have been separated, the solution is saturated with hydrogen sulfide and then an excess of aqueous ammonia is added to the solution. Under these conditions the sulfides of cobalt, nickel, manganese, iron, and zinc, and the hydroxides of aluminum and chromium, are precipitated.

The Metals of Analytical Group IV. The Group IV metals, barium, strontium, and calcium, are precipitated as the carbonates from the filtrate or centrifugate of Group III separation by ammonium carbonate in the presence of aqueous ammonia and ammonium chloride.

The Metals of Analytical Group V. The filtrate from the Group IV separation contains the ions of sodium, potassium, magnesium, and ammonium, which constitute Group V.

A "flow sheet" illustrating the schematic separations of the metal ions into the various analytical groups is given in Table 33·1. The chapters which follow Chapter 34 are devoted to a consideration of the descriptive chemistry of the metals as they are grouped according to the analytical scheme. An additional chapter is included on the less common metals, which are not considered in the qualitative scheme.

TABLE 33·1 Flow Sheet of Group Separations

Ions	Reagent		Reagent		Reagent		Reagent		Group
		Hg_2Cl_2							*Group I Chlorides*
		$AgCl$							
Hg_2^{++}		$PbCl_2$							
Ag^+									
Pb^{++}		Pb^{++}		PbS					*Group II Sulfides*
Bi^{+++}		Bi^{+++}		Bi_2S_3					
Cu^{++}		Cu^{++}		CuS					
Cd^{++}		Cd^{++}		CdS					
Hg^{++}		Hg^{++}		HgS					
As^{+++}		As^{+++}		As_2S_3					
Sb^{+++}		Sb^{+++}		Sb_2S_3					
Sn^{++++}		Sn^{++++}		SnS_2					
Co^{++}		Co^{++}		Co^{++}		CoS			*Group III Sulfides and Hydroxides*
Ni^{++}		Ni^{++}	0.3 M HCl	Ni^{++}		NiS			
Mn^{++}	HCl	Mn^{++}	→	Mn^{++}		MnS			
Fe^{+++}	→	Fe^{+++}	H_2S	Fe^{++}	NH_4Cl	FeS			
Al^{+++}		Al^{+++}		Al^{+++}	NH_3+H_2O	$Al(OH)_3$			
Cr^{+++}		Cr^{+++}		Cr^{+++}		$Cr(OH)_3$			
Zn^{++}		Zn^{++}		Zn^{++}	→	ZnS		$BaCO_3$	*Group IV Carbonates*
Ba^{++}		Ba^{++}		Ba^{++}	H_2S	Ba^{++}		$SrCO_3$	
Sr^{++}		Sr^{++}		Sr^{++}		Sr^{++}	NH_3+H_2O	$CaCO_3$	
Ca^{++}		Ca^{++}		Ca^{++}		Ca^{++}	NH_4Cl		
Mg^{++}		Mg^{++}		Mg^{++}		Mg^{++}	→	Mg^{++}	*Group IV Soluble Group*
NH_4^+		NH_4^+		NH_4^+		NH_4^+	$(NH_4)_2CO_3$	NH_4^+	
Na^+		Na^+		Na^+		Na^+		Na^+	
K^+		K^+		K^+		K^+		K^+	

33.2 Metals and Nonmetals

One of the first attempts by chemists to classify the elements was based upon the observation that the oxides of many of the elements react with water to form acids, whereas others react with water to form bases. For example, sulfur dioxide and carbon dioxide react with water to form sulfurous acid and carbonic acid, respectively; sulfur and carbon are nonmetals. Sodium oxide and calcium oxide react with water to form sodium hydroxide and calcium hydroxide, respectively; sodium and calcium are metals. Metals are good conductors of heat and electricity; they are usually opaque to light, and have metallic luster. These are properties of metals that are familiar to everyone. Few nonmetals have luster, and nearly all are poor conductors.

The difference in chemical properties between metals and nonmetals lies chiefly in the fact that atoms of nonmetals can readily fill their valence shells by sharing electrons with or transferring electrons from other atoms. Atoms of chlorine, a typical nonmetal, readily enter into chemical combination by adding one electron to an outer shell of seven — gaining an electron from another atom or by sharing an electron pair. On the other hand, an atom of sodium, a typical metal, enters into chemical combination only by the loss of its single valence electron. Metallic character decreases and nonmetallic character increases with increased number of valence electrons. Furthermore, metallic character increases with the number of electron shells. Thus the properties of succeeding elements change gradually in progressing across the periods of the Periodic Table (with increasing number of valence electrons from left to right), and down the groups (with increasing number of electron shells). This means that there is no sharp dividing line between metals and nonmetals, and most elements fall between the extremes. Elements which are definitely on the borderline and show hybrid behavior are sometimes referred to as **metalloids.** This class of elements includes boron, silicon, germanium, arsenic, antimony, tellurium, and astatine. Silicon, for example, has the physical properties characteristic of metals, but many of its chemical reactions are like those of the typical nonmetals. Of the 103 elements now known, only 17 show primarily nonmetallic character, 7 others are metalloids, and 79 may be classed as metals.

Some characteristic properties of the metals and nonmetals have been summarized in Table 33·2 on page 530, but it follows from the foregoing statements that there are many exceptions to these generalizations.

33.3 Occurrence of the Metals

The metals above hydrogen in the activity series (Table 6·1) are rarely found in the free state in nature. The less active metals, which are below hydrogen in the activity series, oftentimes occur in the free or **native state.** Among the latter are copper, silver, gold, and platinum. Some metals, such as copper and silver, are found both free and combined.

It is not surprising that the metallic compounds occurring in the earth's crust

TABLE 33·2 Comparison of Metals and Nonmetals

Metals	*Nonmetals*
Physical Properties	*Physical Properties*
1. Are good conductors of heat and electricity	1. Are poor conductors
2. Are malleable and ductile in solid state	2. Are brittle, nonductile in solid state
3. Show metallic luster	3. Show no metallic luster
4. Are opaque	4. May be transparent or translucent
5. Have high density	5. Have low density
6. Are solids (except mercury)	6. Are gases, liquids, or solids
7. Have crystal structure in which each atom is surrounded by eight to twelve near neighbors; metallic bonds between atoms	7. Form molecules which consist of atoms covalently bonded; the rare gases are monatomic
Chemical Properties	*Chemical Properties*
1. Have one to four electrons in outermost shell; usually not more than three	1. Usually have four to eight electrons in outermost shell
2. Have low ionization potential; readily form cations by losing electrons	2. Have high electron affinity; readily form anions by gaining electrons (except rare gases)
3. Are good reducing agents	3. Are good oxidizing agents (except rare gases)
4. Have hydroxides which are basic or amphoteric	4. Have hydroxides which are acidic
5. Are electropositive; oxidation states are positive	5. Are electronegative; oxidation states may be either positive or negative

are low in water solubility while the more soluble compounds are found in sea water, or in large salt beds which have been formed by the evaporation of inland seas. Water is such an excellent solvent that warm rains soaking into the earth dissolve a lot of salts, carrying them slowly to the nearest stream, then to the nearest river, and finally down to the sea. The ocean is continually becoming richer in salt and other minerals, although man has not been observing it long enough to notice any real change. It is interesting that the age of the ocean as calculated from its salt content is between 1 and 7 billion years. This is of the same order of magnitude as that (2.6 billion years) calculated for the age of the earth by methods involving radioactive minerals (Section 30.3).

The natural materials in which metals or their compounds occur in the earth and from which the metals may be extracted economically are known as **ores.** They usually contain large percentages of rocky material which is called **gangue.** The important classes of ores, based on the nonmetallic element or acid radical with which the metal is combined (if any), are listed below.

1. *Native ores:* Gold, silver, platinum, copper, mercury, arsenic, antimony, and bismuth.

2. *Oxide ores:* Iron, aluminum, manganese, and tin.

3. *Sulfide ores:* Zinc, cadmium, mercury, copper, lead, nickel, cobalt, silver, arsenic, and antimony.

4. *Carbonate ores:* Iron, lead, zinc, and copper. These are less important as sources of the metals than are the oxides or sulfides of the same metals. The carbonates of calcium, barium, strontium, and magnesium are important as sources for the preparation of various compounds of these metals.

5. *Halides:* The chlorides of sodium and potassium are important sources of these metals and their compounds. The halides of magnesium, calcium, and silver are also important.

6. *Sulfates:* Calcium, strontium, barium, and lead.

7. *Silicates:* Most silicates are unsuitable as ores because it is difficult to extract the metals from them. The silicates of beryllium, zinc, and nickel are important.

33.4 The Ocean as a Source of Minerals

The vast oceans that cover a large fraction of the earth's surface have been termed "the world's greatest mine." A ton of sea water contains about 55 lbs. of common salt, 2.54 lbs. of magnesium, 1.75 lbs. of sulfur, 0.8 lb. of calcium, 0.75 lb. of potassium, 0.125 lb. of bromine, and lesser quantities of such elements as strontium, boron, fluorine, iodine, iron, copper, lead, zinc, uranium, silver, gold, and even radium. The ocean contains 8.5 million tons of gold that would be worth over 7,000 billion dollars at $35.00 an ounce. Our mineral deposits in the earth's crust are being depleted at an ever increasingly rapid rate, so it is necessary to look to the oceans for future supplies of the metals which have become so essential to our modern way of life.

The first mineral to be "mined" from sea water was undoubtedly salt. If sea water is trapped at high tide, and the sun evaporates the water, "solar" salt with all the other solids that were in the water is obtained. This salt can be purified by fractional crystallization. Solar salt is still made in large quantities on our west coast. Many chemical industries use salt as their raw material, especially the alkali and chlorine industries. Scandinavian sea salt has served as a starting point for the manufacture of soda ash (sodium carbonate) for many years.

Processes are now in use by which magnesium (Section 39.20) and bromine (Section 17.3) are extracted from sea water. We may ask about the extraction of other elements such as gold, copper, silver, potassium (for fertilizer), and especially uranium, from sea water. It is too expensive to extract these elements from the sea with our present methods. Indirect methods may be the answer; for example, plants have the curious ability to remove certain materials from soil or water and to store them in their own tissues. The horsetail (*Equisetum*) removes silica and gold from the soil, the locoweed takes up barium, while certain seaweeds extract large amounts of potassium and iodine from sea water. When the weeds are burned, these elements are left in the ashes, from which they can be obtained.

The ocean is a potential source of uranium which may well be our chief energy fuel when our deposits of coal and petroleum are exhausted. The ocean contains three pounds of uranium to every hundred pounds of iodine, and iodine is easily extracted from certain seaweeds — in fact, iodine was first discovered in the ashes of seaweeds. Perhaps some marine plant will be found or developed which will extract uranium from sea water and make the metal available to us.

EXTRACTIVE METALLURGY

Extractive metallurgy pertains to the processes involved in the production of metals from their ores. Most such metallurgical processes include three principal steps: (1) preliminary treatment, (2) smelting, and (3) refining.

33.5 Preliminary Treatment

Most ores must be subjected to certain preliminary treatments to put them in a form suitable for chemical extraction of the metals. The first step is usually that of pulverizing the ore by crushing and grinding. This is followed by **concentration** of the metal-bearing portions by removing most of the gangue. Sometimes this is accomplished by washing away the lighter particles of gangue. Slightly inclined shaking tables are widely used to separate the heavier ore particles from the lighter rocky material (Fig. 33–1). Metal-bearing particles which are affected by

Fig. 33–1 Concentration tables in use with tin ore. These concentration tables separate the heavy tin ore from the lighter earthy material (gangue). They move back and forth somewhat as a miner operates his pan in separating gold from river sand. *Pan American Union*

a magnetic field are often separated from nonmagnetic impurities by passing the finely ground ore through a magnetic field (Fig. 33–2). Certain ores are affected by an electrostatic field, and in such cases electrostatic separation may be employed. The "flotation" process is a concentration method particularly applicable to sulfide ores of lead, zinc, and copper, but is used also for carbonates and silicates. In this process, the pulverized ore is mixed with water to which a carefully selected oil has been added. A froth is produced by blowing air into the mixture. The hydrophobic metal-bearing particles are preferentially coated by the oil and adhere to the air bubbles in the froth which floats on the surface (see Sections 13.4 and 13.6). The hydrophilic particles of gangue (sand, rock, clay, etc.) are wetted by water more readily than by the oil and sink to the bottom of the flotation vat. The

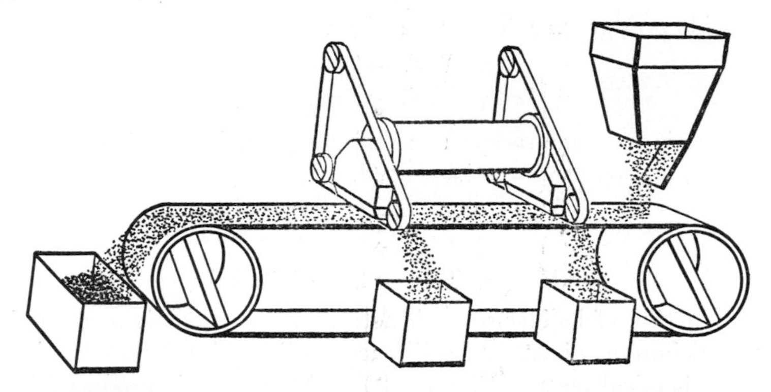

Fig. 33–2 Diagram of a machine for the magnetic separation of ores.

froth containing the metal-bearing particles is removed and the ore is recovered in a highly concentrated form.

The preliminary treatment of ores often includes chemical changes by which the metallic compounds are converted into substances that may be more readily reduced to give the metals. Ores containing moisture or water chemically combined in hydrates or hydroxides, or ores containing metallic carbonates, are heated to expel water and other volatile matter and to decompose the carbonates. This treatment is known as **calcination.** The following equations illustrate typical changes which may occur during calcination.

$$2\ M(OH)_3 \rightarrow M_2O_3 + 3\ H_2O \quad (M = \text{metal})$$
$$MCO_3 \rightarrow MO + CO_2$$

Most sulfide ores are heated in air to change the sulfides to oxides, and to expel sulfur as sulfur dioxide. This treatment is known as **roasting.** The following equation illustrates the reaction.

$$2\ MS + 3\ O_2 \rightarrow 2\ MO + 2\ SO_2$$

33.6 Smelting

The next step in the metallurgical process involves the extraction of the metal in the fused state, a process called **smelting.** The chemical reaction involved in smelting is one of reduction of the metallic compound. Most ores still contain some gangue at this stage of the process; removal of this material is accomplished by the addition of a **flux** (from the Latin "fluo," meaning flow). This is a chemical which will react with the gangue to form a substance of low melting point — a **slag.** When the gangue is silica or a silicate, a basic flux such as lime or limestone is used. At the high temperature of the furnace in which the reduction is carried out, the lime reacts with the silica to produce fused calcium silicate. The molten slag is easily separated from the fused metal because of the difference in their densities and because they are insoluble in each other.

The methods commonly employed in the smelting of various ores are illustrated by the equations on the following page.

(1) The oxide ores are usually reduced by carbon.

$$ZnO + C \rightarrow Zn + CO$$
$$SnO_2 + 2\ C \rightarrow Sn + 2\ CO$$

When carbon is for some reason unsatisfactory, such reducing agents as aluminum, hydrogen, or iron are sometimes used.

$$Cr_2O_3 + 2\ Al \rightarrow 2\ Cr + Al_2O_3$$
$$WO_3 + 3\ H_2 \rightarrow W + 3\ H_2O$$
$$Sb_2S_3 + 3\ Fe \rightarrow 2\ Sb + 3\ FeS$$

(2) The reduction of halides of such active metals as sodium, potassium, magnesium, and calcium may be more readily accomplished by electrochemical methods than by pure chemical means (Chapter 20). Aluminum is produced by the electrolysis of aluminum oxide dissolved in fused cryolite, Na_3AlF_6.

(3) Metals which occur in the native state are smelted by heating the ore until the metals are melted. The fused metals are then drained away from the gangue.

33.7 Refining of Metals

Smelting usually results in the production of metals which contain greater or lesser amounts of impurities such as other metals (or nonmetals), slag, and dissolved gases. The removal of impurities is usually necessary in the preparation of a metal for at least some of its uses. The low boiling metals, such as zinc and mercury, may be purified from less volatile impurities by distillation. Other low melting metals, such as tin, when fused on an inclined table, may flow away from higher melting impurities. Electrolysis is the most widely used method of refining. Electrolytic refining is accomplished by making the impure metal the anode and the pure metal the cathode of an electrolytic cell (see Section 20.7). Among the metals which are purified by this process are copper, gold, lead, zinc, and aluminum.

A process known as **zone refining** provides the ultrahigh-purity materials essential to semiconductor and transistor devices such as described earlier for the solar battery (Section 20.17). When a molten section (or zone) of a solid bar of metal is made to progress longitudinally through the bar, the zone carries certain impurities with it. The procedure can be repeated with increasing purification each time. The process depends upon the lowering of the melting point of a substance as a result of impurities present. It is applicable to a wide range of substances and impurities.

33.8 Hydrometallurgy

Certain metals may be extracted from their ores by causing the metal to go into aqueous solution as the result of chemical changes, and then precipitating the metal in the free state by means of a suitable reducing agent. The following equations illustrate the method.

$$4\ Ag + 8\ CN^- + O_2 + 2\ H_2O \rightarrow 4\ Ag(CN)_2^- + 4\ OH^-$$

or

$$AgCl + 2\ CN^- \rightarrow Ag(CN)_2^- + Cl^-$$
$$2\ Ag(CN)_2^- + Zn \rightarrow 2\ \underline{Ag} + Zn(CN)_4^{=}$$

33.9 Chemical Bonding in Metals

We have noted that the atoms of the nonmetals have a sufficient number of valence electrons to combine with each other by sharing electron pairs. For example, two chlorine atoms share an electron pair in the Cl_2 molecule, two nitrogen atoms share three electron pairs in the N_2 molecule, and each carbon atom in the diamond crystal shares electron pairs with each of four neighboring carbon atoms. However, most of the metal atoms have less than four valence electrons (many only one or two), and each atom is surrounded by eight or twelve "closest neighbors" in the crystal. With only one valence electron, it would be impossible for an atom of sodium to be linked by electron-pair bonds to eight neighboring atoms. The evidence now available indicates that in solid or liquid metals the valence electrons are free to pass from one atom to another in such a way that they may be shared among several atoms. These shared electrons serve to hold the atoms together and constitute what is known as a "metallic" bond, which may be looked upon as a modified covalent bond in which more or less mobile electrons are shared by more than two atoms. Such characteristic properties of metals as high electrical and thermal conductivity, luster, and high reflectivity are thought to be due to these relatively free, mobile valence electrons. These considerations are in accord with the fact that metallic character exists only when the material is in the massive solid or liquid state. Gaseous mercury, zinc, and sodium do not have metallic luster and the other characteristic metallic properties; their gaseous molecules are monatomic and metallic bonding is, of course, absent.

33.10 Classification of the Metals

It is convenient to classify the metals in terms of electronic structure as **representative** and **transition metals** (see Section 3.14). The representative metals have all their valence electrons in one shell, whereas the transition metals have valence electrons in more than one shell. Those representative metals with one or two valence electrons use them in bond formation and usually exhibit only one oxidation state: e.g., sodium, +1; calcium, +2; and magnesium, +2. Most of the representative metals that have three or more valence electrons have two oxidation states: e.g., lead, +2 and +4; tin, +2 and +4; and bismuth, +3 and +5.

The transition metals include the elements of subgroups IIIB through IB in each of the long periods of the Periodic Table. The first series of transition metals includes Sc, Ti, V, Cr, Mn, Fe, Co, Ni, and Cu. Because of the carry-over in properties, elements in subgroup IIB (Zn, Cd, and Hg) have many characteristics analogous to those of the transition elements, and for this reason they are often classed with the latter elements. However, in terms of our definition of transition and representative metals, the metals of subgroup IIB are classified as representative metals. The electron distribution and common oxidation states of the transition metals of the fourth period of the Periodic Table are given in Table 33·3.

The transition metals are noted for their variability in oxidation state; this is attributed to the presence of valence electrons in more than one shell. Thus,

TABLE 33·3 The Transition Metals of the Fourth Period

Atomic Number	*Metal*	*Electronic Structure*	*Some Oxidation States*
21	Scandium	$1s^2\ 2s^2\ 2p^6\ 3s^2\ 3p^6\ 3d^1\ 4s^2$	+3
22	Titanium	$3d^2\ 4s^2$	+2, +3, +4
23	Vanadium	$3d^3\ 4s^2$	+2, +3, +4, +5
24	Chromium	$3d^5\ 4s^1$	+2, +3, +6
25	Manganese	$3d^5\ 4s^2$	+1, +2, +3, +4, +6, +7
26	Iron	$3d^6\ 4s^2$	+2, +3, +6
27	Cobalt	$3d^7\ 4s^2$	+2, +3, +4
28	Nickel	$3d^8\ 4s^2$	+2, +3, +4
29	Copper	$3d^{10}\ 4s^1$	+1, +2, +3

manganese has two electrons in its outside shell and five electrons in the next underlying $3d$ subshell and exhibits oxidation states of +1, +2, +3, +4, +6, and +7. An atom of iron may lose the two electrons in its outermost shell and form an iron (II) ion, Fe^{++}, or it may lose also an electron from its underlying $3d$ subshell and form an iron (III) ion, Fe^{+++}. By sharing electrons with oxygen in K_2FeO_4, iron exhibits an oxidation state of +6.

The transition metals are further characterized by the fact that as we get well into the series and go from left to right across the Periodic Table, the properties of succeeding metals do not differ greatly (Table 33·4). This is attributed to the fact that, generally speaking, succeeding elements differ in electronic structure by one electron in the next to the outer valence shell rather than the outer valence shell (with two exceptions).

TABLE 33·4

Property	*Sc*	*Ti*	*V*	*Cr*	*Mn*	*Fe*	*Co*	*Ni*	*Cu*
Atomic number	21	22	23	24	25	26	27	28	29
Density g./cm.^{3}	2.5	4.5	5.96	7.19	7.21	7.87	8.90	8.90	8.91
Melting point, °C	1200	1725	1710	1890	1260	1535	1490	1452	1083
Atomic radius, Å	1.51	1.45	1.31	1.25	1.29	1.26	1.25	1.24	1.28
Ionization potential, electron volts	6.56	6.83	6.74	6.76	7.432	7.896	7.86	7.633	7.723

TABLE 33·5

Property	*Na*	*Mg*	*Al*
Atomic number	11	12	13
Density, g./cm.^{3}	0.97	1.74	2.71
Melting point, °C	97.6	651	658.7
Atomic radius, Å	1.86	1.60	1.48
Ionization potential, electron volts	5.138	7.644	5.984

In contrast to the properties of the transition metals, those of succeeding representative ones in a period differ extensively (Table 33·5). The electronic structures of succeeding elements in this series differ by one electron in the outer shell.

The transition metal ions containing incomplete underlying electron shells are usually colored, both in solid salts and in solution. The color exhibited depends upon the oxidation state of the metal as indicated by the following examples: Cr^{++} (blue), Cr^{+++} (violet); Mn^{++} (pink), Mn^{+++} (violet); and Fe^{++} (green), Fe^{+++} (yellow). The color is also modified by the nature of the nonmetallic element or acid radical with which the metal is combined. For example, CuO is black; $Cu(OH)_2$, pale blue; $CuCl_2$, yellow; $CuBr_2$, black; CuS, black; $CuSO_4$, white; and $CuSO_4 \cdot 5\,H_2O$, blue. When the underlying electron shell is filled, as in the case of Cu^+ and Zn^{++}, the substance containing the ion is usually colorless. This is also usually true of compounds containing the representative metals, i.e., those with valence electrons only in the outer shells.

33.11 The Transition Metals and Magnetism

Most of the transition metals and their compounds in oxidation states involving incomplete inner electron subshells are **paramagnetic**; i.e., they are substances that tend to move into a strong magnetic field, such as that between the poles of a magnet.

Paramagnetism is characteristic of systems containing one or more unpaired electrons. An electron in an atom spins about its own axis. Because the electron is electrically charged, the spin about its axis gives it the properties of a small magnet, with north and south poles. The two electrons of a pair spin in opposite directions. This means that their magnetic moments will cancel each other because their north and south poles are opposed. On the other hand, when an electron in an atom is unpaired, the magnetic moment due to its spin confers paramagnetism upon the entire atom or ion, and in turn upon the specimen containing such atoms or ions.

The magnetic moment of a system containing unpaired electrons is related directly to the number of unpaired electrons, i.e., the greater the number of such electrons, the larger the magnetic moment. The observed magnetic moment is used to indicate the number of unpaired electrons present.

The unpaired electrons in the transition metal atoms or ions are located in the *d* or *f* subshells. When a subshell is being filled by the stepwise addition of single electrons, the added electrons enter only unoccupied orbitals before any pairing occurs. This is illustrated in Table 33·6 for the 3*d* subshell of the transition metal atoms of the fourth period. The magnetic moment of the metal ions of this series

TABLE 33·6

Element	*Order of Filling of 3d Subshell*					
Scandium	$3d^1$	$3d$	$3d$	$3d$	$3d$	$4s^2$
Titanium	$3d^1$	$3d^1$	$3d$	$3d$	$3d$	$4s^2$
Vanadium	$3d^1$	$3d^1$	$3d^1$	$3d$	$3d$	$4s^2$
Chromium	$3d^1$	$3d^1$	$3d^1$	$3d^1$	$3d^1$	$4s^1$
Manganese	$3d^1$	$3d^1$	$3d^1$	$3d^1$	$3d^1$	$4s^2$
Iron	$3d^2$	$3d^1$	$3d^1$	$3d^1$	$3d^1$	$4s^2$
Cobalt	$3d^2$	$3d^2$	$3d^1$	$3d^1$	$3d^1$	$4s^2$
Nickel	$3d^2$	$3d^2$	$3d^2$	$3d^1$	$3d^1$	$4s^2$
Copper	$3d^2$	$3d^2$	$3d^2$	$3d^2$	$3d^2$	$4s^1$

reaches a maximum with Mn^{+2} and Fe^{+3}, both of which have the *d* subshell configuration $3d^1\ 3d^1\ 3d^1\ 3d^1\ 3d^1$; i.e., they have the greatest number of unpaired electrons. Note that both manganese and iron lose their two 4*s* electrons and iron one 3*d* electron in forming the Mn^{++} and Fe^{+3}, respectively.

Ferromagnetism is an extreme form of paramagnetism, or at least closely related to it; and ferromagnetic substances may become permanently magnetized whereas paramagnetism is shown only in the presence of an applied magnetic field. Only iron, cobalt, nickel, and gadolinium (a rare earth element) exhibit ferromagnetism. In order for an element to be ferromagnetic, (1) it must have an incompletely filled *d* or *f* subshell, (2) the atoms must not be too close together in the crystal lattice, or the singly occupied orbitals of neighboring atoms overlap and the electrons become paired with those with opposed spins, and (3) the atoms must not be too far apart in the crystal, or the unpaired electrons of one atom cannot align the electron spins in the neighboring atoms.

The dependence of ferromagnetism upon a critical interatomic distance is well illustrated by the fact that some compounds of manganese (five unpaired 3*d* electrons) are ferromagnetic while the metal itself is not. The reason for this is that the atoms are close enough together in the metal to cause sharing (pairing up) of the unpaired 3*d* electrons between neighboring atoms. In a compound such as manganese nitride, the manganese atoms have been pushed apart somewhat by the nitrogen atoms, making the sharing of 3*d* electrons between atoms impossible.

The same explanation may account for the ferromagnetism of the **Heusler alloys,** which consist of Cu, Al, and Mn in proportions approximating the atomic composition Cu_2AlMn.

33.12 Compounds of the Metals

The metals which have relatively large atomic radii and only one or two valence electrons show a marked tendency to react with the typical nonmetals by electron transfer, with the formation of ionic compounds. For example, NaCl, KBr, CaF_2, MgO, and BaS are ionic compounds. However, those metals with relatively small atomic radii and having three or more valence electrons tend to share electrons with other atoms and form covalent molecules. For example, anhydrous aluminum chloride, anhydrous tin (IV) chloride, and titanium tetrachloride are covalent compounds.

The most metallic metals are distinguished from the nonmetals in the basic nature of their hydroxyl compounds (see Section 15.1, part 7). The hydroxides of the highly electropositive metals such as sodium and potassium are ionic in the solid state and yield hydroxide ions in solution. The bonding in the less soluble metal hydroxides such as magnesium hydroxide and calcium hydroxide is largely ionic and they are fairly strong bases. The hydroxides of metals such as aluminum, iron, and tin are largely covalent; they are sparingly soluble in water and extremely weak as hydroxide bases.

The hydroxides of some metals such as zinc, tin, and aluminum are **amphoteric;** i.e., they can act as either acids or bases and hence are soluble in either strongly basic or strongly acidic solutions.

$$Al(H_2O)_3(OH)_3 + OH^- \rightleftharpoons [Al(H_2O)_2(OH)_4]^- + H_2O$$
$$Al(H_2O)_3(OH)_3 + H_3O^+ \rightleftharpoons [Al(H_2O)_4(OH)_2]^+ + H_2O$$

The hydroxyl compounds of metals which have several oxidation states, such as manganese, become less basic and more acidic as the oxidation state is increased (see Table 33·7).

It should be noted that manganese is typically metallic in the +2 oxidation state as indicated by the basic character of $Mn(OH)_2$. In permanganic acid,

TABLE 33·7

Hydroxide	*Oxidation State*	*Character*
$Mn(OH)_2$	Mn (II)	Moderately basic
$Mn(OH)_3$	Mn (III)	Weakly basic
H_2MnO_3, $(HO)_2MnO$	Mn (IV)	Weakly acidic
H_2MnO_4, $(HO)_2MnO_2$	Mn (VI)	Definitely acidic
$HMnO_4$, $(HO)MnO_3$	Mn (VII)	Strongly acidic

$HMnO_4$, manganese has an oxidation state of +7 and behaves as a nonmetal; it is similar to chlorine in perchloric acid, $HClO_4$.

An important difference between the metals and the nonmetals is demonstrated in the extent and reversibility of the hydrolysis of their chlorides. The chlorides of the more nonmetallic elements usually hydrolyze extensively — in many cases, irreversibly. The chlorides of very active metals (Na, K) are not hydrolyzed appreciably at ordinary temperatures.

$$PCl_3 + 3\ H_2O \rightarrow H_3PO_3 + 3\ HCl \quad \text{(irreversible)}$$
$$AlCl_3 + 3\ H_2O \rightleftharpoons Al(OH)_3 + 3\ HCl \quad \text{(reversible)}$$

Mercury and the metals preceding it in the activity series (Section 6.9) react directly with oxygen. The metal hydroxides, except those of the alkali and alkaline earth metals, yield oxides upon heating. The heating of metallic carbonates and nitrates, except those of the alkali metals, produces oxides. Most of the metals react with the halogens and sulfur to form halides and sulfides, respectively. Sodium and the metals above it in the activity series displace hydrogen from cold water while the metals above hydrogen liberate hydrogen from acids and form salts. The metals below hydrogen in the series ordinarily will not liberate hydrogen from acids, but most of them react with oxidizing acids forming salts or oxides. Salts of metals may also be produced by the reaction of oxides, hydroxides, carbonates, or other salts with acids or other salts (see Chapter 21).

33.13 Alloys

An **alloy** is usually composed of two or more metals, or it may be made up of a metallic element and one of the less nonmetallic elements such as carbon, silicon, nitrogen, or phosphorus. Such systems are considered alloys only when they have metallic properties.

Alloys are usually prepared by fusing metals together and allowing the melt to cool, but they are sometimes produced by simultaneous electrodeposition of two or more metals at a cathode. For example, many iron hardware fittings such as doorknobs are plated with brass (Cu 60–80 per cent, Zn 40–20 per cent) by electrodeposition from a bath containing copper and zinc in the form of soluble cyanide complexes. In general, alloys are solids, but they may be liquids, as in the case of certain amalgams, i.e., alloys of mercury. The study of alloys by X-ray methods has shown that they may be grouped into three classes based upon their structures.

1. *Simple mixtures*, in which the component metals are mutually insoluble and the solid alloy is composed of an intimate mixture of crystals of each metal. For example, tin and lead (in plumber's solder) are insoluble in each other in the solid state.

2. *Solid solutions*, in which the atoms of one of the component metals take up positions in the crystal lattice of the other. The solute atoms may replace some of the atoms at the lattice points of the solvent crystal to form **substitutional solid solutions.** For example, chromium dissolves in nickel to form a solid solution in which the chromium atoms replace nickel atoms in the face-centered cubic nickel lattice. The very small atoms of the elements H, C, B, and N may occupy

the holes in the lattice of a metal, forming **interstitial solid solutions.** The solid solution of carbon in gamma-iron (austenite) is an example of this type; the iron atoms are on the face-centered cubic lattice points, and the carbon atoms occupy the interstitial positions.

3. *Intermetallic compounds*, in which atoms of the components of the alloy appear in atomic ratios: Cu_5Zn_8, Ag_3Al, and $AuMg_3$. In general, the formulas of such intermetallic compounds are not those which might be predicted on the basis of valence rules. Instead, the ratio of the total number of electrons in the outer shells to the total number of atoms appears to be important in determining the composition and structure of these intermetallic compounds.

33.14 Properties of Alloys

Alloys which are solid solutions are always harder than the pure solvent metal and are apt to be less ductile; for example, brass, which is a solution of zinc in copper, is much harder than pure copper. As one metal is dissolved in another, the electrical conductivity of the solvent metal is usually lowered very sharply. Thus copper must be quite free of impurities if it is to be used for transmission of electricity. The thermal conductivity of a solid solution is less than that of the solvent metal. The melting point of a metal is usually lowered when another metal is dissolved in it. The practical application of a great many alloys depends upon their low melting or freezing points. For example, fuse metal, type metal, solder,

TABLE 33·8 Composition of Some Common Alloys

Trade Name	*Composition, Per Cent by Weight*
White cast iron	97 Fe, 3 C
Stainless steel	82.5 Fe, 16.5 Cr, 0.65 C, 0.35 Mn
Nickel coin, U.S.A.	75 Cu, 25 Ni
Bronze	70–95 Cu, 1–25 Zn, 1–18 Sn
Type metal	70 Pb, 18 Sb, 10 Sn, 2 Cu
Wood's metal	50 Bi, 12.5 Cd, 25 Pb, 12.5 Sn
Plumber's solder	67 Pb, 33 Sn
Battery plate	94 Pb, 6 Sb
Dentist amalgam	70 Hg, 30 Cu
Sterling silver	92.5 Ag, 7.5 Cu
Silver coin, U.S.A.	90 Ag, 10 Cu
Gold coin, U.S.A.	90 Au, 10 Cu
18 carat yellow gold	75 Au, 12.5 Ag, 12.5 Cu
18 carat white gold	75 Au, 3.5 Cu, 16.5 Ni, 5 Zn
14 carat gold	58 Au, 4–28 Ag, 14–28 Cu
Yellow brass	67 Cu, 33 Zn
Red brass	90 Cu, 10 Zn

and the alloys for sprinkler heads are low melting alloy systems. Alloys of iron, cobalt, and nickel with each other are strongly magnetic (ferromagnetic). The effect of solid solution upon color is impossible to predict. Copper turns gray with the addition of 23 per cent of nickel or 50 per cent of zinc. Certain gold-iron solid solutions are blue; copper-antimony is green; and gold-silver-cadmium is green. The compositions of some common alloys are given in Table 33·8.

QUESTIONS

1. What physical properties distinguish metallic elements from nonmetallic elements?
2. Compare metals with nonmetals with regard to (a) number of valence electrons, (b) ionization potential, (c) electron affinity, (d) electronegativity, and (e) acidic or basic nature of hydroxides.
3. Is the distinction between metals and nonmetals well defined? Explain.
4. Explain the concentration of sulfide ores by flotation.
5. What is accomplished by roasting an ore before smelting?
6. In what ways are the metallic and covalent bonds similar and how do they differ?
7. Which metals are more likely to form ionic compounds and which ones are apt to form covalent compounds?
8. Contrast the hydrolysis of the chlorides of metals and nonmetals.
9. Account for the fact that most compounds of the transition metals are colored.
10. What is the basis for the classification of metals as representative and transition?
11. How does the basicity of the hydroxyl compounds of manganese vary with the oxidation state of the metal? Why is this so?
12. Compare the thermal stability of the hydroxides of the alkali and alkaline earth metals with that of the other metal hydroxides.
13. How may alloys be produced? What are alloys containing mercury called?
14. Contrast the structures of substitutional and interstitial solid solutions.

REFERENCES

"Magnetic Materials," R. M. Bozorth, *Sci. American*, Jan., 1955; p. 68.

"The World's Greatest Mine," S. J. Lloyd, *J. Chem. Educ.*, **24** (6) 273 (June, 1947).

"Nature of the Metallic State," W. C. Fernelius and R. F. Robey, *J. Chem. Educ.*, **12** (2) 53 (Feb., 1935).

"Modern Views on Alloys," W. Hume-Rothery, *J. Inst. Metals*, **70** (6) 229 (1944).

"Pure Metals," L. P. Lessing, *Sci. American*, July, 1954; p. 36.

"The Origin of Ores," H. G. Bachmann, *Sci. American*, June, 1960; p. 146.

"A Short History of Oceanography with Emphasis on the Role Played by Chemistry," T. G. Thompson, *J. Chem. Educ.*, **35** (3) 108 (1958).

"Minerals on the Ocean Floor," J. L. Mero, *Sci. American*, Dec., 1960; p. 64.

"New Solid-State-Chemistry Methods Yield Ultrapure Materials," (Zone Refining), R. E. Johnson, *Chem. Eng.*, Jan. 23, 1961; p. 147.

CHAPTER THIRTY-FOUR

Coordination Compounds

In other chapters of this text, a considerable number of examples of compounds and ions is given in which negative groups or neutral polar molecules are attached to metal ions or atoms. This type of compound, which is known as a **coordination** or **complex compound,** has many important applications in such areas as soil treatment, corrosion control, electroplating of metals, and water softening. Typical examples of such compounds or ions are $[Ag(NH_3)_2]^+$, $[Cu(NH_3)_4]^{++}$, $[Fe(CN)_6]^{-4}$, $[Fe(CN)_6]^{\equiv}$, $[Co(NH_3)_6]^{+++}$, $[Co(NH_3)_3(NO_2)_3]$, $[Pt(NH_3)_2Cl_4]$, and $[Fe(CO)_5]$.

Formation of a complex ion requires the combination of an ion or molecule, which has at least one pair of electrons available for bonding, with a metal ion or atom which has a sufficient attraction for electrons to form a coordinate covalent bond with the attaching group. As would be expected, metallic ions or atoms with small size and high nuclear charge attract electrons most readily and form the most stable complex ions. Ions of the transition metals, inner transition metals, and a few metals near these series in the Periodic Table are especially prone to react in this way.

34.1 Definitions of Terms

It is important to understand the meaning of several terms which are commonly used in discussing coordination compounds.

The **coordination number** is the number of electron pairs which an acceptor metal ion attracts in forming a complex ion. The coordination number for the silver ion in $[Ag(NH_3)_2]^+$ is *two;* that for the copper ion in $[Cu(NH_3)_4]^{++}$ is *four;* and that for the iron (III) ion in $[Fe(CN)_6]^{\equiv}$ is *six.* In each of these examples, the coordination number is also equal to the number of coordinating groups attached to the metal ion, but such is not always the case. Some groups such as ethylenediamine,

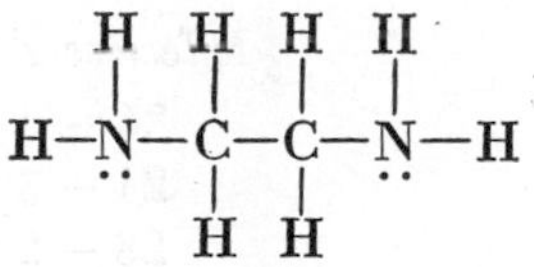

```
   H  H  H  H
   |  |  |  |
 H—N—C—C—N—H
   ••  |  |  ••
      H  H
```

furnish two pairs of electrons per molecule. Thus, the coordination number for $[Co(H_2NCH_2CH_2NH_2)_3]^{+++}$ is *six.* Although only three coordinating molecules are attached to the metal ion, *six electron pairs* are utilized in the bonding of the three groups to the metal ion. The most common coordination numbers are 2, 4, and 6, but in some complex ions coordination numbers of 3, 5, 7, or 8 occur. The coordination number is sometimes twice the oxidation state of the acceptor metal, but it is important to realize that this is not always the case. For example, $[Fe(CN)_6]^{-4}$ has a coordination number of six, whereas the oxidation state of iron in the complex is +2.

The groups attached to the central metal ion are referred to as **coordinating groups** or **ligands.** These may be either ions or neutral molecules. Within the coordinating group, the atom which is attached directly to the metal is called the **donor atom.**

The **coordination sphere,** which is usually enclosed in brackets in the formula, represents the central metal ion plus the coordinating groups (ligands) attached to it.

When one molecule of a ligand attaches itself, by the use of two or more electron pairs, to more than one coordination position of the central metal ion, it is referred to as a **chelating group.** The resulting complex is referred to as a metal chelate; an example is $[Co(H_2NCH_2CH_2NH_2)_3]^{+++}$.

The **effective atomic number** is the total number of electrons in the orbitals of the central metal ion of the complex after coordination takes place. It is interesting to note that the total electronic configuration of the central ion in many complexes corresponds to that of a rare gas, a fact which may be related to the great stability of such complexes. For example, in the $[Co(NH_3)_6]^{+++}$, the cobalt (III) ion, which has 24 electrons (27 − 3), obtains 12 additional electrons (two from each $:NH_3$) to make a total of 36 electrons in the atomic orbitals of the cobalt. Thus, **36** is the "effective atomic number" for the $[Co(NH_3)_6]^{+++}$ ion and is equal to the number of electrons possessed by the rare gas, krypton. Other examples are as follows:

Complex Ion	*Effective Atomic Number*	*Rare Gas Structure*
$[Fe(CN)_6]^{-4}$	$26 - 2 + 12 = 36$	Krypton
$[Cd(NH_3)_4]^{++}$	$48 - 2 + 8 = 54$	Xenon
$[PtCl_6]^{=}$	$78 - 4 + 12 = 86$	Radon

It should be emphasized, however, that an effective atomic number equal to the atomic number of a rare gas is not required for stability, as is shown by the following examples:

Complex Ion	*Effective Atomic Number*
$[Fe(CN)_6]^{=}$	$26 - 3 + 12 = 35$
$[Cr(NH_3)_6]^{+++}$	$24 - 3 + 12 = 33$
$[Ni(NH_3)_6]^{++}$	$28 - 2 + 12 = 38$

The manner in which the pairs of electrons from the ligands enter the electron orbitals of the metal ion will be discussed later in this chapter.

34.2 The Naming of Complex Compounds

The nomenclature of coordination compounds is patterned after a system originally suggested by Alfred Werner, a Swiss chemist, who in the latter part of the nineteenth century and early part of the twentieth century did much outstanding work which laid the foundation for a clearer understanding of complex ions and coordination compounds. The following rules of nomenclature will be useful.

1. The cation is named first and then the anion, in accord with usual nomenclature rules.

2. In naming the coordination sphere, whether it be a cation, an anion, or a neutral molecule, the ligands are named first and then the central metal.

3. The order of indicating the ligands within the coordination sphere is to name the negative ligands first, neutral ligands next, and positive ligands last. The prefixes, *di–*, *tri–*, *tetra–*, etc., (or sometimes *bis–*, *tris–*, *tetrakis–*, etc., for certain larger ligands) are used with the name of the ligand when more than one ligand of a particular kind occurs within the coordination sphere. The names used for some common ligands are: fluoro (F^-), chloro (Cl^-), bromo (Br^-), iodo (I^-), cyano (CN^-), nitro (NO_2^-), nitrito (ONO^-), nitrato (NO_3^-), hydroxo (OH^-), oxo ($O^=$), amido (NH_2^-), oxalato ($C_2O_4^=$), carbonato ($CO_3^=$), ammine (NH_3), and aquo (H_2O).

4. When the coordination sphere is either a cation or a neutral molecule, the name of the central metal remains intact, followed by a Roman numeral designation in parentheses to indicate the oxidation state of the metal. When the coordination sphere is an anion, the ending *–ate* is added to the stem for the name of the central metal (or sometimes to the stem of the Latin name for the metal), followed by the Roman numeral designation of the oxidation state of the metal.

Examples in which the coordination sphere is a cation:

$[Co(NH_3)_6]Cl_3$	Hexaamminecobalt (III) chloride
$[Pt(NH_3)_4Cl_2]^{++}$	Dichlorotetraammineplatinum (IV) ion
$[Ag(NH_3)_2]^+$	Diamminesilver (I) ion
$[Cr(H_2O)_4Cl_2]Cl$	Dichlorotetraaquochromium (III) chloride
$[Co(H_2NCH_2CH_2NH_2)_3]_2(SO_4)_3$	Tris(ethylenediamine)cobalt (III) sulfate

Examples in which the coordination sphere is neutral:

$[Pt(NH_3)_2Cl_4]$	Tetrachlorodiammineplatinum (IV)
$[Co(NH_3)_3(NO_2)_3]$	Trinitrotriamminecobalt (III)

Examples in which the coordination sphere is an anion:

$K_3[Co(NO_2)_6]$	Potassium hexanitrocobaltate (III)
$[PtCl_6]^=$	Hexachloroplatinate (IV) ion
$Na_2[SnCl_6]$	Sodium hexachlorostannate (IV)

34.3 The Structural Chemistry of Complexes

In 1893, Alfred Werner presented a concept of coordination compounds which laid the foundation for the further study of these substances. He proposed, as one part of his theory, that when ions or polar molecules are coordinated to a metal ion, they arrange themselves in a definite geometrical pattern about the central metal ion. In this way, he was able to account for the properties of hydrates, ammonates, and various double salts of the types $CoCl_2 \cdot 6H_2O$, $CoCl_3 \cdot 6NH_3$, and $SnCl_4 \cdot 2NaCl$, respectively. Werner assigned the formulas $[Co(H_2O)_6]Cl_2$, $[Co(NH_3)_6]Cl_3$, and $Na_2[SnCl_6]$ to these compounds and pointed out that the properties of the complexes $[Co(H_2O)_6]^{++}$, $[Co(NH_3)_6]^{+++}$, and $[SnCl_6]^{=}$ could be explained by postulating that the six coordinated groups are arranged about the central ion at the corners of a regular octahedron (Fig. 34–1). In such an octahedral

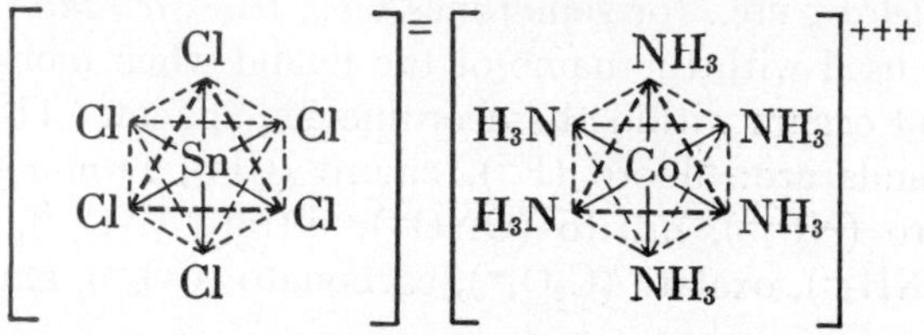

Fig. 34–1 Octahedral structures of the $[SnCl_6]^{=}$ and the $[Co(NH_3)_6]^{+++}$.

structure, the six pairs of electrons from the six coordinated groups may be considered as entering the orbitals of the metal ion. An isolated cobalt atom in its normal state has the electron configuration $1s^2\,2s^2\,2p^6\,3s^2\,3p^6\,3d^7\,4s^2$ (see Section 3.17). Each atomic orbital (Section 3.16) can accommodate two electrons of opposing spin. The electrons enter each orbital of a given type singly before any pairing of electrons occurs within those orbitals — a rule known as **Hund's Rule.** The orbitals for the cobalt atom, each orbital represented by a circle, can be diagrammed as follows.

Co atom:

1s	2s	2p	3s	3p	3d	4s
(··)	(··)	(··)(··)(··)	(··)	(··)(··)(··)	(··)(··)(·)(·)(·)	(··)

Measurements of magnetic moment indicate three unpaired electrons, in accord with the above diagram.

When the cobalt (III) ion, Co^{+++}, is formed, three electrons are lost, resulting in a structure possessing four unpaired electrons.

Co^{+++}:

1s	2s	2p	3s	3p	3d	4s
(··)	(··)	(··)(··)(··)	(··)	(··)(··)(··)	(··)(·)(·)(·)(·)	( )

When six ammonia molecules bond to the cobalt (III) ion, six pairs of electrons are available for sharing with the cobalt. The postulation is usually made that the electrons which are already present in the 3*d* orbitals of the metal (indicated above and below by dots) pair up to allow the incoming electrons from the ammonia (indicated below by small crosses) to remain paired. It should be noted, however, that once the structure is formed, it is impossible to distinguish the source of the electrons, inasmuch as all electrons are identical regardless of their origin. The six bonds to the central ion arise from the hybridization of two *d*, one *s*, and three *p* orbitals; this is spoken of as d^2sp^3 hybridization. In the notation, the superscripts refer to the number of orbitals of each type involved in the bonding.

$[Co(NH_3)_6]^{+++}$ (no unpaired electrons):

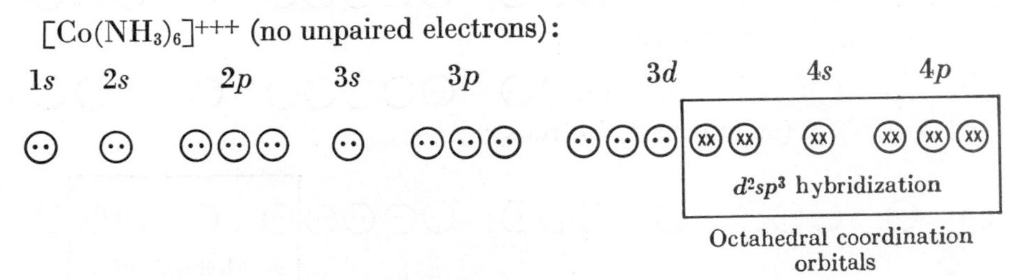

All 6-coordinate complexes, such as $[Co(NH_3)_6]^{+++}$, $[SnCl_6]^{=}$, $[Co(H_2O)_6]^{++}$, $[Co(CN)_6]^{\equiv}$, $[Fe(CN)_6]^{-4}$, and $[Fe(CN)_6]^{\equiv}$, show d^2sp^3 hybridization of bonding orbitals (or sometimes sp^3d^2 hybridization as discussed in a later chapter in connection with $[Zn(NH_3)_6]^{++}$) and have the octahedral configuration.

The 6-coordinate complexes of cobalt (II) contain one more electron than those of cobalt (III). To permit d^2sp^3 bonding, this extra electron must be promoted to a 4*d* orbital (or perhaps 5*s*), where it is loosely held. This electron is readily removed, as indicated by the ease with which Co (II) complexes are oxidized to Co (III) complexes.

$[Co(CN)_6]^{-4}$ (one unpaired electron):

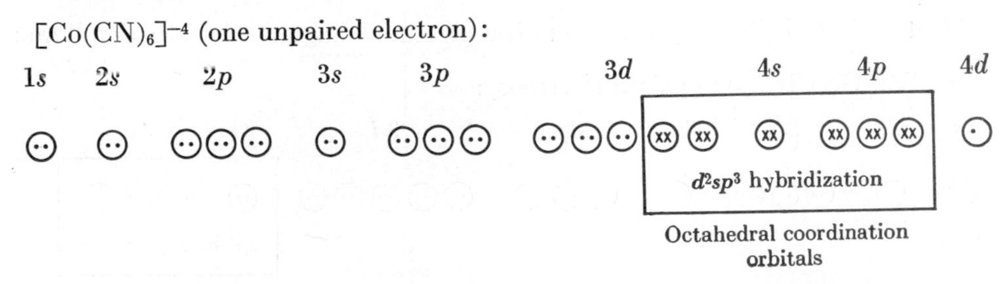

Complexes in which the metal shows a coordination number of four exist in two different geometric arrangements, the planar and the tetrahedral configurations. Examples of 4-coordinate complex ions with the planar configuration are $[Ni(CN)_4]^{=}$ and $[Cu(NH_3)_4]^{++}$, and with the tetrahedral configuration are $[Zn(CN)_4]^{=}$ and $[Zn(NH_3)_4]^{++}$ (Fig. 34–2).

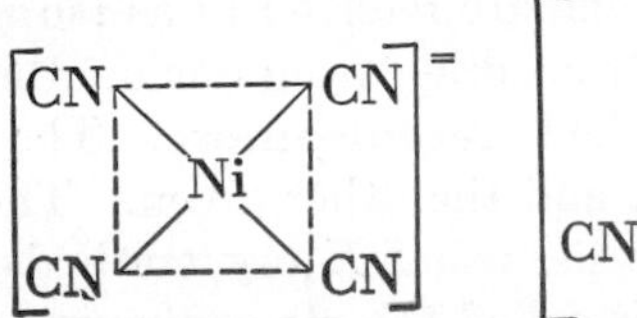

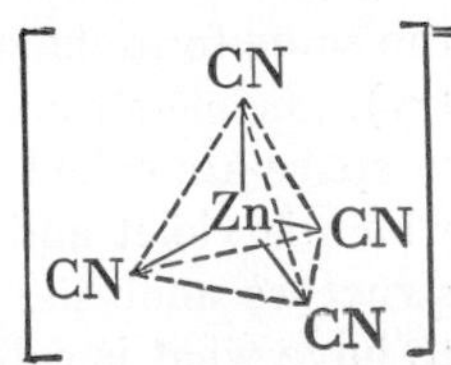

Fig. 34–2 The planar configuration of the $[Ni(CN)_4]^{=}$ ion, and the tetrahedral configuration of the $[Zn(CN)_4]^{=}$ ion.

In the case of 4-coordinate structures with a planar configuration, the four bonds of the central atom arise from dsp^2 hybridization, as illustrated below for $[Ni(CN)_4]^{=}$.

Ni atom (two unpaired electrons):

1s	2s	2p	3s	3p	3d	4s	4p
(··)	(··)	(··)(··)(··)	(··)	(··)(··)(··)	(··)(··)(··)(·)(·)	(··)	( )( )( )

Ni^{++} (two unpaired electrons):

1s	2s	2p	3s	3p	3d	4s	4p
(··)	(··)	(··)(··)(··)	(··)	(··)(··)(··)	(··)(··)(··)(·)(·)	( )	( )( )( )

$[Ni(CN)_4]^{=}$ (no unpaired electrons):

1s	2s	2p	3s	3p	3d	4s	4p
(··)	(··)	(··)(··)(··)	(··)	(··)(··)(··)	(··)(··)(··)(··)(xx)	(xx)	(xx)(xx)( )

dsp^2 hybridization (boxed: the last 3d orbital, 4s, and two 4p orbitals)

Planar coordination orbitals

For 4-coordinate complexes with a tetrahedral structure, the four bonds of the central atom arise from the hybridization of one *s* and three *p* orbitals; this is referred to as sp^3 hybridization. This is analogous to the filling of the carbon orbitals in methane or carbon tetrachloride to produce a tetrahedral sp^3 configuration (see Section 28.1), except that in the present instance coordinate covalent bonds are being formed in which both electrons of each shared pair come from the ligand.

The tetrahedral $[Zn(CN)_4]^{=}$ complex is represented diagrammatically as follows:

$[Zn(CN)_4]^{=}$ (no unpaired electrons):

1s	2s	2p	3s	3p	3d	4s	4p
(··)	(··)	(··)(··)(··)	(··)	(··)(··)(··)	(··)(··)(··)(··)(··)	(xx)	(xx)(xx)(xx)

sp^3 hybridization (boxed: 4s and the three 4p orbitals)

Tetrahedral coordination orbitals

34.4 Isomerism in Complexes

Certain complexes such as $[Co(NH_3)_4Cl_2]^+$, the dichlorotetraamminecobalt (III) ion, have more than one form. These different forms of the substance, possessing the same formula, are referred to as **isomers** (see also chapter on organic chemistry). Isomers that differ from one another *only* in the way the atoms are oriented in space are called **stereoisomers.** The $[Co(NH_3)_4Cl_2]^+$ has two isomers, one of which is violet and the other green. The violet form has been shown by crystal structure analysis, using X-ray methods, and by other experimental techniques to have what is called the **cis** configuration (the chloride ions on adjacent corners of the octahedron), and the green form to have what is called the **trans** configuration (the chloride ions on opposite corners), as shown in Fig. 34–3.

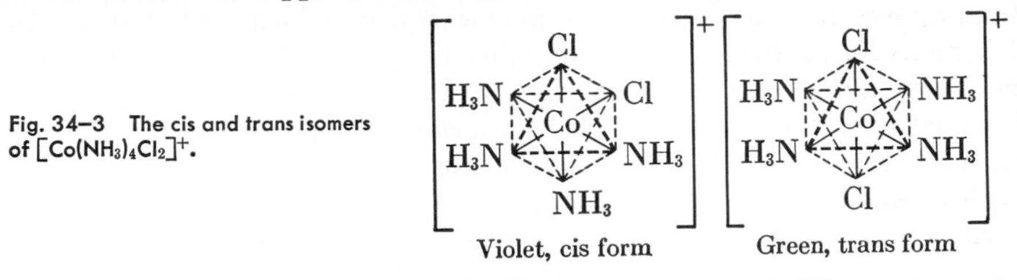

Fig. 34–3 The cis and trans isomers of $[Co(NH_3)_4Cl_2]^+$.

A complex such as $[Cr(NH_3)_2(H_2O)_2(Br)_2]^+$ has a variety of different isomeric forms. Each coordinating group can be trans to one like it:

$[NH_3;\ Br,\ H_2O;\ Cr;\ H_2O,\ Br;\ NH_3]^+$

The ammonia molecules can be trans to each other but the water and bromine molecules cis to groups like themselves:

$[NH_3;\ H_2O,\ Br;\ Cr;\ H_2O,\ Br;\ NH_3]^+$

Similarly, the water molecules or the bromine atoms can be trans to each other with the other groups cis to groups like themselves:

$[H_2O;\ Br,\ NH_3;\ Cr;\ Br,\ NH_3;\ H_2O]^+$ $[Br;\ H_2O,\ NH_3;\ Cr;\ H_2O,\ NH_3;\ Br]^+$

Finally, each group can be cis to one like itself. In this latter case, it can be shown that there are actually two arrangements which are different from each other, as follows:

$[NH_3;\ H_2O,\ NH_3;\ Cr;\ H_2O,\ Br;\ Br]^+$ $[NH_3;\ H_3N,\ H_2O;\ Cr;\ Br,\ H_2O;\ Br]^+$

These two forms are mirror images of each other but are not superimposable on each other and therefore are not identical. They are called **optical isomers,** a term applied to isomers which are mirror images of each other but not identical. Diagrams for mirror images of the other isomers of $[Cr(NH_3)_2(H_2O)_2(Br)_2]^+$ can be drawn, but it can be shown in each case that the additional form can be superimposed upon the one for which it is a mirror image and is therefore identical with it. For example, the following mirror image forms are actually identical to each other, inasmuch as either may be turned 180° on an axis through the two corners occupied by the ammonia molecules to superimpose it upon the other.

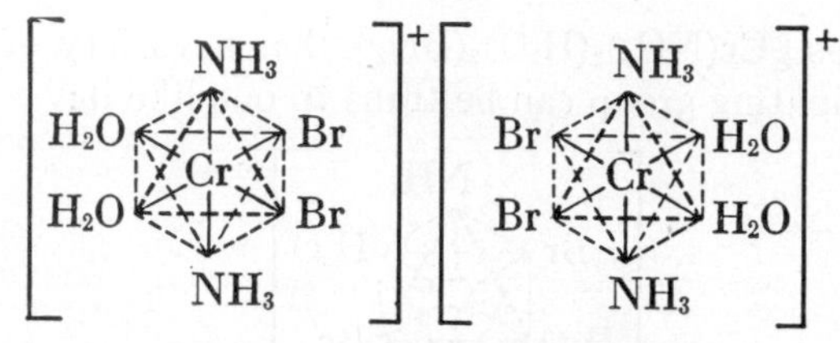

(Identical geometric forms)

The $[Cr(NH_3)_2(H_2O)_2(Br)_2]^+$, thus, has a total of six stereoisomers, two of which are optical isomers of each other.

The tris(ethylenediamine)cobalt (III) ion, $[Co(H_2NCH_2CH_2NH_2)_3]^{+++}$, has two optical isomers, as shown in Fig. 34–4.

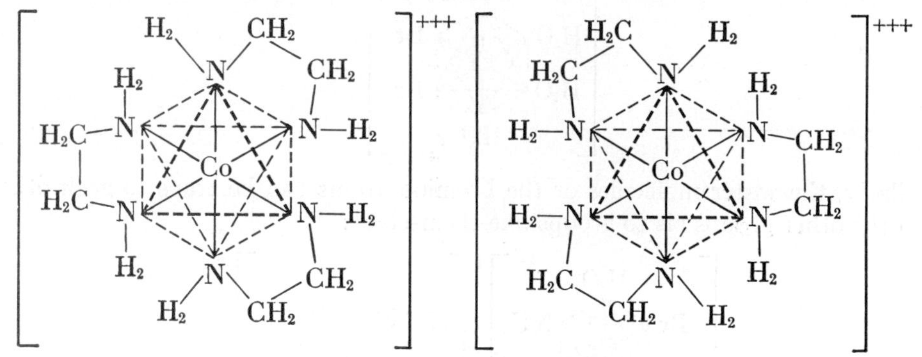

(or in abbreviated form where en = $H_2NCH_2CH_2NH_2$):

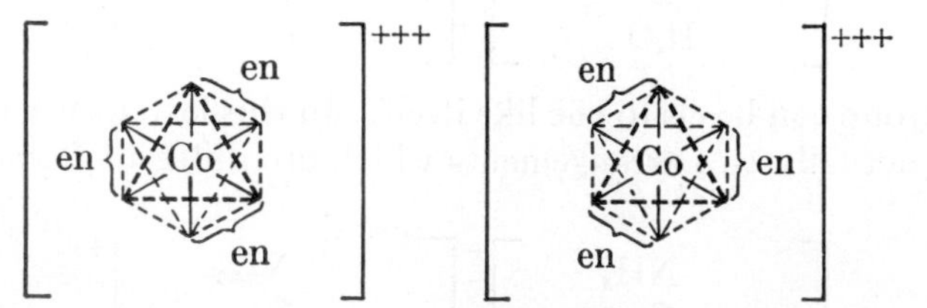

Fig. 34–4 Optical isomers of $[Co(H_2NCH_2CH_2NH_2)_3]^{+++}$.

The $[Co(en)_2Cl_2]^+$ has two cis isomers, which are optical isomers of each other, and one trans isomer. The trans form is symmetrical and has no possible optical isomerism. Its mirror image is superimposable on it and is therefore identical. The three isomers are shown in Fig. 34–5.

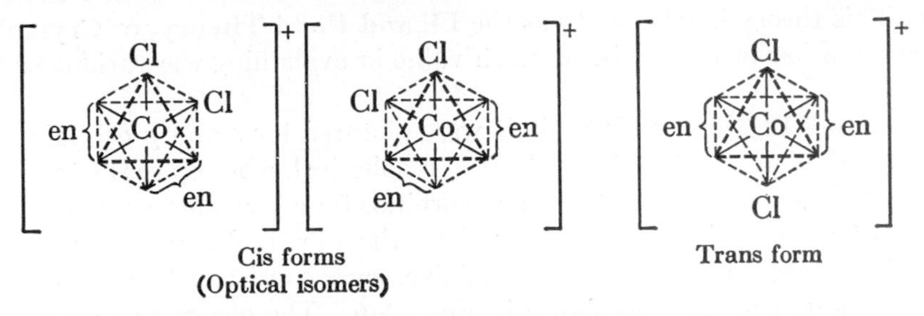

Fig. 34–5 The three isomeric forms of $[Co(en)_2Cl_2]^+$.

34.5 Brief Introduction to the Ligand Field Theory

The discussion, thus far, has assumed that the bonding of the ligands to the central metal ion is primarily covalent in complex ions and compounds. This assumption has been used for many years and explains a number of the properties of complexes quite satisfactorily. Some questions arise, nevertheless, that cannot be explained perfectly with the assumption of covalent bonding. For example, measurements of magnetic moments for a group of iron (II) complexes indicate that $[Fe(CN)_6]^{-4}$ has no unpaired electrons, whereas $[Fe(H_2O)_6]^{++}$ has four unpaired electrons. On the assumption of covalent bonding, no unpaired electrons would be predicted. It is not contradictory, therefore, to assume that $[Fe(CN)_6]^{-4}$ is covalently bonded as follows:

$[Fe(CN)_6]^{-4}$:

1s	2s	2p	3s	3p	3d	4s	4p
(··)	(··)	(··)(··)(··)	(··)	(··)(··)(··)	(··)(··)(··) [(xx)(xx)	(xx)	(xx)(xx)(xx)]

However, a contradiction does arise in considering $[Fe(H_2O)_6]^{++}$, with four unpaired electrons, as being covalently bonded. If, instead, the ion is assumed to be essentially ionically bonded without the ligand electrons entering the orbitals of the iron through sharing, the electron structure contains four unpaired electrons just as in the simple iron (II) ion.

Fe^{++} and $[Fe(H_2O)_6]^{++}$:

1s	2s	2p	3s	3p	3d	4s	4p
(··)	(··)	(··)(··)(··)	(··)	(··)(··)(··)	(··)(·)(·)(·)(·)	( )	( )( )( )

Such a differentiation between $[Fe(CN)_6]^{-4}$ and $[Fe(H_2O)_6]^{++}$ is not unreasonable, inasmuch as the cyanide ion usually makes an electron pair more readily available for sharing with the central metal ion and forms more stable complexes than does water. The concept of ionic bonding, however, does not adequately explain certain other properties of complexes such as their structural configurations.

An alternative explanation which provides a useful modification of the concept of ionic or electrostatic bonding has received much attention during the last few years. This theory is referred to as the **Ligand Field Theory,** or **Crystal Field Theory,** and has proved to be of much value in explaining the various properties of complexes.

In Section 3.18, the atomic orbitals were pictured for *s* and *p* orbitals. It will be recalled that the orbital of an *s* electron is spherical, whereas that of a *p* electron is a dumbbell shape, and that the three *p* orbitals for a given major energy level are oriented at right angles to each other along the *x*, *y*, and *z* axes (see Fig. 3–20).

The *d* orbitals, which occur in sets of five, each consist of lobe-shaped regions and are arranged in space as shown in Fig. 34–6. The one or two electrons that

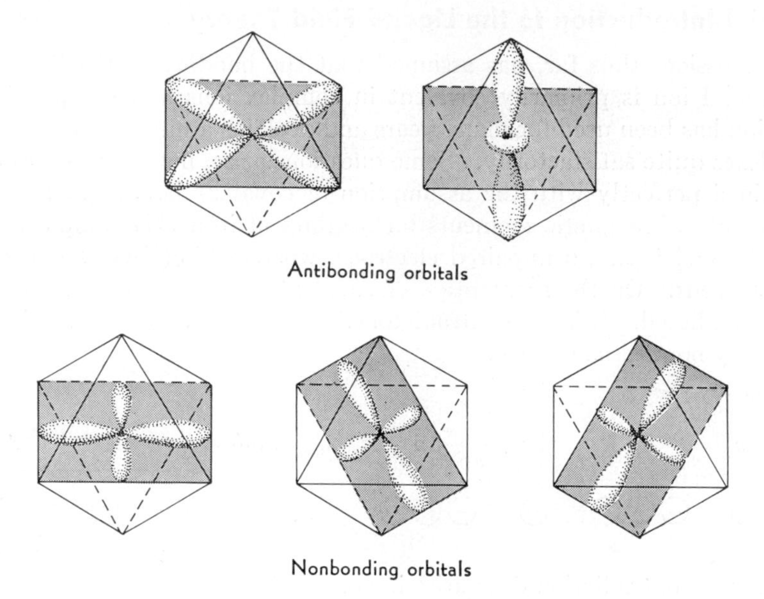

Fig. 34–6 Diagram showing the directional characteristics of the five *d* orbitals.

can occupy each orbital may be any place within these regions and over a period of time will effectively occupy all the lobes of the orbital. As shown in Fig. 34–6, the lobes in two of the five orbitals point toward the corners of the octahedral configuration for the metal. These orbitals are referred to as **antibonding orbitals,** inasmuch as any electrons which occupy these lobes will be repelled by electron pairs of ligand groups at the corners of the octahedron. The lobes in each of the other three orbitals point in between the corners of the octahedron and are called **nonbonding orbitals,** inasmuch as they are not directly affected by the electron pairs of approaching ligands.

In a simple metal ion, the electrons will be distributed among the five 3*d* orbitals in accord with Hund's Rule, inasmuch as they all have the same energy.

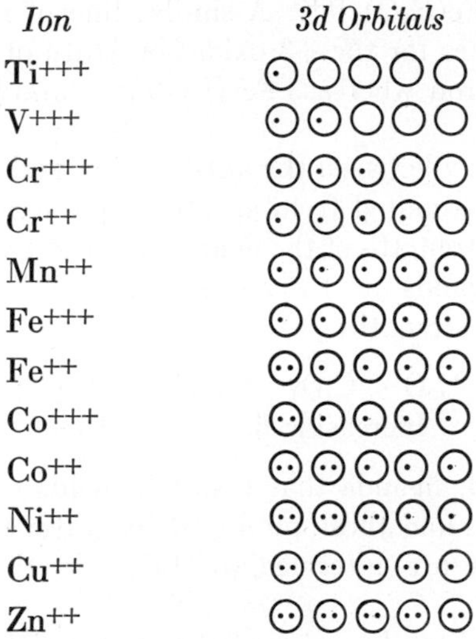

Ion	*3d Orbitals*
Ti^{+++}	(·) ( ) ( ) ( ) ( )
V^{+++}	(·) (·) ( ) ( ) ( )
Cr^{+++}	(·) (·) (·) ( ) ( )
Cr^{++}	(·) (·) (·) (·) ( )
Mn^{++}	(·) (·) (·) (·) (·)
Fe^{+++}	(·) (·) (·) (·) (·)
Fe^{++}	(··) (·) (·) (·) (·)
Co^{+++}	(··) (·) (·) (·) (·)
Co^{++}	(··) (··) (·) (·) (·)
Ni^{++}	(··) (··) (··) (·) (·)
Cu^{++}	(··) (··) (··) (··) (·)
Zn^{++}	(··) (··) (··) (··) (··)

If a negative ion or a neutral polar molecule approaches with an electron pair pointing toward a corner of the octahedral structure of the central metal ion, the 3*d* electrons of the metal will be repelled by the electron pair and will tend to seek nonbonding orbitals with lobes pointing in between the corners of the octahedron. Thus, the nonbonding orbitals become somewhat lower in energy than the antibonding orbitals. Two opposing forces are set up with the approach of the ligand, one force tending to concentrate the 3*d* electrons of the central metal in the nonbonding orbitals and the other force tending to keep the electrons distributed within all the 3*d* orbitals according to Hund's Rule. Some ligands, such as water and the fluoride ion, produce weak fields and have very little tendency to repel the 3*d* electrons of the central ion, whereas other ligands, such as the cyanide ion, set up strong fields in which the 3*d* electrons of the metal are significantly repelled.

Hence, in $[Fe(CN)_6]^{-4}$ the strong field of the six cyanide ions concentrates the six 3*d* electrons of the iron into the three nonbonding orbitals, leaving no unpaired electrons. This result is in agreement with the experimentally measured magnetic moment.

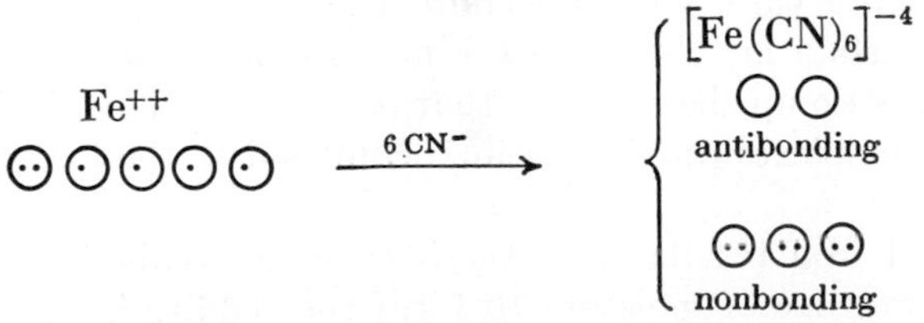

Fe^{++} (··) (·) (·) (·) (·) $\xrightarrow{6\,CN^-}$ $[Fe(CN)_6]^{-4}$: ( ) ( ) antibonding; (··) (··) (··) nonbonding

In $[Fe(H_2O)_6]^{++}$, on the other hand, with the weak field of the water molecules, the repulsive forces between the 3*d* electrons, themselves, predominate over the slight tendency toward repulsion by the incoming ligand, and the electrons remain distributed through all five 3*d* orbitals, in accord with Hund's Rule. Thus, four unpaired electrons are present, in agreement with the magnetic moment measurement, in Fe^{++} and in $[Fe(H_2O)_6]^{++}$. A similar line of reasoning can be followed to show why in complexes for the +3 oxidation state of iron the $[Fe(CN)_6]^{\equiv}$ has only one unpaired electron whereas $[Fe(H_2O)_6]^{+++}$ and $[FeF_6]^{\equiv}$ each possess five unpaired electrons.

The difference in energy between the antibonding and nonbonding orbitals for a given complex can be estimated from spectroscopic experiments and serves as a measure of the relative strengths of the fields produced by various ligands. Several of the more common ligands are thereby shown to fall in the following order in terms of increasing field strength:

$$I^- < Br^- < Cl^- < F^- < H_2O < C_2O_4^{=} < NH_3 < \text{ethylenediamine} < NO_2^- < CN^-$$
$$\text{Increasing field strength} \rightarrow$$

As would be expected, ligands that result in fields of strength between those produced by cyanide ion and those produced by water form complexes for which the magnetic moments are intermediate between those of $[Fe(CN)_6]^{-4}$ and $[Fe(H_2O)_6]^{++}$.

Actually, there is no sharp boundary between covalent and ionic bonding and, in fact, a modification of the Ligand Field Theory in which certain proportions of both ionic and covalent bonding are recognized as being present in complexes is necessary for a still more exact description of the properties of complexes. A theory known as the Molecular Orbital Theory seeks to introduce a covalent component into the electrostatic viewpoint.

The subject of structure of complexes points out that the explanations of chemical processes are never complete and are constantly open to modification as more information is obtained through research. Thus, one is constantly reminded in the study of science that there is a continuing need for research and that previous research, impressive as it is, has scarcely scratched the surface of that which is possible for the future. It is quite possible that some of the present readers of this book will, after further training, be among those contributing to a more complete knowledge of this subject or some other area of chemistry.

34.6 Uses of Complexes

Complexes have a variety of important uses. Some complexing groups, when coordinated to certain metals, make the metal more easily assimilated by plants and in other cases tie up the metal so that it cannot be effectively utilized by the plant. Hence, complexes provide an important aid to the farmer in effective soil treatment.

The rusting of iron results from the iron metal combining with oxygen from the air in the presence of moisture to form the reddish-brown iron (III) oxide, $Fe_2O_3 \cdot xH_2O$, which is known as iron rust. If, however, the iron is treated with a suitable coordinating group to form an iron complex, the iron on the surface can be tied up in the complex so that it cannot readily react to form $Fe_2O_3 \cdot xH_2O$. Under some conditions, the iron in rust which has already formed can be complexed to form a soluble complex ion which can then be washed free from the iron. Thus, a number of commercial products are on the market which can prevent or control corrosion through coordination.

In the electroplating industry, it has been found that many metals plate out in a smoother, more uniform plate which adheres better and has better appearance when the metal is plated from a bath which contains the metal in the form of a complex ion. Thus, complexes such as $[Ag(CN)_2]^-$ and $[Au(CN)_2]^-$ are used extensively in the electroplating industry.

Complexing groups are used in medicines and sometimes in the formulation of diets to make certain metals more readily, or occasionally less readily, assimilated by the body in its metabolic processes. Vitamin B_{12}, itself, is a dark-red complex of cobalt, in which the cobalt is coordinated to a large organic complexing group.

Various chelating groups may be of aid, through their complexing action with metals, in diminishing the effects of radioactive contamination following nuclear reactions.

Chlorophyll, the green pigment in plants, is a magnesium complex.

Hemoglobin, present in the red corpuscles of mammals, is an important iron complex.

Complexing agents are often used in water softening, because they tie up such ions as Ca^{++}, Mg^{++}, and Fe^{++} which are responsible for the hardness in water (see Section 10.6).

Complexes are used extensively in analytical laboratory work, both in qualitative and quantitative analysis.

A considerable and growing quantity of research is being undertaken currently to develop inorganic complexes which are polymeric, in the hope that such polymeric materials may be more chemically resistant and more stable at high temperatures than polymers heretofore developed.

The foregoing discussion is a brief introduction to one of the most fascinating fields of chemistry. Many significant advances have been made during the last several years, and a rapidly expanding number of useful applications have been and continue to be developed.

QUESTIONS

1. Calculate the "effective atomic number" for each of the following:
   (a) $[Pt(NH_3)_6]^{++++}$
   (b) $[PdCl_6]^{=}$
   (c) $[Zn(NH_3)_4]^{++}$
   (d) $[PtCl_4]^{=}$
   (e) $[Cr(CN)_6]^{\equiv}$
   (f) $[Co(NH_3)_4Cl_2]^+$
   (g) $[IrCl_6]^{\equiv}$
2. Explain what is meant by the terms (a) coordination sphere, (b) effective atomic number, (c) ligand, (d) coordination number, (e) coordination compound, and (f) chelating group.
3. Name each of the following:
   (a) $[Co(NH_3)_3(NO_2)_3]$
   (b) $[Ag(NH_3)_2]^+$
   (c) $K[Cr(NH_3)_2Cl_4]$

(d) $[Co(H_2NCH_2CH_2NH_2)_3]Cl_3$
(e) $[Pd(CN)_6]^{=}$
(f) $[Co(C_2O_4)_3]^{\equiv}$
(g) $[Pt(NH_3)_2Cl_2]$
(h) $[Cr(NH_3)_6][Co(CN)_6]$

4. Write formulas for each of the following:
(a) Hexaamminenickel (II) ion
(b) Dichlorotetraamminecobalt (III) chloride
(c) Chloronitrobis(ethylenediamine)cobalt (III) ion
(d) Potassium pentachloroammineplatinate (IV)
(e) Chlorodiaquotriamminecobalt (III) bromide
(f) Tetraamminecopper (II) tetrachloroplatinate (II)
(g) Tris(ethylenediamine)cadmium (II) ion
(h) Carbonatobis(ethylenediamine)cobalt (III) carbonate

5. Show orbital diagrams, indicate the type of hybridization you would expect, and draw a diagram showing the geometrical structure for each of the following: (a) $[Co(NH_3)_6]^{+++}$; (b) $[Fe(CN)_6]^{-4}$; (c) $[Cu(NH_3)_4]^{++}$; (d) $[Zn(NH_3)_4]^{++}$; (e) $[Cd(CN)_4]^{=}$.

6. Draw diagrams for any cis, trans, and optical isomers that could exist for each of the following:
(a) $[Pt(NH_3)_2Cl_4]$
(b) $[Cr(en)_3]^{+++}$ (where *en* is ethylenediamine)
(c) $[Co(en)_2Cl_2]^{+}$
(d) $[Co(en)_2(NO_2)Cl]^{+}$
(e) $[Pt(NH_3)_2Cl_2]$
(f) $[Cr(NH_3)_2(H_2O)_2Br_2]^{+}$

7. Determine the number of unpaired electrons you would expect for $[Fe(CN)_6]^{\equiv}$ and for $[Fe(H_2O)_6]^{+++}$. Explain in terms of the Ligand Field Theory.

8. Explain how coordination compounds may aid in (a) corrosion control; (b) soil treatment; (c) electroplating; (d) water softening.

REFERENCES

"Inorganic Coordination Compounds in General Chemistry," S. Kirschner, *J. Chem. Educ.*, **35** (3) 139 (1958).

"Chelation," H. F. Walton, *Sci. American*, June, 1953; p. 68.

"Crystal Field Explains Inorganic Behavior," R. G. Pearson, *Chem. Eng. News*, June 29, 1959; p. 72.

"The Coordinate Bond and the Nature of Complex Inorganic Compounds," D. H. Busch, *J. Chem. Educ.*, **33** (8) 376 (1956); **33** (10) 498 (1956).

"Some Recent Developments in the Theory of Bonding in Complex Compounds of the Transition Metals," L. E. Sutton, *J. Chem. Educ.*, **37** (10) 498 (1960).

"The Numbers and Structures of Isomers of Hexacovalent Complexes," J. C. Bailar, Jr., *J. Chem. Educ.*, **34** (7) 334 (1957).

"Inorganic Polymerization Reactions. Coordination Polymerization," D. B. Sowerby and L. F. Audrieth, *J. Chem. Educ.*, **37** (3) 134 (1960).

"Lone Pair Electrons," G. W. A. Fowles, *J. Chem. Educ.*, **34** (4) 187 (1957).

"Use of Metal Complexes in Organic Dyes and Pigments," O. Stallmann, *J. Chem. Educ.*, **37** (5) 220 (1960).

"Polymerization of Metal Chelates in Aqueous Solution," R. L. Gustafson, *J. Chem. Educ.*, **37** (11) 603 (1960).

CHAPTER THIRTY-FIVE

The Metals of Analytical Group I

MERCURY, SILVER, AND LEAD

Mercury (I), silver, and lead (II) ions are precipitated as chlorides by the use of a slight excess of hydrochloric acid, whereas the chlorides of all the other common metal ions are soluble in dilute acid. Thus Hg_2^{++}, Ag^+, and Pb^{++} make up Group I of our analytical scheme. If the less familiar ions were also considered, Analytical Group I would include Cu^+, Au^+, and Tl^+ because the chlorides of all these ions are insoluble.

The solubilities of mercury (I) chloride, Hg_2Cl_2, and silver chloride, AgCl, are low enough so that the mercury (I) ion and the silver ion are completely precipitated by the chloride ion in acid solution. However, lead chloride is somewhat soluble and may even fail to precipitate if the concentration of the lead ion is too low or the temperature is too high (lead chloride is readily soluble in hot water). Because of the relatively high solubility of the chloride, lead is found in Group II as well as in Group I.

Some properties of the metals of Analytical Group I are listed in Table 35·1.

TABLE 35·1 Some Properties of the Metals of Analytical Group I

Property	*Mercury*	*Silver*	*Lead*
Atomic number	80	47	82
Atomic weight	200.59	107.870	207.19
Electronic structure	2,8,18,32,18,2	2,8,18,18,1	2,8,18,32,18,4
Oxidation potential, volts	(Hg/Hg_2^{++}) -0.80 (Hg/Hg^{++}) -0.79	(Ag/Ag^+) -0.80	(Pb/Pb^{++}) $+0.13$
Oxidation states	+1, +2	+1, +2, +3	+2, +4
Density, g./cm.^{3}, at 20°	13.546	10.50	11.34
Melting point, °C	−38.87	960.8	327.4
Boiling point, °C	356.57	2193	1750

MERCURY

35.1 Periodic Relationships of Mercury

The three elements of Periodic Group IIB are zinc, cadmium, and mercury. Cadmium is in Analytical Group II (Chapter 36), and zinc is in Group III (Chapter 37). Each of these elements has two electrons in its outer shell and eighteen in the underlying shell. They are representative metals and the +2 oxidation state prevails, although the +1 state of mercury (Hg_2^{++}) is important. The melting points, boiling points, and heats of vaporization for the Group IIB members are lower than for any other group of metals except the alkali metals (Group IA). Of the three elements, zinc is the most reactive and mercury the least. The ions of all three elements are small in relation to their charges, so they show strong tendencies toward the formation of complex ions, like the transition metals which they immediately follow in the Periodic Table. The most frequently encountered complex ions of this family are the halo-, cyano-, and ammine complexes. Coordination numbers of both 4 and 6 are quite common in the complexes of these elements. The 4-coordinate complexes are generally tetrahedral (sp^3 configuration). The 6-coordinate complexes have octahedral structures but the bonding is not of the d^2sp^3 type, for the inner d orbitals of the simple ions are completely filled with electrons. Instead, an sp^3d^2 structure results, in which the d orbitals are of the same major energy level as the s and p orbitals. Hybridization of the sp^3d^2 type is represented diagrammatically for $[Zn(NH_3)_6]^{++}$ as

$[Zn(NH_3)_6]^{++}$ $3d^2$ $3d^2$ $3d^2$ $3d^2$ $3d^2$ | $4s^2$ $4p^2$ $4p^2$ $4p^2$ $4d^2$ $4d^2$ sp^3d^2 hybridization |

Octahedral coordination

35.2 History of Mercury

Mercury was one of the few metals known to the ancients. The Greek philosopher Aristotle refers to the metal as "liquid silver" or "quick silver" because of its appearance and liquid state. The Latin term "hydrargyrum" means "liquid silver" and the symbol Hg for mercury is the abbreviation of this name. The alchemists named the element after Mercury, the swift messenger of the gods of Roman mythology. One of its early uses was for the extraction of gold from its ores. The alchemists used mercury in their attempts to transmute base metals into gold.

35.3 Occurrence and Metallurgy

Elementary mercury is sometimes found in rocks and as an amalgam of silver and gold. However, the most important commercial source of the metal is the dark red sulfide, HgS, known as **cinnabar,** and found in Italy, Spain, the United States (California and Nevada), Russia, and Mexico.

Metallic mercury is produced by roasting cinnabar. The mercury distills from the furnace and is condensed to the liquid.

$$HgS + O_2 \rightarrow Hg + SO_2$$

Ordinarily, the roasting of a mineral in air results in the oxidation of the metal. However, the oxides of mercury are thermally unstable and decompose at the temperature of the furnace. Mercury may be purified by filtering it through chamois, washing it with nitric acid to oxidize the metallic impurities, or by distilling it in an atmosphere of oxygen to remove the more active metals.

35.4 Properties and Uses

Mercury is a silvery-white metal and is the only metal which is liquid at room temperature. Due to its low freezing point (−38.87° C), its high boiling point (356.6° C), its uniform coefficient of expansion, and the fact that it does not wet glass, mercury is an excellent thermometric substance. Because of its chemical inactivity, mobility, high density, and electrical conductivity, it is used extensively in barometers, vacuum pumps, liquid seals, and for electrical contacts. With the exception of iron and platinum, all metals readily dissolve in, or are wet by, mercury to form amalgams. Sodium amalgam is used as a reducing agent because it is less active than the alkali metal alone. Amalgams of tin, silver, and gold are used in dentistry. Mercury is used in the extraction of native gold from its ores due to ready amalgam formation. It is usually stored and shipped in iron flasks which hold 76 pounds of the metal.

Mercury vapor lamps and fluorescent lamps make use of the fact that mercury vapor is a conductor of electricity, and while conducting, it emits light which is rich in ultraviolet rays.

Mercury is permanent in air at ordinary temperatures but is slowly oxidized when heated, forming mercury (II) oxide, HgO, which decomposes at still higher temperatures. Being below hydrogen in the activity series, mercury is not attacked by hydrochloric acid but does dissolve in an excess of cold nitric or hot concentrated sulfuric acid.

$$3\ Hg + 8\ H^+ + 2\ NO_3^- \rightarrow 3\ Hg^{++} + 2\ NO\uparrow + 4\ H_2O$$

$$Hg + 2\ H_2SO_4 \rightarrow Hg^{++} + SO_4^= + SO_2\uparrow + 2\ H_2O$$

When the mercury is in excess, these oxidizing acids convert the metal to the corresponding mercury (I), Hg_2^{++}, salts rather than to the mercury (II), Hg^{++}, salts.

The halogens attack mercury forming the halides, and sulfur combines with it to produce mercury (II) sulfide. Mercury is displaced from solutions of its ions by all metals except silver, the platinum metals (Ru, Rh, Pd, Os, Ir, and Pt), and gold. A copper wire soon becomes amalgamated when immersed in a solution of a mercury compound.

Mercury forms two series of compounds; in these, the metal shows oxidation states of +1 and +2, respectively. The mercury atom uses both its valence electrons in bonding in all of its compounds. For example, in mercury (II) chloride,

$HgCl_2$, the chlorine atoms are covalently bonded to the mercury atom in a linear molecule.

$${}_{\times}^{\times}\overset{\times\times}{\underset{\times\times}{\text{Cl}}}{}_{\times}^{\circ}\text{Hg}{}_{\times}^{\circ}\overset{\times\times}{\underset{\times\times}{\text{Cl}}}{}_{\times}^{\times}$$

With the strongly electronegative sulfate and nitrate groups, mercury (II) forms ionic compounds in which dipositive mercury (II) ions, Hg^{++}, are present. In the series of compounds in which mercury exhibits a +1 oxidation state, one valence electron of each mercury atom serves to form an electron-pair bond with a second mercury atom. Hg_2Cl_2 has a linear covalent structure.

$${}_{\times}^{\times}\overset{\times\times}{\underset{\times\times}{\text{Cl}}}{}_{\circ}^{\times}\text{Hg}\,{}^{\bullet}_{\bullet}\,\text{Hg}{}_{\times}^{\circ}\overset{\times\times}{\underset{\times\times}{\text{Cl}}}{}_{\times}^{\times}$$

The equal sharing of the electron pair between the two mercury atoms does not contribute to the oxidation state of either atom, but the unequal sharing of an electron pair by each mercury atom with an electronegative chlorine atom gives each mercury atom an oxidation state of +1. When the second electron of each mercury atom is lost completely by electron transfer, as in the formation of $Hg_2(NO_3)_2$, the double mercury (I) ion, $\overset{+}{\text{Hg}}:\overset{+}{\text{Hg}}$ is formed.

The Hg_2^{++} ion is the only common ionic species with a **metal-metal bond.** Evidence from various sources points to the dimeric nature of this ion. X-ray studies of crystalline mercury (I) chloride show Hg–Hg bonds to be present, and magnetic studies of solutions containing univalent mercury show that it is not paramagnetic, meaning that there are no unpaired electrons as there would be if such solutions were to contain Hg^+ ions with an odd number of electrons per ion. On the contrary, $Hg{:}Hg^{++}$ contains an even number of electrons so that all the electrons present are assumed to exist in pairs. Thus, it is correct to write the formulas of mercury (I) compounds as Hg_2X_2, instead of HgX, where X is an acid radical.

35.5 Mercury (I) Compounds

A number of compounds containing univalent mercury are known. One of these, **mercury (I) chloride,** Hg_2Cl_2 (commonly called mercurous chloride), is a white, insoluble crystalline compound which is of analytical importance because its insolubility serves to precipitate the mercury (I) ion in Group I.

$$Hg_2^{++} + 2\ Cl^- \rightarrow \underline{Hg_2Cl_2}$$

Mercury (I) chloride is manufactured by heating a mixture of mercury (II) sulfate, mercury, and sodium chloride.

$$HgSO_4 + Hg + 2\ NaCl \rightarrow Hg_2Cl_2 + Na_2SO_4$$

Mercury (I) chloride is volatile and sublimes from the reaction mixture.

On exposure to light, mercury (I) chloride decomposes ($Hg_2Cl_2 \rightarrow HgCl_2 + Hg$); hence the salt is usually stored in amber-colored bottles.

Mercury (I) chloride is used in medicine under the name "calomel" as a cathartic and diuretic (i.e., it stimulates the organs of secretion).

When mercury dissolves in cold, dilute nitric acid (with the mercury in excess), **mercury (I) nitrate, $Hg_2(NO)_2$,** is formed. This compound is commonly called mercurous nitrate and it is important because it is the only readily soluble salt of univalent mercury. This salt hydrolyzes in aqueous solution to form the basic nitrate, $Hg_2(OH)NO_3$. The addition of nitric acid reverses the hydrolysis.

$$Hg_2(NO_3)_2 + H_2O \rightleftharpoons \underline{Hg_2(OH)NO_3} + H^+ + NO_3^-$$

On standing in contact with air, solutions of mercury (I) nitrate readily oxidize to mercury (II) nitrate. The accumulation of Hg^{++} can be prevented by keeping some metallic mercury in the bottle in which the solution is stored ($Hg^{++} + Hg \rightarrow Hg_2^{++}$).

Mercury (I) sulfide, Hg_2S, is unstable and immediately decomposes into mercury and mercury (II) sulfide when it is formed by passing hydrogen sulfide into a solution containing mercury (I) ions.

$$Hg_2^{++} + H_2S \rightarrow \underline{Hg_2S} + 2\ H^+$$

$$\underline{Hg_2S} \rightarrow \underline{Hg} + \underline{HgS}$$

Aqueous ammonia reacts with mercury (I) chloride in an oxidation-reduction reaction to form metallic mercury and a complex salt containing bivalent mercury.

$$Hg_2Cl_2 + 2\ NH_3 \rightarrow \underline{Hg} + \underline{HgNH_2Cl} + NH_4^+ + Cl^-$$

The formation of a black material when the white mercury (I) chloride is treated with aqueous ammonia is used as the test for the mercury (I) ion in qualitative analysis. The finely divided mercury is black and the **mercury (II) amido chloride** is white.

Alkali hydroxides precipitate black Hg_2O, which is unstable and decomposes into Hg and HgO.

Reducing agents, such as tetrachlorostannate (II) ion, readily reduce mercury (I) compounds to metallic mercury. This property is used in qualitative tests for the ion.

$$Hg_2Cl_2 + SnCl_4^{=} \rightarrow 2\ \underline{Hg} + SnCl_6^{=}$$

35.6 Mercury (II) Compounds

When a strong base is added to a solution of a mercury (II) compound, the oxide, HgO, precipitates. When precipitated in the cold, **mercury (II) oxide** is yellow, but formed from hot solutions, it is red. This difference in color has been attributed to a difference in the state of subdivision of the substance, the crystal structure being the same in the two cases. The hydroxide of mercury (II) is unstable, losing the elements of a molecule of water to form the oxide.

Mercury (II) chloride (mercuric chloride), $HgCl_2$, may be formed by heating the metal with an excess of chlorine, by dissolving mercury (II) oxide in hydrochloric acid, or by the action of aqua regia upon mercury. It is prepared commercially by heating mercury (II) sulfate with sodium chloride; the $HgCl_2$ sublimes from the reaction mixture.

$$2\,NaCl + HgSO_4 \rightarrow Na_2SO_4 + HgCl_2$$

The compound $HgCl_2$ is also called "bichloride of mercury" and "corrosive sublimate." In dilute solutions it is used as an antiseptic. It is moderately soluble in water, but only slightly ionized, as indicated by the low electrical conductivity of its solutions. Its solubility can be increased by adding an excess of chloride ions, which cause the formation of the complex **tetrachloromercurate** (**II**) ion according to the equation

$$HgCl_2 + 2\,Cl^- \rightleftharpoons [HgCl_4]^=$$

Mercury (II) chloride hydrolyzes in water somewhat, and ammonolyzes in aqueous ammonia. These reactions are similar, as can readily be seen by studying the equations

$$Cl{-}Hg{-}Cl + 2\,H_2O \rightarrow Cl{-}Hg{-}OH + H_3O^+ + Cl^-$$
$$Cl{-}Hg{-}Cl + 2\,NH_3 \rightarrow Cl{-}Hg{-}NH_2 + NH_4^+ + Cl^-$$

Mercury (II) amido chloride, $Hg(NH_2)Cl$, is called "infusible white precipitate" because upon being heated it decomposes without fusing.

Iodide ions precipitate mercury (II) ions from solution as HgI_2, which is orange in color. It is soluble in a solution containing an excess of iodide ions, tetraiodomercurate ions being formed, according to the equation

$$HgI_2 + 2\,I^- \rightarrow HgI_4^=$$

Hydrogen sulfide precipitates **mercury (II) sulfide,** HgS, from solutions of mercury (II) salts even in strongly acidic solutions. Because of this, bivalent mercury is a member of Analytical Group II. The precipitate formed by the interaction of $HgCl_2$ in solution and H_2S is first white, then yellow, then red, and finally black. The white compound has the formula $HgCl_2 \cdot 3\,HgS$. When heated, HgS becomes bright red; the red sulfide is isomeric with the black and has, in the past, been used as a pigment under the name of **vermilion.**

Mercury (II) sulfide is dissolved by aqueous solutions of sodium sulfide, Na_2S, in the presence of an excess of hydroxyl ions and forms the **thiomercurate** ion.

$$HgS + S^= \rightleftharpoons HgS_2^=$$

This reaction is used in the Group II procedures of the analytical scheme (Section 46.2).

Mercury (II) fulminate, $Hg(ONC)_2$, is an explosive compound formed by the action of nitric acid on mercury in the presence of alcohol. It is used in making detonators and percussion caps because it explodes when struck. Mercury fulminate probably has the structure

$$Hg(\,{}^{\circ}_{\times}\overset{\times\times}{\underset{\times\times}{O}}{}^{\circ}_{\times}N{}^{\circ\circ\times}_{\circ\circ\times}C{}^{\times}_{\times})_2$$

35.7 Physiological Action of Mercury

Metallic mercury is an accumulative poison; the breathing of air containing mercury vapor or contact of the liquid metal with the skin should be avoided.

All soluble mercury compounds are poisonous, but in small doses they may be medicinal. The fatal dose of mercury (II) chloride is 0.2 to 0.4 gram. The mercury (II) ion combines with the protein tissue of the kidney and destroys the ability of this organ to remove waste products from the blood. Antidotes for mercury poisoning are egg white and milk; their proteins precipitate the mercury in the stomach.

35.8 Properties of Mercury of Analytical Importance

The mercury (I) ion is colorless and is precipitated as a white crystalline solid by hydrochloric acid, a property which makes it a member of Analytical Group I. Aqueous ammonia converts Hg_2Cl_2 to a black or gray mixture of Hg, black, and $HgNH_2Cl$, white.

The mercury (II) ion of Analytical Group II is also colorless, but $HgCl_2$ is soluble in hydrochloric acid; with hydrogen sulfide, black HgS is formed. This compound is insoluble in most acids but dissolves in aqua regia or a mixture of hydrochloric and hypochlorous acids. It is dissolved also by a mixture of NaOH and Na_2S, the complex ion, $HgS_2^{=}$, being formed. This property is often used in separating HgS from the sulfides of lead, copper, cadmium, and bismuth, which do not form soluble thiocomplexes.

Both unipositive and dipositive mercury ions are readily reduced by tin (II) chloride. A black precipitate of finely divided mercury is the final product in both cases (when an excess of $SnCl_2$ is employed). Mercury is displaced from solutions of its ions by all the metals which lie above it in the activity series. A copper strip or wire soon becomes amalgamated when dipped in a solution of a mercury compound, a change which may be used as a simple test for mercury.

SILVER

35.9 Periodic Relationships of Silver

Copper, silver, and gold are known as the coinage metals and have been used from very early times for the manufacture of ornamental objects and coins. They comprise Group IB of the Periodic Table and may be classified as transition elements in that they have valence electrons in two shells. Each has one electron in its outermost shell and eighteen in the underlying shell. Because both the alkali metals of Group IA and the coinage metals of Group IB each have one electron in their outermost shell, the members of these two families might be expected to behave similarly. The elements of both families are good conductors of electricity and form a series of univalent compounds with analogous formulas (Na_2O, Ag_2O; NaCl, AgCl; and Na_2SO_4, Ag_2SO_4), but beyond this, similarities between the two families are almost entirely lacking. For example, the alkali metals are highly reactive while the coinage metals are quite unreactive. This results in part from the fact that the atoms of the IB family are smaller than those of the IA family and they hold their valence electrons more closely to the nucleus. Unlike the alkali metals, copper, silver, and gold can use one or two electrons from the underlying shell in bond formation. Thus, copper, silver, and gold each exhibit +1, +2, and +3 oxidation states. However, the most common oxidation state for copper is +2; for silver, +1; and for gold, +3. Many of the ions and compounds of the coinage metals are colored, whereas the ions of the alkali metals are colorless and their only colored compounds are those having a color associated with the anion (e.g., $K_2Cr_2O_7$ and $KMnO_4$). The hydroxides of the alkali metals are soluble and strongly basic whereas those of copper and gold are insoluble and weakly basic. Silver hydroxide is slightly soluble and strongly basic. Most compounds of the alkali metals are soluble in water, while the majority of those of the coinage metals are insoluble. Finally, the alkali metals show little tendency toward the formation of complex ions, while many stable complexes, such as $[Cu(CN)_2]^-$, $[Ag(CN)_2]^-$, $[Au(CN)_2]^-$, $[Cu(NH_3)_2]^+$, $[Cu(NH_3)_4]^{++}$, and $[Ag(NH_3)_2]^+$, are known for the coinage metals.

Among the coinage metals, trends in properties are not very regular nor readily interpreted. The chemical activity, elasticity, tensile strength, and specific heat decrease in the order: copper, silver, gold; and the density increases in this order. All three metals in their +1 oxidation states form insoluble chlorides, but only silver is included in Analytical Group I. Compounds of univalent copper are not common and are not as important as those of divalent copper, which is a member of Analytical Group II. Gold is considered a less common metal, and its chemical properties are relatively unimportant. For these reasons it is not included in our analytical scheme at all.

35.10 History of the Coinage Metals

These metals were the first to be used by primitive races because they are found in the native state, they tarnish slowly, and their appearance is pleasing to the eye. Ornaments of gold have been found in Egyptian tombs which were constructed in the prehistoric Stone Age. Gold and silver coins were used as a medium of exchange in India and Egypt long before the Christian era.

It is believed that copper was the first metal to be fashioned into utensils, instruments, and weapons, its use for such purposes beginning sometime during the Stone Age. The practice of alloying copper with tin and the use of the resulting bronze in place of stone introduced the Bronze Age.

The chemical symbol for gold (Au) is derived from the Latin name "aurum," that for silver (Ag) from "argentum," and that for copper (Cu) from "cuprum." The alchemists associated gold, "the most perfect of all metals," with the sun, and silver, which they called "luna," with the moon.

35.11 Occurrence and Metallurgy of Silver

Silver is sometimes found in large nuggets but more frequently in veins and related deposits. It frequently is found alloyed with gold, copper, or mercury. It occurs combined as the chloride, AgCl (horn silver), and as the sulfide, Ag_2S, which is usually mixed with the sulfides of lead, copper, nickel, arsenic, and antimony. The principal silver-producing countries are Mexico, Canada, and the United States. Most of the silver of commerce is a product of the mining of other metals such as lead and copper.

The lead obtained from lead sulfide ore contains some silver. The silver is extracted from the fused lead by the use of zinc, in which silver is about 3000 times more soluble than it is in lead. The lead is fused and thoroughly mixed with a small quantity of zinc. Lead and zinc are immiscible. Most of the silver leaves the lead and dissolves in the zinc. When mixing is stopped, the zinc rises to the surface of the lead and solidifies. The zinc-silver alloy is removed from the lead and the more volatile zinc is separated from the silver by distillation. This extraction procedure is known as the **Parkes process** (Fig. 35–1).

Fig. 35–1 Desilvering kettles. The zinc-silver alloy is being removed with a huge skimmer, while molten lead drains back into the kettle. *International Lead Refining Co.*

The extraction of silver from its ores is dependent upon the formation of the complex dicyanoargentate ion, $[Ag(CN)_2]^-$. Silver metal and all of its compounds are readily dissolved by alkali cyanides in the presence of air. Representative equations for the hydrometallurgy of silver are given below.

$$4\ Ag + 8\ CN^- + O_2 + 2\ H_2O \rightarrow 4\ [Ag(CN)_2]^- + 4\ OH^-$$
$$2\ Ag_2S + 8\ CN^- + O_2 + 2\ H_2O \rightarrow 4\ [Ag(CN)_2]^- + 2\ S + 4\ OH^-$$
$$AgCl + 2\ CN^- \rightleftharpoons [Ag(CN)_2]^- + Cl^-$$

The silver is precipitated from the cyanide solution upon the addition of zinc or aluminum.

$$2\ [Ag(CN)_2]^- + Zn \rightarrow 2\ \underline{Ag} + [Zn(CN)_4]^=$$

Much silver is also obtained from the anode mud formed during the electrolytic refining of copper (Section 36.9).

Sometimes silver is extracted from ores containing free silver or silver chloride by an amalgamation process, in which the pulverized ore is agitated with water and mercury. Mercury dissolves the free silver and reduces the chloride to the metal, which also dissolves in the excess mercury.

$$2\ AgCl + 2\ Hg \rightarrow Hg_2Cl_2 + 2\ Ag$$

The amalgam, Ag-Hg, is separated from the gangue and distilled in iron retorts.

The volatile mercury is condensed and used again, while the silver remains in the retort.

35.12 Properties of Silver

Silver is a white, lustrous metal and its surface is an excellent reflector of light. It is the best conductor of heat and electricity that we have, and it is noted for its ductility and malleability.

Silver is not attacked by oxygen of the air under ordinary conditions but tarnishes quickly in the presence of hydrogen sulfide or upon contact with sulfur-containing food materials such as eggs and mustard. Its reaction with hydrogen sulfide in the presence of air is

$$4\ Ag + 2\ H_2S + O_2 \rightarrow 2\ Ag_2S + 2\ H_2O$$

Silver tarnish is a thin film of silver sulfide. The halogens react with silver forming the halides, and the metal is soluble in such oxidizing acids as nitric and hot sulfuric.

$$3\ Ag + 4\ H^+ + NO_3^- \rightarrow 3\ Ag^+ + NO\uparrow + 2\ H_2O$$

Because silver lies below hydrogen in the activity series, it is not soluble in non-oxidizing acids such as hydrochloric. Most silver salts are sparingly soluble in water, but the nitrate is quite soluble. The common oxidation state exhibited by silver is +1, although the oxides AgO and Ag_2O_3 and many complex compounds containing Ag(II) and Ag(III) are known.

35.13 Uses of Silver

Considerable silver is used for the making of coins, silverware, and ornaments. For most of its uses, silver is too soft to wear well, and it is therefore hardened by alloying it with other metals, particularly copper. British silver coins contain 7.5 per cent copper, the composition of "sterling silver." Silver coins of the United States (dimes, quarters, half dollars, and dollars) contain 10 per cent copper. Jewelry silver contains 20 per cent copper. Large amounts of silver are also used in the preparation of dental alloys, photographic films, and mirrors.

When the copper supply is very short, as it was during World War II, silver is used as an electrical conductor to some extent. Silver has been used recently in various alloys such as bearing metal for automobiles, airplanes, and locomotives, and in the production of a high grade stainless steel (0.26–0.28 per cent silver).

35.14 Plating with Silver

The electroplating industry uses a large percentage of the metal produced. The object to be plated with silver is made the cathode in an electrolytic cell containing a solution of sodium dicyanoargentate, $Na[Ag(CN)_2]$, as the electrolyte. The anode is a bar of pure silver which dissolves to replace the silver ions removed from solution as plating at the cathode proceeds. The electrode reactions are

Cathodic reduction: $[Ag(CN)_2]^- + e^- \rightarrow Ag + 2\ CN^-$
Anodic oxidation: $Ag + 2\ CN^- \rightarrow [Ag(CN)_2]^- + e^-$

The film of deposited silver has a flat white appearance, but it can be made to assume a brilliant luster by burnishing.

The characteristic luster can be restored to tarnished silverware by the following application of the activity series. The tarnished silver object is immersed in a solution of baking soda and salt containing a teaspoonful of each to a quart of water held in an aluminum vessel. (A piece of aluminum metal in a glass vessel will serve equally well.) The aluminum and silver must be in contact. After the tarnish is removed, the silver object should be thoroughly washed. The chemistry involved may be explained in this way: the silver sulfide of the film of tarnish dissolves somewhat in the solution, forming silver and sulfide ions. The more active aluminum displaces the silver from solution, causing it to plate out on the silver object, according to the equation

$$3\ Ag^{+} + Al \rightarrow 3\ \underline{Ag} + Al^{+++}$$

The tarnish is removed with little loss of silver. The use of silver polish restores the bright surface but with loss of the silver in the tarnish.

Silver mirrors are formed by depositing a thin layer of silver on glass. This is accomplished by reducing an ammoniacal solution of silver nitrate with some mild reducing agent, such as glucose or formaldehyde. The equation for the reaction may be written as follows:

$$[Ag(NH_3)_2]^{+} + e^{-}\ \text{(from reducing agent)} \rightarrow Ag + 2\ NH_3$$

The film of silver deposited on the glass is washed, dried, and varnished.

35.15 Compounds of Silver

1. *Silver oxide.* Silver oxide can be formed in a variety of ways. For example, it is formed when silver is exposed to ozone, or when finely divided silver is heated in oxygen under pressure. The alkalies act upon silver nitrate to give a dark-brown amorphous precipitate of silver oxide. Although the oxide is but slightly soluble in water, it dissolves enough to give a distinctly alkaline solution. The equilibrium is given by the equation

$$Ag_2O + H_2O \rightleftharpoons 2\ Ag^{+} + 2\ OH^{-}$$

Silver oxide is a convenient reagent, in both inorganic and organic chemistry, for preparing soluble hydroxides from the corresponding halide because the silver halide formed at the same time may be removed conveniently by filtration. Cesium hydroxide, for example, may be prepared according to the equation

$$(2\ Cs^{+}) + 2\ Cl^{-} + Ag_2O + H_2O \rightarrow (2\ Cs^{+}) + 2\ OH^{-} + 2\ \underline{AgCl}$$

This reaction proceeds to the right because AgCl is much less soluble than Ag_2O. Silver oxide dissolves readily in aqueous ammonia to form the strong base, diamminesilver hydroxide.

$$Ag_2O + 4\ NH_3 + H_2O \rightarrow 2\ [Ag(NH_3)_2]^{+} + 2\ OH^{-}$$

When the oxide is heated at atmospheric pressure in air, it readily gives up its oxygen according to the equation

$$2\ Ag_2O \rightarrow 4\ Ag + O_2$$

Very strong oxidizing agents in alkaline solution oxidize the Ag(I) ion with the formation of AgO and Ag_2O_3, in which silver has oxidation states of +2 and +3, respectively.

2. *The silver halides.* It is of interest that **silver fluoride,** AgF, is very soluble in water, whereas the chloride, bromide, and iodide are insoluble — the higher the atomic weight of the halogen, the less the solubility. The insoluble silver halides are formed as curdy precipitates when halide ions are added to solutions of silver salts. The chloride is white, silver bromide is pale yellow, and silver iodide is yellow. Upon exposure to light, the halides of silver turn violet at first and finally black; they are decomposed into their elements.

$$2\ AgX + \text{light} \rightarrow 2\ Ag + X_2\ (X = \text{halogen})$$

Silver chloride is readily soluble in an excess of dilute aqueous ammonia to form the diamminesilver complex, $[Ag(NH_3)_2]^+$.

$$AgCl + 2\ NH_3 \rightarrow [Ag(NH_3)_2]^+ + Cl^-$$

This reaction is used in separating silver chloride from mercury (I) chloride in the qualitative scheme. Silver bromide will dissolve only if the ammonia is concentrated, and the iodide is scarcely soluble at all in this reagent. Use is made of these facts in the separation and identification of the halide ions in the anion analytical scheme (Section 50.11).

3. *Silver nitrate.* **Silver nitrate,** $AgNO_3$, is the only simple silver salt which is found to be usefully soluble; its solutions are essentially neutral, indicating but little hydrolysis. This shows that silver hydroxide is a strong base, even though it is only slightly soluble. Silver nitrate is obtained by dissolving silver in nitric acid and evaporating the solution. It is sold under the name "lunar caustic" and is used to cauterize sores. Organic materials, such as the skin, readily reduce silver nitrate to give free silver, which forms a black stain. Some indelible inks are based upon this reaction. Much silver nitrate is used in the production of photographic materials, as a laboratory reagent, and in the manufacture of other silver compounds.

35.16 The Photographic Process (Black and White)

1. *The photographic film.* Photographic films are thin sheets of cellulose acetate coated with a colloidal suspension of small silver halide crystals in gelatin. Pure solutions of silver nitrate (Fig. 35–2, page 570), potassium bromide, and potassium iodide are mixed in the presence of the gelatin in the preparation of the photographic emulsion ($Ag^+ + X^- \rightarrow AgX$). The size of the silver halide particles and the relative amounts of bromide and iodide used determine the "sensitivity" or "speed" of the film.

2. *Exposure.* The film is exposed by focusing an image upon the light-sensitive photographic emulsion on the film. The silver halide crystals become "activated" when exposed to light, so that they are more readily reduced than before. The chemical change occurring during exposure is not well understood, but the silver halide crystals receiving the most light (from the light areas of the object) are

Fig. 35–2 Silver to be used in the manufacture of light-sensitive emulsion. *Eastman Kodak Co.*

more readily reduced, during development of the film, than those receiving little light (from the dark areas of the object). Exposure causes no visible change in the appearance of the film.

3. *Developing.* After exposure, the film is developed by placing it in an alkaline solution of an organic reducing agent such as hydroquinone or pyrogallol. The reducing agent acts upon the grains of silver halide with a speed proportional to the intensity of the illumination during exposure, and reduces them to metallic silver.

$$AgX + e^- \text{ (reducing agent)} \rightarrow \underline{Ag} + X^-$$

4. *Fixing.* After developing, the film is fixed by treating it with a solution of sodium thiosulfate (hypo) to dissolve the unreduced silver halide.

$$AgX + 2\ S_2O_3^{=} \rightleftharpoons [Ag(S_2O_3)_2]^{-3} + X^-$$

The metallic silver remaining on the film forms the visible image and is called a **negative,** since the light portions of the original image are now dark and the dark portions of the original are now light.

5. *Printing.* The process of printing is essentially the same as that of making a negative, but due to the fact that the sensitive printing paper is illuminated through the negative, the image is once again reversed, and now corresponds to the original image as regards light and dark areas on the print.

The print may be **toned** by replacing part of the silver of the image by gold or platinum. To do this, the print is treated with solutions of $Na[AuCl_4]$ or $K_2[PtCl_6]$. The more active silver displaces these noble metals from their salts to give a thin deposit of gold (red tone) or platinum (dark gray).

35.17 Properties of Silver of Analytical Importance

The silver ion yields a white, curdy precipitate with chloride ions in acid solution, making it a member of Analytical Group I. Silver chloride is soluble in aqueous ammonia, forming diamminesilver chloride, and is reprecipitated by acids. Silver ions are precipitated by iodide, bromide, chromate, sulfide, phosphate, and cyanide ions, yielding pale yellow AgI, yellow AgBr, red Ag_2CrO_4, black Ag_2S, yellow Ag_3PO_4, and white AgCN, respectively. Silver cyanide is soluble in an excess of soluble cyanide ($AgCN + CN^- \rightleftharpoons [Ag(CN)_2]^-$).

LEAD

35.18 Periodic Relationships of Lead

The first two elements of Periodic Group IVA, carbon and silicon, have already been discussed in Chapters 28 and 29, respectively. The remaining three members of this family are germanium, tin, and lead.

Carbon and silicon are primarily nonmetallic in character, while germanium, tin, and lead become increasingly metallic in properties with increasing atomic weight. In ionic compounds, carbon and silicon are always found in the anion. On the other hand, germanium, tin, and lead form bivalent cations, Ge^{++}, Sn^{++}, and Pb^{++}. The fact that the hydroxides of these ions are amphoteric is a reflection of some nonmetallic character. All members of this periodic group form covalent compounds or anions in which the +4 oxidation state is exhibited; for example, CCl_4, $SiCl_4$, $GeCl_4$, $SnCl_4$, and $PbCl_4$ are all low-boiling covalent liquids, and Na_2CO_3, Na_2SiO_3, Na_2GeO_3, Na_2SnO_3, and Na_2PbO_3 are ionic compounds.

Germanium and the members of Periodic Group IVB (Ti, Zr, and Hf) are among the less familiar elements; these elements are discussed in Chapter 40. The members of the B group usually show an oxidation state of +4 in their compounds; they are transition metals with two electrons in their outer shells and ten electrons in the next to the outer shells.

35.19 History of Lead

Because lead is easily extracted from its ores, it was known to the early Egyptians and Babylonians and it is mentioned in the Bible in Job and in Numbers. Lead pipes were commonly used by the Romans for conveying water, and in the Middle Ages lead was used as a roofing material. The stained glass windows of the great cathedrals of this age were set in lead. The symbol (Pb) is derived from the Latin word for lead, "plumbum," meaning heavy.

35.20 Occurrence and Metallurgy of Lead

The principal lead ore is the sulfide, PbS, commonly called **galena.** Other common ores of lead are the carbonate, **cerrusite** ($PbCO_3$), and the sulfate, **anglesite** ($PbSO_4$), which appear to have been formed by the weathering of sulfide ores. Lead is quite widely distributed in many parts of the world. The principal lead-producing countries are the United States, Spain, and Mexico.

Lead ores are first concentrated by a series of selective flotation processes to remove the gangue materials and a large part of the zinc sulfide which is usually associated with lead ores. The concentrated ore is then roasted in air to convert most of the sulfide to the oxide.

$$2\ PbS + 3\ O_2 \rightarrow 2\ PbO + 2\ SO_2$$

The roasted product is reduced in a blast furnace with coke and scrap iron.

$$PbO + C \rightarrow Pb + CO$$
$$PbO + CO \rightarrow Pb + CO_2$$
$$PbS + Fe \rightarrow Pb + FeS$$

The lead obtained from the blast furnace contains copper, antimony, arsenic, bismuth, gold, and silver. The crude lead is melted and stirred to bring about the oxidation of antimony, arsenic, and bismuth. The oxides of these metals rise to the surface and the molten lead is drained off for further refining. Gold and silver may be extracted from the lead by the Parkes process (Section 35.11), or by the electrolytic **Betts process.** In the electrolytic process, thin sheets of pure lead are made the cathodes, plates of impure lead the anodes, and the electrolyte is a solution containing lead hexafluosilicate, $PbSiF_6$, and hexafluosilicic acid, H_2SiF_6.

A recent method of metallurgy for lead involves the electrolysis of lead sulfide dissolved in molten lead chloride. Lead is liberated at the cathode, and sulfur at the anode.

35.21 Properties and Uses of Lead

Lead is a soft metal having little tensile strength, and it is the heaviest of the common metals excepting gold and mercury. It has a metallic luster when freshly cut but quickly acquires a dull gray color when exposed to moist air. In air which contains moisture and carbon dioxide it becomes oxidized on the surface, forming a protective layer which is both compact and adherent; this film is probably the basic carbonate.

Unlike silver and mercury of Analytical Group I, lead lies above hydrogen in the activity series and therefore dissolves slowly in dilute nonoxidizing acids. Concentrated nitric acid attacks it readily. It is not dissolved by pure water in the absence of air, but in the presence of air it reacts with water to form the hydroxide.

$$2\ Pb + 2\ H_2O + O_2 \rightarrow 2\ Pb(OH)_2$$

The presence of carbonate or sulfate in the water checks the solvent action of the water (lead carbonate and sulfate are insoluble) so that hard water may be conveyed in lead pipes without danger of lead poisoning. When heated in a stream of air, lead burns. It is also attacked by sulfur, fluorine, and chlorine.

The uses of lead depend mainly upon the ease with which it is worked, its low melting point, and its resistance to corrosion. It is used in the manufacture of plumbing articles ("plumber" originally meant "worker in lead"), coverings for electric cables, lead chambers in sulfuric acid plants, and in storage batteries. Lead alloyed with 0.5 per cent arsenic is used in making shot and bullets. Other important alloys of lead include solder, fuse metals, bearing metals, and pewter. Large quantities of lead are converted into the basic carbonate, white lead, which is used as a paint pigment.

35.22 Compounds of Lead

Lead forms two well-defined series of compounds in which its oxidation states are +2 and +4, respectively. An atom of lead (like those of its congeners carbon, silicon, germanium, and tin) has four valence electrons; two of these are *s* electrons and the other two are *p* electrons. All four of the valence electrons are seldom, if ever, completely removed from the atom but are very often shared with electronegative elements. This leads to the +4 oxidation state which is typical of the Group IVA elements. Lead (and also tin) forms many compounds in which its two *s* valence electrons do not participate in the bonding but remain associated with the core of the atom as a stable electron pair. When this happens, the element assumes the +2 oxidation state. Because of the high oxidation potential of tetravalent lead ($Pb^{++} \rightarrow PbO_2$, −1.5 volts), the +2 oxidation state of this element is often considered to be the characteristic oxidation state.

1. *Oxides of lead.* When lead is heated in air the yellow, powdery **monoxide,** PbO, is obtained. When this material is fused and then pulverized, a buff-colored powder, named **litharge,** results. It is used in the manufacture of lead glass and enamels.

Lead dioxide, PbO_2, is a chocolate-brown powder formed by oxidizing lead (II) compounds in alkaline solution. With sodium hypochlorite as the oxidizing agent, the equation for the oxidation of the plumbite ion is

$$Pb(OH)_3^- + ClO^- \rightarrow \underline{PbO_2} + Cl^- + OH^- + H_2O$$

Lead dioxide is the principal constituent of the cathode of the charged lead storage battery during its use to deliver current (Section 20.16). It is formed by the anodic oxidation of lead (II) ions during the charging of the battery, according to the equation

$$Pb^{++} + 2\ H_2O \rightarrow \underline{PbO_2} + 4\ H^+ + 2\ e^-$$

Since lead +4 tends to revert to the stable +2 state by gaining two electrons, lead dioxide is a powerful oxidizing agent.

The oxide Pb_3O_4, called "red lead" or **trilead tetroxide,** is prepared by carefully heating the monoxide in air at temperatures between 400 and 500°. When red lead is treated with nitric acid, two thirds of the lead dissolves as lead nitrate (oxidation state +2), and the remaining third remains as lead dioxide (oxidation state +4). The equation for the reaction is

$$Pb_3O_4 + 4\ H^+ + (NO_3^-) \rightarrow \underline{PbO_2} + 2\ Pb^{++} + (NO_3^-) + 2\ H_2O$$

Trilead tetroxide is used chiefly in making storage batteries, paints, ceramic products, and flint glass. Paint containing it is particularly effective as a rust inhibitor for ironwork.

2. *Lead hydroxide.* When alkali hydroxides are added to solutions of lead (II) compounds, white **lead hydroxide,** $Pb(OH)_2$, precipitates. An excess of alkali causes the hydroxide to dissolve according to the equation

$$Pb(OH)_2 + OH^- \rightarrow Pb(OH)_3^-$$

showing the amphoteric character of the compound. Its reaction with hydrogen ions is given by the equation

$$Pb(OH)_2 + 2\ H^+ \rightarrow Pb^{++} + 2\ H_2O$$

3. *Lead chloride.* Lead chloride, $PbCl_2$, may be formed by the direct union of the elements, by the action of hydrochloric acid upon lead monoxide, or by precipitation from solutions containing lead (II) ions and chloride ions. It is soluble in hot water and in solutions of high chloride concentration, tetrachloroplumbate (II) ions being formed in the latter case.

$$PbCl_2 + 2\ Cl^- \rightleftharpoons PbCl_4^=$$

These properties are important in the analysis of lead.

4. *Lead nitrate.* When metallic lead or the monoxide is dissolved in nitric acid, $Pb(NO_3)_2$ is formed. This salt is readily soluble in water, but unless the solution is slightly acid with nitric acid, hydrolysis occurs, and basic nitrates are precipitated.

$$Pb^{++} + NO_3^- + H_2O \rightleftharpoons \underline{Pb(OH)NO_3} + H^+$$

Lead nitrate is unstable at moderately high temperatures and decomposes in the same manner as do the nitrates of other heavy metals.

$$2\ Pb(NO_3)_2 \rightarrow 2\ PbO + 4\ NO_2 + O_2$$

5. *Carbonates of lead.* The normal carbonate, $PbCO_3$, may be prepared by the action of sodium hydrogen carbonate upon lead chloride. The basic carbonate, $Pb_3(OH)_2(CO_3)_2$, is formed when alkali carbonates are added to solutions of the lead ion. This compound is important commercially as the paint pigment "white lead." It is prepared commercially by the action of air, carbon dioxide, and acetic acid vapor upon lead metal. The essential reactions for the process may be represented by the equations

$$2\ Pb + O_2 + 2\ HOAc \rightarrow 2\ Pb(OH)OAc \quad \text{(HOAc represents acetic acid)}$$
$$6\ Pb(OH)OAc + 2\ CO_2 \rightarrow Pb_3(OH)_2(CO_3)_2 + 3\ Pb(OAc)_2 + 2\ H_2O$$

The $Pb(OAc)_2$ which is formed in the second reaction is eventually used up in the process, with the regeneration of acetic acid.

Although the covering power of white lead paints is excellent, it has the disadvantage of turning dark in the presence of hydrogen sulfide due to the formation of black lead sulfide.

6. *Other lead compounds.* **Lead sulfate,** $PbSO_4$, formed by ionic combination, is insoluble in water, but readily dissolved by solutions containing an excess of alkali or acetate ions. **Lead acetate,** $Pb(OAc)_2$, is one of the few soluble compounds of lead; it is a weak electrolyte, indicating that it dissolves mainly as a covalent compound rather than as an ionic one. The **chromate,** $PbCrO_4$, is in-

soluble in water but dissolves readily in acids and alkalies. Because of its yellow color it is widely used as a paint pigment and dye under the name "chrome yellow." Hydrogen sulfide precipitates black **lead sulfide,** PbS, which is insoluble in dilute acids and alkali sulfides.

The organometallic **lead tetraethyl,** $Pb(C_2H_5)_4$, is a covalent compound which is liquid at ordinary temperatures. It is used extensively in the production of "antiknock" gasoline. It is prepared by the reaction of ethyl chloride with a sodium-lead alloy, according to the equation

$$4\ C_2H_5Cl + Na_4Pb \rightarrow Pb(C_2H_5)_4 + 4\ NaCl$$

All soluble lead salts are poisonous. They act as cumulative poisons because their elimination, which is through the kidneys, is very slow. Extreme care is exercised to prevent lead poisoning in the industries dealing with lead and its compounds. Poisoning often results from the entrance of lead into the body through the mouth or nose.

35.23 Properties of Lead of Analytical Importance

Lead chloride, white, is precipitated from cold solutions which are fairly concentrated in Pb^{++}, but not from dilute, hot solutions. Lead sulfide, black, is precipitated by hydrogen sulfide in dilute acid solutions. The sulfide is insoluble in dilute nonoxidizing acids and alkali sulfides but is dissolved by dilute nitric acid. The precipitation of the insoluble salts, lead sulfate (white) and lead chromate (yellow), is important in the detection of lead ions in solution.

QUESTIONS

1. What chemical property do mercury, silver, and lead have in common that is of analytical importance?
2. The electrode potentials of mercury and silver are negative while that of lead is positive. What is the action, if any, of hydrochloric acid upon each of these metals?
3. The roasting of an ore of a metal usually results in the conversion of the metal to the oxide. Why does the roasting of cinnabar produce metallic mercury rather than an oxide of mercury?
4. What properties make mercury valuable as a thermometric substance?
5. Why is mercury not attacked by hydrochloric acid even though it dissolves readily in nitric acid or hot sulfuric acid?
6. Why are mercury (II) halides spoken of as weak electrolytes?
7. Write electronic formulas for $HgCl_2$ and Hg_2Cl_2.
8. Compare by equations the hydrolysis and ammonolysis of mercury (II) chloride.
9. Describe the Parkes process for extracting silver from lead.
10. What properties of silver have made it valuable as a coinage metal down through the ages?

11. Explain the tarnishing of silver in the presence of materials containing sulfur.

12. Compare the solubilities of the silver halides in water and in aqueous ammonia.

13. Silver nitrate does not hydrolyze in aqueous solutions. What does this indicate in regard to the strength of silver hydroxide as a base?

14. Write equations for the electrode reactions when $Na[Ag(CN)_2]$ is used as the electrolyte in silver plating.

15. Outline the chemistry of the photographic process.

16. Describe the Betts process for the refining of lead.

17. How are silvered mirrors made?

18. Why should soft water not be conveyed in lead pipes?

19. Compare the nature of the bonds in $PbCl_2$ to those in $PbCl_4$. Would you expect the existence of Pb^{++++} ions? Explain.

20. Show by suitable equations that lead (II) hydroxide is amphoteric.

21. Account for the solubility of $PbCl_2$ in solutions of high chloride concentration.

22. How is the paint pigment "white lead" prepared commercially?

23. What is a commercial use of lead tetraethyl?

REFERENCES

"Lead and Its Alloys," G. O. Hiers, *Ind. and Eng. Chem.*, **41** (10) 2124 (1949).

"Lead Poisoning," J. E. Hatfield, *Chem. Ind.*, **62** (3) 401 (March, 1948).

"Photographic Development," T. H. James, *Sci. American*, Nov., 1952; p. 30.

CHAPTER THIRTY-SIX

The Metals of Analytical Group II

DIVISION A — LEAD, BISMUTH, COPPER, CADMIUM

Analytical Group II consists of the metals whose ions form chlorides which are soluble in dilute acid but whose sulfides are precipitated by hydrogen sulfide in 0.3 molar hydrochloric acid. Lead appears in Group II as well as in Group I because its chloride is of intermediate solubility in cold water. Mercury occurs in both Groups I and II because mercury (I) chloride is insoluble whereas mercury (II) chloride is soluble in dilute hydrochloric acid.

The ions Pb^{++}, Bi^{+++}, Cu^{++}, and Cd^{++}, which comprise **Division A,** form sulfides insoluble in sodium sulfide solutions. This property permits the separation of these ions from those of **Division B,** Hg^{++}, As^{+++}, Sb^{+++}, and Sn^{++++}, whose sulfides are soluble in water containing an excess of sodium sulfide.

If the ions of the less common metals were to be included in our scheme of analysis, Group II would contain ions of such metals as Au, Pt, Mo, Ru, Rh, Pd, Ir, Os, W, Re, Ge, and Te as well as the ones listed above.

The chemistry of lead was considered in Chapter 35 with that of the metals of

TABLE 36·1 Some Properties of the Division A Metals of Analytical Group II

Property	*Lead*	*Bismuth*	*Copper*	*Cadmium*
Atomic number	82	83	29	48
Atomic weight	207.21	208.98	63.54	112.40
Electronic structure	2,8,18,32,18,4	2,8,18,32,18,5	2,8,18,1	2,8,18,18,2
Oxidation states	+2, +4	−3, +3, +5	+1, +2, +3	+2
Oxidation potential	(Pb/Pb^{++}) +0.13	(Bi/Bi^{+++}) −0.32	(Cu/Cu^{++}) −0.34	(Cd/Cd^{++}) +0.40
Density, g./cm.^{3}, at 20°	11.34	9.78	8.92	8.65
Melting point, °C	327.4	271.0	1083	320.9
Boiling point, °C	1750	1420.0	2582	767

Analytical Group I. The other metals of Division A will be considered here and those of Division B will be discussed later in this chapter. Some of the more important properties of the Division A metals are listed in Table 36·1 on page 577.

BISMUTH

36.1 Periodic Relationships of Bismuth

Bismuth is a member of Periodic Group VA, which also includes nitrogen, phosphorus, arsenic, and antimony. The elements of this group furnish an excellent illustration of the gradation in properties characteristic of groups of the periodic system. Nitrogen, the lightest member of the group, is a typical nonmetal in that it accepts electrons from active metals and forms the nitride ion $N^{\equiv}$, as in magnesium nitride, Mg_3N_2, and lithium nitride, Li_3N. Bismuth is the heaviest member of the group, and it is almost entirely metallic in character. It gives up three of its five valence electrons to active nonmetals to form the tripositive ion, Bi^{+++}. The nonmetallic character of nitrogen and the metallic character of bismuth, each of which has five valence electrons, can be attributed for the most part to the greater distance of the valence shell from the nucleus in atoms of bismuth. This means that the attraction of the positive nucleus for valence electrons is much smaller in an atom of bismuth than in an atom of nitrogen.

The properties of phosphorus, arsenic, and antimony are intermediate between those of nitrogen and bismuth, with the nonmetallic character becoming less pronounced with increasing atomic weights. Atoms of each member of this family have five valence electrons and exhibit oxidation states of +3 and +5. Consult Chapters 25 and 27 for additional considerations of group relationships among the members of this periodic group.

36.2 History of Bismuth

Bismuth was known to the alchemists as early as the fifteenth century, although it was often confused with antimony, tin, and lead. The element was first described accurately by J. H. Pott in 1739. The name "bismuth" is supposedly derived from the German term "Weissmuth."

36.3 Occurrence and Metallurgy of Bismuth

Bismuth is most often found in the free state in nature. It also occurs in combination as **bismuth ocher,** Bi_2O_3, and **bismuth glance,** Bi_2S_3. The chief sources of the metal and its compounds are Bolivia, Canada, Spain, and the United States. It is produced in the United States as a by-product of the refining of other metals, particularly lead. Ores containing the free metal are treated by heating them in inclined iron pipes, whereupon the metal melts and flows away from the gangue. The oxide and sulfide are roasted and then heated with charcoal. As the bismuth is set free, it melts and collects beneath the less dense material.

36.4 Properties and Uses of Bismuth

Bismuth is a lustrous, hard, and brittle metal with a reddish tint. The metal burns when heated in air, giving the oxide, Bi_2O_3, but oxidizes only superficially in moist air at ordinary temperatures to form a coating of oxide which protects it against further oxidation. Bismuth reduces steam and combines directly with the halogens and sulfur. Oxidizing acids, such as hot sulfuric and nitric, dissolve it, forming salts. It is dissolved slowly by hydrochloric acid in the presence of air, forming the chloride, $BiCl_3$. An unstable hydride of bismuth, BiH_3, exists; it is called **bismuthine.**

Melted bismuth expands upon solidifying, a most unusual property. Because of this, it is used in the formation of alloys to prevent them from shrinking upon solidification. Alloys of bismuth, tin, and lead have low melting points, which make them useful for electrical fuses, safety plugs for boilers, and automatic sprinkler systems (Fig. 36–1). Some of these alloys melt even in hot water. For example, **Rose's metal** (Bi, 50 per cent; Pb, 25 per cent; Sn, 25 per cent) melts at 94°; and **Wood's metal** (Bi, 50 per cent; Pb, 25 per cent; Sn, 12.5 per cent; Cd, 12.5 per cent) melts at 65.5°. Such low-melting alloys are used occasionally in heating baths in the laboratory, when customary substances for this purpose are found to be unsuitable. Bismuth alloys are also used to some extent as antifriction metals, as solders, as dental alloys, and as alloys for taking impressions of engravings such as wood cuts.

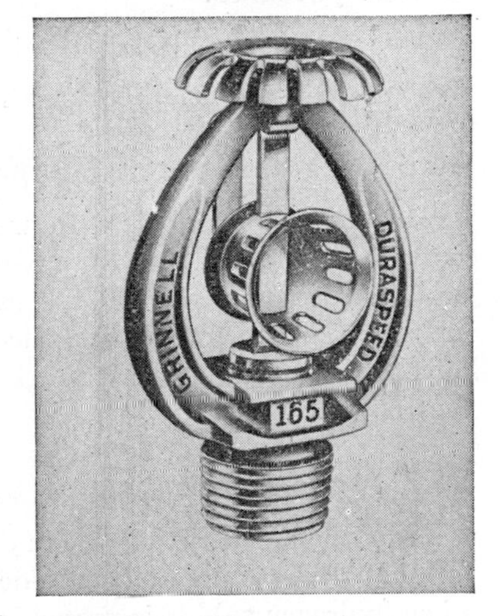

Fig. 36–1 Sprinkler head for an automatic fire extinguisher. *Grinnell Co.*

36.5 Compounds of Bismuth

1. *Oxides and hydroxides.* When bismuth is burned in air or when the nitrate is ignited, yellow **bismuth (III) oxide,** Bi_2O_3, is formed. This oxide reveals the basic character of the lower oxidation state by dissolving in acids to form salts. It does not exhibit acidic properties such as the ability to react with bases. Alkali hydroxides or aqueous ammonia precipitate the white **hydroxide,** $Bi(OH)_3$, from solutions of trivalent bismuth salts. When a suspension of bismuth hydroxide is boiled, it loses the elements of a molecule of water, forming bismuth oxyhydroxide, $BiO(OH)$.

Bismuth (V) oxide, Bi_2O_5, is produced by the action of very strong oxidizing agents upon the trioxide. This oxide shows its acidic character by dissolving in concentrated sodium hydroxide to form **sodium bismuthate,** $NaBiO_3$. This salt reacts with nitric acid to give **bismuthic acid,** $HBiO_3$, which is a very strong oxidizing agent. It is used in analytical chemistry in the detection and estimation of manganese, which it oxidizes from Mn^{++} to MnO_4^-.

2. *Bismuth (III) sulfide.* When hydrogen sulfide is passed into a solution of a bismuth salt, brown **bismuth (III) sulfide,** Bi_2S_3, is precipitated. Bi_2S_3 does not dissolve in concentrated sulfide solutions to form thiosalts. This property is utilized in separating bismuth from arsenic and antimony, which do form soluble thiosalts.

3. *Salts of bismuth.* Bismuth (III) oxide dissolves in acids forming the corresponding salts, such as the chloride, $BiCl_3 \cdot 2\ H_2O$; the nitrate, $Bi(NO_3)_3 \cdot 5\ H_2O$; and the sulfate, $Bi_2(SO_4)_3$. Bismuth salts hydrolyze readily when water is added, forming **hydroxysalts.**

$$BiCl_3 + 2\ H_2O \rightleftharpoons Bi(OH)_2Cl + 2\ H^+ + 2\ Cl^-$$
$$Bi(NO_3)_3 + 2\ H_2O \rightleftharpoons \underline{Bi(OH)_2NO_3} + 2\ H^+ + 2\ NO_3^-$$

The **dihydroxychloride** loses the elements of a molecule of water to form **bismuth oxychloride.**

$$Bi(OH)_2Cl \rightarrow BiOCl + H_2O$$

The **dihydroxynitrate** when repeatedly washed with water is converted to **bismuth hydroxide.**

$$Bi(OH)_2NO_3 + H_2O \rightarrow \underline{Bi(OH)_3} + H^+ + NO_3^-$$

When dried, bismuth dihydroxynitrate forms the **oxynitrate,** $BiONO_3$.

36.6 Uses of Bismuth Compounds

The compounds of bismuth are not widely nor extensively used. The **oxycarbonate,** $(BiO)_2CO_3$, and the oxynitrate (under the names **bismuth subcarbonate** and **bismuth subnitrate**) are used in medicine for the treatment of stomach disorders, such as gastritis and ulcers, and of skin diseases, such as eczema. The oxychloride is known as "pearl white" and is used as a paint pigment and in face powders.

36.7 Properties of Bismuth of Analytical Importance

Bismuth chloride is soluble in dilute hydrochloric acid, but hydrolyzes in water, forming the insoluble oxychloride. Bismuth (III) sulfide, brown, is precipitated when hydrogen sulfide is passed into a solution of a bismuth salt; it is insoluble in dilute hydrochloric acid and alkali sulfides, but is dissolved by dilute nitric acid. Bismuth hydroxide, white, is precipitated by aqueous ammonia. Upon the addition of a sodium stannite solution, bismuth (III) is reduced to metallic bismuth, black; this reaction serves as a confirmatory test for the element.

COPPER

The history and periodic relationships of copper were considered in Sections 35.10 and 35.9, respectively.

36.8 Occurrence of Copper

Copper occurs in both the native and combined forms. The most important deposit of native copper in the world is that in the Michigan peninsula near

Houghton. The largest single mass of native copper yet found weighs 420 tons, and it is now on display in the Smithsonian Institution in Washington. The most important copper ores are the sulfides, such as **chalcocite,** Cu_2S, and **chalcopyrite,** $CuFeS_2$. Others are **cuprite,** Cu_2O; **melaconite,** CuO; and **malachite,** $Cu_2(OH)_2CO_3$.

The United States has been the leading producer of copper (Fig. 36–2). The largest known deposit of copper sulfide ore, however, is in the Andes Mountains in Chile. Chile ranks second in the production of copper to the United States; Rhodesia, the Congo, and Canada also rank high.

Fig. 36–2 An open-pit copper mine at Morenci, Arizona. The size of the parked automobiles and the buildings in the foreground will help you get some notion of the extent of this mine. *Copper and Brass Research Association*

Copper is found in trace amounts in plants in regions where there are copper ores. It is also found in the brightly colored feathers of certain birds, and in the blood of certain marine animals such as lobsters, oysters, and cuttlefish, where it serves the same oxygen-carrying function as iron in the blood of higher animals (Section 32.26).

36.9 Metallurgy of Copper

Native copper ores are pulverized, the gangue is washed away, and then the copper is melted and poured into molds to cool. Oxide and carbonate ores are often leached with sulfuric acid to produce copper (II) sulfate solutions, from which copper metal may be obtained by electrodeposition. High grade oxide or carbonate ores are reduced by heating with coke mixed with a suitable flux.

Sulfide ores are usually low grade, containing less than 10 per cent copper, but they are frequently accompanied by small quantities of gold, silver, the platinum group metals, antimony, bismuth, selenium, and tellurium. The recovery of the precious metals from copper ores is important to the economics of the copper industry.

Low grade sulfide ores of copper are first concentrated by the flotation process (Section 33.5). The concentrate (or a high grade sulfide ore if concentration was unnecessary) is then roasted in a furnace at a temperature below the fusion point of the ore. Roasting drives off the moisture, removes part of the sulfur as sulfur dioxide, and leaves a mixture called "calcine," which consists of Cu_2S, FeS, FeO, and SiO_2. The roasted ore is smelted by mixing it with limestone, to serve as a flux, and heating the mixture above its melting point. The reactions taking place during the formation of the slag are given by the following equations:

$$CaCO_3 + SiO_2 \rightarrow CaSiO_3 + CO_2$$
$$FeO + SiO_2 \rightarrow FeSiO_3$$

The Cu_2S, impure with FeS, which remains after smelting is called "matte."

Reduction of the matte is accomplished in a "converter" by blowing air through the molten material. The air first oxidizes the iron (II) sulfide to iron (II) oxide and sulfur dioxide. Sand is added to form a slag of iron (II) silicate with the iron (II) oxide. After the iron has been removed, the air blast converts the Cu_2S to Cu_2O, and as soon as copper (I) oxide is formed, it is reduced by copper (I) sulfide to metallic copper. The equations are

$$2\ Cu_2S + 3\ O_2 \rightarrow 2\ Cu_2O + 2\ SO_2$$
$$2\ Cu_2O + Cu_2S \rightarrow 6\ Cu + SO_2$$

The last traces of copper (II) oxide produced by the air blast are removed by stirring the molten metal with poles of green wood, the resulting gases acting as reducing agents (Fig. 36–3), or, recently in some industries, by reduction with H_2 and CO produced catalytically from methane or natural gas. The copper obtained in this way has a characteristic appearance due to the air blisters which it contains, and is called "blister copper."

Fig. 36–3 In making blister copper, the last traces of copper (II) oxide are removed by stirring the molten copper with poles of green wood. *Encyclopaedia Britannica Films, Inc.*

The impure copper is cast into large plates, which are used as anodes in the electrolytic purification of the metal (Section 20.7). Thin sheets of pure copper serve as the cathodes, and copper (II) sulfate, acidified with sulfuric acid, serves as the electrolyte. The impure copper passes into solution from the anodes and pure copper plates out on the cathodes as electrolysis proceeds. Gold and silver in the anodes do not oxidize but fall to the bottom of the electrolytic cell as anode mud along with bits of slag and Cu_2O. Silver, gold, and the platinum group metals are recovered from the anode mud as valuable by-products. The metals more active than copper, such as zinc and iron, are oxidized; and their cations pass into solution, where they remain. The copper deposited on the cathode has an average purity of 99.955 per cent. The value of the precious metals recovered from the anode mud is often sufficient to pay the cost of the electrolytic refining.

36.10 Properties of Copper

Copper is a reddish-yellow metal. It is ductile and malleable, so that it is readily fashioned into wire, tubing, and sheets. Copper is the best conductor of the cheaper metals but when used for this purpose it must be quite pure, since small amounts of impurities reduce its electrical conductivity greatly.

Copper is relatively inactive chemically. In moist air, it first turns brown, due to the formation of a very thin, adherent film of oxide or sulfide. Prolonged weathering of copper causes it to become coated with a green film of the basic carbonate, $Cu_2(OH)_2CO_3$, which is similar to the mineral malachite.

$$2\ Cu + O_2 + CO_2 + H_2O \rightarrow Cu_2(OH)_2CO_3$$

This compound, or the basic sulfate, is responsible for the green color of copper roofs, gutters, and downspouts that have been weathered for a considerable time. When heated in air, copper oxidizes and forms copper (II) oxide along with some copper (I) oxide. Oxidizing acids, and nonoxidizing acids in the presence of air, convert copper to the corresponding copper (II) salts. Aqueous ammonia in the presence of air will dissolve copper and give a blue solution containing $[Cu(NH_3)_4]^{++}$. Alkali hydroxides do not act upon the metal. Sulfur vapor reacts with hot copper to give both Cu_2S and CuS. Hot copper burns in chlorine to give $CuCl$.

36.11 Uses of Copper

The extent and wide range of the uses of copper cause it to be regarded as second in importance to iron. The chief use of copper is in the production of electrical wiring for a wide variety of uses. Because of its resistance to corrosion it is extensively used as roofing material, for covering bottoms of wooden ships, for utensils used in the cooking of foods and in the fermentation industries, and for coins.

The fact that copper may be electrolytically deposited in thin sheets which are smooth and tough makes it useful in electrotyping. An impression of the type is made in wax, and this is rubbed with graphite to make its surface an electrical conductor. This is used as the cathode in an electrolytic cell containing copper sulfate as the electrolyte and an anode of copper. Copper is plated out on the graphite film until the deposit becomes the thickness of a sheet of paper. The copper sheet is removed from the wax and is then strengthened by covering its back surface with lead. Plates prepared in this way are used in printing books.

Copper is also used in the production of a great many alloys. Among the more important ones are **brass** (Cu, 60–82 per cent; Zn, 18–40 per cent), **bronze** (Cu, 70–95 per cent; Zn, 1–25 per cent; Sn, 1–18 per cent), **aluminum bronze** (Cu, 90–98 per cent; Al, 2–10 per cent), **German silver** (Cu, 50–60 per cent; Zn, 20 per cent; Ni, 20–25 per cent), and **nickel coin** (Cu, 75 per cent; Ni, 25 per cent). Other alloys containing copper are bell metal, gun metal, silver coin, sterling silver, gold coin, jewelry gold, and jewelry silver.

36.12 Oxidation States of Copper

Copper forms two principal series of compounds which are based upon the oxidation states of +1 and +2, respectively. When the one electron in the outermost shell of the copper atom is involved in bond formation, the oxidation state of +1 is exhibited. When an additional electron from the underlying shell is removed, the copper (II) ion results. When two electrons from the underlying shell are used in bonding, copper exhibits an oxidation state of +3; copper (III) compounds are rare and relatively unimportant, however. Copper (I) forms a complete series of binary compounds such as the halides and the oxide, but the ternary oxygen salts are few in number and readily decomposed by water. In contrast, copper (II) forms a complete series of oxygen salts while some of its binary compounds are unstable and break down spontaneously.

36.13 Copper (I) Compounds

Compounds containing univalent copper are frequently referred to as "cuprous" compounds, e.g., CuCl, cuprous chloride, and Cu_2O, cuprous oxide. Solid salts of copper (I) show a variety of colors, but solutions are colorless.

1. *Copper (I) oxide.* Cu_2O may be prepared as a reddish-brown precipitate by boiling copper (I) chloride with sodium hydroxide.

$$2\ CuCl + 2\ OH^- \rightarrow \underline{Cu_2O} + 2\ Cl^- + H_2O$$

When basic solutions of copper (II) salts are heated with reducing agents, copper (I) oxide precipitates.

$$2\ Cu^{++} + 2\ OH^- + 2\ e^-\ (\text{reducing agent}) \rightarrow \underline{Cu_2O} + H_2O$$

This reaction is the basis for the test for the presence of reducing sugars in the urine in the diagnosis of diabetes (Section 32.8). The reagent most often used for this purpose is Benedict's solution, which is a solution of copper (II) sulfate, sodium carbonate, and sodium citrate. The addition of a reducing sugar, such as glucose, causes the precipitation of the reddish-brown copper (I) oxide.

Copper (I) oxide is used in the manufacture of red glass and the red glaze on porcelain.

2. *Copper (I) hydroxide.* This compound is formed as a yellow precipitate when

a cold solution of copper (I) chloride in hydrochloric acid is treated with sodium hydroxide. The hydroxide is unstable and decomposes into the oxide and water upon heating.

3. *Copper (I) chloride.* When copper metal is added to a solution of copper (II) chloride acidified with hydrochloric acid, an oxidation-reduction reaction takes place with the precipitation of copper (I) chloride.

$$Cu^{++} + 2\ Cl^- + Cu \rightarrow 2\ \underline{CuCl}$$

This white crystalline compound is readily soluble in concentrated hydrochloric acid, forming the complex ion $[CuCl_2]^-$.

$$CuCl + Cl^- \rightleftharpoons [CuCl_2]^-$$

The two chlorides of the $[CuCl_2]^-$ ion are bonded to the copper by covalent bonds.

$$\left[\ \overset{\times\times}{\underset{\times\times}{\vdots Cl \vdots}} Cu \overset{\times\times}{\underset{\times\times}{\vdots Cl \vdots}}\ \right]^-$$

Dilution with water brings about reprecipitation of the copper (I) chloride.

Among other stable and insoluble copper (I) binary salts are Cu_2S (black), CuCN (white), CuBr (white), and CuI (white).

36.14 Copper (II) Compounds

The more common compounds of copper are those in which the metal is bivalent (cupric compounds). In the solid state, the copper (II) compounds may be blue, black, green, yellow, or white. However, dilute solutions of all soluble copper (II) compounds have the blue color of the hydrated copper (II) ion, $[Cu(H_2O)_4]^{++}$.

1. *Copper (II) oxide.* Copper (II) oxide, CuO, is a black insoluble compound that may be obtained by heating the carbonate or nitrate, as shown by the following equations:

$$CuCO_3 \rightarrow CuO + CO_2$$
$$2\ Cu(NO_3)_2 \rightarrow 2\ CuO + 4\ NO_2 + O_2$$

Copper (II) oxide can also be prepared by heating finely divided copper in oxygen. Because of the ease with which the copper can be reduced to a valence of one or to the metal, hot copper (II) oxide is a good oxidizing agent. As such, it is used in the analysis of organic compounds to determine the percentage of carbon that they contain. Copper (II) oxide oxidizes the carbon to carbon dioxide, which is absorbed by sodium hydroxide, and the gain in weight is taken as a measure of the quantity of carbon dioxide produced and absorbed.

2. *Copper (II) hydroxide.* When hydroxide ions are added to cold solutions of copper (II) salts, a bluish-green gelatinous precipitate of the hydroxide, $Cu(OH)_2$, is formed. If hot solutions are employed, CuO is formed. Copper (II) hydroxide is somewhat amphoteric and dissolves slightly in solutions of concentrated alkalies, the cuprate ion, $[Cu(OH)_4]^{=}$, being formed. The hydroxide is also soluble in aqueous ammonia, giving **tetraamminecopper (II) hydroxide,** $[Cu(NH_3)_4](OH)_2$, which is a strong base.

$$Cu(OH)_2 + 4\ NH_3 \rightarrow [Cu(NH_3)_4]^{++} + 2\ OH^-$$

The tetraamminecopper (II) ion, $[Cu(NH_3)_4]^{++}$, has a deep blue color. The formation of this color is used as a qualitative test for the presence of the copper (II) ion in solution. Solutions of $[Cu(NH_3)_4]SO_4 \cdot H_2O$ are used in industry to dissolve cellulose in one of the methods for the manufacture of rayon (Section 32.14).

Bordeaux mixture contains copper (II) hydroxide and calcium sulfate. It is made by adding a suspension of calcium hydroxide to a solution of copper (II) sulfate, and it is used in the form of a spray as a fungicide and insecticide.

3. *Copper (II) sulfate.* The sulfate is the most important of the copper salts. The anhydrous salt is colorless, but when crystallized from aqueous solution, the blue pentahydrate, $[Cu(H_2O)_4]SO_4 \cdot H_2O$, known as **blue vitriol,** is formed. As indicated by the formula, four of the water molecules are coordinated to the copper (II) ion and the fifth is attached to the sulfate and to two of the coordinated water molecules by hydrogen bonds. The structure of the pentahydrate may be represented as follows:

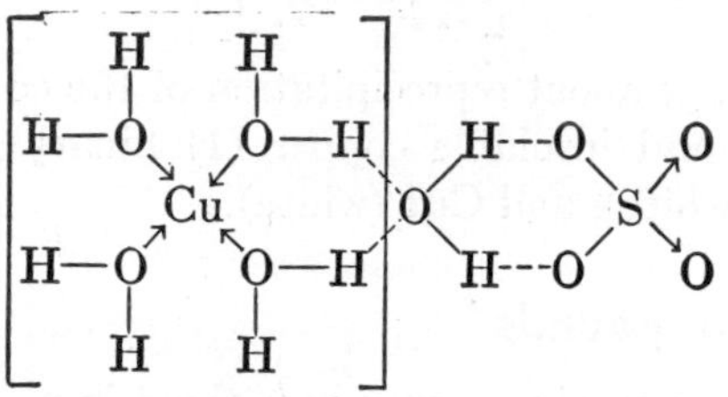

```
┌                ┐
    H     H
    |     |
 H—O      O—H    H--O    O
     ↘  ↙       /     \  ↗
      Cu       O        S
     ↗  ↖       \     /  ↘
 H—O      O—H    H--O    O
    |     |
    H     H
└                ┘
```

The dehydration of this salt proceeds in steps, yielding successively $CuSO_4 \cdot 3\ H_2O$ (with loss of the two nonhydrogen-bonded waters), $CuSO_4 \cdot H_2O$ (with loss of the other two water molecules coordinated to the Cu(II) ion), and finally $CuSO_4$ (with loss of the water molecule attached to the sulfate ion).

The sulfate is produced commercially by oxidizing the sulfide, either directly to the sulfate, or to the oxide, which may be converted to the sulfate by reaction with sulfuric acid. In the laboratory, the anhydrous sulfate may be prepared by oxidizing copper with hot concentrated sulfuric acid.

$$Cu + 2\ H_2SO_4 \rightarrow CuSO_4 + SO_2 \uparrow + 2\ H_2O$$

Aqueous solutions of copper (II) sulfate are acidic by hydrolysis:

$$[Cu(H_2O)_4]^{++} + H_2O \rightleftharpoons [Cu(H_2O)_3OH]^{+} + H_3O^{+}$$

or simply,

$$Cu^{++} + H_2O \rightarrow CuOH^{+} + H^{+}$$

Copper (II) sulfate is used in the electrolytic refining of copper, in electroplating, in the Daniell cell, in the manufacture of pigments, as a mordant in the textile industry, and to prevent the growth of algae in reservoirs and swimming pools. Because anhydrous copper (II) sulfate readily takes up water, turning blue, this salt is used in detecting water in liquids such as alcohol and ether, and it is also used to remove water from these liquids.

4. *Copper (II) halides.* Anhydrous **copper (II) chloride,** $CuCl_2$, may be prepared as a yellow crystalline salt by direct union of the elements. The blue-green hydrated salt $Cu(H_2O)_2Cl_2$ may be obtained by treating the carbonate or hydroxide of copper (II) with hydrochloric acid and evaporating the solution.

Concentrated solutions of copper (II) chloride are green because they contain both the hydrated copper (II) ion $[Cu(H_2O)_4]^{++}$, which is blue, and the **tetrachlorocuprate** ion $[CuCl_4]^{=}$, which is yellow. Upon dilution, water molecules replace the chloro groups of the $[CuCl_4]^{=}$ ion, and the solution becomes blue.

Copper (II) bromide, $CuBr_2$, is a black solid which may be obtained by direct union of the elements or by the action of hydrobromic acid upon the oxide or carbonate.

It is interesting that **copper (II) iodide,** CuI_2, does not exist. When a solution containing the copper (II) ion is treated with an excess of iodide, an oxidation-reduction reaction occurs, with precipitation of copper (I) iodide and the formation of elementary iodine.

$$2\ Cu^{++} + 4\ I^{-} \rightarrow 2\ \underline{CuI} + I_2$$

This reaction is used in the quantitative determination of copper by titration of the liberated iodine with a standard solution of sodium thiosulfate.

5. *Copper (II) sulfide.* CuS, black, is precipitated by passing hydrogen sulfide into acid, alkaline, or neutral solutions of copper (II) salts. The sulfide readily dissolves in warm dilute nitric acid with the formation of elementary sulfur and nitric oxide.

$$3\ CuS + 8\ H^{+} + 2\ NO_3^{-} \rightleftharpoons 3\ Cu^{++} + 3\ \underline{S} + 2\ NO\uparrow + 4\ H_2O$$

Copper (II) sulfide dissolves only to a slight extent in solutions of alkali sulfides.

36.15 Complex Copper Salts

Copper possesses the property of forming both complex cations and anions which are quite stable. Copper (II) ions coordinate with four neutral ammonia molecules and form the deep blue tetraamminecopper (II) ion.

$$[Cu(H_2O)_4]^{++} + 4\ NH_3 \rightleftharpoons [Cu(NH_3)_4]^{++} + 4\ H_2O$$

The fact that the ammonia molecules displace the coordinated water molecules indicates the greater stability of the ammine complex. In fact, the ammine complex is so stable that most slightly soluble copper (II) compounds are dissolved by aqueous ammonia. The copper ion is located at the center of a square formed by the four attached groups, whether they be water or ammonia molecules or negative ions, $[Cu(H_2O)_4]^{++}$, $[Cu(NH_3)_4]^{++}$, $[CuCl_4]^{=}$, $[Cu(OH)_4]^{=}$.

Monovalent copper forms linear complexes with ammonia, $[Cu(NH_3)_2]^{+}$, with the halides, $[CuX_2]^{-}$, and with cyanide ions, $[Cu(CN)_2]^{-}$. In contrast to the divalent copper complexes, the copper (I) complexes are colorless.

36.16 Properties of Copper of Analytical Importance

Chloride ions cause CuCl, white, to precipitate from solutions containing Cu(I) ions, but copper (II) chloride is soluble in water and in dilute hydrochloric acid. Sulfide ions precipitate CuS, black, from acidic, neutral, or alkaline solutions containing Cu(II) ions. This sulfide is readily dissolved by warm, dilute nitric acid, elementary sulfur and nitric oxide being formed. Alkali cyanides dissolve copper

(II) sulfide with the formation of the complex dicyanocuprate (I) ion, $[Cu(CN)_2]^-$. An excess of aqueous ammonia changes light blue $[Cu(H_2O)_4]^{++}$ ions to deep blue $[Cu(NH_3)_4]^{++}$ ions. The precipitation of pink $Cu_2Fe(CN)_6$ serves as a delicate test for the copper (II) ion.

CADMIUM

The periodic relationships of cadmium were discussed in Section 35.1, along with its congeners zinc and mercury.

36.17 History and Occurrence of Cadmium

Cadmium was discovered in 1817 by Stromeyer and about the same time, but independently, by Hermann. Stromeyer named the metal "cadmia fornacum," meaning "furnace zinc," because it was found in the residues of a zinc furnace.

Cadmium is found in the rare mineral **greenockite,** CdS, and in small amounts (less than 1 per cent) in some zinc ores. Most of our supply of cadmium comes from zinc smelters and from the sludge obtained from the electrolytic refining of zinc.

36.18 Metallurgy and Uses of Cadmium

In the smelting of cadmium-containing zinc ores, the two metals are reduced together. Because cadmium is more volatile (b.p. 767°) than zinc (b.p. 907°), they may be separated by fractional distillation. Separation of the two metals is also possible by selective electrolytic deposition. Cadmium is less active than zinc and is deposited at a lower voltage.

A large part of the cadmium produced is used in electroplating metals, such as iron and steel, to protect them from corrosion. The electrolytic bath contains tetracyanocadmate ions, $[Cd(CN)_4]^{=}$, made by mixing cadmium cyanide and sodium cyanide. The equation for the cathodic reduction is

$$[Cd(CN)_4]^{=} + 2\ e^- \rightarrow Cd + 4\ CN^-$$

Cadmium-plated metals are more resistant to corrosion, more easily soldered, and more attractive in appearance than galvanized (zinc-coated) metals.

Cadmium is used in making a number of alloys. Certain ones are easily fusible; these include **Wood's metal** (12.5 per cent Cd), melting at 65.5°, and **Lipowitz alloy** (10 per cent cadmium), melting at 70°. Some antifriction bearing metals contain cadmium. These alloys melt at a higher temperature and have a lower friction coefficient than **Babbitt metal** (Section 36.30). Amalgamated cadmium, along with cadmium sulfate, is used in the Weston standard cell for measuring electrical potentials. Rods of cadmium are used in nuclear reactors (Section 30.11) to absorb neutrons and thus control the chain reaction in the reactor or pile.

36.19 Properties and Compounds of Cadmium

Cadmium is a silvery, crystalline metal resembling zinc. Since it is only slightly tarnished by air or water at ordinary temperatures, it is used as a coating to protect other metals from corrosion. Cadmium dissolves slowly in hot, moderately dilute hydrochloric or sulfuric acid, with the evolution of hydrogen. It is also dissolved by nitric acid, the oxides of nitrogen being evolved.

The oxide, CdO, is formed as a brown solid when cadmium burns in air. Alkali hydroxides react with cadmium salts and produce the white hydroxide, $Cd(OH)_2$, which is soluble in aqueous ammonia by forming the **tetraammine complex,** $[Cd(NH_3)_4]^{++}$. Solutions of cadmium chloride are poor conductors of electricity; the compound dissolves as covalent molecules which ionize only slightly:

$$CdCl_2 \rightleftharpoons Cd^{++} + 2\ Cl^-$$

Cadmium chloride is converted almost completely into $[CdCl_4]^=$ by high concentrations of the chloride ion. **Cadmium sulfide,** CdS, is formed as a bright yellow precipitate by the action of hydrogen sulfide upon solutions of cadmium salts. It is used as a paint pigment called **cadmium yellow.** The carbonate, phosphate, cyanide, and ferrocyanide are all insoluble in water. All cadmium compounds are soluble in an excess of sodium iodide, due to the formation of the complex, $[CdI_4]^=$.

36.20 Properties of Cadmium of Analytical Importance

Cadmium ions are not precipitated by chloride ions. Yellow cadmium sulfide is formed when cadmium ions and sulfide ions are brought together in basic, neutral, or weakly acidic solutions. The sulfide is dissolved by strong acids, but is insoluble in alkali sulfide solutions. Alkali hydroxides precipitate cadmium hydroxide, white, which is dissolved by aqueous ammonia with the formation of $[Cd(NH_3)_4]^{++}$. The white, insoluble salt, $Cd_2Fe(CN)_6$, is useful in detecting cadmium in solution.

DIVISION B — MERCURY, ARSENIC, ANTIMONY, TIN

The chemistry of mercury was considered in Chapter 35 with the metals of Analytical Group I. Some properties of the Division B metals are listed in Table 36·2.

TABLE 36·2 Some Properties of the Division B Metals of Analytical Group II

Property	*Mercury*	*Arsenic*	*Antimony*	*Tin*
Atomic number	80	33	51	50
Atomic weight	200.59	74.9216	121.75	118.69
Electronic structure	2,8,18,32,18,2	2,8,18,5	2,8,18,18,5	2,8,18,18,4
Oxidation states	+1, +2	+3, +5	+3, +5	+2, +4
Oxidation potential	(Hg/Hg^{++}) −0.79	(As/As^{+++}) −0.25	(Sb/Sb^{+++}) −0.21	(Sn/Sn^{++}) +0.14
Density, g./cm.³, at 20°	13.546	5.73	6.68	7.31
Melting point, °C	−38.87	817 (36 atm.)	630.5	231.9
Boiling point, °C	356.57	610 (sublimes)	1440	2337

ARSENIC

The periodic relationships of arsenic, a member of the nitrogen family (Periodic Group VA), have been discussed in Section 36.1.

36.21 History of Arsenic

Compounds of arsenic were known and used extensively by the ancients. The early Romans and Greeks used some of the naturally occurring arsenic compounds as pigments because of their bright colors. The Greeks associated the yellow sulfide, orpiment, with the male sex to indicate its potency. They called it "arsenikon," which means "masculine," and from which the element takes its name. The free element was first isolated in 1250 by Albertus Magnus. "White arsenic," As_4O_6, was commonly used as a poison during the medieval period, and, of course, is still used for this purpose.

36.22 Occurrence and Preparation of Arsenic

Arsenic is found both as the free element and combined. Its principal native compounds are **arsenopyrite,** FeAsS; **realgar,** As_2S_2; and **orpiment,** As_2S_3. Arsenic is widely distributed in trace amounts in the sulfide ores of many metals; consequently, the metals and the sulfuric acid obtained from these sulfides frequently contain arsenic as an impurity. A large part of the arsenic used in the United States is a by-product from the gases of copper furnaces, from which it is collected by Cottrell precipitators (Section 13.10).

Pure arsenic is obtained by subliming native arsenic. When arsenopyrite is heated, it decomposes according to the equation

$$4\ FeAsS \rightarrow 4\ FeS + As_4 \uparrow$$

When arsenic ores are roasted, As_4O_6 is formed. Reduction of the oxide by heating with carbon produces the element.

$$As_4O_6 + 6\ C \rightarrow As_4 \uparrow + 6\ CO \uparrow$$

36.23 Properties and Uses of Arsenic

Elementary arsenic exists in several allotropic modifications. Ordinary gray arsenic is monatomic (As), is metallic in appearance, and sublimes at 615°, forming tetratomic As_4 molecules which are tetrahedral in structure. When arsenic vapor is cooled rapidly, an unstable yellow crystalline modification is produced. This allotrope consists of As_4 molecules and is soluble in carbon disulfide. Arsenic vapor has the odor of garlic and is yellow in color. Arsenic is a member of an intermediate class of elements which possess in some degree the properties of both metals and nonmetals. It is a metalloid (Section 33.2). Arsenic ignites when heated, producing white clouds of As_4O_6. It is slowly attacked by hot hydrochloric acid in the presence of air, forming arsenic (III) chloride, $AsCl_3$. Hot nitric acid readily oxidizes arsenic to arsenic acid, H_3AsO_4. Arsenic combines directly with sulfur, the halogens, and many metals. The trihalides (AsX_3) are either liquids or low melting solids with properties suggestive of covalent rather than ionic bonding, as observed in the absence of saltlike character.

Certain alloys contain arsenic as a hardening agent. Examples are bronze and lead shot.

36.24 Compounds of Arsenic

1. *Arsine.* Arsenic forms **arsine,** AsH_3, a compound which has a formula analogous to that of ammonia (NH_3). This gaseous compound has a "garlic" odor and is quite poisonous. It does not react with nor dissolve in water or acids to form compounds corresponding to ammonium compounds. Arsine is formed by reducing arsenic compounds by zinc in acid solution or by the action of a metallic arsenide, such as zinc arsenide, with acids.

$$As_4O_6 + 12\ Zn + 24\ H^+ \rightarrow 4\ AsH_3\uparrow + 12\ Zn^{++} + 6\ H_2O$$
$$Zn_3As_2 + 6\ H^+ \rightarrow 3\ Zn^{++} + 2\ AsH_3\uparrow$$

Arsine is unstable and decomposes into its elements when heated ($4\ AsH_3 \rightarrow As_4 + 6\ H_2$). In the Marsh test for arsenic (Fig. 36–4), the element is deposited as a black mirror from burning arsine when a cold glazed porcelain dish is held in the flame. This test is very sensitive and is commonly employed in the detection of arsenic poisoning.

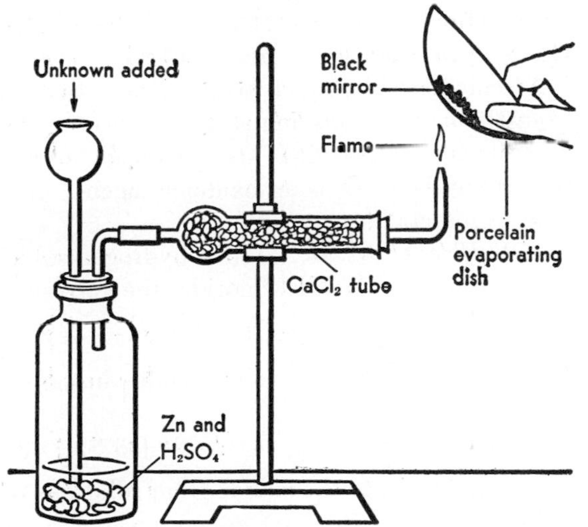

Fig. 36–4 The Marsh test for arsenic.

2. *Arsenic (III) oxide and arsenous acid.* The substance commonly referred to as "arsenic" or "white arsenic" is actually the oxide, As_4O_6. For convenience, the formula is often written As_2O_3 although the formula As_4O_6 corresponds to the vapor density. It is the product of the combustion of the element or its compounds. It has a sweet taste and is a violent poison. Arsenic (III) oxide is slowly dissolved by water with the formation of **arsenous acid,** H_3AsO_3.

$$As_4O_6 + 6\ H_2O \rightleftharpoons 4\ H_3AsO_3$$

Arsenous acid is amphoteric; i.e., it can behave either as an acid or as a base, as shown by the equations

$$As(OH)_3 \rightleftharpoons As(OH)_2^+ + OH^- \rightleftharpoons AsOH^{++} + OH^- \rightleftharpoons As^{+3} + OH^-$$
$$H_3AsO_3 \rightleftharpoons H^+ + H_2AsO_3^-$$

It acts as a base in the presence of hydrochloric acid, and as an acid in the presence of sodium hydroxide.

$$As(OH)_3 + 3\ H^+ + 3\ Cl^- \rightleftharpoons AsCl_3 + 3\ H_2O$$
$$H_3AsO_3 + (Na^+) + OH^- \rightarrow (Na^+) + H_2AsO_3^- + H_2O$$

Arsenous acid is known only in solution; when attempts are made to isolate it as a solid, it loses water and forms the oxide. All arsenites except those of the alkali metals are insoluble in water. **Copper (II) arsenite-acetate,** $Cu_3(AsO_3)_2 \cdot Cu(C_2H_3O_2)_2$, or **Paris green,** is used as an insecticide.

3. *Arsenic (V) oxide and arsenic acid.* **Arsenic (V) oxide,** As_2O_5, may be produced by heating **arsenic acid,** H_3AsO_4.

$$2\ H_3AsO_4 \rightarrow As_2O_5 + 3\ H_2O$$

Arsenic acid is formed when arsenic (III) oxide is oxidized by concentrated nitric acid.

$$As_4O_6 + 8\ HNO_3 + 2\ H_2O \rightarrow 4\ H_3AsO_4 + 8\ NO_2 \uparrow$$

By careful heating, H_3AsO_4 may be converted stepwise into **pyroarsenic acid,** $H_4As_2O_7$, **meta-arsenic acid,** $HAsO_3$, and finally the oxide, As_2O_5.

Arsenic acid is a much stronger acid than arsenous acid, as would be expected from the higher oxidation state (see Section 19.2), and it does not react as a base with strong acids as does arsenous acid. Arsenic acid is rather easily reduced, so that it can be used as an oxidizing agent. The arsenates of calcium and lead are used as insecticides.

4. *Sulfides of arsenic.* When hydrogen sulfide is passed into a hydrochloric acid solution of arsenic (III) chloride, the corresponding yellow sulfide is precipitated.

$$2\ AsCl_3 + 3\ H_2S \rightarrow \underline{As_2S_3} + 6\ H^+ + 6\ Cl^-$$

Arsenic (III) sulfide dissolves readily in sodium sulfide, forming the **thioarsenite,** Na_3AsS_3.

$$As_2S_3 + 3\ S^= \rightarrow 2\ AsS_3^{-3}$$

Acids reprecipitate the sulfide from solutions of thioarsenites.

$$2\ AsS_3^{-3} + 6\ H^+ \rightarrow \underline{As_2S_3} + 3\ H_2S \uparrow$$

Arsenic (V) sulfide, As_2S_5, is a yellow compound obtained very slowly as a precipitate when hydrogen sulfide is passed into a solution of arsenic acid in hydrochloric acid.

$$2\ H_3AsO_4 + 5\ H_2S \rightarrow \underline{As_2S_5} + 8\ H_2O$$

The arsenic acid oxidizes hydrogen sulfide in cold, weakly acidic solutions.

$$2\ H_3AsO_4 + 5\ H_2S \rightarrow \underline{As_2S_3} + 2\ \underline{S} + 8\ H_2O$$

Iodide ions catalyze the reduction of pentavalent arsenic by sulfide ions.

$$2\ I^- + AsO_4^{-3} + 8\ H^+ \rightarrow As^{+++} + 4\ H_2O + I_2$$

$$I_2 + H_2S \rightarrow 2\ H^+ + 2\ I^- + \underline{S}$$

Arsenic (V) sulfide dissolves in sodium sulfide with the formation of the **thioarsenate,** Na_3AsS_4. The addition of an acid reprecipitates the sulfide, As_2S_5.

36.25 Uses of Arsenic Compounds

The most important uses of arsenic compounds depend upon their poisonous character. They are used as weed killers, cattle and sheep dips, and insecticides. The compounds most widely used for these purposes are Paris green, lead arsenate, calcium arsenate, sodium arsenite, and arsenous acid.

In very small doses, 0.005 gram or less, white arsenic (As_4O_6) is used as a medicine for the treatment of anemia and skin diseases. Persons who use arsenic regularly (arsenic eaters) develop a tolerance for it and can take larger doses than ordinary persons, to whom doses of 0.125 to 0.25 gram are usually fatal. The best antidote for arsenic poisoning is freshly precipitated iron (III) hydroxide (ferric hydroxide), which forms a compound with As_4O_6 that is insoluble in the body fluids.

A considerable amount of arsenic is used in making dyes, drugs, and glass. **Salvarsan (606)** is a synthetic organo-arsenic compound, which is used as a specific remedy for such diseases as syphilis, relapsing fever, and the tropical disease known as frambesia. **Neoarsphenamine** or **Neosalvarsan** is a drug similar in nature to salvarsan, but preferred to the latter because it is less toxic and has milder after-effects. Antibiotics such as penicillin are replacing organo-arsenic drugs to a large degree.

36.26 Properties of Arsenic of Analytical Importance

Arsenic is precipitated from solution as the yellow sulfide, As_2S_3, which is insoluble in dilute hydrochloric acid, but dissolved by alkali sulfides. Acids reprecipitate the sulfide from alkali thioarsenite solutions. Arsenic (III) sulfide is not dissolved by 6 M hydrochloric acid, but a mixture of aqueous ammonia and hydrogen peroxide dissolves it by converting it to the arsenate ion. The arsenate ion can be detected by precipitating it as white, crystalline **magnesium ammonium arsenate,** $MgNH_4AsO_4$. The Marsh test (Section 36.24) is useful for detecting traces of arsenic compounds.

ANTIMONY

36.27 History of Antimony

Antimony has been used, both as a metal and in compounds, for at least 5000 years. The Chaldeans used the metal in making vases and ornaments. The sulfide, Sb_2S_3, was used by the Egyptians as a pigment and for painting eyebrows at least as early as 3000 B.C. Compounds of antimony were also used in medicine. Basil Valentine, a Benedictine monk of the fifteenth century, collected all that the alchemists knew about this element in his treatise, "The Triumphal Chariot of Antimony." The symbol, Sb, is derived from the Greek term "stibium" (Sb_2S_3), which was translated into Latin by Geber as "antimonium."

36.28 Occurrence and Metallurgy of Antimony

The principal ore of antimony is **stibnite,** Sb_2S_3, most of which is supplied to the world by China, Mexico, Argentina, Bolivia, and Chile. The sulfide is separated from earthy material of the ore by melting it, and it is then reduced by heating with iron.

$$Sb_2S_3 + 3\ Fe \rightarrow 2\ Sb + 3\ FeS$$

The ore may also be roasted to the oxide, from which antimony may be obtained by reduction with carbon.

$$Sb_4O_6 + 6\ C \rightarrow 4\ Sb + 6\ CO$$

36.29 Properties of Antimony

Antimony is a lustrous silver-white metal, brittle, and readily pulverized. It is but little tarnished in dry air but oxidizes slowly in moist air. The metal is readily attacked by the halogens, phosphorus, and sulfur. It is attacked, but not dissolved, by hot nitric acid, forming Sb_4O_6. It is slowly dissolved by hot concentrated sulfuric acid, forming $Sb_2(SO_4)_3$ and evolving SO_2. The fact that the metal and its oxides do not react with nitric acid to give the nitrate indicates a lack of pronounced base-forming properties. However, the metallic nature of the element is more pronounced than that of arsenic, which lies immediately above it in Group VA of the Periodic Table.

"Explosive antimony" is an interesting material in that it explodes when it is subjected to a sharp blow, an electric spark, or when heated to 110°–120°. It appears to be a solid solution of unstable α-antimony in $SbCl_3$, and it is formed on the cathode as a shiny black deposit when a solution of antimony trichloride is carefully electrolyzed. The explosion involves a change from amorphous (α-antimony) to the more stable crystalline modification (β-antimony) with the evolution of 2,440 calories of heat per gram-atom.

36.30 Uses of Antimony

Lead hardened by the addition of 10 to 20 per cent of antimony is suitable for shrapnel, bullets, and bearings. Because of its resistance to corrosion by acids, it is used in making storage battery plates. Babbitt metal is an alloy of antimony with tin and copper, which is used as an antifriction metal. Since antimony, like bismuth, expands on freezing, it is used as a constituent of type metal, to which it confers this property, thus giving a sharp and distinct imprint of the type.

Antimony trisulfide has been used in range-finding shells, which give dense clouds of white smoke when they explode.

36.31 Compounds of Antimony

1. *Stibine*, SbH_3, is prepared by reducing antimony compounds with zinc in acid solution. Stibine is poisonous and unstable towards heat. It gives a mirror with the Marsh test, as does arsine. The two compounds may be distinguished by the fact that the antimony deposit is insoluble in sodium hypochlorite, whereas the arsenic deposit is dissolved by this reagent.

2. *Oxides and acids of antimony.* **Antimony (III) oxide,** Sb_4O_6, and **antimony (V) oxide,** Sb_2O_5, resemble the oxides of arsenic in their preparation and properties. Both oxides form acids, and antimony (III) oxide exhibits some basic properties in forming salts with acids. The antimony in **antimonic acid** has a coordination number of 6, the formula being $HSb(OH)_6$. **Sodium antimonate,** $NaSb(OH)_6$, is one of the very few slightly soluble salts of sodium. Sb_2O_4 is also known; it is formed when either Sb_4O_6 or Sb_2O_5 is heated with a free access of air.

3. *Antimony halides.* Antimony forms all of the **trihalides** and **pentahalides** except the pentabromide and the pentaiodide. They are prepared by direct union of the elements, and by the action of the hydrohalic acids on the oxides of antimony. Hydrolysis of antimony (III) chloride, known as "butter of antimony," forms the **dihydroxychloride**

$$SbCl_3 + 2\ H_2O \rightleftharpoons \underline{Sb(OH)_2Cl} + 2\ H^+ + 2\ Cl^-$$

which loses water and forms the **oxychloride,** which is white and insoluble.

$$Sb(OH)_2Cl \rightarrow \underline{SbOCl} + H_2O$$

An excess of hydrochloric acid changes the oxychloride to **tetrachloroantimonous acid,** $HSbCl_4$.

4. *Sulfides of antimony.* **Antimony (III) sulfide,** Sb_2S_3, is interesting in that it occurs in two strikingly different modifications. A black form is found in nature as the mineral stibnite; this is also the form which results when antimony and sulfur are heated together. However, the precipitate obtained by the reaction of hydrogen sulfide with slightly acidified solutions of compounds of trivalent antimony is brilliant orange-red. The orange-red modification changes to the black one upon heating or upon standing in contact with a dilute solution of an acid. Antimony (III) sulfide is used in the manufacture of matches (Section 27.5) and as a pigment in the production of red rubber.

Antimony (III) sulfide dissolves in sodium sulfide solutions, forming **thioantimonite** ions.

$$Sb_2S_3 + 3\ S^{=} \rightarrow 2\ SbS_3^{-3}$$

Acidification of the solution causes the sulfide to reprecipitate.

$$2\ SbS_3^{\equiv} + 6\ H^+ \rightarrow \underline{Sb_2S_3} + 3\ H_2S \uparrow$$

The addition of hydrochloric acid in excess to antimony (III) sulfide causes it to dissolve, with the **tetrachloroantimonate (III) ion,** $SbCl_4^-$, and hydrogen sulfide being formed.

$$Sb_2S_3 + 6\ H^+ + 8\ Cl^- \rightarrow 2\ SbCl_4^- + 3\ H_2S \uparrow$$

Antimony (V) sulfide, Sb_2S_5, is also known. It is orange in color and is similar to Sb_2S_3 in many of its reactions. However, treatment of this sulfide with an excess of hydrochloric acid causes reduction of the antimony to the trivalent state.

$$Sb_2S_5 + 6\ H^+ + 8\ Cl^- \rightarrow 2\ SbCl_4^- + 3\ H_2S \uparrow + 2\ \underline{S}$$

5. *Potassium antimonyl tartrate.* When antimony (III) oxide is heated with a solution of potassium hydrogen tartrate, $KHC_4H_4O_6$, there is formed **potassium antimonyl tartrate,** $KSbOC_4H_4O_6$, which is also known as "tartar emetic." Like the oxychloride, this compound contains the univalent **antimonyl group** (SbO). Tartar emetic is used in medicine and in the dyeing of fabrics.

36.32 Properties of Antimony of Analytical Importance

Antimony (III) sulfide is an orange-red colored compound which precipitates when hydrogen sulfide is passed into a solution of the trichloride or weakly acidic solutions of antimonites and other compounds of trivalent antimony. When compounds of pentavalent antimony are employed, **antimony (V) sulfide,** Sb_2S_5, is precipitated. Both sulfides of antimony, like those of arsenic, dissolve in solutions of alkali sulfides. When solutions containing the thiosalts are acidified, antimony (III) sulfide is precipitated. This sulfide dissolves in 6 M hydrochloric acid with the formation of the complex ion, $SbCl_4^-$. Aluminum (and other active metals) reduces antimony to the metallic state. The metal can be dissolved in a mixture of nitric acid and oxalic acid, the compound $SbOHC_2O_4$ being formed. Hydrogen sulfide precipitates the orange-red sulfide, Sb_2S_3, from solutions of $SbOHC_2O_4$.

TIN

36.33 History and Occurrence of Tin

Tin has been found in early Egyptian tombs, showing that the metal was known from the very early periods of history. The metal was obtained from deposits of cassiterite in England by the Romans and Phoenicians. The symbol for tin, Sn, comes from the Latin name "stannum."

The most important and abundant ore of tin is called **cassiterite** or **tinstone,** SnO_2, the main deposits of which occur in England, the East Indies, Bolivia, the Congo, and Nigeria. No important deposits have been found in the United States; yet more than half of the world's production of tin is used in this country.

Some tin is reclaimed from the bright scrap which is left from the manufacture of tin cans. Formerly the detinning process involved treatment with an excess of chlorine. Volatile tin tetrachloride is formed which can be readily removed by distillation from the underlying iron, which is little affected by the chlorine. Most detinning of tin plate is now based upon the removal of the tin by alkali solutions with the formation of stannites and hydrogen.

36.34 Metallurgy of Tin

The tin ore is crushed and washed with water to separate the lighter rocky material from the heavier ore. Roasting of the ore removes arsenic and sulfur as volatile oxides, and oxides of other metals are extracted by means of hydrochloric acid. The purified ore is reduced by carbon.

$$SnO_2 + 2\ C \rightarrow Sn + 2\ CO$$

The molten tin which collects on the bottom of the furnace is drawn off and cast into blocks (block tin). The crude tin is remelted and permitted to flow away from the higher-melting impurities, which are chiefly compounds of iron and arsenic. Further purification of the tin is accomplished by electrolysis. Impure tin anodes, pure tin cathodes, and a bath of fluosilicic acid (H_2SiF_6) and sulfuric acid are used in the electrolytic purification of the metal.

36.35 Properties of Tin

Tin exists in three solid allotropic forms. They are **gray tin** (cubic crystals), **malleable tin** (tetragonal crystals), and **brittle tin** (rhombic crystals). The malleable form is silvery-white with a bluish tinge. When a rod of it is bent, the crystals slip over one another, producing a sound described as "tin cry." When malleable or "white tin" is heated, it changes to the brittle modification. White tin changes slowly at low temperatures (below 13.2°) into gray tin, a powdery form of the element. Consequently, articles made of tin are likely to disintegrate in cold weather, particularly if kept cold for a long time. The change progresses slowly from a spot of origin, with the gray tin which is formed catalyzing its own formation. An effect is thus produced which, in a way, is similar to the spread of an infection in a plant or animal body. For this reason, it is called "tin disease" or "tin pest" (Fig. 36–5).

Fig. 36–5 Tin disease. A full-sized pig of tin which was delayed in shipment during the winter. The name Banka shows that the metal came from an East Indian island famous for high-purity tin. One corner has crumbled and the metal is distinctly granular at both top and bottom. *American Sheet and Tinplate Co.*

The metal dissolves slowly in hydrochloric acid when the acid is cold and dilute but rapidly when hot and concentrated, $SnCl_2$ and H_2 being produced. Very dilute cold nitric acid converts tin to tin (II) nitrate. Concentrated nitric acid rapidly converts tin into insoluble, hydrated metastannic acid, H_2SnO_3. Aklali hydroxides dissolve tin, forming stannites and hydrogen.

$$Sn + 2\ OH^- + 2\ H_2O \rightarrow [Sn(OH)_4]^= + H_2 \uparrow$$

The reactions with concentrated nitric acid and sodium hydroxide show that tin is not entirely metallic in character. Dry chlorine oxidizes tin to the tetrachloride, $SnCl_4$, and oxygen converts it to tin (IV) oxide, SnO_2; tin burns with a white flame. At ordinary temperatures tin is permanent in air or water, a property which makes it valuable for plating.

36.36 Uses of Tin

The principal use of tin is in the production of **tin plate,** i.e., iron plate coated with tin. Tin plate is widely used in the manufacture of the familiar "tin" cans and utensils of various sorts. The older method of applying tin plate involves the thorough cleaning of the surface of the iron by "pickling" in a bath of sulfuric acid, and then running the sheet of metal through molten tin. This is known as the "hot-dip" method. A thin film of tin adheres to the surface of the iron and protects it from corrosion. Most tin plate is now applied electrolytically because this uses only about 50 per cent as much metal as the hot-dip process, and it gives a more uniform coating. Electroplating with tin involves passing a continuous strip of sheet steel through an alkaline bath containing sodium or potassium stannate. The thickness of the plate is determined by the speed at which the sheet passes through the bath and by the current density employed. After the tin plate has been cleaned, it is heated to the melting point of tin to make it adhere well and to give it a bright appearance. Iron is more active than tin and will corrode more rapidly when in contact with tin than otherwise. Iron and tin in contact with each other, and both in contact with moist air, comprise an electrolytic cell which promotes corrosion (Section 37.31). As a result, when a scratch through the tin plate exposes the iron, corrosion sets in rapidly.

Solid tin, called **block tin,** has been used in the fabrication of stills for the preparation and distribution of distilled water. Tinfoil was formerly used for wrapping foods, but in recent years it has been largely replaced by aluminum foil and cellophane. Tin is also used in making alloys, such as bronze (Cu and Sn), solder (Sn and Pb), and type metal (Sn, Pb, and Sb). A plate of nickel and tin, in about equal proportions, is being used widely in Europe as a substitute for chromium plate. It has good appearance and is cheaper to produce.

36.37 Compounds of Tin

1. *Oxides of tin.* Depending upon the method of preparation, **tin (II) oxide** (stannous oxide), SnO, is a black or green powder. It may be prepared by treating a hot solution of a tin (II) compound with an alkali carbonate, or by heating tin (II) oxalate in the absence of air. The equations are

$$Sn^{++} + CO_3^{=} \rightarrow \underline{SnO} + CO_2$$
$$SnC_2O_4 \rightarrow \underline{SnO} + CO_2 + CO$$

When tin is burned in air, **tin (IV) oxide** (stannic oxide), SnO_2, is formed. The product is white when cold, but yellow when hot. This oxide is used as an opacifier in the manufacture of opaque glass and enamels such as found on sinks and bathtubs.

2. *Tin (II) hydroxide.* Soluble bases precipitate tin (II) ions from solution as tin (II) hydroxide, $Sn(OH)_2$, which is white and gelatinous in character. An excess of alkali causes the hydroxide to dissolve, forming **stannites** such as $NaSn(OH)_3$.

$$Sn(OH)_2 + OH^- \rightarrow Sn(OH)_3^-$$

The stannite ion is an active reducing agent. It is used in qualitative analysis to test for bismuth by reducing white bismuth hydroxide to black metallic bismuth.

$$2\ \underline{Bi(OH)_3} + 3\ Sn(OH)_3^- + 3\ OH^- \rightarrow 2\ \underline{Bi} + 3\ Sn(OH)_6^{=}$$

3. *Tin (II) chloride (stannous chloride).* **Tin (II) chloride** can be obtained as the **dihydrate** ($SnCl_2 \cdot 2\ H_2O$) by evaporating a solution formed by the reaction of tin or tin (II) oxide with hydrochloric acid. The salt is hydrolyzed by water, forming the basic **hydroxychloride,** $Sn(OH)Cl$.

$$SnCl_2 + H_2O \rightleftharpoons \underline{Sn(OH)Cl} + H^+ + Cl^-$$

Tin (II) chloride finds wide use as a reducing agent because of the ease with which tin is oxidized to the tin (IV) condition. It follows that aqueous solutions of tin (II) must be protected against air oxidation. Tin (II) chloride dihydrate is called "tin salt" in industry, where it is used as a mordant in dyeing fabrics, in the weighting of silk, and in the manufacture of tin-coated metal articles such as pins and paper clips.

4. *Tin (IV) chloride (stannic chloride).* Tin (IV) chloride is formed when an excess of chlorine reacts with metallic tin. It is a colorless liquid, soluble in organic solvents, such as carbon tetrachloride, and it is a nonconductor of electricity. These properties are typical of covalent compounds. When dissolved in water, the tetrachloride is highly hydrolyzed, whereas in hydrochloric acid, **hexachlorostannic acid** is produced.

$$SnCl_4 + 2\ HCl \rightarrow H_2SnCl_6$$

The ammonium salt of hexachlorostannic acid, $(NH_4)_2SnCl_6$, is known as **pink salt** and is used as a mordant in dyeing.

5. *Sulfides of tin.* Dark brown **tin (II) sulfide,** SnS, is precipitated when hydrogen sulfide is passed into a solution of a tin (II) salt. Unlike tin (IV) sulfide, the tin (II) compound is not dissolved by alkali sulfides.

Tin (IV) sulfide is prepared as a yellow precipitate by the interaction of hydrogen sulfide and a moderately acid solution of tetravalent tin. It dissolves in alkali sulfides with the formation of thiostannate ions, $SnS_3^{=}$. The addition of acid reprecipitates the sulfide.

$$SnS_3^{=} + 2\ H^+ \rightarrow \underline{SnS_2} + H_2S \uparrow$$

Concentrated hydrochloric acid dissolves tin (IV) sulfide according to the equation

$$SnS_2 + 4\ H^+ + 6\ Cl^- \rightarrow SnCl_6^{=} + 2\ H_2S \uparrow$$

Under the name "mosaic gold" tin (IV) sulfide is used as a gilding pigment.

36.38 Hydrolysis of Covalent Halides

Except for the carbon compounds, the tetrahalides of the Group IVA elements hydrolyze when dissolved in water, for the most part as indicated by the general equation

$$MX_4 + 2\ H_2O \rightarrow MO_2 \text{ (or hydrate thereof)} + 4\ HX$$

The mechanism by which the tetrahalides of silicon, germanium, tin, and lead hydrolyze may be as follows: Taking the hydrolysis of silicon tetrachloride as an example, the silicon atom carries a partial net positive charge because it is less electronegative than chlorine in the $SiCl_4$ molecule. During hydrolysis, the positively charged silicon atom may attract hydroxide ions of water, forming a pentacovalent intermediate, according to the following equation:

$$SiCl_4 + :OH^- \rightarrow [Cl_4Si{:}OH]^-$$

One of the highly negative chlorines is then easily lost from the intermediate as a chloride ion.

$$[Cl_4Si{:}OH]^- \rightarrow Cl_3SiOH + Cl^-$$

This process continues until all four chlorine atoms are replaced by hydroxide groups, $Si(OH)_4$ being the final hydrolytic product. The conversion of the hydroxide ions of water to coordinated hydroxo groups leaves an excess of hydrogen ions in solution, and hydrochloric acid is formed. Resistance of the carbon tetrahalides to hydrolysis is probably due to the fact that carbon is coordinately saturated (all its bonding orbitals are filled with electrons) in these compounds and it cannot form intermediates of the type suggested for silicon tetrachloride. Other halides such as sulfur hexafluoride, SF_6, do not hydrolyze because the central element is already coordinately saturated in each case. On the other hand, tungsten hexachloride, WCl_6, hydrolyzes because the maximum coordination number for tungsten is 8. It is interesting to note that preliminary studies show that the new compound XeF_4 (see Section 24.7) can hydrolyze; further work is necessary to establish the exact nature of this hydrolysis reaction.

The silicon halides undergo complete hydrolysis, but with halides of more ionic character, hydrolysis is often less complete and it may be suppressed by the addition of acids. Thus aqueous solutions of tin tetrachloride can be prepared in the presence of hydrochloric acid.

36.39 Stannic Acids and Stannates

When an alkali is added to a solution of a tin (IV) compound, a white precipitate forms. We would expect this compound to have the formula $Sn(OH)_4$ and to be acidic in character. However, neither the acid nor salts derived from it have been found. On the other hand, alkali stannates are known which appear to be derived from an **orthostannic acid** which may be formulated as $H_2[Sn(OH)_6]$; its sodium salt, for example, may be written as $Na_2[Sn(OH)_6]$. Orthostannic acid readily loses water, yielding a **metastannic acid,** H_2SnO_3, and finally the anhydride, SnO_2. When this anhydride is fused with sodium hydroxide, sodium metastannate, Na_2SnO_3, is formed. The metastannic acid mentioned above is sometimes called **alpha-stannic acid** to distinguish it from **beta-stannic acid,** which is formed when hot concentrated nitric acid reacts with tin. Beta-stannic acid has the same composition as the alpha form but it is insoluble in acids and very slightly soluble in strongly alkaline solutions.

36.40 Properties of Tin of Analytical Importance

The colorless tin (II) ion forms a dark brown precipitate when hydrogen sulfide gas is passed into a solution which is dilute in hydrochloric acid. Tin (II) sulfide is insoluble in alkali sulfides, but is dissolved by polysulfide solutions, with the formation of thiostannate ions, $SnS_3^{=}$. Solutions of tin (IV) compounds yield a yellow precipitate of tin (IV) sulfide when treated with hydrogen sulfide; this sulfide is soluble in alkali sulfides, forming alkali thiostannates, and is dissolved by concentrated hydrochloric acid, the hexachlorostannate ion, $SnCl_6^{=}$, being formed. Active metals, such as aluminum, reduce $SnCl_6^{=}$ to $SnCl_3^{-}$ or to metallic tin. When mercury (II) chloride is added to a solution containing tin (II) ions, mercury (I) chloride (white) or metallic mercury (black) is formed.

QUESTIONS

1. Write balanced equations for the reaction of metallic bismuth with each of the following: O_2, H_2O (steam), Cl_2, S, HNO_3, and HCl (in air).
2. What are the properties of metallic bismuth that make it commercially useful?
3. Compare the basicity and acidity of Bi_2O_3 and Bi_2O_5.
4. Write equations to show the hydrolysis of $BiCl_3$.
5. Describe the electrolytic refining process for metallic copper.
6. Why must copper be quite free of impurities when used as an electrical conductor?
7. Account for the green coloration of copper which has been weathered.
8. In terms of electronic structure, explain the existence of copper in three oxidation states.
9. Compare the stability of the copper (I) halides to that of copper (II) halides.
10. Explain the use of copper (II) sulfate in urine analysis.
11. Write the structure for $Cu(H_2O)_4SO_4 \cdot H_2O$.
12. Write an equation to explain the acidic nature of copper (II) sulfate solutions.
13. Relate CuI to an analytical method for determining copper (II) quantitatively.

14. Why are most slightly soluble copper salts readily dissolved by aqueous ammonia?

15. What property makes cadmium effective as a protective coating for other metals?

16. Why is cadmium chloride considered to be a weak electrolyte?

17. Arsenic is classed as a metalloid. Explain.

18. Compare and contrast arsine and ammonia.

19. Describe the Marsh test for arsenic.

20. What substance is commonly referred to as "arsenic" or "white arsenic"?

21. What are the composition and use of Paris green?

22. Account for the oxidation states +3 and +5 of arsenic in terms of electronic structure.

23. Which is the more acidic, As_4O_6 or As_2O_5?

24. Write equations to show the action of Na_2S upon As_2S_3 and As_2S_5.

25. Why is antimony used as a constituent of type metal?

26. Compare the metallic character of arsenic with that of antimony.

27. What is the coordination number of antimony in the antimonate ion?

28. What is meant by "tin pest," which is also known as "tin disease"?

29. What is the action of metallic tin with HCl, with HNO_3, and with NaOH?

30. How and why is tin plate applied to the surface of iron?

31. Write the equation for the thermal decomposition of tin (II) oxalate.

32. Write the equations for the reactions involved when aqueous NaOH is slowly added to a solution of tin (II) chloride.

33. Why cannot $SnCl_4$ be classified as a salt?

34. Why must aqueous solutions of $SnCl_2$ be protected from the air?

REFERENCES

"Gas Reduction — New Route to Copper Refining," (Staff) *Chem. Eng.*, June 12, 1961; p. 100.

"Electroplating Cadmium," Z. Iranas, *Mo. Rev. Electroplaters' Soc.*, **30** (7) 603 (July, 1943).

"New Insecticides," H. L. Haller, *J. Chem. Educ.*, **19** (7) 315 (1942).

"Cornwall as a Tin Producer," G. H. M. Farley, *Eng. and Mining Journal*, **147** (11) 78 (Nov., 1946).

"Tin Plating with Potassium Stannate," M. M. Sternfelds and F. A. Lowenkeim, *Trans. Am. Electrochem. Soc.*, **81**, 265 (1942).

"Acid Tin Plating," P. R. Pine, *Trans. Am. Electrochem. Soc.*, **80**, 631 (1941).

CHAPTER THIRTY-SEVEN

The Metals of Analytical Group III

NICKEL, COBALT, MANGANESE, IRON, ALUMINUM, CHROMIUM, ZINC

Analytical Group III consists of those common cations which are precipitated as sulfides or hydroxides in solutions of aqueous ammonia saturated with hydrogen sulfide, but which are not precipitated by hydrochloric acid nor by hydrogen sulfide in solutions that are 0.3 M in hydrogen ions. The sulfides of cobalt (II), nickel (II), manganese (II), iron (II), and zinc, and the hydroxides of chromium (III) and aluminum precipitate in ammonium sulfide solutions.

Five of the metals whose ions constitute Analytical Group III (Cr, Mn, Fe, Co, and Ni) are members of the first transition series (Period 4) of the Periodic Table. This series begins with scandium and ends with copper; it is a series in which the electron shell underlying the valence shell is being increased from 9 to 18 electrons. These elements have valence electrons in two shells; associated with this property are such characteristics as variation in valence, color of the ions, and tendency toward the formation of stable complex ions. It has already been pointed out that successive members of each of the transition series show striking resemblances to each other (Section 33.10). Atomic and ionic sizes of elements with similar electronic structures are important in determining the properties of the elements. Note that the following elements of Periodic Series 4 (and Analytical Group III) have atoms of very nearly the same radius (Å): Cr, 1.25; Mn, 1.29; Fe, 1.26; Co, 1.25; Ni, 1.24. Zinc and aluminum are representative metals (valence electrons in one shell) with atomic radii of 1.33 and 1.48, respectively. Some properties of the Analytical Group III metals are given in Table 37·1.

NICKEL

Iron, cobalt, and nickel comprise the first triad of Group VIII of the Periodic Table. The second triad consists of ruthenium, rhodium, and palladium, and the third, of osmium, iridium, and platinum. In each of these horizontal series the tendency to lose electrons decreases as the nuclear charge increases. Thus iron exhibits oxidation states of +2, +3, and +6; cobalt, +2, +3, and +4; while with nickel, oxidation states higher than +2 are extremely rare.

TABLE 37·1 Some Properties of the Metals of Analytical Group III

Property	*Aluminum*	*Chromium*	*Manganese*	*Iron*	*Cobalt*	*Nickel*	*Zinc*
Atomic number	13	24	25	26	27	28	30
Atomic weight	26.9815	51.996	54.9380	55.847	58.9332	58.71	65.37
Electronic structure	2 8 3	2 8 13 1	2 8 13 2	2 8 14 2	2 8 15 2	2 8 16 2	2 8 18 2
Oxidation states	+3	+2 +3 +6	+2 +3 +4 +6 +7	+2 +3 +6	+2 +3 +4	+2 +3 +4	+2
Oxidation potential	$\left(\frac{Al}{Al^{+++}}\right)$ +1.66	$\left(\frac{Cr}{Cr^{+++}}\right)$ +0.71	$\left(\frac{Mn}{Mn^{++}}\right)$ +1.18	$\left(\frac{Fe}{Fe^{++}}\right)$ +0.44	$\left(\frac{Co}{Co^{++}}\right)$ +0.28	$\left(\frac{Ni}{Ni^{++}}\right)$ +0.25	$\left(\frac{Zn}{Zn^{++}}\right)$ +0.76
Density g./cm.^{3} at 20°	2.70	7.1	7.20	7.86	8.71	8.9	7.14
Melting point, °C	660	1900	1244	1535	1493	1455	419.5
Boiling point, °C	2327	2642	2087	2800	3100	2800	907

37.1 History and Occurrence of Nickel

Because nickel ores are difficult to reduce, early attempts to produce the metal from its ores were unsuccessful. It was thought by the seventeenth century metallurgists that these nickel ores were copper ores because of their similarity in appearance; but when they failed to yield copper, they were called "Kupfer-nickel" (German). "Kupfer" means copper, and "nickel" refers to the devil which was thought to prevent the extraction of copper from the ores. The metal was first obtained by Cronstedt in 1751.

Nickel occurs, along with iron, as an alloy in meteorites (Fig. 37–1). Metallic nickel and iron probably constitute most of the core of the earth. The most important ores of nickel are **pentlandite,** (Ni, Cu, Fe)S, and **garnierite,** which is a hydrated magnesium-nickel silicate of variable composition. A large part of the nickel produced comes from Ontario, Canada. Other producing areas include Cuba, New Caledonia, the Scandinavian countries, South Africa, and Russia.

37.2 Metallurgy of Nickel

Pentlandite, (Ni, Cu, Fe)S, is roasted and then reduced with carbon. This process results in the production of an alloy containing nickel, iron, and copper

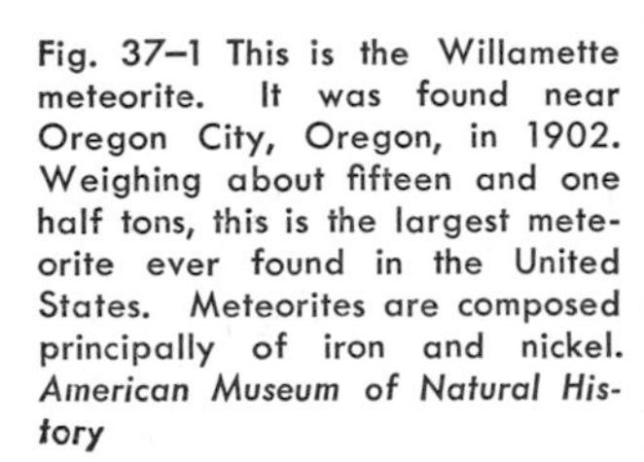

Fig. 37–1 This is the Willamette meteorite. It was found near Oregon City, Oregon, in 1902. Weighing about fifteen and one half tons, this is the largest meteorite ever found in the United States. Meteorites are composed principally of iron and nickel. *American Museum of Natural History*

which is known as "Monel metal." This alloy, because of its resistance to corrosion, has many important industrial uses. The process used most extensively in the production of pure metallic nickel in recent years involves the separation of the sulfides of nickel, copper, and iron by selective flotation. After separation, the nickel sulfide is converted to the oxide by roasting and the oxide is reduced by carbon. The metal obtained in this way is approximately 96 per cent pure. It is cast into huge anodes (425 pounds each) and refined electrolytically in a nickel (II) sulfate bath. The nickel which deposits on the cathode is 99.98 per cent pure. Noble metals, especially platinum, are recovered from the anode mud.

37.3 Properties and Uses

Nickel is a silvery-white metal that is hard, malleable, and ductile. Like iron and cobalt, it is highly magnetic. It is not oxidized by air under ordinary conditions, and it is resistant to the action of alkalies. Dilute acids slowly dissolve nickel, hydrogen being evolved. It is made **passive,** so that it no longer displaces hydrogen from dilute acids by exposure to concentrated nitric acid.

Because of its hardness, resistance to corrosion, and high reflectivity when polished, nickel is widely used in the plating of iron, steel, and copper. It is also a constituent of many important alloys. **Monel metal** (Ni, Cu, and a little Fe) is used as a corrosion-resistant alloy. **Permalloy** (Ni and Fe) is remarkably permeable to the magnetic field; it is used in instruments for the electrical transmission and reproduction of sound. **German silver** is a nickel-zinc-copper alloy. **Nichrome** and **chromel** are alloys containing nickel, iron, and chromium; they are resistant to oxidation at high temperatures and show high electrical resistance, so are used in electrical heating units such as electric stoves, pressing irons, and toasters. **Alnico** contains aluminum, nickel, iron, and cobalt; it is highly magnetic, being able to lift 4000 times its own weight of iron. **Platinite** and **invar** are nickel alloys which have the same coefficient of expansion as glass and are used for "seal-in" wires through glass, such as electric light bulbs. **Nickel coins** contain 75 per cent copper. Finely divided nickel is used as a catalyst in the hydrogenation of oils.

37.4 Compounds of Nickel

In combination, nickel exhibits an oxidation state of +2 almost exclusively. One notable exception is tetravalent nickel in the dioxide, NiO_2, a black hydrous substance formed by the oxidation of nickel (II) salts in alkaline solution. This oxide forms the anode in the Edison storage cell (Section 20.16).

Nickel (II) oxide, NiO, is prepared by heating the hydroxide, the carbonate, or the nitrate. When alkali hydroxides are added to solutions of nickel (II) salts, pale green **nickel (II) hydroxide,** $Ni(OH)_2$, precipitates. Both the oxide and the hydroxide are dissolved by aqueous ammonia with the formation of the deep blue **hexaamminenickel (II) hydroxide,** $[Ni(NH_3)_6](OH)_2$.

$$\underline{Ni(OH)_2} + 6\ NH_3 \rightarrow Ni(NH_3)_6^{++} + 2\ OH^-$$

The soluble salts of nickel are prepared from the oxide, hydroxide, or carbonate by treatment with the proper acid. The important soluble salts of the metal are the acetate, chloride, nitrate, sulfate, and the hexaamminenickel (II) sulfate. Ammoniacal solutions of the latter compound are used in nickel-plating baths. The hydrated nickel (II) ion, $[Ni(H_2O)_6]^{++}$, imparts a pale green color to the solutions and crystallized salts of the nickel (II) ion.

Nickel (II) sulfide is produced as a black precipitate by the action of ammoniacal sulfide solutions upon nickel (II) salts. This compound exists in at least two crystalline modifications of different degrees of solubility in mineral acids; this property is of value in the analytical scheme (Section 47.2).

Nickel carbonyl, $Ni(CO)_4$, is formed as a colorless volatile liquid (boiling at 43°) when carbon monoxide is led over finely divided nickel. It readily decomposes at higher temperatures and deposits pure nickel metal. The **Mond process** for separating nickel from other metals is based upon the formation and decomposition of nickel carbonyl. When carbon monoxide is passed over the mixture of metals, nickel carbonyl is formed and carried along with the excess carbon monoxide, leaving the other metals behind. When heated to 200°, the nickel carbonyl deposits the metal as a fine dust.

37.5 Properties of Nickel of Analytical Importance

Aqueous solutions of nickel salts are green. The addition of aqueous ammonia first causes pale green nickel hydroxide to precipitate, but an excess of ammonia dissolves the precipitate by forming the deep blue complex, $[Ni(NH_3)_6]^{++}$. Hydrogen sulfide causes the precipitation of brown or black nickel sulfide from neutral or alkaline solutions of nickel salts. This is readily soluble in acids, but it very quickly changes to another crystalline form that is nearly insoluble in dilute acid solutions. Nickel salts in nearly neutral solutions form a red precipitate with dimethylglyoxime.

COBALT

37.6 History of Cobalt

The name of this metal is derived from the German word "Kobold," which means "goblin." The reason for this was that the early metallurgists believed that goblins carefully guarded the cobalt ores and prevented man from liberating the metal. Brandt finally succeeded in isolating the metal in 1735. Even today, the metallurgy of both cobalt and nickel is difficult and complicated.

37.7 Occurrence and Metallurgy of Cobalt

The common cobalt minerals are **cobaltite,** $CoAsS$, and **smaltite,** $CoAs_2$, with the richest deposits of these minerals being found in Ontario, Canada. However, nearly all the world's production of cobalt is obtained as a by-product of the metallurgy of nickel, copper, iron, silver, and other metals. The leading producers are the Congo, Northern Rhodesia, and Canada. The metallurgy of cobalt involves its separation from nickel, copper, and iron, conversion to Co_3O_4, and the reduction of the oxide with aluminum or hydrogen.

$$3\ Co_3O_4 + 8\ Al \rightarrow 9\ Co + 4\ Al_2O_3$$

Purification of the metal is effected by electrolytic deposition on a rotating, stainless steel cathode.

37.8 Properties and Uses of Cobalt

The metal is similar to iron in appearance except that it has a faint tinge of pink. Like iron and nickel, it is magnetic. It is slowly soluble in warm dilute hydrochloric or sulfuric acid, and more rapidly soluble in dilute nitric acid. Like iron and nickel, cobalt is rendered passive by contact with concentrated nitric acid. It is not oxidized on exposure to the air, but at red heat it reduces steam with the evolution of hydrogen. The halogens, except fluorine, convert it to cobalt (II) halides. When cobalt is heated with fluorine, cobalt (III) fluoride, CoF_3, is formed.

Cobalt is alloyed with iron and small percentages of other metals in making high-speed cutting tools and surgical instruments. Permanent magnets are made from **Alnico** (Al, Ni, Co, Fe), **Hiperco** (Co, Fe, Cr), and **Vicalloy** (Co, Fe, V). Certain cobalt alloys, such as **Hastelloy** (Co, Ni) and **Vitallium** (Co, Cr, Mo, Ni, Fe), are used for high temperature work because they maintain their strength and resist wear and corrosion at elevated temperatures, even at bright red heat (800° C).

Finely divided cobalt metal is used as a catalyst in the hydrogenation of carbon monoxide and carbon dioxide with the formation of hydrocarbons, and for the oxidation of ammonia.

37.9 Compounds of Cobalt

1. *Hydroxides and oxides of cobalt.* Cobalt (II) hydroxide, $Co(OH)_2$, is formed as a blue flocculent precipitate when an alkali is added to a solution of a cobalt (II) salt. The blue color of the precipitate changes to violet and then pink, probably as a result of hydration. The hydroxide is readily soluble in aqueous ammonia to form **hexaamminecobalt (II) hydroxide,** $[Co(NH_3)_6](OH)_2$. Solutions of the latter compound are oxidized by air to the various cobalt (III) compounds; the oxidation is accompanied by a darkening of the solution.

When cobalt (II) hydroxide is heated in the absence of air, cobalt (II) oxide, CoO, results. This oxide is a black substance which dissolves in fused glass to give it a blue color; such glass is called "cobalt glass," and it contains cobalt (II) silicate. Ignition of the hydroxide or oxide in air gives rise to cobalt (II,III) oxide, Co_3O_4. Cobalt (III) oxide may be produced by gently heating cobalt (II) nitrate.

$$4\ Co(NO_3)_2 \rightarrow 2\ Co_2O_3 + 8\ NO_2 + O_2$$

2. *Cobalt (II) chloride.* Cobalt (II) oxide and hydroxide readily dissolve in hydrochloric acid. Concentration of the solution causes crystallization of **cobalt (II) chloride 6-hydrate,** $CoCl_2 \cdot 6\ H_2O$, which is red in color. The hydrated cobalt (II) ion, $[Co(H_2O)_6]^{++}$, exhibits a pink color in solution. When partially dehydrated, cobalt (II) chloride changes to a deep blue color. This is believed to result from a change in the coordination number of the cobalt (II) ion from six to four:

$$\underset{\text{pink}}{[Co(H_2O)_6]Cl_2} \rightarrow \underset{\text{blue}}{[Co(H_2O)_4]Cl_2} + 2\ H_2O$$

The same change in color is effected by dissolving $CoCl_2 \cdot 6\ H_2O$ in alcohol. Writing made on paper with a dilute solution of the hydrated salt is almost invisible, but when the paper is warmed, dehydration of the salt occurs, and the writing becomes blue. It fades again as hydration takes place from moisture of the air. This is the chemistry of one kind of invisible ink.

3. *Cobalt (II) sulfide.* Black **cobalt (II) sulfide,** CoS, is completely precipitated only from basic solutions. However, once precipitated, this sulfide is but slightly soluble in hydrochloric acid (see Section 37.10). Aqua regia readily dissolves it.

4. *Complex cobalt compounds.* In addition to the simple salts, oxides, and hydroxides, cobalt forms a large number of complex compounds. Cobalt (II) simple salts are more stable than are those of cobalt (III); complex cobalt (III) compounds, in contrast, are much more stable than the corresponding cobalt (II) salts. Thus, the majority of the more stable complex salts of cobalt contain the metal in the +3 oxidation state. Some of the more important cobalt (III) complexes are **hexaamminecobalt (III) chloride,** $[Co(NH_3)_6]Cl_3$; **potassium hexacyanocobaltate (III),** $K_3[Co(CN)_6]$; and **potassium hexanitrocobaltate (III),** $K_3[Co(NO_2)_6]$. In these complex compounds, the six coordinated groups, such as NH_3, CN^-, and NO_2^-, occupy the corners of a regular octahedron with the cobalt at the center (see Section 34.3).

37.10 Properties of Cobalt of Analytical Importance

Solutions of simple cobalt (II) compounds are pink. Hydrogen sulfide precipitates black cobalt (II) sulfide from basic solutions of cobalt. The sulfide changes quickly to another crystalline form which is only slightly soluble in dilute hydrochloric acid but readily soluble in aqua regia. When a concentrated solution of ammonium thiocyanate is added to a solution of a cobalt (II) salt, the complex ion $[Co(CNS)_4]^=$ is formed. The characteristic blue color of the ion is accentuated by the addition of acetone to the solution. Another test for cobalt involves its oxidation by the nitrite ion from +2 to +3, and precipitation of the insoluble yellow complex salt, $K_3[Co(NO_2)_6]$.

$$Co^{++} + 6\ NO_2^- \rightarrow [Co(NO_2)_6]^{-4}$$
$$[Co(NO_2)_6]^{-4} + NO_2^- + 2\ H^+ \rightarrow [Co(NO_2)_6]^{-3} + NO\uparrow + H_2O$$
$$3\ K^+ + [Co(NO_2)_6]^{-3} \rightarrow \underline{K_3[Co(NO_2)_6]}$$

MANGANESE

37.11 Periodic Relationships of Manganese

Manganese, technetium, and rhenium comprise Periodic Group VIIB. Although rhenium was not discovered until 1925, its chemistry has now been widely studied. No stable isotope of technetium is known; however, the chemistry of the element has been studied by means of radioactive isotopes prepared synthetically. Each of these elements has valence electrons in two shells, the outermost one of which contains two electrons. Contrasted with these elements are the halogens of Periodic Group VIIA, which have seven electrons in their outer and only valence shell. The halogens are active nonmetals whereas the Group VIIB elements are metals. However, in the higher oxidation states, there are striking similarities between the elements of these two subgroups. Thus Mn_2O_7 and Cl_2O_7 are both volatile, explosively unstable liquids; $KMnO_4$ and $KClO_4$ are both strong oxidizing agents which form isomorphous crystals of nearly the same solubility.

37.12 History of Manganese

Compounds of manganese have been used since early times, but they were often confused with those of other metals, making it difficult to say just when their use began. Before 1774, **pyrolusite,** MnO_2, and **magnetite,** Fe_3O_4, were thought to be the same substance. In that year, Scheele proved that these two substances are fundamentally different. The name manganese is derived from the Latin word "magnes," meaning a magnet.

37.13 Occurrence and Metallurgy of Manganese

The most important ore of manganese is **pyrolusite,** MnO_2. The name "pyrolusite" comes from two Greek words meaning "fire" and "to wash," because it has been used for many centuries in glass manufacture to remove objectionable colors, especially the green tint produced by iron (II) silicate. Other manganese ores include **braunite,** Mn_2O_3, **manganite,** $MnO(OH)$ or $Mn_2O_3 \cdot H_2O$, **hausmannite,** Mn_3O_4, and **psilomelane,** MnO_2 (BaO, K_2O, H_2O, etc.). Some manganese is obtained as a by-product from other ores, especially those of iron. The principal producers of manganese are India, Africa, Cuba, Russia, Chile, and Brazil. The United States imports most of her manganese, although a considerable quantity is mined in Montana.

Nearly pure manganese may be produced by the high temperature reduction of the dioxide by aluminum according to the equation

$$3\,MnO_2 + 4\,Al \rightarrow 3\,Mn + 2\,Al_2O_3$$

Since alloys of manganese and iron are extensively used in the production of steel, such alloys are usually produced instead of the pure manganese. They are prepared by reducing the mixed oxides of manganese and iron with coke in a blast furnace. The alloys high in manganese are called **ferromanganese,** and those low in manganese are called **spiegeleisen,** meaning "mirror iron" (German).

37.14 Properties

Manganese is a gray-white metal with a slightly reddish tinge. It is brittle and has the general appearance of cast iron. It is readily oxidized by moist air and decomposes water slowly, forming manganese (II) hydroxide and hydrogen. It dissolves readily in dilute acids forming manganese (II) salts. Manganese forms five oxides and five corresponding series of salts (Table 37·2). These compounds are to be considered in the following sections.

TABLE 37·2 Classes of Manganese Compounds

Oxidation State	*Oxide*	*Hydroxide*	*Character*	*Derivative*	*Name*	*Color*
+2	MnO	$Mn(OH)_2$	Moderately basic	$MnCl_2$	Manganese (II) chloride	Pink
+3	Mn_2O_3	$Mn(OH)_3$	Weakly basic	$MnCl_3$	Manganese (III) chloride	Violet
+4	MnO_2	H_2MnO_3	Weakly acidic	$CaMnO_3$	Calcium manganite	Brown
+6	MnO_3	H_2MnO_4	Acidic	K_2MnO_4	Potassium manganate	Green
+7	Mn_2O_7	$HMnO_4$	Strongly acidic	$KMnO_4$	Potassium permanganate	Purple

37.15 Compounds of Divalent Manganese

Although manganese forms compounds in which it exhibits oxidation states of +2, +3, +4, +6, and +7, the only stable cation is the divalent manganese ion.

Mn^{++}. The common soluble manganese (II) salts are the chloride, sulfate, and nitrate. They impart a faint pink color to their solutions.

Alkalies precipitate pale pink **manganese (II) hydroxide,** $Mn(OH)_2$, which is oxidized on exposure to air to the dark brown **manganese (III) oxyhydroxide,** $MnO(OH)$. Manganese (II) hydroxide is only partially precipitated by aqueous ammonia and is dissolved by solutions of ammonium salts, according to the equation

$$Mn(OH)_2 + 2\ NH_4^+ \rightleftharpoons Mn^{++} + 2\ NH_3 + 2\ H_2O$$

Manganese (II) hydroxide is entirely basic in character as indicated by the fact that it dissolves in acids but not in hydroxide bases such as sodium hydroxide. Manganese (II) oxide, MnO, may be produced by heating the corresponding hydroxide in the absence of air.

From manganese (II) solutions, alkali sulfides precipitate the pink sulfide, MnS, which is readily soluble in dilute acids.

37.16 Compounds of Trivalent Manganese

Dimanganese trioxide, Mn_2O_3, and $MnO(OH)$ occur naturally, but the manganese (III) ion is unstable in aqueous solution and is readily reduced to the manganese (II) ion. **Manganese (III) chloride** is formed in solution by the action of hydrochloric acid upon manganese dioxide at low temperature, but when the solution is warmed, the manganese (III) chloride decomposes, manganese (II) chloride and chlorine being formed. The reactions are

$$MnO_2 + 4\ H^+ + 4\ Cl^- \rightarrow MnCl_4 + 2\ H_2O$$
$$2\ MnCl_4 \rightarrow 2\ MnCl_3 + Cl_2 \uparrow$$
$$2\ MnCl_3 \rightarrow 2\ Mn^{++} + 4\ Cl^- + Cl_2 \uparrow$$

37.17 Compounds of Tetravalent Manganese

The most important compound of tetravalent manganese is the **dioxide,** MnO_2. This oxide is amphoteric but is relatively inert towards acids and alkalies. Cold, concentrated hydrochloric acid acts upon the dioxide, giving a green solution of the unstable manganese (IV) chloride. The **sulfate,** $Mn(SO_4)_2$, is also unstable, but the complex salt K_2MnF_6 is not readily decomposed. When the dioxide is fused with calcium oxide, **calcium manganite,** $CaMnO_3$, is formed. This is a salt of the hypothetical **manganous acid,** H_2MnO_3.

When manganese dioxide is heated to 535°, it is transformed to **trimanganese tetroxide,** Mn_3O_4, and oxygen, according to the equation

$$3\ MnO_2 \rightarrow Mn_3O_4 + O_2$$

37.18 Manganates, Hexavalent Manganese

When an oxide of manganese is fused with an alkali hydroxide or carbonate in the presence of air or some other oxidizing agent (such as potassium chlorate or potassium nitrate), a **manganate** is formed.

$$2\ MnO_2 + 4\ KOH + O_2 \rightarrow 2\ K_2MnO_4 + 2\ H_2O$$

Manganates are green in color and are stable only in alkaline solution. The addition of water to solutions of manganates may bring about auto-oxidation-reduction with the precipitation of manganese dioxide and the formation of purple permanganate, MnO_4^-.

$$3\ MnO_4^{=} + 2\ H_2O \rightarrow 2\ MnO_4^- + 4\ OH^- + \underline{MnO_2}$$

Free **manganic acid,** H_2MnO_4, is too unstable to be prepared and isolated. Solutions containing the manganate ion become active oxidizing agents when acidified. The half-reaction is given by the equation

$$MnO_4^{=} + 8\ H^+ + 4\ e^- \rightarrow Mn^{++} + 4\ H_2O$$

37.19 Permanganates, Heptavalent Manganese

An important compound of manganese is **potassium permanganate,** $KMnO_4$. It is prepared commercially by oxidizing potassium manganate in alkaline solution by means of chlorine.

$$2\ MnO_4^{=} + Cl_2 \rightarrow 2\ MnO_4^- + 2\ Cl^-$$

The resultant purple solution deposits crystals when sufficiently concentrated. Potassium permanganate is a valuable laboratory reagent because it acts as a strong oxidizing agent. A solution of the free **permanganic acid,** $HMnO_4$, may be prepared by the reaction of dilute sulfuric acid and barium permanganate.

$$Ba^{++} + 2\ MnO_4^- + (2\ H^+) + SO_4^{=} \rightarrow \underline{BaSO_4} + (2\ H^+) + 2\ MnO_4^-$$

Mn_2O_7, a dark brown, highly explosive liquid, is the anhydride of permanganic acid.

37.20 Uses of Manganese and Its Compounds

Manganese metal forms a number of important alloys. Two of these were mentioned in Section 37.13; they are **spiegeleisen,** which is a bright and lustrous iron alloy containing 5–20 per cent manganese, and **ferromanganese,** which contains 70–80 per cent manganese. Both of these alloys are used in making very hard steels which are suitable for the manufacture of rails, safes, and heavy machinery. About 12.5 pounds of manganese metal are used in the production of every ton of steel to remove oxygen, nitrogen, and sulfur. An alloy called **manganin** (Cu, 84 per cent; Mn, 12 per cent; Ni, 4 per cent) is used in instruments for making electrical measurements because the electrical resistance of the alloy does not change much with changes in temperature.

Manganese dioxide is used in glassmaking to correct the green color produced by iron (II) compounds, to color glass and enamels black, to act as an oxidizing agent or "dryer" in black paints, and as a depolarizer in dry cells. Manganates are important in the manufacture of permanganates, as oxidizing agents, and as disinfectants. Potassium permanganate is used as a disinfectant, a deodorant, and a germicide. It is used in the treatment of skin eruptions caused by poison ivy. The brown stain which it leaves on the skin can be removed by treatment with oxalic acid. Potassium permanganate is also used extensively as an oxidizing agent in analytical determinations.

37.21 Properties of Manganese of Analytical Importance

When solutions containing Mn^{++} are treated with ammonium sulfide, flesh-colored MnS precipitates. This sulfide is soluble in acids. White $Mn(OH)_2$ is precipitated by alkalies; it soon turns brown upon exposure to the air. Manganese (II) hydroxide is soluble in solutions of ammonium salts. Bismuthate ion, BiO_3^-, in acid solution readily oxidizes Mn^{++} to MnO_4^-, as indicated by the purple color of the resulting permanganate.

IRON

37.22 History and Importance of Iron

Iron was known at least as early as 4000 B.C. and probably has been used to some extent since prehistoric times. Because free iron is not commonly found in nature, that first used by man may well have been of meteoric origin. The early discovery and application of iron to the manufacture of tools and weapons resulted from the wide distribution of iron ores and the ease with which these ores are reduced by carbon. Charcoal was used for a long time in the reduction of iron ores, but the production and use of iron on a large scale began about 1620, when coal was introduced as the reducing agent. The English name "iron" is of uncertain origin, and the symbol Fe is derived from the Latin word "ferrum."

Iron is the most important and widely used metal. This results from the fact that its ores are abundant and widely distributed, the metal is easily and cheaply produced from the ores, and its properties can be varied over a wide range by the addition of other substances and by different methods of treatment, such as tempering and annealing. More iron is used than all the other metals combined (14 times as much).

37.23 Occurrence of Iron

Iron ranks second in abundance among the metals (aluminum is first) and fourth among all elements in the earth's crust. The central core of the earth is largely iron, as has been indicated by studies of the earth's density and the rate of transmission of earthquake shock. Metallic meteors are usually about 90 per cent iron, and the remainder is principally nickel. Practically all rocks, minerals, and soils, as well as plants, contain some iron. Iron is present in the hemoglobin of the blood, which acts as a carrier of oxygen (Section 32.26).

The important iron-bearing ores are **hematite,** Fe_2O_3, and **magnetite,** Fe_3O_4 (Fig. 37–2, page 614). The name "hematite," from the Greek word for blood, was given to the ore because of its red color. The presence of this ore accounts largely for the red coloration of many rocks and soils. Hematite often occurs as the hydrate $2\ Fe_2O_3 \cdot 3\ H_2O$, which is called **limonite.** It is soft and reddish-brown in color, sometimes called "yellow ocher," and it is used in the manufacture of paint. Magnetite is a black, crystalline mineral, which is strongly magnetic, sometimes possessing polarity, in which case it is called "loadstone." Black crystalline

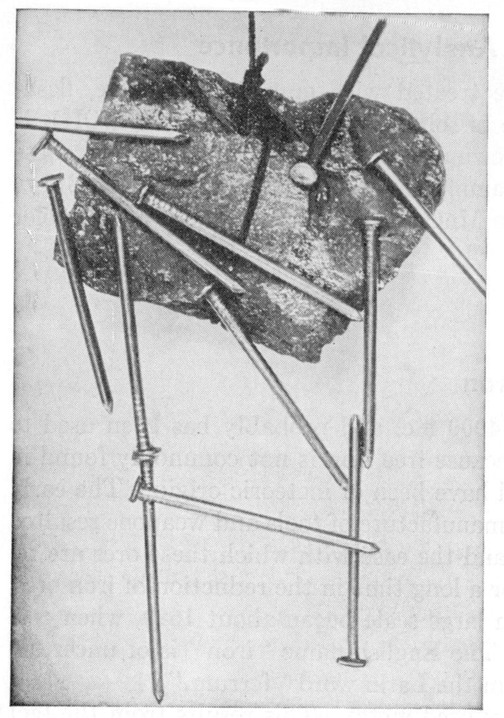

Fig. 37–2 This photograph of magnetite, Fe_3O_4, illustrates its magnetic properties. See Section 37.33, also. *Ward's Natural Science Establishment, Inc.*

magnetite interlocked with crystals of silica in the form of hard rock is called **taconite.** **Siderite** is a white or brownish carbonate, $FeCO_3$. **Pyrite,** FeS_2, occurs as pale yellow crystals with a metallic luster which are easily mistaken for gold; hence the name "fool's gold." Pyrite is quite abundant and useful as a source of sulfur for the manufacture of sulfuric acid; but because roasting does not remove all of the sulfur, pyrite is usually considered unsatisfactory for the smelting of iron, although low-grade pig iron can be made from it.

Nearly ninety per cent of the iron ore mined in the United States comes from the tremendous ore deposits of the Lake Superior district of Minnesota (Fig. 37–3) and Michigan (80 per cent) and the Birmingham, Alabama, district (10 per cent). The main producers of iron ore besides the United States are France, Germany, Russia, Great Britain, Sweden, Canada, and several South American countries. Large de-

Fig. 37–3 This open-pit iron mine at Hibbing, Minnesota, is the largest man-made hole on the earth. It is 350 feet deep at its deepest point, one mile wide, and $2\frac{1}{2}$ miles long. The ore is hematite. *U.S. Steel Corp.*

posits of iron ore in Brazil, Labrador, and Venezuela, which have recently been discovered and are being developed, will insure a supply of this valuable ore for many generations. The United States formerly produced sufficient iron ore to satisfy its needs, but gradual depletion of high-grade iron ore deposits has made it necessary in recent years to import considerable quantities of this ore from other parts of the world. The world-wide production of iron metal is over 200 million tons annually.

37.24 Metallurgy of Iron

The first step in the metallurgy of iron ores is usually that of roasting to remove water, decompose carbonates, and oxidize sulfides. The oxides of iron are then reduced in a blast furnace (Fig. 37–4) with coke.

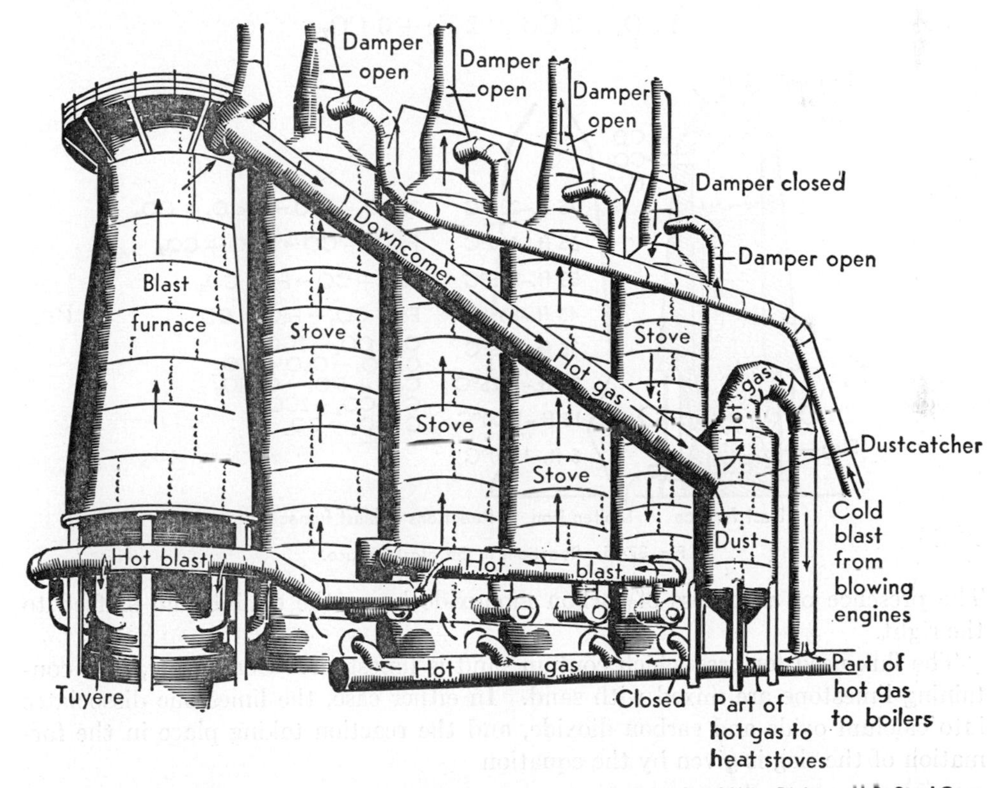

Fig. 37–4 The exterior of a blast furnace and its four stoves. *American Steel and Wire Division, U.S. Steel Corp.*

The blast furnace is made of steel and lined with refractory brick. It is in the shape of a large, cylindrical stack, 80–100 feet high and 25 feet in diameter. Near the bottom of the furnace are nozzles or "tuyères" through which preheated air is blown into the furnace under pressure. The charge of ore, coke, and flux (limestone or sand) is introduced into the top of the furnace through two successive cone-shaped valves, at least one of which is always closed. The shape and location of the lower valve (or bell) is such that the charge is deposited uniformly around the circumference of the furnace near the walls. As the charge melts, or is burned in the lower regions of the furnace, the stock column gradually settles, thus leaving room for additional charges at the top, and making the operation of the blast furnace a continuous process. The entire stock in the furnace weighs several hundred tons.

As soon as the preheated air (500°) under pressure enters the furnace, the coke in the region of the tuyères is oxidized to carbon dioxide with the liberation of much heat which raises the temperature to about 1500°. As the carbon dioxide passes upward through the overlying layer of white-hot coke, it is reduced to carbon monoxide ($CO_2 + C \rightarrow 2\ CO$). The carbon monoxide thus produced serves as the reducing agent in the upper regions of the furnace. The reduction reactions (indicated in Fig. 37–5) can be summarized as a single reversible reaction as follows:

$$Fe_2O_3 + 3\ CO \rightleftharpoons 2\ Fe + 3\ CO_2$$

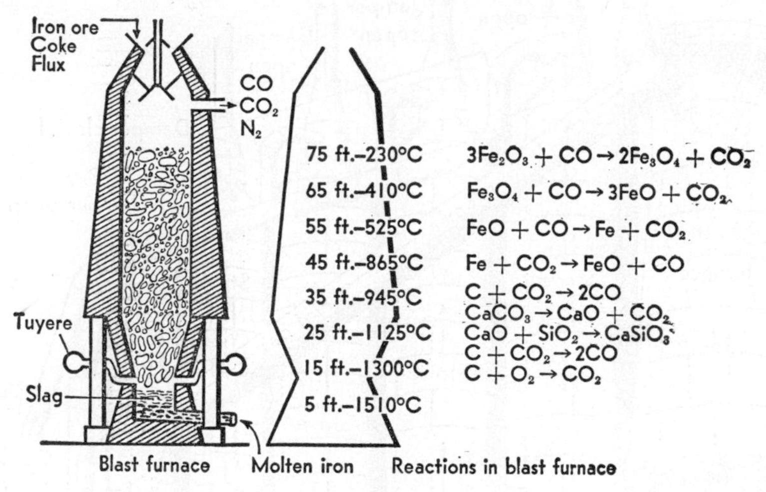

Fig. 37–5 Reactions in the blast furnace.

The presence of an excess of carbon monoxide keeps the equilibrium shifted to the right.

The flux used for ores which contain sand is limestone. Conversely, ores containing limestone are mixed with sand. In either case, the limestone dissociates into calcium oxide and carbon dioxide, and the reaction taking place in the formation of the slag is given by the equation

$$CaO + SiO_2 \rightarrow CaSiO_3$$

The iron ore is completely reduced before the formation of the slag begins in the middle region of the furnace; otherwise, part of the iron would be lost due to the reaction $FeO + SiO_2 \rightarrow FeSiO_3$.

Just below the middle of the furnace, the temperature is high enough to melt both the iron and the slag which have been produced. The molten iron and slag collect in two layers at the bottom of the furnace, the less dense slag floating on the iron and protecting it against oxidation. Every hour or two, the liquid slag is withdrawn from the furnace. Blast furnace slag is often used in the manufacture of Portland cement. Four or five times a day, the molten iron is withdrawn through a tap hole into a large ladle lined with fire brick that holds several hundred tons of the hot metal. The ladle containing the hot metal is then transferred to the pig casting machine or to the steelmaking plant, which may be several miles away. The daily production of a blast furnace is about 1200 tons of iron.

The hot exhaust gases, which issue from the top of the blast furnace and contain some unoxidized carbon monoxide, are mixed with air and burned to preheat the air used in the operation of the blast furnace.

37.25 Pig Iron and Cast Iron

The metal obtained from the blast furnace is called **pig iron.** It contains as impurities several per cent of carbon, silicon, phosphorus, manganese, and smaller amounts of sulfur. Pig iron is brittle and is usually converted to cast iron or steel. When pig iron is remelted and recooled, it is called **cast iron.** When it is cooled rapidly, the carbon remains chemically combined with the iron in the form of the carbide, Fe_3C, which is known as **cementite.** The product has a light color because Fe_3C is white, and is therefore called **white cast iron.** It is brittle but hard and resistant to wear. When pig iron is allowed to cool slowly, the carbon separates from the iron as black graphite. This gives the product a gray color so it is called **gray cast iron.** In contrast to white cast iron, the gray variety is soft and tough. It is possible to control the cooling of cast iron in such a way that the surface cools rapidly, while the body of the casting cools slowly. This treatment results in a casting which has the toughness of gray cast iron and the wearing qualities of white cast iron.

Cast iron is especially adapted to making castings, because it expands upon solidification and consequently fills all details of the mold completely.

37.26 Wrought Iron

This is a rather pure form of iron made by melting pig iron with an excess of iron oxide which oxidizes most of the impurities. The carbon and sulfur escape as carbon dioxide and sulfur dioxide, respectively. The silicon and phosphorus oxides which are formed react with oxides of iron and manganese or with limestone, which may be added as a flux, to form a slag. The fused mass is stirred with hand-operated rods, an operation called **puddling.** As the impurities are removed, the mass becomes stiff enough so that finally it is taken out of the furnace in balls (called blooms) which weigh about one hundred pounds each. These are hammered or rolled to remove part of the slag. Wrought iron contains less than 0.2 per cent carbon and it is malleable and ductile. It has a fibrous structure, which in part is due to thin films of slag between layers of pure iron. It is used in the manufacture of articles which are to be subjected to sudden stresses, such as chains, anchors, bolts, and for making ornamental framework. In recent years, wrought iron has been displaced largely by mild steel (Section 37.28).

37.27 The Manufacture of Steel

The term **steel** is used to denote many widely different alloys of iron. It is made from pig iron by removing the impurities and later adding substances such as manganese, chromium, nickel, tungsten, molybdenum, and vanadium to produce alloys with properties which make them suitable for specific uses. Most steels contain small but definite percentages of carbon. Thus, a large part of the carbon contained in pig iron must be removed in the manufacture of steel. Two processes are used chiefly in the production of steel; they are the "open-hearth process" and the "Bessemer process." Steels for special purposes are made by the crucible and electric furnace methods.

1. *The open-hearth process.* The bulk of the steel produced in the United States (about 90 per cent) is manufactured by the open-hearth method (Fig. 37–6).

Fig. 37–6 Charging one of a long row of open-hearth furnaces. When tests indicate that the desired percentages have been attained, the molten steel is withdrawn from the other end of the furnace. *National Tube Co.*

A diagram of the open-hearth furnace is given in Fig. 37–7. The charge, which may weigh from fifty to two hundred tons, consists of pig iron, scrap iron, and iron ore. It is placed on a shallow hearth and heated from above by a gaseous fuel containing an excess of air. The mixture of fuel and air required for the oxidation of such impurities as carbon and sulfur in the iron is preheated by passage through a checkerwork of hot brick. The bricks are heated by the hot gases which are produced during the oxidation of the impurities in the iron. The directions of the entering gases and the gaseous products are reversed at intervals so that each chamber of bricks is alternately heated and used to preheat the incoming fuel and air mixture. The iron ore and the rust on the scrap iron, which are parts of the charge, aid in the oxidation of the impurities.

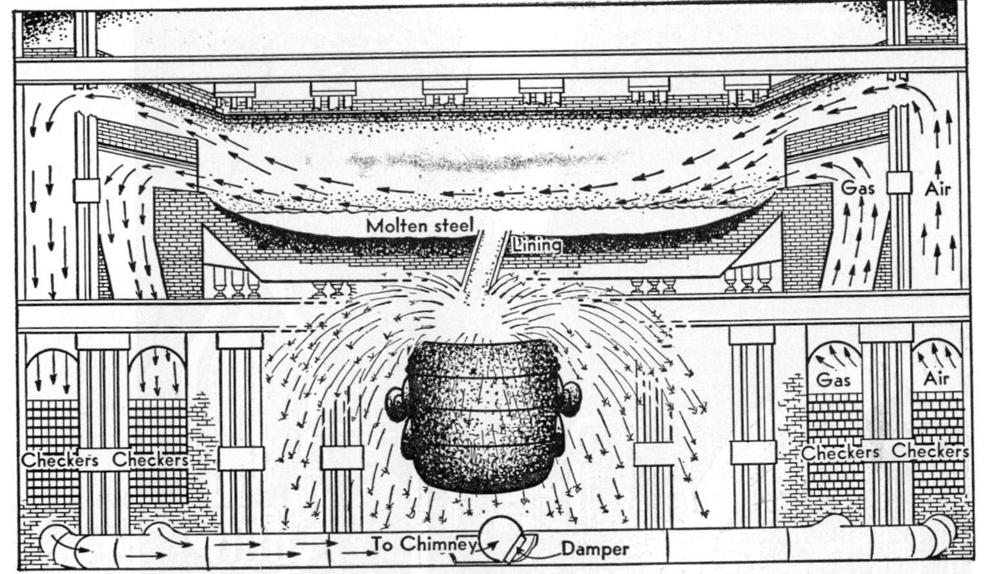

Fig. 37–7 A diagram of an open-hearth steel furnace. See the text for a description. *American Steel and Wire Division, U.S. Steel Corp.*

When the pig iron contains elements whose oxides are acidic (e.g., silicon, phosphorus, and sulfur) the lining of the hearth is made of basic materials, principally magnesium and calcium oxides. The acidic oxides react with the basic lining, forming a slag. Most of the open-hearth steel is made in basic furnaces. If the pig iron contains basic oxides, an acid lining composed chiefly of sand or siliceous materials is employed.

About eight hours are required to oxidize most of the carbon. At intervals, samples of the metal are removed for testing, the oxidation being continued until the desired composition is obtained. Before the steel is poured, the required amounts of alloying substances, such as manganese, chromium, and other elements, are added.

Open-hearth steel is high-grade and uniform in quality. It is used in making products which are subject to frequent vibration or sudden strains such as girders, heavy rails, guns, and armor plate.

2. *The Bessemer process.* A diagram of the Bessemer converter is shown in Fig. 37–8, page 620. A blast of air is blown through a charge of 10–25 tons of molten pig iron for seven to fifteen minutes to oxidize the impurities. The carbon monoxide thus formed burns at the mouth of the converter, the character of the flame indicating the amount of carbon remaining in the iron. A considerable portion of the iron is lost, due to oxidation. After the impurities are burned out, the composition is adjusted by adding calculated quantities of carbon and manganese or other metals, to produce a steel of the desired properties. The converter is so designed that it can be tipped to a horizontal position for pouring the finished product. The metal is poured first into a ladle, and then into molds, where it is allowed

Fig. 37–8 Three views of a Bessemer converter. The cutaway at the right shows the construction. The converter is about 20 feet high and 12 feet in diameter. While tipped on its side, the converter is charged with molten pig iron. It is then turned upright and a blast of air under about 20 pounds pressure is forced through the iron. The blast is continued for 10 to 15 minutes, depending upon the purity of the pig iron. Then, carefully measured amounts of alloying materials are added. Finally, the converter is tipped on its side and the molten steel is poured out. *American Steel and Wire Division, U.S. Steel Corp.*

to solidify in the form of ingots. The ingots are rolled or hammered into articles of the desired shape. The Bessemer converter is usually lined with silica brick; the silica constitutes an "acid" lining, which acts as a flux toward basic oxides that are produced by the oxidation of impurities, but not toward the oxides of nonmetals such as phosphorus and sulfur. Therefore, the acid Bessemer process is not suitable for the production of steels from pig iron containing appreciable quantities of these two elements. For some applications, the Bessemer converter is used with a basic lining.

The Bessemer process is so rapid that it does not permit the careful regulation which is possible in the open-hearth process. Consequently, Bessemer steel is a low-grade, inexpensive product, which is used in making steel frameworks for buildings, bridges, etc.

3. *The duplex process.* This process for the manufacture of steel combines the best features of the acid Bessemer and basic open-hearth methods. Processing the pig iron first in the acid Bessemer converter removes most of the impurities other than phosphorus. The product is then transferred to the basic open-hearth furnace, in which the phosphorus and the remainder of the carbon are removed. The duplex process yields a steel of high quality that is very low in phosphorus.

4. *Other processes.* Certain high-grade carbon steels are refined in crucibles made of graphite. The process is carefully controlled, the carbon (0.75 to 1.5 per cent) is uniformly distributed, and the finished product contains almost no slag or dissolved gases. Steel made in this way is called "crucible steel" and is used for making such articles as files, drills, knives, razor blades, watch springs, and axes.

Various types of electric furnaces are used in the United States for the refining of steel. Two distinct advantages of the electric furnace are (1) the temperature can be controlled within a few degrees, and (2) higher temperatures are attainable than with other methods, making possible the production of special steels with high melting points. "Electric steel" is used as tool steel and for production of articles of the types made by the crucible process.

37.28 Carbon Steels

Carbon is the most important alloying element used in the manufacture of steel. It may be present in three forms — in combination with iron as cementite, Fe_3C, in relatively large crystals of graphite, and as very small crystals of graphite.

Steel containing cementite in solid solution in iron contains up to about 1.5 per cent carbon and is made by quenching the hot metal in water or oil. This steel is hard, brittle, and light colored. If the metal is cooled slowly, the carbon is deposited largely as separate crystals of cementite or as particles of graphite, and the product is softer, more pliable, and has a much higher tensile strength than steel which has been cooled rapidly.

Steels of low carbon content (up to 0.2 per cent) are quite ductile and are known as **mild steels.** These are used in the manufacture of such products as sheet iron, wire (Fig. 37–9), and pipe. Medium steels contain 0.2 to 0.6 per cent carbon,

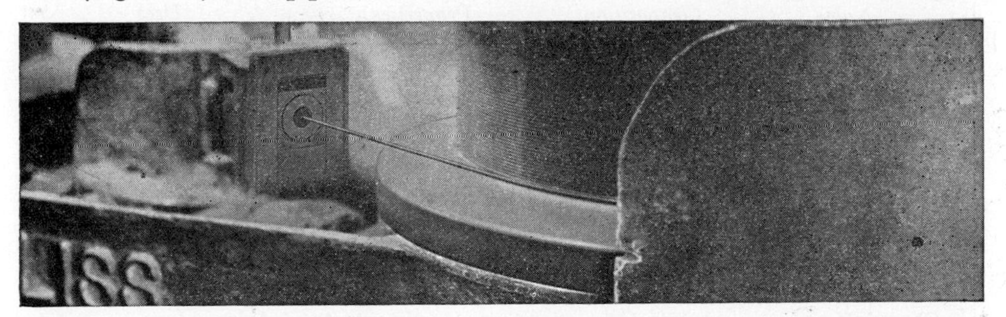

Fig. 37–9 In making wire, cold iron rods are drawn through smaller and smaller dies. *American Iron and Steel Institute*

and are used in rails, structural steel, and boiler plate. Both mild and medium steels can be forged and welded. High-carbon steels contain from 0.6 to 1.5 per cent carbon. They are hard and brittle and are used in surgical instruments, razor blades, springs, and cutlery.

Steel which has been heated to redness and allowed to cool slowly is said to be "annealed." Steel is "tempered" by rapid cooling in water or oil followed by controlled reheating to obtain the desired proportion of cementite and graphite. **Case-hardened steel** is made by heating low-carbon steel in closed containers with powdered carbon, followed by quenching it in oil. The carbon reacts with the iron on the surface forming cementite. Such a steel is very hard on its surface and tough in the interior. It is used in making axles and other articles which must resist wear and, at the same time, be tough and flexible so as not to break when subjected to sudden strains and shocks. Steel can also be case-hardened using nitrogen compounds. A very hard iron nitride is formed in the process, which is called **nitriding.**

37.29 Alloy Steels

Certain materials, called **scavengers,** are added to iron in the manufacture of steel to remove impurities, especially oxygen and nitrogen, and improve the quality of the product. The most important scavengers are aluminum, ferrosilicon, ferromanganese, and ferrotitanium. They react with dissolved oxygen and nitrogen forming oxides and nitrides, respectively. The compounds formed are removed in the slag.

For every ton of steel produced, about 25–30 pounds of nonferrous metals are added or used as coatings. By the appropriate choice of the number and percentages of these elements, steels of widely varying properties can be manufactured. Some of the important alloy steels and their features are given in Table 37·3.

TABLE 37·3 Alloy Steels

Name	*Composition*	*Characteristic Properties*	*Uses*
Manganese	10–18% Mn	Hard, tough, resistant to wear	Railroad rails, safes, armor plate, rock-crushing machinery
Silicon	1–5% Si	Hard, strong, highly magnetic	Magnets
Duriron	12–15% Si	Resistant to corrosion, acids	Pipes, kettles, condensers, etc.
Invar	36% Ni	Low coefficient of expansion	Meter scales, measuring tapes, pendulum rods
Chrome-Vanadium	1–10% Cr 0.15% V	Strong, resistant to strains	Axles
Stainless steel	14–18% Cr 7–9% Ni	Resistant to corrosion	Cutlery, instruments
Permalloy	78% Ni	High magnetic susceptibility	Ocean cables
High-speed steels	14–20% W or 6 to 12% Mo	Retain temper at high temperatures	High-speed cutting tools
Nickel	2–4% Ni	Hard and elastic, resistant to corrosion	Drive shafts, gears, cables

37.30 Taconite Ores and the Steel Industry

With the rather rapid depletion of our domestic high-grade iron ore (over 50 per cent iron) deposits, the steel industry has turned to the conquest of the taconite ores (25–30 per cent iron) which it once regarded as useless. Taconite is the extremely hard rock that makes up some 95 per cent by volume of the famous Mesabi Range's vast iron-bearing deposits in upper Minnesota.

Until the greatly accelerated depletion of high-grade ore deposits, starting with World War II, there was little incentive for the development of taconite. Its low iron content makes it impossible to reduce it directly in the blast furnace, and its extreme hardness defied all attempts to develop simple, economical mining and concentration methods.

However, after 20 years of research, a method has been developed for processing taconite; this is based on magnetic separation of the iron-bearing particles from the gangue. Super-hard taconite rock is blasted loose at the mine, and large pieces are reduced to a fine powder in a series of crushers and grinders. The iron oxide particles are separated magnetically, and then rolled in a damp condition into small balls. When heated to 2300° F in a vertical furnace, these balls lose moisture and fuse into hard pellets, which are suitable for charging the blast furnace.

After an investment of half a billion dollars, the total production of taconite pellets from the various plants in Minnesota is expected to rise to about 60 million tons per year by 1972. In comparison, about 80 million tons of high-grade ore were shipped from the Lake Superior ranges in 1952, before the taconite ores became an appreciable factor.

37.31 Corrosion

Many metals, particularly iron, undergo corrosion when exposed to air and water. Pure iron corrodes (or rusts) slowly, whereas impure iron corrodes more rapidly. The reaction is slow in pure water, but rapid in solutions of electrolytes. Losses caused by corrosion of metals cost the United States billions of dollars annually. The phenomenon of corrosion and its prevention has been studied extensively by many investigators, both in industry and in universities, and it has been found that many factors affect corrosion.

It has been shown that iron will not rust in dry air, nor in water which is free from dissolved oxygen. It follows that both air and water are involved in the corrosion process. The presence of an electrolyte in the water accelerates corrosion, particularly when the solution is acidic. Strained metals corrode more rapidly than unstrained ones. Heated portions of a metal corrode more rapidly than unheated ones. Finally, iron in contact with a less active metal such as tin, lead, or copper corrodes more rapidly than when alone, or when in contact with a more active metal such as zinc.

An electrochemical theory helps to explain these facts. It appears that minute primary electrochemical cells are set up when corrosion takes place. When iron is in contact with water containing an electrolyte, the half-reaction given below tends to occur.

$$\text{(Anodic oxidation) } Fe \rightarrow Fe^{++} + 2\ e^-$$

Sometimes, one portion of the iron is more active than the rest and tends to go into solution more easily. This means that the active portion of the iron has a higher potential than the rest, and this portion tends to dissolve in the electrolyte. On the less active portions of the iron (lower electrode potential), hydrogen tends to form according to the half-reaction

$$\text{(Cathodic reduction) } 2\ H^+ + 2\ e^- \rightarrow H_2$$

The accumulation of hydrogen on the surface of iron tends to polarize the electrode and stop the cell action. However, dissolved oxygen gradually removes the hydrogen in the same manner that MnO_2 depolarizes the dry cell, and the electrochemical reaction proceeds; i.e., corrosion occurs.

$$2\ H_2 + O_2 \rightarrow 2\ H_2O$$

Iron (II) ions combine with hydroxide ions of the electrolytic solution, forming $Fe(OH)_2$. Iron (II) hydroxide is then readily oxidized by air to $Fe_2O_3 \cdot x\ H_2O$, which is **iron rust.**

Many methods and devices have been employed to prevent or retard corrosion. Some of these methods are given below.

Iron can be protected against corrosion by coating it with (1) an organic material such as paint, lacquer, grease, or asphalt, (2) another metal such as zinc, copper, nickel, chromium, tin, cadmium, or lead, (3) a ceramic enamel, like that used on sinks, bathtubs, stoves, refrigerators, and washers, or (4) an adherent oxide, which may be formed by exposing iron to superheated steam, thereby giving it an adherent coating of magnetic oxide, Fe_3O_4.

Iron may also be treated with a suitable coordinating group, such as phosphate, which ties the surface iron up in a complex such that it cannot react to form $Fe_2O_3 \cdot x\ H_2O$ (Section 34.6).

Alloys of iron with certain other elements are often corrosion resistant. Typical examples are stainless steel (Fe, Cr, and Ni) and duriron (Fe and Si).

Another method of preventing the corrosion of iron or steel involves an application of electrochemistry called **cathodic protection.** For example, corrosion of iron or steel water tanks can be retarded by suspending several stainless steel anodes in the tank; the tank serves as a cathode. A small current is passed continuously through the system, with the natural salts in the water making it conducting. A slight cathodic evolution of a protective coat of hydrogen takes place on the wall of the tank. Cathodic protection against corrosion is also used on iron and steel which is in contact with soil, such as underground pipe lines. Other applications of cathodic protection do not involve the use of a current from an external source. In these cases, the iron becomes cathodic when connected by a wire to a more active metal such as zinc, aluminum, or magnesium. The difference in activity of the two metals causes a current to flow between them, producing corrosion on the more active metal and furnishing cathodic protection to the iron.

37.32 Properties of Iron

Pure iron is silvery white, capable of taking a high polish, ductile, relatively soft, and high in tensile strength. These properties are greatly modified by the amount and nature of the impurities present, especially carbon. Pure iron is attracted by a magnet but does not retain its magnetism. Iron dissolves in hydrochloric acid and dilute sulfuric acid, forming hydrogen and iron (II) ions, Fe^{++}. Hot concentrated sulfuric acid forms Fe^{+++}, and SO_2 is evolved. Cold concentrated nitric acid induces **passivity** in iron. When in the passive condition, iron does not react with dilute acids which would otherwise readily dissolve it. The passivity is easily destroyed by a scratch or by shock. Hot dilute nitric acid oxidizes iron to Fe^{+++} with the evolution of nitric oxide. When heated to redness, iron reduces steam to produce hydrogen and iron (II,III) oxide, Fe_3O_4, which is the same oxide that is produced when iron burns in oxygen. When exposed to moist air at ordinary temperatures iron becomes oxidized with the formation of a loose coating of partially hydrated iron (III) oxide, $Fe_2O_3 \cdot x\ H_2O$ (Section 37.31).

Iron forms two principal series of compounds in which the oxidation states are +2 and +3; compounds in which iron is +6 are rare and less important. The +2 and +3 series are called iron (II), or ferrous, and iron (III), or ferric, respectively. The oxides and hydroxides of iron (II) and (III) are basic in character with little or no acid-forming property.

37.33 Oxides and Hydroxides of Iron

The black **iron (II) oxide,** FeO, may be obtained by the thermal decomposition of iron (II) oxalate, FeC_2O_4.

$$FeC_2O_4 \rightarrow FeO + CO + CO_2$$

The corresponding **hydroxide,** $Fe(OH)_2$, is white when pure; it precipitates upon the addition of alkali hydroxides to solutions of iron (II) salts. Ammonium salts and many organic acids greatly increase the solubility of iron (II) hydroxide. In the air the white hydroxide quickly turns green and then reddish-brown, due to oxidation to iron (III) hydroxide.

$$4\ Fe(OH)_2 + O_2 + 2\ H_2O \rightarrow 4\ \underline{Fe(OH)_3}$$

Iron (III) oxide, Fe_2O_3, occurs in nature as the mineral **hematite.** It may also be prepared by igniting $Fe(OH)_3$ or by roasting pyrite, FeS_2, in the air. It is a red powder which is used as a paint pigment under the names "rouge" and "Venetian red." When treated with alkali hydroxides or aqueous ammonia, solutions of Fe^{+++} yield $Fe(OH)_3$, which is reddish-brown and insoluble in an excess of reagent.

Iron (II,III) oxide, Fe_3O_4, is a mixed oxide $FeO \cdot Fe_2O_3$ and is called magnetic oxide of iron or "loadstone" (Fig. 37–2, page 614). It is a valuable ore of iron.

37.34 Iron (II) Salts

Iron (II) chloride 4-hydrate, $FeCl_2 \cdot 4\ H_2O$, is produced by the action of dilute hydrochloric acid upon iron. It is pale green in color. Sulfuric acid dissolves iron or iron (II) oxide forming "green vitriol" or "copperas," which crystallizes as the 7-hydrate, $FeSO_4 \cdot 7\ H_2O$. This salt is used as a deodorant, disinfectant, weed-killer, and wood preservative as well as in the manufacture of inks, dyes, and pigments, and as a substitute for aluminum sulfate in the purification of water (Section 10.5).

Iron (II) ammonium sulfate 6-hydrate, $(NH_4)_2SO_4 \cdot FeSO_4 \cdot 6\ H_2O$, is a double salt which crystallizes from an equimolar solution of ammonium sulfate and iron (II) sulfate. It is called **Mohr's salt,** and because it is readily obtained in a pure state, it is used extensively in laboratory work as a reducing agent, the iron being readily oxidized to the +3 state.

Iron (II) carbonate, $FeCO_3$, occurs in nature as the mineral **siderite.** It may be produced, also, as a white precipitate by the reaction of alkali carbonates with solutions of iron (II) in the absence of air. The carbonate dissolves in carbonic acid to form the **hydrogen carbonate,** $Fe(HCO_3)_2$, a common constituent of hard waters. The conversion of this salt to iron (III) hydroxide by oxygen and water is responsible for the familiar brown stain produced when water containing iron hydrogen carbonate is allowed to stand in the air.

Iron (II) sulfide, FeS, is precipitated when an alkali sulfide is added to a solution of an iron (II) salt. It is prepared commercially by heating a mixture of iron and sulfur. Acids act upon it to form hydrogen sulfide.

37.35 Iron (III) Compounds

An important iron (III) compound is the chloride, $FeCl_3$, which may be obtained by heating iron with chlorine. It is appreciably covalent, as is indicated by its volatility and its solubility in nonpolar solvents. When the anhydrous chloride is dissolved in water, much heat is liberated due to hydration of the ions. From water, it crystallizes as the brownish-yellow hydrate, $[Fe(H_2O)_6]Cl_3$. This compound [and all soluble iron (III) salts] gives an acid reaction by hydrolysis.

$$[Fe(H_2O)_6]^{+++} + H_2O \rightarrow [Fe(H_2O)_5(OH)]^{++} + H_3O^+$$

or simply

$$Fe^{+++} + H_2O \rightarrow Fe(OH)^{++} + H^+$$

These solutions are usually yellow or brown due to the formation of hydroxo complexes.

Hydrated iron (III) chloride is used in medicine to coagulate blood, and thus stop bleeding, and in the treatment of anemia. It is also used as a mordant and in the manufacture of pigments and dyes.

When a solution of an iron (III) salt is added to a solution containing a thiocyanate, a blood-red color appears, whereas an iron (II) salt yields only a colorless solution. Use is made of these facts in the detection of iron (III) ions in the presence of iron (II) ions. It appears that the species responsible for the red color is the cation, $Fe(CNS)^{++}$.

Other iron (III) salts include the sulfate, $Fe_2(SO_4)_3$, and the iron alums formed from this salt, such as $NH_4Fe(SO_4)_2 \cdot 12\ H_2O$.

37.36 Inks

Some inks contain **iron (II) tannate,** a soluble and nearly colorless compound made by mixing tannic acid with iron (II) sulfate. Iron (II) tannate is readily oxidized by air to the black, insoluble **iron (III) tannate.** A blue dye is added to the ink to make it visible before oxidation takes place. Ink stains due to iron (III) tannate may be removed by soaking the stained material in a solution of ammonium oxalate for several hours. This treatment reduces the iron (III) tannate to the soluble iron (II) tannate, which may be washed away with water.

37.37 Complex Cyanides of Iron

When an excess of potassium cyanide is added to a solution of an iron (II) salt, **potassium hexacyanoferrate (II),** $K_4Fe(CN)_6$ (also called potassium ferrocyanide), is formed in solution.

$$Fe^{++} + 6\ CN^- \rightarrow Fe(CN)_6^{-4}$$

The complex hexacyanoferrate (II) ion is so stable that it gives none of the common qualitative tests for the iron (II) or cyanide ions. When the hexacyanoferrate (II) ion is oxidized by chlorine, the **hexacyanoferrate (III) ion,** $Fe(CN)_6^{-3}$ (also called ferricyanide), is produced.

$$2\ Fe(CN)_6^{-4} + Cl_2 \rightarrow 2\ Fe(CN)_6^{-3} + 2\ Cl^-$$

Solutions of potassium hexacyanoferrate (III) do not give the usual tests for iron (III) ions or cyanide ions.

The addition of iron (II) ions to hexacyanoferrate (III) solutions yields a blue precipitate known as **Turnbull's blue.** Iron (III) ions react with hexacyanoferrate (II) ions to form **Prussian blue.** These precipitates are evidently the same and have the approximate composition $KFeFe(CN)_6 \cdot H_2O$; both have a deep blue color. When solutions of iron (III) ions and hexacyanoferrate (III) are mixed, no precipitate forms, but only a brown solution. Iron (II) ions and hexacyanoferrate (II) ions produce a white precipitate, $K_2FeFe(CN)_6$. These reactions serve as sensitive tests to distinguish between Fe^{++} and Fe^{+++} in solution.

Prussian blue is used as a paint pigment, as a constituent of certain inks, and as laundry bluing.

37.38 Blueprints

Blueprint paper is coated with a mixture of iron (III) ammonium citrate and potassium hexacyanoferrate (III); this gives the paper the bronze-green color of iron (III) hexacyanoferrate (III). When a drawing in black ink on tracing cloth is placed over the blueprint paper and the paper is exposed to light, the iron (III) ions are reduced by the citrate ions to iron (II) wherever light transmission occurs.

The iron (II) ion immediately reacts with the hexacyanoferrate (III) ion to form an insoluble blue precipitate. After exposure, the paper is washed with water to remove the unchanged iron (III) hexacyanoferrate (III), leaving the body of the paper blue with white lines produced by the tracing.

37.39 Properties of Iron of Analytical Importance

Hydrogen sulfide in acid solution reduces iron (III) ions to iron (II) ions. Sulfide ions in alkaline solution precipitate FeS, which is black and readily dissolved by acids. Alkalies precipitate white $Fe(OH)_2$ from solutions of pure iron (II) salts, and reddish-brown $Fe(OH)_3$ from solutions containing iron (III) ions. Iron (II) hydroxide is readily oxidized to iron (III) hydroxide by air. Neither hydroxide is dissolved by alkalies or aqueous ammonia, but each dissolves readily in acids. Iron (III) ions give a red solution with thiocyanate ions and a blue precipitate or colloidal solution with $Fe(CN)_6^{-4}$ ions. Iron (II) ions give colorless solutions with thiocyanate ions, a white precipitate with $Fe(CN)_6^{-4}$ ions, and a blue precipitate or colloidal solution with $Fe(CN)_6^{-3}$ ions. Pure Fe (II) salts are seldom obtained because they are so readily oxidized to Fe (III) compounds.

ALUMINUM

37.40 Periodic Relationships of Aluminum

Group IIIA of the Periodic Table contains boron, aluminum, gallium, indium, and thallium. Boron is a nonmetallic element which has already been considered (Chapter 29). Aluminum is a common and abundant metal, whereas gallium, indium, and thallium are all scarce and almost without useful application (see Chapter 40). The Group IIIB elements (scandium, yttrium, the lanthanide elements, and the actinide elements) are considered in Chapter 40. All the elements of Periodic Group III are generally trivalent. Oxidation states other than +3 are exhibited by most of these elements. The rare earths are extremely similar in properties because the atoms of these elements have the same number of electrons in their outer two shells, the differences in electronic structure occurring in the third from the outermost shell.

37.41 History of Aluminum

To the alchemists the term "alum" meant a group of substances all of which had an astringent taste. Aluminum oxide was recognized as a distinct substance, related to alum, long before aluminum was isolated as a free element. Oersted (1825) and Wöhler (1828) first prepared aluminum by reducing aluminum chloride with potassium ($AlCl_3 + 3\ K \rightarrow Al + 3\ KCl$). The aluminum thus produced sold for $150 per pound because the method was expensive. In 1854, Deville, in France, produced aluminum by substituting the cheaper sodium for potassium as the reducing agent. As improvements in technology brought the cost of sodium down, the price of aluminum dropped to about $4 per pound by 1886. Bunsen had produced aluminum in 1854 by the electrolysis of aluminum chloride, but the cost was prohibitively high. The metal is now produced by an electrolytic process (Section 37.42) discovered in 1886 by Charles M. Hall (Fig. 37–10), who began work on the problem while he was a student at Oberlin College, and, independently, a month or two later by Héroult in France. The discovery made cheap aluminum possible, and, by the beginning of World War II in 1939, the price had dropped to 20 cents per pound. By 1962, however, the price had risen to 25 cents per pound.

Fig. 37–10 Charles Martin Hall (1863–1914) invented the inexpensive electrolytic process of refining aluminum now in use. Largely because of this invention the price of aluminum is now quoted in pennies rather than in dollars per pound. *Aluminum Company of America*

37.42 Occurrence and Metallurgy of Aluminum

Aluminum is the most abundant metal and the third most abundant element in the earth's crust. It is too active chemically to occur free in nature and is usually found combined with oxygen. The most important ore of aluminum is the hydrated oxide, $Al_2O_3 \cdot 2\,H_2O$, which is called **bauxite.** The mineral **cryolite,** Na_3AlF_6, occurs in nature and is used in the metallurgy of aluminum, though it is not an ore of aluminum. Very large and widely distributed quantities of aluminum are found in complex aluminosilicate minerals, such as **clays** and **feldspars.** Anhydrous aluminum oxide occurs as **corundum, ruby,** and **sapphire. Emery** is a mixture of Al_2O_3 and Fe_3O_4.

Aluminum can be produced from clays, which are largely hydrated aluminum silicates, but the higher cost involved in the preliminary treatment makes it impossible for aluminum from this source to compete with that produced from high-grade bauxite at the present time. However, as the deposits of bauxite become depleted, our supplies of aluminum will probably come from clays, of which we have practically inexhaustible quantities. In March, 1962, the world's first commercial plant designed to obtain aluminum sulfate from coal shale by treatment with sulfuric acid was put into production at Powhatan, Ohio. The company intends later to make Al_2O_3 from $Al_2(SO_4)_3$.

The first step in the production of metallic aluminum from bauxite consists in the purification of the mineral. It is dried and pulverized and then digested with sodium hydroxide under steam pressure. The aluminum oxide is thereby converted to soluble sodium aluminate, while the oxides of iron and silicon, which are present as impurities, remain undissolved.

$$Al_2O_3 \cdot 2\,H_2O + 2\,OH^- + H_2O \rightarrow 2\,Al(OH)_4^- \text{ (aluminate ion)}$$

After the insoluble iron oxide and silicates are filtered from the solution, the aluminum hydroxide is precipitated by hydrolysis of the aluminate. The hydrolysis is hastened by boiling and thoroughly aerating the solution. The precipitated aluminum hydroxide is ignited to the oxide, which is dissolved in fused cryolite, Na_3AlF_6. This solution is electrolyzed, whereupon aluminum metal is liberated at the cathode and oxygen, carbon monoxide, and carbon dioxide are formed at the anode (Fig. 37–11).

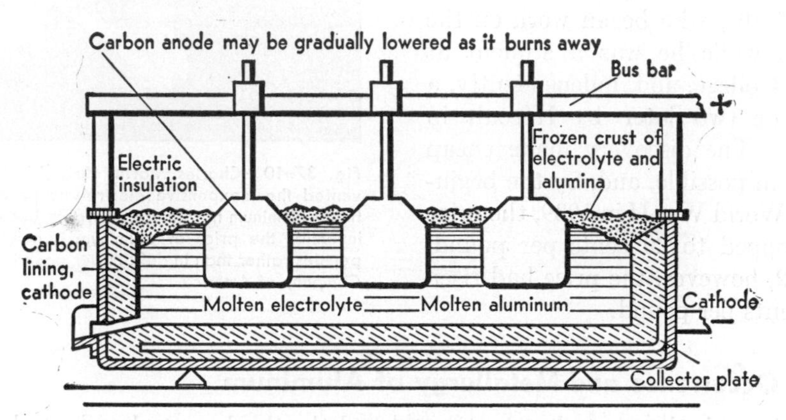

Fig. 37–11 Diagram of the electrolytic cell used in the production of metallic aluminum.

As the molten aluminum is drawn off, more aluminum oxide is added to the fused electrolyte. The carbon anodes are consumed, being converted to carbon monoxide and carbon dioxide.

In modern practice, an artificial mixture of fluorides replaces cryolite as the electrolyte. Typical is a mixture which approaches the composition $2\ AlF_3 \cdot 6\ NaF \cdot 3\ CaF_2$. Aluminum prepared by electrolysis is about 99 per cent pure, the impurities being small amounts of copper, iron, silicon, and aluminum oxide.

Aluminum of 99.9 per cent purity is obtained by the **Hoopes electrolytic process** (Fig. 37–12), which employs a fused bath consisting of three layers. The bottom layer is a fused alloy of copper and aluminum, the top layer is pure molten aluminum, and the middle layer (the electrolyte) consists of a fused mixture of the fluorides of barium, aluminum, and sodium, and nearly enough aluminum oxide to saturate it. The densities of the layers are such that their separation is maintained during electrolysis. The bottom layer serves as the anode and the top layer as the cathode. As electrolysis proceeds, the aluminum in the bottom layer passes into solution in the electrolyte as Al^{+++}, leaving the copper, iron, and silicon behind in the anode, for they are not oxidized under these conditions. The aluminum ion is reduced at the cathode. During electrolysis, purified aluminum is drawn off from the upper layer, and the impure metal is added to the lower layer through a carbon-lined funnel.

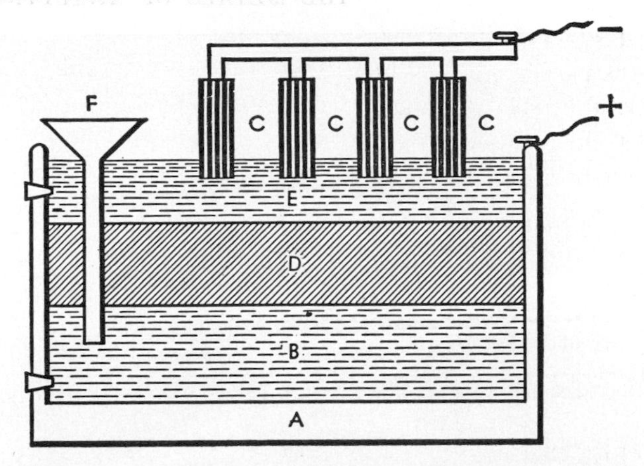

Fig. 37–12 Furnace for the purification of aluminum. A is bottom portion of cell in contact with the anodes; B is heavy impure aluminum-copper alloy; D an electrolyte of fused fluorides; E the layer of pure aluminum deposited at cathode CC. F is a funnel arrangement by which impure aluminum may be added to the bottom of the cell.

37.43 Properties and Uses of Aluminum

When freshly cut, aluminum has a silvery appearance, but it soon becomes superficially oxidized and assumes a dull white luster. The metal is very light and possesses high tensile strength. Weight for weight, it is twice as good a conductor of electricity as copper. Although aluminum is a relatively reactive metal, the tenacious coating of the oxide which forms on it prevents further atmospheric corrosion. When heated in the air finely divided aluminum burns with a brilliant light. Because of the formation of a protective coat of oxide, aluminum does not decompose water. It is readily dissolved by hydrochloric acid and sulfuric acid, but is rendered passive by nitric acid. Aluminum dissolves in concentrated alkalies with the formation of aluminates and hydrogen.

$$2\ Al + 2\ OH^- + 6\ H_2O \rightarrow 2\ Al(OH)_4^- + 3\ H_2 \uparrow$$

This behavior is in accord with the amphoteric character of aluminum hydroxide. When heated, aluminum combines directly with the halogens, nitrogen, carbon, and sulfur.

The fact that aluminum is an excellent conductor of heat, together with its light weight and resistance to corrosion, accounts for its use in the manufacture of cooking utensils. The most important uses of aluminum are in the airplane and other transportation industries (Fig. 37–13, page 632). Here the lightness, toughness, and tensile strength of the metal are important. The average 1962 automobile contains 66.5 pounds of aluminum, compared to only six pounds in each 1948 automobile. Aluminum is also used in the manufacture of electrical transmission wire, as a paint pigment, and, in the form of foil, as a wrapping material.

Aluminum is one of the best reflectors of heat and light, including the wave lengths in the ultraviolet. For this reason it is used as an insulating material, and

Fig. 37–13 Much aluminum is used in the construction of modern airplanes. Boeing 720B turbofan jet. *TWA*

as a mirror in reflecting telescopes. The 200-inch mirror in the world's largest telescope at Mount Palomar, California, is coated with aluminum.

About half of the aluminum produced in this country is converted to alloys for special uses. **Duralumin** is an alloy containing aluminum, copper, manganese, and magnesium. It is light but nearly as strong as steel, so it is useful in the construction of aircraft. **Aluminum bronzes** contain copper, and occasionally some silicon, manganese, iron, nickel, and zinc. These light-weight alloys have high tensile strength and great resistance to corrosion, so they are used extensively in the manufacture of crankcases and connecting rods for gasoline motors. **Alnico** is a magnetic alloy containing 50 per cent iron, 20 per cent aluminum, 20 per cent nickel, and 10 per cent cobalt, which will lift more than 4000 times its own weight of iron. It is made by pressing together the constituent metals in powder form and heating the mixture just below the melting point. This is an example of **powder metallurgy** — a branch of science which is growing rapidly in importance.

When powdered aluminum and iron (III) oxide are mixed and ignited by means of a magnesium fuse a vigorous and highly exothermic reaction occurs.

$$2\ Al + Fe_2O_3 \rightarrow 2\ Fe + Al_2O_3 + \Delta$$

This is known as the **thermite** or **Goldschmidt** reaction. The temperature of the reaction mixture rises to about 3000° so the iron and aluminum oxide become liquid. The process is frequently used in welding large pieces of iron or steel (Fig. 37–14). Thermite bombs were used for incendiary purposes during World War II because of the high temperature generated by the thermite reaction and because the reaction is not readily quenched by water. The thermite reaction is used in the reduction of metallic oxides (such as MoO_3 and WO_3) which are not readily reduced by carbon, or others (such as MnO_2 and Cr_2O_3) which do not give pure metal when reduced by carbon.

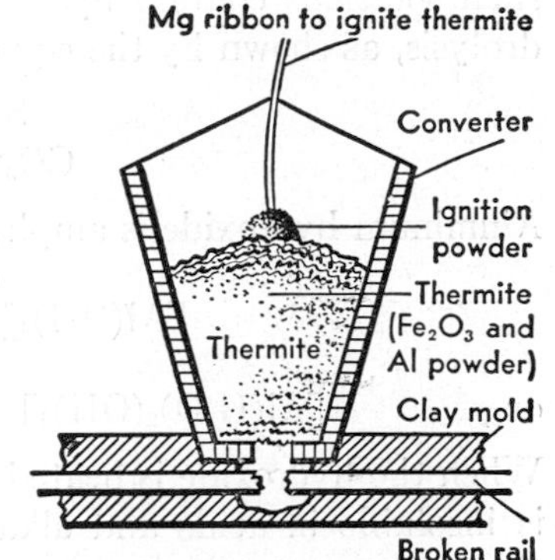

Fig. 37–14 Thermite welding. Molten iron flows out the bottom of the converter welding together the parts of the broken rail. What reaction occurs in the converter?

37.44 Aluminum Oxide

The oxide, Al_2O_3, occurs in nature in pure form as the mineral **corundum,** a very hard substance which is used as an abrasive for grinding and polishing. **Emery** is aluminum oxide mixed with Fe_3O_4; it is also used as an abrasive. Artificial corundum, sold under the name **alundum,** is produced by fusing bauxite in an electric furnace. It is used as an abrasive, refractory, and as a filtering medium for corrosive liquids. Several precious stones are composed of aluminum oxide. These stones are colored by impurities: ruby (red, by chromium compounds); sapphire (blue, by compounds of cobalt, chromium, or titanium); oriental amethyst (violet, by manganese compounds); and oriental topaz (yellow, by iron). Artificial rubies and sapphires are now manufactured by melting aluminum oxide (m.p. 2050°) with small amounts of oxides to produce the desired color, and cooling the melt in such a way as to produce large crystals. These gems are indistinguishable from natural stones, except for microscopic, rounded air bubbles in the synthetic ones and flattened bubbles in the natural stones. These are used not only as jewelry, but as bearings ("jewels") in watches and other instruments, and as dies through which wires are drawn. Very finely divided aluminum oxide, called "activated alumina," is used as a dehydrating agent and as a catalyst.

Various aluminum articles, such as drinking tumblers, are given a wear resistant coating of oxide by anodic oxidation in a bath of chromic, sulfuric, or oxalic acid. This surface readily adsorbs dyes and pigments which give a pleasing decorative effect to the article.

37.45 Aluminum Hydroxide

When an alkali is added to a solution of an aluminum salt, a white, gelatinous precipitate is formed.

$$Al^{+++} + 3\ OH^- \rightarrow \underline{Al(OH)_3}$$

or

$$[Al(H_2O)_6]^{+++} + 3\ OH^- \rightarrow \underline{[Al(OH)_3(H_2O)_3]} + 3\ H_2O$$

Solutions of sulfides or carbonates also precipitate aluminum hydroxide because such solutions contain hydroxide ions in considerable concentrations due to hydrolysis, as shown by the equations

$$S^{=} + H_2O \rightleftharpoons HS^{-} + OH^{-}$$
$$CO_3^{=} + H_2O \rightleftharpoons HCO_3^{-} + OH^{-}$$

Aluminum hydroxide is amphoteric and is dissolved by both acids and bases.

$$[Al(OH)_4]^{-} \underset{}{\overset{OH^-}{\leftrightharpoons}} \underline{Al(OH)_3} \overset{3\ H^+}{\rightleftharpoons} Al^{+++} + 3\ H_2O$$

or $$[Al(H_2O)_2(OH)_4]^{-} \overset{OH^-}{\leftrightharpoons} \underline{[Al(H_2O)_3(OH)_3]} \overset{3\ H^+}{\rightleftharpoons} [Al(H_2O)_6]^{+++}$$

When the hydroxide is heated above 850°, a form of aluminum oxide results which is insoluble in acids and alkalies. Products obtained below 600° are soluble in these reagents.

Aluminum hydroxide is widely used to fix dyes to fabrics. Cloth which is soaked in a hot solution of aluminum acetate becomes impregnated with the aluminum hydroxide formed by hydrolysis of the salt. If the hydroxide is precipitated from a solution containing a dye, the precipitate is colored. The aluminum hydroxide adsorbs the dye and holds it fast to the cloth. When used in this way, the aluminum hydroxide is called a **mordant,** and the colored product is called a **lake.**

Aluminum hydroxide is also used in the purification of water, for its gelatinous character enables it to carry down with it any suspended material in the water, including bacteria. The aluminum hydroxide is ordinarily produced by the reaction of aluminum sulfate with lime.

$$2\ Al^{+++} + 3\ SO_4^{=} + 3\ Ca^{++} + 6\ OH^{-} \rightarrow 2\ \underline{Al(OH)_3} + 3\ \underline{CaSO_4}$$

37.46 Aluminum Chloride

Anhydrous aluminum chloride is a white crystalline solid which sublimes at 180° and is soluble in organic solvents. Measurements of its density show that in the vapor state it is dimeric, and the formula should be written Al_2Cl_6. In these molecules each aluminum atom is tetrahedrally bonded to four chlorine atoms; two of these chlorine atoms are each bonded to two aluminum atoms, as shown below.

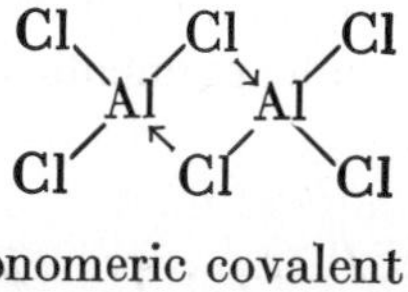

```
Cl     Cl     Cl
  \   /  ↘   /
   Al     Al
  /  ↖   /  \
Cl     Cl     Cl
```

One chlorine atom of each monomeric covalent molecule donates a pair of electrons to be shared by the aluminum atom of the other molecule, and thus two "chlorine bridges" are formed, and each aluminum atom then possesses an octet of electrons. X-ray studies show that there are no Al_2Cl_6 molecules in solid aluminum chloride, and the formula for the compound in the solid state is written $AlCl_3$.

Aluminum chloride can be prepared by direct chlorination of aluminum or by heating bauxite with carbon and chlorine.

$$2\ Al + 3\ Cl_2 \rightarrow 2\ AlCl_3$$
$$Al_2O_3 + 3\ C + 3\ Cl_2 \rightarrow 2\ AlCl_3 + 3\ CO$$

Anhydrous aluminum chloride is used as a catalyst in many organic reactions as in the cracking processes for making gasoline.

If aluminum or aluminum hydroxide is treated with hydrochloric acid and the solution is evaporated, crystals of the hexahydrate, $AlCl_3 \cdot 6\ H_2O$, are formed. When this salt is heated, hydrolysis occurs according to the equation

$$2[AlCl_3 \cdot 6\ H_2O] \rightarrow \underline{Al_2O_3} + 6\ HCl \uparrow + 9\ H_2O$$

37.47 Aluminum Sulfate

The sulfate, $Al_2(SO_4)_3 \cdot 18\ H_2O$, is prepared by treating bauxite or clay with sulfuric acid.

$$\underset{\text{Clay}}{Al_2Si_2O_5(OH)_4} + 6\ H^+ + (3\ SO_4^{=}) \rightarrow 2\ \underline{H_2SiO_3} + 2\ Al^{+++} + (3\ SO_4^{=}) + 3\ H_2O$$

The metasilicic acid formed is removed by filtration. The sulfate is the cheapest soluble salt of aluminum, so it is used as a source of aluminum hydroxide for the purification of water, the waterproofing of fabrics, the sizing of paper, and the dyeing of fabrics.

37.48 Alums

When solutions of potassium sulfate and aluminum sulfate are mixed and concentrated by evaporation, crystals of potassium alum are formed. The salt may best be formulated as $KAl(SO_4)_2 \cdot 12\ H_2O$. It is the commonest of a class of double salts known as alums and is frequently referred to simply as "alum." The univalent ion in an alum may be that of an alkali metal, silver, or ammonium, and the trivalent ion may be aluminum, chromium, iron, manganese, or some other. The selenate ion, $SeO_4^{=}$, may replace the sulfate ion. Thus we have **ammonium alum,** $NH_4Al(SO_4)_2 \cdot 12\ H_2O$; **sodium iron (III) alum,** $NaFe(SO_4)_2 \cdot 12\ H_2O$; and **potassium chrome alum,** $KCr(SO_4)_2 \cdot 12\ H_2O$. The alums are all isomorphous; i.e., they have the same crystal structure.

37.49 Aluminum Silicates

As we saw in Section 29.17, many of the most important silicate rocks contain aluminum. Clay and sand are formed as disintegration products by the weathering of these rocks. Weathering involves the thawing and freezing of water in the rocks, and the chemical action of water and carbon dioxide upon them. For example, the chemical disintegration of feldspar may be represented by the equation

$$2\ \underset{\text{Feldspar}}{KAlSi_3O_8} + 2\ H_2O + CO_2 \rightarrow 2\ K^+ + CO_3^{=} + \underset{\text{Clay}}{\underline{Al_2Si_2O_5(OH)_4}} + 4\ \underset{\text{Sand}}{\underline{SiO_2}}$$

The soluble potassium carbonate formed is largely removed by water, and the residue of sand and clay remains as soil. Pure clay has the formula shown above;

it is white and is called **kaolin.** Ordinary clay is colored by compounds of iron and other metals. **Porcelain** and **china** are made of kaolin, while impure clays are used in the manufacture of earthenware products such as **tile** and **brick.** The buff or red color of such products is due to the presence of iron (III) silicate. When articles fashioned of clay are strongly heated, the products are porous, but may be made watertight by being glazed. In the glazing of cheap ware, common salt is introduced in the kiln after the article has been fired. The salt reacts with the clay on the surface, forming vitreous sodium aluminosilicate, which fills the pores. More expensive wares, such as porcelain and china, are glazed by treatment with a mixture of powdered feldspar and silica and often lead oxide and then refired at a higher temperature. Oxides of suitable metals are used to produce colored glazes.

37.50 Properties of Aluminum of Analytical Importance

Aluminum hydroxide forms as a white gelatinous precipitate when solutions containing aluminum ions are treated with aqueous ammonia or alkali hydroxides, sulfides, or carbonates. The precipitate is practically insoluble in an excess of aqueous ammonia, but dissolves readily in excess alkali, aluminate ions being formed. The dye aurin tricarboxylic acid (aluminon) forms a red lake with aluminum hydroxide; this is the basis of a sensitive test for aluminum ions.

CHROMIUM

37.51 Periodic Relationships of Chromium

The elements which constitute Group VIB of the Periodic Table are chromium, molybdenum, and tungsten. These metals differ distinctly from the nonmetals of Periodic Group VIA, which we have already considered in Chapter 22. Chromium, molybdenum, and tungsten are each used in the production of commercially important alloy steels. These metals are typical transition metals; they show a variety of oxidation states, form highly colored compounds, and enter into the formation of stable complex ions. Like those of the other transition metals, their lowest oxides are basic, the intermediate ones are amphoteric, and the highest ones are primarily acidic. The members of the A and B families show similarities in the higher oxidation states; thus the sulfates (e.g., K_2SO_4) and the chromates (K_2CrO_4) are analogous in formula and in physical and chemical properties.

37.52 History and Occurrence of Chromium

In 1797 the French chemist, Vauquelin, discovered chromium in a red mineral which had been found in Siberia in 1766. The mineral has the composition $PbCrO_4$ and is now known as **crocoite.** The name "chromium" was chosen for the element because of the variety and intensity of color shown by its compounds, and is derived from the Greek word "chroma," which means color.

Chromium does not occur free in nature. Its most important ore is **chromite,** $FeCr_2O_4$, sometimes called "chrome iron ore." The leading producing countries of high-grade chrome ore are Rhodesia, Turkey, and the Union of South Africa. Lower-grade ores are obtained from India and Greece. The United States imports practically all of the chromium which she consumes. Because chromium is essential to the production of special alloy steels and the supply is often short, it is a strategic metal.

37.53 Metallurgy and Properties of Chromium

Reduction of chromite by carbon in an electric furnace yields an alloy of iron and chromium, called **ferrochrome,** which is used in making chromium steels.

$$FeCr_2O_4 + 4\ C \rightarrow Fe + 2\ Cr + 4\ CO$$

The pure metal is prepared by reducing chromium (III) oxide with aluminum.

$$Cr_2O_3 + 2\ Al \rightarrow Al_2O_3 + 2\ Cr$$

Chromium may also be produced by the electrolytic reduction of its compounds from aqueous solution, a process which is used in chromium plating.

Chromium is a very hard, silvery-white, crystalline metal. It assumes a passive state by becoming coated with a thin layer of oxide, which protects it against further corrosive attack. This property, along with its metallic luster, accounts for its extensive use in the plating of iron and copper objects, such as plumbing fixtures and automobile trim. Passivity is produced by the action of concentrated nitric acid, chromic acid, or exposure of the metal to air. When not in the passive state, chromium dissolves readily in dilute acids with the evolution of hydrogen. Chromium is a transition metal which shows several oxidation states, the principal ones being +2, +3, and +6. The compounds of chromium are highly colored, each color exhibited being dependent to some extent upon a particular oxidation state and upon the structure of the compound.

37.54 Compounds of Chromium

1. *Chromium (II) compounds.* **Chromium (II) chloride,** $CrCl_2$, can be prepared by dissolving chromium in hydrochloric acid or by reducing a solution of chromium (III) chloride by zinc in the presence of acids. The anhydrous salt is colorless, but its solutions have the bright blue color of the hydrated ion, $[Cr(H_2O)_6]^{++}$. This ion is rapidly oxidized by air to the chromium (III) ion, $[Cr(H_2O)_6]^{+++}$; for this reason solutions of chromium (II) salts are frequently employed to remove the last traces of oxygen from gases. The **sulfate,** $CrSO_4 \cdot 7\ H_2O$, is prepared by dissolving the metal in sulfuric acid. The **acetate,** $Cr(C_2H_3O_2)_2$, forms as a red precipitate when a saturated solution of sodium acetate is added to a solution of chromium (II) chloride. In general, acetates are soluble (Section 12.9). Chromium (II) acetate is one of the few exceptions to this rule. **Chromium (II) hydroxide** is basic, and chromium (II) salts are only slightly hydrolyzed.

2. *Chromium (III) compounds.* Green **chromium (III) oxide,** Cr_2O_3, is formed by heating the metal in air, by igniting ammonium dichromate, or by reducing a dichromate with sulfur.

$$(NH_4)_2Cr_2O_7 \rightarrow N_2 + 4\ H_2O + Cr_2O_3$$
$$Na_2Cr_2O_7 + S \rightarrow Na_2SO_4 + Cr_2O_3$$

This oxide finds use as a pigment called "chrome green." The bluish-green, gelatinous **chromium (III) hydroxide** is precipitated when an alkali, a soluble sulfide, or a carbonate is added to a solution of a chromium (III) compound. It is amphoteric, dissolving in both acids and bases.

$$Cr(OH)_3 + 3\ H^+ \rightarrow Cr^{+++} + 3\ H_2O$$
$$Cr(OH)_3 + OH^- \rightarrow [Cr(OH)_4]^- \text{ (chromite ion)}$$

Chromium (III) chloride 6-hydrate, $CrCl_3 \cdot 6\ H_2O$, and the **sulfate,** $Cr_2(SO_4)_3 \cdot 18\ H_2O$, are the best known salts of trivalent chromium. Dilute solutions of the chloride are violet, the hexaaquochromium (III) ion, $[Cr(H_2O)_6]^{+++}$ being responsible for the color. In more concentrated solutions of the chloride, the green $[Cr(H_2O)_4Cl_2]^+$ is formed. The hydrates of chromium (III) sulfate also exist in violet and green modifications. Trivalent chromium forms alums (Fig. 37–15) of the type $KCr(SO_4)_2 \cdot 12\ H_2O$, solutions of which are bluish-violet when cold but green when hot. **Chrome alum** is used in the tanning of leather, the printing of calico, the waterproofing of fabrics, and as a mordant. It is the most important of the soluble chromium salts.

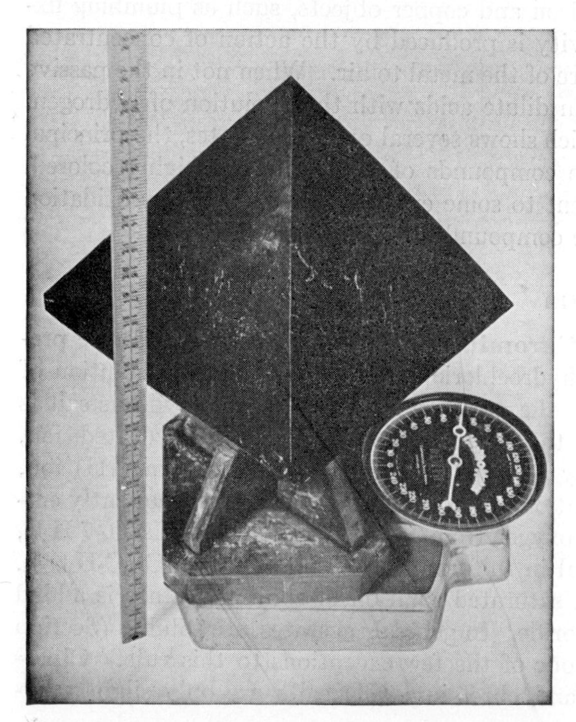

Fig. 37–15 A large crystal of chrome alum. Notice that the crystal and stand weigh approximately 70 pounds, and that the largest dimension of the crystal is approximately two feet.

3. *Chromium (VI) compounds.* In the +6 oxidation state, chromium is usually combined with oxygen in the form of the oxide **chromium trioxide,** CrO_3, or the oxyanions, **chromate,** $CrO_4^{=}$, and **dichromate,** $Cr_2O_7^{=}$. **Potassium chro-**

mate, K_2CrO_4, is produced commercially by the atmospheric oxidation of chromite ore admixed and heated with potassium carbonate.

$$4\ FeCr_2O_4 + 8\ K_2CO_3 + 7\ O_2 \rightarrow 2\ Fe_2O_3 + 8\ K_2CrO_4 + 8\ CO_2$$

The yellow potassium chromate is extracted with water and recrystallized. It is used in dyeing and in manufacturing ink. **Lead chromate** ($PbCrO_4$) and **barium chromate** ($BaCrO_4$) are both insoluble in water and are used as yellow pigments. The former is called "chrome yellow." **Basic lead chromate,** $PbO \cdot PbCrO_4$, is called "chrome red"; when mixed with chrome yellow it gives "chrome orange."

When an acid is added to a solution containing chromate ions, the solution changes from yellow to orange-red due to the formation of the dichromate ion, $Cr_2O_7^{=}$.

$$2\ CrO_4^{=} + 2\ H^+ \rightleftharpoons Cr_2O_7^{=} + H_2O$$

The addition of a base reverses the reaction.

$$Cr_2O_7^{=} + 2\ OH^- \rightleftharpoons 2\ CrO_4^{=} + H_2O$$

The conversion of chromate to dichromate involves the formation of an oxygen linkage between two chromium atoms. The electronic structure of the dichromate ion is given in Fig. 37–16. In very strongly acid solutions, further condensation of chromate ions to **trichromate** ions, $Cr_3O_{10}^{=}$, occurs.

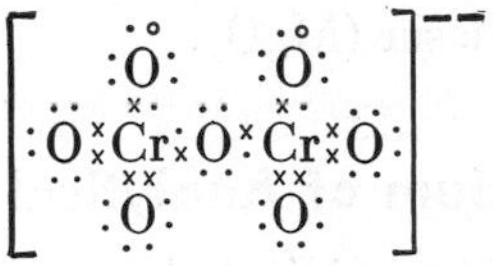

```
[      ·°       ·°      ]--
      :O:      :O:
 ··    ×·   ··  ×·   ··
:O×Cr×O×Cr×O:
 ··    ××   ··  ××   ··
      :O:      :O:
[      ··       ··      ]
```

Fig. 37–16 Electronic structure of $Cr_2O_7^{=}$.

A mixture of sodium dichromate and sulfuric acid is used as a cleaning solution for glassware in the laboratory. The cleansing action is due to the strong oxidizing power of the dichromate and the dehydrating action of the concentrated sulfuric acid. The dichromates are used as oxidizing agents in many reactions. The dichromate ion is readily reduced to the chromium (III) ion by reducing agents such as sulfurous acid.

$$Cr_2O_7^{=} + 3\ H_2SO_3 + 2\ H^+ \rightarrow 2\ Cr^{+++} + 3\ SO_4^{=} + 4\ H_2O$$

As the reduction progresses, one may observe a change from the orange color of the dichromate to the green color of the chromium (III) ion.

Potassium and sodium dichromates have many uses. These include use in tanning, dyeing, printing, and waterproofing, as astringents and cauterizing agents in medicine, and as laboratory reagents.

The **trioxide,** CrO_3, is produced as scarlet needle-shaped crystals by the action of concentrated sulfuric acid upon a concentrated solution of potassium dichromate.

$$Cr_2O_7^{=} + 2\ H^+ \rightarrow 2\ \underline{CrO_3} + H_2O$$

The anhydride, CrO_3, reacts with water in different proportions, forming **chromic acid,** H_2CrO_4, **dichromic acid,** $H_2Cr_2O_7$, and **trichromic acid,** $H_2Cr_3O_{10}$.

$$3\ CrO_3 + H_2O \rightarrow 2\ H^+ + Cr_3O_{10}^{=}$$
$$2\ CrO_3 + H_2O \rightarrow 2\ H^+ + Cr_2O_7^{=}$$
$$CrO_3 + H_2O \rightarrow 2\ H^+ + CrO_4^{=}$$

These solutions are used as active oxidizing agents. When heated, the anhydride decomposes, liberating oxygen and forming the green chromium (III) oxide.

$$4\ CrO_3 \rightarrow 2\ Cr_2O_3 + 3\ O_2$$

37.55 Uses of Chromium

A large portion of the chromium produced goes into steel alloys which are very hard and strong. These are used in armor plate, projectiles, bank vaults, safes, cutting tools, and automobile parts. **Stainless steel** usually contains chromium and some nickel. It is used in the manufacture of cutlery because it is corrosion resistant. Nonferrous chromium alloys include nichrome and chromel (Ni and Cr), which are used for electrical resistance in various heating devices. Chromium is widely used as a protective and decorative coating for other metals, such as plumbing fixtures and automobile trim.

The compounds of chromium have many uses. These include use as paint pigments and mordants and in the tanning of leather. Certain refractories which are used as lining for high-temperature furnaces are made by mixing pulverized chromite ore with clay or magnesia (MgO).

37.56 Properties of Chromium of Analytical Importance

Chromium (III) hydroxide is precipitated from solutions containing chromium (III) ions by aqueous ammonia, alkalies, and ammonium sulfide or carbonate. The bluish-green gelatinous precipitate is soluble in acids and in excess of alkali. The hydroxide is converted to soluble sodium chromate (yellow) by sodium peroxide. Acids convert the chromate to the dichromate (orange-red). Either chromate or dichromate ions precipitate lead chromate (yellow) from solutions of lead salts. Hydrogen peroxide converts dichromate ions in acid solution to a blue soluble compound whose formula has not been established but which is believed to be a peroxychromate.

ZINC

37.57 History and Occurrence of Zinc

The ancients used brass, an alloy of zinc and copper, a very long time ago without knowing its composition. The alloy was produced by smelting ores containing both metals. Zinc was first recognized as a distinct element by Paracelsus in the sixteenth century and was first prepared in a fairly pure state by Henckel in 1720.

Sphalerite, or zinc blende, ZnS, is the principal ore of zinc. Less important ores include **zincite,** ZnO; **smithsonite,** $ZnCO_3$; **franklinite,** a mixture of oxides of zinc, iron, and manganese; and **willemite,** Zn_2SiO_4. Zinc ores are widely distributed and the metal is produced in many countries. The most productive areas in the United States are the Joplin region of Missouri, Kansas, and Oklahoma; New Jersey; Idaho; and New Mexico.

37.58 Metallurgy of Zinc

Zinc sulfide ores are first concentrated by flotation and then roasted to convert the sulfide to the oxide.

$$2\,ZnS + 3\,O_2 \rightarrow 2\,ZnO + 2\,SO_2$$

In the case of carbonate ores, the oxide is obtained by simple heating. The zinc oxide formed by roasting the sulfide or carbonate ores is reduced by heating it with coal in a fire-clay retort (Fig. 37–17, 18). As rapidly as the zinc is produced, it distills out and is condensed. The zinc so produced is impure with cadmium, iron, lead, and arsenic. It may be purified by careful redistillation.

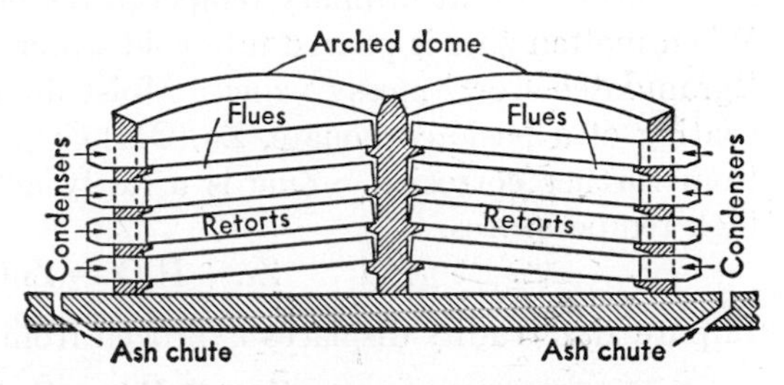

Fig. 37–17 Zinc retort furnace.

Fig. 37–18 A zinc furnace in operation. Zinc oxide and carbon (coal and charcoal) are heated in retorts which are connected to the condensers seen projecting from the furnace. The flame at the mouth of each condenser is burning carbon monoxide gas. *U.S. Steel Corp.*

An electrolytic process is also employed to produce zinc. The ore is roasted in special furnaces under such conditions that most of the sulfide is converted to the sulfate and the remainder changed to the oxide. The roasted ore is leached with sulfuric acid to dissolve the zinc sulfate and zinc oxide, as well as the sulfates and oxides of other metals. Silver sulfate and lead sulfate remain in the residue, for they are insoluble. The resulting solution of zinc sulfate is treated with powdered zinc to reduce the less active metals such as copper, arsenic, and antimony to the elementary condition. Any manganese present is oxidized by passing air through the solution. Manganese and iron are precipitated as hydroxides by adding lime. After the solution is purified in this way, it is electrolyzed, zinc being deposited on aluminum cathodes. Sulfuric acid is regenerated as electrolysis proceeds and is used in the leaching of more roasted ore. At intervals, the cathodes are removed, the zinc scraped off, melted, and cast into ingots. Electrolytic zinc has a purity of 99.95 per cent. Much of it is used in the production of brass.

37.59 Properties and Uses of Zinc

The periodic relationships of zinc were discussed in Section 35.1. Zinc is a silvery metal that quickly tarnishes to a blue-gray appearance. The metal is hard and brittle at ordinary temperatures but ductile and malleable at 100–150°. When molten zinc is poured into cold water, it solidifies in irregular masses called "granulated" or "mossy" zinc. Moist air acts upon zinc, forming an adherent coating of a basic carbonate, $Zn_2(OH)_2CO_3$, which protects the underlying metal from further corrosion. Zinc is a fairly active metal and will reduce steam at high temperatures.

$$Zn + H_2O \rightarrow ZnO + H_2 \uparrow$$

Impure zinc readily displaces hydrogen from dilute hydrochloric or sulfuric acids,

$$Zn + 2\ H^+ \rightarrow Zn^{++} + H_2 \uparrow$$

but pure zinc reacts slowly or not at all with these acids due to the formation of a protecting layer of hydrogen on the surface of the metal. Impure zinc contains small particles of impurities from which hydrogen is discharged rather than from the zinc.

Zinc dissolves in strong bases, liberating hydrogen and forming zincate ions.

$$Zn + 2\ OH^- + 2\ H_2O \rightarrow [Zn(OH)_4]^= + H_2 \uparrow$$

A considerable amount of zinc is used in the manufacture of dry cells and in the production of alloys such as brass and bronze. About half of the zinc metal produced is used to protect iron and other metals from corrosion by air and water. Its protective action depends upon the property of forming a basic carbonate film on its surface. Furthermore, it protects less active metals such as iron because it corrodes first, being a more active metal (see Section 37.31).

The zinc coating on iron may be applied in several ways, and the product is called **galvanized iron.** In the "hot galvanizing" method, the iron or steel is first thoroughly freed from grease and oxide. A wash with hot caustic removes the grease, and then the oxide is removed by "pickling" in dilute sulfuric acid (Fig. 37–19). The zinc coating is put on by dipping the sheet iron or wire into molten zinc and then running the metal through rollers. The zinc on a "hot galvanized" piece of iron consists of an alloy of the two metals in direct contact with the iron with a layer of pure zinc outside of this.

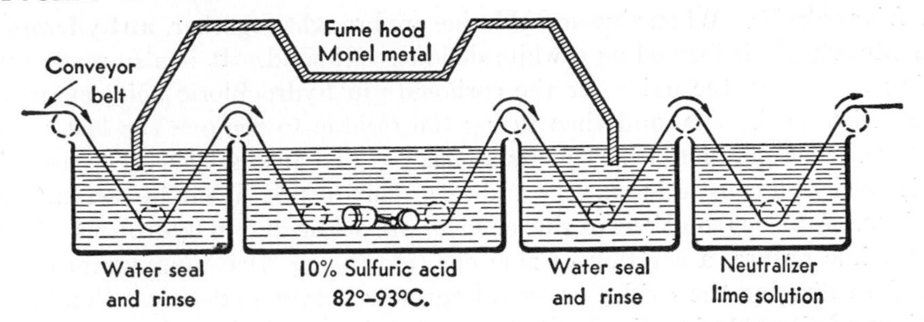

Fig. 37–19 Modern hood for use in pickling metal parts for electroplating and galvanizing. Annoyance from acid fumes is avoided even in plants which consume as much as 50 tons of acid daily.

Electrogalvanizing (cold galvanizing) involves the continuous passage of strips or wires through a plating bath, while individual articles, such as automobile parts, are carried through the bath on a conveyor. The electrogalvanizing method has the advantages that the thickness of the zinc layer can be varied at will, and the layer is uniform in thickness, thus giving a product which has a higher resistance to corrosion.

A layer of zinc may be applied to small iron objects by placing them in a revolving drum with zinc dust, and heating to such a temperature that the zinc dissolves in the surface of the iron, forming a corrosion resistant alloy. This process is called **sherardizing** and is particularly applicable to objects of intricate form such as pulleys and bolts. A fourth method of producing a protective coating of zinc on iron is called the **metallizing process.** The iron objects are coated by spraying atomized zinc against the iron with great force. The resulting layer of zinc is quite adherent.

37.60 Compounds of Zinc

1. *Zinc oxide and zinc hydroxide.* The **oxide,** ZnO, is produced when zinc vapor is burned and when zinc ores are roasted in an excess of air. The oxide is yellow when hot, but pure white when cold. It is used as a paint pigment, called **zinc white** or **Chinese white;** unlike white lead, it does not blacken in hydrogen sulfide, because zinc sulfide is white. It is also used in the manufacture of automobile tires and other rubber goods, and in the preparation of medical ointments.

Zinc hydroxide, $Zn(OH)_2$, is formed as a white, gelatinous precipitate when a soluble hydroxide is added to a solution of a zinc salt.

$$Zn^{++} + 2\ OH^- \rightarrow \underline{Zn(OH)_2}$$

The hydroxide is amphoteric and dissolves in an excess of alkali as well as in acids.

$$Zn(OH)_2 + 2\ OH^- \rightarrow [Zn(OH)_4]^= \text{ (zincate ion)}$$
$$Zn(OH)_2 + 2\ H^+ \rightarrow Zn^{++} + 2\ H_2O$$

Zinc hydroxide is soluble in aqueous ammonia, forming **tetraamminezinc hydroxide.**

$$Zn(OH)_2 + 4\ NH_3 \rightarrow [Zn(NH_3)_4]^{++} + 2\ OH^-$$

2. *Zinc chloride.* When zinc and chlorine are brought together, **anhydrous zinc chloride,** $ZnCl_2$, is formed as a white deliquescent solid. It is also made by dissolving the metal, the oxide, or the carbonate in hydrochloric acid, evaporating the solution to dryness, and then fusing the residue to remove the last traces of moisture. The product, which melts at 262°, is cast into sticks. The anhydrous salt is used as a caustic in surgery and as a dehydrating agent in certain organic reactions. Aqueous solutions of zinc chloride are acidic due to hydrolysis. Because of its acidic nature, a solution of zinc chloride (along with ammonium chloride) is used to dissolve the oxides on metal surfaces before soldering. Concentrated solutions of zinc chloride dissolve cellulose, forming a gelatinous mass, which may be molded into various shapes. Fiberboard is made of this material. Zinc chloride is used to preserve wood because it forms an impervious gelatinous layer on the surface of the wood and also because it is toxic to decay-producing organisms. Because zinc compounds are poisonous, they should be handled with care; the best antidote is soda and milk, or white of egg. Zinc oxide dissolves in concentrated solutions of zinc chloride, producing a **basic zinc chloride,** Zn_2OCl_2, which sets to a hard mass, and is used as a cement.

3. *Zinc sulfate.* **Zinc sulfate** is produced in large quantities by roasting zinc blende at low red heat.

$$ZnS + 2\ O_2 \rightarrow ZnSO_4$$

The product is extracted with water and recovered by recrystallization to form crystals of the **heptahydrate,** $ZnSO_4 \cdot 7\ H_2O$, which is called "white vitriol." It is used principally in the production of the white paint pigment **lithopone,** which is a mixture of barium sulfate and zinc sulfide, formed by the reaction

$$BaS + Zn^{++} + SO_4^{=} \rightarrow \underline{BaSO_4} + \underline{ZnS}$$

The product is not darkened by hydrogen sulfide.

4. *Zinc sulfide.* **Zinc sulfide,** ZnS, is found in nature as zinc blende and is formed in the laboratory when ammonium sulfide is added to a solution of a zinc salt. The sulfide is insoluble in acetic acid but dissolves readily in stronger acids such as hydrochloric or sulfuric.

$$ZnS + 2\ H^+ \rightarrow Zn^{++} + H_2S \uparrow$$

Zinc sulfide is used as a white paint pigment, either alone or mixed with zinc oxide.

37.61 Properties of Zinc of Analytical Importance

Solutions containing the zinc ion are colorless. Zinc chloride is soluble in water, and the sulfide is soluble in dilute acids but insoluble in alkaline solutions. The white hydroxide is precipitated by ammonia and by alkalies but is dissolved by an excess of these reagents.

QUESTIONS

1. What is the composition of the reagent used for the precipitation of the Group III metals?

2. What is the physical nature of nickel carbonyl? How is this compound used in the separation of nickel from other metals?

3. What is meant by the term "passivity"? How is nickel rendered passive?

4. Write the equation for the dissolution of nickel (II) hydroxide in aqueous ammonia.

5. What is the composition of Alnico? What use is made of this alloy?

6. Give the chemistry of an invisible ink.

7. Sketch the spatial configuration of $[Co(CN)_6]^{\equiv}$.

8. How are the alloys known as ferromanganese produced?

9. Write the names and formulas for compounds in which manganese exhibits each of the following oxidation states: +2, +3, +4, +6, and +7.

10. Outline the chemistry of the action of manganese dioxide upon hydrochloric acid.

11. Explain the dissolution of manganese (II) hydroxide in aqueous ammonium chloride in terms of an acid-base reaction.

12. Mention two uses of manganese dioxide.

13. How is potassium permanganate prepared commercially?

14. Write the names and formulas of the principal ores of iron.

15. List the equations for the reactions that take place in the reduction of iron (III) oxide in the blast furnace.

16. What use is made of the hot exhaust gases from the blast furnace?

17. Give the composition and distinguishing physical properties of pig iron, wrought iron, and steel.

18. How can passivity in iron be destroyed?

19. What is the composition of iron rust?

20. Identify each of the following: hematite, magnetic oxide of iron, rouge, Mohr's salt, and Prussian blue.

21. What compound of iron is a common constituent of hard water?

22. What is the odoriferous gas produced when iron (II) sulfide is treated with an acid?

23. Give the general equation for the hydrolysis of iron (III) salts.

24. Describe the production of metallic aluminum by electrolytic reduction.

25. Why can aluminum, which is an active metal, be used so successfully as a structural metal?

26. What is the action of sodium hydroxide upon aluminum?

27. Illustrate the amphoteric nature of aluminum hydroxide by suitable equations.

28. Explain the function of aluminum hydroxide in water purification.

29. What is the composition of alums as a class of double salts?

30. What is the Goldschmidt or thermite process?

31. Account for the extensive use of chromium in the plating of iron and copper objects, such as the trim on automobiles.

32. Chromium, iron, cobalt, nickel, and manganese are among the elements referred to as "transition metals." Explain.

33. Write the equation for the decomposition of ammonium dichromate by ignition.

34. What is the composition of the pigment known as chrome green?

35. What is the action of hydrogen ions upon chromate ions? This is called a condensation reaction. Explain.

36. Write an equation to illustrate the action of the dichromate ion as an oxidizing agent.

37. What is the composition and chemical action of the "cleaning solution" of the laboratory?

38. How is zinc metal separated from the impurities cadmium, iron, lead, and arsenic during the refining process?

39. Why does pure zinc react only slowly or not at all with dilute hydrochloric or sulfuric acids?

40. How is galvanized iron produced?

41. What is lithopone and how is it produced? In what way is lithopone superior to white lead as a paint pigment?

REFERENCES

"Nickel and Its Alloys," H. O. Teeple, *Ind. and Eng. Chem.*, **42** (10) 1990 (1950).

"From Cabul to Cobalt — A Historical View of the Mischievous Metal," F. R. Morral, *J. Chem. Educ.*, **34** (4) 185 (1957).

"Blast Furnace Practice," R. H. Sweester, *Metals and Alloys*, **17** (1) 50 (Jan., 1943).

"Stainless Steels and Other Ferrous Alloys," M. H. Brown and W. B. DeLong, *Ind. and Eng. Chem.*, **41** (10) 2139 (1949); also W. B. DeLong and P. H. Permar, *ibid.*, **42** (10) 2009 (1950).

"Theory of Corrosion," W. L. Orr and H. A. Stafford, *J. Chem. Educ.*, **27** (4) 202 (1950).

"Conquering the Outer Space of Corrosion Science," H. H. Uhlig, *J. Electrochem. Soc.*, **109** (1) 9 C (1962).

"Steel Tanks for Rocket Fuels," J. Halbig, *Chem. Eng.*, Dec. 25, 1961; p. 108.

"Mechanism of Passivity," R. B. Mears, *J. Electrochem. Soc.*, **95** (1) 1 (1949).

"Ink Chemistry," C. A. Schmidt, *Chem. Met. Eng.*, **51** (11) 183 (Nov., 1944).

"The Story of Hall and Aluminum," H. N. Holmes, *J. Chem. Educ.*, **7** (2) 232 (1930).

"Aluminum from Clay," Bureau of Standards, *J. Chem. Educ.*, **25** (3) 159 (1948).

"Genuine and Synthetic Rubies and Sapphires," A. E. Alexander, *J. Chem. Educ.*, **23** (9) 418 (1946).

"Flame-Grown Gem Stones Enjoy Broadened Use in Optics and Fashion Jewelry," (Synthetic Gems), (Staff) *Chem. Eng.*, Dec. 25, 1961; p. 26.

"Electrowinning of Chromium," R. R. Lloyd, *et al.*, *J. Electrochem. Soc.*, **97** (7) 227 (July, 1950).

"Better Chrome Plate," (Staff) *Chem. Eng. News*, July 25, 1960; p. 48.

"Story of Zinc," H. R. Hanley, *J. Chem. Educ.*, **10** (10) 600, (11) 682 (1933); **11** (1) 33, (2) 111 (1934).

"Chemicals and the Auto Industry," (Staff) *Chem. Eng. News*, Oct. 22, 1962; p. 114.

CHAPTER THIRTY-EIGHT

The Metals of Analytical Group IV

CALCIUM, STRONTIUM, AND BARIUM

Analytical Group IV contains those common cations which are precipitated as carbonates by ammonium carbonate from an aqueous ammonia solution containing ammonium chloride, but which are not precipitated by the reagents used in the precipitation of Groups I, II, and III. All the other cations, except magnesium, which form insoluble carbonates have been separated in Groups I, II, and III. If ammonium chloride were not present, magnesium carbonate would precipitate with the ions of Group IV. However, this is not desirable because this compound is moderately soluble and of indefinite composition. The precipitation of the Mg^{++} is therefore postponed. Some properties of the Analytical Group IV metals are given in Table 38·1.

TABLE 38·1 Some Properties of the Metals of Analytical Group IV

Property	*Calcium*	*Strontium*	*Barium*
Atomic number	20	38	56
Atomic weight	40.08	87.62	137.34
Electronic structure	2,8,8,2	2,8,18,8,2	2,8,18,18,8,2
Oxidation state	+2	+2	+2
Oxidation potential	(Ca/Ca^{++}) +2.87	(Sr/Sr^{++}) +2.89	(Ba/Ba^{++}) +2.90
Density, g./cm.^{3} at 20°	1.54	2.60	3.5
Melting point, °C	850	770	704
Boiling point, °C	1490	1384	1638

38.1 Periodic Relationships of Calcium, Strontium, and Barium

The elements of Periodic Group IIA (Be, Mg, Ca, Sr, Ba, and Ra) have two electrons in their outer shells. All exhibit a single oxidation state, +2. They are all light, very reactive metals, the reactivity increasing with increasing atomic number.

The members of the B subgroup (Zn, Cd, and Hg), on the other hand, are heavy, and their reactivity decreases with increasing atomic number. Beryllium, the first member of Group IIA, is a bridge element in that it resembles aluminum, the second member of Group IIIA of the Periodic Table, in its chemical behavior. Beryllium and magnesium are somewhat different in chemical properties from the other elements of this group. For example, the hydroxides of beryllium and magnesium are nearly insoluble in water and are easily decomposed by heat into water and metallic oxides. The hydroxide of beryllium, the smallest and most electronegative element of the group, is amphoteric, whereas the hydroxides of barium, strontium, and calcium are strong bases and their hydrated ions do not hydrolyze appreciably. Beryllium ion forms stable complex ions, but with a few exceptions the other ions of this group do not. In contrast to the salts of the alkali metals (Chapter 39), many of the common salts of the metals of Periodic Group IIA are insoluble in water. Most of the salts of these metals (called the alkaline earth metals) with weak or moderately strong acids are sparingly soluble — e.g., the phosphates, oxalates, and carbonates. A number of the salts are quite soluble in water, however, especially the cyanides, sulfides, and acetates. The solubility of the hydroxides of these metals in water increases with increasing atomic number, whereas the solubility of the carbonates and sulfates decreases in this order.

The term "earth" was formerly used by chemists to denote slightly soluble metal oxides. The oxides of barium, strontium, and calcium resemble alumina (Al_2O_3), a typical "earth," but form alkaline mixtures with water. For this reason barium, strontium, and calcium were called alkaline earth metals. This name has now been extended to include all of the elements of Periodic Group IIA.

38.2 History of Calcium, Strontium, and Barium

Lime (CaO) was used for mortar by the ancients. They obtained it by heating limestone, as is still done. In 1774, Scheele distinguished baryta (BaO) from lime, and in 1790 Crawford distinguished strontia (SrO) from baryta. The name calcium is derived from "calx," the Latin word for lime; strontium is named after the town of Strontian in Scotland; and the name barium comes from "barus," a Greek word meaning heavy, chosen because many of the compounds of this element are of high density.

Until the early part of the nineteenth century, the alkaline earths were thought to be elements. In 1808, Davy succeeded in decomposing the fused hydroxides of the alkaline earth metals by electrolysis, and thus obtained the metals calcium, strontium, and barium.

38.3 Occurrence of Calcium, Strontium, and Barium

Because of their high chemical activity, these metals never occur free in nature. Their most abundant native compounds are the carbonates and the sulfates.

1. *Calcium.* Calcium is the fifth most abundant element in the earth's crust and is widely distributed in nature. The common rock known as **limestone** is

an impure calcium carbonate. Other natural forms of calcium carbonate include **calcite, aragonite, chalk, marl, marble, marine shells,** and **pearls. Dolomitic limestone** (dolomite) is $CaCO_3 \cdot MgCO_3$. Calcium sulfate occurs as **anhydrite,** $CaSO_4$, and **gypsum,** $CaSO_4 \cdot 2\,H_2O$. Other common minerals include **fluorite** or **fluorspar,** which is CaF_2, and **apatite,** which may be formulated as $Ca_{10}(PO_4)_6(OH, Cl, F)_2$. Hydroxylapatite is the chief constituent of the bones and teeth of animals.

2. *Strontium.* The minerals containing strontium are much rarer than those of calcium. The chief ones are **celestite,** $SrSO_4$, and **strontianite,** $SrCO_3$.

3. *Barium.* Barium occurs more abundantly than strontium, but less so than calcium. Its chief minerals are **barite** or **heavy spar,** $BaSO_4$, and **witherite,** $BaCO_3$.

38.4 Preparation of Calcium, Strontium, and Barium

The most important methods for producing these metals are those in which their molten salts (generally the chlorides) are electrolyzed. Because of the high chemical activity of these metals, their salts are not readily reduced by other methods.

1. *Calcium.* The commercial preparation of calcium is carried out electrolytically in a furnace lined with graphite, which serves as the anode (Fig. 38–1). The cathode is copper, tipped with iron, which at the beginning of the process dips below the surface of the fused calcium chloride. As the metal is deposited the cathode is slowly raised, and there is formed an irregular rod of calcium, which serves as the cathode during the latter part of the process. As the rod is raised, the electrolyte which adheres to it freezes and keeps the metal from burning. Calcium metal obtained in this way is about 85 per cent pure. When nearly pure metal is desired, the rods are melted and cast in an atmosphere of argon or distilled under high vacuum.

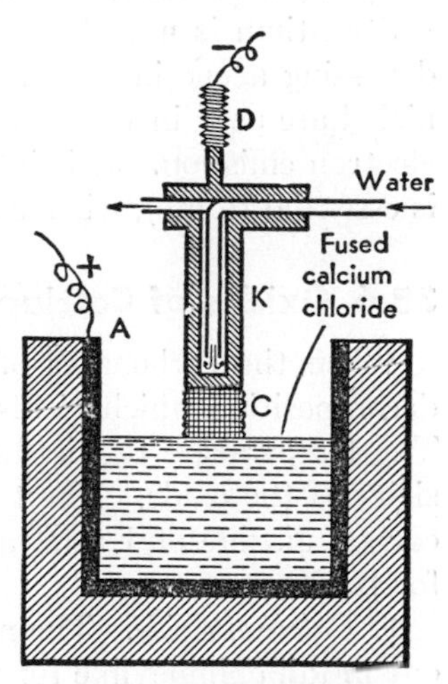

Fig. 38–1 Furnace for production of metallic calcium. The graphite lining of the furnace, A, serves as the anode. The cathode, K, is water-cooled and is slowly raised by the screw device, D, as the electrolysis continues. Calcium metal, C, collects on the end of the cathode; it just touches the surface of the fused calcium chloride.

2. *Strontium.* This metal is prepared by the electrolysis of its fused chloride mixed with potassium chloride in a cell like that described for the preparation of calcium.

3. *Barium.* Several methods of producing barium, in addition to the electrolysis of the fused chloride, have been developed. One of these involves the electrolysis of solutions of barium chloride, using a mercury cathode. The amalgam of barium and mercury that is formed yields metallic barium when the mercury is distilled off in a vacuum.

In the King process for producing the metal, a mixture of barium oxide and barium peroxide is reduced with aluminum in a vacuum furnace (Fig. 38–2). A temperature of 950° to 1100° is required for the reaction to take place; and at the very low pressure (10^{-3} to 10^{-4} mm.) which is maintained in the furnace, the metallic barium distills off and is collected on a cold surface.

38.5 Properties and Uses of Calcium, Strontium, and Barium

These metals are silvery-white and crystalline but malleable and ductile. Calcium is harder than lead, strontium is about as hard as lead, and barium is quite soft. Calcium, strontium, and barium are all active metals, their activity increasing in the order named. For example, calcium does not react with oxygen unless it is heated, while strontium oxidizes rapidly when exposed to air, and barium is spontaneously inflammable in moist air. When heated these metals combine with hydrogen, forming hydrides; with sulfur, forming sulfides; with halogens, forming halides; with nitrogen, forming nitrides; and with phosphorus, forming phosphides. Each of these metals displaces hydrogen from water, and the corresponding hydroxide is formed.

Calcium is used as a dehydrating agent for certain organic solvents; as a reducing agent in the production of certain metals; as a scavenger (to remove gases in fused metals) in metallurgy; as a hardening agent for lead used for covering cables, making storage battery grids, and making bearings; in steelmaking when alloyed with silicon; and for many other purposes.

Strontium is not abundant and has no commercial uses. Barium is used as a degassing agent in the manufacture of vacuum tubes, and alloys of barium and nickel are used in vacuum tubes and spark plugs because of their high thermionic electron emission. It is interesting that Mg^{++} and Ca^{++} are not poisonous (Ca^{++} is essential to life), whereas Be^{++} and Ba^{++} are very toxic.

38.6 Oxides of Calcium, Strontium, and Barium

When the carbonates of these metals are heated sufficiently, they undergo a decomposition which yields the oxides and carbon dioxide ($MCO_3 \rightarrow MO + CO_2$). The temperature required for these decompositions increases with increasing basicity of the oxide. The temperatures required to attain equilibrium pressures of carbon dioxide of 1 atm. are about 900° for $CaCO_3$, 1250° for $SrCO_3$, and 1450° for $BaCO_3$.

1. *Calcium oxide.* The manufacture of **calcium oxide** or **quicklime** is carried out in tall chimneylike furnaces which are known as **kilns** (Fig. 38–3). In a continuous process, the limestone, which is fed in at the top of the kiln, is heated and decomposed by a draft of hot gas, and the quicklime is removed at the bottom of the kiln.

$$CaCO_3 \rightarrow CaO + CO_2$$

The blast of hot gases through the furnace keeps the partial pressure of the carbon dioxide at a minimum and permits the reaction to go to completion at a much lower temperature than would otherwise be required. Coal or gas is used as fuel in these kilns.

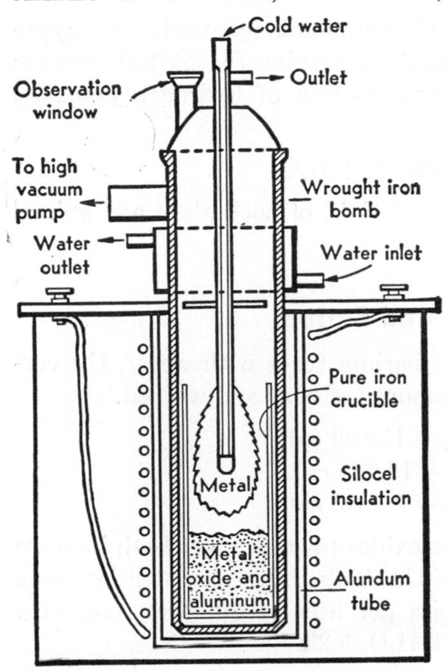

Fig. 38–2 Furnace for the production of barium.

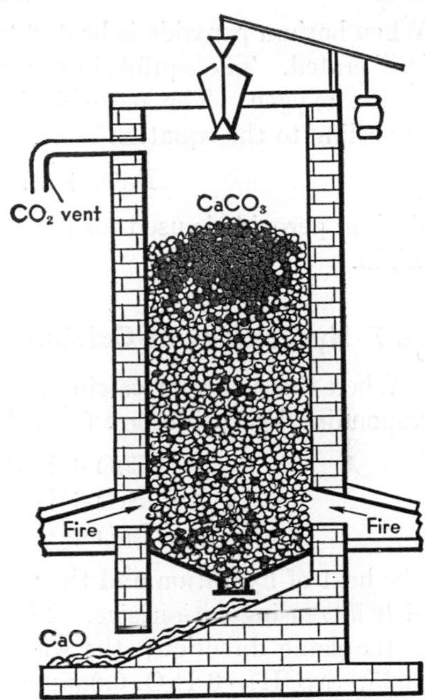

Fig. 38–3 A lime kiln. Such kilns may be operated for weeks without shutting down.

Pure calcium oxide is a white amorphous substance that emits an intense light, called "limelight," when heated to a high temperature. Lime reacts vigorously and exothermally with water, forming the hydroxide. This reaction is called **slaking** and the hydroxide is called **slaked lime** or **hydrated lime.**

$$CaO + H_2O \rightarrow Ca(OH)_2 + 15{,}500 \text{ calories}$$

Calcium oxide is often employed as a drying agent, for example, in the preparation of anhydrous alcohol and in the drying of ammonia. A mixture of calcium oxide and sodium hydroxide, called **soda lime,** is often used to remove both water and carbon dioxide from gases.

2. *Barium oxide.* In the production of barium oxide, the carbonate is heated with finely divided carbon. The purpose of the carbon is to reduce the carbon dioxide which is produced, and thus to shift the equilibrium $BaCO_3 \rightleftharpoons BaO + CO_2$ to the right. This makes possible the conversion of the carbonate to the oxide at a lower temperature than the 1450° otherwise necessary. This means a considerable saving of fuel in the commercial production of barium oxide. The oxide is also prepared from barium nitrate, which easily decomposes upon being heated. Like calcium oxide, barium oxide is an effective drying agent. Most of the barium oxide produced is used in the preparation of barium peroxide.

3. *Barium peroxide.* Calcium, strontium, and barium form peroxides of the general formula MO_2. Only barium peroxide is easily formed and important. It is produced when barium oxide is heated in air or oxygen to 500°–600°.

$$2\ BaO + O_2 \rightleftharpoons 2\ BaO_2$$

When barium peroxide is heated to 700°–800°, the reaction is reversed, and oxygen is liberated. The equilibrium can also be shifted by varying the partial pressure of the oxygen. The peroxide is used in the production of hydrogen peroxide, according to the equation

$$BaO_2 + 2\ H^+ + SO_4^= \rightarrow \underline{BaSO_4} + H_2O_2$$

Barium peroxide is used for bleaching various materials, of both plant and animal origin.

38.7 Hydroxides of Calcium, Strontium, and Barium

When the oxides of calcium, strontium, and barium react with water, the corresponding hydroxides are formed and large amounts of heat are evolved.

$$CaO + H_2O \rightarrow Ca(OH)_2 + 15{,}600\ \text{cal.}$$
$$SrO + H_2O \rightarrow Sr(OH)_2 + 19{,}900\ \text{cal.}$$
$$BaO + H_2O \rightarrow Ba(OH)_2 + 24{,}500\ \text{cal.}$$

The heat of hydration and the reactivity of the oxides toward water both increase with increasing cation size. The solubility of the hydroxides in water increases in the same direction; the solubilities in moles per liter at 20° are: $Ca(OH)_2$, 0.025; $Sr(OH)_2 \cdot 8\ H_2O$, 0.066; and $Ba(OH)_2 \cdot 8\ H_2O$, 0.23.

1. *Calcium hydroxide.* Calcium oxide is known by various names, such as **lime, quicklime,** and **unslaked lime,** while the product formed from its reaction with water is known commercially as **slaked** or **hydrated lime.** Calcium hydroxide is a dry white powder that forms a pasty mass with an excess of water. Because of the high heat of reaction of quicklime with water, it should always be stored where it cannot come in contact with water, for the slaking reaction generates enough heat to ignite paper or wood. Dry hydrated lime rather than quicklime is usually sold because it can be shipped and stored in paper bags without risk of fire.

Calcium hydroxide is classed as a strong base and, because of its activity and cheapness, it is used more extensively in commercial processes than any other base. It is only sparingly soluble in water, 1.7 grams dissolving in a liter of water at room temperature. A saturated solution of calcium hydroxide is often called **limewater.** A suspension of calcium hydroxide in water is known as **milk of lime.** Even though calcium hydroxide has a limited solubility, milk of lime furnishes a ready supply of hydroxide ions because the solid continues to dissolve as hydroxide ions are removed from solution during chemical reaction, i.e., the following equilibrium shifts to the right:

$$\underset{\text{solid}}{Ca(OH)_2} \rightleftharpoons \underset{\text{dissolved}}{Ca^{++} + 2\ OH^-}$$

Mortar is prepared by mixing slaked lime with sand and water. One part of slaked lime is used with about three or four parts of sand, and enough water is added to give the mixture the consistency of paste. It dries and becomes hard (sets) on exposure to the air by adsorbing carbon dioxide and forming crystalline calcium carbonate.

$$Ca(OH)_2 + CO_2 \rightarrow CaCO_3 + H_2O$$

The calcium carbonate cements together the particles of sand and unchanged calcium hydroxide. Many years are required for the complete conversion of the calcium hydroxide to carbonate, especially in heavy wall construction.

Ordinary **lime plaster** for coating walls and ceilings is similar to mortar, with some binding material such as hair or fiber to help hold it in place. Cement was considered in Section 29.20.

In the manufacture of beet sugar, the sugar is purified by precipitation with calcium hydroxide, with which it forms a very slightly soluble compound. This is filtered off and washed, and the sugar is regenerated from it by treatment with carbon dioxide, which converts the lime to calcium carbonate.

The manufacture of at least 150 important industrial chemicals requires the use of lime. In fact, only five other raw materials are used more frequently than lime (or limestone, from which lime is made); these are salt, coal, sulfur, air, and water.

2. *Strontium hydroxide.* Strontium hydroxide is a rather active base, which is made by treating strontium carbonate with superheated steam.

$$SrCO_3 + H_2O \rightarrow Sr(OH)_2 + CO_2$$

Strontium hydroxide is fairly soluble in hot water and crystallizes from solution as the octahydrate, $Sr(OH)_2 \cdot 8\ H_2O$.

3. *Barium hydroxide.* Barium hydroxide is made by slaking barium oxide and by treatment of the carbonate with superheated steam. Solutions of barium hydroxide are called "baryta water." Barium hydroxide is the most soluble of the alkaline earth hydroxides, and it crystallizes from solution in the form of the hydrate, $Ba(OH)_2 \cdot 8\ H_2O$. It is widely used in analytical chemistry because it has an advantage over hydroxides of sodium and potassium in that any carbonate which is formed due to contact with the air precipitates out as barium carbonate, leaving the solution relatively pure.

38.8 Calcium Carbonate

Calcium carbonate occurs in two distinctly different crystal forms which are known as **calcite** and **aragonite.** The first is common while the second is comparatively rare. Calcite crystallizes in rhombohedra; it is the "low-temperature" form of calcium carbonate and results when precipitation occurs below 30°. Above this temperature, calcium carbonate crystallizes in rhombic prisms of aragonite, the "high-temperature" form.

Calcite is known in many varieties, such as **Iceland spar, oriental alabaster,** and **onyx.** This crystal form possesses the property of **birefringence,** or **double refraction;** i.e., when a beam of light enters the crystal it is broken up into two beams (Fig. 38–4 on page 654).

Limestone is by far the most abundant source of calcium carbonate, being second in abundance only to silicate rocks in forming the earth's crust. Beds of impure calcium carbonate have been formed from the exoskeletons of very small marine organisms, many fossilized remains of which are evident in the deposits. Limestone is used more extensively than any other building stone in the United States;

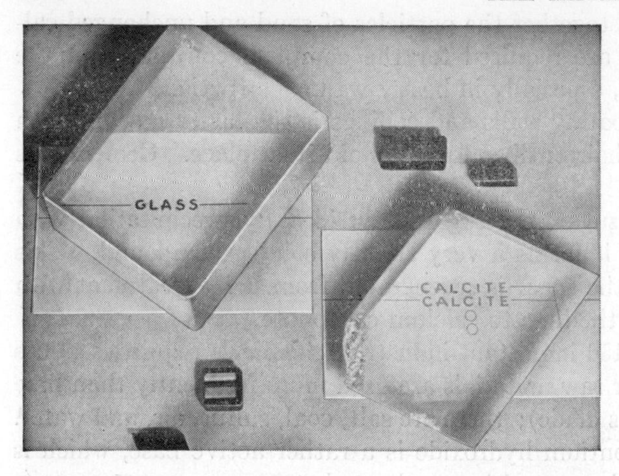

Fig. 38–4 Calcite, or Iceland spar, at the lower right in the photograph, refracts doubly. *Bausch and Lomb Optical Co.*

more than 80 per cent of it is supplied by southern Indiana. Coral reefs are composed largely of calcium carbonate of marine-animal origin. A pearl is built up of concentric layers of calcium carbonate deposited upon a foreign particle such as a small grain of sand which has entered the shell of an oyster.

Calcium carbonate is only slightly soluble in pure water. However, it dissolves readily in water containing dissolved carbon dioxide because of the conversion to the more soluble hydrogen carbonate, $Ca(HCO_3)_2$.

$$CaCO_3 + H_2O + CO_2 \rightleftharpoons Ca^{++} + 2\ HCO_3^-$$

This reaction is involved in the formation of limestone caves when water containing carbon dioxide comes in contact with limestone rocks. If water containing $Ca(HCO_3)_2$ finds its way into a cave where it may liberate carbon dioxide, calcium carbonate may again be deposited, according to the reaction

$$Ca^{++} + 2\ HCO_3^- \rightarrow CaCO_3 + H_2O + CO_2 \uparrow$$

This reaction is the basis for the formation of **stalactites,** which hang from the ceiling of limestone caves, and of **stalagmites,** which grow upward from the floor of the cave, where the water has dripped (Fig. 38–5).

Calcium hydrogen carbonate is readily converted to the normal carbonate when its solutions are heated. This reaction is involved in the formation of scale in kettles and boilers, and is the basis for one method of removing carbonate hardness from water (Section 10.6).

38.9 Chlorides of Calcium, Strontium, and Barium

1. *Calcium chloride.* This salt is obtained commercially as a by-product of the Solvay process for the manufacture of sodium carbonate (see Section 39.10). Calcium chloride may be produced in the laboratory by treating the oxide, hydroxide, or carbonate of calcium with hydrochloric acid. The salt crystallizes from water as the hexahydrate, $CaCl_2 \cdot 6\ H_2O$, which is converted upon heating to

Fig. 38–5 Stalactites and stalagmites ($CaCO_3$) in one of the Carlsbad Caverns of New Mexico. *David W. Corson from A. Devaney*

the monohydrate, $CaCl_2 \cdot H_2O$. Complete dehydration occurs upon heating to a higher temperature, but some hydrolysis always takes place during the dehydration.

$$CaCl_2 + H_2O \rightarrow CaO + 2\ HCl \uparrow$$

The anhydrous salt and the monohydrate are used extensively as drying agents for gases and liquids. Calcium chloride forms compounds with ammonia, $CaCl_2 \cdot 8\ NH_3$, and with alcohol, $CaCl_2 \cdot 4\ C_2H_5OH$, and so cannot be used for drying these substances. Calcium chloride hexahydrate is very soluble in water and forms with ice an excellent freezing mixture, giving temperatures as low as $-55°$. Solutions of calcium chloride are quite commonly used as the cooling brine in refrigeration plants. Because it is a very deliquescent salt, $CaCl_2 \cdot 6\ H_2O$ is used to keep dust down on highways and in coal mines. Calcium chloride is frequently used to remove snow and ice from roads and walks.

2. *Strontium chloride hexahydrate.* This salt, $SrCl_2 \cdot 6\ H_2O$, is made by treating the carbonate with hydrochloric acid and evaporating the resulting solution. It is used, as are other salts of strontium, in the production of a red color in fireworks, railway fusees, and military flares.

3. *Barium chloride.* This salt is prepared by heating barium sulfate with carbon and calcium chloride.

$$BaSO_4 + 4\ C + CaCl_2 \rightarrow BaCl_2 + CaS + 4\ CO$$

Upon evaporation of solutions of the chloride, the dihydrate, $BaCl_2 \cdot 2\ H_2O$, separates. Whenever the barium ion is required in solution, this salt is usually employed. Like all other soluble barium salts, the chloride is very poisonous.

38.10 Sulfates of Calcium, Strontium, and Barium

The solubilities of the sulfates of Ca, Sr, and Ba in water decrease with increasing atomic weight of the metal; in moles per liter at 20° they are: $CaSO_4 \cdot 2\ H_2O$, 1.5×10^{-2}; $SrSO_4$, 7×10^{-4}; and $BaSO_4$, 1×10^{-5}.

1. *Calcium sulfate.* **Anhydrous calcium sulfate** occurs in nature as the mineral **anhydrite,** $CaSO_4$, and as the dihydrate, **gypsum,** $CaSO_4 \cdot 2\ H_2O$. The latter is found in enormous deposits. The largest producers of gypsum in the United States are New York, Michigan, Iowa, and Texas. The dihydrate is occasionally found in crystalline forms of fine texture, called **alabaster.** Even though it is low in solubility, calcium sulfate is largely responsible for the noncarbonate hardness of ground waters (Section 10.6).

When gypsum is heated, it loses water, forming the hemihydrate, $(CaSO_4)_2 \cdot H_2O$, according to the equation

$$2\ [CaSO_4 \cdot 2\ H_2O] \rightarrow (CaSO_4)_2 \cdot H_2O + 3\ H_2O$$

The hemihydrate is known as **plaster of Paris.** When it is ground to a fine powder and mixed with water, it sets by forming small interlocking crystals of gypsum. The setting results in an increase in volume and hence the plaster fits tightly any mold into which it is poured. Plaster of Paris is used extensively as a component of plaster for the interiors of buildings. It is also used in making statuary, stucco, wallboard, and casts of various kinds.

Gypsum is also used in making Portland cement (Section 29.20), blackboard crayon (erroneously called "chalk"), plate glass, terra cotta, pottery, and orthopedic and dental plasters. Powdered gypsum is used as "land plaster" to correct the alkalinity of soils. Anhydrous calcium sulfate is sold under the name "Drierite" as a drying agent for gases and organic liquids.

2. *Strontium sulfate.* This compound occurs in nature in the mineral **celestite,** which is sometimes found in the form of beautiful crystals in caves, where a faint tinge of blue suggested the name of the mineral.

3. *Barium sulfate.* The mineral **barite,** $BaSO_4$, is frequently used in the production of other barium compounds. Since the sulfate is insoluble in acids, it is first converted to the sulfide by a high temperature reduction with carbon.

$$BaSO_4 + 4\ C \rightarrow BaS + 4\ CO$$

The sulfide may then be dissolved in acids such as hydrochloric or nitric to produce the desired salts.

A mixture of $BaSO_4$ and ZnS is known as **lithopone** and is used as a white paint pigment. It is made by the reaction of aqueous solutions of barium sulfide and zinc sulfate.

$$Ba^{++} + S^{=} + Zn^{++} + SO_4^{=} \rightarrow \underline{BaSO_4} + \underline{ZnS}$$

Barium sulfate is used in taking X-ray photographs of the intestinal tract due to the fact that it is opaque to X-rays (Fig. 38–6). It is so slightly soluble that it is nonpoisonous. Because barium sulfate is only very slightly soluble in water, its formation is useful in the quantitative determination of barium or sulfate ions.

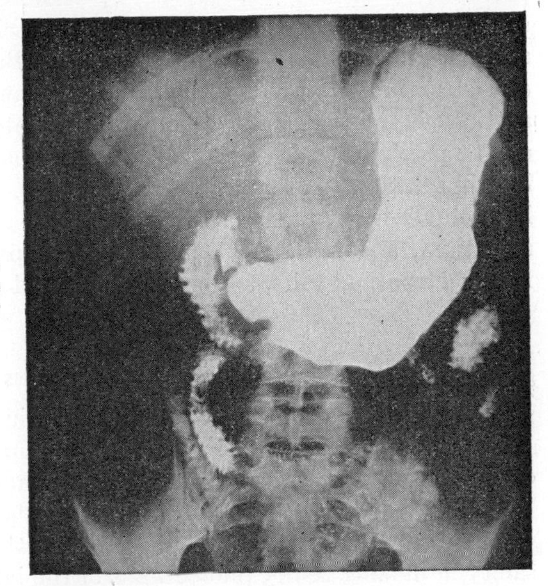

Fig. 38–6 An X-ray photograph of the stomach is possible because barium and bismuth salts are largely opaque to X-rays. *General Electric X-Ray Corp.*

38.11 Other Compounds of Calcium, Strontium, and Barium

Calcium carbide, CaC_2, is important in the production of acetylene (Section 31.3); calcium cyanamide, $CaCN_2$, in the manufacture of many organic nitrogen compounds; calcium hydrogen sulfite, $Ca(HSO_3)_2$, in the manufacture of wood pulp (Section 32.15); calcium chlorohypochlorite, $CaCl(ClO)$, as bleaching powder (Section 19.3); calcium nitrate, $Ca(NO_3)_2$, as a fertilizer; calcium phosphates as fertilizers (Section 27.11); calcium silicate in glassmaking (Section 29.19); and calcium tungstate, $CaWO_4$, in the production of luminous paints and X-ray screens.

Calcium fluoride, CaF_2, occurs in nature as fluorite or fluorspar, and is used as the principal source of fluorine and fluorine compounds. It is also used as a flux in certain metallurgical processes because of its slag-forming properties; in the manufacture of white enamel and opaque glass; and, in the form of single crystals, for making certain optical instruments.

Barium fluosilicate, $BaSiF_6$, is often used as an insecticide upon fruits and vegetables where the use of compounds of arsenic is undesirable. **Barium carbonate** is used as a rat poison. **Barium nitrate** and **chlorate** are used in pyrotechnics to give a green flame. **Barium perchlorate** is sold under the name "Desicchlora" as an effective agent for drying gases.

38.12 Properties of Calcium, Strontium, and Barium of Analytical Importance

The ions of the alkaline earth metals are colorless. Ammonium carbonate precipitates white crystalline carbonates of calcium, barium, and strontium from solutions of salts of these metals. The precipitated carbonates are dissolved by acetic acid as well as by all mineral acids. Barium can be separated from calcium and strontium by precipitation of its yellow chromate in a solution containing acetic acid buffered with ammonium acetate. The yellow strontium chromate can be precipitated from ammoniacal solutions if alcohol is added, leaving calcium ions in solution. Calcium ions are best detected by the fact that calcium oxalate is insoluble in water. Flame tests may be used to identify the salts of calcium, strontium, and barium. Calcium salts impart a brick-red color to the Bunsen flame; strontium salts, a crimson color; and barium salts, a greenish-yellow color.

QUESTIONS

1. Why are barium, strontium, and calcium called alkaline earth metals?
2. Give equations for the reaction of barium with each of the following: oxygen, carbon dioxide, hydrogen, nitrogen, sulfur, and water.
3. Why does baryta water turn milky when exposed to the air?
4. The barium ion is poisonous. Why, then, can barium sulfate be used with safety in making X-ray photographs of the intestinal tract?
5. Give the formula for each of the following naturally occurring calcium compounds: limestone, chalk, gypsum, fluorite, and hydroxylapatite.
6. How is metallic calcium produced commercially?
7. What is the chemical meaning of the term "limelight"?
8. Identify each of the following: quicklime, slaked lime, milk of lime, and soda lime.
9. What is the essential reaction involved in the setting of mortar?
10. Explain the formation of limestone caves, stalactites, and boiler scale.
11. Why cannot anhydrous calcium chloride be used for drying alcohol or ammonia?
12. Give the chemistry of the preparation and setting of plaster of Paris.
13. On the basis of atomic structure, explain why barium is more reactive than calcium.
14. Crushed limestone is used in the treatment of soils which are acid. Write equations to explain the reactions involved.
15. Why is carbon added to barium carbonate when the latter is calcined to make barium oxide?

REFERENCES

"Oxides of the Alkali and Alkaline Earth Metals," W. H. Schechter and J. Kleinberg, *J. Chem. Educ.*, **24** (6) 302 (1947).

"Lime — An Industrial Chemical," R. S. Boynton, *Chem. Eng.*, **57** (7) 104 (July, 1950).

"Calcium and Life," L. V. Heilbrunn, *Sci. American*, June, 1951; p. 60.

Discovery of the Elements, M. E. Weeks, Publ. by the Journal of Chemical Education, Easton, Pa., Sixth Edition, 1956; pp. 505–521.

CHAPTER THIRTY-NINE

The Metals of Analytical Group V

SODIUM, POTASSIUM, MAGNESIUM, AND AMMONIUM

The metals comprising Analytical Group V are those whose cations fail to form precipitates with the reagents used in the precipitation of the first four groups. For this reason, Group V is called the soluble group, and no single reagent will precipitate all four cations. Some properties are listed in Table 39·1.

Magnesium falls in the same group of the Periodic Table as do barium, strontium, and calcium and is closely related chemically to these metals, but it is not precipitated by ammonium carbonate in the presence of other ammonium salts.

The ammonium ion is chemically similar to those of the alkali metals, particularly potassium. The cation, NH_4^+, has not been isolated as a neutral molecule, NH_4. However, it does form an amalgam when solutions of ammonium salts are electrolyzed with a mercury cathode, as do the alkali metals.

TABLE 39·1 Some Properties of the Metals of Analytical Group V

Property	*Sodium*	*Potassium*	*Magnesium*
Atomic number	11	19	12
Atomic weight	22.9898	39.102	24.312
Electronic structure	2,8,1	2,8,8,1	2,8,2
Oxidation states	+1	+1	+2
Oxidation potential	(Na/Na^+) +2.71	(K/K^+) +2.92	(Mg/Mg^{++}) +2.37
Density, g./cm.^{3} at 20°	0.97	0.86	1.74
Melting point, °C	98	63.4	650
Boiling point, °C	889	757	1120

39.1 Periodic Relationships of the Alkali Metals

The elements of Group IA of the Periodic Table are lithium, sodium, potassium, rubidium, cesium, and francium. The heaviest of them, francium, occurs in nature in very small quantities as a short-lived radioactive isotope. The alkali metals and the alkaline earth metals (Group IIA) are often called the **light metals** because of their relatively low densities. The alkali metals have the largest atomic radii (Table 39·2) of the elements in their respective periods of the Periodic Table.

TABLE 39·2

	Atomic Number	*Atomic Weight*	*Atomic Radius, Å*	*Ionic Radius, Å*	*Density at 20°*	*Melting Point, °C*	*Boiling Point, °C*
Lithium	3	6.939	1.50	0.60	0.534	180	1326
Sodium	11	22.9898	1.86	0.95	0.97	98	889
Potassium	19	39.102	2.27	1.33	0.86	63.4	757
Rubidium	37	85.47	2.44	1.48	1.53	38.8	679
Cesium	55	132.905	2.62	1.69	1.87	28.7	690
Francium	87	223	2.7	—	—	—	—

There is a single electron in the outermost shell of each of the alkali metals. Since this electron is far removed from the rest of the atom, it is easily lost and the alkali metals readily form stable positive ions. The difficulty with which their ions are reduced to the metal accounts for the fact that none of the alkali metals were isolated until Sir Humphry Davy, in 1807, produced sodium and potassium by the electrolytic reduction of their respective hydroxides. The ease with which the valence electron is lost increases with increasing atomic radius. Of those members of the group which have been extensively studied, cesium is the most reactive; however francium, the atoms of which are even larger than those of cesium, should be more reactive than cesium.

The alkali metals all react vigorously with water, liberating hydrogen and giving solutions of the corresponding strong bases. They also react directly with oxygen, sulfur, nitrogen, hydrogen, and the halogens. Most of the salts of the alkali metals are readily soluble in water; however, Li_2CO_3, Li_3PO_4, and LiF are relatively insoluble. In this respect, lithium resembles magnesium, the second member of Group IIA. Lithium is a bridge element (Chapter 29).

SODIUM AND POTASSIUM

39.2 History of Sodium and Potassium

Sodium chloride (common salt) is essential to life and has been known and used by man from the earliest times. The term **alkali** is derived from the Arabian word "alqili," which means "ashes of the saltwort plant," for sodium carbonate was obtained from the ashes of sea plants. Potassium carbonate was obtained from the ashes of land plants and called "vegetable alkali." At one time, potassium carbonate was obtained by leaching wood ashes in iron pots, and hence the names "potash" for K_2CO_3 and "caustic potash" for KOH. The symbol K for potassium comes from the German name "Kali." The symbol Na for sodium is the abbreviation of the word "natron," meaning sodium carbonate.

Metallic sodium and potassium were first prepared by Sir Humphry Davy in 1807. He obtained the metals by electrolyzing the fused hydroxides, and he described the products as "inflammable substances very like metals." Previous to this time, the substances now recognized as sodium and potassium hydroxides were considered to be elements, for they resisted all attempts to decompose them by heat or chemical reagents; because of this, they were called "fixed alkalies."

39.3 Occurrence of Sodium and Potassium

Compounds of sodium and potassium occur widely distributed in nature. They appear in many complex silicate rocks such as feldspars, of which the very abundant **albite,** $NaAlSi_3O_8$, and **orthoclase,** $KAlSi_3O_8$, are typical. As these minerals are disintegrated by weathering, the sodium and potassium are converted to soluble compounds, most of which are leached out of the soil by water and are eventually carried to the sea. In passing through the soil, some of the potassium compounds are adsorbed by the colloidal particles of the soil and held there until used by plants for growth. Sodium compounds are much less retained by the soil and little sodium is needed for plant growth.

Changes in the earth's crust during past geological ages have at various times and places caused sections of the sea to become isolated and to have gradually evaporated. Such geological changes have resulted in the formation of certain large salt beds.

Sodium occurs in sodium nitrate in deposits found in Chile (Section 26.1); in sodium carbonate and sodium hydrogen carbonate, as the mineral called **trona,** in Egypt and California; and in **borax** ($Na_2B_4O_7$), in the Death Valley region of southern California. Large deposits of such potassium salts as **sylvite,** KCl, and **carnallite,** $MgCl_2 \cdot KCl \cdot 6\ H_2O$, are found in Stassfurt, Germany, and in the Alsace region of France. The United States obtains potassium from large deposits of **langbeinite** ($K_2SO_4 \cdot 2\ MgSO_4$), **sylvite** (KCl), and **polyhalite** ($K_2SO_4 \cdot MgSO_4 \cdot 2\ CaSO_4$) in the Carlsbad section of New Mexico. A large part of the production of potassium compounds goes into American agriculture as fertilizer.

39.4 Preparation of Sodium and Potassium

For many years metallic sodium was obtained by reducing the carbonate with carbon.

$$Na_2CO_3 + 2\ C \rightarrow 2\ Na + 3\ CO$$

With the development of the dynamo for the production of cheap electricity, Davy's original electrolytic method of obtaining sodium from fused sodium hydroxide came to be the industrial process for producing the metal. Most of our sodium is now prepared by the electrolysis of fused sodium chloride, admixed with sodium carbonate or calcium chloride to lower the melting point of the salt. The energy required to melt sodium chloride and the high vapor pressure of metallic sodium at this temperature prohibit the use of sodium chloride alone; the melting point of sodium chloride is 801°, while that of the mixture is about 600°.

The cell used in the United States for the electrodeposition of sodium is the Downs cell, a cross section of which is shown in Fig. 39–1. The graphite anode is encircled by an iron or copper cathode, and the two are separated by an iron screen partition. This arrangement allows the electric current to pass, but keeps the sodium and chlorine from coming in contact after they have been set free at the cathode and anode, respectively. The fused sodium rises in a special compartment from which it may be drawn off, and dry chlorine is collected in the dome above the anode.

Sodium is shipped in the form of 12-pound bricks in air-tight steel barrels (Fig. 39–2), or in tank cars which are loaded by pumping in the fused metal. To unload the cars, the metal is melted and the liquid forced out by nitrogen under pressure. The heat to melt the sodium is provided by passing hot oil through a system of coils in the tank car.

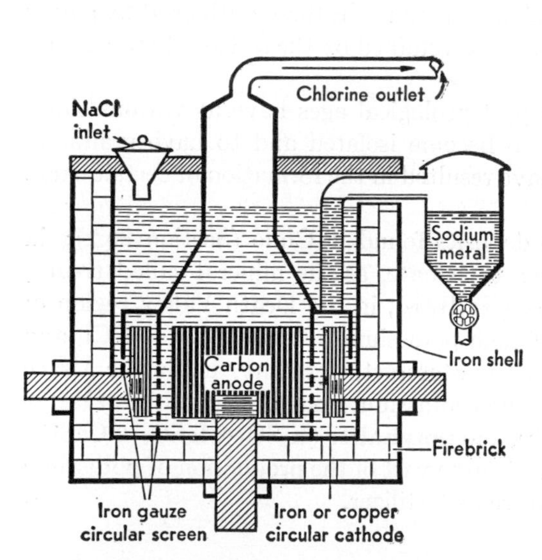

Fig. 39–1 Cross section of the circular cell used in the Downs process for the production of metallic sodium.

Fig. 39–2 Barrels of sodium, each containing twenty-four 12-pound bricks. *E. I. du Pont de Nemours and Co.*

Because electrolysis requires the use of electrical energy, plants for the production of metallic sodium usually are located where water power is readily available; Niagara Falls is a notable example. In terms of volume, sodium is the cheapest metal available.

Potassium is produced on a relatively small scale, since this element offers few technical advantages over the less costly sodium. Sodium has been sold at 16–17 cents a pound since 1938, while potassium sells at $2.50 per pound. However, if a lot of potassium were used, its price would probably fall a great deal. The metal may be made by the electrolytic reduction of either molten potassium chloride or potassium hydroxide but is now produced in the United States by the reaction of sodium with fused potassium chloride ($Na + KCl \rightleftharpoons K + NaCl$). The sodium is fed into the bottom of a column of melted potassium chloride, and potassium metal escapes at the top. It should be noted that for fused salts the regular electromotive series does not apply exactly. A variety of chemical factors determine the course of the reaction. Apparently, this particular reaction proceeds, although potassium is above sodium in the electromotive series, because metallic potassium is more volatile than is sodium, thereby causing a shift in the equilibrium to the right.

39.5 Properties of Sodium and Potassium

These metals are soft enough to be cut by a knife, silvery-white in color, and are excellent conductors of heat and electricity. Both metals tarnish immediately in moist air, and react vigorously with water and acids, liberating hydrogen and forming hydroxides or salts of the acids, respectively. The heat of reaction between these metals and water may cause the evolved hydrogen to ignite. One should never touch sodium or potassium with the hands because the heat of reaction with the moisture on the skin may cause the metal to ignite. These metals are stored under kerosene or in sealed containers.

Sodium dissolves in mercury, forming an amalgam. This alloy is an active reducing agent which is more suitable for many uses than pure sodium because the mercury, being an inactive metal, retards the action of the sodium. Sodium forms alloys with many other metals such as potassium, tin, and antimony, but not with iron.

Sodium and its compounds impart a yellow color to a Bunsen flame, and potassium and its compounds color the flame violet (Fig. 3–13). The color of the potassium flame is best detected by observing it through cobalt glass (blue in color), which absorbs all wave lengths of light except blue and violet.

In general, potassium is more reactive than sodium; otherwise the chemical properties of the two metals are quite similar. Potassium and sodium differ primarily in regard to the solubilities of their salts, the potassium salts being in general slightly less soluble than those of sodium; there are exceptions to this generalization, however.

39.6 Uses of Sodium and Potassium

Sodium is used as a reducing agent in the production of other metals, such as titanium and zirconium, from their chlorides or oxides. Its properties as a reducing agent make it useful in the manufacture of certain dyes, drugs, and perfumes. It is used in the preparation of sodium-lead alloys which in turn are used in the production of tetraethyl lead from ethyl chloride. It is used in sodium lights for lighting highways because its yellow light penetrates fog well. The synthetic rubber industry consumes a considerable amount of sodium. The largest uses are in manufacture of compounds such as sodium peroxide and sodium cyanide, which cannot be made directly from sodium chloride.

Because potassium has no major uses for which sodium cannot be substituted, its production is quite limited. A sodium-potassium alloy provides an extremely convenient way of handling sodium or potassium and is growing in importance as an interesting tool for achieving new organic reactions and as an industrial heat transfer medium. Alloys of from about 40 to 90 weight per cent potassium are liquid at room temperature and are thus handled with greater ease than the component metals (sodium melts at 98° and potassium at 63.4°). The low density, low viscosity, wide liquid range, and high thermal conductivity of the alloy combine to make it a very attractive heat transfer medium. For these reasons and the fact that it has a low neutron cross section (does not capture many neutrons) it is of interest as a cooling liquid for atomic reactors. However, the relatively high cost of potassium has favored the use of pure sodium, and molten sodium is being used as the heat transfer medium in the Hallam, Nebraska, nuclear reactor, which began producing commercial power in 1962. Other potential uses of the sodium-potassium alloy include its use as a bath in heat-treating furnaces, as a jacket fluid in high temperature reaction kettles, and as a heat exchanger for reheating steam in boiler systems.

39.7 Hydrides of Sodium and Potassium

The hydrides NaH and KH are prepared by the direct union of the elements at slightly elevated temperatures and are decomposed at higher temperatures. They are saltlike compounds, with a crystal structure like that of sodium chloride. When the fused hydrides are electrolyzed, the metal is formed at the cathode and hydrogen is evolved at the anode, so the hydrides must be composed of metal ions and hydride ions, $:H^-$. The hydrides are readily decomposed by water with the evolution of hydrogen, the hydride ions combining with hydrogen ions of the water ($H^+ + :H^- \rightarrow H_2$), and leaving an excess of hydroxide ions in solution.

$$NaH + H_2O \rightarrow Na^+ + OH^- + H_2 \uparrow$$

Sodium hydride is used widely in organic chemistry as a reducing agent, and in the descaling of steel before it is plated or enameled.

39.8 Oxides of Sodium and Potassium

Metallic oxides usually are produced by heating the hydroxides, nitrates, or carbonates. The oxides of the more active alkali metals cannot be prepared in this way because their hydroxides, nitrates, and carbonates are stable toward heat, decomposing only at extremely high temperatures.

Sodium forms both the **normal oxide,** Na_2O, and the **peroxide,** Na_2O_2. Sodium oxide was formerly prepared by heating sodium hydroxide, sodium peroxide, or sodium nitrate with sodium.

$$2\ NaOH + 2\ Na \rightarrow 2\ Na_2O + H_2$$
$$Na_2O_2 + 2\ Na \rightarrow 2\ Na_2O$$
$$2\ NaNO_3 + 10\ Na \rightarrow 6\ Na_2O + N_2$$

It is now prepared in commercial quantities by heating sodium in a limited supply of air under carefully controlled conditions. The product is a white powder that is called "super-caustic" because of its extremely alkaline character. It is a very effective drying agent, and it is used wherever strong caustic is needed.

The peroxide is the more important of the two oxides of sodium. It is manufactured by passing chips of sodium on aluminum trays through a furnace held at 300° to 400°, while a current of air is moving in the opposite direction. This is an application of the "counter current principle," which is widely used in the manufacture of chemicals; the sodium moves in one direction, while the air with which it reacts moves in the opposite direction. This procedure allows fresh metallic sodium to come in contact first with air from which most of the oxygen has been removed; and at the opposite end of the furnace, the sodium, which is nearly completely oxidized, comes in contact with fresh air. This plan allows the oxidation to proceed more slowly and under better control than would be possible if the sodium were simply heated in air.

Sodium peroxide is a yellowish-white powder, which is used extensively as an oxidizing agent and as a bleaching agent. Solutions of the compound are alkaline by hydrolysis, as shown by the equations

$$O_2^{=} + H_2O \rightleftharpoons HO_2^- + OH^-$$
$$HO_2^- + H_2O \rightleftharpoons H_2O_2 + OH^-$$

The hydrogen peroxide thus formed decomposes into water and oxygen. Sodium peroxide containing a little copper oxide is sold under the trade name "Oxone" for the preparation of oxygen.

Potassium oxide, K_2O, may be obtained by heating potassium nitrate with elementary potassium in the absence of air. The **peroxide,** K_2O_2, is formed by burning the metal in the calculated quantity of air. When exposed to an excess of air, potassium oxide combines readily with oxygen to give **potassium superoxide,** KO_2, in which the superoxide ion has an oxidation state of −1. The superoxide of potassium is most readily formed by burning the metal in an excess of oxygen.

39.9 Hydroxides of Sodium and Potassium

Sodium hydroxide is frequently called "caustic soda" in commerce, and its solutions are sometimes referred to as "lye" or "soda lye." It is produced commercially by two processes. The older method involves the action of slaked lime, $Ca(OH)_2$, on soda, Na_2CO_3, and is rightly called the "lime-soda process." The reaction is given by the equation

$$(2\ Na^+) + CO_3^{=} + Ca^{++} + (2\ OH^-) \rightarrow \underline{CaCO_3} + (2\ Na^+) + (2\ OH^-)$$

The insoluble calcium carbonate is filtered out and the filtrate is evaporated to yield solid sodium hydroxide. The residue is fused to remove the last traces of water and is then molded into sticks or pellets.

A second and equally important industrial process for the production of sodium hydroxide is the electrolysis of aqueous sodium chloride (see Section 17.3).

$$(2\ Na^+) + 2\ Cl^- + 2\ H_2O \rightarrow (2\ Na^+) + 2\ OH^- + H_2\uparrow + Cl_2\uparrow$$

Hydrogen is formed at the cathode and chlorine is evolved at the anode. Sodium ions and hydroxyl ions accumulate in the solution. The cell is so designed that the chlorine is not permitted to react with the hydroxide ions to form hypochlorite.

Electrolytic sodium hydroxide is impure with sodium chloride, most of which is removed when the solution resulting from electrolysis is evaporated. The less soluble chloride crystallizes, and the very soluble sodium hydroxide remains in solution. The solution is then evaporated completely to obtain solid sodium hydroxide, which still contains a little sodium chloride. This can be removed by dissolving the product in alcohol, in which the chloride is insoluble.

Pure sodium hydroxide can be obtained electrolytically from aqueous sodium chloride by using a mercury cathode cell. Carbon electrodes serve as anodes. Sodium, rather than hydrogen, is liberated at the cathode, where the sodium then reacts with mercury to form an amalgam. The amalgam is decomposed by water in a separate compartment to produce hydrogen and very pure sodium hydroxide, containing no chlorides.

$$2\ Na^+ + 2\ Cl^- + 2x\ Hg \xrightarrow{\text{electrolysis}} 2\ Na(Hg)_x + Cl_2\uparrow$$
$$2\ Na(Hg)_x + 2\ H_2O \rightarrow 2\ Na^+ + 2\ OH^- + 2x\ Hg + H_2\uparrow$$

In the De Nora cell (Fig. 39–3), which is typical of the mercury cathode type, a plastic lining is used. The bottom of the cell slopes gradually from one end to the other. A thin layer of mercury, spread over the bottom of the cell, serves as the cathode. The carbon anodes hang from the lid of the cell. As the brine is electrolyzed, chlorine escapes, and a dilute sodium amalgam is formed which flows out the bottom end of the cell to react with water to produce sodium hydroxide and hydrogen.

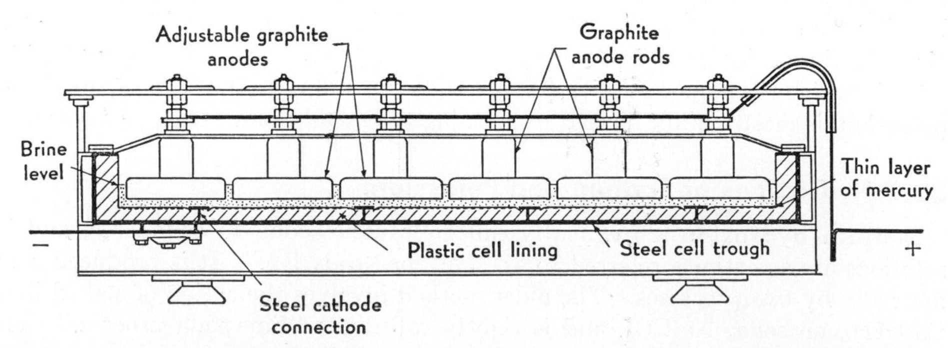

Fig. 39–3 Cross section of the De Nora mercury cathode cell, which is used in the production of sodium hydroxide. *Monsanto Chemical Co.*

The electrolytic methods of producing sodium hydroxide are more costly than the lime-soda process, but the valuable by-products, chlorine and hydrogen, make the electrolytic methods process competitive with the lime-soda process.

Sodium hydroxide is an ionic compound that melts and boils without decomposition. When fused or in aqueous solution, sodium hydroxide attacks silicate minerals and glass. The solid hydroxide and its solutions readily absorb carbon dioxide from the air with the formation of sodium carbonate and water.

$$2\,OH^- + CO_2 \rightarrow H_2O + CO_3^{=}$$

Sodium hydroxide dissolves extensively in water with the evolution of a great deal of heat, and yields strongly basic solutions. This compound is often referred to as "caustic soda" by virtue of the fact that it acts upon vegetable and animal matter, particularly when hot, converting them to soluble substances.

Sodium hydroxide is used extensively in the production of chemicals, rayon, lye, cleaners, textiles, soap, paper and pulp, and in petroleum refining. Between five and six million tons of sodium hydroxide are produced and consumed each year in the United States.

Potassium hydroxide is manufactured in a manner similar to that described for the production of sodium hydroxide. The method involving the treatment of aqueous potassium carbonate with slaked lime has largely given way to the electrolytic method. In either case, the solution of potassium hydroxide is evaporated, the product heated until it melts, and then cast into sticks, which contain 15 to 20 per cent of water. Potassium hydroxide is strongly deliquescent, very soluble, and it is used as a dehydrating agent. It forms strongly alkaline solutions with water. Because it is more expensive than sodium hydroxide, which almost always serves equally well, its use is limited.

39.10 Carbonates of Sodium and Potassium

Sodium carbonate is the most important manufactured compound of sodium. It has the formula Na_2CO_3 and it is commonly called **soda ash,** or simply **soda.**

Practically all the sodium carbonate produced in America is made by the **Solvay process.** This process is based upon the reaction of ammonium hydrogen carbonate with a saturated solution of sodium chloride. Sodium hydrogen carbonate precipitates, since it is insoluble in the reaction medium.

$$Na^+ + (Cl^-) + (NH_4^+) + HCO_3^- \rightarrow \underline{NaHCO_3} + (NH_4^+) + (Cl^-)$$

The basic raw materials used in the process are limestone and salt. The carbon dioxide is generated by heating limestone.

$$(1) \qquad CaCO_3 \rightarrow CaO + CO_2$$

The ammonia is obtained by treating the ammonium chloride, formed as a by-product of the process, with calcium hydroxide.

$$(2) \quad 2\,NH_4^+ + (2\,Cl^-) + (Ca^{++}) + 2\,OH^- \rightarrow 2\,NH_3\uparrow + 2\,H_2O + (Ca^{++}) + (2\,Cl^-)$$

Calcium hydroxide results from slaking the lime produced in reaction (1).

$$(3) \qquad CaO + H_2O \rightarrow Ca^{++} + 2\,OH^-$$

Aqueous ammonia reacts with an excess of carbon dioxide yielding ammonium hydrogen carbonate.

$$(4) \qquad NH_3 + CO_2 + H_2O \rightarrow NH_4^+ + HCO_3^-$$

The only by-product of the entire process is calcium chloride.

Sodium hydrogen carbonate is the first product of the Solvay process; and after being freed of ammonium chloride by recrystallization, it is made commercially available. The major portion of the sodium hydrogen carbonate is converted to sodium carbonate by heating.

$$(5) \qquad 2\ NaHCO_3 \rightarrow Na_2CO_3 + H_2O + CO_2$$

The carbon dioxide from this reaction is used to produce more sodium hydrogen carbonate.

Sodium carbonate is produced to a limited extent by an electrolytic process, but here it is regarded as a by-product of the chlorine industry. We saw in Section 17.3 that the electrolysis of aqueous sodium chloride produces chlorine, hydrogen, and sodium hydroxide. By saturating the sodium hydroxide solution with carbon dioxide, sodium hydrogen carbonate is produced.

$$(Na^+) + OH^- + CO_2 \rightarrow (Na^+) + HCO_3^-$$

The use of less carbon dioxide gives rise to the normal carbonate.

$$(2\ Na^+) + 2\ OH^- + CO_2 \rightarrow (2\ Na^+) + CO_3^= + H_2O$$

The carbon dioxide used in the process is obtained by calcining limestone, and the lime thus produced is used in the manufacture of bleaching powder (Section 19.3). Thus the raw materials, salt and limestone, are the same as those used in the Solvay process. However, the cost of the electricity used and the fact that the process must be carried out in small units constitute disadvantages of the process. On the other hand, all the products of the electrolytic method are valuable, whereas the by-product calcium chloride of the Solvay process has little commercial value.

About nine million tons of soda are produced yearly in the United States. It is used extensively in the manufacture of glass, caustic soda, other chemicals, soap, paper and pulp, cleansers, water softeners, and in petroleum refining.

When a solution of sodium carbonate is evaporated below 35.2°, the decahydrate $Na_2CO_3 \cdot 10\ H_2O$, known as **washing soda,** crystallizes out; above this temperature the monohydrate, $Na_2CO_3 \cdot H_2O$, separates. Heating of the hydrates produces the anhydrous compound. Solutions of sodium carbonate are basic due to hydrolysis of the carbonate ion, as shown by the equation

$$CO_3^= + H_2O \rightarrow HCO_3^- + OH^-$$

For this reason it is generally used in commercial processes requiring an alkali which is less strong than sodium hydroxide.

Sodium hydrogen carbonate, $NaHCO_3$, is commonly known as "bicarbonate of soda" or "baking soda." Its solutions are weakly basic due to hydrolysis of the hydrogen carbonate:

$$HCO_3^- + H_2O \rightleftharpoons H_2CO_3 + OH^-$$

Acids act upon sodium hydrogen carbonate with the formation of carbon dioxide according to the equation

$$HCO_3^- + H_3O^+ \rightarrow 2\ H_2O + CO_2 \uparrow$$

This reaction is involved in the leavening process in baking. Baking powders contain baking soda admixed with an acidic substance, such as potassium hydrogen tartrate, $KHC_4H_4O_6$ (cream of tartar); calcium dihydrogen phosphate, $Ca(H_2PO_4)_2$; or sodium aluminum sulfate, $NaAl(SO_4)_2 \cdot 12\ H_2O$. When the mixture is kept dry, no reaction takes place; but as soon as water is added, carbon dioxide is given off. Starch or flour is added to keep the material dry until it is to be used. When water is added to baking powder, the acidic substance gives hydrogen ions in solution which in turn react with the baking soda with the formation of carbon dioxide.

$$HC_4H_4O_6^- + H_2O \rightleftharpoons H_3O^+ + C_4H_4O_6^{=}$$
$$H_2PO_4^- + H_2O \rightleftharpoons H_3O^+ + HPO_4^{=}$$
$$[Al(H_2O)_x]^{+++} + H_2O \rightleftharpoons H_3O^+ + [Al(OH)(H_2O)_{x-1}]^{++}$$
$$HCO_3^- + H_3O^+ \rightarrow CO_2 \uparrow + 2\ H_2O$$

The lactic acid of sour milk or the acetic acid in vinegar will furnish hydrogen ions and thus serve the same purpose as the acidic constituent of baking powder.

When plants remove potassium salts from the soil, they convert them into potassium salts of organic acids. Burning of plant materials changes these salts into **potassium carbonate,** so this substance is found in wood ashes. In pioneer days wood ashes were leached with water, and the resulting solution containing potassium carbonate was evaporated in iron pots; the residue formed was called "potash." This salt was converted to **potash lye** or **caustic potash,** KOH, by allowing a solution of it to flow through a bed of slaked lime.

$$(2\ K^+) + CO_3^{=} + Ca^{++} + (2\ OH^-) \rightarrow \underline{CaCO_3} + (2\ K^+) + (2\ OH^-)$$

Potash and potash lye made in this way were heated with fat to make a soft soap. Some potassium carbonate is still obtained by leaching wood ashes, and some from the ash from spent sirup of the sugar-beet industry. This salt cannot be prepared by the Solvay process because of the high solubility of potassium hydrogen carbonate in solutions of aqueous ammonia. Instead, it is obtained by treating electrolytic potassium hydroxide with carbon dioxide, or from potassium chloride. The latter method involves heating potassium chloride under pressure with magnesium carbonate, water, and carbon dioxide, whereby the slightly soluble double salt $KHCO_3 \cdot Mg(HCO_3)_2 \cdot 4\ H_2O$ is formed.

$$2\ K^+ + (2\ Cl^-) + 3\ MgCO_3 + 3\ CO_2 + 11\ H_2O \rightarrow$$
$$2\ [KHCO_3 \cdot Mg(HCO_3)_2 \cdot 4\ H_2O] + Mg^{++} + (2\ Cl^-)$$

The complex salt is removed from the solution by filtration and heated to 120°, which causes the following reaction to take place:

$$2\ [KHCO_3 \cdot Mg(HCO_3)_2 \cdot 4\ H_2O] \rightarrow K_2CO_3 + 2\ MgCO_3 + 11\ H_2O + 3\ CO_2 \uparrow$$

Finally, the potassium carbonate is leached from the solid mass, leaving a residue of insoluble magnesium carbonate, which is used again in the first step.

Potassium carbonate forms three hydrates, containing one, two, and three molecules of water of crystallization, respectively. It is usually sold in the form of an anhydrous powder. It is deliquescent and very soluble in water, forming a strongly alkaline solution. It is used in the manufacture of soft soap, glass, pottery, and various potassium compounds.

When a solution of potassium carbonate is saturated with carbon dioxide and concentrated by evaporation, crystals of **potassium hydrogen carbonate,** $KHCO_3$, are deposited. Solutions of this salt are nearly neutral (just slightly alkaline). When heated, the hydrogen carbonate is converted to the normal carbonate.

39.11 Sodium Chloride

Sodium chloride is one of our most abundant minerals. Sea water contains 2.7 per cent sodium chloride, and the waters of the Dead Sea and the Great Salt Lake contain 23 per cent. There are vast deposits of rock salt in the Stassfurt region of Germany, and in the United States large deposits are found in New York, Michigan, West Virginia, California, and a very extensive bed (about 400 to 500 feet thick) underlies parts of Oklahoma, Texas, and Kansas. Most of the salt consumed comes from beds which lie below the surface of the earth, rather than from sea water. The salt is removed from these underground beds by mining (Fig. 39–4) or by forcing water down into the deposits to form saturated brines, which are then pumped to the surface. Natural salt contains other soluble salts which make it unsuitable for many of its uses. Salt is purified by dissolving it in water, concentrating the solution by evaporation (often under reduced pressure), and allowing the crystals to form again. Most of the impurities are more soluble than the salt and remain in solution when the salt crystallizes. Some of the impurities which are less soluble than salt do not crystallize out because they are present in small amounts. Other of the less soluble impurities, such as calcium

Fig. 39–4 A quarter of a mile below the city of Detroit is located one of the largest salt mines in the world. The mine covers 200 acres and has 25 miles of passageways. The salt is used by the chemical industry, by meat packers, for water softening, and for many other purposes. *International Salt Co., Inc.*

sulfate, do crystallize out with the salt and are then removed by a process called **counter-current washing.** Advantage can also be taken of the decreasing solubility of calcium sulfate in sodium chloride solution as the temperature is raised above 80° C. Thus, if the brine is filtered hot, the resulting solution will not contain enough calcium sulfate to be saturated when cooled. Hence, calcium sulfate cannot precipitate with the sodium chloride, and the sodium chloride crystallizes relatively free of the impurity.

Pure salt absorbs water when the relative humidity is above 75%, causing the salt to "cake" and thus clog the salt shaker. Basic magnesium carbonate or calcium aluminosilicate is usually added to serve as a drier or "anti-caking" agent.

Pure sodium chloride for small-scale laboratory uses is obtained by passing hydrogen chloride gas into a saturated brine, which causes the sodium chloride to precipitate. This is a practical illustration of the effect of adding a common ion to a saturated solution (Section 42.4).

Sodium chloride is the usual source of all other sodium and chlorine compounds. Its most extensive use is in the manufacture of chlorine, hydrochloric acid, sodium hydroxide, and sodium carbonate. Salt is an essential constituent of the foods of animals. It not only makes food more palatable, but it is the source of chlorine from which hydrochloric acid, a constituent of gastric juice, is produced. Sodium chloride is also a constituent of the blood and it is essential for the life processes of the human body.

39.12 Halogen Compounds of Potassium

The source of potassium metal and all its compounds is **potassium chloride.** The supply of this compound is obtained from the mineral **sylvite,** which is very pure potassium chloride, and from the mineral **carnallite,** $KCl \cdot MgCl_2 \cdot 6\ H_2O$. Potassium chloride is obtained from carnallite by passing hydrogen chloride gas into a saturated solution of the mineral, which causes the less soluble potassium chloride to precipitate, leaving the magnesium chloride in solution. The crude product is extensively used in the manufacture of fertilizers, while lesser quantities of the purer salt are used in the production of other potassium compounds such as the hydroxide, nitrate, and carbonate.

Potassium bromide is made by dissolving bromine in a hot solution of potassium hydroxide, whereupon both potassium bromide and potassium bromate are formed.

$$6\ OH^- + 3\ Br_2 \rightarrow 5\ Br^- + BrO_3^- + 3\ H_2O$$

When the resulting solution is evaporated to dryness and the residue ignited, the bromate is decomposed and the bromide remains.

$$2\ KBrO_3 \rightarrow 2\ KBr + 3\ O_2$$

Potassium bromide is used in the manufacture of photographic film and paper, in medicine, and as a laboratory reagent.

The method of preparation, the properties, and the uses of potassium iodide are very similar to those of the bromide.

39.13 Nitrates of Sodium and Potassium

Sodium nitrate, or **Chile saltpeter,** is a very important compound that was discussed in connection with nitrogen and nitric acid (Chapters 25 and 26).

Potassium nitrate was one of the principal reagents used by the alchemists. It takes the name **saltpeter** from "sal petrae," as it was called by Geber. It is formed in nature by the decay of organic matter and is prepared commercially from sodium nitrate and potassium chloride.

$$Na^+ + (NO_3^-) + (K^+) + Cl^- \rightarrow \underline{NaCl} + (K^+) + (NO_3^-)$$

The sodium nitrate and potassium chloride are dissolved in hot water and the solution is evaporated by boiling. Of the four compounds possible in a solution containing Na^+, NO_3^-, K^+, and Cl^-, sodium chloride is the least soluble in hot water, and hence it is the first to crystallize out when the concentration of the solution is increased by evaporation. On the other hand, potassium nitrate is very soluble in hot water, making it possible to separate the two salts by filtration. Sodium chloride has about the same solubility in cold as in hot water, so very little more of it crystallizes out when the filtrate is cooled. However, potassium nitrate is but slightly soluble in cold water, and thus it crystallizes out as the filtrate is cooled.

A second method of producing potassium nitrate involves the action of nitrogen dioxide upon potassium chloride, according to the equation

$$KCl + 2\ NO_2 \rightarrow KNO_3 + NOCl$$

Potassium nitrate is a valuable fertilizer because it furnishes both potassium and nitrogen in forms which are readily utilized by growing plants. It is also used to some extent in preserving ham and corned beef, to which it imparts a red color.

39.14 Gunpowder

Potassium nitrate is used in the manufacture of gunpowder and fireworks. **Black gunpowder** is an intimate mixture containing 75 per cent potassium nitrate, 13 per cent charcoal, and 12 per cent sulfur. The constituents are first ground separately, then mixed, moistened with water, and ground together. The mass is then pressed into grains of desired size and allowed to dry. The potassium nitrate furnishes oxygen for the combustion of the charcoal and sulfur. The value of an explosive depends upon the liberation of a lot of heat and a large volume of gas nearly instantaneously. The gases formed when black gunpowder explodes are free nitrogen, sulfur dioxide, carbon monoxide, and carbon dioxide. Several solid substances are also produced. These include the carbonate, sulfide, and sulfate of potassium. These substances, together with particles of unburned carbon and sulfur, make up the smoke that results from the explosion.

Black gunpowder was used in warfare from about 1346 until about 1904, but since that time it has been replaced by smokeless powders, such as guncotton, which is a cellulose nitrate (Section 32.17).

39.15 Sulfates of Sodium and Potassium

Extensive deposits of **sodium sulfate** occur in Canada, North Dakota, and the southwestern section of the United States, but most of the sodium sulfate used commercially is obtained as a by-product in the manufacture of hydrochloric acid from salt and sulfuric acid. The sodium sulfate thus formed is commonly called **salt cake** and is used in the manufacture of glass, paper, rayon, coal-tar dyes, and soap.

When sodium sulfate is crystallized from solution at temperatures below 32.28°, the decahydrate, $Na_2SO_4 \cdot 10\ H_2O$, is formed. This hydrate is called **Glauber's salt,** in honor of the alchemist Glauber, who used it as a medicine in the seventeenth century. The anhydrous salt, Na_2SO_4, crystallizes from solutions at temperatures above the transition point of 32.28°. This temperature is so constant that it is used as a fixed point on the thermometer scale.

Sodium hydrogen sulfate, $NaHSO_4$, is used in the production of hydrochloric acid from salt.

$$NaCl + NaHSO_4 \rightarrow Na_2SO_4 + HCl \uparrow$$

It is prepared by heating sodium chloride or sodium nitrate with sulfuric acid.

$$NaCl + H_2SO_4 \rightarrow NaHSO_4 + HCl \uparrow$$
$$NaNO_3 + H_2SO_4 \rightarrow NaHSO_4 + HNO_3 \uparrow$$

Potassium forms two sulfates, the **normal salt,** K_2SO_4, and the **hydrogen salt,** $KHSO_4$. The normal sulfate is obtained from natural salt deposits, and it is used as a fertilizer and in the preparation of alums. **Potassium hydrogen sulfate** is made by heating the normal sulfate with the proper quantity of sulfuric acid. It is used in analytical chemistry to convert metal oxides and silicates into sulfates. Heat converts it to potassium pyrosulfate, according to the equation

$$2\ KHSO_4 \rightarrow K_2S_2O_7 + H_2O$$

When the pyrosulfate is strongly ignited, it gives up sulfur trioxide, which is a very reactive acid anhydride at high temperatures.

$$K_2S_2O_7 \rightarrow K_2SO_4 + SO_3 \uparrow$$

39.16 Other Sodium Compounds

Sodium hydrogen sulfite, $NaHSO_3$, is prepared by passing an excess of sulfur dioxide into a solution of sodium carbonate or sodium hydroxide.

$$(2\ Na^+) + CO_3^{=} + 2\ SO_2 + H_2O \rightarrow (2\ Na^+) + 2\ HSO_3^- + CO_2 \uparrow$$
$$(Na^+) + OH^- + SO_2 \rightarrow (Na^+) + HSO_3^-$$

The product is used as a source of sulfur dioxide, and as an "antichlor" in the manufacture of paper and dyestuffs.

The **normal sulfite,** Na_2SO_3, is prepared by adding an equivalent of sodium hydroxide or sodium carbonate to a solution of the hydrogen sulfite.

$$(Na^+) + HSO_3^- + (Na^+) + OH^- \rightarrow (2\ Na^+) + SO_3^{=} + H_2O$$
$$(2\ Na^+) + 2\ HSO_3^- + (2\ Na^+) + CO_3^{=} \rightarrow (4\ Na^+) + 2\ SO_3^{=} + CO_2 \uparrow + H_2O$$

The normal sulfite is used chiefly in the manufacture of sodium thiosulfate (Section 23.12).

Sodium cyanide, NaCN, may be produced in a number of ways. However, most of it is made commercially by heating a mixture of calcium cyanamide, carbon, and salt in an electric furnace.

$$CaCN_2 + C + 2\ NaCl \rightarrow CaCl_2 + 2\ NaCN$$

Sodium cyanide is used in the extraction of gold and silver from their ores (Section 33.8), in electroplating various metals, and as a source of hydrogen cyanide for the extermination of lower forms of animals. All cyanides must be used with extreme caution, for they are extremely poisonous.

The phosphates, silicates, nitrite, thiosulfate, borates, chromates, halides, sulfides, and certain other salts of sodium have been mentioned in previous chapters under the corresponding acids.

39.17 Other Potassium Compounds

Potassium hydrogen tartrate, $KHC_4H_4O_6$, is commonly known as **cream of tartar.** It is found in grape juice and is obtained from the sediments which collect in the manufacture of wine. It is used in medicine and in tartrate baking powders. The sour taste of such plants as sorrel and rhubarb is due to the presence of **potassium hydrogen oxalate,** $KHC_2O_4 \cdot H_2O$, and **potassium tetraoxalate,** $KHC_2O_4 \cdot H_2C_2O_4 \cdot 2\ H_2O$. **Potassium cyanide,** KCN, is an exceedingly poisonous salt that is employed in photography and for extracting gold and silver from their ores. **Potassium cyanate,** KOCN, is made by fusing potassium cyanide in air, or with an oxidizing substance such as lead oxide.

$$KCN + PbO \rightarrow KOCN + Pb$$

Similarly, **potassium thiocyanate** is made by heating potassium cyanide with sulfur.

$$KCN + S \rightarrow KSCN$$

39.18 Properties of Sodium and Potassium of Analytical Importance

1. *Sodium.* Most of the salts of sodium are soluble in water. Notable exceptions are **sodium hexafluosilicate,** Na_2SiF_6, and **sodium hexahydroxoantimonate (V),** $NaSb(OH)_6$.

Of qualitative and quantitative analytical importance is the yellow complex salt, **sodium zinc uranyl acetate,** $NaZn(UO_2)_3(OAc)_9 \cdot 6\ H_2O$. Sodium ions may be almost completely precipitated from solution by adding a concentrated solution of zinc uranyl acetate, saturated with the sodium salt, to a concentrated solution containing sodium ions.

The characteristic yellow color imparted to the Bunsen flame by sodium compounds serves as a qualitative test for the sodium ion.

2. *Potassium.* With hexachloroplatinic acid, potassium ions produce **potassium hexachloroplatinate (IV),** $K_2[PtCl_6]$, a yellow salt which is somewhat soluble

in water but sparingly soluble in alcohol. Other slightly soluble salts are the yellow **hexanitrocobaltate (III),** $K_2Na[Co(NO_2)_6]$, and the **tripotassium hexanitrocobaltate (III),** $K_3[Co(NO_2)_6]$. Tartaric acid, $H_2C_4H_4O_6$, reacts with potassium ions in high concentrations and in neutral solutions to form white **potassium hydrogen tartrate,** $KHC_4H_4O_6$. Concentrated solutions of potassium salts react with perchloric acid precipitating $KClO_4$, and with fluosilicic acid precipitating K_2SiF_6.

Potassium compounds impart a violet color to a Bunsen flame, a property which is of value in detecting the element qualitatively.

MAGNESIUM

The periodic relationships of magnesium were discussed with those of the other alkaline earth metals in Section 38.1.

39.19 History and Occurrence of Magnesium

The name "magnesia" was taken from the district Magnesia in Asia Minor from which magnesium compounds were obtained in early times. In 1695 Nehemiah Grew isolated the substance called **Epsom salts** (magnesium sulfate) from the mineral water at Epsom, England. Davy, in 1808, isolated impure magnesium metal by electrolysis.

Magnesium never occurs free in nature because of its reactivity, but, in combination, is abundant and widely distributed. The chloride and sulfate of magnesium are readily soluble in water and, consequently, are found in ground waters, to which they give noncarbonate hardness (Section 10.6). Sea water contains both the chloride and the sulfate, and compounds of magnesium concentrate in the mother liquor of brines from which sodium chloride has been crystallized. The Stassfurt salt beds contain **carnallite,** $KCl \cdot MgCl_2 \cdot 6\ H_2O$, and extensive deposits of magnesium sulfate are found in Washington, and in Searles Lake, California. Magnesium is found in many insoluble mineral forms such as **magnesite,** $MgCO_3$; and whole mountain ranges are formed of **dolomite,** $MgCO_3 \cdot CaCO_3$. Most limestones contain some magnesium carbonate. Other insoluble minerals containing magnesium include the complex silicates **asbestos,** $H_4Mg_3Si_2O_9$; **meerschaum,** $Mg_2Si_3O_8 \cdot 2\ H_2O$; and **talc** or **soapstone,** $Mg_3SiO_{10}(OH)_2$. The mineral **brucite** is magnesium hydroxide, $Mg(OH)_2$.

39.20 Preparation of Magnesium

Magnesium metal is obtained from several different sources and prepared by several different methods.

1. *From underground brines.* Magnesium chloride is obtained from the underground brines of Michigan, which contain about 3 per cent magnesium chloride, 9 per cent calcium chloride, 14 per cent sodium chloride, and 0.1 per cent bromine as bromide ion. The bromine is first extracted (Section 17.3), the brine is treated

with a suspension of magnesium hydroxide to precipitate the hydroxides of iron and certain other metals, and then the filtrate is evaporated to crystallize out the sodium chloride. The magnesium and calcium chlorides are separated by fractional crystallization. Crystalline magnesium chloride hexahydrate, $MgCl_2 \cdot 6\ H_2O$, is then completely dehydrated in an atmosphere of hydrogen chloride. The hydrogen chloride prevents the formation of magnesium oxide by hydrolysis (Section 39.24). Electrolysis of the fused chloride produces magnesium metal and chlorine. Sodium chloride is usually added to lower the melting point and increase the electrical conductivity of the electrolyte. Cast-steel pots serve as cathodes, and the anodes are graphite bars. The anode is protected by a porcelain hood through which the liberated chlorine gas escapes. The magnesium rises to the surface of the electrolytic bath as it is liberated and is removed at intervals by a ladle. The product has a purity of 99.9 per cent.

2. *From sea water.* Sea water now serves as an important and inexhaustible source of magnesium. Nearly 6 million tons of magnesium, as the chloride and sulfate, are contained in each cubic mile of sea water. Dow Chemical extracts magnesium from sea water at Freeport, Texas, on the Gulf of Mexico.

The raw materials for the process are sea water, oyster shells ($CaCO_3$) from Galveston Bay, salt from salt domes, fresh water, and natural gas. Nearly 800 tons of sea water must be processed to obtain one ton of magnesium metal. Oyster shells are calcined to produce lime, which is slaked by adding water. The same sea water that was used for the recovery of bromine (Section 17.3) is treated with slaked lime to precipitate magnesium hydroxide. After filtration, the magnesium hydroxide is treated with hydrochloric acid to produce the chloride. The magnesium chloride is crystallized from solution by evaporation. The crystallized salt is then partially dehydrated. The resulting magnesium chloride has a composition corresponding to $MgCl_2 \cdot 1\frac{1}{2}\ H_2O$. It is placed in electrolytic cells which are cast-steel tanks and which serve as cathodes, while the anodes are made of graphite. The by-product chlorine produced by this method is impure with hydrogen chloride. It is burned with natural gas to produce the hydrogen chloride used in the process.

3. *Other methods.* At one time, an electrolytic method resembling the Hall process for the preparation of aluminum (Section 37.42) was used in Europe. In this process, magnesium oxide was dissolved in a bath of a fused mixture of the fluorides of magnesium, barium, and sodium. Electrolysis liberated magnesium at the cathode and oxygen at the anode.

Magnesium has been obtained by reducing the oxide with carbon.

$$MgO + C \rightarrow Mg + CO$$

The oxide is obtained by calcining magnesite, $MgCO_3$, and brucite, $Mg(OH)_2$. A high temperature is required for the reduction, and the magnesium leaves the furnace in vapor state, along with carbon monoxide. This mixture of gases must be cooled very rapidly to prevent the reverse reaction $Mg + CO \rightarrow MgO + C$.

During World War II, the Pidgeon process was developed for reducing magnesium oxide by ferrosilicon under reduced pressure. The iron oxide forms a slag, $FeSiO_3$, with the silica.

$$MgO + Fe \rightarrow Mg + FeO$$
$$2\ MgO + Si \rightarrow 2\ Mg + SiO_2$$
$$FeO + SiO_2 \rightarrow FeSiO_3$$

The process, which had not had appreciable use since the war, has now been reinstated and has been a market competitor since 1959.

39.21 Properties and Uses of Magnesium

Magnesium is a silvery-white metal which is malleable and ductile at higher temperatures. It is the lightest of the widely used structural metals. Although it is very active, magnesium is not readily attacked by air or water due to the formation of a protective basic carbonate film on its surface. Magnesium is soluble in acids, including carbonic, evolving hydrogen.

$$Mg + H_2CO_3 \rightarrow MgCO_3 + H_2 \uparrow$$
$$MgCO_3 + H_2CO_3 \rightarrow Mg^{++} + 2\ HCO_3^-$$

It is also attacked by alkali hydrogen carbonates and various salts which give an acid reaction by hydrolysis.

Magnesium decomposes boiling water very slowly, but it rapidly reduces steam, forming magnesium oxide and hydrogen. The affinity of magnesium for oxygen is so great that it will burn in an atmosphere of carbon dioxide, reducing it to elementary carbon.

$$2\ Mg + CO_2 \rightarrow 2\ MgO + C$$

The great reducing power of hot magnesium is utilized in separating many metals and nonmetals, such as silicon and boron, from their oxides.

The metal will unite with most nonmetals. The brilliant white light emitted from burning magnesium affects a photographic film, so extensive use is made of it in flashlight powders, as well as military flares and incendiary bombs. When magnesium burns in air, both the oxide, MgO, and the nitride, Mg_3N_2, are formed.

Most of the production of magnesium is used in making light-weight alloys, the most important of which are those of aluminum and zinc. **Magnalium** (1–15 per cent Mg, 0–1.75 per cent Cu and the remainder Al) is lighter, harder, stronger, and more easily machined than aluminum. Other important magnesium alloys include **duralumin** (0.5 per cent Mg, 0.5 per cent Mn, 3.5–5.5 per cent Cu, remainder Al), and **Dowmetal** (8.5 per cent Al, 0.15 per cent Mn, 2.0 per cent Cu, 1.0 per cent Cd, 0.5 per cent Zn, 87.85 per cent Mg). Magnesium and its alloys are used chiefly in the construction of airplanes, automobiles, speed boats, and dirigibles. They are used in the manufacture of pistons, crankcases, propellers, and devices for producing and amplifying sound. One to three pounds of magnesium are used per automobile in the United States (1962). One European make (Volkswagen) uses 42 pounds of magnesium in each automobile.

39.22 Magnesium Oxide and Hydroxide

The oxide of magnesium, MgO, is sometimes called **magnesia.** It is formed commercially by heating **magnesite,** $MgCO_3$, to 600°–800°, which drives off most of the carbon dioxide. The product is a light, fluffy powder which still contains a few per cent of magnesium carbonate, and it is called "light burnt" or "caustic" magnesia. It reacts slowly with water, forming magnesium hydroxide, and it is soluble in aqueous carbon dioxide forming magnesium hydrogen carbonate, a constituent of hard water. On the other hand, when magnesite is ignited at 1400° or above, "dead burnt" magnesia is formed. This product contains no magnesium carbonate and is a powder which is much more dense than the light form of the oxide. It does not react with water, and it conducts heat poorly. Since magnesium oxide melts at 2800°, it is used in making fire brick and crucibles, as a lining in furnaces, and in heat insulation.

Light magnesium oxide is used as an ingredient of toilet powders and certain dentifrices, and in medicine for the correction of hyperacidity. **Sorel's cement** is made by grinding the light oxide to a fine powder and mixing it with a solution of magnesium chloride. This mixture sets to a strong and durable cement, which is thought to be the basic salt, $MgO \cdot MgCl_2$.

Since magnesium oxide does not slake readily, the hydroxide is best prepared by treating a solution of a magnesium salt with an alkali hydroxide. The hydroxide is slightly soluble in water, but readily soluble in solutions of ammonium salts because of the acidity of the NH_4^+.

$$Mg(OH)_2 + 2\ NH_4^- \rightarrow Mg^{++} + 2\ NH_3 + 2\ H_2O$$

A suspension of magnesium hydroxide in water is called "milk of magnesia" and is used in medicine to correct hyperacidity of the stomach.

39.23 Magnesium Carbonates

The **normal carbonate,** $MgCO_3$, is found in nature as the mineral magnesite. A **basic carbonate** of approximately the composition $3\ MgCO_3 \cdot Mg(OH)_2 \cdot 3\ H_2O$ is produced by precipitation. This compound is known commercially as "magnesia alba," and is used as a dental abrasive, as a medicine, as a cosmetic, and as a silver polish. **Magnesium hydrogen carbonate,** $Mg(HCO_3)_2$, is a constituent of many hard waters.

39.24 Magnesium Chloride

This salt occurs in sea water and as a constituent of the mineral **carnallite,** $KCl \cdot MgCl_2 \cdot 6\ H_2O$. Magnesium chloride crystallizes from aqueous solutions as the hydrated salt, $MgCl_2 \cdot 6\ H_2O$. The hexahydrate is deliquescent, becoming moist in damp air. When heated, the salt undergoes hydrolysis and forms the oxide, hydrogen chloride, and water.

$$MgCl_2 \cdot 6\ H_2O \rightarrow MgO + 2\ HCl \uparrow + 5\ H_2O$$

The anhydrous salt may be obtained by heating the hydrate in a current of hydrogen chloride, by burning magnesium in chlorine, or by carefully heating the double salt $NH_4Cl \cdot MgCl_2 \cdot 6\ H_2O$, in which case the water of crystallization is driven off first and then the ammonium chloride is volatilized.

39.25 Other Magnesium Salts

Magnesium sulfate is found as the minerals **kieserite,** $MgSO_4 \cdot H_2O$, and **epsomite,** $MgSO_4 \cdot 7\,H_2O$. The heptahydrate in pure form is familiar as **Epsom salts.** It is used in medicine as a purgative, particularly in veterinary practice, in weighting cotton and silk, in polishing powders, and in insulation against heat.

Magnesium ammonium phosphate, $MgNH_4PO_4$, is a slightly soluble crystalline salt, which is formed whenever a soluble phosphate is added to a solution containing magnesium, ammonium, and hydroxide ions. This white substance is used in the detection and estimation of either magnesium or phosphate ions in analytical chemistry.

Anhydrous **magnesium perchlorate,** $Mg(ClO_4)_2$, is a highly efficient drying agent, called "Anhydrone." It rapidly absorbs up to 35 per cent of its weight of water. The anhydrous salt is easily regenerated by heating the hydrate.

Several silicates of magnesium are of commercial importance. The mineral known as **talc** or **soapstone** is a hydrated magnesium silicate which feels greasy to the touch. It can be sawed and turned on a lathe, so is useful in the fabrication of tables, sinks, switchboards, and window sills. **Asbestos** is a calcium-magnesium silicate with a fibrous structure (Section 29.17), from which incombustible fabrics of considerable strength and durability can be made. Such materials are used in making automobile brake linings, paper, drop curtains for theaters, cardboard, flooring, roofing, and covering for heating pipes and boilers.

39.26 Properties of Magnesium of Analytical Importance

The alkali and alkaline earth hydroxides precipitate the magnesium ion as magnesium hydroxide, which is white and gelatinous. With aqueous ammonia alone, magnesium is partially precipitated as the hydroxide. If enough ammonium ions are present, no precipitation is effected.

The alkali carbonates precipitate basic magnesium carbonate of indefinite composition. Ammonium carbonate in the presence of other ammonium salts does not precipitate magnesium ions at all.

In the presence of ammonium and hydroxide ions, soluble phosphates precipitate magnesium as the white, crystalline **magnesium ammonium phosphate,** which is readily soluble in acids.

$$Mg^{++} + NH_4^+ + HPO_4^= \rightleftharpoons \underline{MgNH_4PO_4} + H^+$$

This compound serves as the basis for the qualitative and quantitative determination of magnesium.

THE AMMONIUM ION AND ITS SALTS

39.27 The Ammonium Ion

The ammonium ion behaves chemically like the ions of the alkali metals, and in particular, like that of potassium, the two ions being of nearly the same size and having the same charge. The resemblance of ammonium and potassium salts is especially noticeable as regards the formation of slightly soluble salts. There are two notable exceptions to the similarity between the salts of the ammonium and potassium ions: (1) The ammonium ion undergoes hydrolysis whereas the potassium ion does not,

$$NH_4^+ + H_2O \rightleftharpoons NH_3 + H_3O^+$$

and (2) ammonium salts decompose when heated.

$$NH_4Cl \rightarrow NH_3 + HCl$$
$$NH_4NO_3 \rightarrow N_2O + H_2O$$
$$NH_4NO_2 \rightarrow N_2 + H_2O$$
$$(NH_4)_2Cr_2O_7 \rightarrow N_2 + 4\ H_2O + Cr_2O_3$$

The ammonium group, NH_4, cannot be isolated as a neutral species but is always found as a positively charged ion, NH_4^+, in combination with a negative ion. When attempts have been made to isolate the neutral NH_4 unit, ammonia and hydrogen have always resulted. When ammonium ions are electrolytically reduced at a mercury cathode, a voluminous, semisolid amalgam, $NH_4(Hg)_x$, is produced.

$$\text{(Cathodic reduction) } NH_4^+ + x\ Hg + e^- \rightarrow NH_4(Hg)_x$$

Ammonium amalgam can also be obtained by stirring a concentrated solution of ammonium chloride into sodium amalgam.

$$NH_4Cl + Na(Hg)_x \rightarrow NaCl + NH_4(Hg)_x$$

Ammonium amalgam is quite unstable and soon decomposes with the formation of mercury, ammonia, and hydrogen. The fact that ammonium amalgams can be formed indicates that the neutral ammonium group is somewhat metallic in character.

39.28 Ammonium Chloride

This salt, NH_4Cl, is known in commerce as "sal ammoniac." It is produced by the reaction of ammonia with hydrochloric acid, and is purified by sublimation. Ammonium chloride decomposes at 350° into ammonia and hydrogen chloride.

$$NH_4Cl \rightleftharpoons NH_3 + HCl$$

For this reason, it is used as a flux in soldering because the hydrogen chloride which is formed when the salt is heated reacts with the films of metal oxide, converting them into chlorides which are either fusible or volatile, thus cleansing the metal surfaces to be joined by the solder. Ammonia and hydrogen chloride gases in the air of chemical laboratories combine to form the familiar white deposits of ammonium chloride so commonly seen on glassware and window panes.

Most of the ammonium chloride produced is used in the manufacture of dry cells (Section 20.15). It is also used in medicine, in dyeing, in calico printing, as a laboratory reagent, and as a fertilizer.

39.29 Ammonium Nitrate

Aqueous ammonia and nitric acid react to form **ammonium nitrate,** NH_4NO_3. a white crystalline salt. It has been used as an ingredient of explosives for warfare. When heated to 166° it fuses and decomposes smoothly with the formation of nitrous oxide and water. When detonated, it decomposes with explosive violence. The enormous explosion which destroyed a large part of Texas City (Fig. 39–5) and took 576 lives in April, 1947, was due to the decomposition of ammonium nitrate which was intended for use as a fertilizer and which was being loaded in the harbor.

Fig. 39–5 View near the dock in Texas City after the explosion of ammonium nitrate, April 1947. *Fire Prevention and Engineering Bureau, Dallas, Texas*

39.30 Ammonium Carbonates

The **hydrogen carbonate,** NH_4HCO_3, is prepared by evaporating a solution made by treating an aqueous solution of ammonia with an excess of carbon dioxide. When heated, the white crystalline salt decomposes rapidly.

$$NH_4HCO_3 \rightleftharpoons NH_3 + H_2O + CO_2$$

Even at ordinary temperatures, it has a faint odor of ammonia. By treating a solution of the hydrogen carbonate with an excess of ammonia, the **normal carbonate** results.

$$HCO_3^- + NH_3 \rightleftharpoons NH_4^+ + CO_3^=$$

When exposed to the air, $(NH_4)_2CO_3$ gives off ammonia more readily than does the hydrogen carbonate and thus is useful in the form of "smelling salts," since ammonia is an effective heart stimulant.

39.31 Other Ammonium Salts

Large quantities of **ammonium sulfate,** $(NH_4)_2SO_4$, are produced by absorbing ammonia in sulfuric acid. Its chief use is as a fertilizer to supply nitrogen to the soil.

When aqueous ammonia is saturated with hydrogen sulfide, **ammonium hydrogen sulfide,** NH_4HS, is formed. If the resulting solution is then treated with an equivalent amount of aqueous ammonia, the **normal sulfide,** $(NH_4)_2S$, is formed. This compound is a valuable reagent in analytical chemistry. When freshly prepared, it is colorless and is called colorless ammonium sulfide. On standing in air in the presence of sunlight, a solution of ammonium sulfide absorbs oxygen and liberates sulfur.

$$2\ S^{=} + O_2 + 2\ H_2O \rightarrow 2\ \underline{S} + 4\ OH^-$$

The sulfur thus formed unites with the undecomposed colorless ammonium sulfide to produce a yellow solution, called **yellow ammonium sulfide,** or **ammonium polysulfide;** its formula may be written $(NH_4)_2S_x$, where x is 1–5. Yellow ammonium sulfide is prepared for use in the laboratory by dissolving sulfur in solutions of the normal sulfide. It is an important reagent in analytical processes.

39.32 Properties of the Ammonium Ion of Analytical Importance

Most ammonium salts are soluble in water. The slightly soluble salts that may be employed in the detection of the ammonium ion are: **ammonium hexanitrocobaltate (III),** $(NH_4)_3[Co(NO_2)_6]$; **ammonium hydrogen tartrate,** $NH_4HC_4H_4O_6$; and **ammonium hexachloroplatinate (IV),** $(NH_4)_2[PtCl_6]$. Since potassium forms similar insoluble compounds, ammonium ions must be removed from solution prior to the precipitation of potassium salts. Unlike potassium, the ammonium ion does not give a precipitate with perchloric acid.

The alkali hydroxides and carbonates and the alkaline earth hydroxides liberate ammonia from solutions of the ammonium ion in the cold, and more rapidly upon heating.

QUESTIONS

1. Why is a consideration of the chemistry of the ammonium ion and its salts introduced at this point?
2. What evidence is there that the neutral ammonium molecule is metallic in character?
3. Correlate the positive oxidation states of sodium, potassium, and magnesium with their respective atomic structures.
4. Why do not the alkali metals occur free in nature?
5. Why is sodium carbonate or calcium chloride added to the electrolyte in the electrolysis of fused sodium chlorides?
6. Why should metallic sodium never be handled with the fingers?
7. What evidence is available to show that hydrogen is present as the negative hydride ion in sodium hydride?
8. Why must the chlorine and sodium hydroxide be kept separate in the electrolysis of aqueous sodium chloride?
9. Outline the chemistry of the Solvay process for the production of sodium carbonate.
10. Why is sodium hydroxide called "caustic soda"?

11. Why cannot potassium hydrogen carbonate be manufactured by the Solvay process?

12. What is the principal reaction involved when baking powder acts as a leavening agent?

13. What is the commercial process for the manufacture of sodium cyanide?

14. Give two examples of slightly soluble sodium salts.

15. Identify by formulas: potash, caustic potash, dolomitic limestone, magnesia, and sal ammoniac.

16. Outline the extraction of magnesium from sea water.

17. Why cannot a magnesium fire be extinguished by either water or carbon dioxide?

18. Explain the dissolution of magnesium hydroxide in solutions of ammonium salts.

19. Why cannot $MgCl_2 \cdot 6\,H_2O$ be dehydrated by heating in air? How may it be dehydrated?

20. Compare the solubilities of potassium and ammonium salts.

21. Write equations for the thermal decomposition of the following salts: NH_4Cl, NH_4NO_3, NH_4NO_2, and $(NH_4)_2Cr_2O_7$.

22. Describe a chemical test for the ammonium ion.

REFERENCES

"Production of Salt," J. E. Hyler, *J. Chem. Educ.*, **12** (5) 203 (1935).

"Potassium," W. O. Fenn, *Sci. American*, Aug., 1949; p. 16.

Discovery of the Elements, M. E. Weeks, Publ. by the Journal of Chemical Education, Easton, Pa., Sixth Edition, 1956; pp. 455–471, 473–484, and 521–528.

"Magnesium from Sea Water," G. E. Stedman, *Metals and Alloys*, **20** (4) 941 (1944).

"Magnesium Producer Shuns Electrolysis," (Pidgeon Process), R. E. Barnes, *Chem. Eng.*, May 29, 1961; p. 70.

"Magnesium Battery," (Staff) *Chem. Eng. News*, **27** (27) 1936 (1949).

"Magnesium Looks for Gains," (Staff) *Chem. Eng. News*, Jan. 15, 1962; p. 36.

CHAPTER FORTY

The Less Common Metals

In the preceding five chapters we have studied the metals whose ions are usually included in qualitative analytical schemes and certain other metals closely related to these. There are several other metals which are often spoken of as the "less common" or "less familiar" metals that deserve attention. In fact, a few of these metals actually have greater commercial importance than some of those included in the analytical scheme. For example, platinum, gold, tungsten, molybdenum, and titanium have much more value and use than do strontium and barium.

The discussion of the metals in this chapter follows their grouping according to the Periodic Table.

GOLD — GROUP IB

The history and periodic relationships of gold were discussed in Sections 35.10 and 35.9, respectively, along with silver and copper, the other elements of Group IB.

40.1 Occurrence of Gold

Gold is found chiefly as the metal, occasionally in nuggets scattered through gravel but more frequently as small particles in veins of quartz or in sands formed by the disintegration of gold-bearing rock. Native gold always contains silver and some platinum metals (Ru, Rh, Pd, Os, Ir, and Pt). In the combined state, gold is found in a few minerals such as the telluride, $AuTe_2$, and as the double telluride, $AuAgTe_4$, which is called **silvanite.** The main gold-producing countries are the Union of South Africa, Canada, Russia, the United States, various South American countries, India, Japan, and Mexico.

40.2 Metallurgy of Gold

For centuries gold has been obtained by processes known as "panning," "sluicing," or "placer mining," in which the gold-bearing sand and gravel was washed with water to separate the lighter particles from the heavier gold particles. Nowadays, powerful streams of water are thrown against the deposits, which are washed into the sluices (long troughs). This process is called "hydraulic mining."

The amalgamation process for the extraction of gold has also been used for many centuries. In this process finely powdered ore is washed over plates of copper coated with mercury, in which about half the gold dissolves. At intervals, the amalgam is scraped off, the mercury removed by distillation in an iron retort, and the gold residue refined.

The cyanide process for gold is similar to that used in obtaining silver from its ores (Section 35.11); in fact the two metals are usually extracted together. This process involves the action of solutions of sodium or potassium cyanide on the finely pulverized ore. Oxygen of the air is essential to the reaction.

$$4\ Au + 8\ CN^- + 2\ H_2O + O_2 \rightarrow 4\ [Au(CN)_2]^- + 4\ OH^-$$

The gold is recovered from the solution by displacement using zinc.

$$Zn + 2\ [Au(CN)_2]^- \rightarrow 2\ Au + [Zn(CN)_4]^=$$

Gold obtained by any of the above processes is impure with silver; and other metals, such as lead, copper, and zinc may be present. The refining or "parting" of the impure gold may be accomplished by electrolysis or by dissolving the impurities by a chemical reagent. The electrolyte employed for **electrolytic parting** is a mixture of chlorauric acid, $H[AuCl_4]$, and hydrochloric acid; the anode is the impure gold and the cathode is a strip of pure gold. The gold passes into solution and is deposited on the cathode while the silver is precipitated as silver chloride. **Chemical parting** involves treatment of the impure gold with sulfuric or nitric acid, which dissolves the silver and the base metals. Separation of the silver by acids is impossible when the gold content is more than about 25 per cent. Under such circumstances it is necessary to fuse a suitable amount of silver with the alloy before the parting can be accomplished.

40.3 Properties of Gold

Gold is a yellow, soft metal, and the most malleable and ductile of all metals. Gold foil can be made by hammering the metal into sheets so thin that 300,000 of them would be required to make a pile one inch thick; one gram of gold can be drawn into a wire more than a mile and a half in length. Pure gold is too soft to be used for jewelry and coinage; for such purposes it is always alloyed with copper, silver, or some other metal. The purity of gold is expressed by the number of **carats,** a designation that indicates the number of parts by weight of gold in 24 parts of alloy. Thus 24-carat gold is the pure metal, while a 10-carat gold alloy is $\frac{10}{24}$ gold by weight. Red or yellow gold alloys contain copper, whereas white gold alloys are made using palladium, nickel, or zinc.

Gold is a very inactive metal. It neither combines directly with oxygen nor corrodes in the atmosphere. The metal is not affected by any single common acid nor by alkalies. It is acted upon, however, by selenic acid, H_2SeO_4, and it dissolves readily in aqua regia.

$$Au + 4\ H^+ + NO_3^- + 4\ Cl^- \rightarrow [AuCl_4]^- + NO\uparrow + 2\ H_2O$$

It is also dissolved by a solution of chlorine, and by cyanide in the presence of air.

Gold is a transition metal with one valence electron in its outermost shell. It forms principally compounds in which it is univalent or trivalent. When gold dissolves in aqua regia and the solution is evaporated, yellow crystals of **chlorauric acid,** $HAuCl_4 \cdot 4\,H_2O$, are formed. When this complex compound is heated, hydrogen chloride is evolved, and red crystalline **gold (III) chloride,** $AuCl_3$, remains. When this compound is heated to 175° it is changed to **gold (I) chloride,** $AuCl$, and at higher temperatures the metal is obtained. The thermal instability of these compounds is typical, for all compounds of gold are decomposed by heat. Gold (I) chloride undergoes an auto-oxidation-reduction reaction in water, forming gold (III) chloride and the metal. Gold forms two oxides, Au_2O and Au_2O_3, and the corresponding hydroxides, $AuOH$, which is a weak base, and $Au(OH)_3$. The trihydroxide is a weak acid capable of reacting with strong bases to form salts called **aurates,** such as $NaAuO_2$. Potassium cyanide acts upon gold (I) and gold (III) compounds giving the complex salts $Na[Au(CN)_2]$ and $Na[Au(CN)_4]$, respectively. These soluble compounds are important in the extraction of gold from its ores and in gold plating and gilding operations.

A sensitive test for gold consists of the treatment of a dilute solution of gold (III) chloride with tin (II) chloride. Colloidal gold with a deep purple color, known as the "purple of Cassius," is formed by the reducing action of the divalent tin.

BERYLLIUM AND RADIUM — GROUP IIA

Beryllium and radium are the first and last members, respectively, of Group IIA of the Periodic Table. The periodic relationships of the elements of this group were discussed in Section 38.1.

40.4 Beryllium

Beryllium was discovered by Vauquelin in 1798 in the mineral **beryl,** which is beryllium aluminosilicate, $Be_3Al_2Si_6O_{18}$. Beryl is still the main source of beryllium, and it is sometimes found in the transparent gem stones aquamarine, emerald, and beryl.

Beryllium metal is produced commercially by electrolysis of the fused chloride. It is a light, silvery-white metal, which possesses considerable strength, rigidity, and elasticity. The metal is used for making windows in X-ray tubes because, among the very light metals, it is the most penetrable to X-rays. Its most common use is as a constituent of special alloys. For example, beryllium-copper alloys are especially suitable for use in springs which are subject to frequent vibration. These alloys are also important because of their high thermal and electrical conductivity and their nonsparking character when struck. Beryllium oxide was formerly used in fluorescent lamps and on fluorescent screens, but this use has been abandoned because the oxide is poisonous. In fact, all compounds of beryllium are poisonous, and merely breathing the dust of the metal or its oxide may cause serious illness (berylliosis).

Beryllium closely resembles aluminum in its chemical properties; it is one of the bridge elements. For example, its salts are readily hydrolyzed when dissolved in water, and the hydroxide, $Be(OH)_2$, is amphoteric. Compounds of the type Na_2BeO_2 are formed when the hydroxide is dissolved in concentrated solutions of alkalies. On boiling or diluting the alkaline solution, the salt hydrolyzes and beryllium hydroxide precipitates.

40.5 Radium

Metallic radium was first obtained in 1910 by Marie Curie, who accomplished this by electrolyzing a solution of radium chloride with a mercury cathode. The mercury was removed from the amalgam thus obtained, leaving radium. In 1898, Marie Curie and her husband, Pierre, had obtained a few hundredths of a gram of radium bromide from a large quantity of pitchblende after a long and tedious process of extraction and fractional crystallization.

Radium occurs in all uranium minerals in extremely small proportions, about one part in three million. The early supplies of radium were obtained from **pitchblende** deposits of Bohemia, which contain U_3O_8 in a very complicated mixture of the oxides of many other metals. Later this source was supplanted by **carnotite,** $K_2(UO_2)_2(VO_4)_2 \cdot 8\ H_2O$, from Colorado and Utah. At present most of the world's production of radium comes from the pitchblende deposits found near Great Bear Lake in Canada's Northwest Territories, and the rich carnotite ores of the Congo. The rarity of radium, the difficulty in extraction, and its usefulness combine to make it one of the most costly substances known. The price of radium compounds was once as high as $150,000 per gram of radium.

Radium is quite similar to barium in its physical and chemical properties. It is the most reactive metal of Group IIA; its hydroxide is fairly soluble and is a strong base; and its sulfate is even less soluble than that of barium.

The important property of radium and its compounds is its radioactivity. Its nucleus decomposes spontaneously giving off alpha particles and the element radon. This change is accompanied by the liberation of a tremendous quantity of energy, which causes many crystalline substances to fluoresce when exposed to the rays of radium. Among these substances are zinc sulfide, fluorspar, and diamond. Certain luminous paints contain one part of radium mixed with several thousand parts of impure zinc sulfide.

The most important application of radium is its use in the treatment of cancer (Section 30.1).

GALLIUM, INDIUM, AND THALLIUM — GROUP IIIA

Group IIIA of the Periodic Table contains the nonmetallic element boron (Chapter 29), the important metal aluminum (Chapter 37), and the metals gallium, indium, and thallium, which are neither common nor abundant, but which resemble aluminum.

40.6 Gallium

The existence of the rare element gallium was predicted by Mendeleev, who called it "eka-aluminum," about four years before it was discovered in 1875. The element was found by de Boisbaudran in specimens of zinc blende, ZnS, by means of a spectroscope. He named it **gallium** after his native country, France (Gallia).

Gallium is a soft, white metal with a melting point (29.78°) slightly above room temperature and a specific gravity of 5.91. It forms two series of compounds in which it is bivalent and trivalent. The trihydroxide, $Ga(OH)_3$, is slightly more basic than aluminum hydroxide; otherwise the compounds of trivalent gallium closely resemble those of aluminum.

40.7 Indium

Reich and Richter first observed lines of indium in the spectrum of zinc blende in 1863, and gave this element its name from the two indigo-blue lines characteristic of its spectrum.

Indium is a soft, gray-white metal that melts at 157° and has a specific gravity of 7.36. It is used to some extent in dental alloys and as a hardening layer on moving parts of machinery.

Two series of indium compounds are known. Compounds of trivalent indium are similar to those of aluminum and gallium, except that indium (III) hydroxide is more basic than the hydroxides of either of the other two metals. A few monovalent indium compounds such as the halides, InX, have been prepared.

40.8 Thallium

Crookes discovered thallium in 1861 while examining the flue dust of a zinc smelter by means of a spectroscope. He named the element **thallium** from the Greek word meaning "a green twig" because of the prominent green line characteristic of its spectrum. Thallium is much more abundant than gallium and indium, and is often found with the sulfides of heavy metals. It is a soft, white metal with a bluish tinge, resembling lead in appearance. Its specific gravity is high (11.85) and it melts at 303.6°.

Thallium forms two distinct classes of compounds. The compounds of the thallium (I) series resemble the alkali metal compounds and those of silver. For example, the soluble salts, such as the sulfate and carbonate, resemble those of potassium, while the insoluble salts, such as the halides and cyanide, are like the corresponding silver salts. The thallium (III) compounds resemble those of aluminum. The hydroxide, $Tl(OH)_3$, is brown in color and is a stronger base than aluminum hydroxide.

Thallium compounds are used in making optical glass of high index of refraction, and for destroying vermin such as rats, gophers, and ants. This metal and its salts are also exceedingly poisonous to man.

THE LESS COMMON ELEMENTS OF GROUP IIIB

Division B of Group III includes scandium, yttrium, the lanthanide elements (rare earths), and the elements of the actinide series. Because scandium and yttrium resemble the rare earths so closely, they are often included in the study of that series.

40.9 The Rare Earth Elements (the Lanthanide Series)

The **rare earths** include elements of atomic numbers 57 to 71, inclusive. These elements have physical and chemical properties which are very similar. The unusual similarity is attributed to the fact that their electron configurations differ principally in the number of electrons in the 4*f* and 5*d* subshells rather than in their outer, 6*s*, subshell (see Table 40·1). Although lanthanum (At. No. 57) is a **transition element** (see Section 3.14), it is often included as a rare earth along with elements 58 to 71, which are **inner transition elements,** because of the similarity in properties.

TABLE 40·1 Electron Configurations of the Rare Earth Elements

Atomic Number	*Element*	*Electron Configuration*					
57	La	$1s^2$	$2s^2\ 2p^6$	$3s^2\ 3p^6\ 3d^{10}$	$4s^2\ 4p^6\ 4d^{10}\ 4f^0$	$5s^2\ 5p^6\ 5d^1$	$6s^2$
58	Ce				$4f^2$	$5s^2\ 5p^6\ 5d^0$	$6s^2$
59	Pr				$4f^3$	$5s^2\ 5p^6\ 5d^0$	$6s^2$
60	Nd				$4f^4$	$5s^2\ 5p^6\ 5d^0$	$6s^2$
61	Pm				$4f^5$	$5s^2\ 5p^6\ 5d^0$	$6s^2$
62	Sm				$4f^6$	$5s^2\ 5p^6\ 5d^0$	$6s^2$
63	Eu				$4f^7$	$5s^2\ 5p^6\ 5d^0$	$6s^2$
64	Gd				$4f^7$	$5s^2\ 5p^6\ 5d^1$	$6s^2$
65	Tb				$4f^9$	$5s^2\ 5p^6\ 5d^0$	$6s^2$
66	Dy				$4f^{10}$	$5s^2\ 5p^6\ 5d^0$	$6s^2$
67	Ho				$4f^{11}$	$5s^2\ 5p^6\ 5d^0$	$6s^2$
68	Er				$4f^{12}$	$5s^2\ 5p^6\ 5d^0$	$6s^2$
69	Tm				$4f^{13}$	$5s^2\ 5p^6\ 5d^0$	$6s^2$
70	Yb				$4f^{14}$	$5s^2\ 5p^6\ 5d^0$	$6s^2$
71	Lu				$4f^{14}$	$5s^2\ 5p^6\ 5d^1$	$6s^2$

The rare earths are found in many rare minerals which exist in a few widely separated localities. These minerals are often complex silicates or phosphates and usually contain several of the rare earth elements. **Monazite sand** is the most important source of these minerals and it contains the various elements of the group in the form of phosphates, excepting promethium (atomic number 61), which does not occur in nature at all. Monazite sand is found along the seacoast in Brazil, India, and the Carolinas.

The rare earth elements resemble each other so closely that their separation has been an exceedingly laborious task. Formerly, the only effective method of separation has been that of fractional crystallization of certain of their salts, involving many hundreds of crystallizations. Now, ion-exchange techniques, which provide a much more rapid and effective separation, are used. This method consists in the selective adsorption of the ions of the various rare earths on a column of an ion-exchange resin (Section 10.7), followed by fractional elution of the adsorbed material by a suitable solvent.

The rare earth elements are metallic in character and all form oxides of the general formula M_2O_3. Their usual valence is 3, but some of the members have other valences as well, such as 2 or 4. As would be expected, the basicity of the hydroxides, $M(OH)_3$, decreases with increasing atomic number of the elements (see Section 15.1, part 7).

An alloy of iron with a mixture of the rare earth metals, known commercially as "misch metal," is used in making the "flints" in cigarette lighters. A mixture of the fluorides of these metals forms the core of the carbon arcs used in motion picture projectors. Recently, the rare earths have been found to have great catalytic power in some reactions, and large quantities soon will be used in this way, chiefly in petroleum cracking and reforming.

40.10 The Actinide Series

The series of elements beginning with actinium, element 89, and extending through lawrencium, element 103, is called the **actinide series.** All the elements of this series are radioactive. They are analogous to the rare earths in that the electron configurations of succeeding elements in the series differ by one electron, in this case in the $5f$ or $6d$ subshells. The properties of the actinide elements are similar to those of the "lanthanide" rare earths. These elements have a characteristic valence of 3, but show a much wider variation in oxidation states than do those of the rare earth series. Thorium resembles cerium in that it shows a valence of 4.

Elements 93 through 103 are prepared synthetically by nuclear reactions (Section 30.5). However, since they were first synthesized, it has been discovered that plutonium and neptunium occur in nature in small amounts. The most important elements in the actinide series are thorium, uranium, and plutonium, the importance of the latter two being related to their use in atomic energy (Sections 30.10 and 30.11).

Thorium occurs as the dioxide in monazite sand, along with the rare earths. Deposits of monazite in Brazil and India run as high as 10 per cent of **thoria,** ThO_2. Metallic thorium is obtained by reducing the tetrachloride, $ThCl_4$, with sodium; the thorium tetrachloride is prepared by the action of chlorine on a heated mixture of the dioxide and carbon. Thorium is very similar to the elements of Group IVB, which are discussed later in this chapter. It is tetravalent in its compounds. Its hydroxide, $Th(OH)_4$, is entirely basic, and its salts are hydrolyzed to a limited extent in water. Thorium is used principally as the dioxide, mixed with 1 per cent of cerium dioxide, in the manufacture of Welsbach gas mantles. Tungsten filaments for electric lamps are thoriated to increase their efficiency and retard their disintegration.

Uranium, the first radioactive element to be discovered, is found in the minerals **pitchblende,** U_3O_8, and **carnotite,** $K_2(UO_2)_2(VO_4)_2 \cdot 8\ H_2O$. The principal sources of uranium minerals are the Congo, the Great Bear Lake Region of Canada, Colorado, and Utah. The metal may be obtained by reduction of the oxide with carbon, calcium, or aluminum. It is a white, lustrous metal of high density (18.9 g./cm.^{3}), and it melts at 1132°. The metal is moderately active and forms compounds in which it shows oxidation states of +2, +3, +4, +5, and +6. The "uranium" salts of commerce contain the bipositive uranyl ion, UO_2^{++}. These include uranyl nitrate, $UO_2(NO_3)_2 \cdot 6\ H_2O$, and the acetate, $UO_2(C_2H_3O_2)_2 \cdot 2\ H_2O$. There are several series of uranates, the most important of which are the diuranates, such as sodium diuranate, $Na_2U_2O_7 \cdot 6\ H_2O$. Uranium compounds are used for producing yellow glazes on ceramic ware and as mordants in the dye industry. The chief interest in uranium at present is in its release of nuclear energy and its conversion to elements that will release nuclear energy (see Chapter 30).

GERMANIUM — GROUP IVA

The periodic relationships of germanium are given in Section 35.18.

40.11 Germanium

As mentioned in Section 15.2, Mendeleev predicted in 1871 the existence of an element that he named "eka-silicon." Less than two decades later (1886) this element was discovered by Clemens Winkler, professor of chemistry at Freiburg, Germany, who named it "germanium" in honor of that country.

Germanium minerals are quite rare. This element occurs in the mineral **argyrodite,** Ag_4SeS_4, but its most common occurrence is in the form of sulfide ores associated with other metal sulfides, particularly those of lead, zinc, silver, and tin. Some germanium is recovered during the processing of these ores. The metal is easily obtained from the dioxide, GeO_2, by reduction with carbon or hydrogen.

Germanium metal is a gray-white, crystalline solid that retains its luster in air at ordinary temperatures. It is not affected by hydrochloric acid, dilute sulfuric acid, or concentrated sodium hydroxide. However, the metal is tarnished by concentrated nitric acid and dilute sodium hydroxide. Fused alkalies dissolve it, forming germanates, such as Na_2GeO_3.

This metal forms germanium (II) and germanium (IV) compounds, but few of the former are known for they are unstable and easily oxidized or reduced. Its two oxides, GeO and GeO_2, are both amphoteric, and the tetrachloride, $GeCl_4$, is a volatile covalent liquid, resembling the corresponding halide of silicon, $SiCl_4$, in its properties. Germanium also shows a marked similarity to silicon in the formation of a number of hydrides such as GeH_4, Ge_2H_6, and Ge_3H_8, and numerous organometallic compounds such as $(C_2H_5)_4Ge$ and $(C_6H_5)_4Ge$.

The compounds of germanium have little use. When the metal is alloyed with small amounts of certain other elements, it has the unique property of permitting an electric current to pass in only one direction. This rectifying power makes crystals of the metal useful in special apparatus, such as radar. In a highly purified form, it is also used in place of ordinary vacuum tubes in "transistors" for amplifying currents of electricity.

TITANIUM, ZIRCONIUM, AND HAFNIUM—GROUP IVB

These elements are classed as transition metals with valence electrons in their two outermost electron shells. They are most commonly tetravalent, with two electrons of the incomplete inner subshell and the two electrons of the outer shell being used in bonding. These elements, however, show the oxidation states of +2 and +3, as well as +4.

40.12 Titanium

Although titanium is commonly classed as a "less common" element, it is one of the more abundant elements. It is ninth among the elements in abundance in the earth's crust, thus ranking in abundance above such useful metals as nickel, copper, zinc, lead, tin, and mercury.

The most important ores of titanium from the commercial standpoint are **ilmenite,** $FeTiO_3$, and **rutile,** TiO_2. Ilmenite is obtained mainly from the United States, Canada, Norway, and India, whereas rutile is supplied by the United States and Australia. Most of the ilmenite consumed in the United States is used in making a form of the dioxide, TiO_2, which has great light-scattering power. The dioxide is used as an excellent white pigment for paints and in the preparation of white rubber and white leather. The total annual output of TiO_2 (1962) is about 540,000 tons, of which 60% is used in paints, varnishes, and lacquers. Crystals of titanium dioxide colored with small amounts of other metal oxides have been made recently for use as gems.

Titanium is very difficult to obtain in the pure state because it has a high melting point (1812°), it combines readily with such nonmetals as oxygen, nitrogen, hydrogen, and carbon, and it readily forms alloys with the common metals. The free metal has been most successfully prepared by reducing titanium tetrahalides with active metals such as sodium, potassium, magnesium, and calcium. Titanium metal is very strong, light (specific gravity 4.49), high melting, and resistant to corrosion. These properties make the metal and its special alloys valuable in the production of jet motors and high-speed aircraft. An alloy, ferrotitanium, is used in making special steels of great strength and toughness, with the titanium acting to remove nitrogen and other undesirable impurities.

Titanium forms three oxides, TiO, Ti_2O_3, and TiO_2, and their corresponding hydroxides. The dioxide may be prepared from ilmenite by the reaction

$$2\ FeTiO_3 + 4\ HCl + Cl_2 \rightarrow 2\ FeCl_3 + 2\ TiO_2 + 2\ H_2O$$

The temperature is held high enough to volatilize the iron (III) chloride which is formed.

Titanium (IV) chloride, $TiCl_4$, is a liquid boiling at 136.4°. It is produced by passing chlorine over a heated mixture of carbon and titanium dioxide.

$$TiO_2 + C + 2\ Cl_2 \rightarrow TiCl_4 + CO_2$$

The tetrachloride hydrolyzes quickly in moist air, producing a dense white smoke. It is used in producing smoke screens and in skywriting.

The trichloride, $TiCl_3$, and the sulfate, $Ti_2(SO_4)_3$, are powerful reducing agents, and in this capacity are used in the chemical laboratory as reducing agents. Fused alkalies react with titanium dioxide, forming titanates such as sodium titanate, Na_2TiO_3.

40.13 Zirconium

Zirconium is not so abundant as titanium but it is far more abundant than such familiar metals as lead, copper, nickel, zinc, mercury, and tin. Its chief ores are **zircon,** $ZrSiO_4$, and **baddeleyite,** ZrO_2, extensive deposits of which occur in Brazil, India, and New South Wales. The metal is obtained by heating K_2ZrF_6 with sodium, potassium, or aluminum. Ferrozirconium has been used with some success in the steel industry in the production of a tough steel.

Zirconium dioxide, ZrO_2, which is called **zirconia,** is the most important compound of the element because of its excellent refractory qualities. These include a high melting point (about 2700°), a low coefficient of expansion, and a high resistance to corrosion. It is used as a refractory for lining furnaces and for producing crucibles and other high-temperature vessels. It has not been used extensively, however, because its high cost has been prohibitive.

Although zirconia is scarcely attacked by any acid except hydrofluoric, it reacts with fused alkalies, forming **zirconates** such as Na_2ZrO_3. Insoluble zirconates are formed when the dioxide is used in the production of enamels and opaque glass.

Zirconium forms the **tetrachloride,** $ZrCl_4$, which is not so readily hydrolyzed as titanium tetrachloride; hydrolysis results in the formation of derivatives such as the **oxychloride,** $ZrOCl_2$, instead of the oxide as is the case with $TiCl_4$.

Zircon, the naturally occurring silicate, $ZrSiO_4$, is found in a variety of colors, and because of its beauty and hardness, the mineral is used in jewelry as a semiprecious stone.

40.14 Hafnium

This element was discovered in zircon from Norway by means of spectroscopic analysis in 1923 by Coster and Hevesy. It is found in nearly all zirconium minerals, most of which contain about 5 per cent hafnium. Hafnium has chemical properties quite similar to those of zirconium, making the separation of the two elements difficult. Thus far the metal and its compounds have been used but little.

VANADIUM, NIOBIUM, AND TANTALUM — GROUP VB

These elements are typical transition metals; they exhibit a wide range of oxidation states and form highly colored compounds.

40.15 Vanadium

Vanadium is the most important element of Group VB. Its importance lies in the fact that addition of **ferrovanadium** to steel serves the purpose of removing impurities and forming an alloy steel of special properties. Vanadium steel is tough and strong, and it is used wherever a steel is needed that will withstand strain, vibration, and shock, such as in automobile crankshafts and heavy machinery. The principal ores of vanadium are **vanadinite,** $Pb_5(VO_4)_3Cl$, and **carnotite,** $K_2(UO_2)_2(VO_4)_2 \cdot 8\,H_2O$. Most of the vanadium consumed in the United States comes from Colorado and other western states, and from Peruvian coal, the ashes of which may contain up to 48 per cent V_2O_5. The metal is obtained by reducing the pentoxide with such reducing agents as carbon, hydrogen, or aluminum.

Vanadium forms compounds in which it shows oxidation states of +2, +3, +4, and +5. As might be expected, the oxides VO and V_2O_3 are basic, while VO_2 is amphoteric and V_2O_5 is acidic. The compounds of vanadium in its different oxidation states exhibit strikingly varied colors. Compounds of V^{+2} are lavender; V^{+3}, green; V^{+4}, blue; and V^{+5}, orange.

Vanadium (V) oxide, V_2O_5, is the most important of the vanadium compounds. It is used as a catalyst in a variety of industrial processes, including the "contact process" for making sulfuric acid.

40.16 Niobium (Columbium) and Tantalum

The principal mineral of niobium is **columbite,** $Fe(NbO_3)_2$, which usually occurs associated with the tantalum mineral known as **tantalite,** $Fe(TaO_3)_2$. The world's supply of these minerals comes from Australia, Africa, the United States, and Brazil. Fusion of the mixture of pulverized columbite and tantalite with potassium fluoride, followed by extraction of the melt with water, gives a solution containing complex fluorides of niobium and tantalum. Potassium fluotantalate, K_2TaF_7, forms crystals which are less soluble than those of the niobium salt, K_2NbOF_5, thus permitting the two compounds to be separated by fractional crystallization. The metals are obtained by the electrolysis of the fused complex fluorides.

Stainless steel containing a fraction of a per cent of niobium resists corrosion at high temperatures, making it possible for the steel to be welded. Other niobium alloys are used in the manufacture of motors for jet-propelled airplanes and in exhaust systems of conventional airplane engines. Tantalum has the same effect upon steel as niobium, particularly to make a product which is less subject to corrosion. Tantalum alloys are used for making rust-proof tools and dental and surgical instruments which are so corrosion resistant that they can be sterilized in a flame without dulling their cutting edges. Tantalum is also used in making laboratory utensils, electrodes, standard weights, spinnerets in rayon manufacture, and as a gas remover or "getter" in vacuum tubes. Tantalum forms an extremely hard carbide which is employed as an abrasive and as a cutting tool for machining steel.

Niobium and tantalum in most of their compounds have an oxidation state of +5. In fact, only a few compounds appear to exist in which they show a lower oxidation state. The pentoxides, Nb_2O_5 and Ta_2O_5, are formed by heating the corresponding acids or by burning the metals in air. The acids may be formulated as $HNbO_3$ and $HTaO_3$, although their composition is variable and hence they may be considered as hydrous oxides. Salts of these acids are known. Examples are $NaNbO_3$, $Fe(NbO_3)_2$, $NaTaO_3$, and $Fe(TaO_3)_2$. The pentahalides of niobium and tantalum, NbX_5 and TaX_5, are formed by the direct union of the elements.

MOLYBDENUM AND TUNGSTEN — GROUP VIB

All the elements of Group VIB, chromium (Chapter 37), molybdenum, and tungsten, are not only well known in the free state and in the form of their compounds, but also have important industrial uses. These three transition elements are tough, heavy metals with very high melting points. Each has a maximum oxidation state of +6. They also exhibit a number of lower oxidation states.

40.17 Molybdenum

Molybdenite, MoS_2, is the most important ore of molybdenum. **Wulfenite,** $PbMoO_4$, and **molybdic ocher,** $Fe_4(MoO_4)_6 \cdot 15\ H_2O$, are other important sources of this metal. Extensive deposits of these ores occur in Colorado, California, Canada, Australia, and Norway.

Roasting of molybdenite ore, MoS_2, converts it to **molybdenum trioxide,** MoO_3, which is then extracted from the gangue with aqueous ammonia. The resulting solution is then evaporated until **ammonium molybdate,** $(NH_4)_2MoO_4$, crystallizes out. The oxide, obtained by heating the ammonium salt, is reduced with carbon, aluminum, or hydrogen to produce the metal. Molybdenum produced in this way is in the form of a gray powder, which is converted to the compact metal by the application of high pressure, followed by hammering at high temperatures in an atmosphere of hydrogen. Molybdenum is a silvery-white metal that is malleable and ductile when pure, but when it contains impurities such as carbon it becomes hard and brittle. It melts at 2610° and has a specific gravity of 9.0. Although it is relatively unreactive at ordinary temperatures, molybdenum combines readily with oxygen and other nonmetals when heated.

Metallic molybdenum is used in electric lamps as a support for tungsten filaments, for windings in electric resistance furnaces, as terminals for spark plugs, and in other high temperature electrical devices. Most of the molybdenum produced, however, goes into the manufacture of alloys. **Ferromolybdenum,** which is used in the steel industry, is the most important of its alloys. Molybdenum increases the hardness and strength of steel at high temperatures, and is used in making steel for high-speed machine tools. The high temperatures developed in the operation of high-speed machine tools would cause ordinary tools to lose their hardness.

A familiar compound of molybdenum is ammonium molybdate, which is used in the qualitative and quantitative analysis of the phosphates. In the presence of nitric acid, orthophosphates give with ammonium molybdate a canary yellow precipitate, the composition of which varies with the conditions under which it is formed, but is usually shown by the formula $(NH_4)_3PO_4 \cdot 12\ MoO_3 \cdot x\ H_2O$. The oxide, MoO_3, is used as a catalyst in the hydrogenation of coal and mineral oil. **Lead molybdate,** $PbMoO_4$, precipitated together with lead chromate and sulfate, produces the pigment "molybdate red." Other compounds of molybdenum are used in coloring fabrics and the glazes of porcelain and china.

40.18 Tungsten

This element takes its name from the mineral $CaWO_4$, now called "scheelite," but formerly known as "tungsten" from the Swedish for "heavy stone." The symbol W was obtained from the German name "Wolfram." Tungsten occurs chiefly as **wolframite,** $(Fe, Mn)WO_4$, and **scheelite.** Most of the world supply is found in China, Burma, Bolivia, Japan, and the United States.

The extraction of tungsten from its ores involves several steps. The ore is first fused with sodium carbonate, which gives **sodium tungstate,** Na_2WO_4, a soluble compound that can be extracted with water. When the solution of the tungstate is acidified, **tungstic acid,** H_2WO_4, is precipitated. Ignition of the acid yields the **trioxide,** WO_3, which is then purified by dissolution in aqueous ammonia and recrystallization as the ammonium salt. The purified trioxide is then obtained by ignition of the ammonium salt. The pure metal is finally produced by reducing the oxide by hydrogen in an electric furnace. The fine, gray powder thus formed is reheated in an atmosphere of hydrogen and pressed into bars of compact metal. Hammering and rolling of these bars, still at high temperature and in hydrogen, results in a product that is coherent and ductile. The metal in this form may be drawn into extremely fine wires.

Tungsten is one of the heaviest and hardest of metals, and its melting point (3380°) is the highest of that of any metal. It is used for filaments in electric lamps, contact points in spark plugs, and targets in X-ray tubes. Tungsten steel is noted for its retention of hardness even at red heat, making it useful in the production of cutting tools for high-speed machinery. **Tungsten carbide,** WC, is an extremely hard substance, which is used as an abrasive.

Tungsten forms compounds in which its oxidation states are +2, +3, +4, +5, and +6. The most important compounds are those in which its valence is 6, and in which it serves as an acid-forming element. One of the simple tungstates, Na_2WO_4, is used as a mordant in dyeing and as an agent for making fabrics nonflammable. Calcium and magnesium tungstates are fluorescent, a property which makes these salts valuable when used as coatings in fluorescent tubes.

THE LESS COMMON ELEMENTS OF GROUP VIIB

40.19 Technetium and Rhenium

Group VIIB of the Periodic Table contains three elements: manganese (Mn), technetium (Tc), and rhenium (Re). Manganese, of great commercial importance, was discussed in Chapter 37. However, technetium is known only in the form of radioactive isotopes, prepared in the cyclotron in very small amounts. Rhenium is fairly abundant, and its properties have been rather extensively investigated. It is an unreactive metal that does not resemble any other element very closely in its chemistry. It forms compounds in which all oxidation states from -1 to $+7$ are represented. Neither the metal nor its compounds have any important uses at present.

THE PLATINUM METALS — GROUP VIII

The six metals ruthenium, rhodium, palladium, osmium, iridium, and platinum, which comprise the second and third triads of Group VIII, are grouped together under the name "platinum metals." These are transition metals, each of which shows more than one oxidation state; ruthenium and osmium show a maximum oxidation state of $+8$. There is a close resemblance in properties throughout this group of elements. Some of the physical properties of these elements are given in Table 40·2.

TABLE 40·2 Some Physical Properties of the Platinum Metals

	Atomic Number	*Atomic Weight*	*Melting Point, °C*	*Density (g./cm.³) at 20°*	*Hardness Moh's Scale*
Ruthenium	44	101.07	2500	12.2	6.5
Rhodium	45	102.905	1960	12.5	5.2
Palladium	46	106.4	1550	12.0	4.8
Osmium	76	190.2	2700	22.48	7.0
Iridium	77	192.2	2443	22.42	6.5
Platinum	78	195.09	1769	21.45	4.3

40.20 History of the Platinum Metals

Platinum is the most important of this group of metals. It takes its name from the Spanish word "platina," which means "little silver." The early Spaniards found this white metal, resembling silver in appearance, in Mexico and South America. In 1819, platinum was discovered in the Ural Mountains of Russia, which for a long time was the most important producer of this metal.

The other platinum metals were unknown until the discovery of osmium, iridium, rhodium, and palladium in the period between 1802 and 1804. They were separated from the black residue which remains after the extraction of platinum from an ore. The remaining platinum metal was discovered by Klaus in 1844 and was called ruthenium after "Ruthenia," meaning Russia. Osmium, iridium, and rhodium were named after the Greek words characterizing their properties: osmium from "osme" (smell); iridium from "iris" (rainbow); and rhodium from "rhodon" (a rose).

40.21 Occurrence of the Platinum Metals

The platinum metals occur mainly in the native state, almost always associated with each other and mixed with other metals such as gold, silver, copper, nickel, and iron. The metals are usually found in the form of fine black grains in alluvial deposits of heavy sands. Platinum usually comprises about 75 per cent of the native metal ores. The principal producers of the platinum metals are Canada and Russia; Colombia, the United States, and several other localities produce smaller amounts.

40.22 Platinum

Platinum is a soft, white metal which is extremely malleable and ductile. It has a relatively low electrical conductivity and its coefficient of expansion is the lowest of all the metals. The latter property makes it easy to seal platinum into glass.

Platinum is one of the most permanent metals, and retains its silvery appearance even when heated in air. Pure platinum is not affected by any single acid, but it dissolves in aqua regia, and it is attacked by chlorine, fused hydroxides, peroxides, and nitrates. Because platinum readily forms alloys with many of the less active metals, easily reducible metal oxides should not be heated in platinum vessels.

Platinum and its alloys are used for the manufacture of many types of equipment for handling corrosive liquids and gases, such as reaction vessels, tubing, valves, laboratory ware, and rayon spinnerets. It is very useful as a catalyst for making sulfuric acid by the contact process (Section 23.6), for the oxidation of ammonia in the manufacture of nitric acid (Section 26.2), and in the hydrogenation of organic substances. Platinum is frequently employed as a catalyst when in the form of "platinum sponge" or "platinum black." Platinum sponge is a finely divided form of the metal which is made by strongly heating **ammonium hexachloroplatinate (IV),** $(NH_4)_2PtCl_6$. Platinum black is a fine powder produced by the reduction of platinum (IV) chloride by zinc.

Platinum is very useful in the electrical industry for the manufacture of electrodes, electrical contacts, thermocouples, and many electrical instruments. Because of its pleasing appearance and high degree of permanence, platinum is in great demand in the manufacture of jewelry. Considerable quantities of this metal are used also in the manufacture of dental alloys for use as bridges, bracings, inlays, and orthodontic appliances.

Although platinum does not combine directly with many elements, numerous compounds have been prepared by indirect methods. When platinum dissolves in aqua regia, **hexachloroplatinic acid,** H_2PtCl_6, is formed. Evaporation of the solution yields crystals of $H_2PtCl_6 \cdot 6\,H_2O$, which forms strongly acidic solutions. The acid is used to precipitate **potassium hexachloroplatinate (IV),** K_2PtCl_6, as yellow crystals from solutions of soluble potassium salts. This reaction is used in the estimation of both potassium and platinum. The chloroplatinates of the other alkali metals and ammonium can also be formed in this way.

Platinum (IV) chloride, $PtCl_4$, is obtained as a red compound by heating the chloroplatinic acid to a temperature of 165° in an atmosphere of hydrogen chloride. The **brown dichloride,** $PtCl_2$, is produced when platinum (IV) chloride is heated to 580° in chlorine.

Other compounds of platinum include **platinum (II) oxide,** PtO, and the corresponding **hydroxide,** $Pt(OH)_2 \cdot 2\,H_2O$; **platinum (IV) oxide,** PtO_2, and the corresponding **hydroxide,** $Pt(OH)_4 \cdot 2\,H_2O$ or $H_2Pt(OH)_6$; and many complex compounds such as $[Pt(NH_3)_4]Cl_2$ and $Ba[Pt(CN)_4] \cdot 4\,H_2O$. The latter compound is a yellow fluorescent powder used in the manufacture of X-ray screens.

40.23 Ruthenium and Osmium

These are gray metals somewhat resembling iron in appearance. Osmium is the heaviest substance known (sp. gr., 22.48). These metals form tetraoxides, RuO_4 and OsO_4, which are solids with low melting and boiling points, and in which they show an oxidation state of +8. The vapors of these oxides are poisonous and very irritating, especially that of OsO_4, which has an odor similar to that of chlorine. **Osmium tetraoxide,** incorrectly called "osmic acid," is used in histology to stain tissues through its reduction to the metal by organic matter. It also has the property of hardening tissue without distorting it. Ruthenium is used, with platinum, in dental alloys and jewelry.

40.24 Rhodium and Iridium

These metals are very hard and extremely unreactive, not being attacked by aqua regia. Iridium is alloyed with platinum to produce very hard and permanent alloys, which are used for the tips of pen-points, surgical tools, electrical equipment, and chemical utensils. The international standard kilogram and standard meter are made of a platinum-iridium alloy (10.1% iridium) because of the permanence and low coefficient of thermal expansion of this alloy. Rhodium is sometimes alloyed with platinum to harden the latter and to reduce its volatility. It is also very useful in making reflectors.

40.25 Palladium

Palladium resembles platinum in appearance, but it is somewhat harder, less ductile, and less malleable than platinum. Like platinum, it forms two important series of compounds in which it shows oxidation states of +2 and +4. These compounds are very similar in properties to the corresponding platinum compounds.

The most characteristic property of palladium metal is its ability to adsorb hydrogen selectively. In the colloidal condition it adsorbs 3000 times its own volume of hydrogen. Because of its ability to adsorb and activate hydrogen and certain other gases, palladium is used as a catalyst in a number of industrial processes, particularly those involving reactions of hydrogen.

Palladium is also used, when alloyed with platinum and gold, in jewelry, dentistry, and laboratory ware.

QUESTIONS

1. Account for the variable oxidation state of gold in terms of the electronic structure of its atoms.
2. Would you expect salts of the gold (I), Au^+, ion to be colored? Explain.
3. Write balanced equations for the following changes: $Au \rightarrow [Au(CN)_2]^- \rightarrow Au$.
4. Show several ways in which coordination compounds play an important part in the chemistry of gold.
5. List the alkaline earth metals in order of increasing basicity of their hydroxides; increasing solubility of their sulfates.
6. Why is beryllium classed as a "bridge element"?
7. Why is radium found associated with uranium ores?
8. Name two uranium ores from which radium is obtained. What factors combine to make radium one of the most costly substances known?
9. From the electronic structure of thallium, what would you predict concerning the solubility of thallium (I) chloride? the basicity of thallium (I) hydroxide?
10. Why are the rare earths associated in their natural occurrence?
11. Point out the analogy in structure between the elements of the rare earths and those of the actinide series.
12. Write the electronic structures you would expect elements 104, 105, 106, 107, and 108 to have if and when they are synthesized.
13. List five properties of germanium and its compounds that were predicted by Mendeleev.
14. Why is titanium difficult to obtain in the pure state?
15. What chemistry is involved in skywriting using titanium tetrachloride?
16. What properties make zirconia effective as a refractory?
17. Represent the electronic structure of the vanadium atom using subshell notation and account for its various oxidation states (+2, +3, +4, and +5) in terms of its valence electrons.
18. What special properties are given to alloy steels by vanadium? tantalum? molybdenum? tungsten?
19. What precautions should be exercised in the use of platinum ware for chemical reactions?

REFERENCES

"The Gold Content of the Sea," G. L. Putnam, *J. Chem. Educ.*, **30** (11) 576 (1953).

"Beryllium and Berylliosis," J. Schubert, *Sci. American*, Aug., 1958; p. 27.

"Gallium," G. H. Wagner and W. H. Gitzen, *J. Chem. Educ.*, **29** (4) 162 (1952).
"The Rare Earths," F. H. Spedding, *Sci. American*, Nov., 1951; p. 26.
"Carl Auer von Welsbach," (History of the rare earths), F. Lieber, *J. Chem. Educ.*, **35** (5) 230 (1958).
The Chemistry of Uranium, J. Katz and E. Rabinowitch, McGraw-Hill Book Co., Inc., New York, 1951. (Reprinted, paperbound, by Dover Publications, New York).
"Development of Uranium Metal Production in America," H. A. Wilhelm, *J. Chem. Educ.*, **37** (2) 56 (1960).
"Titanium," G. A. W. Boehm, *Sci. American*, April, 1949; p. 48.
"Titanium Expected to Grow Faster Than Any Other Metal," (Staff) *Chem. Eng. News*, **29** (48) 5047 (1951).
"Chemicals in the Manufacture of Paint," W. C. Weber, *J. Chem. Educ.*, **37** (6) 323 (1960).
"Titanium: Where It Stands," (Staff) *Chem. Eng.*, April 16, 1962; p. 194.
"Behind Titanium Dioxide Buildup," (Staff) *Chem. Week*, April 28, 1962; p. 87.
"Vanadium," H. A. Knight, *Mat. and Meth.*, **24** (1) 5 (July, 1946).
"The Story of Tantalum," C. W. Balke, *Chem. and Ind.*, **1948,** 83 (Feb. 7).
"Tungsten and Tantalum," J. A. Lee, *Chem. Eng.*, Sept., 1948; p. 110.
"The Platinum Group Metals," J. Cochrane, *J. Chem. Educ.*, **31** (8) 407 (1954).
"The Platinum Metals," *Discovery of the Elements*, M. E. Weeks, Publ. by the Journal of Chemical Education, Easton, Pa., 1956; Chapter 16 (pp. 407–453).
"Richard Chenevix (1774–1839) and the Discovery of Palladium," D. Reilley, *J. Chem. Educ.*, **32** (1) 37 (1955).
"Zirconium Chemistry in Industry," W. B. Blumenthal, *J. Chem. Educ.*, **39** (12) 604 (1962).

PART 3

Ionic Equilibria

CHAPTER FORTY-ONE

Ionic Equilibria Involving Weak Electrolytes

We saw in Section 12.3 that aqueous solutions of electrolytes contain ions, and that strong electrolytes are virtually completely ionic in solution. The strong electrolytes include strong inorganic acids such as HCl, HBr, HI, HNO_3, and $HClO_4$, the hydroxides of the alkali metals and the alkaline earth metals, and salts. In solutions of weak electrolytes, ions and un-ionized molecules of the electrolyte are both present. The weak electrolytes include some inorganic acids such as H_3PO_4, H_2SO_3, HCN, HF, and H_2CO_3, most organic acids, some inorganic hydroxides such as ammonium hydroxide (aqueous ammonia) and most divalent and trivalent hydroxides, and most of the organic bases. The polar covalent halides and cyanides of Hg, Cd, Zn, and a few other metals are also classed as weak electrolytes.

From the viewpoint of chemical equilibrium the weak electrolytes are of great importance, and in this chapter we shall deal extensively with equilibria involving this class of compounds. The weak acids are the most important of all the weak electrolytes, not only in the interpretation of the many processes and reactions of a purely chemical nature including those of qualitative analysis, but also those in living systems involving the blood, the tissue and cell materials, and the glandular secretions.

41.1 Ionic Concentrations in Solutions of Strong Electrolytes

Because strong electrolytes are completely in the ionic condition in aqueous solution, the ion concentrations may be found directly from the molar concentration of the solution. For example, in a 0.01 M solution of hydrochloric acid ($HCl \rightarrow H^+ + Cl^-$), the hydrogen ion concentration $[H^+]$ is equal to the chloride concentration $[Cl^-]$, and both concentrations have the value 0.01 M, or 1×10^{-2} M. On the other hand, in a 0.01 M solution of potassium sulfate ($K_2SO_4 \rightarrow 2\ K^+ + SO_4^=$), the potassium ion concentration $[K^+]$ is 2×0.01 M, or 2×10^{-2} M, whereas the sulfate ion concentration $[SO_4^=]$ is 0.01 M, or 1×10^{-2} M. This follows because each formula unit of potassium sulfate yields two potassium ions but only one sulfate ion. In a 0.001 M silver sulfate solution ($Ag_2SO_4 \rightarrow 2Ag^+ + SO_4^=$), the silver ion concentration $[Ag^+]$ is 2×10^{-3} M and the sulfate ion concentration $[SO_4^=]$ is 1×10^{-3} M. This is due to the fact that crystals (and solutions) of silver sulfate contain twice as many silver ions as sulfate ions.

41.2 Ionic Concentrations in Solutions of Weak Acids

In aqueous solution a weak acid, such as acetic acid (HOAc), is only partly ionized into hydrogen ions and acid anions, and the remaining portion of the acid is present in solution in the un-ionized or molecular form. For acetic acid, the ionization equation is

$$\text{HOAc} \rightleftharpoons \text{H}^+ + \text{OAc}^- \text{ (where OAc}^- \text{ is the acetate ion)}$$

This ionization reaction is reversible and equilibrium is attained almost instantly after the acetic acid is dissolved in the water. Therefore, in any dilute solution of acetic acid the law of chemical equilibrium (Section 16.7) may be applied.

$$\frac{[\text{H}^+][\text{OAc}^-]}{[\text{HOAc}]} = \text{K}_\text{i}$$

For this particular kind of equilibrium the constant K_i is called an **ionization constant.** Concentrations of ions and molecules in the mathematical expression must always be given in moles per liter. The data in Table 41·1 show that K_i remains

TABLE 41·1

Molarity	*Per Cent Ionized*	*[H⁺] and [OAc⁻]*	*[HOAc]*	*K_i*
0.1	1.34	0.00134	0.09866	1.82×10^{-5}
0.08	1.50	0.0012	0.0788	1.83×10^{-5}
0.03	2.45	0.000735	0.02927	1.85×10^{-5}
0.01	4.15	0.000415	0.009585	1.797×10^{-5}

practically the same over a considerable range of concentrations. Note that the extent to which acetic acid ionizes increases with decreasing concentration. For example, 0.1 M acetic is 1.34 per cent ionized (98.66 per cent is in the molecular form), while the 0.01 M acid is 4.15 per cent ionized (95.85 per cent is in the molecular form). This results from the fact that an increase in the amount of water used in dissolving a given quantity of the acid causes the following equilibrium to shift to the right:

$$\text{HOAc} + \text{H}_2\text{O} \rightleftharpoons \text{H}_3\text{O}^+ + \text{OAc}^-$$

We may ask why the water in the above equation may be omitted from the expression for the ionization constant. This is because the number of moles of water consumed in the formation of hydronium ions is negligibly small compared with the total number of moles of water present in dilute solution. Under such conditions it may be assumed that the molar concentration of the water remains unchanged during the ionization of the acetic acid.

The ionization constants of a number of weak acids are given in Table 41·2, and a more complete list is given in Appendix I.

TABLE 41·2 Ionization Constants of Some Weak Acids

Acid		*Ionization*	K_i *at 25°*
HCN	$\rightleftharpoons$	$H^+ + CN^-$	4×10^{-10}
HBrO	$\rightleftharpoons$	$H^+ + BrO^-$	2×10^{-9}
HClO	$\rightleftharpoons$	$H^+ + ClO^-$	3.5×10^{-8}
HOAc	$\rightleftharpoons$	$H^+ + OAc^-$	1.8×10^{-5}
HCNS	$\rightleftharpoons$	$H^+ + CNS^-$	1×10^{-4}
HCNO	$\rightleftharpoons$	$H^+ + CNO^-$	1.2×10^{-4}
HCOOH	$\rightleftharpoons$	$H^+ + HCOO^-$	1.8×10^{-4}
HNO_2	$\rightleftharpoons$	$H^+ + NO_2^-$	4.5×10^{-4}
HF	$\rightleftharpoons$	$H^+ + F^-$	7.2×10^{-4}

The acids in this table are listed in order of increasing strength as indicated by the increasing size of the ionization constant. As the size of the constant increases, the fraction of the acid in the ionized form increases; thus HF with its constant of 7.2×10^{-4} is a much stronger acid than HCN, which has a K_i of 4×10^{-10}.

41.3 The Solution of Problems Involving the Ionization of Acetic Acid

The following types of problems, all based upon the partial ionization of weak electrolytes, are important to the understanding of the reactions of qualitative analysis and chemical reactions in general.

EXAMPLE 1. In 0.100 M solution, acetic acid is 1.34 per cent ionized. Calculate $[H^+]$, $[OAc^-]$, and $[HOAc]$ in the solution.

First write the equation for the ionization of acetic acid.

$$HOAc \rightleftharpoons H^+ + OAc^-$$

The equation shows that for each mole of HOAc that ionizes, one mole of H^+ and one mole of OAc^- are formed. Since 1.34 per cent of 0.100 mole per liter of acid ionizes, then

$$[H^+] = [OAc^-] = 0.100 \text{ M} \times 0.0134 = 0.00134 \text{ M}$$

and

$$[HOAc] = (0.100 \text{ M} - 0.00134 \text{ M}) = 0.099 \text{ M}$$

EXAMPLE 2. Using the concentrations found in Example 1, calculate the ionization constant of acetic acid.

Write down the expression for the ionization constant of acetic acid, substitute in it the values found above, and solve for K_i.

$$\frac{[H^+][OAc^-]}{[HOAc]} = \frac{(0.00134) \times (0.00134)}{0.099} = 1.8 \times 10^{-5} = K_i$$

EXAMPLE 3. Taking the K_i for acetic acid to be 1.8×10^{-5} at 25° C, calculate the $[H^+]$ and the per cent ionization in a 0.010 M solution of the acid.

In a 0.010 molar solution of acetic acid the total amount of acetic acid, i.e., the ionized plus the un-ionized, contained in one liter of solution is 0.010 mole. If we let X be the concentration of hydrogen ion $[H^+]$, then the concentration of acetate ion $[OAc^-]$ is also X, and the concentration of un-ionized acid [HOAc] is (0.010 − X). Then,

$$\frac{[H^+][OAc^-]}{[HOAc]} = \frac{X^2}{0.010 - X} = 1.8 \times 10^{-5} = K_i$$

The small value of K_i indicates that the ratio $X^2/(0.010 - X)$ is small and that X will be small compared to 0.010 from which it is to be subtracted. Thus 0.010 − X is virtually equal to 0.010, and the foregoing expression may be simplified for an approximate solution as follows:

$$\frac{X^2}{0.010} = 1.8 \times 10^{-5}$$

$$X^2 = 1.8 \times 10^{-7} = 18.0 \times 10^{-8}$$

$$X = \sqrt{18.0 \times 10^{-8}} = 4.3 \times 10^{-4} \text{ mole per liter}$$

The concentration of H^+ and OAc^- is thus calculated to be 4.3×10^{-4} molar. It can readily be seen that we were justified in neglecting X in the expression (0.010 − X) since (0.010 − .00043) = 0.00957, which is very nearly equal to 0.010. One may use the approximate solution when X is less than about 5 per cent of the total concentration of the acid; if X is greater than 5 per cent, then the quadratic equation should be solved (see Appendix A.4 for the solution of quadratic equations).

Calculation of the per cent of ionization in the 0.010 M solution of acetic acid is made by dividing the concentration of the acid in the ionic form, which is equal to the $[H^+]$, by the total concentration of the acid, and then multiplying by 100. Thus, we have

$$\frac{\text{Ionic HOAc}}{\text{Total HOAc}} \times 100 = \frac{4.3 \times 10^{-4}}{0.010} \times 100 = 4.3 \text{ per cent ionized}$$

41.4 The Ionization of Weak Bases

Equilibria involving the ionization of weak bases may be treated in the same manner as those of weak acids. The most common weak base is aqueous ammonia (ammonium hydroxide). When ammonia gas is dissolved in water, the solution is distinctly basic, and the reaction is given by the equation

$$NH_3 + H_2O \rightleftharpoons NH_4^+ + OH^-$$

Application of the law of chemical equilibrium to this system gives the expression

$$\frac{[NH_4^+][OH^-]}{[NH_3][H_2O]} = K_e$$

Because only a small fraction of the water is consumed in the reaction, the concentration of water is practically constant and the above equation may be written

$$\frac{[NH_4^+][OH^-]}{[NH_3]} = K_e[H_2O] = 1.8 \times 10^{-5}$$

Aqueous ammonia as a base has about the same strength that acetic acid has as an acid; the ionization constants for the two substances are very nearly the same. The ionization constants of several bases are given in Table 41·3.

TABLE 41·3 Ionization Constants of Some Weak Bases

Base		*Ionization*	K_i *at 25°*
$NH_3 + H_2O$ ammonia	$\rightleftharpoons$	$NH_4^+ + OH^-$	1.8×10^{-5}
$CH_3NH_2 + H_2O$ methylamine	$\rightleftharpoons$	$CH_3NH_3^+ + OH^-$	5×10^{-4}
$(CH_3)_2NH + H_2O$ dimethylamine	$\rightleftharpoons$	$(CH_3)_2NH_2^+ + OH^-$	7.4×10^{-4}
$(CH_3)_3N + H_2O$ trimethylamine	$\rightleftharpoons$	$(CH_3)_3NH^+ + OH^-$	7.4×10^{-5}
$C_6H_5NH_2 + H_2O$ phenylamine (aniline)	$\rightleftharpoons$	$C_6H_5NH_3^+ + OH^-$	4.6×10^{-10}

It should be emphasized that the law of chemical equilibrium does not apply to aqueous solutions of strong acids such as HCl and HNO_3 and strong bases such as NaOH and KOH, for these are completely ionic in dilute solution; there are no equilibria.

41.5 Salt Effect on Ionization

The expression for the ionization constant holds for dilute solutions of weak electrolytes when the solutions are pure. However, the extent of ionization of a weak electrolyte may be influenced by the presence of other ions in the solution. For example, the ionization constant of acetic acid is increased from 1.8×10^{-5} to 2.2×10^{-5} when the solution is made 0.1 M with respect to sodium chloride. This means that the addition of a salt has slightly increased the degree of ionization of the weak acid, and this effect is known as the **salt effect.** This effect is due to the fact that the presence of the ions of a strong electrolyte reduces the activity of the ions (Section 12.11) in a solution of a weak electrolyte as a result of interionic attraction. The ionization constant is, therefore, not strictly constant, but varies slightly with the ionic strength of the solution. For our purposes, the expression for the ionization constant may be used without regard to slight errors which may arise due to the salt effect.

41.6 Common Ion Effect on Degree of Ionization

It has been found by experiment that the acidity of a solution of acetic acid is decreased by the addition of sodium acetate. This can be explained by the fact that, according to the law of mass action (Section 16.6), the addition of acetate ions to a solution of acetic acid causes the following equilibrium to shift to the left.

$$\mathrm{HOAc} \rightleftharpoons \mathrm{H^+} + \mathrm{OAc^-}$$

This decreases the $[H^+]$ and the extent of ionization of the acid. The NaOAc has the acetate ion in common with HOAc, so the influence is known as the **common ion effect.** Since the equilibrium was disturbed by the increase in the concentration of OAc^-, a shift in the equilibrium will occur which will reduce the concentration of OAc^-. This is accomplished by the union of H^+ with OAc^- to form molecular acetic acid. Consequently, the $[H^+]$ of the solution is reduced.

The extent to which the concentration of the hydrogen ion is decreased by the addition of the acetate ion may be calculated from the expression for the ionization constant of acetic acid.

EXAMPLE 1. Let us calculate the $[H^+]$ in a 0.10 M solution of HOAc which is 0.50 M with respect to NaOAc. At equilibrium the concentration of the acetate ion is equal to the concentration of NaOAc, which is completely dissociated into Na^+ and OAc^-, plus the concentration of the acetate ion derived from the ionization of acetic acid. Let X equal the concentration of acetate ions derived from the ionization of acetic acid. Then (0.50 M + X) will equal the total concentration of the acetate ion. The concentration of the hydrogen ions will be equal to X and the concentration of un-ionized acetic acid will be equal to (0.10 M − X). Substituting in the expression for the ionization constant for acetic acid we have

$$\frac{[\mathrm{H^+}][\mathrm{OAc^-}]}{[\mathrm{HOAc}]} = \frac{X(0.50 + X)}{0.10 - X} = 1.8 \times 10^{-5}$$

Even in the absence of NaOAc the concentration of the acetate ion derived from the ionization of 0.10 M acetic acid is small (0.00134 mole per liter) compared to 0.50 mole per liter derived from NaOAc. Since the degree of ionization is even smaller in the presence of the high concentration of sodium acetate, it follows that the concentration of acetate ion may be taken as equal to the concentration of the sodium acetate, or that X may be neglected in the term (0.50 + X). Likewise, the concentration of the un-ionized acetic acid is very nearly equal to 0.10 M, and X in the term (0.10 − X) may be dropped. Thus, in an approximate solution to the problem we have

$$\frac{[\mathrm{H^+}][\mathrm{OAc^-}]}{[\mathrm{HOAc}]} = \frac{(0.50)X}{0.10} = 1.8 \times 10^{-5}$$

$$X = \frac{0.10}{0.50} \times 1.8 \times 10^{-5} = 3.6 \times 10^{-6}\ \mathrm{M} = [\mathrm{H^+}]$$

Consequently, the concentration of the hydrogen ion is reduced from 0.00134 mole per liter to 0.0000036 mole per liter by the presence of the 0.50 M sodium acetate in the 0.10 M acetic acid solution.

EXAMPLE 2. A 0.10 M solution of aqueous ammonia, also containing ammonium chloride, has a hydroxide ion concentration of 2.8×10^{-6} M. What is the concentration of the ammonium ion in the solution? First write the equation for the ionization of ammonia.

$$NH_3 + H_2O \rightleftharpoons NH_4^+ + OH^-$$

The ammonium ion of the ammonium chloride present in the solution causes the ionization of ammonia to be decreased (the equilibrium to be shifted to the left) because of the common ion effect. Let X be the total ammonium ion concentration at equilibrium; this value will be the sum of the ammonium ion concentration resulting from the slight ionization of ammonia and that from the ammonium chloride. The hydroxide ion concentration is given as 2.8×10^{-6} M, and the concentration of ammonia will be $(0.10 - 2.8 \times 10^{-6})$ M, which is very nearly 0.10 M. Substituting in the expression for the ionization constant of ammonia, we have

$$\frac{[NH_4^+][OH^-]}{[NH_3]} = \frac{X(2.8 \times 10^{-6})}{0.10} = 1.8 \times 10^{-5}$$

Solving for X, we find

$$X = \frac{(0.10)(1.8 \times 10^{-5})}{2.8 \times 10^{-6}} = \frac{1.8}{2.8} = 0.64$$

Thus, we find the concentration of the ammonium ion to be 0.64 M at equilibrium. Of this amount, 2.8×10^{-6} mole is formed by the ionization of ammonia and the remainder comes from the added ammonium chloride.

EXAMPLE 3. Ten ml. of 4.0 M acetic acid is added to 20 ml. of 1.0 M sodium hydroxide. Calculate the hydrogen ion concentration of the resulting solution. Before mixing, the 10 ml. of 4.0 M HOAc contains 10 ml. $\times$ 4.0 M = 40 millimoles of HOAc, and the 20 ml. of 1.0 M NaOH contains 20 ml. $\times$ 1.0 M = 20 millimoles of NaOH. The 20 millimoles of NaOH neutralize 20 millimoles of HOAc, producing 20 millimoles of NaOAc and leaving 40 − 20 = 20 millimoles of HOAc not neutralized. After reaction, the 20 millimoles of NaOAc and 20 millimoles of HOAc are contained in (10 + 20) ml. = 30 ml. of solution, so the concentrations are 20 millimoles/30 ml. = 0.67 M and 20 millimoles/30 ml. = 0.67 M, respectively.

The sodium acetate in the solution exhibits the common ion effect upon the ionization of the acetic acid. Let X equal the concentration of the hydrogen ion. Then the concentration of the molecular acetic acid will be (0.67 − X) M and that of the acetate ion will be (0.67 + X) M. Neglecting the X's in the terms (0.67 − X) and (0.67 + X) and substituting in the expression for the ionization constant of acetic acid, we have

$$\frac{[H^+][OAc^-]}{[HOAc]} = \frac{X(0.67)}{(0.67)} = 1.8 \times 10^{-5}$$

$$X = \frac{(0.67)}{(0.67)} \times 1.8 \times 10^{-5} = 1.8 \times 10^{-5} \text{ M}$$

Thus the concentration of the hydrogen ion in the solution is 1.8×10^{-5} M.

The common ion effect is of importance in the adjustment of the hydrogen ion concentration for many of the precipitations and separations in the qualitative analysis scheme and in other chemical processes.

41.7 The Ionization of Water

Water is an extremely weak electrolyte which undergoes self-ionization according to the equation

$$H_2O + H_2O \rightleftharpoons H_3O^+ + OH^-$$

or simply

$$H_2O \rightleftharpoons H^+ + OH^-$$

Application of the law of chemical equilibrium yields the following expression:

$$\frac{[H^+][OH^-]}{[H_2O]} = K_e$$

As long as we work with dilute aqueous solutions, the concentration of water may be considered as constant. We may therefore write

$$[H^+][OH^-] = K_e[H_2O] = K_w$$

In all problems of acidity and basicity or aqueous solutions of electrolytes, K_w is a constant of great importance. It is called the **ion-product constant of water,** and at 25° it has the value 1×10^{-14}. The value of K_w increases rapidly with the temperature and at 100° is approximately 1×10^{-12}, thus being 100 times as large at 100° as at 25°. This means simply that the degree of ionization of water and the concentration of the hydrogen and hydroxide ions increase with rising temperature.

The ionization of water yields the same number of hydrogen and hydroxide ions. Therefore in pure water at 25° it is found that $[H^+] = [OH^-]$, and

$$[H^+]^2 = [OH^-]^2 = 10^{-14}$$

$$[H^+] = [OH^-] = \sqrt{10^{-14}} = 10^{-7}\text{ M}$$

All aqueous solutions contain both hydrogen ions and hydroxide ions. If by the addition of hydrogen ions (as an acid) the $[H^+]$ is made larger than 10^{-7}, then the $[OH^-]$ will become smaller than 10^{-7}; in basic solutions the $[OH^-]$ will be greater than 10^{-7} and the $[H^+]$ will be less than 10^{-7}. The product of the $[H^+]$ and $[OH^-]$ always remains constant. For example, what is the $[H^+]$ of 0.01 M NaOH?

$$[H^+][OH^-] = K_w$$

$$[H^+](10^{-2}) = 10^{-14}$$

$$[H^+] = \frac{10^{-14}}{10^{-2}} = 10^{-12}\text{ M}$$

In a 0.001 M solution of hydrochloric acid, the concentration of hydroxide ion is

$$[H^+][OH^-] = (10^{-3})[OH^-] = 10^{-14}$$

$$[OH^-] = \frac{10^{-14}}{10^{-3}} = 10^{-11}\text{ M}$$

41.8 The pH Method of Expressing the Concentration of the Hydrogen Ion

The concentration of the hydrogen ion is a measure of the acidity or basicity of a solution. It has been found convenient to express the concentration of the hydrogen ion in terms of the negative logarithm of the hydrogen ion concentration. This is called the pH of the solution. Expressed mathematically, we have

$$pH = -\log [H^+]$$

or

$$pH = \log \frac{1}{[H^+]}$$

The pH value is the negative power to which 10 must be raised to equal the hydrogen ion concentration.

$$[H^+] = 10^{-pH}$$

The following problems will serve to illustrate the calculation of pH values from hydrogen or hydroxide ion concentrations:

EXAMPLE 1. Calculate the pH of 0.01 M HCl. Hydrochloric acid is completely ionized in dilute solution so the concentration of the hydrogen ion is 0.01 M, or 10^{-2} M. Substituting, we have

$$pH = -\log [H^+] = -\log 10^{-2} = -(-2) = 2$$

(The use of logarithms is explained in Appendix A.3.)

EXAMPLE 2. Calculate the pH of 0.0050 M HNO_3. The hydrogen ion concentration of nitric acid is the same as the molar concentration of the acid, for it is a strong electrolyte. Thus, we have

$$\begin{aligned} pH &= -\log (5.0 \times 10^{-3}) = -(\log 5.0 + \log 10^{-3}) = -(0.7 - 3.0) \\ &= -(-2.3) = 2.3 \end{aligned}$$

EXAMPLE 3. Calculate the pH of 0.0001 M NaOH. Because pH is defined in terms of hydrogen ion concentration, it is first necessary to find the concentration of this ion by substituting in the ion-product expression for water. The $[OH^-]$ from the sodium hydroxide is given as 10^{-4} M.

$$[H^+][OH^-] = K_w$$

$$[H^+](10^{-4}) = 10^{-14}$$

$$[H^+] = \frac{10^{-14}}{10^{-4}} = 10^{-10}$$

The hydrogen ion concentration thus found is then converted to pH as follows:

$$pH = -\log [H^+] = -\log 10^{-10} = -(-10) = 10$$

EXAMPLE 4. Water in equilibrium with the air contains 0.030 volume per cent of carbon dioxide. The resulting carbonic acid, H_2CO_3, gives to the solution a hydrogen ion concentration about twenty times larger than that of pure water, or 2.0×10^{-6} as compared to 1.0×10^{-7}. The pH of the solution is calculated as follows:

$$\begin{aligned} pH &= -\log [H^+] = -\log (2.0 \times 10^{-6}) = -(\log 2.0 + \log 10^{-6}) \\ &= -(0.3 - 6.0) = -(-5.7) = 5.7 \end{aligned}$$

Thus we see that water in contact with air is acidic, rather than neutral, due to dissolved carbon dioxide.

EXAMPLE 5. Calculate the pH of 0.100 M HOAc, which is 1.34 per cent ionized. The hydrogen ion concentration of this weak acid is 0.100 M × 0.0134 = 0.00134 M = 1.34×10^{-3} M.

$$\begin{aligned} pH &= -\log [H^+] = -\log (1.34 \times 10^{-3}) = -(\log 1.34 + \log 10^{-3}) \\ &= -(0.13 - 3.00) = -(-2.87) = 2.87 \end{aligned}$$

The following problems illustrate the conversion of pH values to hydrogen ion concentrations.

EXAMPLE 1. Calculate the hydrogen ion concentration of a solution the pH of which is 9.

$$\begin{aligned} pH = -\log [H^+] &= 9 \\ \log [H^+] &= -9 \\ [H^+] &= \text{antilog of } (-9) = 10^{-9} \end{aligned}$$

EXAMPLE 2. Calculate the hydrogen ion concentration of a solution whose pH is 4.4.

$$\begin{aligned} pH = -\log [H^+] &= 4.4 \\ \log [H^+] &= -4.4 \end{aligned}$$

It is readily seen that −4.4 is equal to (−5 + 0.6). Then we may write

$$\begin{aligned} \log [H^+] &= 0.6 - 5 \\ [H^+] &= \text{antilog of } (0.6 - 5) \\ [H^+] &= (\text{antilog of } 0.6) \times (\text{antilog of } -5) \\ [H^+] &= 4.0 \times 10^{-5}\ M \end{aligned}$$

41.9 The pOH Method of Expressing the Concentration of the Hydroxide Ion

We may define pOH as the negative logarithm of the hydroxide ion concentration (pOH = − log [OH⁻]). Similarly, we may define pK_w as the negative logarithm of the ion-product constant (K_w) for water. Now we can write the ion-product expression for water in terms of pH, pOH, and pK_w.

$$\begin{aligned} [H^+][OH^-] &= K_w \\ (-\log [H^+]) + (-\log [OH^-]) &= -\log K_w \\ pH + pOH &= pK_w \end{aligned}$$

Because K_w has the value 10^{-14}, then

$$pK_w = -\log 10^{-14} = -(-14) = 14$$

It follows that

$$\begin{aligned} pH + pOH &= 14 \\ pH &= 14 - pOH \\ pOH &= 14 - pH \end{aligned}$$

The relationship between the hydrogen ion and hydroxide ion concentration, and the pH and pOH of certain aqueous solutions is given in Table 41·4.

TABLE 41·4 Relation of $[H^+]$, $[OH^-]$, pH, and pOH

$[H^+]$	$[OH^-]$	pH	pOH	Solution
10^1	10^{-15}	−1	15	strongly acidic
10^0 or 1	10^{-14}	0	14	
10^{-1}	10^{-13}	1	13	
10^{-2}	10^{-12}	2	12	
10^{-3}	10^{-11}	3	11	
10^{-4}	10^{-10}	4	10	
10^{-5}	10^{-9}	5	9	
10^{-6}	10^{-8}	6	8	
10^{-7}	10^{-7}	7	7	neutral
10^{-8}	10^{-6}	8	6	
10^{-9}	10^{-5}	9	5	
10^{-10}	10^{-4}	10	4	
10^{-11}	10^{-3}	11	3	
10^{-12}	10^{-2}	12	2	
10^{-13}	10^{-1}	13	1	strongly basic

41.10 Acid-Base Indicators

Certain organic substances have the property of changing color in dilute solution when the hydrogen ion concentration of the solution attains a definite value. For example, phenolphthalein is a colorless substance in any aqueous solution of which the hydrogen ion concentration is greater than 10^{-9} M, or the pH is less than 9. In solutions for which the hydrogen ion concentration is less than 10^{-9} the phenolphthalein imparts a red or pink color to the solution. Substances like phenolphthalein are called **acid-base indicators,** and they are often employed for the determination of the pH of solutions. Acid-base indicators are either weak organic acids, HIn, or weak organic bases, InOH, in which the symbol "In" represents a complex organic group.

The equilibrium existing in a solution of a certain acid-base indicator called methyl orange, which is a weak acid, may be represented by the following equation:

$$\underset{\text{Red}}{HIn} \rightleftharpoons H^+ + \underset{\text{Yellow}}{In^-}$$

The anion of the indicator is yellow, and the un-ionized form is red. An increase in the concentration of the hydrogen ion brought about by the addition of an acid to the solution shifts the equilibrium toward the red form in accordance with the law of mass action. Application of the law of chemical equilibrium to this reversible reaction gives the expression for the ionization constant of this acid.

$$\frac{[H^+][In^-]}{[HIn]} = K_i$$

The color exhibited by the indicator is determined by the ratio of the concentrations of the two species HIn and In^-. For methyl orange

$$\frac{[In^-]}{[HIn]} = \frac{[\text{Substance with yellow color}]}{[\text{Substance with red color}]} = \frac{K_i}{[H^+]}$$

When $[H^+]$ has the same numerical value as K_i, the ratio of $[In^-]$ to $[HIn]$ becomes equal to one, meaning that 50 per cent of the indicator is present in the acid (yellow form) and 50 per cent in the alkaline (red form). Under these conditions the solution appears orange in color. When the hydrogen ion concentration has been increased until the pH is 3.1, about 90 per cent of the indicator is present in the red form and 10 per cent is present in the yellow form. The eye cannot detect any change in color with further increase in the hydrogen ion concentration.

Addition of a base to the system reduces the concentration of hydrogen ions ($H^+ + OH^- \rightarrow H_2O$), and shifts the equilibrium to the yellow form. At a pH of 4.4 about 90 per cent of the indicator is in the form of the yellow ion and a further decrease in the hydrogen ion concentration does not produce a color change easily detected by the eye. The pH range between 3.1 (red) and 4.4 (yellow-orange) is called the color-change interval of the indicator. This means that the pronounced color change takes place between these two pH values.

A large number of acid-base indicators are known, covering a wide range of pH values. A number of indicators may be used in determining the pH of any solution, and by a process of elimination the pH of a solution can be fixed within rather narrow limits. Table 41·5 lists a series of indicators, together with their colors for the corresponding pH values.

The measurement and control of the hydrogen ion concentration are important in scientific investigations, in industry, and in agriculture. In analytical chemistry the separation and identification of many of the metallic ions depend upon the pH of the solutions containing these ions.

TABLE 41·5 Some Acid-Base Indicators

Indicator	*Color in the More Acid Range*	*pH Range*	*Color in the More Basic Range*
Methyl violet	yellow	0–2	violet
Thymol blue	pink	1.2–2.8	yellow
Brom-phenol blue	yellow	3.0–4.7	violet
Methyl orange	pink	3.1–4.4	yellow
Brom-cresol green	yellow	4.0–5.6	blue
Brom-cresol purple	yellow	5.2–6.8	purple
Litmus	red	4.7–8.2	blue
Phenolphthalein	colorless	8.3–10.0	pink
Thymolphthalein	colorless	9.3–10.5	blue
Alizarin yellow G	colorless	10.1–12.1	yellow
Trinitrobenzene	colorless	12.0–14.3	orange

41.11 Buffer Solutions

Mixtures of weak acids and their salts or of weak bases and their salts are called **buffer solutions.** They resist a change in hydrogen-ion concentration upon the addition of small amounts of acids or bases. An example of a buffer solution is a mixture of 0.10 M acetic acid and 0.10 M sodium acetate. The pH of the solution may be found as follows:

$$HOAc \rightleftharpoons H^+ + OAc^-$$

$$\frac{[H^+][OAc^-]}{[HOAc]} = K_i$$

$$[H^+] = \frac{[HOAc]}{[OAc^-]} K_i = \frac{0.10}{0.10} \times 1.8 \times 10^{-5} = 1.8 \times 10^{-5}$$

$$pH = -\log [H^+] = -\log (1.8 \times 10^{-5}) = 4.745$$

$$= 4.7 \text{ (to justifiable limit in significant figures)}$$

Now let an amount of base equivalent to 1.0 ml. of 0.10 M sodium hydroxide be added to 100 ml. of this buffer mixture. An equivalent amount of acetic acid is neutralized by the sodium hydroxide, and sodium acetate is formed.

$$HOAc + OH^- \rightarrow H_2O + OAc^-$$

Before reaction, 100 ml. of the buffer mixture contains 100 ml. × 0.10 M = 10 millimoles of HOAc, and 100 ml. × 0.10 M = 10 millimoles of NaOAc. One ml. of 0.10 M sodium hydroxide contains 1.0 ml. × 0.10 M = 0.10 millimole of NaOH. The 0.10 millimole of NaOH neutralizes 0.10 millimole of HOAc, leaving 10 − 0.10 = 9.9 millimoles of HOAc, and producing 0.10 millimole of NaOAc; this makes a total of 10 + 0.10 = 10.1 millimoles of NaOAc. After reaction, the 9.9 millimoles of HOAc and 10.1 millimoles of NaOAc are contained in 101 ml. of solution, so the concentrations are 9.9 millimoles/101 ml. = 0.098 M HOAc, and 10.1 millimoles/101 ml. = 0.100 M NaOAc. The final pH of the solution is then calculated as follows:

$$[H^+] = \frac{[HOAc]}{[OAc^-]} \times K_i = \frac{0.098}{0.100} \times 1.8 \times 10^{-5} = 1.76 \times 10^{-5}$$

$$pH = -\log [H^+] = -\log (1.76 \times 10^{-5}) = 4.754$$

$$= 4.8 \text{ (to justifiable limit in significant figures)}$$

Thus the addition of this small amount of base barely changes the pH of the solution. The explanation for this buffering action lies in the fact that as the sodium hydroxide is added, the hydroxide ions unite with the few hydrogen ions present, and then more of the acetic acid ionizes, thus restoring the concentration of the hydrogen ions to near its original value. If a small amount of hydrochloric acid were to be added to the acetic acid–sodium acetate buffer solution, most of the hydrogen ions from the hydrochloric acid would unite with acetate ions from the large reserve of these ions, forming un-ionized acetic acid.

$$H^+ + OAc^- \rightarrow HOAc$$

Thus there would be very little increase in the concentration of the hydrogen ion, and the pH would remain practically unchanged.

Some **buffer pairs** that find extensive application are $HOAc—OAc^-$, $NH_3—NH_4^+$, $H_2CO_3—HCO_3^-$, and $H_2PO_4^-—HPO_4^=$. Blood is an important example of a buffer solution with the principal acid and ion responsible for the buffering action being H_2CO_3 and HCO_3^-. When excess hydrogen ion enters the blood stream, it is removed principally through the reaction

$$H^+ + HCO_3^- \rightarrow H_2CO_3$$

and when excess hydroxide is formed, it is absorbed by the reaction

$$OH^- + H_2CO_3 \rightarrow H_2O + HCO_3^-$$

The pH of human blood thus remains very nearly 7.35, that is, slightly alkaline.

41.12 The Ionization of Weak Polyprotic Acids

Polyprotic acids, those from which more than one proton may be removed, ionize in water in successive steps. A typical example is phosphoric acid, a triprotic acid.

$$H_3PO_4 \rightleftharpoons H^+ + H_2PO_4^-$$
$$H_2PO_4^- \rightleftharpoons H^+ + HPO_4^=$$
$$HPO_4^= \rightleftharpoons H^+ + PO_4^{-3}$$

For each step in the ionization there is a corresponding ionization constant. The expressions for the ionization constants of the three stages in the ionization of phosphoric acid are

$$\frac{[H^+][H_2PO_4^-]}{[H_3PO_4]} = K_{H_3PO_4} = 7.5 \times 10^{-3}$$
$$\frac{[H^+][HPO_4^=]}{[H_2PO_4^-]} = K_{H_2PO_4^-} = 6.3 \times 10^{-8}$$
$$\frac{[H^+][PO_4^{-3}]}{[HPO_4^=]} = K_{HPO_4^=} = 3.6 \times 10^{-13}$$

It will be noted that the ionization in the successive steps becomes progressively less extensive. This is a general characteristic of polyprotic acids, and successive ionization constants for most such acids differ by about 10^5.

41.13 The Ionization of Hydrogen Sulfide

An example of a weak diprotic acid of prime importance in analytical chemistry is hydrogen sulfide in aqueous solution (hydrosulfuric acid). The first step in its ionization yields hydrogen and hydrosulfide ions.

$$H_2S \rightleftharpoons H^+ + HS^-$$

The expression for the ionization constant for the primary ionization of H_2S is

$$\frac{[H^+][HS^-]}{[H_2S]} = K_{H_2S} = 1.0 \times 10^{-7}$$

The hydrosulfide ion in turn ionizes and forms hydrogen and sulfide ions.

$$HS^- \rightleftharpoons H^+ + S^=$$

The expression for the ionization constant for the hydrosulfide ion is

$$\frac{[H^+][S^=]}{[HS^-]} = K_{HS^-} = 1.3 \times 10^{-13}$$

Note that K_{HS^-} is smaller than K_{H_2S} by almost 10^6 times. This means that very little of the HS^- formed by the ionization of H_2S ionizes to give hydrogen ions and sulfide ions. Thus the concentrations of H^+ and HS^- are practically equal in a pure aqueous solution of H_2S. The concentration of H_2S in a saturated aqueous solution of the gas at one atmosphere of pressure and room temperature is approximately 0.10 molar. If we let X equal $[H^+]$, then $[HS^-]$ will also be equal to X, and $[H_2S]$ will be equal to $0.10 - X$. Since X will be quite small compared to 0.10, it may be dropped from the term $(0.10 - X)$. Solving for X, we have

$$\frac{[H^+][HS^-]}{[H_2S]} = \frac{X^2}{0.10} = 1.0 \times 10^{-7}$$

$$X^2 = 1.0 \times 10^{-8}$$

$$X = 1.0 \times 10^{-4}\ M = [H^+] = [HS^-]$$

Since, in any solution, all possible equilibria must be satisfied simultaneously, the $[H^+]$ and $[HS^-]$ must be the same for the equilibria involved in both the ionization of HS^- and H_2S. Thus, substituting in the expression for the ionization constant for HS^-, we have

$$\frac{[H^+][S^=]}{[HS^-]} = \frac{(1.0 \times 10^{-4})}{(1.0 \times 10^{-4})}[S^=] = K_{HS^-} = 1.3 \times 10^{-13}$$

$$[S^=] = 1.3 \times 10^{-13}\ M$$

Note that in a pure aqueous solution of H_2S the $[S^=]$ is equal to K_{HS^-}. In fact, for any weak diprotic acid the concentration of the divalent anion is equal to the secondary ionization constant.

By multiplying the expressions for the ionization constants K_{H_2S} and K_{HS^-}, we obtain

$$\frac{[H^+][HS^-]}{[H_2S]} \times \frac{[H^+][S^=]}{[HS^-]} = K_{H_2S} \times K_{HS^-}$$

or

$$\frac{[H^+]^2[S^=]}{[H_2S]} = K_{H_2S}K_{HS^-} = 1.3 \times 10^{-20}$$

Since a saturated solution of hydrogen sulfide in water is 0.10 M with respect to the gas, we have

$$\frac{[H^+]^2[S^=]}{0.10} = 1.3 \times 10^{-20}$$

$$[H^+]^2[S^=] = 1.3 \times 10^{-21} \text{ (for a saturated } H_2S \text{ solution only)}$$

Thus in a solution saturated with hydrogen sulfide the concentration of the sulfide ion varies inversely as the square of the hydrogen ion concentration. This equation may be used to calculate the concentration of the sulfide ion when hydrogen ions in the form of a strong acid are added to a saturated hydrogen sulfide solution. Let us calculate the concentration of sulfide ion in a saturated solution of hydrogen sulfide to which sufficient hydrochloric acid has been added to make the hydrogen ion concentration of the solution 0.1 molar. Substituting in the above equation, we have

$$[H^+]^2[S^=] = (0.1)^2[S^=] = 1.3 \times 10^{-21}$$

$$[S^=] = \frac{1.3 \times 10^{-21}}{(0.1)^2} = 1 \times 10^{-19}\ M$$

We may use the same equation in calculating the hydrogen ion concentration necessary to produce a given sulfide ion concentration.

QUESTIONS

1. Compare the extent of ionization or dissociation in water of strong electrolytes and weak electrolytes.
2. Classify each of the following compounds as a weak or strong electrolyte: HCl, NaOH, NaCl, HOAc, H_2SO_4, $CaCl_2$, $Hg(CN)_2$, $CdCl_2$, $Ca(OH)_2$, H_3PO_4, NH_3, $Fe(OH)_3$, and HCN.
3. What are the ionic and molecular species present in an aqueous solution of acetic acid? a solution of hydrochloric acid? a solution of phosphoric acid?
4. Why does the law of chemical equilibrium apply to solutions of weak electrolytes but not to solutions of strong electrolytes?
5. How would the extent of ionization of acetic acid in a solution be changed by the addition of some potassium acetate? some hydrogen chloride?
6. What is meant by the self-ionization of water?
7. Define pH both in words and by a mathematical equation.
8. Explain the change of color of acid-base indicators in terms of ionic equilibria.
9. What constitutes a buffer solution?
10. Of what practical value are buffer solutions?

PROBLEMS

1. Calculate the per cent ionization of each of the following solutions:
   (a) 0.020 M HCN; $K_i = 4.0 \times 10^{-10}$ *Ans.* $1.4 \times 10^{-2}\%$
   (b) 0.50 M H_3BO_3; $K_i = 5.8 \times 10^{-10}$ *Ans.* $3.4 \times 10^{-3}\%$
   (c) 0.15 M HBrO; $K_i = 2.0 \times 10^{-9}$. *Ans.* $1.1 \times 10^{-2}\%$
   (d) 0.10 M HNO_2; $K_i = 4.5 \times 10^{-4}$. Calculate (1) with simplifying assumption and (2) without using simplifying assumption and with use of the quadratic formula. Compare the values. *Ans.* (1) 6.7%; (2) 6.5%
2. Calculate the concentration of each of the ions in the following solutions: (a) 0.05 M HCl, (b) 0.003 M $Ba(OH)_2$, (c) 1.3 M H_2SO_4.
   Ans. (a) $[H^+] = 0.05\ M$; $[Cl^-] = 0.05\ M$. (b) $[Ba^{++}] = 0.003\ M$; $[OH^-] = 0.006\ M$. (c) $[H^+] = 2.6\ M$; $[SO_4^=] = 1.3\ M$.
3. A 0.050 M solution of HF is 11 per cent ionized. Calculate $[H^+]$, $[F^-]$, and $[HF]$, and the ionization constant for HF.
   Ans. $[H^+] = [F^-] = 5.7 \times 10^{-3}\ M$; $[HF] = 4.4 \times 10^{-2}\ M$; $K_i = 7.2 \times 10^{-4}$
4. A dilute solution of acetic acid, containing 0.20 mole of acid in 350 liters of solution, is 16.4% dissociated into ions. Calculate the ionization constant of acetic acid. *Ans.* 1.8×10^{-5}

5. Calculate the molarity of a solution of acetic acid which is 2.0% ionized. $K_i = 1.8 \times 10^{-5}$. *Ans.* *0.045 M*

6. Calculate the ionization constant for acetic acid, which is 12.6 per cent ionized in a 1.00×10^{-3} M solution. *Ans.* 1.82×10^{-5}

7. The degree of ionization of 0.030 M benzoic acid is 4.5×10^{-2}. Calculate its ionization constant. *Ans.* 6.3×10^{-5}

8. The ionization constant of HCN is 4.0×10^{-10}. Calculate $[H^+]$, $[CN^-]$, and the per cent ionization of a 0.010 M solution of the acid.

Ans. $[H^+] = [CN^-] = 2.0 \times 10^{-6}$ *M*; 2.0×10^{-2}%

9. The ionization constant of aqueous ammonia is 1.8×10^{-5}. Calculate the hydroxyl ion concentration in a 2.0 M aqueous ammonia solution.

Ans. 6.0×10^{-3} *M*

10. Calculate the pH of a solution which contains 1.5×10^{-5} g. of hydrogen ion per liter of solution. *Ans.* *4.8*

11. Calculate the hydrogen ion concentration and the pH of a 0.40 M solution of benzoic acid, C_6H_5COOH, for which $K_i = 6.6 \times 10^{-5}$.

Ans. $[H^+] = 5.1 \times 10^{-3}$ *M*; *pH = 2.3*

12. Calculate the pH and percentage ionization for a 0.050 M methylamine, CH_3NH_2, solution. K_i for methylamine is 4.40×10^{-4}.

Ans. *pH = 11.7; per cent ionization = 9.8%*

13. The ionization constant of HNO_2 is 4.5×10^{-4}. What total concentration of HNO_2 would be required to give a solution having a hydrogen ion concentration 1.0×10^{-2} M? *Ans.* 2.3×10^{-1} *M*

14. The ionization constant of acetic acid is 1.8×10^{-5}. What will be the hydrogen ion concentration of a 0.050 M HOAc solution which is 1.0 M in NaOAc?

Ans. 9.0×10^{-7}

15. The ionization constant for formic acid (HCOOH) is 1.8×10^{-4}. How many moles and how many grams of HCOONa must be added to one liter of a 0.30 M solution of HCOOH to maintain a hydrogen ion concentration of 1.0×10^{-3} M?

Ans. 5.4×10^{-2} *mole; 2.5 g.*

16. A 0.100 M solution of aqueous ammonia is 1.20% ionized. What volume of this solution contains the same quantity of hydroxyl ions as 200 ml. of 1.00×10^{-4} M NaOH, which is completely dissociated? *Ans.* *16.7 ml.*

17. Calculate the pH and pOH of water at 100°; at this temperature, $K_w = 1 \times 10^{-12}$. *Ans.* *pH = 6; pOH = 6*

18. The pH of a given formic acid solution is 2.33. What is the per cent ionization of the acid? $K_i = 1.8 \times 10^{-4}$. *Ans.* *3.8%*

19. What is the pH of a solution which is 0.100 M in acetic acid and 0.100 M in sodium acetate? *Ans.* *4.75*

20. What is the pH of a solution containing aqueous ammonia and ammonium chloride in (a) a molar ratio of 1.0 to 4.0, and (b) a molar ratio of 4.0 to 1.0?

Ans. *(a) 8.7; (b) 9.9*

21. Forty ml. of 0.10 M HCl is mixed with 30 ml. of 0.30 M aqueous ammonia. Calculate the concentration of hydroxyl ions in the solution.

Ans. 2.3×10^{-5} *M*

22. Calculate the hydrogen and hydroxyl ion concentrations in pure water. $K_w = 1 \times 10^{-14}$. *Ans.* $[H^+] = [OH^-] = 1 \times 10^{-7}$ *M*

23. Ten ml. of 4.0 M acetic acid is added to 80 ml. of 0.50 M sodium acetate solution. Calculate the hydrogen ion concentration of this solution.
Ans. 1.8×10^{-5} *M*

24. Calculate the $[H^+]$, $[OH^-]$, pH, and pOH of the following solutions:
(a) 0.01 M HCl *Ans.* 10^{-2} *M*; 10^{-12} *M*; *2*; *12*
(b) 0.00001 M $Ca(OH)_2$ *Ans.* 5×10^{-10} *M*; 2×10^{-5} *M*; *9.3*; *4.7*
(c) 0.005 M H_2SO_4 *Ans.* 10^{-2} *M*; 10^{-12} *M*; *2.0*; *12.0*
(d) 0.10 M NaOH *Ans.* 10^{-13} *M*; 10^{-1} *M*; *13*; *1*
(e) 0.080 M HOAc (1.50 per cent ionized)
Ans. 1.2×10^{-3} *M*; 8.3×10^{-12} *M*; *2.9*; *11.1*
(f) 1.00 M aqueous NH_3 (0.420 per cent ionized)
Ans. 2.38×10^{-12} *M*; 4.20×10^{-3} *M*; *11.6*; *2.4*

25. Calculate the pH of a solution that is prepared from
(a) 30 ml. of 1.0 M HOAc and 20 ml. of 1.0 M NaOH. *Ans.* 5.0
(b) 10 ml. of 1.0 M aqueous ammonia and 10 ml. of 0.25 M HCl.
Ans. *9.7*

26. Calculate the pH of a solution which contains
(a) 0.500 g. of NaOH in 500 ml. of solution. *Ans.* *12.4.*
(b) 20.0 g. of NH_3 in 100 ml. of solution. *Ans.* *12.2*
(c) 5.00 g. H_2SO_4 in 500 ml. of solution. *Ans.* *0.69*

27. What is the hydrogen ion concentration corresponding to each of the following pH values: 1.0; 7.0; 14.0; 3.5; 10.4; and 0.0?
Ans. *0.1 M*; 10^{-7} *M*; 10^{-14} *M*; 3.2×10^{-4} *M*; 4.0×10^{-11} *M*; *1 M*

28. Calculate the hydroxyl ion concentration for a solution having a pH of 7.8.
Ans. 6.3×10^{-7} *M*

29. Calculate the molarity of a solution of H_2SO_4 which has a pH of 1.8.
Ans. 8.0×10^{-3} *M*

30. It is desired to prepare a buffer solution for which the pH is 5.5. How much solid $NaC_2H_3O_2 \cdot 3\,H_2O$ must be added to 100 ml. of 0.10 M acetic acid ($K_i = 1.8 \times 10^{-5}$) to produce such a buffer solution? *Ans.* *7.6 g.*

31. Given a 0.10 M solution of acetic acid which is also 0.10 M in sodium acetate (a buffer mixture), and also a solution of 1.80×10^{-5} M HCl. Calculate (a) the initial pH in each solution, (b) the pH when a liter of each of the original solutions is treated with 0.050 mole of solid sodium hydroxide, and (c) the pH when a liter of each of the original solutions is treated with 0.050 mole of HCl. (Assume no volume change with the addition of the NaOH or the HCl).
Ans. *(a) 4.7 for each solution; (b) 5.2; 12.7; (c) 4.3; 1.3*

32. What relative number of moles of acetic acid and sodium acetate should be used in making up a buffer solution with a pH of 4.8?
Ans. *1 mole of HOAc to 1.1 mole of NaOAc*

33. A 50.0 ml. solution of a 0.20 M monoprotic acid was mixed with 10 ml. of 0.10 M potassium hydroxide, and the resulting mixture was diluted to 100 ml. The pH of the solution was found to be 3.8. What is the ionization constant of the acid?
Ans. $K_i = 1.8 \times 10^{-5}$

34. The ionization constant for lactic acid, $CH_3CHOHCOOH$, at 25°, is 1.36×10^{-4}. If a 2.0 g. quantity of lactic acid is diluted with water to a volume of 1.0 l., what is the concentration of hydrogen ion in the solution?
Ans. 1.7×10^{-3} *M*

35. What is the pH of a 0.010 M solution of HF, for which K_i is 7.2×10^{-4}?
Ans. 2.6

36. Calculate the per cent ionization of 0.10 M H_3PO_4, if the ionization constant for the first ionization step is 7.5×10^{-3}. (Consider that the second and third ionization steps are negligible compared to the first). *Ans.* 27%

37. A 2.00 g. sample of NaOAc was dissolved in water, to which was added 25.0 ml. of 0.100 M HCl. The resulting solution was diluted to 100 ml. Calculate the pH of the resulting solution. K_i for acetic acid is 1.8×10^{-5}. *Ans.* 5.7

38. The pH of a 0.105 M solution of a particular monoprotic acid is 2.85. Calculate the K_i for the acid. *Ans.* 1.87×10^{-5}

39. Calculate the concentration of sulfide ion in a saturated solution of hydrogen sulfide which is 0.2 M with respect to hydrochloric acid. ($K_{H_2S} = 1 \times 10^{-7}$, and $K_{HS^-} = 1 \times 10^{-13}$). *Ans.* 3×10^{-20} *M*

40. Calculate the hydrogen ion concentration of a 0.005 M solution of hydrogen sulfide. (Neglect the second stage in the ionization of H_2S). *Ans.* 2×10^{-5} *M*

41. Calculate the pH of a 0.0010 M solution of carbonic acid (H_2CO_3). The ionization constant for the reaction $H_2CO_3 = H^+ + HCO_3^-$ is 4.3×10^{-7}. (Neglect the second stage in the ionization of H_2CO_3). *Ans.* 4.7

42. A buffer solution is made up of equal volumes of 0.100 M acetic acid and 0.500 M sodium acetate. (a) What is the pH of this solution? (b) What is the pH of the solution which results from adding 1.00 ml. of 0.100 M HCl to 200 ml. of the original buffer solution? (K_i for acetic acid is 1.8×10^{-5}).
Ans. *(a) 5.444; (b) 5.441 (but note that for each answer only two significant figures, or 5.4, are justified by the data provided in the problem).*

43. What is the concentration of an acetic acid solution which is (a) 2.0% ionized; (b) 0.40% ionized? ($K_i = 1.8 \times 10^{-5}$). *Ans.* *(a) 0.045 M; (b) 1.1 M*

44. Calculate the ionization constant in general terms for the degree of ionization, α, and concentration, C.
Ans. $\frac{\alpha^2 C}{1 - \alpha}$

45. How many grams of lactic acid, $CH_3CHOHCOOH$, are necessary to prepare 1.5 l. of a solution for which the hydrogen ion concentration is 3.0×10^{-3} mole/l. K_i for lactic acid is 1.4×10^{-4}. *Ans.* *8.6 g.*

46. Calculate the carbonate ion concentration in a 0.060 M solution of carbonic acid which is also 0.125 M in hydrochloric acid. ($K_1 = 4.3 \times 10^{-7}$, and $K_2 = 7 \times 10^{-11}$ for the two steps in the dissociation of H_2CO_3). *Ans.* 1.2×10^{-16} *M*

47. What will be the final pH of a solution made by mixing 1.0 mole of HCl and 1.0 mole $LiC_2H_3O_2$ in enough water to make 1.0 l. of solution? *Ans.* 2.4

48. Calculate the pH for each of the following solutions:

(a) 250 ml. of 0.100 M acetic acid + 50.0 ml. of 0.100 M potassium hydroxide.
Ans. 4.14

(b) 250 ml. of 0.100 M acetic acid + 100 ml. of 0.100 M potassium hydroxide.
Ans. 4.57

(c) 250 ml. of 0.100 M acetic acid + 200 ml. of 0.100 M potassium hydroxide.

Ans. *5.35*

49. How many grams of lactic acid, $CH_3CHOHCOOH$, are there in 5.00 liters of a solution of this acid, if the pOH of the solution is 11.9? *Ans.* *200 g.*

50. Assuming that the hydrogen ion concentration in the solution is controlled by the reaction $H_2PO_4^- = H^+ + HPO_4^=$, calculate the ratio of concentrations of $HPO_4^=$ and $H_2PO_4^-$ necessary to make up a buffer solution of pH equal to (a) 5.0, (b) 7.0, and (c) 9.0. (K_i for the reaction $H_2PO_4^- = H^+ + HPO_4^=$ is 6.2×10^{-8}).

Ans. (*a*) 6.2×10^{-3}; (*b*) *0.62*; (*c*) *62*

Explain exactly how such a solution, for pH 7.0, could be made in the laboratory.

REFERENCE

"pH," Duncan A. MacInnes, *Sci. American*, Jan., 1951; p. 40.

CHAPTER FORTY-TWO

The Solubility Product Principle

In analyses which involve precipitations, we deal with slightly soluble substances which are strong electrolytes. Equilibrium systems composed of slightly soluble ionic substances in contact with their saturated aqueous solutions are particularly important in analytical chemistry. In this chapter we shall be concerned with the theory and application of the precipitation and dissolution of slightly soluble ionic substances.

42.1 The Solubility Product Constant

A slightly soluble electrolyte dissolves in water to the extent that a saturated solution of its ions is formed. A **saturated solution** is defined as one which is in equilibrium with the undissolved solute. It can be shown by the use of radioactive tracers that at equilibrium the solid continues to dissolve but that the process of crystallization is also taking place and that the opposing processes have equal rates. Let us consider a saturated solution of silver chloride in equilibrium with some crystals of silver chloride. The equilibrium can be expressed by the following equation:

$$\text{AgCl (solid)} \underset{\text{crystallization}}{\overset{\text{dissolution}}{\rightleftharpoons}} Ag^+ + Cl^- \text{ (saturated solution)}$$

Applying the law of chemical equilibrium to this system, we obtain the mathematical expression

$$\frac{[Ag^+][Cl^-]}{[AgCl]} = K_e$$

Because the concentration of the solid silver chloride remains essentially constant, we may write

$$[Ag^+][Cl^-] = K_e[AgCl] = K_{sp}$$

The constant K_{sp} is called the **solubility product constant,** or sometimes simply the **solubility product.** In a saturated solution of a slightly soluble electrolyte the product of the molar concentrations of its ions is a constant at a given temperature if the different kinds of ions are formed in equal numbers. If the slightly soluble electrolyte contains more than one ion of one kind in its formula, the concentration of that ion is raised to the corresponding power in the expression for the solubility product constant. For example, calcium phosphate dissociates according to the equation

$$Ca_3(PO_4)_2 \rightleftharpoons 3\ Ca^{++} + 2\ PO_4^{-3}$$

and the expression for its solubility product constant is

$$[Ca^{++}]^3[PO_4^{-3}]^2 = K_{sp}$$

For a salt like magnesium ammonium phosphate, which dissociates according to the equation $MgNH_4PO_4 \rightleftharpoons Mg^{++} + NH_4^{+} + PO_4^{-3}$, we have

$$[Mg^{++}][NH_4^{+}][PO_4^{-3}] = K_{sp}$$

The solubility product principle is based upon experimental studies of saturated solutions of slightly soluble electrolytes and does not hold for moderately soluble salts such as NaCl or $KClO_3$. Furthermore, the presence of high concentrations of ions of an added electrolyte causes an increase in the solubility of a slightly soluble substance — the salt effect (Section 41.5). The salt effect varies with the concentration of the added electrolyte and with the charges on the ions the salt supplies to the solution. Hence, the solubility product principle is strictly valid only for saturated solutions in which the total ionic concentration is fairly small.

42.2 Calculation of Solubility Products from Molar Solubilities

When the solubility of a slightly soluble electrolyte is known, its solubility product constant can be calculated. In all calculations involving solubility product constants, the concentrations must be expressed in moles per liter. Thus, when the concentrations are given in other units, such as grams per liter, they must be converted to moles per liter. Some examples are given below.

EXAMPLE 1. The solubility of $BaSO_4$ in water is 2.42×10^{-3} gram per liter. Calculate the solubility product constant for $BaSO_4$.

First calculate the molar solubility of $BaSO_4$. The formula weight of $BaSO_4$ is 233.4.

$$\frac{2.42 \times 10^{-3}\ \text{g./liter}}{233.4\ \text{g./mole}} \doteq 1.04 \times 10^{-5}\ \text{mole per liter}$$

Since $BaSO_4$ dissolves to give Ba^{++} and $SO_4^{=}$ in equal amounts, $[Ba^{++}] = [SO_4^{=}] = 1.04 \times 10^{-5}$ M. When these values are substituted in the expression for the solubility product constant of $BaSO_4$, the numerical value of the constant may be obtained.

$$\underline{BaSO_4 \rightleftharpoons Ba^{++} + SO_4^{=}}$$

$$[Ba^{++}][SO_4^{=}] = K_{sp}$$

$$(1.04 \times 10^{-5})(1.04 \times 10^{-5}) = 1.08 \times 10^{-10} = K_{sp}$$

Thus the solubility product constant for barium sulfate is calculated to be 1.08×10^{-10}.

EXAMPLE 2. Calculate the solubility product constant for silver chromate, whose molar solubility is 1.3×10^{-4} mole per liter.

Writing the equation for the dissolution of Ag_2CrO_4

$$\underline{Ag_2CrO_4} \rightleftharpoons 2\ Ag^+ + CrO_4^=$$

we see that the concentration of silver ion will be twice the molar solubility of Ag_2CrO_4, and that the concentration of chromate ion will be equal to the molar solubility of the salt, or that $[Ag^+] = 2 \times 1.3 \times 10^{-4}$, and $[CrO_4^=] = 1.3 \times 10^{-4}$. Substituting in the expression for the solubility product constant, we find

$$[Ag^+]^2[CrO_4^=] = K_{sp}$$
$$(2 \times 1.3 \times 10^{-4})^2(1.3 \times 10^{-4}) = 9 \times 10^{-12} = K_{sp}$$

A table of solubility product constants of some slightly soluble electrolytes is given in Appendix G.

42.3 Calculation of the Molar Solubility from the Solubility Product

When the solubility product constant for a slightly soluble electrolyte is known, its solubility in moles per liter can be readily calculated.

EXAMPLE 1. The solubility product constant for silver chloride is 1.2×10^{-10}. Calculate the molar solubility of silver chloride.

Silver chloride dissolves in water to form a saturated solution according to the equation

$$\underline{AgCl} \rightleftharpoons Ag^+ + Cl^-$$

Let X be the solubility of AgCl in moles per liter. The molar concentration of Ag^+ and Cl^- will also be X since the salt is completely dissociated in aqueous solution. Substituting in the expression for the solubility product constant for AgCl, we have

$$[Ag^+][Cl^-] = K_{sp} = 1.2 \times 10^{-10}$$
$$X^2 = 1.2 \times 10^{-10}$$
$$X = \sqrt{1.2 \times 10^{-10}} = 1.1 \times 10^{-5} \text{ mole/l.}$$

Thus the molar solubility of silver chloride is 1.1×10^{-5}.

EXAMPLE 2. The solubility product constant of $Fe(OH)_3$ is 1.1×10^{-36}. Calculate the molar solubility of iron (III) hydroxide.

Let X be the molar solubility of iron (III) hydroxide. From the equation for the dissolution of iron (III) hydroxide, $\underline{Fe(OH)_3} \rightleftharpoons Fe^{+++} + 3\ OH^-$, it is apparent that each mole of $Fe(OH)_3$ that dissolves yields one mole of Fe^{+++} and three moles of OH^-. Thus if the molar solubility of $Fe(OH)_3$ is X, then $[Fe^{+++}] = X$, and $[OH^-] = 3X$. These values are substituted in the expression for the solubility product constant of ferric hydroxide, and the value of X is calculated.

$$[Fe^{+++}][OH^-]^3 = K_{sp} = 1.1 \times 10^{-36}$$
$$X(3\ X)^3 = 1.1 \times 10^{-36}$$
$$27\ X^4 = 1.1 \times 10^{-36}$$
$$X^4 = 0.0407 \times 10^{-36} = 407 \times 10^{-40}$$
$$X = 4.5 \times 10^{-10} \text{ mole/l.}$$

Thus 4.5×10^{-10} = molar solubility of $Fe(OH)_3 = [Fe^{+++}]$; and $[OH^-] = 3\ X = 13.5 \times 10^{-10}$, or 1.4×10^{-9}.

42.4 The Precipitation of Slightly Soluble Electrolytes

In order to precipitate a slightly soluble electrolyte, it is necessary to bring together in the same solution the ions of that electrolyte in such quantities that the product of the ion concentrations, raised to the appropriate powers, exceeds the solubility product constant of the compound. Thus, when equal volumes of a 2×10^{-4} M solution of $AgNO_3$ and a 2×10^{-4} M solution of NaCl are mixed, we can show that silver chloride will precipitate. Because the volume is doubled by mixing equal volumes of the two solutions, each concentration is reduced to half its initial value. Consequently, both the $[Ag^+]$ and $[Cl^-]$ will be $2 \times 10^{-4}/2 = 1 \times 10^{-4}$ immediately upon mixing. Substituting in the expression for the solubility product constant of silver chloride,

$$[Ag^+][Cl^-] = K_{sp} = 1.2 \times 10^{-10}$$
$$(1 \times 10^{-4})(1 \times 10^{-4}) = 1 \times 10^{-8} > K_{sp}$$

we see that, momentarily, the product of $[Ag^+]$ and $[Cl^-]$ is greater than (>) K_{sp} for AgCl. According to the principle of chemical equilibrium, some of the silver and chloride ions will unite under these conditions with the formation of crystalline silver chloride, and the precipitation will continue until the product of $[Ag^+]$ and $[Cl^-]$ still remaining in solution attains a value equal to the solubility product constant for silver chloride.

In the above case, the Ag^+ and Cl^- were present in equal concentrations. Since an equal number of Ag^+ and Cl^- combine to form solid AgCl, the saturated solution in contact with the precipitate will contain Ag^+ and Cl^- in equal concentrations, their product being just equal to the solubility product constant of AgCl. If to this saturated solution of silver chloride we add more NaCl, we again shall momentarily have the product of $[Ag^+]$ and $[Cl^-]$ greater than the solubility product constant of AgCl, and then more Ag^+ and Cl^- will unite and form solid AgCl until the product of $[Ag^+]$ and $[Cl^-]$ again attains the value of K_{sp}. In the new equilibrium which results, $[Ag^+]$ will be smaller and $[Cl^-]$ will be larger than those in a saturated solution of AgCl in pure water. The larger we make $[Cl^-]$, the smaller $[Ag^+]$ will become. However, we can never reduce $[Ag^+]$ to zero because the product of $[Ag^+]$ and $[Cl^-]$ will always be equal to the solubility product constant.

42.5 Calculation of the Concentration of an Ion Necessary to Form a Precipitate

When the concentration of one of the ions of a slightly soluble electrolyte and the solubility product constant are known, we can calculate the concentration which the other ion must exceed before precipitation can occur. For example, if a solution contains 0.001 mole of $CrO_4^{=}$ per liter, what concentration of Ag^+ ion must be exceeded by adding $AgNO_3$ to the solution before Ag_2CrO_4 will begin to precipitate? K_{sp} is 9×10^{-12}. The equilibrium involved in the problem is

$$\underline{Ag_2CrO_4} \rightleftharpoons 2\ Ag^+ + CrO_4^{=}$$

The expression for the solubility product constant is

$$[Ag^+]^2[CrO_4^{=}] = K_{sp}$$

Substituting in the above expression the values for the $[CrO_4^{=}]$ and K_{sp}, we have

$$[Ag^+]^2(0.001) = 9 \times 10^{-12}$$
$$[Ag^+]^2 = \frac{9 \times 10^{-12}}{10^{-3}} = 9 \times 10^{-9} = 90 \times 10^{-10}$$
$$[Ag^+] = 9.5 \times 10^{-5}$$
$$= 1 \times 10^{-4}\ M \text{ (to the limit of significant figures available)}$$

A concentration of Ag^+ greater than 1×10^{-4} M is necessary to cause precipitation of Ag_2CrO_4.

42.6 Calculation of the Concentration of an Ion Left in Solution after Precipitation

What is the concentration of Ag^+ left in solution if AgCl is precipitated by adding sufficient hydrochloric acid to a solution of $AgNO_3$ to make the final chloride concentration 0.10 M?

$$[Ag^+][Cl^-] = K_{sp}$$
$$[Ag^+](0.10) = 1.2 \times 10^{-10}$$
$$[Ag^+] = \frac{1.2 \times 10^{-10}}{1.0 \times 10^{-1}} = 1.2 \times 10^{-9}\ M$$

The concentration of Ag^+ left in solution is 1.2×10^{-9} mole per liter.

42.7 Supersaturation of Slightly Soluble Electrolytes

When the product of the concentrations of the ions, raised to the proper powers, exceeds the value of the solubility product constant, precipitation does not always occur; sometimes a supersaturated solution is formed. For example, if magnesium is being precipitated as magnesium ammonium phosphate from a solution of low magnesium ion content, the solution may stand several hours before a visible precipitate appears. Furthermore, even though precipitation may be immediate under ordinary conditions, it does not follow that it is complete. The first crystals to precipitate are often very small and more soluble than the larger ones which form as the solution stands in contact with the precipitate (see Section 42.8). Hence, the solution should be allowed to stand before filtering to insure maximum precipitation.

42.8 Solubility and Crystal Size

It has been shown by experiment that small crystals of any substance are more soluble than larger ones. A notable example of this is barium sulfate. The solubility of "fine" crystals of barium sulfate has been found to be about twice as great as that of "coarse" crystals of this salt. This results from the fact that ions in the interior of a crystal are bound with greater forces than those of the faces and edges. A greater fraction of the ions occupy surface positions in small rather than large crystals, making the tendency for ions to enter the solution greater for the smaller crystal. Because small crystals are more soluble than large crystals, the smallest crystals will in time dissolve and the larger ones will grow still larger. True equilibrium is not reached until large, perfect crystals are formed. The solubility product constants are calculated for solutions in contact with relatively large crystals.

Because very small crystals will pass through filters, or may resist sedimentation by centrifugation, precipitates are often "digested" to increase the size of the crystals. Heat increases the rate at which large crystals will grow from the smaller ones. Allowing the suspended precipitate to stand for a time will also often result in larger crystals.

42.9 Calculations Involving Both Ionization Constants and Solubility Product Constants

In the theory and practice of precipitation analysis we often deal with systems which involve more than one equilibrium. The following problems will serve to illustrate the point.

EXAMPLE 1. Calculate the concentration of hydrogen ion required to prevent the precipitation of ZnS in a solution which is 0.10 M in $ZnCl_2$ and saturated with H_2S. The maximum concentration of sulfide ion that can be present without causing ZnS to precipitate may be calculated from the solubility product expression for ZnS, as shown below.

$$[Zn^{++}][S^{=}] = K_{sp} = 1.1 \times 10^{-21}$$

$$[S^{=}] = \frac{K_{sp}}{[Zn^{++}]} = \frac{1.1 \times 10^{-21}}{0.10} = 1.1 \times 10^{-20} \text{ M}$$

The sulfide ion concentration varies inversely with the square of the hydrogen ion concentration in a saturated solution of hydrogen sulfide containing a strong acid such as HCl (see Section 41.13).

$$[H^{+}]^2[S^{=}] = 1.3 \times 10^{-21}$$

Substituting in this equation the sulfide ion concentration found above, we have

$$[H^{+}]^2 = \frac{1.3 \times 10^{-21}}{[S^{=}]} = \frac{1.3 \times 10^{-21}}{1.1 \times 10^{-20}} = 1.2 \times 10^{-1}$$

$$[H^{+}] = \sqrt{0.12} = 0.35 \text{ M}$$

Thus it is found that a hydrogen ion concentration of 0.35 M will prevent the precipitation of zinc sulfide in the solution described in the problem.

EXAMPLE 2. Calculate the quantity of Cd^{++} which will remain unprecipitated in a 0.30 M HCl solution which is saturated with H_2S. The concentration of $[Cd^{++}]$ remaining in the solution will be determined by the final sulfide ion concentration which in turn is determined by the hydrogen ion concentration of the 0.30 M HCl solution. Solving for the sulfide ion concentration, we have

$$[H^+]^2[S^=] = (0.30)^2[S^=] = 1.3 \times 10^{-21}$$

$$[S^=] = \frac{1.3 \times 10^{-21}}{(0.30)^2} = \frac{1.3 \times 10^{-21}}{0.090} = 1.4 \times 10^{-20}\ M$$

Substituting the value of the sulfide ion concentration in the expression for the solubility product of CdS, we have

$$[Cd^{++}][S^=] = [Cd^{++}](1.2 \times 10^{-22}) = K_{sp} = 3.6 \times 10^{-29}$$

$$[Cd^{++}] = \frac{3.6 \times 10^{-29}}{1.4 \times 10^{-20}} = 2.8 \times 10^{-9}\ M$$

Multiplying the molar concentration of Cd^{++} by the gram-atomic weight of Cd, we find

2.8×10^{-9} mole/liter $\times$ 112.4 g./mole $= 3.1 \times 10^{-7}$ g./liter or 3.1×10^{-7} mg./ml.

Hence the precipitation of Cd^{++} as CdS in a 0.30 M HCl solution saturated with H_2S is fairly complete.

Calculations of the type shown in Examples 1 and 2 are important in the separation of the metal ions of Analytical Group II from those of Group III as discussed in Section 46.1.

EXAMPLE 3. Calculate the concentration of ammonium ion, supplied by NH_4Cl, required to prevent the precipitation of $Mg(OH)_2$ in a liter of solution containing 0.10 mole of ammonia and 0.10 mole of Mg^{++}. To find the maximum concentration of OH^- that can be present in solution without precipitating $Mg(OH)_2$, we use the solubility product expression for $Mg(OH)_2$.

$$[Mg^{++}][OH^-]^2 = (0.10)[OH^-]^2 = K_{Mg(OH)_2} = 1.5 \times 10^{-11}$$

$$[OH^-]^2 = \frac{1.5 \times 10^{-11}}{0.10} = 1.5 \times 10^{-10}$$

$$[OH^-] = 1.2 \times 10^{-5}\ M$$

Thus $Mg(OH)_2$ will not precipitate if the $[OH^-]$ does not exceed 1.2×10^{-5} M.

To calculate the $[NH_4^+]$, supplied by NH_4Cl and needed to repress the ionization of NH_3 so that the $[OH^-]$ will not exceed 1.2×10^{-5}, we use the expression for the ionization constant of aqueous ammonia.

$$\frac{[NH_4^+][OH^-]}{[NH_3]} = K_{NH_3} = 1.8 \times 10^{-5}$$

$$[NH_4^+] = \frac{[NH_3]}{[OH^-]} \times K_{NH_3} = \frac{(0.10)}{(1.2 \times 10^{-5})} \times 1.8 \times 10^{-5} = 0.15\ M$$

The total concentration of ammonium ion that must be present is 0.15 M. Because the amount of ammonium ion formed by the ionization of ammonia is very small, it can be neglected.

42.10 Fractional Precipitation

When two anions form sparingly soluble compounds with the same cation or when two cations form sparingly soluble compounds with the same anion, the less soluble compound will precipitate first on the addition of a precipitant to a solution containing both. An additional quantity of the less soluble ion will precipitate along with the precipitation of the more soluble ion, if addition of the precipitant is continued (**coprecipitation**).

Consider the case in which a solution containing both iodide and chloride ions is treated with silver nitrate. Silver iodide, being less soluble than silver chloride, is precipitated first, and only after most of the iodide is precipitated will chloride begin to precipitate.

For example, a solution contains 0.010 mole of KI and 0.10 mole of KCl per liter. $AgNO_3$ is gradually added to this solution. Which will be precipitated first, AgI or AgCl?

(a) Calculate the $[Ag^+]$ necessary to start the precipitation of AgI.

$$[Ag^+][I^-] = K_{AgI} = 1.5 \times 10^{-16}$$

$$[Ag^+] = \frac{K_{AgI}}{[I^-]} = \frac{1.5 \times 10^{-16}}{0.010} = 1.5 \times 10^{-14}\ M$$

(b) Calculate the $[Ag^+]$ necessary to start the precipitation of AgCl.

$$[Ag^+][Cl^-] = K_{AgCl} = 1.2 \times 10^{-10}$$

$$[Ag^+] = \frac{K_{AgCl}}{[Cl^-]} = \frac{1.2 \times 10^{-10}}{0.10} = 1.2 \times 10^{-9}\ M$$

A greater concentration of Ag^+ is necessary to cause precipitation of AgCl than AgI, so AgI will precipitate first.

(c) What will be the concentration of I^- in this solution when AgCl begins to precipitate as a result of the continued addition of Ag^+? The $[Ag^+]$ necessary to initiate the precipitation of AgCl is 1.2×10^{-9}. For this concentration of Ag^+, the I^- concentration will be

$$[I^-] = \frac{K_{AgI}}{[Ag^+]} = \frac{1.5 \times 10^{-16}}{1.2 \times 10^{-9}} = 1.3 \times 10^{-7}\ M$$

(d) What fraction of the amount of I^- originally present remains in solution when AgCl begins to precipitate?

$$\frac{[I^-] \text{ when precipitation of AgCl begins}}{[I^-] \text{ originally present}} = \frac{1.3 \times 10^{-7}}{0.010} = 1.3 \times 10^{-5}$$

(e) What will be the concentration of I^- in the solution after half the Cl^- initially present is precipitated as AgCl?

$$[Ag^+] = \frac{K_{AgCl}}{[Cl^-]} = \frac{1.2 \times 10^{-10}}{0.050} = 2.4 \times 10^{-9}\ M$$

$$[I^-] = \frac{K_{AgI}}{[Ag^+]} = \frac{1.5 \times 10^{-16}}{2.4 \times 10^{-9}} = 0.625 \times 10^{-7} = 6.3 \times 10^{-8}\ M$$

Note that half of the I^- remaining in solution when AgCl begins to precipitate is *coprecipitated* as half of the Cl^- is precipitated.

THE DISSOLUTION OF PRECIPITATES

When the product of the molar concentrations of the ions, raised to the appropriate powers, can be made less than (<) the solubility product constant, the solid electrolyte completely dissolves or dissolves until the ion product is again equal to the solubility product constant. For example, calcium carbonate dissolves when

$$[Ca^{++}][CO_3^{=}] < K_{sp}$$

To achieve this condition it becomes necessary to make the concentration of at least one of the ions of the electrolyte smaller than that in a saturated solution.

Ions can be removed from saturated solutions of sparingly soluble electrolytes, and hence solid electrolytes dissolved, in the following ways: (1) by the formation of a weak electrolyte; (2) by a change in the charge on an ion; (3) by formation of a complex ion.

42.11 Dissolution of a Precipitate by the Formation of a Weak Electrolyte

Slightly soluble electrolytes which are derived from weak acids may often be dissolved by strong acids. For example, $CaCO_3$, FeS, and $Ca_3(PO_4)_2$ are dissolved by HCl due to the fact that H_2CO_3, H_2S, and $H_2PO_4^-$ are weak acids.

When hydrochloric acid is added to a precipitate of calcium carbonate in equilibrium with a saturated solution of its ions, the hydrogen ion from the acid combines with the carbonate ion and forms the slightly ionized hydrogen carbonate ion as follows:

$$H^+ + CO_3^{=} \rightleftharpoons HCO_3^-$$

Then, as the concentration of the hydrogen carbonate ion increases, it unites with hydrogen ions from the hydrochloric acid, according to the equation

$$H^+ + HCO_3^- \rightleftharpoons H_2CO_3$$

Finally, the solution becomes saturated with the slightly ionized and unstable carbonic acid, and carbon dioxide gas is evolved, as shown by the equation

$$H_2CO_3 \rightleftharpoons H_2O + CO_2$$

The above reactions cause the carbonate ion concentration to be reduced and maintained at such a low level that the product of the calcium and carbonate ion concentrations is less than the solubility product constant of calcium carbonate.

$$[Ca^{++}][CO_3^{=}] < K_{sp}$$

Consequently, the calcium carbonate dissolves. An acid as weak as acetic acid gives a concentration of hydrogen ion sufficiently high to bring about the dissolution of calcium carbonate because its ionization constant is greater than that for either the hydrogen carbonate ion or carbonic acid.

The dissolution of magnesium hydroxide in aqueous ammonium chloride is brought about by the formation of the weak electrolyte aqueous ammonia.

$$\underline{Mg(OH)_2} + 2\ NH_4^+ \rightleftharpoons Mg^{++} + 2\ NH_3 + 2\ H_2O$$

When an excess of ammonium ion is added to a suspension of magnesium hydroxide, the following reaction takes place

$$NH_4^+ + OH^- \rightleftharpoons NH_3 + H_2O$$

Consequently, the hydroxide ion concentration is lowered to the level such that

$$[Mg^{++}][OH^-]^2 < K_{sp}$$

and the magnesium hydroxide dissolves.

Slightly soluble lead sulfate dissolves readily in solutions of ammonium acetate because the formation of slightly ionized (but soluble) lead acetate reduces the product of the lead and sulfate ion concentrations below the value of the solubility product constant for lead sulfate.

$$\underline{PbSO_4} \rightleftharpoons Pb^{++} + SO_4^{=}$$

$$Pb^{++} + 2\ OAc^- \rightleftharpoons Pb(OAc)_2$$

$$[Pb^{++}][SO_4^{=}] < K_{sp}$$

The formation of slightly ionized water causes many sparingly soluble metal hydroxides such as $Mg(OH)_2$, $Al(OH)_3$, and $Fe(OH)_3$ to dissolve in solutions of acids.

$$\underline{Mg(OH)_2} + 2\ H^+ \rightarrow Mg^{++} + 2\ H_2O$$

$$[Mg^{++}][OH^-]^2 < K_{sp}$$

$$\underline{Al(OH)_3} + 3\ H^+ \rightarrow Al^{+++} + 3\ H_2O$$

$$[Al^{+++}][OH^-]^3 < K_{sp}$$

42.12 Dissolution of a Precipitate by a Change in the Charge on an Ion

Many metal sulfides have solubility product constants sufficiently large that the hydrogen ion of strong acids will lower the sulfide ion concentration enough by forming the weak electrolyte, hydrogen sulfide, to dissolve the sulfide. For example, iron (II) sulfide is readily dissolved by hydrochloric acid according to the equation

$$\underline{FeS} + 2\ H^+ \rightleftharpoons Fe^{++} + H_2S \uparrow$$

$$[Fe^{++}][S^{=}] < K_{sp}$$

However, a number of metal sulfides furnish such low concentrations of sulfide ion in their saturated solutions that the high concentration of hydrogen ion furnished by a strong acid is not sufficient to exceed the ion product constant of hydrogen sulfide and bring about the evolution of this gas. For the dissolution of such sulfides as lead sulfide, the sulfide ion concentration may be decreased by oxidizing it to elementary sulfur with nitric acid.

$$3\ S^{=} + 2\ NO_3^- + 8\ H^+ \rightarrow 3\ \underline{S} + 2\ NO \uparrow + 4\ H_2O$$

Lead sulfide dissolves in nitric acid, then, because

$$[Pb^{++}][S^{=}] < K_{sp}$$

resulting from the fact that much of the sulfide ion is oxidized to sulfur by the nitric acid.

42.13 Dissolution of a Precipitate by the Formation of a Complex Ion

Many slightly soluble electrolytes are dissolved through the formation of complex ions. Several examples which are important to qualitative analysis follow.

$$\underline{AgCl} + 2\ NH_3 \rightleftharpoons Ag(NH_3)_2^+ + Cl^-$$
$$\underline{CuCN} + CN^- \rightleftharpoons Cu(CN)_2^-$$
$$\underline{Zn(OH)_2} + 2\ OH^- \rightleftharpoons Zn(OH)_4^=$$
$$\underline{Sn(OH)_2} + OH^- \rightleftharpoons Sn(OH)_3^-$$
$$\underline{Al(OH)_3} + OH^- \rightleftharpoons Al(OH)_4^-$$
$$\underline{As_2S_3} + 3\ S^= \rightleftharpoons 2\ AsS_3^{-3}$$
$$\underline{HgS} + S^= \rightleftharpoons HgS_2^=$$
$$\underline{Sb_2S_3} + 3\ S^= \rightleftharpoons 2\ SbS_3^{-3}$$

Let us consider the case of the dissolution of silver chloride in aqueous ammonia. When silver ions and ammonia molecules are brought together in solution, the complex diamminesilver ion, $Ag(NH_3)_2^+$, is formed. This complex ion dissociates reversibly in aqueous solution according to the equation

$$Ag(NH_3)_2^+ \rightleftharpoons Ag^+ + 2\ NH_3$$

Applying the law of chemical equilibrium to this system, we obtain

$$\frac{[Ag^+][NH_3]^2}{[Ag(NH_3)_2^+]} = K_d = 6.8 \times 10^{-8}$$

The equilibrium constant, K_d, is a measure of the stability of the complex ion and is called the **dissociation constant;** the smaller the value of the constant, the more stable the complex. In a saturated solution of silver chloride, the Ag^+ concentration is determined by the value of the solubility product, K_{sp}. This Ag^+ concentration is greater than that which can exist in equilibrium with the ammonia which has been added.

$$\frac{[Ag^+][NH_3]^2}{[Ag(NH_3)_2^+]} > K_d$$

Therefore, silver ions and ammonia molecules combine, thus lowering the concentration of silver ions and bringing the product of the silver ion concentration and chloride ion concentration below the solubility product constant for silver chloride,

$$[Ag^+][Cl^-] < K_{sp}$$

and dissolution of some silver chloride results. If the concentration of ammonia is great enough, equilibrium will be reached only after all of the silver chloride has dissolved.

The copper (II) ion coordinates with four ammonia molecules and forms the complex, $Cu(NH_3)_4^{++}$. The expression for the dissociation constant is

$$\frac{[Cu^{++}][NH_3]^4}{[Cu(NH_3)_4^{++}]} = K_d$$

When a copper (II) solution is treated with dilute aqueous ammonia, copper (II) hydroxide first precipitates because the hydroxide ion concentration of the dilute ammonia solution is sufficiently large that the solubility product constant is exceeded.

$$[Cu^{++}][OH^-]^2 > K_{sp}$$

As the concentration of ammonia is increased, the dissociation constant of the complex ion, $Cu(NH_3)_4^{++}$ is exceeded.

$$\frac{[Cu^{++}][NH_3]^4}{[Cu(NH_3)_4^{++}]} > K_d$$

Note that the concentration of the copper (II) ion varies inversely as the fourth power of the concentration of ammonia and with the second power of the concentration of hydroxide ion. The combination of copper (II) ion with ammonia molecules makes the concentration of Cu^{++} so small that the condition for the dissolution of copper (II) hydroxide is attained.

$$[Cu^{++}][OH^-]^2 < K_d$$

42.14 Calculations Involving Complex Ions

EXAMPLE 1. Calculate the concentration of the silver ion in a solution which is 0.10 M with respect to $Ag(NH_3)_2^+$. The dissociation of the complex ion may be represented by the equilibrium

$$Ag(NH_3)_2^+ \rightleftharpoons Ag^+ + 2\ NH_3$$

Let X be the number of moles of $Ag(NH_3)_2^+$ which dissociate per liter. Then at equilibrium $[Ag^+]$ will be X, and $[NH_3]$ will be 2 X. From the small value of the dissociation constant we know that the dissociation must be small, and we can assume that the complex is practically 0.10 M at equilibrium. Therefore

$$\frac{[Ag^+][NH_3]^2}{[Ag(NH_3)_2^+]} = \frac{X(2\ X)^2}{0.10} = K_d = 6.8 \times 10^{-8}$$

$$4\ X^3 = 6.8 \times 10^{-9}$$

$$X^3 = 1.7 \times 10^{-9}$$

$$X = 1.2 \times 10^{-3}\ M = [Ag^+]$$

$$2\ X = 2.4 \times 10^{-3}\ M = [NH_3]$$

EXAMPLE 2. Calculate the number of moles of ammonia that must be added to one liter of water just to dissolve 1.0×10^{-3} mole of silver chloride. Writing the equation for the reaction

$$\underline{AgCl} + 2\ NH_3 \rightleftharpoons Ag(NH_3)_2^+ + Cl^-$$

we see that when 1.0×10^{-3} mole of AgCl is dissolved, 1.0×10^{-3} mole of $Ag(NH_3)_2^+$ and 1.0×10^{-3} mole of Cl^- are formed. Two equilibria are involved when AgCl dissolves in aqueous ammonia.

$$AgCl\ (solid) \rightleftharpoons Ag^+ + Cl^-$$

$$Ag(NH_3)_2^+ \rightleftharpoons Ag^+ + 2\ NH_3$$

The $[Ag^+]$ in solution applies to both equilibria when both solid AgCl and $Ag(NH_3)_2^+$ ions are present in the system. Since the $[Cl^-]$ is 1.0×10^{-3}, we may calculate the $[Ag^+]$ using the solubility product expression for AgCl.

$$[Ag^+][Cl^-] = [Ag^+](1.0 \times 10^{-3}) = 1.2 \times 10^{-10}$$

$$[Ag^+] = \frac{1.2 \times 10^{-10}}{1.0 \times 10^{-3}} = 1.2 \times 10^{-7}\ M$$

By substituting in the expression for the dissociation constant of $Ag(NH_3)_2^+$ the values for $[Ag^+]$ and $[Ag(NH_3)_2^+]$, we can calculate the $[NH_3]$ required at equilibrium.

$$\frac{[Ag^+][NH_3]^2}{[Ag(NH_3)_2^+]} = \frac{(1.2 \times 10^{-7})[NH_3]^2}{1.0 \times 10^{-3}} = 6.8 \times 10^{-8}$$

$$[NH_3]^2 = \frac{(1.0 \times 10^{-3})(6.8 \times 10^{-8})}{1.2 \times 10^{-7}} = 5.7 \times 10^{-4}$$

$$[NH_3] = 2.4 \times 10^{-2}\ M$$

In this calculation the amount of ammonia consumed in forming the complex ion is $2(1.0 \times 10^{-3})$ or 0.002 mole, which is to be added to the 2.4×10^{-2} or 0.024 mole of ammonia required at equilibrium. Thus, the total ammonia required for dissolution of 1.0×10^{-3} mole of AgCl in a liter of water is 0.026 mole.

QUESTIONS

1. A saturated solution of a slightly soluble electrolyte in contact with some of the solid phase of the electrolyte is a system in equilibrium. Explain. Why is such a system called a heterogeneous equilibrium?

2. Write the expression for the solubility product constant of each of the following slightly soluble electrolytes: AgBr, $PbCl_2$, Ag_2S, $MgNH_4AsO_4$, and $Ba_3(PO_4)_2$.

3. If solid silver bromide is in equilibrium with a saturated solution of its ions, Ag^+ and Br^-, will this equilibrium be affected and in what manner if (a) more solid silver bromide is added? (b) silver nitrate is added? (c) sodium bromide is added? (d) the temperature is raised (the solubility increases with tempera ture)?

4. State the rule regarding the precipitation of slightly soluble electrolytes.

5. Can an ion ever be completely removed from solution by the use of a large excess of the precipitant? Explain.

6. Explain why the concentration of a solid is a constant.

7. What is meant by fractional precipitation?

8. What is the rule regarding the dissolution of precipitates relative to the product of the concentration of its ions?

9. What three general methods are used to dissolve slightly soluble electrolytes?

10. What is meant by the dissociation of a complex ion? Illustrate.

PROBLEMS

1. Calculate the solubility product constant of each of the following from the molar solubility given: (a) AgI (1.23×10^{-8} mole/liter); (b) Ag_2CO_3 (1.27×10^{-4} mole/liter). *Ans.* (*a*) 1.5×10^{-16}; (*b*) 8.2×10^{-12}

2. The solubility of SrF_2 is 1.22×10^{-2} g./liter. Calculate its solubility product constant. *Ans.* 3.7×10^{-12}

3. Calculate the solubility in moles per liter for each of the following substances from its solubility product constant:

(a) $CaCO_3$, $K_{sp} = 4.8 \times 10^{-9}$ *Ans.* 6.9×10^{-5}

(b) BaF_2, $K_{sp} = 1.7 \times 10^{-6}$ *Ans.* 6.8×10^{-3}

(c) $Pb(OH)_2$, $K_{sp} = 2.8 \times 10^{-16}$ *Ans.* 4.8×10^{-6}

(d) $Fe(OH)_3$, $K_{sp} = 1.1 \times 10^{-36}$ *Ans.* 4.5×10^{-10}

(e) CaC_2O_4, $K_{sp} = 2.27 \times 10^{-9}$ *Ans.* 4.76×10^{-5}

4. The K_{sp} for AgI is 1.5×10^{-16}. Calculate the maximum concentration of silver ion that can exist in a solution that is 0.10 M in HI.

Ans. 1.5×10^{-15} *mole/liter*

5. (a) Calculate the silver ion concentration in a saturated aqueous solution of silver bromide for which K_{sp} is 3.3×10^{-13}. *Ans.* 5.7×10^{-7} *M*

(b) What will be the $[Ag^+]$ when enough NaBr has been added to make $[Br^-] = 0.20$ M? *Ans.* 1.6×10^{-12} *M*

(c) What will be the $[Br^-]$ when enough $AgNO_3$ has been added to make $[Ag^+] = 0.010$ M? *Ans.* 3.3×10^{-11} *M*

6. Calculate $[Ca^{++}]$ required to start the precipitation of calcium fluoride from a solution that is 0.0050 M in fluoride ions. ($K_{sp} = 3.9 \times 10^{-11}$.)

Ans. 1.6×10^{-6} *M*

7. Calculate the maximum concentration of barium ion in a solution in which the molar concentration of sulfate ion is 0.030. ($K_{sp} = 1.08 \times 10^{-10}$.)

Ans. 3.6×10^{-9} *M*

8. In one experiment, a precipitate of $BaSO_4$ was washed with 100 ml. of distilled water; in another experiment, a precipitate of $BaSO_4$ was washed with 100 ml. of 0.010 M H_2SO_4. Calculate the quantity of $BaSO_4$ which dissolved in each experiment, assuming that the wash liquid became saturated with $BaSO_4$. (K_{sp} of $BaSO_4 = 1.08 \times 10^{-10}$.) *Ans.* 1.04×10^{-6} *mole;* 1.08×10^{-9} *mole*

9. With what volume of water must a precipitate of AgBr be washed in order for 0.200 mg. of AgBr to be dissolved? Assume that the wash water becomes saturated with AgBr. (K_{sp} of AgBr $= 3.30 \times 10^{-13}$.) *Ans.* *1.86 l.*

10. Calculate the minimum chromate ion concentration required to initiate the precipitation of $BaCrO_4$ from a solution that is 0.001 M in barium ion. ($K_{sp} = 2 \times 10^{-10}$.) *Ans.* 2×10^{-7}

11. What is the concentration of Ca^{++} and $CO_3^{=}$ in a saturated solution of calcium carbonate? ($K_{sp} = 4.8 \times 10^{-9}$.) *Ans.* $[Ca^{++}] = [CO_3^{=}] = 6.9 \times 10^{-5}$ *M*

12. A 20 ml. volume of a solution which is 1×10^{-6} M in barium chloride is added to 80 ml. of a 1×10^{-2} M sodium sulfate solution. Will barium sulfate precipitate? (K_{sp} for $BaSO_4$ is 1.08×10^{-10}.) *Ans.* *Yes*

13. The solubility product constant of $CaSO_4 \cdot 2\,H_2O$ is 2.4×10^{-5}. Calculate the number of moles of this salt that will dissolve in 1.0 liter of 0.10 M K_2SO_4.

Ans. 2.4×10^{-4}

14. A 50 ml. volume of solution containing 1.2 g. of $MgCl_2$ is mixed with an equal volume of 1.8 M aqueous ammonia. What weight of solid NH_4Cl must be added to the resulting solution to prevent the precipitation of $Mg(OH)_2$? (K_{sp} of $Mg(OH)_2 = 1.5 \times 10^{-11}$; K_i of NH_3 is 1.8×10^{-5}.) *Ans.* *7.9 g.*

15. What pH is necessary for the initiation of precipitation of cobalt (II) hydroxide from a solution of cobalt (II) sulfate which contains 1.00 mg./ml. of cobalt (II) ion? (K_{sp} of $Co(OH)_2 = 2.0 \times 10^{-16}$.) *Ans.* *7.0*

16. What concentration of Zn^{++} must be present in a solution that has a pH of 9.0 in order to initiate precipitation of $Zn(OH)_2$? (K_{sp} for $Zn(OH)_2$ is 4.5×10^{-17}.) *Ans.* *4.5×10^{-7} M*

17. What is the molar solubility of Fe^{+++} in a solution having a pH of 12.0? (K_{sp} for $Fe(OH)_3$ is 1.1×10^{-36}.) *Ans.* *1.1×10^{-30}*

18. Calculate the maximum pH that a solution must have in order that CoS will not precipitate in a solution that contains 0.010 mole of $CoCl_2$ per liter and is saturated with hydrogen sulfide. A saturated solution of hydrogen sulfide is 0.10 M. (K_{sp} for CoS is 5.9×10^{-21}; $[H^+]^2[S^=] = 1.3 \times 10^{-21}$.) *Ans.* *1.3*

19. With what volume of water must a precipitate of PbF_2 be washed to dissolve 0.50 mg. of the salt? Assume that the wash water becomes saturated with PbF_2. (K_{sp} of PbF_2 is 3.7×10^{-8}.) *Ans.* *0.97 ml.*

20. The K_{sp} for $PbBr_2$ is 6.3×10^{-6}. How much Pb^{++} in moles per liter may be added to a solution containing 30 grams of KBr in 300 ml. of solution without causing lead bromide to precipitate? *Ans.* *7.5×10^{-6} mole/liter*

21. A solution is made 0.01 M in Ca^{++} and 0.04 M in OH^-. The K_{sp} of $Ca(OH)_2$ is 7.9×10^{-6}. Will this substance precipitate under the conditions stated? *Ans.* *Yes*

22. The K_{sp} of $Mg(OH)_2$ is 1.5×10^{-11}. Calculate the pH of a saturated solution of magnesium hydroxide. *Ans.* *10.5*

23. The K_{sp} of PbF_2 is 3.7×10^{-8}; that of $PbCl_2$, 1.7×10^{-5}; and that of $PbBr_2$, 6.3×10^{-6}. Calculate the maximum concentrations of lead ion in separate solutions which are 0.1 M with respect to HF, HCl, and HBr, respectively. *Ans.* *3.7×10^{-6} M; 1.7×10^{-3} M; 6.3×10^{-4}* M

24. A liter of solution contains 0.010 mole of Na_2SO_4 and 0.010 mole of NaI. Solid $Pb(NO_3)_2$ is gradually added to this solution. (a) Which will precipitate first, $PbSO_4$ or PbI_2? (b) What will be the concentration of $SO_4^=$ in the solution when PbI_2 begins to precipitate upon the continued addition of $Pb(NO_3)_2$? (K_{sp} for $PbSO_4 = 1.8 \times 10^{-8}$; K_{sp} for $PbI_2 = 8.7 \times 10^{-9}$.) *Ans.* *(a) $PbSO_4$; (b) 2.1×10^{-4} M*

25. To a saturated aqueous solution of silver chloride, sufficient hydrochloric acid is added to make the total chloride ion concentration 0.30 M. Calculate the concentration of Ag^+. (K_{sp} for silver chloride is 1.2×10^{-10}.) *Ans.* *6.4×10^{-10} M*

26. A 0.20 M solution of $CdCl_2$ is made 0.10 M in hydrogen ion by the addition of hydrochloric acid and then saturated with hydrogen sulfide. What concentration of cadmium ion will remain in solution? (K_{sp} for CdS is 3.6×10^{-29}.) (Do not neglect the hydrogen ions produced by the reaction of Cd^{++} with H_2S.) *Ans.* *6.9×10^{-9} M*

27. A solution is 0.10 M in $FeCl_2$. What concentration of hydrogen ion must be present so that no iron (II) sulfide will precipitate when the solution is saturated with hydrogen sulfide? A saturated solution of hydrogen sulfide is 0.10 M. (K_{sp} for FeS is 1.0×10^{-19}.) *Ans.* *3.6×10^{-2} M*

28. How many moles of ammonium chloride must be added to 50 ml. of 0.10 M aqueous ammonia to prevent precipitation of $Mn(OH)_2$, when this solution is added to 50 ml. of a 0.04 M solution of $MnCl_2$? ($K_{NH_3} = 1.8 \times 10^{-5}$; K_{sp} for $Mn(OH)_2 = 4.5 \times 10^{-14}$.) *Ans.* *0.06 mole*

29. To a liter of solution that is 0.10 M in $CrO_4^=$ and 0.10 M in $SO_4^=$, solid strontium chloride is added slowly. Assuming no volume change, (a) at what $[Sr^{++}]$ will $SrSO_4$ begin to precipitate? (K_{sp} for $SrSO_4$ is 2.8×10^{-7}; K_{sp} for $SrCrO_4$ is 3.6×10^{-5}.) *Ans.* 2.8×10^{-6} *M*
(b) at what $[Sr^{++}]$ will $SrCrO_4$ begin to precipitate? *Ans.* 3.6×10^{-4} *M*
(c) which strontium salt will precipitate first, $SrSO_4$ or $SrCrO_4$? *Ans.* $SrSO_4$
(d) what will be the concentration of $SO_4^=$ in the solution when $SrCrO_4$ begins to precipitate? *Ans.* 7.8×10^{-4} *M*
(e) what will be the ratio of $[CrO_4^=]$ to $[SO_4^=]$ at this point? *Ans.* *128 to 1*

30. What concentration of silver ion remains in solution when a 0.10 M solution of $AgNO_3$ is treated with solid NaCl in a quantity 10% in excess of the amount equivalent to the silver nitrate present in the solution? (K_{sp} for $AgCl = 1.2 \times 10^{-10}$.) *Ans.* 1.2×10^{-8} M

31. What would be the concentration of Pb^{++} in a solution made by washing a precipitate of $PbSO_4$ with 100 ml. of 0.01 M K_2SO_4 solution? (K_{sp} for $PbSO_4 = 1.8 \times 10^{-8}$.) *Ans.* 1.8×10^{-6} *M*

32. Calculate the $[Cu^{++}]$ in a solution of 0.067 M $[Cu(NH_3)_4]SO_4$. ($K_d = 4.6 \times 10^{-14}$.) *Ans.* 4.1×10^{-4} *M*

33. Calculate the $[Ag^+]$ in a 0.2 M solution of $Na[Ag(CN)_2]$. ($K_d = 1 \times 10^{-20}$.) *Ans.* 8×10^{-6} *M*

34. In the preparation of 0.10 M $[Ag(NH_3)_2]^+$, an excess of NH_3 was used, making the resulting solution 5.1 M with respect to NH_3. Calculate the concentration of silver ion in the solution. (K_d for $[Ag(NH_3)_2]^+$ is 6.8×10^{-8}.) *Ans.* 2.6×10^{-10} *M*

35. Calculate the concentration of free Fe^{+++} ions in a 0.1 M solution of $K_3[Fe(CN)_6]$. ($K_d = 1 \times 10^{-44}$.) *Ans.* 8×10^{-8} *M*

36. Calculate the minimum number of moles of cyanide ion that must be added to 50 ml. of water to dissolve 1×10^{-2} moles of AgCN. (K_{sp} for AgCN is 1.2×10^{-16}; K_d for $[Ag(CN)_2]^-$ is 1×10^{-20}.) *Ans.* 1×10^{-2} *mole*

37. Calculate the volume of 4.0 M HOAc required to dissolve a precipitate composed of 200 mg. each of $CaCO_3$, $BaCO_3$, and $SrCO_3$. *Ans.* *2.2 ml.*

REFERENCE

"The Solubility Product Constants of the Metallic Sulfides," W. H. Waggoner, *J. Chem. Educ.*, **35** (7) 339 (1958).

CHAPTER FORTY-THREE

Hydrolysis

When a salt is dissolved in water the resulting solution may be neutral, basic, or acidic, depending upon the nature of the salt. A salt formed from a strong acid and a strong base, such as NaCl, yields an aqueous solution which is practically neutral. A salt of a strong base and a weak acid, such as NaOAc, forms aqueous solutions which are basic. A salt of a weak base and a strong acid, such as NH_4Cl, gives an acidic reaction in water. A salt of a weak acid and a weak base may form neutral, basic, or acidic solutions, depending upon the relative strengths or solubilities of the acid and the base. Many of the substances reacting with water do so in such a way as to disturb the normal concentration of the hydrogen and hydroxide ions formed through the auto-ionization of water. A reaction of this type, in which water is one of the reactants, is called **hydrolysis.** The theory of the hydrolysis of salts of the types listed above will be given in the sections which follow.

As has been pointed out in earlier chapters, ions known to be hydrated in water solution are often indicated, for convenience, in abbreviated form without showing the hydration; for example, H^+ for H_3O^+, and Cu^{++} for $[Cu(H_2O)_4]^{++}$. However, when water is a participant in the reaction, as in hydrolysis reactions, indication of the hydration of the ions becomes important. In this chapter, therefore, we will use formulas which show the hydration when important for an understanding of the reaction involved.

43.1 Salt of a Strong Acid and a Strong Base

A salt consisting of a cation from a strong hydroxide base (such as NaOH) and an anion from a strong acid (such as HCl) forms neutral aqueous solutions. This means that the ions of sodium chloride do not react with water in such a way as to alter the normal concentration of the hydrogen and hydroxyl ions which are formed through the ionization of the solvent ($H_2O \rightleftharpoons H^+ + OH^-$, or $2\,H_2O \rightleftharpoons H_3O^+ + OH^-$). The salts of the alkali metals and alkaline earth metals with the halogen acids, nitric acid, sulfuric acid, and perchloric acid are examples of salts that give neutral aqueous solutions; i.e., these salts do not undergo appreciable hydrolysis.

43.2 Salt of a Strong Base and a Weak Acid

Experiment shows that when sodium acetate is dissolved in water, the solution becomes alkaline. This result must be due to an increase in the concentration of the hydroxide ion and a decrease in the concentration of the hydrogen ion (or, more exactly, hydronium ion) of the solution. The acetate ion is the anion of a weak acid, acetic acid. The concentration of hydrogen ion supplied by the water, 10^{-7} M, is too large to exist in equilibrium with the high concentration of acetate ion supplied by the salt sodium acetate. As a consequence, some undissociated acetic acid forms, according to the equation

$$OAc^- + H^+ \rightleftharpoons HOAc$$

or

$$OAc^- + H_3O^+ \rightleftharpoons HOAc + H_2O$$

The hydrogen ion is formed by the ionization of water.

$$H_2O \rightleftharpoons H^+ + OH^- \quad (\text{or} \quad 2\,H_2O \rightleftharpoons H_3O^+ + OH^-)$$

As acetate ions combine with hydrogen ions derived from the ionization of water, the second equilibrium shifts to the right, and more hydrogen ions and hydroxide ions are formed. The net result is that the solution becomes slightly basic due to the accumulation of hydroxide ions in the solution. The net reaction may be expressed by the equation

$$OAc^- + H_2O \rightleftharpoons HOAc + OH^-$$

Applying the law of chemical equilibrium to the reaction of the acetate ion with water, we obtain the following expression for the equilibrium constant:

$$\frac{[HOAc][OH^-]}{[OAc^-][H_2O]} = K_e$$

Because the number of moles of water consumed in the reaction is negligibly small compared with the total number of moles of water present in dilute solution, we may assume that the molar concentration of the water remains unchanged during the hydrolysis. Hence, we have

$$\frac{[HOAc][OH^-]}{[OAc^-]} = K_e[H_2O] = K_h$$

The constant K_h is called the **hydrolysis constant.** When K_h is small, the degree of hydrolysis is slight; when it is large, hydrolysis is extensive.

We may obtain the value of K_h for the hydrolysis of sodium acetate from the values for the ionization constants of water and of acetic acid. This follows because the hydrolysis involves the two equilibria, (a) the ionization of water, $H_2O \rightleftharpoons H^+ + OH^-$, and (b) the ionization of acetic acid, $HOAc \rightleftharpoons H^+ + OAc^-$. For every aqueous solution

$$[H^+][OH^-] = K_w, \quad \text{or} \quad [OH^-] = \frac{K_w}{[H^+]}$$

Substituting $K_w/[H^+]$ for $[OH^-]$ in the expression for the hydrolysis constant, we obtain

$$\frac{[HOAc][OH^-]}{[OAc^-]} = \frac{[HOAc]K_w}{[OAc^-][H^+]} = K_h$$

But the expression $\frac{[HOAc]}{[OAc^-][H^+]}$ is the reciprocal of K_i and is therefore equal to $\frac{1}{K_i \text{ (for HOAc)}}$. Therefore

$$\frac{K_w}{K_i} = K_h = \frac{1.0 \times 10^{-14}}{1.8 \times 10^{-5}} = 5.6 \times 10^{-10}$$

43.3 Salt of a Weak Base and a Strong Acid

Now let us consider the hydrolysis of ammonium chloride, which is a salt of a weak base and a strong acid. The chloride ion is such a weak base that it does not combine appreciably with the hydrogen ion of water. However, the ammonium ion tends to react with the hydroxide ion of water according to the equation

$$NH_4^+ + OH^- \rightleftharpoons NH_3 + H_2O$$

Removal of hydroxide ions from solution causes the equilibrium

$$2\ H_2O \rightleftharpoons H_3O^+ + OH^-$$

to shift to the right and leaves an excess of hydronium ions in solution. The hydrolysis of the ammonium ion may be represented by the net equation obtained by adding the two equations given above. Thus, we have

$$NH_4^+ + H_2O \rightleftharpoons NH_3 + H_3O^+$$

It is not sufficient in this case to write

$$NH_4^+ \rightleftharpoons NH_3 + H^+$$

for this implies a spontaneous loss of a proton by the ammonium ion. Actually, such loss takes place only because the solvent water attracts the proton more strongly than does the ammonia.

The expression for the hydrolysis constant for the hydrolysis of the ammonium ion, based on the equation $NH_4^+ + H_2O \rightleftharpoons NH_3 + H_3O^+$, is written as

$$\frac{[NH_3][H_3O^+]}{[NH_4^+]} = K_h$$

Substituting $K_w/[OH^-]$ for $[H_3O^+]$ in the above equation, we obtain

$$\frac{[NH_3]\ K_w}{[NH_4^+][OH^-]} = K_h$$

Because the expresssion $\frac{[NH_3]}{[NH_4^+][OH^-]}$ is equal to $\frac{1}{K_i \text{ (for } NH_3)}$ we may write

$$K_h = \frac{K_w}{K_i} = \frac{1.0 \times 10^{-14}}{1.8 \times 10^{-5}} = 5.6 \times 10^{-10}$$

43.4 Salt of a Weak Base and a Weak Acid

When ammonium acetate is dissolved in water we have, in solution, ammonium ions and acetate ions, both of which undergo hydrolysis. The equations are

$$NH_4^+ + H_2O \rightleftharpoons NH_3 + H_3O^+$$
$$OAc^- + H_2O \rightleftharpoons HOAc + OH^-$$

The extent to which these reactions take place is approximately the same because aqueous ammonia and acetic acid have nearly equal ionization constants. Therefore the hydrolytic products are present in equal concentrations at equilibrium. As hydronium and hydroxide ions are produced by these reactions they unite to form water, for the product of their concentrations cannot exceed 1×10^{-14}. Because these ions are formed and removed from solution in equal amounts, the solution remains neutral as hydrolysis proceeds.

The net reaction involved in the hydrolysis may be looked upon as the sum of the three equations

$$\begin{array}{l} NH_4^+ + H_2O \rightleftharpoons NH_3 + H_3O^+ \\ OAc^- + H_2O \rightleftharpoons HOAc + OH^- \\ \underline{H_3O^+ + OH^- \rightleftharpoons 2\,H_2O} \\ NH_4^+ + OAc^- \rightleftharpoons HOAc + NH_3 \end{array}$$

Applying the law of chemical equilibrium to this system, we obtain

$$\frac{[NH_3][HOAc]}{[NH_4^+][OAc^-]} = K_h$$

To evaluate the hydrolysis constant in terms of the ion product constant for water and the ionization constants for aqueous ammonia and acetic acid, multiply the numerator and denominator of the above equation by $[H_3O^+] \times [OH^-]$.

$$\frac{[NH_3]}{[NH_4^+][OH^-]} \times \frac{[HOAc]}{[H_3O^+][OAc^-]} \times \frac{[H_3O^+][OH^-]}{1} = K_h$$

Thus it may readily be seen that

$$K_h = \frac{K_w}{K_i \text{ (for } NH_3) \times K_i \text{ (for HOAc)}} = \frac{1.0 \times 10^{-14}}{(1.8 \times 10^{-5})(1.8 \times 10^{-5})} = 3.1 \times 10^{-5}$$

When the hydrolytic products of a salt of a weak base and a weak acid do not have the same ionization constants, the aqueous solution of the salt is either basic or acidic, depending upon which electrolyte has the larger ionization constant. For example, ammonium cyanide hydrolyzes to give a basic solution because K_i for NH_3 is larger than K_i for HCN. This means that the hydrolysis of the cyanide ion, $CN^- + H_2O \rightleftharpoons HCN + OH^-$, is more extensive than that of the ammonium ion, $NH_4^+ + H_2O \rightleftharpoons NH_3 + H_3O^+$, and that an excess of hydroxide ions will accumulate in the solution.

43.5 Calculations Involving the Hydrolysis of Salts

EXAMPLE 1. Calculate the hydroxide ion concentration, the degree of hydrolysis, and the pH of a 0.10 M solution of sodium acetate.

We have seen that the equation for the hydrolysis of sodium acetate is

$$OAc^- + H_2O \rightleftharpoons HOAc + OH^-$$

and that the expression for the hydrolysis constant is

$$\frac{[HOAc][OH^-]}{[OAc^-]} = K_h = \frac{K_w}{K_i} = 5.6 \times 10^{-10}$$

If we let X equal the concentration of molecular acetic acid formed by the hydrolysis of the acetate ion, then the concentration of hydroxide ion will also be equal to X, and the concentration of acetate ion at equilibrium will be 0.10 – X. Substituting in the hydrolysis constant expression above, we have

$$\frac{X^2}{0.10 - X} = 5.6 \times 10^{-10}$$

Since X is very small compared with 0.10, we may drop it in the denominator. Then,

$$X^2 = 0.10 \times 5.6 \times 10^{-10} = 56 \times 10^{-12}$$
$$X = 7.5 \times 10^{-6} = [HAc] = [OH^-]$$

Thus the concentration of hydroxide ion is 7.5×10^{-6} M, and the percentage hydrolysis is equal to

$$\frac{[HOAc]}{[OAc^-]} \times 100 = \frac{7.5 \times 10^{-6}}{0.10} \times 100 = 0.0075 \text{ per cent}$$

We can calculate the pH of the solution by first finding the hydronium ion concentration

$$[H_3O^+] = \frac{K_w}{[OH^-]} = \frac{1.0 \times 10^{-14}}{7.5 \times 10^{-6}} = 1.3 \times 10^{-9}$$

and then,

$$pH = -\log [H_3O^+] = -\log (1.3 \times 10^{-9}) = -(0.1 - 9) = 8.9$$

EXAMPLE 2. Calculate the sulfide ion concentration and the degree of hydrolysis in a 0.0010 M solution of sodium sulfide.

The sulfide ion hydrolyzes according to the equation

$$S^= + H_2O \rightleftharpoons HS^- + OH^-$$

The hydrosulfide ion thus formed also undergoes hydrolysis, but its extent is so slight compared with that of the sulfide ion that it can be neglected. The expression for the hydrolysis constant of the sulfide ion is

$$\frac{[HS^-][OH^-]}{[S^=]} = K_h = \frac{K_w}{K_i \text{ (for } HS^-)} = \frac{1.0 \times 10^{-14}}{1.3 \times 10^{-13}} = 7.7 \times 10^{-2}$$

The large value for the hydrolysis constant indicates that most of the sulfide ion undergoes hydrolysis. For this reason we shall let X equal the $S^=$ concentration when hydrolytic equilibrium has been established. Then the concentrations of HS^-

and OH^-, which are equal to each other, may each be represented by 0.0010 − X. Substituting these values in the expression, we have

$$\frac{[HS^-][OH^-]}{[S^=]} = \frac{(0.0010 - X)(0.0010 - X)}{X} = 7.7 \times 10^{-2}$$

But since hydrolysis is nearly complete, X is now small as compared to 0.0010 and may be neglected in the numerator. The expression then becomes

$$\frac{(0.0010)^2}{X} = 7.7 \times 10^{-2}$$

$$X = \frac{(1.0 \times 10^{-3})^2}{7.7 \times 10^{-2}} = 1.3 \times 10^{-5} = [S^=]$$

The degree of hydrolysis may be found by dividing the amount of $S^=$ hydrolyzed (0.0010 M − 0.000013 M = 0.00099 M) by the total amount of $S^=$ originally present. Then the percentage hydrolysis is obtained by multiplying by 100.

$$\frac{0.00099}{0.0010} \times 100 = 99 \text{ per cent}$$

Example 3. Calculate the degree of hydrolysis and the pH of a solution that is 1.0 M in NH_4CN.

When ammonium cyanide is dissolved in water, both the ammonium ion and the cyanide undergo hydrolysis. The equations are

$$NH_4^+ + H_2O \rightleftharpoons NH_3 + H_3O^+$$
$$CN^- + H_2O \rightleftharpoons HCN + OH^-$$
$$H_3O^+ + OH^- \rightleftharpoons 2\,H_2O$$

The net reaction is given by the equation

$$NH_4^+ + CN^- \rightleftharpoons NH_3 + HCN$$

The expression for the hydrolysis constant may be written

$$\frac{[NH_3][HCN]}{[NH_4^+][CN^-]} = K_h = \frac{K_w}{K_i\text{ (for }NH_3) \times K_i\text{ (for HCN)}} = \frac{1.0 \times 10^{-14}}{(1.8 \times 10^{-5})(4 \times 10^{-10})} = 1.4$$

It can be shown that it is justifiable to assume that for every NH_4^+ that hydrolyzes, a CN^- also hydrolyzes, provided the NH_4CN concentration is not extremely low. Let X equal the number of moles of NH_4^+ and the number of moles of CN^- undergoing hydrolysis. At equilibrium, then, the $[NH_4^+] = (1.0 - X)$ and the $[NH_3] = [HCN] = X$. Substituting, we have

$$\frac{[NH_3][HCN]}{[NH_4^+][CN^-]} = \frac{X^2}{(1.0 - X)^2} = 1.4$$

Extracting the square root of both sides of the equation, we find

$$\frac{X}{1.0 - X} = 1.18$$

$$X = 1.18 - 1.18\,X$$

$$2.18\,X = 1.18$$

$$X = 0.54 = [NH_3] = [HCN]$$

The degree of hydrolysis is the amount of NH_4CN hydrolyzed divided by the total amount of NH_4CN originally present. The per cent hydrolysis is

$$\frac{0.54}{1.0} \times 100 = 54 \text{ per cent}$$

At equilibrium, $[NH_4^+] = [CN^-] = (1.0 - X) = (1.0 - 0.54) = 0.46$, and substituting in the expression for the ionization constant for HCN, we find

$$\frac{[H^+][CN^-]}{[HCN]} = \frac{[H^+](0.46)}{0.54} = 4 \times 10^{-10}$$

$$[H^+] = \frac{0.54}{0.46} \times (4 \times 10^{-10}) = 4.7 \times 10^{-10}$$

$$pH = -\log (4.7 \times 10^{-10}) = 9$$

43.6 The Hydrolysis of Metal Ions

A large number of metal ions hydrolyze to give acidic solutions. They disturb the normal hydronium and hydroxide concentration of water by removing hydroxide ions from solution. For example, the aluminum ion reacts with water according to the equations

$$Al^{+++} + 6\ H_2O \rightleftharpoons [Al(H_2O)_6]^{+++}$$

$$[Al(H_2O)_6]^{+++} + H_2O \rightleftharpoons [Al(OH)(H_2O)_5]^{++} + H_3O^+$$

leaving an excess of hydronium ions in solution. The aluminum ion hydrolyzes in stages just as polyprotic acids ionize in more than one stage, as shown by the equations

$$[Al(OH)(H_2O)_5]^{++} + H_2O \rightleftharpoons [Al(OH)_2(H_2O)_4]^+ + H_3O^+$$

$$[Al(OH)_2(H_2O)_4]^+ + H_2O \rightleftharpoons [Al(OH)_3(H_2O)_3] + H_3O^+$$

Just as in the ionization of polyprotic acids, such as H_3PO_4, the hydrolysis of cations carrying more than one charge is not extensive beyond the first stage. Additional examples of the first stage in the hydrolysis of metal ions are provided by the following equations

$$[Fe(H_2O)_6]^{+++} + H_2O \rightleftharpoons [Fe(OH)(H_2O)_5]^{++} + H_3O^+$$

$$[Cu(H_2O)_4]^{++} + H_2O \rightleftharpoons [Cu(OH)(H_2O)_3]^+ + H_3O^+$$

$$[Zn(H_2O)_4]^{++} + H_2O \rightleftharpoons [Zn(OH)(H_2O)_3]^+ + H_3O^+$$

Let us calculate the pH of a 0.10 M solution of aluminum chloride, given that the hydrolysis constant for the reaction $[Al(H_2O)_6]^{+++} + H_2O \rightleftharpoons [Al(OH)(H_2O)_5]^{++} + H_3O^+$ is 1.4×10^{-5}. The expression for the hydrolysis constant is written as

$$\frac{[Al(OH)(H_2O)_5{}^+][H_3O^+]}{[Al(H_2O)_6{}^{+++}]} = K_h = 1.4 \times 10^{-5}$$

Let X equal the concentration of the hydronium ion, which is in turn equal to the concentration of $[Al(OH)H_2O)_5]^{++}$. Then $0.10 - X$ will equal the concentration of $[Al(H_2O)_6]^{+++}$. Substituting in the expression for the hydrolysis constant, we have

$$\frac{[Al(OH)(H_2O)_5{}^{++}][H_3O^+]}{[Al(H_2O)_6{}^{+++}]} = \frac{X^2}{0.10 - X} = 1.4 \times 10^{-5}$$

Because K_h is small, X will also be small, and we may drop the X in the term $0.10 - X$ in an approximate solution of the problem. Thus, we obtain

$$\frac{X^2}{0.10} = 1.4 \times 10^{-5}$$
$$X = 1.2 \times 10^{-3}\,M = [H^+]$$
$$pH = -\log(1.2 \times 10^{-3}) = 2.9$$

Because the constants for the different stages of hydrolysis are not known for most metal ions, we cannot calculate the degree of hydrolysis for most metal ions which we know to be hydrolyzed in solution. However, if the hydroxide of a metal ion is insoluble in water, we may conclude that the metal ion will hydrolyze to give an acidic solution. In fact, practically all metal ions other than those of the alkali and alkaline earth metals hydrolyze to give acidic solutions.

43.7 Additional Examples of Hydrolysis

Many salts hydrolyze when they are dissolved in water with the formation of precipitates, with the evolution of gases, or both. For example, when aluminum sulfide (Al_2S_3) is dissolved in water, insoluble aluminum hydroxide is formed and hydrogen sulfide gas is evolved. The aluminum ions combine with the hydroxide ions of water, and the sulfide ions unite with the hydrogen ions of water according to the equations

$$2\,[Al(H_2O)_6]^{+++} + 6\,OH^- \rightleftharpoons 2\,\underline{[Al(OH)_3(H_2O)_3]} + 6\,H_2O$$
$$3\,S^= + 6\,H_3O^+ \rightleftharpoons 3\,H_2S\uparrow + 6\,H_2O$$
$$12\,H_2O \rightleftharpoons 6\,H_3O^+ + 6\,OH^-$$

The net reaction is given by the equation

$$2\,[Al(H_2O)_6]^{+++} + 3\,S^= \rightleftharpoons 2\,\underline{[Al(OH)_3(H_2O)_3]} + 3\,H_2S\uparrow$$

The aluminum sulfide cannot be recovered by crystallization after it has undergone hydrolytic decomposition. Many other salts behave similarly toward water.

When a relatively insoluble sulfide such as lead sulfide, PbS, is dissolved in water until a saturated solution is formed, an appreciable amount of the sulfide ion hydrolyzes to form the hydrosulfide ion.

$$\underline{PbS} \rightleftharpoons Pb^{++} + S^=$$
$$S^= + H_2O \rightleftharpoons HS^- + OH^-$$

For this reason the lead ion concentration is not the same as that of the sulfide ion under these conditions. The concentration of the lead ion is very nearly equal to the sum of the concentrations of the sulfide and hydrosulfide ions. This means that in calculating the solubility of a relatively insoluble sulfide from the solubility product constant, one must take into account the hydrolysis of the sulfide ion.

Let us first calculate the solubility of PbS in water neglecting the hydrolysis of the sulfide ion. (K_{sp} for PbS is 8.4×10^{-28}.) Let X equal the molar solubility of lead sulfide in water. Then X will also be equal to the concentration of the lead ion and the sulfide ion. Substituting in the expression for the solubility product constant, we obtain

$$[Pb^{++}][S^{=}] = K_{sp}$$
$$X^2 = 8.4 \times 10^{-28}$$
$$X = 2.9 \times 10^{-14}$$

Thus we find the solubility of PbS in water to be 2.9×10^{-14} mole per liter when hydrolysis of the sulfide ion is neglected.

Now let us solve the problem, taking into consideration the hydrolysis of the sulfide ion. We shall consider only the first stage in the hydrolysis of the sulfide ion because the second stage is negligibly small.

$$S^{=} + H_2O \rightleftharpoons HS^- + OH^-$$

We found K_h for this reaction to be 7.7×10^{-2} in Example 2 of Section 43.5, and the sulfide ion in a 0.0010 M sodium sulfide solution was calculated to be 99 per cent hydrolyzed. The extent to which the sulfide ion from lead sulfide is hydrolyzed is practically complete because its concentration is initially only 2.9×10^{-14}. The hydroxide ion concentration due to the hydrolysis of the sulfide ion, $S^{=} + H_2O \rightleftharpoons HS^- + OH^-$, would be of the order of 3×10^{-14} M. However, this hydroxide ion concentration is so small compared with that of water, 1.0×10^{-7} M, that the $[OH^-]$ of the solution will still have a value of 1.0×10^{-7} M. Using 1.0×10^{-7} M for the $[OH^-]$, we can now calculate the ratio of the concentration of the hydrosulfide ion to that of the sulfide ion by substituting in the expression for the hydrolysis constant of the sulfide ion.

$$\frac{[HS^-][OH^-]}{[S^{=}]} = \frac{[HS^-](1.0 \times 10^{-7})}{[S^{=}]} = K_h = 7.7 \times 10^{-2}$$
$$\frac{[HS^-]}{[S^{=}]} = 7.7 \times 10^5, \quad \text{or} \quad [S^{=}] = \frac{[HS^-]}{7.7 \times 10^5}$$

Hence, we find that there are 770 thousand times as many hydrosulfide ions as sulfide ions in the solution. This means that hydrolysis of the sulfide ion is nearly complete. From the two equilibria involved in the system,

$$PbS \rightleftharpoons Pb^{++} + S^{=}$$
$$\overline{S^{=} + H_2O \rightleftharpoons HS^- + OH^-}$$

it is readily seen that for every sulfide ion which undergoes hydrolysis, one lead ion and one hydrosulfide ion are produced. It follows that the concentrations of lead ion and hydrosulfide ion will be nearly the same, or $[Pb^{++}] = [HS^-]$. Substituting the value for $[S^{=}]$ found above in the expression for the solubility product constant for lead sulfide, we have

$$[Pb^{++}][S^{=}] = [Pb^{++}]\frac{[HS^-]}{7.7 \times 10^5} = K_{sp} = 8.4 \times 10^{-28}$$

Because $[Pb^{++}] = [HS^-]$, we can write

$$\frac{[Pb^{++}]^2}{7.7 \times 10^5} = 8.4 \times 10^{-28}$$

$$[Pb^{++}]^2 = 6.5 \times 10^{-22}$$

$$[Pb^{++}] = 2.5 \times 10^{-11} = \text{molar solubility of PbS}$$

We have found, then, that the solubility of lead sulfide in water is 2.5×10^{-11} M when hydrolysis of the sulfide ion is considered. This value is about one thousand times greater than that calculated (2.9×10^{-14} M) when hydrolysis was neglected. If one were to take into account the fact that the lead ion hydrolyzes slightly to give $Pb(OH)^+$ and $Pb(OH)_2$, the solubility of lead sulfide would be found to be somewhat larger yet.

The relatively insoluble carbonates behave similarly to the sulfides. When a relatively insoluble carbonate such as barium carbonate, $BaCO_3$, is dissolved in water, its solubility is increased due to hydrolysis of the carbonate ion, $CO_3^{=} + H_2O \rightleftharpoons HCO_3^- + OH^-$, and the concentration of the barium ion is practically equal to the sum of the concentrations of the carbonate and hydrogen carbonate ions.

QUESTIONS

1. Classify solutions of the following salts as acidic, neutral, or basic: KCl, $NaNO_3$, $FeCl_3$, NH_4NO_3, KCN, $Al_2(SO_4)_3$, $CuSO_4$, NH_4OAc, and Na_2CO_3.
2. Write equations for the hydrolysis of the following ions: NH_4^+, CN^-, OAc^-, $CO_3^{=}$, $HPO_4^{=}$, $SO_3^{=}$, HCO_3^-, NO_2^-, F^-, Cu^{++}, Al^{+++}, and Zn^{++}.
3. What determines whether a salt of a weak base and a weak acid will hydrolyze to give a solution that is acidic, neutral, or basic?
4. Bringing together equivalents of what kinds of acids and bases results in the formation of neutral solutions?
5. Write equations to show the stepwise hydrolysis of the following metal ions: $[Al(H_2O)_6]^{+++}$, $[Cu(H_2O)_4]^{++}$, $[Cr(H_2O)_6]^{+++}$, $[Sn(H_2O)_6]^{+4}$, and $[Zn(H_2O)_4]^{++}$.
6. The ions of which groups of metals in the Periodic Table do not undergo hydrolysis?
7. Explain why aluminum sulfide cannot be recrystallized from water.
8. How does hydrolysis affect the solubility of relatively insoluble metal sulfides and carbonates?

PROBLEMS

1. Calculate the hydrolysis constant for each of the following ions:
   (a) CN^- (K_i for HCN $= 4 \times 10^{-10}$.) *Ans.* 3×10^{-5}
   (b) F^- (K_i for HF $= 7.2 \times 10^{-4}$.) *Ans.* 1.4×10^{-11}
   (c) ClO^- (K_i for HClO $= 3.5 \times 10^{-8}$.) *Ans.* 2.9×10^{-7}
   (d) NO_2^- (K_i for $HNO_2 = 4.5 \times 10^{-4}$.) *Ans.* 2.2×10^{-11}
2. The ionization constant for HCN is 4.0×10^{-10}. Calculate the pH and percentage hydrolysis in a 0.050 M KCN solution. *Ans. 11; 2.4 per cent*

3. Calculate the pH of (a) a 0.10 M solution of ammonium chloride, (b) a 0.05 M solution of $NaNO_2$. (K_i for NH_3 is 1.8×10^{-5}, and K_i for HNO_2 is 4.5×10^{-4}.)
Ans. (a) *5.1;* (b) *8*

4. How many moles (and grams) of sodium acetate must be added to one liter of water to give a solution with a hydroxide concentration of 3.0×10^{-5} M?
Ans. *1.6 mole; 130 g.*

5. Calculate the pH of a 0.20 M Na_2CO_3 solution. (Neglect the second stage in the hydrolysis of the carbonate ion.) (K_i for HCO_3^- is 7.0×10^{-11}.) *Ans.* *12*

6. What is the concentration of molecular acetic acid in a 2.0 M solution of sodium acetate? *Ans.* 3.3×10^{-5} *M*

7. A 0.01 M solution of NaCN is found to be hydrolyzed to the extent of 5.0 per cent. Calculate the value of the ionization constant for HCN.
Ans. 4×10^{-10}

8. Calculate the pH of a 0.050 M solution of $ZnCl_2$. (The K_h for the reaction, $[Zn(H_2O)_4]^{++} + H_2O \rightleftharpoons [Zn(OH)(H_2O)_3]^+ + H_3O^+$, is 2.45×10^{-10}.) *Ans.* *5.5*

9. Calculate the pH of a solution resulting from mixing 20 ml. of 0.10 M NaOH with 80 ml. of 0.025M acetic acid. *Ans.* *8.5*

10. Calculate the K_i of the HNO_2 from the hydrolysis constant of KNO_2. The hydrolysis constant is equal to 2.2×10^{-11}. *Ans.* 4.5×10^{-4}

11. The hydrogen ion concentration of a 0.010 M solution of KCN is 2.0×10^{-11} gram ions per liter. Calculate (a) the hydrolysis constant for KCN, and (b) the ionization constant for HCN. *Ans.* (a) 2.5×10^{-5}; (b) 4.0×10^{-10}

12. Ten milliliters of 0.20 M acetic acid is mixed with 10 ml. of 0.10 M sodium acetate. The pH of the resulting solution is 4.4. Calculate the K_i of the acetic acid.
Ans. 1.8×10^{-5}

13. Calculate the pH of a saturated solution of $Ba(OH)_2$. (K_{sp} for $Ba(OH)_2$ $= 5.0 \times 10^{-3}$.) *Ans.* *13*

14. Calculate the concentration of aluminum chloride required to give a solution with pH = 4.0. The hydrolysis constant for the reaction, $[Al(H_2O)_6]^{+++} + H_2O \rightleftharpoons [Al(OH)(H_2O)_5]^{++} + H_3O^+$, is 1.4×10^{-5}. *Ans.* 7.1×10^{-4}

15. How many moles of NH_4Cl must be added to 1.5 liters of water to give a solution with pH = 4.8? (K_i for $NH_3 = 1.8 \times 10^{-5}$.) *Ans.* *0.69*

16. Calculate the pH of a solution made by mixing equal volumes of 0.15 M aqueous ammonia and 0.15 M nitric acid. (K_i for $NH_3 = 1.8 \times 10^{-5}$.)
Ans. *5.2*

17. Calculate the final pH of a solution which is made by adding 2.0 ml. of 0.10 M NaOH to 200 ml. of 1.0 M NaOAc. (K_i for HOAc $= 1.8 \times 10^{-5}$.) *Ans.* *11*

10. Calculate the concentration of molecular NH_3 in a 1.5 M solution of NH_4Br. (K_i for $NH_3 = 1.8 \times 10^{-5}$.) *Ans.* 2.9×10^{-5} *M*

19. What concentration of potassium acetate will give a solution in which the *per cent* hydrolysis is 1.8×10^{-2}? (K_i for HOAc $= 1.8 \times 10^{-5}$.)
Ans. 1.7×10^{-2} *M*

PART 4

Semimicro Qualitative Analysis

CHAPTER FORTY-FOUR

General Laboratory Directions

Your course in Qualitative Analysis has two principal objectives. One of these is to give you the reasons for the analytical procedures and results in terms of the theory of ionic equilibria, especially that relating to weak electrolytes, solubility products, complex ions, and oxidation-reduction. The other is on the practical side and is for the purpose of teaching you careful laboratory manipulation, critical observation, and logical interpretation of observed results.

Semimicro qualitative analysis is a method of analysis employing techniques whereby the reactions and procedures used in macro work may be reliably carried out on a reduced scale. Analysis on the macro scale is made on volumes of solutions of the order of 10 to 100 ml. and with ordinary test tubes, beakers, and funnels. In semimicro analysis, volumes of solutions from 1 drop to about 5 ml. are employed, and small test tubes, centrifuge tubes, capillary syringes, and medicine droppers are used to carry out the separations and identification tests. This leads to a striking reduction in the consumption of reagents and usually the analyses can be carried out more rapidly than by macro methods.

Even though rather definite directions are given for the analysis to be carried out, no two analyses will be exactly alike. For this reason, directions should never be followed to the letter, but with careful thought, procedures should be adapted to the particular problem at hand.

44.1 Equipment

In Appendices C and D will be found a list of apparatus and of solutions and solid reagents which each student will need in carrying out the laboratory work of the course. After a laboratory desk has been assigned, check the apparatus in the desk according to the specific directions given by your instructor. Get from the stockroom any apparatus which may be required but is not in the desk. Wash all of the apparatus that will be employed in the course before beginning your laboratory work.

44.2 Laboratory Assignments

Below is listed a set of suggested laboratory assignments. The number of unknowns required will be specified by the instructor.

1. Construct a wash bottle, stirring rods, and capillary syringes.
2. Analyze a known solution containing all the cations of Group I.
3. Analyze an unknown solution based on the Group I cations.
4. Analyze a known solution containing all the cations of Group II.
5. Analyze an unknown solution based on the Group II cations.
6. Analyze a known solution containing all the cations of Group III.
7. Analyze an unknown solution based on the Group III cations.
8. Analyze a known solution containing all the cations of Group IV.
9. Analyze a known solution containing all the cations of Group V.
10. Analyze an unknown solution based on the cations of Groups IV and V.
11. Analyze a general unknown solution based on all the cations of all the groups.
12. Analyze a known salt mixture containing no oxidizing anions.
13. Analyze an unknown salt mixture containing no oxidizing anions.
14. Analyze a known salt mixture containing no reducing anions.
15. Analyze an unknown salt mixture containing no reducing anions.
16. Analyze a salt mixture for both cations and anions.
17. Analyze an alloy.

44.3 Wash Bottle

Using a 250 ml. Florence flask and 6 mm. glass tubing, construct a wash bottle of the type shown in Fig. 44–1. Make uniform bends with no constrictions, and fire-polish all ends of glass tubing. Keep the wash bottle filled with distilled water for use in the analytical procedures. Ordinary tap water contains such ions as Ca^{++}, Mg^{++}, Fe^{+++}, Al^{+++}, Cl^{-}, $SO_4^{=}$, and HCO_3^{-}. Since these ions are among those to be tested for in the unknown solutions, all water used in the procedures and in the cleaning of glassware must be distilled.

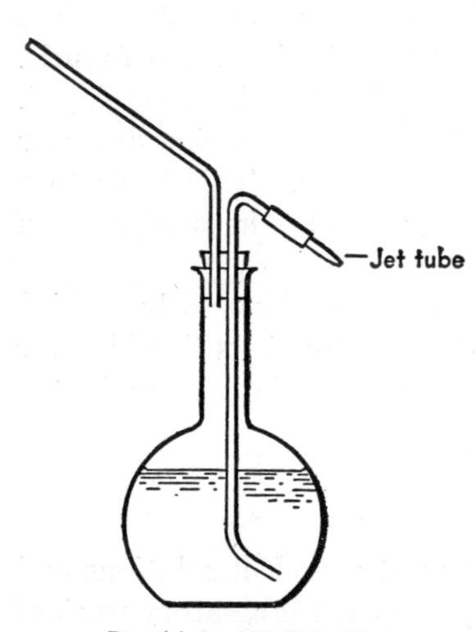

Fig. 44–1 Wash bottle.

44.4 Stirring Rods

Make at least five glass stirring rods, approximately 15 cm. in length and 3 mm. in diameter. Fire-polish each end of each rod in the flame.

44.5 Capillary Syringes

Standard medicine droppers of approximately 1 ml. capacity are used for measuring and transferring solutions of reagents. These droppers deliver about 20 drops per milliliter. A second type of dropper, called a capillary syringe, is needed for the removal of liquids from precipitates held in small test tubes or centrifuge tubes.

These may be supplied. If not available, the capillary syringes may be made from glass tubing as follows: Heat the middle portion of a 7 inch section of 8 mm. glass tubing over a Bunsen flame with rotation until the glass softens. Remove the tube from the flame and slowly draw it out until the bore is about 1 mm. When the tube has cooled, cut the capillary at the mid-point and fire-polish the capillary ends. Flare the wide ends of the tubes by heating until soft and quickly pressing down against a flat metal surface. When the syringes are cold, attach medicine dropper bulbs to the flared ends. These syringes will deliver approximately 40 drops per ml.

44.6 Reagents

The solids and solutions which are called for in the analytical procedures will be stored in the 10 ml. reagent bottles (Fig. 44–2) to be found in your desk. Fill these reagent bottles with the chemicals required in the analysis of each group prior to starting the analysis of that group. See Appendix D for a list of these reagents. Only a small quantity of the starred reagents will be needed during the course, so fill the bottles only about one-fourth full of these reagents.

Before filling a reagent bottle, make sure that it is perfectly clean. To avoid mistakes, it is well to label each bottle before filling it.

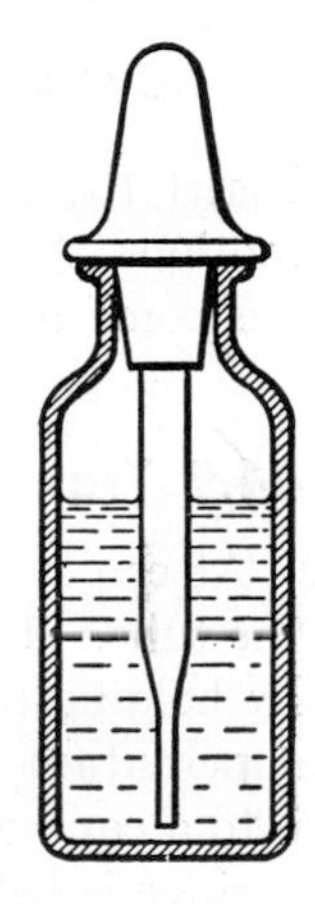

Fig. 44–2 Reagent bottle with dropper.

44.7 Precipitation

Practically all of the precipitations are carried out either in 4 ml. pyrex test tubes or 2 ml. conical test tubes. Check for completeness of precipitation by adding a drop of reagent to the solution (centrifugate) obtained in the separation of the precipitate. If the addition of more reagent to the solution shows that precipitation is incomplete, separate the mixture and test the second solution for completeness of precipitation.

The precipitating agent should be added slowly, preferably from a medicine dropper, and with vigorous shaking or stirring of the reaction mixture. The formation of larger crystals of the precipitate is favored by warming the solution, and separation of the precipitate should not be attempted before the crystals become large enough to settle.

A slight excess of the precipitating agent is added to reduce the solubility of the precipitate by the common ion effect (Section 41.6). On the other hand, a very large excess of the precipitating agent should be avoided, as it may actually increase the solubility of the precipitate. For example, in precipitating silver chloride a large excess of Cl^- will bring about the formation of $AgCl_2^-$, and thereby increase the solubility of AgCl. Many precipitates are dissolved, at least partially, by the formation of complexes of this type.

44.8 Centrifugation of Precipitates

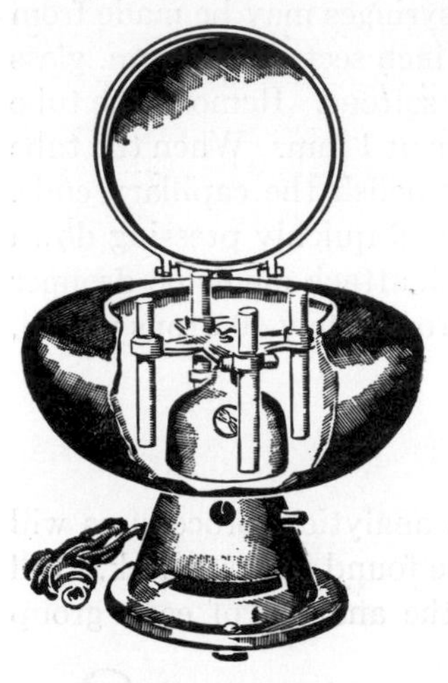

Fig. 44–3 Centrifuge.

A precipitate may be separated from a liquid by means of a centrifuge (Fig. 44–3). By rotating a mixture of solid and liquid at high speed in a centrifuge, the more dense precipitate is forced to the bottom of the containing tube by a centrifugal force which is many times the force of gravity. This accounts for the much shorter time required for settling of the precipitate when centrifugation is employed. Colloidal precipitates require longer centrifugation than do crystalline precipitates because of the small size of the colloidal particles.

Before centrifuging a precipitate contained in a test tube or centrifuge tube, prepare another tube to balance it in the centrifuge by filling an empty tube with water until the liquid levels in both tubes are the same. Insert the tubes in opposite positions in the centrifuge, and set the machine in motion. Allow the centrifugation to continue for 30 seconds. After the machine has come to rest, remove the tubes.

44.9 Transfer of the Centrifugate

After centrifugation, the precipitate should be found packed in the bottom of the tube. The supernatant liquid or centrifugate is separated from the precipitate by holding the tube at an angle of about 30 degrees (Fig. 44–4) and removing the supernatant liquid by slowly drawing it into a capillary syringe. The tip of the syringe is held just below the surface of the liquid and as the pressure on the bulb is slowly released, causing the liquid to rise in the syringe, the capillary is lowered into the tube until all of the liquid is removed. As the capillary approaches the bottom of the tube, the tip must not be allowed to stir up the mixture by touching the precipitate.

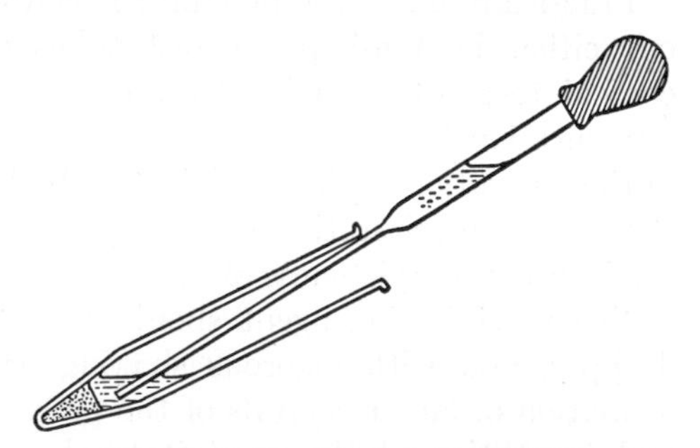

Fig. 44–4 Transfer of the centrifugate.

44.10 Washing of the Precipitate

The precipitate left in the tube after the removal of a supernatant liquid is still wet with a solution containing the ions of this liquid. The precipitate must be washed, usually with water, to dilute the solution adhering to the precipitate. The wash liquid is added to the precipitate, and the mixture is stirred thoroughly. The mixture is then centrifuged to cause the precipitate to settle again. After centrifugation, the washings are removed by a capillary syringe as previously described. Usually a precipitate is washed at least twice. The first wash liquid is ordinarily saved and added to the first centrifugate. If the precipitate must be transferred to another container, the reagent to be used is added, the mixture is well stirred, and then it is poured into the other container. After the precipitate has settled, the supernatant liquid may be employed to remove any precipitate remaining in the centrifuge tube.

44.11 Dissolution and Extraction of Precipitates

When all or a part of a precipitate is to be brought into solution by a reagent, the solvent is added to the precipitate which is in the centrifuge tube and the mixture is stirred. The mixture is then separated by centrifugation and the operation is repeated using fresh solvent. Oftentimes the extraction of a precipitate is more efficient at an elevated temperature.

44.12 Heating of Mixtures or Solutions

Whenever it is necessary to heat a mixture for the purpose of bringing about a precipitation or for dissolving or extracting a precipitate, the test tube or centrifuge tube is placed in a water bath (Fig. 44–5) maintained at a suitable temperature. It will be found convenient to keep the water hot in the water bath throughout the work period.

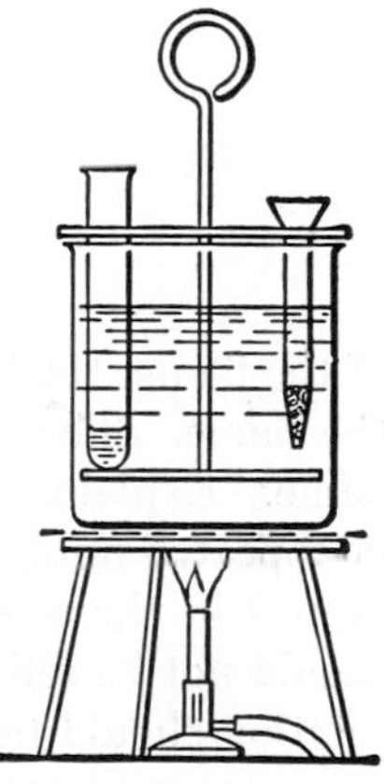

Fig. 44–5 Hot water bath.

44.13 Evaporation

It is often necessary to heat solutions to boiling and to hold them at the boiling temperature in order to concentrate them, or to remove volatile acids or bases, or even to evaporate a solution to dryness. Evaporation should be carried out in a small casserole or porcelain evaporating dish. The contents of the container should be agitated constantly while the heating continues. The evaporation of solutions contained in small test tubes should be avoided because the contents of the tube may be lost due to overheating.

44.14 Cleaning Glassware

Because small amounts of contaminants may give rise to erroneous results, all glassware used in the analytical procedures should be thoroughly cleaned before it is used. The cleaning should be done with a brush and some cleansing powder such as a synthetic detergent. The apparatus should then be rinsed first with tap water and finally with distilled water. Test tube brushes and centrifuge tube brushes are available. Medicine droppers, capillary syringes, and stirring rods should be cleaned, rinsed, and stored in a beaker of distilled water.

44.15 Flame Tests

Flame tests are made using a platinum wire sealed in the end of a piece of glass tubing. The wire is cleaned by first dipping the end of it in 6 M HCl and then heating it in the Bunsen flame (Fig. 44–6). Rather than using the hottest portion

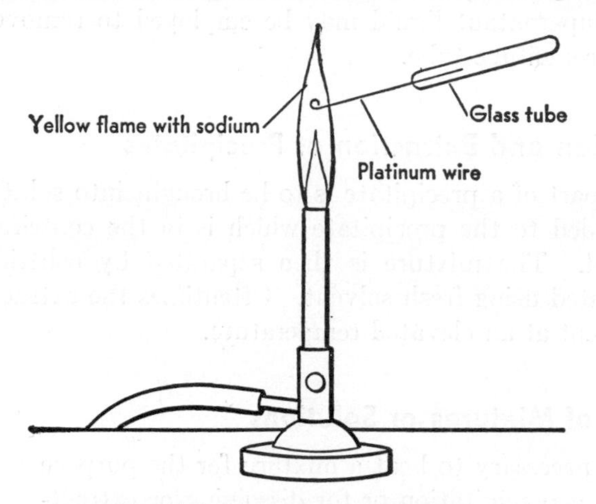

Fig. 44–6 How to make a flame test.

of the flame, the looped end of the wire should be brought slowly up to the edge of the flame. The platinum wire should never come into the reducing part of the flame. Explain. The operation of dipping in acid and heating in the flame should be repeated until the wire no longer imparts a color to the flame. The wire loop is dipped in the solution to be tested and then heated in the flame. The memory should not be relied upon in judging the color imparted to the flame, but a known solution should be tested and the color compared to that given by the unknown.

44.16 Known Solutions

In order to acquaint the student with the details of the analytical procedures before he attempts to analyze a solution of unknown composition, **known** solutions containing all the ions of a given group are provided. The student should satisfy himself that he has become quite familiar with the separations and confirmatory tests for the ions of the group by practicing on a known solution before trying to determine the ions present in an unknown solution. The student should note the quantities of precipitates obtained and the colors of precipitates and solutions as he proceeds with the analysis of a known solution. These observations and the equations for the reactions involved should be recorded in a notebook.

44.17 Unknown Solutions

When the analysis of a known solution has been satisfactorily completed, the student should prepare himself for an oral quiz by his instructor on the details of the analysis of the group. This quiz may include questions on the reactions involved, the theory of the separations and confirmatory tests, and the colors of precipitates, ions, and solutions. After the instructor's questions have been satisfactorily answered, a sample of an unknown may be obtained for analysis. The **unknown** may contain any or all of the ions of the group or groups being studied.

44.18 Unknown Report

A notebook should be provided in which to record the results of the analyses which are performed. All observations which are made should be recorded as soon as they have been completed. Equations should be written in the notebook to indicate the behavior of each ion with the reagents with which it comes in contact.

In reporting the results of the analysis of an unknown, a report sheet should be filled out in a manner similar to that shown below, and presented to the instructor for grading.

SAMPLE UNKNOWN REPORT

*Name:*____________________ *Section:*____________ *Date:*__________

*Instructor's Approval:*________________ *Ions Found:*____________ *Grade:*__________

CATION UNKNOWN REPORT

No.	*Substance*	*Reagent*	*Result*	*Inference or Conclusion*	*Precipitate or Residue*	*Centrifugate or Solution*
1	Group I	HCl	White ppt.	Group I present	One or more of AgCl, $PbCl_2$, Hg_2Cl_2	Possibly Pb^{++}
2	Ppt. from 1	Hot water	No visible action	Hg_2^{++} and/or Ag^+ present Pb^{++} uncertain	Hg_2Cl_2 and/or AgCl	Possibly Pb^{++}
3	Filtrate from 2 or 1	K_2CrO_4	Yellow ppt.	Pb^{++} present	$PbCrO_4$	
4	Residue from 2	$NH_3 + H_2O$	Residue dissolves completely	Hg_2^{++} absent Ag^+ probable		$[Ag(NH_3)_2]^+$
5	Filtrate from 4	HNO_3	White ppt.	Ag^+ present	AgCl	
6						

CHAPTER FORTY-FIVE

The Analysis of Group I

45.1 Introduction

Begin with these procedures for the analysis of a solution of a known or unknown sample containing the metal ions. Depending upon the nature of the known or unknown, the solution may contain only the ions of Group I or it may contain the ions of any or all of the Groups I–V. If your sample is a general unknown, reserve a part of the original solution for the test for the ammonium ion in Group V. Review Section 33.1 for the classification of the metal ions into analytical groups before proceeding with the analysis of Group I. A schematic outline of the analysis for the Group I metals is given in the following "flow sheet."

GROUP I Flow Sheet

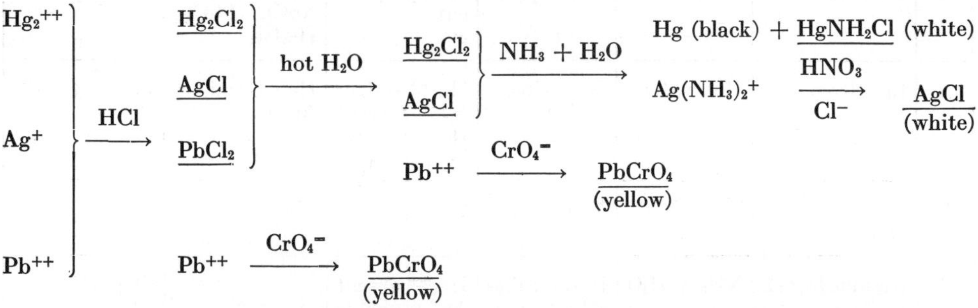

$$\left.\begin{matrix} Hg_2^{++} \\ Ag^+ \\ Pb^{++} \end{matrix}\right\} \xrightarrow{HCl} \left\{\begin{matrix} \left.\begin{matrix} \underline{Hg_2Cl_2} \\ \underline{AgCl} \end{matrix}\right\} \\ \underline{PbCl_2} \end{matrix}\right.$$

$$\left.\begin{matrix} \underline{Hg_2Cl_2} \\ \underline{AgCl} \\ \underline{PbCl_2} \end{matrix}\right\} \xrightarrow{\text{hot } H_2O} \left\{\begin{matrix} \left.\begin{matrix} \underline{Hg_2Cl_2} \\ \underline{AgCl} \end{matrix}\right\} \xrightarrow{NH_3 + H_2O} \begin{matrix} Hg \text{ (black)} + \underline{HgNH_2Cl} \text{ (white)} \\ Ag(NH_3)_2^+ \xrightarrow[Cl^-]{HNO_3} \underline{AgCl} \text{ (white)} \end{matrix} \\ Pb^{++} \xrightarrow{CrO_4^{=}} \underline{PbCrO_4} \text{ (yellow)} \end{matrix}\right.$$

$$Pb^{++} \xrightarrow{CrO_4^{=}} \underline{PbCrO_4} \text{ (yellow)}$$

The flow sheet summarizes the chemistry of the separations and the identification tests in a form easily studied and remembered. Flow sheets similar to the one above are provided in this text to assist the students in the analysis of metals in Groups II–V.

A discussion of the chemistry involved in the various steps of the analysis of each group will be given just prior to the laboratory procedure for each step. Careful study of these discussions will help the student learn the chemistry involved in the analysis.

45.2 Precipitation of Group I

Hydrochloric acid is the reagent which serves as the precipitant for the metal ions of Group I. The chlorides of mercury (I), silver, and lead are the only ones of the cations under consideration in this qualitative scheme which are insoluble in acid solutions. The equations for the precipitation of the metal ions of Group I are

$$Hg_2^{++} + 2\ Cl^- \rightleftharpoons \underline{Hg_2Cl_2}$$
$$Ag^+ + Cl^- \rightleftharpoons \underline{AgCl}$$
$$Pb^{++} + 2\ Cl^- \rightleftharpoons \underline{PbCl_2}$$

The solubilities and solubility product constants of the chlorides of this group are given in Table 45·1.

TABLE 45·1 Solubilities of the Group I Chlorides

Salt	K_{sp}	*Solubility moles/liter*	*Solubility g./ml.*
Hg_2Cl_2	1.1×10^{-18}	6.5×10^{-7}	3.1×10^{-7}
$AgCl$	1.2×10^{-10}	1.1×10^{-5}	1.6×10^{-6}
$PbCl_2$	1.7×10^{-5}	1.6×10^{-2}	4.5×10^{-3}

These values show that the solubility of lead chloride in g./ml. is about 2800 times greater than that of silver chloride and about 14,500 times greater than that of mercury (I) chloride. Thus, it can be seen that the mercury (I) ion and the silver ion are in effect completely removed from solution when hydrochloric acid is added to a solution containing these ions. On the other hand, lead is not completely precipitated by chloride, and some of it is carried through to Group II.

A slight excess of hydrochloric acid is used in the precipitation of the group to prevent the precipitation of bismuth oxychloride and antimony oxychloride by hydrolysis of their chloride salts.

$$Bi^{+++} + Cl^- + H_2O \rightleftharpoons \underline{BiOCl} + 2\ H^+$$
$$Sb^{+++} + Cl^- + H_2O \rightleftharpoons \underline{SbOCl} + 2\ H^+$$

The hydrogen ions of the hydrochloric acid keep the above equilibria shifted to the left. In addition, a slight excess of chloride ions insures more complete precipitation of Hg_2Cl_2, $AgCl$, $PbCl_2$, which is due to the common ion effect (Section 41.6). For example, in a solution which is 0.3 M in chloride ions, the common ion effect will reduce the concentration of Ag^+ from 1.1×10^{-5} M in a saturated solution of AgCl to 4×10^{-10} M. On the other hand, a large excess of chloride ion must be avoided because silver chloride and lead chloride tend to react with chloride ions, forming soluble salts of complex ions. The equations are

$$AgCl + Cl^- \rightleftharpoons [AgCl_2]^-$$
$$PbCl_2 + 2\ Cl^- \rightleftharpoons [PbCl_4]^{=}$$

PROCEDURE 1. To 10 drops of the solution to be analyzed, add enough water to make a total volume of 1 ml. Add 2 drops of 6 M HCl to this solution. Separate the precipitate by centrifugation. If your sample is a general unknown, reserve the solution (centrifugate) for the analysis of Groups II–V. If your sample is a Group I known or unknown, test the solution for lead as directed in Procedure (2) below. Treat the precipitate according to Procedure (2).

45.3 Separation and Identification of the Lead Ion

Lead chloride may fail to precipitate at all if the lead ion concentration is too low or if the temperature is too high. For this reason a test for lead should be made on the centrifugate from the original Group I separation.

The fact that lead chloride is about three times as soluble in hot water as in cold water enables one to separate it from silver and mercury (I) chlorides by extraction of the mixed chlorides with hot water. The presence of the lead ion may be confirmed by precipitation of the slightly soluble yellow chromate. The equation is

$$Pb^{++} + CrO_4 = \rightleftharpoons \underline{PbCrO_4}$$

PROCEDURE 2. *Precipitate from (1): Hg_2Cl_2, AgCl, $PbCl_2$.* Extract the precipitate twice with 10 drops of hot water to dissolve the $PbCl_2$. Reserve the residue for Procedure (3). Add 2 drops of 1 M K_2CrO_4 to the solution (hot water extract). A yellow precipitate of $PbCrO_4$ confirms the presence of lead.

45.4 Separation and Identification of the Mercury (I) Ion

When aqueous ammonia is added to a mixture of silver chloride and mercury (I) chloride, the silver chloride dissolves by forming soluble diamminesilver chloride. The equation is

$$AgCl + 2\ NH_3 \rightleftharpoons [Ag(NH_3)_2]^+ + Cl^-$$

In the presence of ammonia, mercury (I) chloride undergoes auto-oxidation-reduction with the formation of finely divided metallic mercury, which is black, and mercury (II) amido chloride, $HgNH_2Cl$, which is white. The equation is

$$Hg_2Cl_2 + 2\ NH_3 \rightarrow \underline{Hg} + \underline{HgNH_2Cl} + NH_4^+ + Cl^-$$

The formation of this black (or gray) precipitate is sufficient proof of the presence of mercury (I) ions.

PROCEDURE 3. *Residue from (2): Hg_2Cl_2 and AgCl.* Extract the residue twice with 5 drops of 4 M aqueous ammonia. A black or gray residue confirms the presence of the mercury (I) ion. Reserve the aqueous ammonia extract for Procedure (4).

45.5 Identification of the Silver Ion

The presence of the silver ion may be confirmed by treating the aqueous ammonia extract of Hg_2Cl_2 and AgCl with nitric acid. This causes the reprecipitation of white silver chloride. The hydrogen ion supplied by the nitric acid unites with the free ammonia in equilibrium with the diamminesilver ion and causes the equilibrium, $[Ag(NH_3)_2]^+ \rightleftharpoons Ag^+ + 2\ NH_3$, to shift to the right. The free silver ion is then precipitated by the chloride ion which is present in the solution. The net reaction is the sum of three equilibria, as shown below.

$$[Ag(NH_3)_2]^+ \rightleftharpoons Ag^+ + 2\ NH_3$$
$$2\ NH_3 + 2\ H^+ \rightleftharpoons 2\ NH_4^+$$
$$Ag^+ + Cl^- \rightleftharpoons \underline{AgCl}$$
$$\overline{[Ag(NH_3)_2]^+ + Cl^- + 2\ H^+ \rightleftharpoons \underline{AgCl} + 2\ NH_4^+}$$

PROCEDURE 4. ***Solution from (3):*** $[Ag(NH_3)_2]Cl$. **Add 4 M HNO_3 until the solution is acid to litmus. A white precipitate (or cloudiness) of AgCl confirms the presence of silver.**

QUESTIONS

1. Why must a large excess of chloride ion be avoided in the precipitation of the Group I chlorides?
2. In the case of an unknown containing only the cations of Group I, why is it advisable to make a confirmatory test for lead on the filtrate from the Group I precipitation?
3. What general statement can be made concerning the solubility of common chloride salts other than those of the Analytical Group I cations?
4. Give the color of each of the following: AgCl, $PbCl_2$, Hg_2Cl_2, $PbCrO_4$, Hg, $HgNH_2Cl$, and $[Ag(NH_3)_2]Cl$ (in solution).
5. Write out the flow sheet for the Group I analysis.
6. In terms of ionic equilibria and solubility product theory, explain the dissolution of silver chloride in aqueous ammonia and its reprecipitation with nitric acid.
7. Select a reagent used in the analysis of Group I which will in one step separate each of the following pairs: (a) AgCl, $CuCl_2$, (b) AgCl, $PbCl_2$, (c) Hg_2Cl_2, $PbCl_2$, (d) Hg_2Cl_2, AgCl, (e) Hg_2^{++}, Hg^{++}.
8. Why do not the slightly soluble oxychlorides of bismuth and antimony precipitate with the Group I chlorides?
9. Show that the reaction of ammonia with mercury (I) chloride is of the oxidation-reduction type.

PROBLEMS

1. From the data given in Table 45·1, calculate the milligrams per milliliter of the cations present in 1.0 ml. of saturated solutions of Hg_2Cl_2, AgCl, and $PbCl_2$.
Ans. 2.6×10^{-4} *mg. of* Hg_2^{++}; 1.2×10^{-3} *mg. of* Ag^+; 3.3 *mg. of* Pb^{++}
2. Calculate the solubility of silver chloride in 0.050 M HCl. Compare this solubility with that of silver chloride in water. (K_{sp} for AgCl is 1.2×10^{-10}.)
Ans. 2.4×10^{-9} *mole/l.*
3. A solution is 0.010 M with respect to each Pb^{++} and Ag^+. If Cl^- is added to this solution, what is the concentration of Ag^+ when $PbCl_2$ begins to precipitate? (K_{sp} for AgCl is 1.2×10^{-10}, and K_{sp} for $PbCl_2$ is 1.7×10^{-5}.) *Ans.* 2.9×10^{-9} *M*
4. Calculate the concentration of Ag^+ in a 0.010 M solution of $[Ag(NH_3)_2]Cl$ which is 0.10 M in aqueous ammonia. (K_d for $[Ag(NH_3)_2]^+$ is 6.8×10^{-8}.)
Ans. 6.8×10^{-8} *M*

CHAPTER FORTY-SIX

The Analysis of Group II

The solution to be analyzed may be a Group II known or unknown, or it may be the solution from the Group I separation. In either case proceed according to (1) below. See page 769 for the Group II flow sheet.

46.1 Precipitation of Group II Sulfides

1. *Conditions for the separation of Group II from Group III.* Ions of lead, bismuth, copper, cadmium, mercury (II), arsenic, antimony, and tin form sulfides which are insoluble in solutions which are 0.3 M in hydrogen ion. Cadmium sulfide is the most soluble of the sulfides of Group II and zinc sulfide is the least soluble of the sulfides of Group III. Therefore, the separation of the sulfides of Group II from those of Group III is assured if the sulfide ion concentration of the solution is controlled in such a way that the cadmium is completely precipitated as the sulfide without exceeding the solubility product constant of zinc sulfide. In a solution which is saturated with hydrogen sulfide and which is 0.3 M in hydrogen ion, the sulfide ion concentration is just right to effect the separation of cadmium from zinc and, hence, Group II from Group III. The theory for these separations is given in a quantitative manner in Examples 1 and 2 of Section 42.9.

The hydrogen sulfide required for the precipitation of the Group II cations is supplied by thioacetamide, CH_3CSNH_2, which hydrolyzes in hot acidic solutions with the formation of ammonium acetate and hydrogen sulfide.

$$CH_3CSNH_2 + 2\,H_2O \rightarrow CH_3COO^- + NH_4^+ + H_2S$$

The hydrogen sulfide formed ionizes in aqueous solution according to the equation

$$H_2S \rightleftharpoons 2\,H^+ + S^=$$

Hydrochloric acid furnishes hydrogen ions which repress the ionization of hydrogen sulfide, and this causes a decrease in the sulfide ion concentration of the solution. (The ionization of hydrogen sulfide and its control is discussed in detail in Section 41.13.) The precipitation of the Group II sulfides may be represented by the following equations:

$$Pb^{++} + H_2S \rightleftharpoons \underline{PbS} + 2\,H^+$$
$$2\,Bi^{+++} + 3\,H_2S \rightleftharpoons \underline{Bi_2S_3} + 6\,H^+$$
$$Cu^{++} + H_2S \rightleftharpoons \underline{CuS} + 2\,H^+$$
$$Cd^{++} + H_2S \rightleftharpoons \underline{CdS} + 2\,H^+$$
$$Hg^{++} + H_2S \rightleftharpoons \underline{HgS} + 2\,H^+$$
$$2\,As^{+++} + 3\,H_2S \rightleftharpoons \underline{As_2S_3} + 6\,H^+$$
$$2\,Sb^{+++} + 3\,H_2S \rightleftharpoons \underline{Sb_2S_3} + 6\,H^+$$
$$Sn^{++++} + 2\,H_2S \rightleftharpoons \underline{SnS_2} + 4\,H^+$$

It should be noted that the acidity of the solution is increased by such reactions since the hydrogen ion is one of the products of the sulfide precipitation reactions.

2. *Mechanism of the precipitation of the sulfides.* The concentration of the sulfide ion in a solution saturated with hydrogen sulfide and 0.3 M in hydrogen ions is 1.3×10^{-20} mole per liter (Section 41.13). Because there are 6.023×10^{23} ions in one mole, only about 8 sulfide ions are present in each ml. of solution. Yet, practically all the Pb^{++} is precipitated immediately when hydrogen sulfide is passed into an acidic solution of a lead salt. The precipitation is so rapid that it is inconceivable that the reaction is one of simple union of lead and sulfide ions ($Pb^{++} + S^{=} \rightleftharpoons PbS$) when the sulfide ion is present in such a small concentration. However, the concentration of the hydrosulfide ion, HS^-, in a saturated solution of hydrogen sulfide containing 0.3 M hydrogen ion is comparatively large relative to the low concentration of the sulfide ion, as seen from the following calculations:

$$\frac{[H^+][HS^-]}{[H_2S]} = \frac{(0.3)[HS^-]}{0.1} = 1 \times 10^{-7}$$

$$[HS^-] = \frac{0.1}{0.3} \times 1 \times 10^{-7} = 3 \times 10^{-8}$$

Thus, we find that the concentration of HS^- is 3×10^{-8} mole per liter, or about 10^{12} times larger than that of the sulfide ion (1.3×10^{-20}). Therefore, it is reasonable to assume that an unstable intermediate hydrosulfide, $Pb(HS)_2$, could be formed which immediately breaks down to form PbS and H_2S, as shown by the following equations:

$$Pb^{++} + 2\,HS^- \rightleftharpoons \underline{Pb(HS)_2} \rightleftharpoons \underline{PbS} + H_2S$$

Such processes are known for the formation of oxides through the precipitation of unstable hydroxides. A notable example is the formation of silver oxide according to the reaction

$$2\,Ag^+ + 2\,OH^- \rightleftharpoons 2\,\underline{AgOH} \rightleftharpoons \underline{Ag_2O} + H_2O$$

Equilibrium is concerned only with the final result and not with the mechanism by which the result is obtained. This means that calculations involving the precipitation of metal sulfides are valid when concentrations of the sulfide ion are employed even though this ion may not be involved directly in the mechanism for the precipitation of the metal sulfide.

3. *Colors of the sulfides of Group II.* The sulfides of lead (II), copper (II), and mercury (II) are all black. The sulfides of tin (IV), cadmium, and arsenic (III) are

yellow, that of bismuth is dark brown or black, while antimony (III) sulfide is orange-red (sometimes black).

Tin (II) sulfide, SnS, forms a gelatinous precipitate which does not dissolve in sodium sulfide solutions, whereas SnS_2 is readily soluble in this reagent. For this reason tin (II) is oxidized to tin (IV) by adding nitric acid and heating the original solution before the sulfides of the Group II ions are precipitated.

PROCEDURE 1. ***Precipitation of Group II:*** Pb^{++}, Bi^{+++}, Cu^{++}, Cd^{++}, Hg^{++}, As^{+++}, Sb^{+++}, Sn^{++}, Sn^{++++}. **Add 5 drops of 4 M HNO_3 to 10 drops of the known or unknown (or to the centrifugate from the Group I separation) and evaporate the solution to a moist residue (Section 44.13). Cool and add 10 drops of water. Add 1 M aqueous ammonia until the solution (or mixture) is just basic to litmus. (Dip a stirring rod into the solution and then touch the moist end of the rod to a piece of litmus paper in testing for acidity or basicity of solutions.) Add 0.1 M HCl until the solution is just acidic to litmus. Now add 2 drops of 6 M HCl and dilute the solution to 1.5 ml. Add 10 drops of 5 per cent thioacetamide solution. The solution should now be 0.3 M with respect to the hydrogen ion if the directions have been followed carefully. Heat the solution contained in a test tube in a hot water bath for at least five minutes. Add 1 ml. of water and heat the mixture for another five minutes. Separate the precipitate and reserve the centrifugate for the analysis of Groups III–V in the case of a general unknown. Wash the precipitate with 10 drops of 0.1 M HCl twice. Add the first 10 drops of wash solution to the original centrifugate and discard the rest.**

46.2 Separation of the Group II Ions into the A and B Subdivisions

The separation of the Group II ions into subdivisions is based on the fact that HgS, As_2S_3, Sb_2S_3, and SnS_2 form soluble complex sulfides in alkaline sulfide solutions, whereas PbS, Bi_2S_3, CuS, and CdS do not form these complex ions.

The reagent used in this separation is sodium sulfide, which is made by the action of hydrogen sulfide (formed by the hydrolysis of thioacetamide) upon sodium hydroxide. The equation is

$$(2\,Na^+) + 2\,OH^- + H_2S \rightleftharpoons (2\,Na^+) + S^= + 2\,H_2O$$

The presence of the hydroxide ion in high concentration, supplied by an excess of sodium hydroxide, reduces the extent of hydrolysis of the sulfide ion.

$$S^= + H_2O \rightleftharpoons HS^- + OH^-$$

This provides a relatively high concentration of sulfide ion required for the dissolution of the Division B sulfides, particularly of HgS. The equations are

$$HgS + S^= \rightleftharpoons [HgS_2]^= \text{ (thiomercurate)}$$
$$As_2S_3 + 3\,S^= \rightleftharpoons 2\,[AsS_3]^{-3} \text{ (thioarsenite)}$$
$$Sb_2S_3 + 3\,S^= \rightleftharpoons 2\,[SbS_3]^{-3} \text{ (thioantimonite)}$$
$$SnS_2 + S^= \rightleftharpoons [SnS_3]^= \text{ (thiostannate)}$$

The cations whose sulfides fail to dissolve in the presence of a high concentration of sulfide ions constitute Division A of Group II. They are Pb^{++}, Bi^{+++}, Cu^{++}, and Cd^{++}.

GROUP II Flow Sheet

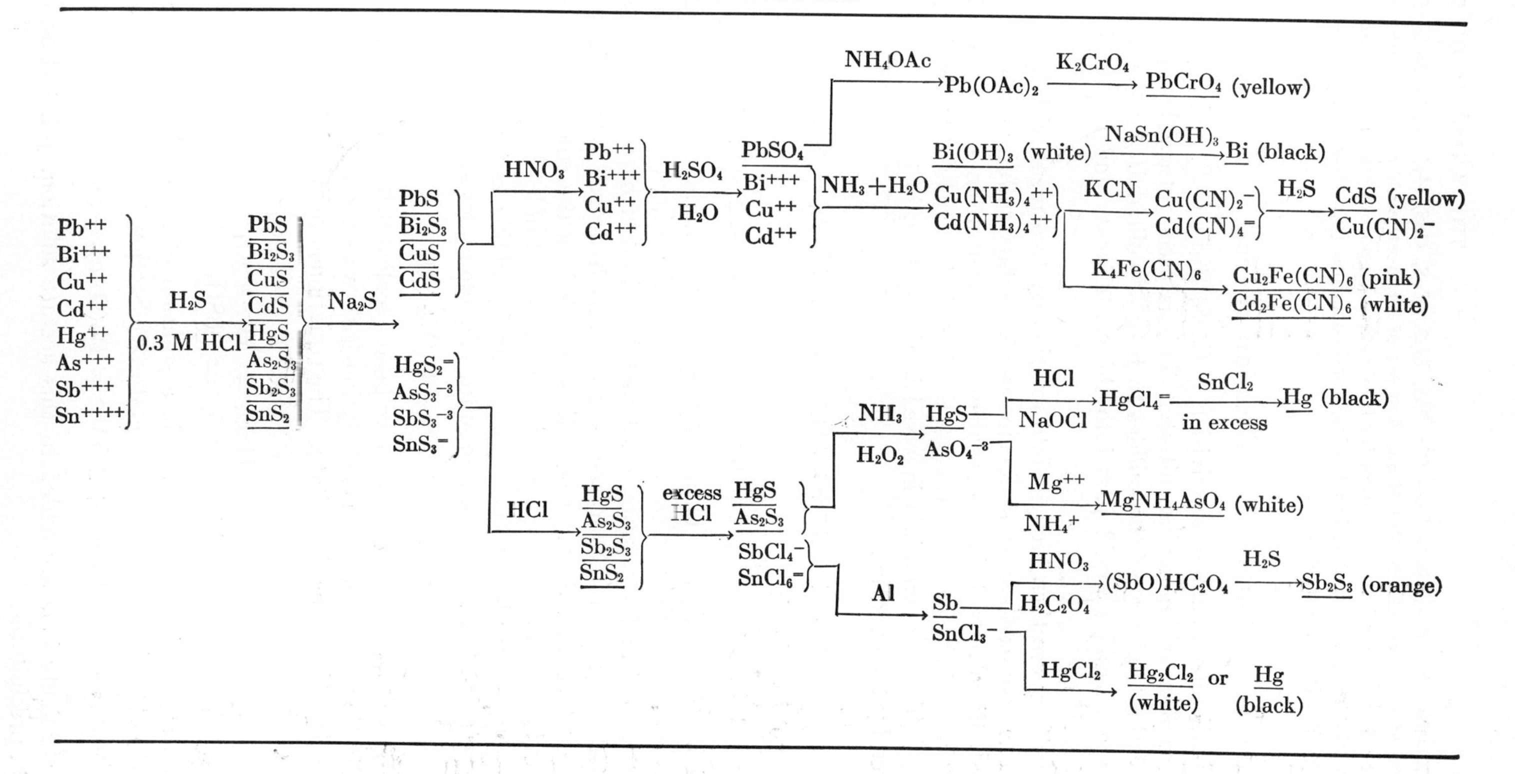

PROCEDURE 2. ***Precipitate from (1): PbS, Bi_2S_3, CuS, CdS, HgS, As_2S_3, Sb_2S_3, SnS_2.*** **Add a mixture of 12 drops of 4 M NaOH and 4 drops of thioacetamide solution to the precipitate. Heat the mixture in a hot water bath for 5 minutes. Separate the mixture and reserve the solution (thiosalts of the Division B ions) for Procedure (6). The residue consists of the sulfides of the ions of Division A.**

46.3 The Separation and Identification of Lead

The undissolved sulfides of Division A (PbS, Bi_2S_3, CuS, and CdS) are washed with a solution of ammonium nitrate. This is used, rather than pure water, to decrease the tendency of the sulfides to become colloidal. In the colloidal condition these sulfides would pass into the centrifugate and be lost in part (see Section 13.10).

The sulfides are then brought into solution by treatment with hot dilute nitric acid. The acid oxidizes the sulfide ion to elementary sulfur, and causes the metal sulfides to dissolve by holding the sulfide ion concentration at such a low level that the product of the concentration of the ions is less than the solubility product constant. The two equilibria involved in the system, in the case of lead sulfide, are given by the equations

$$PbS \rightleftharpoons Pb^{++} + S^{=}$$
$$3\,S^{=} + 8\,H^{+} + 2\,NO_3^{-} \rightleftharpoons 3\,\underline{S} + 2\,NO\uparrow + 4\,H_2O$$

and the net reaction is

$$3\,PbS + 8\,H^{+} + 2\,NO_3^{-} \rightleftharpoons 3\,Pb^{++} + 3\,\underline{S} + 2\,NO\uparrow + 4\,H_2O$$

Lead is separated from bismuth, copper, and cadmium by precipitating the sulfate, $PbSO_4$, which is white. The sulfates of the other three metals are soluble. The nitric acid in the solution must first be removed because the sulfate ion is converted largely to the hydrogen sulfate ion by hydrogen ions in high concentration, $SO_4^{=} + H^{+} \rightleftharpoons HSO_4^{-}$. Under these conditions the concentration of sulfate ion is too low to allow the solubility product constant of lead sulfate to be exceeded. The removal of the nitric acid is accomplished by adding sulfuric acid and evaporating the solution to the point where sulfur trioxide fumes appear.

$$H_2SO_4 \rightarrow H_2O + SO_3$$

The more volatile nitric acid will have been expelled before the SO_3 fumes appear. Upon dilution of the sulfuric acid solution with water, sulfate ions are formed and the lead precipitates as the sulfate. The equations are

$$H_2SO_4 \rightleftharpoons H^{+} + HSO_4^{-}$$
$$HSO_4^{-} \rightleftharpoons H^{+} + SO_4^{=}$$
$$Pb^{++} + SO_4^{=} \rightleftharpoons \underline{PbSO_4}$$

The lead sulfate is then dissolved in a solution of ammonium acetate with the formation of slightly ionized lead acetate (see Section 42.11). The equation is

$$\underline{PbSO_4} + 2\,OAc^{-} \rightleftharpoons Pb(OAc)_2 + SO_4^{=}$$

When chromate ions are added to this acetate solution, yellow lead chromate, $PbCrO_4$, precipitates.

$$Pb(OAc)_2 + CrO_4^{=} \rightleftharpoons \underline{PbCrO_4} + 2\ OAc^-$$

PROCEDURE 3. ***Residue from (2): PbS, CuS, CdS, Bi_2S_3.*** **Wash the residue with 1 ml. of water to which 2 drops of 1 M NH_4NO_3 have been added. Discard the wash solution. Add 15 drops of 6 M HNO_3 to the residue and heat the mixture in a hot water bath for several minutes to dissolve the sulfides. Separate and discard any sulfur which is formed by the oxidation of sulfide ions and transfer the solution to a casserole or evaporating dish. Add 5 drops of 4 M H_2SO_4 and evaporate the solution under the hood to white SO_3 fumes (very important). Cool and add 1 ml. of water to the mixture. Warm the mixture and stir up the precipitate. Separate the mixture. Reserve the solution for Procedure (4). Wash the residue ($PbSO_4$) with a few drops of water and discard the wash solution. Extract the residue (Section 44.11) with a mixture of 5 drops of 1 M NH_4OAc and 1 drop of 1 M HOAc. Add 1 drop of 1 M K_2CrO_4 to the extract. Scratch the inside wall of the test tube with a glass rod to initiate precipitation. The formation of a yellow precipitate confirms the presence of lead as the chromate, $PbCrO_4$.**

46.4 Separation and Identification of Bismuth

Upon the addition of aqueous ammonia to the solution from the lead sulfate separation, the hydroxides of bismuth (white), copper (pale blue), and cadmium (white) are first precipitated. The equations are

$$Bi^{+++} + 3\ NH_3 + 3\ H_2O \rightarrow \underline{Bi(OH)_3} + 3\ NH_4^+$$
$$Cu^{++} + 2\ NH_3 + 2\ H_2O \rightarrow \underline{Cu(OH)_2} + 2\ NH_4^+$$
$$Cd^{++} + 2\ NH_3 + 2\ H_2O \rightarrow \underline{Cd(OH)_2} + 2\ NH_4^+$$

When an excess of aqueous ammonia is added, the hydroxides of copper and cadmium dissolve by forming tetraammine complexes, whereas the bismuth (III) hydroxide does not dissolve.

$$\underline{Bi(OH)_3} + NH_3 \rightarrow \text{no reaction}$$
$$\underline{Cu(OH)_2} + 4\ NH_3 \rightarrow [Cu(NH_3)_4]^{++} + 2\ OH^-$$
$$\underline{Cd(OH)_2} + 4\ NH_3 \rightarrow [Cd(NH_3)_4]^{++} + 2\ OH^-$$

After it is separated from the complexes of copper and cadmium, the bismuth hydroxide is treated with sodium stannite, a strong reducing agent. The bismuth is reduced to the elementary state, in which condition it appears black. The equation is

$$2\ \underline{Bi(OH)_3} + 3\ \underset{\text{Stannite}}{[Sn(OH)_3]^-} + 3\ OH^- \rightarrow 2\ \underline{Bi} + 3\ \underset{\text{Stannate}}{[Sn(OH)_6]^{=}}$$

Because sodium stannite is unstable and darkens upon standing, it must be prepared just prior to use, and the test for bismuth as a black residue must be observed immediately. Sodium stannite is prepared by treating a solution of tin (II) chloride with an excess of sodium hydroxide. The equations are

$$Sn^{++} + 2\ OH^- \rightleftharpoons \underline{Sn(OH)_2}\ \text{(white)}$$
$$\underline{Sn(OH)_2} + \text{excess}\ OH^- \rightleftharpoons [Sn(OH)_3]^-\ \text{(colorless)}$$

The darkening of the stannite solution upon standing is due to the formation of black tin (II) oxide. The equation is

$$[Sn(OH)_3]^- \rightarrow \underline{SnO} + H_2O + OH^-$$

PROCEDURE 4. *Solution from (3): Bi^{+++}, Cu^{++}, Cd^{++}.* **Add 15 M aqueous ammonia dropwise to the solution until it is distinctly basic to litmus (about 5 drops). The development of a deep blue color in the solution indicates the presence of the tetraamminecopper (II) ion, $[Cu(NH_3)_4]^{++}$. The formation of a white precipitate indicates the presence of Bi^{+++} as $Bi(OH)_3$. Separate the mixture and reserve the solution for Procedure (5). Add several drops of freshly prepared sodium stannite solution to the precipitate. The immediate formation of a black residue (finely divided metallic bismuth) confirms the presence of Bi^{+++}. (Preparation of sodium stannite: In a separate test tube, place 1 drop of 1 M $SnCl_2$ and add sufficient 4 M NaOH to dissolve the white precipitate which first forms. Be sure that you are not fooled by an initial precipitate which forms because of a temporary local excess of reagent and dissolves just with stirring.)**

46.5 Identification of Copper and Cadmium

The presence of copper is apparent from the deep blue color exhibited by the complex ion, $[Cu(NH_3)_4]^{++}$. However, if the blue color is too faint to discern, as in the case of a trace of copper, the formation of pink copper (II) hexacyanoferrate (II) serves as a delicate test for the ion. The equation for the reaction is

$$2\,[Cu(NH_3)_4]^{++} + [Fe(CN)_6]^{-4} \rightarrow \underline{Cu_2Fe(CN)_6} + 8\,NH_3$$

If cadmium is present, a white precipitate of cadmium hexacyanoferrate (II), $Cd_2Fe(CN)_6$, will form.

The presence of cadmium ions may be confirmed by forming yellow cadmium sulfide with hydrogen sulfide. However, if one attempts to precipitate CdS in the presence of copper, the black color of CuS obscures the yellow color of CdS. By first adding cyanide ions to a solution containing Cu^{++} and Cd^{++}, the very stable dicyanocopper (I) complex will be formed, which will not react with sulfide ions. The copper (II) ion is reduced to copper (I) by the cyanide ion, and the cyanide ion is oxidized to cyanogen, C_2N_2.

$$2\,[Cu(NH_3)_4]^{++} + 6\,CN^- \rightarrow 2\,[Cu(CN)_2]^- + C_2N_2\uparrow + 8\,NH_3$$
$$[Cu(CN)_2]^- + S^= \rightarrow \text{no reaction}$$

The corresponding tetracyanocadmium complex is much less stable than that of copper and it will react with the sulfide ion to form yellow CdS.

$$[Cd(NH_3)_4]^{++} + 4\,CN^- \rightleftharpoons [Cd(CN)_4]^= + 4\,NH_3$$
$$[Cd(CN)_4]^= + S^= \rightarrow \underline{CdS} + 4\,CN^-$$

PROCEDURE 5. *Solution from (4): $[Cu(NH_3)_4]^{++}$ (blue), $[Cd(NH_3)_4]^{++}$ (colorless).* **If the solution is colorless, a trace of copper may be present. Place 10 drops of the solution in a test tube and add several drops of 0.1 M $K_4Fe(CN)_6$. The formation of a pink precipitate, $Cu_2Fe(CN)_6$, indicates the presence of a small concentration of Cu^{++}; the formation of a white precipitate indicates the absence of Cu^{++} and the probable presence of Cd^{++} as $Cd_2Fe(CN)_6$. If copper (II) ions are present, add 2 drops of 1 M KCN and 2 drops of thioacetamide solution to the remainder of the solution from Procedure (4). Heat the mixture**

in a hot water bath. The formation of a yellow precipitate (CdS) confirms the presence of cadmium. If Cu^{++} is found to be absent, test for Cd^{++} as described above but leave out the KCN.

46.6 Reprecipitation of the Sulfides of the Division B Ions

To reprecipitate the sulfides of mercury, arsenic, antimony, and tin from the solution containing their complex thiosalts, it is necessary to increase the concentration of the cations to a value such that, for example,

$$[Hg^{++}][S^{=}] > K_{sp}$$

This is accomplished by increasing the extent of dissociation of the complex ions through the addition of hydrochloric acid.

$$[HgS_2]^{=} \rightleftharpoons Hg^{++} + 2\,S^{=}$$
$$2\,S^{=} + 4\,H^{+} \rightleftharpoons 2\,H_2S\uparrow$$
$$\text{net reaction } [HgS_2]^{=} + 4\,H^{+} \rightleftharpoons Hg^{++} + 2\,H_2S\uparrow$$

As seen from the above equations, the added acid displaces the equilibria in the direction of an increased concentration of Hg^{++} because of the formation and escape of the weak, gaseous electrolyte H_2S. This results in an increase in the concentration of the cation to such an extent that, for example, the product of the concentration of the mercury (II) ion and the sulfide ion becomes larger than the solubility product constant, and reprecipitation of the sulfide occurs. The net reactions for these reprecipitations are given by the following equations:

$$[HgS_2]^{=} + 2\,H^{+} \rightleftharpoons \underline{HgS} + H_2S\uparrow$$
$$2\,[AsS_3]^{-3} + 6\,H^{+} \rightleftharpoons \underline{As_2S_3} + 3\,H_2S\uparrow$$
$$2\,[SbS_3]^{-3} + 6\,H^{+} \rightleftharpoons \underline{Sb_2S_3} + 3\,H_2S\uparrow$$
$$[SnS_3]^{=} + 2\,H^{+} \rightleftharpoons \underline{SnS_2} + H_2S\uparrow$$

PROCEDURE 6. ***Solution from (2): Thiosalts of the Division B Ions, $[HgS_2]^{=}$, $[AsS_3]^{-3}$, $[SbS_3]^{-3}$, $[SnS_3]^{=}$.*** **Add 1 M HCl until the solution is just acidic to litmus. Heat the mixture in a hot water bath for several minutes. Separate the mixture and discard the solution. The precipitate consists of HgS, As_2S_3, Sb_2S_3, and SnS_2.**

46.7 Separation of Mercury and Arsenic from Antimony and Tin

To dissolve Sb_2S_3 and SnS_2, and leave HgS and As_2S_3 undissolved, the concentrations of the cations and sulfide ion must be made such that

$$[Sb^{+3}]^2[S^{=}]^3 < K_{Sb_2S_3}, \quad \text{and} \quad [Hg^{++}][S^{=}] > K_{HgS}$$

The addition of 6 M HCl reduces the sulfide ion concentration ($S^{=} + 2\,H^{+} \rightleftharpoons 2\,H_2S$), and the concentrations of antimony and tin ions ($Sb^{+3} + 4\,Cl^{-} \rightleftharpoons [SbCl_4]^{-}$, and

$Sn^{+4} + 6\ Cl^- \rightleftharpoons [SnCl_6]^=$) to values such that these sulfides dissolve. The net reactions are given by the equations

$$\underline{Sb_2S_3} + 6\ H^+ + 8\ Cl^- \rightarrow 2\ [SbCl_4]^- + 3\ H_2S \uparrow$$
$$\underline{SnS_2} + 4\ H^+ + 6\ Cl^- \rightarrow [SnCl_6]^= + 2\ H_2S \uparrow$$

The sulfides of mercury and arsenic remain undissolved in the presence of 6 M HCl due to the very small values of their solubility product constants.

PROCEDURE 7. ***Precipitate from (6): HgS, As_2S_3, Sb_2S_3, Sb_2S_3, SnS_2.*** **Add 1 ml. of 6 M HCl to the precipitate and stir the mixture. Heat the mixture in a hot water bath and then separate the residue. Add 15 drops of 6 M HCl to the residue and heat the mixture. Separate the residue and reserve the combined centrifugates for Procedure (11). Treat the residue according to Procedure (8).**

46.8 Separation of Arsenic from Mercury

The concentration of the sulfide ion in saturated solutions of the sulfides of mercury and arsenic is so small that it is not possible to dissolve these sulfides by addition of hydrogen ions. In these cases the product of $[H^+]^2$ and $[S^=]$ does not exceed the ion product constant for H_2S, and equilibrium is established before these sulfides are dissolved.

In order to dissolve HgS and As_2S_3, it is necessary to reduce the concentration of the sulfide ion by oxidation, or the concentration of the cation by the formation of complex ions. A mixture of aqueous ammonia and hydrogen peroxide is used in separating arsenic from mercury. The combined reaction of the hydroxide ion and the hydrogen peroxide with As_2S_3 is given by the equation

$$As_2S_3 + 12\ OH^- + 14\ H_2O_2 \rightarrow 2\ [AsO_4]^{-3} + 3\ SO_4^= + 20\ H_2O$$

Thus the arsenic (III) ion is oxidized to arsenate, $[AsO_4]^{-3}$, and the sulfide ion to sulfate. Consequently, we have

$$[As^{+++}]^2[S^=]^3 < K_{sp} \text{ for } As_2S_3$$

and the As_2S_3 dissolves. Mercury (II) sulfide is not dissolved by this treatment because the sulfide ion concentration in the equilibrium, $HgS \rightleftharpoons Hg^{++} + S^=$, is too small to be appreciably oxidized by hydrogen peroxide.

PROCEDURE 8. ***Residue from (7): HgS and As_2S_3.*** **Add 12 drops of 4 M aqueous ammonia and 6 drops of 3 per cent hydrogen peroxide to the residue. Stir the mixture and heat it in a hot water bath for 5–6 minutes. Separate the residue (HgS) and reserve the solution (AsO_4^{-3}) for Procedure (10).**

46.9 Identification of Mercury

In order to dissolve the extremely insoluble mercury (II) sulfide, it is necessary to reduce the mercury (II) and sulfide ion concentrations to the extent that $[Hg^{++}][S^=]$ will be less than the solubility product of HgS. This may be done by forming the $[HgCl_4]^=$ complex and oxidizing the sulfide ion to sulfur. A mixture of hydrochloric acid and sodium hypochlorite is used to dissolve the HgS. The chloride ions from hydrochloric acid combine with mercury (II) ions and form the complex, $[HgCl_4]^{=}$; hypochlorite ions in acid solution oxidize the sulfide ions to sulfur. The equation is

$$HgS + 2\ H^+ + 3\ Cl^- + ClO^- \rightarrow [HgCl_4]^{=} + \underline{S} + H_2O$$

The solution is then boiled to decompose excess hypochlorite ions which would otherwise interfere with the confirmatory test for mercury by oxidizing tin (II) to tin (IV), thus destroying its reducing power. The decomposition of the hypochlorite ion is according to the equation

$$2\ H^+ + Cl^- + ClO^- \rightarrow H_2O + Cl_2 \uparrow$$

The presence of mercury (II) is confirmed by reducing the $[HgCl_4]^{=}$ to Hg_2Cl_2 (white) or Hg (black) by means of $[SnCl_3]^-$ ions.

$$2\ [HgCl_4]^{=} + [SnCl_3]^- \rightarrow \underline{Hg_2Cl_2} + [SnCl_6]^{=} + 3\ Cl^-$$
$$Hg_2Cl_2 + [SnCl_3]^- + Cl^- \rightarrow \underline{2\ Hg} + [SnCl_6]^{=}$$

The trichlorostannate (II) ion, $[SnCl_3]^-$, is formed when tin (II) chloride is added to the hydrochloric acid solution.

$$SnCl_2 + Cl^- \rightarrow [SnCl_3]^-$$

PROCEDURE 9. ***Residue from (8): HgS.*** **To the black residue add 6 drops of 5 per cent NaClO and 2 drops of 6 M HCl. Stir the mixture, add 1 ml. of water, and separate the sulfur from the solution. Heat the solution to boiling. Add 2 drops of 1 M $SnCl_2$ to the solution. The formation of a white, gray, or black precipitate confirms the presence of mercury.**

46.10 Identification of Arsenic

The presence of arsenic in the form of arsenate ions is confirmed by the formation of white crystalline magnesium ammonium arsenate when magnesia mixture ($MgCl_2$, NH_4Cl, and aqueous ammonia) is added to a solution containing arsenate ions.

$$Mg^{++} + NH_4^+ + AsO_4^{-3} \rightarrow \underline{MgNH_4AsO_4}$$

PROCEDURE 10. ***Solution from (8): AsO_4^{-3}.*** **Add 2 drops of 15 M aqueous ammonia and 5 drops of magnesia mixture to the solution. The formation of a white precipitate, ($MgNH_4AsO_4$), frequently slow in forming, indicates the presence of arsenate ions.**

46.11 Identification of Antimony and Tin

Antimony and tin in hydrochloric acid solutions are in the form of the complex ions, $[SbCl_4]^-$ and $[SnCl_6]^{=}$. Aluminum metal will reduce antimony to the metallic state and tin to the divalent state in hydrochloric acid solution, thus effecting a separation of the two metals.

$$[SbCl_4]^- + Al \rightarrow \underline{Sb} + Al^{+++} + 4\ Cl^-$$
$$3\ [SnCl_6]^{=} + 2\ Al \rightarrow 3\ [SnCl_3]^- + 2\ Al^{+++} + 9\ Cl^-$$

To be exact, aluminum actually reduces tin to the metallic state. When all of the aluminum is gone, the metallic tin dissolves in the hydrochloric acid, forming $[SnCl_3]^-$ ions and liberating hydrogen.

Use is made of the fact that divalent tin is a strong reducing agent in the confirmatory test for the ion. $[SnCl_3]^-$ will reduce mercury (II) to mercury (I), or metallic mercury, depending upon the amount of the tin (II) present in solution.

$$[SnCl_3]^- + 2\ HgCl_4^{=} \rightarrow [SnCl_6]^{=} + \underline{Hg_2Cl_2} + 3\ Cl^-$$
$$[SnCl_3]^- + Hg_2Cl_2 + Cl^- \rightarrow [SnCl_6]^{=} + \underline{2\ Hg}$$

Antimony metal reacts with nitric acid to form the insoluble oxide, Sb_4O_6. This oxide is soluble in oxalic acid, $H_2C_2O_4$, forming antimony (III) oxyhydrogen oxalate, $(SbO)HC_2O_4$.

$$4\ Sb + 4\ H^+ + 4\ NO_3^- \rightarrow \underline{Sb_4O_6} + 4\ NO + 2\ H_2O$$
$$Sb_4O_6 + 4\ H_2C_2O_4 \rightarrow 4(SbO)HC_2O_4 + 2\ H_2O$$

The presence of antimony is then confirmed by precipitating it as the orange-red sulfide, Sb_2S_3.

$$2\ (SbO)HC_2O_4 + 3\ H_2S \rightarrow \underline{Sb_2S_3} + 2\ H_2C_2O_4 + 2\ H_2O$$

PROCEDURE 11. ***Solution from (7): $[SnCl_6]^=$ and $[SbCl_4]^-$.*** **Boil the solution until all of the H_2S has been expelled. Add a volume of water equal to that of the solution and add 2 drops of 6 M HCl. Place a piece of aluminum wire about one-fourth inch long in the solution and heat the mixture until the aluminum has dissolved. Add 1 drop of 6 M HCl to the mixture and heat it for a few minutes. If antimony is present, black flakes of the metal will appear. Separate the mixture. Treat the black flakes with 3 drops of 4 M HNO_3 and several drops of 1 M oxalic acid. Add 2 drops of thioacetamide to the solution and place the test tube in a hot water bath. The formation of a red-orange precipitate of Sb_2S_3 confirms the presence of antimony. To tha solution obtained from the separation of metallic antimony, add a few drops of 0.2 M $HgCl_2$. The formation of a white, gray, or black precipitate confirms the presence of tin.**

QUESTIONS

1. Write the equation for the hydrogen ion catalyzed hydrolysis of thioacetamide. The hydrogen sulfide, as one of the products of the hydrolysis of thioacetamide, is a diprotic acid; illustrate this property of hydrogen sulfide by suitable equations.
2. In terms of ionic equilibria theory, discuss the effect of added hydrochloric acid on the concentration of sulfide ion in a solution of hydrogen sulfide. How would ammonia molecules and hydroxide ions influence the concentration of sulfide ions?
3. Explain in terms of ionic equilibria and solubility product theory, the dissolution of the sulfides of copper, bismuth, cadmium, and lead in nitric acid.
4. Why are the ions of lead and mercury found in both Groups I and II?
5. Explain in terms of ionic equilibria and solubility product theory, why Group II can be separated from Group III by hydrogen sulfide in the presence of hydrogen ions at a concentration of 0.3 M.

6. Why is it necessary to remove the nitric acid present before attempting to precipitate lead as the sulfate?

7. Give the color of each of the following: $[Cu(H_2O)_4]^{++}$, $[Cu(NH_3)_4]^{++}$, $Bi(OH)_3$, CuS, PbS, Bi_2S_3, HgS, As_2S_3, Sb_2S_3, SnS_2, $PbSO_4$, $[Cd(NH_3)_4]^{++}$, $[Cu(CN)_2]^-$, $MgNH_4AsO_4$, Sb, and Bi (finely divided).

8. Explain the dissolution of lead sulfate in ammonium acetate and the reprecipitation of the lead as lead chromate in terms of ionic equilibria and solubility product theory.

9. Why must the sodium stannite, which is used in the identification of bismuth, be prepared just prior to its use?

10. If a yellow precipitate is obtained when an unknown solution for Group II is treated with hydrogen sulfide, what ions are probably absent?

11. The Division A sulfides are washed with water containing ammonium nitrate. What is the function of the ammonium nitrate?

12. If a Group II unknown contains copper in an appreciable concentration, this fact should be evident from an inspection of the unknown solution. Why?

13. Select a reagent used in the analysis of Group I or Group II which will separate each of the following pairs in one step: (a) CdS, HgS; (b) Ag^+, Bi^{+++}; (c) Ag^+, Fe^{+++}; (d) As_2S_3, SnS_2; (e) CuS, CdS; (f) Bi^{+++}, Cd^{++}; (g) $[SbCl_4]^-$, $[SnCl]_6^=$.

14. Outline the separation of the following groups of ions, leaving out all unnecessary steps: (a) Ag^+, Hg^{++}, Co^{++}; (b) Pb^{++}, Cu^{++}, Cd^{++}; (c) Bi^{++}, As^{+++}, Sb^{+++}.

15. How will the separation of Groups II and III be effected if the concentration of hydronium ion in the solution saturated with hydrogen sulfide is 0.1 M? 1 M?

PROBLEMS

1. How many drops of 1 M aqueous ammonia will be required to neutralize the HCl in 2 ml. of a solution to be analyzed for Group II that is 0.5 M in HCl? (1 drop is 0.05 ml.) How many drops of 6 M HCl would be required to make the resulting solution 0.3 M in HCl? *Ans. 20 drops; 3 drops*

2. Calculate the concentration of H^+, HS^-, and $S^=$ in a 0.01 M solution of hydrogen sulfide. *Ans.* $[H^+] = [HS^-] = 3 \times 10^{-5}$; $[S^=] = 1 \times 10^{-13}$

3. Calculate the concentration of $S^=$ in a 0.01 M solution of HCl which is saturated with H_2S. *Ans.* 1×10^{-17} *M*

4. Calculate the concentration of H^+ required to prevent the precipitation of PbS from 0.010 M Pb^{++} that is saturated with H_2S. (K_{sp} for PbS is 8.4×10^{-28}.) *Ans.* 1.2×10^2 *M*

5. Calculate the solubility of CdS in a solution saturated with H_2S and 1.0 M in HCl. (K_{sp} for CdS is 3.6×10^{-29}.) *Ans.* 2.8×10^{-8} *M*

CHAPTER FORTY-SEVEN

The Analysis of Group III

The solution to be analyzed may be a Group III known or unknown, or it may be the solution from the Group II separation. See page 779 for the Group III flow sheet.

47.1 Precipitation of the Group III Ions

Analytical Group III contains the metallic ions, Ni^{++}, Co^{++}, Mn^{++}, Fe^{+++}, Al^{+++}, Cr^{+++}, and Zn^{++}. These ions are not precipitated by hydrochloric acid (the Group I precipitant), nor are they precipitated by sulfide ions in solutions which are 0.3 M in hydrogen ion (the Group II precipitant). However, an ammonium sulfide solution precipitates Ni^{++}, Co^{++}, Mn^{++}, Fe^{++}, and Zn^{++} as sulfides and Al^{+++} and Cr^{+++} as hydroxides.

The concentration of sulfide ions in the 0.3 M hydrogen ion solution of the Group II precipitation is too small to allow the solubility products of the Group III sulfides to be exceeded. Hydrogen sulfide in an aqueous solution of ammonia has a much higher sulfide ion concentration, due to the formation of ammonium sulfide, according to the equation

$$2\ NH_3 + H_2S \rightleftharpoons 2\ NH_4^+ + S^=$$

The resultant sulfide ion concentration is sufficiently large so that the solubility product constants of the sulfides of cobalt, nickel, manganese, iron, and zinc are exceeded and precipitation occurs. Likewise, the hydroxyl ion concentration of the ammonium sulfide solution is great enough to precipitate the hydroxides of aluminum and chromium. The solubility products of aluminum and chromium hydroxides are lower than those of the corresponding sulfides, thus favoring the precipitation of the former.

Hydrogen sulfide is produced for the precipitation of this group by the acidic hydrolysis of thioacetamide. Upon the addition of aqueous ammonia the following precipitations occur.

$$Co^{++} + S^= \rightleftharpoons \underline{CoS} \text{ (brown or black)}$$
$$Ni^{++} + S^= \rightleftharpoons \underline{NiS} \text{ (brown or black)}$$

GROUP III Flow Sheet

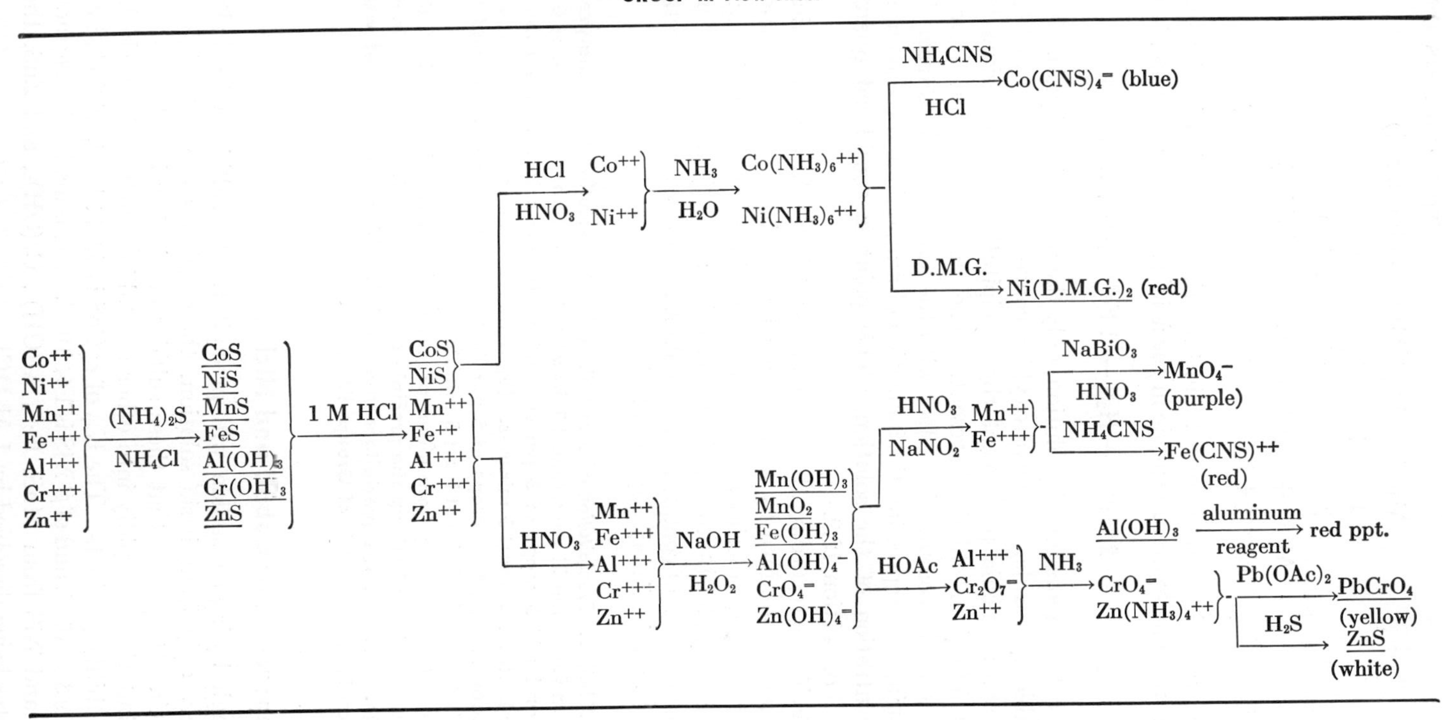

$$Mn^{++} + S^{=} \rightleftharpoons \underline{MnS} \text{ (flesh colored)}$$
$$Fe^{++} + S^{=} \rightleftharpoons \underline{FeS} \text{ (black)}$$
$$Zn^{++} + S^{=} \rightleftharpoons \underline{ZnS} \text{ (white)}$$
$$Al^{+++} + 3\ OH^{-} \rightleftharpoons \underline{Al(OH)_3} \text{ (white)}$$
$$Cr^{+++} + 3\ OH^{-} \rightleftharpoons \underline{Cr(OH)_3} \text{ (blue-green)}$$

In the event that iron is present in the original solution in the Fe^{+++} state, it will be reduced by hydrogen sulfide in the acidic solution, according to the equation

$$2\ Fe^{+++} + H_2S \rightarrow 2\ Fe^{++} + \underline{S} + 2\ H^{+}$$

Of the cations remaining in solution, only the magnesium ion, of Group V, forms an insoluble hydroxide. The hydroxyl ion concentration is kept just low enough in the aqueous ammonia to prevent the precipitation of magnesium hydroxide by having ammonium chloride present. The ammonium ions from ammonium chloride exert the common ion effect with the ammonium ions from the ionization of ammonia, thus repressing the ionization of ammonia and reducing the hydroxyl ion concentration of the solution. This point is considered quantitatively in Example 3 of Section 42.9.

Some evidence regarding the cations present in a solution containing the Group III ions can be obtained by noting the colors of the ions: Co^{++}, pale red; Ni^{++}, pale green; Zn^{++}, colorless; Mn^{++}, colorless in low concentrations; Fe^{++}, pale green; Fe^{+++}, reddish-brown; Al^{+++}, colorless; Cr^{+++}, dark green or blue. Due to the phenomenon of complementary colors, a solution containing certain combinations of colored ions may appear colorless.

PROCEDURE 1. ***Precipitation of Group III.*** **(a) If the solution to be analyzed is a known or unknown for Group III only, take 10 drops of the solution, add 1 drop of 6 M HCl, dilute to 1 ml., and add 5 drops of 5 per cent thioacetamide solution. Heat the solution in a hot water bath for at least 5 minutes. (b) If the solution to be analyzed is that from the Group II separation, add 5 drops of 5 per cent thioacetamide solution and heat the mixture in a hot water bath for at least 5 minutes.**

To the solution resulting from either procedure (a) or (b) above, add 5 drops of 15 M aqueous ammonia and stir up the precipitate. Heat the mixture for 5 minutes in the hot water bath. Separate the precipitate and wash it with a few drops of water. Reserve the solution for the analysis of Groups IV and V.

47.2 Separation of Cobalt and Nickel

Although hydrogen sulfide will precipitate the sulfides of cobalt and nickel completely only from basic solution, these sulfides are but slightly soluble in dilute HCl. It appears that these sulfides precipitate in a form which is soluble in acid, but change rapidly into other crystalline modifications which have much lower solubility products. The K_{sp} of α CoS is 5.9×10^{-21}, of β CoS is 8.7×10^{-23}, of α NiS is 3×10^{-21}, and of β NiS is 1×10^{-26}. Use is made of these facts in separating CoS and NiS from MnS, FeS, $Al(OH)_3$, $Cr(OH)_3$, and ZnS, the latter five precipitates being dissolved by 1 M HCl.

$$\underline{MnS} + 2\ H^+ \rightleftharpoons Mn^{++} + H_2S \uparrow$$
$$\underline{FeS} + 2\ H^+ \rightleftharpoons Fe^{++} + H_2S \uparrow$$
$$\underline{ZnS} + 2\ H^+ \rightleftharpoons Zn^{++} + H_2S \uparrow$$
$$\underline{Al(OH)_3} + 3\ H^+ \rightleftharpoons Al^{+++} + 3\ H_2O$$
$$\underline{Cr(OH)_3} + 3\ H^+ \rightleftharpoons Cr^{+++} + 3\ H_2O$$

PROCEDURE 2. ***Precipitate from (1): CoS, NiS, FeS, MnS, Al(OH)$_3$, Cr(OH)$_3$, and ZnS.*** **Add 10 drops of 1 M HCl to the precipitate and stir the mixture. Separate the mixture immediately because prolonged contact with the acid causes some dissolution of CoS and NiS. Wash the sulfides which remain (CoS and NiS) with 4 drops of 1 M HCl. Reserve the combined centrifugates for Procedure (4).**

47.3 Identification of Cobalt and Nickel

The sulfides of cobalt and nickel readily dissolve in a mixture of nitric and hydrochloric acids due to the higher hydrogen ion concentration and the oxidation of the sulfide ion to sulfur. The equations are

$$3\ CoS + 8\ H^+ + 2\ NO_3^- \rightleftharpoons 3\ Co^{++} + 2\ NO \uparrow\ + 3\ \underline{S} + 4\ H_2O$$
$$3\ NiS + 8\ H^+ + 2\ NO_3^- \rightleftharpoons 3\ Ni^{++} + 2\ NO \uparrow\ + 3\ \underline{S} + 4\ H_2O$$

After boiling the solution containing the cobalt and nickel ions to remove the oxides of nitrogen which would destroy the reagents used in the confirmation of these ions, an excess of aqueous ammonia is added. Ammonia in excess reacts with cobalt and nickel ions to form hexaamminemetal complexes.

$$Co^{++} + 6\ NH_3 \rightleftharpoons [Co(NH_3)_6]^{++}\ \text{(pink)}$$
$$Ni^{++} + 6\ NH_3 \rightleftharpoons [Ni(NH_3)_6]^{++}\ \text{(blue)}$$

In the ammoniacal solution, Ni^{++} will react with dimethylglyoxime to form a very insoluble, bright red complex compound. Co^{++} forms a brown colored soluble complex with dimethylglyoxime which does not interfere with the test.

$$2\ \begin{array}{l} CH_3-C{=}NOH \\ \quad\ \ | \\ CH_3-C{=}NOH \end{array} + Ni(NH_3)_6^{++} \rightarrow \begin{array}{ccccc} & O & \cdots H \cdots & O & \\ & \uparrow & & | & \\ CH_3-C{=} & N & & N & {=}C-CH_3 \\ | & & Ni & & | \\ CH_3-C{=} & N & & N & {=}C-CH_3 \\ & | & & \downarrow & \\ & O & \cdots H \cdots & O & \end{array} + 2\ NH_4^+ + 4\ NH_3$$

Dimethylglyoxime

A concentrated solution of ammonium thiocyanate is used in the identification of the cobalt ion, with which the thiocyanate ion forms a complex ion, $[Co(CNS)_4]^=$, that has a characteristic blue color.

$$[Co(NH_3)_6]^{++} + 4\ CNS^- \rightleftharpoons [Co(CNS)_4]^= + 6\ NH_3$$

When iron (III) ions are present, they interfere with this test by forming a bright red complex ion of the formula $[Fe(CNS)]^{++}$. This interference may be avoided by converting the iron to the colorless and very stable hexafluoroferrate (III) ion, $[FeF_6]^{-3}$. The equation is

$$Fe^{+++} + 6\ F^- \rightleftharpoons [FeF_6]^{-3}$$

A second confirmatory test for cobalt involves its oxidation by the nitrite ion from Co^{++} to Co^{+++} and the precipitation of the complex yellow salt, $K_3[Co(NO_2)_6]$, tripotassium hexanitrocobaltate (III).

$$Co^{++} + 6\ NO_2^- \rightarrow [Co(NO_2)_6]^{-4}$$
$$[Co(NO_2)_6]^{-4} + NO_2^- + 2\ H^+ \rightarrow [Co(NO_2)_6]^{-3} + NO\uparrow + H_2O$$
$$3\ K^+ + [Co(NO_2)_6]^{-3} \rightarrow \underline{K_3[Co(NO_2)_6]}$$

PROCEDURE 3. ***Residue from (2): CoS and NiS.*** **Add 3 drops of 12 M HCl and 1 drop of 14 M HNO_3 to the residue and heat the mixture in a hot water bath. Separate any sulfur that forms and boil the solution to remove any excess nitric acid or oxides of nitrogen. Add sufficient 4 M aqueous ammonia to the solution to make it slightly basic to litmus. Dilute the solution to 1 ml. and divide it into three parts.**

3a. ***Test for Nickel.*** **Add one drop of dimethylglyoxime to one part of the solution. The formation of a pink or red precipitate confirms the presence of nickel.**

3b. ***Test for Cobalt.*** **Acidify a second portion of the solution with 1 M HCl and add several crystals of NH_4CNS to it. Now add an equal volume of acetone and agitate the mixture. The development of a blue color proves the presence of cobalt. If the solution becomes red upon the addition of NH_4CNS, iron (III) ions are present. Add 1 drop of 1 M NaF to the solution. Now, if the solution is bluish green to green, the presence of cobalt is confirmed.**

3c. ***Test for Cobalt.*** **Acidify the third portion of the solution from (3) with 4 M HOAc, and add several large crystals of KNO_2. Warm the mixture. The formation of a yellow precipitate confirms the presence of cobalt.**

47.4 Separation of Iron and Manganese from Aluminum, Chromium, and Zinc

The solution containing the ions of the above metals is treated with nitric acid to remove the sulfide ion by oxidizing it to sulfur, and to oxidize Fe^{++} to Fe^{+++}. The equation for the oxidation of the iron is

$$3\ Fe^{++} + 4\ H^+ + NO_3^- \rightarrow 3\ Fe^{+++} + NO\uparrow + 2\ H_2O$$

It is desirable to have the iron in the +3 condition because $Fe(OH)_3$ is less soluble and less gelatinous in character than is $Fe(OH)_2$.

In order to separate iron and manganese from aluminum, chromium, and zinc, the solution is first treated with sodium hydroxide and then with hydrogen peroxide. The precipitations which first occur, as sodium hydroxide is added to the solution, are described by the following equations.

$$Mn^{++} + 2\ OH^- \rightleftharpoons \underline{Mn(OH)_2}\ \text{(white)}$$
$$Fe^{+++} + 3\ OH^- \rightleftharpoons \underline{Fe(OH)_3}\ \text{(reddish brown)}$$
$$Al^{+++} + 3\ OH^- \rightleftharpoons \underline{Al(OH)_3}\ \text{(white)}$$
$$Cr^{+++} + 3\ OH^- \rightleftharpoons \underline{Cr(OH)_3}\ \text{(dark green or blue)}$$
$$Zn^{++} + 2\ OH^- \rightleftharpoons \underline{Zn(OH)_2}\ \text{(white)}$$

The precipitate is not separated, and the addition of an excess of NaOH dissolves the amphoteric hydroxides of aluminum, chromium, and zinc, but not the hydroxides of iron and manganese.

$$Al(OH)_3 + OH^- \rightleftharpoons [Al(OH)_4]^- \text{ (aluminate) (colorless)}$$
$$Cr(OH)_3 + OH^- \rightleftharpoons [Cr(OH)_4]^- \text{ (chromite) (green)}$$
$$Zn(OH)_2 + 2\ OH^- \rightleftharpoons [Zn(OH)_4]^= \text{ (zincate) (colorless)}$$

Hydrogen peroxide is added to the resulting mixture to oxidize manganese (II) hydroxide to a mixture of manganese dioxide and manganese (III) hydroxide, both of which are much less soluble than $Mn(OH)_2$.

$$Mn(OH)_2 + H_2O_2 \rightarrow MnO_2 + 2\ H_2O$$
$$2\ Mn(OH)_2 + H_2O_2 \rightarrow 2\ Mn(OH)_3$$

Hydrogen peroxide oxidizes the chromite ion, $[Cr(OH)_4]^-$, to the chromate ion, $CrO_4^=$. This is desirable because the reactions of the chromate ion permit better identification of chromium than do those of either Cr^{+3} or $[Cr(OH)_4]^-$.

$$2\ [Cr(OH)_4]^- + 3\ H_2O_2 + 2\ OH^- \rightarrow 2\ CrO_4^= + 8\ H_2O$$

The mixture containing MnO_2 and $Mn(OH)_2$ is brown and solutions of $CrO_4^=$ are yellow.

PROCEDURE 4. ***Solution from (2):*** ***Mn^{++}, Fe^{++}, Al^{+++}, Cr^{+++}, and Zn^{++}.*** **Transfer the solution to a casserole, add 1 ml. of 4 M HNO_3, and evaporate the solution to a moist residue. Take up the residue in 1 ml. of water and transfer the solution to a test tube. Add 10 drops of 4 M NaOH beyond the amount of this reagent that is required to initiate precipitation. Now add 6 drops of 3 per cent hydrogen peroxide to the mixture and heat it in a hot water bath for 5 minutes. Separate the mixture and wash the residue with 10 drops of water to which has been added 1 drop of 4 M NaOH. Save the combined centrifugates for Procedure (6).**

47.5 Separation and Identification of Manganese and Iron

The residue containing MnO_2, $Mn(OH)_3$, and $Fe(OH)_3$ is dissolved by a mixture of HNO_3 and $NaNO_2$. The nitrite ion in acid solution reduces the manganese to the divalent condition. The iron (III) hydroxide is dissolved by nitric acid. The equations for these reactions are

$$2\ Mn(OH)_3 + 4\ H^+ + NO_2^- \rightarrow 2\ Mn^{++} + NO_3^- + 5\ H_2O$$
$$MnO_2 + 2\ H^+ + NO_2^- \rightarrow Mn^{++} + NO_3^- + H_2O$$
$$Fe(OH)_3 + 3\ H^+ \rightarrow Fe^{+++} + 3\ H_2O$$

The presence of Fe^{+++} is confirmed by its reaction with the thiocyanate ion, CNS^-, to produce a blood red complex ion, $[Fe(CNS)]^{++}$, or one of the possible complexes containing from one to six CNS^- groups.

$$Fe^{+++} + CNS^- \rightleftharpoons [Fe(CNS)]^{++}$$

This test for iron may be conducted on a solution containing Mn^{++} without interference by this ion. It should be noted that there are traces of Fe^{+++} existing in many reagents. Therefore a light pink color in this test may be due to iron as an impurity. Blank tests can be run on the reagents used in the test to establish this point.

Manganese may be identified in the presence of iron by oxidizing it to the permanganate ion by means of sodium bismuthate in nitric acid. The MnO_4^- ion is purple but in dilute solutions it may appear pink.

$$2\ Mn^{++} + 5\ BiO_3^- + 14\ H^+ \rightarrow 2\ MnO_4^- + 5\ Bi^{+++} + 7\ H_2O$$

PROCEDURE 5. ***Residue from (4): $Mn(OH)_3$, MnO_2, and $Fe(OH)_3$.*** **Treat the residue with 1 ml. of 4 M HNO_3 and 2 drops of 1 M $NaNO_2$. Stir the mixture and heat it in a hot water bath. Separate any residue that remains. Heat the solution to boiling, then cool it, and divide it into two parts.**

5a. ***Test for Iron.*** **Dilute one part of the solution to 1 ml. and add 2 or 3 crystals of NH_4CNS. If iron is present, a red color will develop in the solution.**

5b. ***Test for Magnanese.*** **To the second part of the solution from (5) add a small quantity of solid $NaBiO_3$ and a few drops of 4 M HNO_3. The formation of a pink or purple color confirms the presence of manganese.**

47.6 Separation and Identification of Aluminum

Acetic acid is added to the solution containing the $[Al(OH)_4]^-$, $CrO_4^=$, and $[Zn(OH)_4]^=$. The aluminum and zinc portray their basic character in the acidic solution and are converted to their cation forms.

$$[Al(OH)_4]^- + 4\ H^+ \rightleftharpoons Al^{+++} + 4\ H_2O$$
$$[Zn(OH)_4]^= + 4\ H^+ \rightleftharpoons Zn^{++} + 4\ H_2O$$

Acids react with yellow chromate, $CrO_4^=$, and convert it in part to the dichromate, $Cr_2O_7^=$, the extent of the conversion depending upon the concentration of the hydrogen ion.

$$2\ CrO_4^= + 2\ H^+ \rightleftharpoons Cr_2O_7^= + H_2O$$

The addition of excess aqueous ammonia precipitates aluminum as the hydroxide, converts $Cr_2O_7^=$ to $CrO_4^=$, and complexes the zinc as the soluble $[Zn(NH_3)_4]^{++}$ ion.

$$Al^{+++} + 3\ NH_3 + 3\ H_2O \rightleftharpoons \underline{Al(OH)_3} + 3\ NH_4^+$$
$$Cr_2O_7^= + 2\ OH^- \rightleftharpoons 2\ CrO_4^= + H_2O$$
$$Zn^{++} + 4\ NH_3 \rightleftharpoons [Zn(NH_3)_4]^{++}$$

The presence of aluminum is confirmed by dissolving the hydroxide in acetic acid and adding the aluminum reagent and $(NH_4)_2CO_3$. Aurin tricarboxylic acid (aluminon) imparts a red color to the $Al(OH)_3$ which is formed.

PROCEDURE 6. ***Solution from (4): $[Al(OH)_4^-]$, $CrO_4^=$, and $[Zn(OH)_4]^=$.*** **Add 4 M HOAc to the solution until it is acid to litmus and then add two or three drops of the acid in excess. Now add 4 M aqueous ammonia until the solution is distinctly alkaline to litmus. If a white gelatinous precipitate forms, it is probably aluminum hydroxide. Separate the precipitate and reserve the solution for Procedure (7). Confirm the presence of aluminum by dissolving the precipitate in 4 M HOAc and adding 2 drops of Aluminum Reagent and enough 1 M $(NH_4)_2CO_3$ to make the solution basic. The formation of a reddish-colored precipitate confirms the presence of aluminum.**

47.7 Identification of Chromium and Zinc

The presence of the chromate ion is confirmed by precipitating yellow lead chromate. Zinc ions do not interfere with the chromate test.

The zinc ions are precipitated by sulfide ions from a thioacetamide solution, white zinc sulfide being formed. The chromate ion may oxidize part of the sulfide ions used in the test to elementary sulfur, but ZnS is soluble in hydrochloric acid whereas sulfur is not. A second confirmatory test for zinc may be made by boiling all of the hydrogen sulfide out of the solution and precipitating the zinc as the hexacyanoferrate (II), which is white.

$$2\ K^{+} + Zn^{++} + Fe(CN)_6^{-4} \rightarrow \underline{K_2Zn[Fe(CN)_6]}$$

PROCEDURE 7. ***Solution from (6):*** $CrO_4^{=}$ ***and*** $[Zn(NH_3)_4]^{++}$**. Divide the solution into two parts.**

7a. Test for Chromium. **To one part of the solution add 1 M HOAc until the solution is acid to litmus. Then add 2 drops of 0.1 M** $Pb(OAc)_2$**. The formation of a yellow precipitate,** $PbCrO_4$**, confirms the presence of chromium.**

7b. Test for Zinc. **To the other part of the solution add 5 drops of 5 per cent thioacetamide solution and heat the mixture in a hot water bath. The formation of a white precipitate, ZnS, which is soluble in 4 M HCl, indicates the presence of zinc. Heat the solution to expel the excess hydrogen sulfide and then neutralize it with 4 M aqueous ammonia. Now add 10 drops of 1 M HCl and 5 drops of 0.1 M** $K_4[Fe(CN)_6]$**. The formation of a white precipitate,** $K_2Zn[Fe(CN)_6]$**, proves the presence of zinc.**

QUESTIONS

1. Why do the sulfides of Co^{++}, Ni^{++}, Mn^{++}, Fe^{++}, and Zn^{++} precipitate in an ammonium sulfide solution but not in a 0.3 M HCl solution of the hydrogen sulfide?
2. What is the function of the ammonium chloride used in the Group III reagent?
3. Why do aluminum and chromium precipitate as hydroxides rather than as sulfides in Group III?
4. Why does iron precipitate as iron (II) sulfide rather than iron (III) sulfide in an ammonium sulfide solution?
5. Account for the fact that CoS and NiS fail to precipitate in the 0.3 M HCl solution of Group II, yet they dissolve only very slowly in 1 M HCl.
6. A Group III unknown is colorless. What cations are probably absent? Why should one not rely definitely upon such an observation?
7. Cite two examples of the use of complex ions in the analysis of Group III.
8. Why will $PbCrO_4$ precipitate when Pb^{++} is added to a solution made up from $K_2Cr_2O_7$?
9. When and why is fluoride added in the test for cobalt using thiocyanate?
10. Write equations showing the amphoteric nature of the hydroxides of zinc, chromium, and aluminum.
11. Show by the proper formulas that manganese can act as either a metal or a nonmetal, depending upon its oxidation state.

12. Select a reagent used in Group III that will separate each of the following pairs. (a) CoS, ZnS; (b) Fe^{+++}, Al^{+++}; (c) $[Zn(NH_3)_4]^{++}$, $CrO_4^{=}$; (d) Al^{+++}, Zn^{++}; (e) Mn^{++}, Mg^{++}.

13. Outline the separation of the following groups of ions leaving out all unnecessary steps. (a) Hg_2^{++}, Hg^{++}, Cu^{++}, Fe^{++}; (b) Cd^{++}, Co^{++}, Ca^{++}; (c) Ni^{++}, Mn^{++}, Zn^{++}.

14. Give the color of each of the following: $Fe(OH)_3$, Fe^{+++}, $Fe(OH)_2$, Fe^{++}, $[Fe(CNS)]^{++}$, $[FeF_6]^{-3}$.

PROBLEMS

1. A solution from the Group II separation is 0.3 M in HCl and has a volume of 2.5 ml. Calculate the number of drops of 15 M aqueous ammonia required to react with the HCl (assume that 1 drop is equal to 0.05 ml.). *Ans. 10 drops*

2. Using 1.1×10^{-20} for the solubility product of ZnS, show that 0.3 M HCl should dissolve or prevent the precipitation of ZnS.
Ans. These conditions will permit a zinc ion concentration of 0.8 M

3. What concentration of NH_4^+ must be present in 0.1 M aqueous ammonia to prevent the precipitation of $Mg(OH)_2$ if the solution contains 0.05 mole of Mg^{++} per liter? (K_{sp} for $Mg(OH)_2$ is 1.5×10^{-11}.) *Ans. 0.1 M*

4. Calculate the concentration of Pb^{++} in a saturated solution of $PbCrO_4$. (K_{sp} for $PbCrO_4$ is 1.8×10^{-14}.) *Ans. 1.3×10^{-7} M*

CHAPTER FORTY-EIGHT

The Analysis of Group IV

The solution to be analyzed may be a Group IV known or unknown, or it may be the solution from the Group III separation. The Group IV flow sheet is given on page 788.

48.1 Precipitation of the Group IV Ions

Analytical Group IV contains the metallic ions, Ba^{++}, Sr^{++}, and Ca^{++}. These metals form chlorides, sulfides, and hydroxides which are soluble under the conditions which prevail in the precipitation of Groups I, II, and III. The carbonates of barium, strontium, and calcium precipitate in aqueous ammonia solutions containing ammonium carbonate.

The concentration of the carbonate ion in a solution of ammonium carbonate is too low to effect a complete precipitation of barium, strontium, and calcium due to the partial hydrolysis of the carbonate ion.

$$CO_3^{=} + H_2O \rightleftharpoons HCO_3^- + OH^-$$

This hydrolysis is repressed by increasing the hydroxide ion concentration of the solution, the additional hydroxide ions being supplied by the buffer pair — aqueous ammonia and ammonium chloride. These conditions permit a carbonate concentration high enough to precipitate $BaCO_3$, $SrCO_3$, and $CaCO_3$, but not $MgCO_3$. At the same time the hydroxide ion concentration in this buffered solution is not high enough to precipitate $Mg(OH)_2$.

In order that the solution may have the required ammonium ion concentration, the centrifugate from the Group III separation, which contains ammonium salts, is first evaporated to dryness and then ignited to expel the ammonium salts present. The equations are

$$NH_4Cl \rightarrow NH_3\uparrow + HCl\uparrow$$
$$NH_4NO_3 \rightarrow NH_3\uparrow + HNO_3\uparrow$$
$$NH_3 + HNO_3 \rightarrow N_2O\uparrow + 2\ H_2O\uparrow$$

The necessary ammonium ion concentration is then obtained by adding the Group IV reagent which consists of ammonium carbonate, ammonium chloride, and

GROUP IV Flow Sheet

- Ba^{++}, Sr^{++}, Ca^{++} $\xrightarrow{(NH_4)_2CO_3,\ NH_4Cl,\ NH_3 + H_2O}$ $\underline{BaCO_3}$, $\underline{SrCO_3}$, $\underline{CaCO_3}$ $\xrightarrow{HOAc}$ Ba^{++}, Sr^{++}, Ca^{++} $\xrightarrow{K_2CrO_4,\ HOAc,\ NH_4OAc}$
  - $\underline{BaCrO_4}$ $\xrightarrow{HCl}$ Ba^{++} $\xrightarrow{H_2SO_4}$ $\underline{BaSO_4}$ (white)
  - Sr^{++}, Ca^{++} $\xrightarrow{NH_3 + H_2O}$ Sr^{++}, Ca^{++} $\xrightarrow{K_2CrO_4,\ alcohol}$
    - $\underline{SrCrO_4}$ (yellow)
    - Ca^{++} $\xrightarrow{(NH_4)_2C_2O_4}$ $\underline{CaC_2O_4}$ (white)

aqueous ammonia in the required concentrations. The equations for the precipitations of the Group IV carbonates are

$$Ba^{++} + CO_3^{=} \rightleftharpoons \underline{BaCO_3} \text{ (white)}$$
$$Sr^{++} + CO_3^{=} \rightleftharpoons \underline{SrCO_3} \text{ (white)}$$
$$Ca^{++} + CO_3^{=} \rightleftharpoons \underline{CaCO_3} \text{ (white)}$$

PROCEDURE 1. ***Precipitation of the Group IV Ions: Ba^{++}, Sr^{++}, Ca^{++}.*** **Evaporate the solution (10 drops of a Group IV known or unknown or the solution from the Group III separation) to dryness and ignite in a casserole to expel ammonium salts. Dissolve the residue in a mixture of 1 drop of 12 M HCl and 12 drops of water. Make the solution alkaline by adding 4 M aqueous ammonia. Add just one drop of aqueous ammonia in excess. Add 2 drops of 1 M $(NH_4)_2CO_3$, or more if necessary, to effect complete precipitation, and warm the mixture in a hot water bath. Allow the mixture to cool; separate the precipitate and reserve the solution for the Group V analysis.**

48.2 The Separation and Identification of Barium

1. *The dissolution of the carbonates.* The carbonates of barium, strontium, and calcium are dissolved readily by strong acids such as hydrochloric acid or by weak acids such as acetic acid. The latter acid is used in these procedures, and the theory involved in these dissolutions is discussed in detail in Section 42.11. The equilibria involved, as applied to barium carbonate, are given by the following equations:

$$\underline{BaCO_3} \rightleftharpoons Ba^{++} + CO_3^{=}$$
$$\underline{HOAc} \rightleftharpoons H^+ + OAc^-$$
$$CO_3^{=} + H^+ \rightleftharpoons HCO_3^-$$
$$HCO_3^- + H^+ \rightleftharpoons H_2CO_3$$
$$H_2CO_3 \rightleftharpoons H_2O + CO_2 \uparrow$$

If the concentration of the hydrogen ion supplied by acetic acid is sufficiently high, the quantity of H_2CO_3 formed will exceed that in a saturated solution of CO_2 at atmospheric pressure and CO_2 will escape from solution. The loss of carbon dioxide from the system in this way causes all the above equilibria to be shifted to the right until the precipitate dissolves completely. The net reaction is given by the equation

$$\underline{BaCO_3} + 2\ HOAc \rightleftharpoons Ba^{++} + 2\ OAc^- + H_2O + CO_2 \uparrow$$

Similar equations may be written for the dissolution of the carbonates of strontium and calcium in acetic acid.

2. *The separation of barium from strontium and calcium by precipitation of barium chromate.* By taking advantage of the fact that barium chromate is less soluble than strontium chromate and calcium chromate, barium can be separated from strontium and calcium. The solubility product constants are 2×10^{-10} for $BaCrO_4$ and 3.6×10^{-5} for $SrCrO_4$. Calcium chromate is relatively very soluble. The problem in this separation, then, is to control the concentration of the chromate ion so that the concentration of the barium ion will be reduced to at least 0.0001 M, and strontium chromate will not be precipitated from a solution 0.1 M in the strontium ion. Let us first calculate the concentration of chromate ion required to reduce the barium ion concentration to 0.0001 M.

$$[Ba^{++}][CrO_4^{=}] = 2 \times 10^{-10}$$

$$[CrO_4^{=}] = \frac{2 \times 10^{-10}}{[Ba^{++}]} = \frac{2 \times 10^{-10}}{1 \times 10^{-4}} = 2 \times 10^{-6} \text{ M}$$

Now let us determine the maximum concentration of chromate ion that we can have without precipitating any strontium chromate when the concentration of the strontium ion is 0.1 M.

$$[Sr^{++}][CrO_4^{=}] = 3.6 \times 10^{-5}$$

$$[CrO_4^{=}] = \frac{3.6 \times 10^{-5}}{[Sr^{++}]} = \frac{3.6 \times 10^{-5}}{10^{-1}} = 3.6 \times 10^{-4} \text{ M}$$

Thus we find that the concentration of the chromate ion must be held between 2×10^{-6} M and 3.6×10^{-4} M to cause a nearly complete precipitation of $BaCrO_4$, but not the precipitation of any $SrCrO_4$.

In a solution containing chromate ions, we have the following equilibrium:

$$Cr_2O_7^{=} + H_2O \rightleftharpoons 2\ CrO_4^{=} + 2\ H^+$$

The concentration of chromate ions in a solution made by dissolving a dichromate in water can be controlled by adjusting the hydrogen ion concentration. Applying the law of chemical equilibrium to this system, we have

$$\frac{[CrO_4^{=}]^2[H^+]^2}{[Cr_2O_7^{=}]} = 2.4 \times 10^{-15}$$

It is readily seen from this expression that the chromate ion concentration is a function of the hydrogen ion concentration. The more acidic the solution, the lower will be the chromate ion concentration; and the more basic the solution, the higher will be the chromate ion concentration. By substituting in the above expression, it can be shown that for a solution which is about 0.01 M in dichromate ions, the hydrogen ion concentration must be adjusted to about 1×10^{-5} M (pH = 5) to maintain the chromate ion concentration at about 5×10^{-4} M. As shown above, this concentration of chromate ions is approximately the value needed for the separation of Ba^{++} from Sr^{++}. A buffered solution composed of acetic acid and ammonium acetate is used to obtain the required hydrogen ion concentration.

As chromate ions are removed from the system through precipitation of barium chromate, the concentration of these ions does not change appreciably. This is true because the excess of dichromate serves as a reservoir for chromate ions; and as $CrO_4^=$ is used up in precipitating $BaCrO_4$, the equilibrium $Cr_2O_7^= + H_2O \rightleftharpoons 2\ CrO_4^= + 2\ H^+$ shifts to the right with the generation of more $CrO_4^=$ from the relatively large supply of $Cr_2O_7^=$. The hydrogen ions that are formed unite with the acetate ions of the buffered solution, and a constant pH is maintained.

3. *The dissolution of barium chromate.* Even though barium chromate is precipitated from a weakly acidic solution, it is readily dissolved by strong acids. The hydrogen ion concentration of solutions of strong acids is sufficiently high to cause a reduction in the chromate ion concentration below the value required to maintain a saturated solution of barium chromate. Thus

$$[Ba^{++}][CrO_4^=] < K_{sp}$$

and the barium chromate dissolves. A solution of 12 M HCl is used in this scheme to bring about the dissolution of $BaCrO_4$.

4. *The identification of barium.* The presence of the barium ion in the solution is confirmed by precipitating it as barium sulfate, with sulfuric acid being used as the precipitant.

Additional evidence for the presence of the barium ion is obtained using the flame test. When heated in the Bunsen flame, barium salts impart to it a yellow-green color.

PROCEDURE 2. ***Precipitate from (1): $BaCO_3$, $SrCO_3$, $CaCO_3$.*** **Dissolve the precipitate in a mixture of 2 drops of 4 M HOAc and 4 drops of 1 M NH_4OAc. Add 1 drop of 1 M K_2CrO_4 to the solution. The formation of a yellow precipitate indicates the presence of barium. Separate the mixture and reserve the solution for Procedure (3). Dissolve the precipitate ($BaCrO_4$) in 2 drops of 12 M HCl. Make a flame test (Section 44.15) on the solution for the barium ion. The barium ion imparts a greenish-yellow color to the Bunsen flame. Add 1 drop of 4 M H_2SO_4 to the remainder of the solution. A white precipitate ($BaSO_4$) confirms the presence of barium.**

48.3 The Separation and Identification of Strontium

1. *The separation of strontium from calcium.* Although the chromate ion concentration in an acetic acid-ammonium acetate buffered solution is too low to exceed the solubility product of strontium chromate, this compound will precipitate when the solution is made basic with aqueous ammonia. The equilibria are

$$Cr_2O_7^= + H_2O \rightleftharpoons 2\ CrO_4^= + 2\ H^+$$
$$2\ OH^- + 2\ H^+ \rightleftharpoons 2\ H_2O$$

and the net reaction is

$$Cr_2O_7^= + 2\ OH^- \rightleftharpoons 2\ CrO_4^= + H_2O$$

The resulting concentration of chromate ions is large enough so that the solubility product constant of strontium chromate is exceeded and precipitation occurs. The complete precipitation of strontium chromate is insured by further reducing its solubility through the addition of enough ethyl alcohol to the solution to make it 50 per cent alcohol by volume. Calcium chromate is soluble in this solution.

2. *The identification of strontium.* The formation of a fine yellow crystalline precipitate of the chromate serves to confirm the presence of strontium. A crimson color imparted to the Bunsen flame is characteristic of the strontium ion.

PROCEDURE 3. ***Solution from (2):*** Sr^{++} ***and*** Ca^{++}. **Add 4 M aqueous ammonia to the solution until the color changes from orange to yellow. Now add a volume of ethyl alcohol equal to the volume of the solution. The formation of a fine yellow precipitate indicates** $SrCrO_4$. **Separate the mixture and reserve the solution for Procedure (4). Dissolve the precipitate in 2 drops of 12 M HCl and make a flame test on the solution for the strontium ion. A crimson color imparted to the flame is characteristic of the strontium ion.**

48.4 The Identification of the Calcium

The solution from the strontium chromate separation contains the calcium ion. The addition of ammonium oxalate will precipitate calcium oxalate, CaC_2O_4, a white crystalline salt.

$$Ca^{++} + C_2O_4^{=} \rightleftharpoons \underline{CaC_2O_4}$$

Calcium ions impart a brick red color to the Bunsen flame.

PROCEDURE 4. ***Solution from (3):*** Ca^{++}. **Heat the solution to boiling and add 2 drops of 0.4 M** $(NH_4)_2C_2O_4$. **The formation of a white precipitate confirms the presence of calcium. Dissolve the precipitate in 12 M HCl and make a flame test on the solution. Calcium ions impart a brick red color to the flame.**

PROCEDURE 5. ***Original Solution:*** Ba^{++}, Sr^{++}, Ca^{++}. **Make flame tests on the original solution and compare with tests on known solutions which you make up yourself.**

QUESTIONS

1. What reagents compose the Group IV precipitant? What is the function of each of these chemicals in the group precipitation?
2. Why are ammonium salts expelled prior to the precipitation of Group IV?
3. Write equations representing the various ionic equilibria involved in the dissolution of barium carbonate in acetic acid.
4. Barium chromate is precipitated from a solution of potassium chromate containing acetic acid. Why is the acetic acid present?
5. In terms of ionic equilibria and solubility product theory, explain the dissolution of $BaCrO_4$ in HCl.
6. What characteristic properties cause Ca^{++}, Sr^{+}, and Ba^{++} to be members of the same group of the analytical scheme?
7. What are the characteristic colors imparted to the Bunsen flame by Ca^{++}, Sr^{++}, and Ba^{++}?
8. Outline the separation of the following groups of ions leaving out all unnecessary steps. (a) Ag^{+}, Cu^{++}, Zn^{++}, Ca^{++}, Na^{+}; (b) Fe^{+++}, Ba^{++}, Mg^{++}; (c) Pb^{++}, Sn^{++++}, Al^{+++}, Sr^{++}.
9. Account for the color change from orange to yellow when aqueous ammonia is added to an acetic acid solution of potassium dichromate.
10. Explain why ammonium carbonate rather than sodium carbonate is used in the precipitation of Group IV.

PROBLEMS

1. What total weight of carbonates can be obtained from a solution containing 2.00 mg. each of Ba^{++}, Sr^{++}, and Ca^{++}? *Ans. 11.2 mg.*

2. How many drops (assume 1 drop = 0.050 ml.) of 1.0 M acetic acid would be required to dissolve the carbonate precipitate in Problem 1? *Ans. 3.5 drops*

3. What concentration of carbonate ion is required to initiate precipitation of (a) $BaCO_3$ from 0.010 M Ba^{++}; (b) $MgCO_3$ from 0.010 M Mg^{++}? (K_{sp} for $BaCO_3$ is 8.1×10^{-9}; K_{sp} for $MgCO_3$ is 4.0×10^{-5}.)
Ans. (a) 8.1×10^{-7} M; (b) 4.0×10^{-3} M

4. Calculate the hydroxide ion concentration of a solution that is 0.10 M in NH_3 and 0.20 M in NH_4^+. *Ans. 9.0×10^{-6} M*

5. Will the concentration of OH^- in Problem 4 be large enough to cause $Mg(OH)_2$ to precipitate in a 0.010 M solution of Mg^{++}? (K_{sp} for $Mg(OH)_2$ is 1.5×10^{-11}.) *Ans. No*

CHAPTER FORTY-NINE

The Analysis of Group V

The solution for analysis may be a Group V known or unknown or it may be the solution from the Group IV separation. The flow sheet for the Group V analytical scheme is given below.

GROUP V Flow Sheet

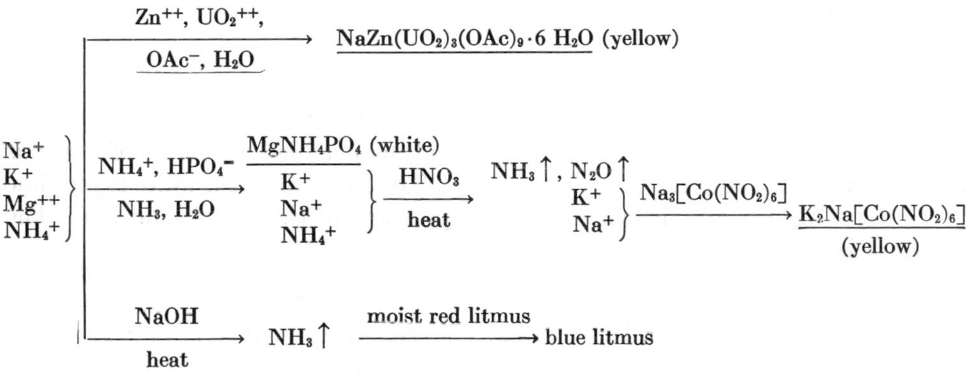

Na^+, K^+, Mg^{++}, NH_4^+

$\xrightarrow[OAc^-,\ H_2O]{Zn^{++},\ UO_2^{++},}$ $NaZn(UO_2)_3(OAc)_9 \cdot 6\ H_2O$ (yellow)

$\xrightarrow[NH_3,\ H_2O]{NH_4^+,\ HPO_4^-}$ $MgNH_4PO_4$ (white); K^+, Na^+, NH_4^+ $\xrightarrow[heat]{HNO_3}$ $NH_3\uparrow$, $N_2O\uparrow$; K^+, Na^+ $\xrightarrow{Na_3[Co(NO_2)_6]}$ $K_2Na[Co(NO_2)_6]$ (yellow)

$\xrightarrow[heat]{NaOH}$ $NH_3\uparrow$ $\xrightarrow{\text{moist red litmus}}$ blue litmus

49.1 Removal of Traces of Calcium and Barium

The cations comprising Group V (Na^+, K^+, Mg^{++}, and NH_4^+) do not form precipitates with the reagents used to separate Groups I, II, III, and IV, and the ions of this group have no precipitant which is common to all four ions.

If ammonium salts were present in excessive quantities during the precipitation of the carbonates of the Group IV ions, then trace amounts of barium and calcium ions may have come through into the Group V solution. Because these ions will interfere with the identification of the Group V ions, they must be removed. Ammonium oxalate is added to precipitate the calcium ions and ammonium sulfate to precipitate the barium ions.

PROCEDURE 1. ***Solution from the Group IV Separation:*** ***Na^+, K^+, Mg^{++}, NH_4^+, (Ca^{++}), (Ba^{++}).*** **Add to this solution 1 drop of 4 M $(NH_4)_2C_2O_4$ and 1 drop of 1 M $(NH_4)_2SO_4$. Separate and discard any precipitate that may form and use the solution for Procedure (2).**

49.2 Identification of Sodium

After the removal of the traces of barium and calcium, the sodium ion may be detected by the formation of the triple salt, sodium zinc uranyl acetate hexahydrate, which is a yellow crystalline compound.

$$Na^+ + Zn^{++} + 3\ UO_2^{++} + 9\ OAc^- + 6\ H_2O \rightleftharpoons \underline{NaZn(UO_2)_3(OAc)_9 \cdot 6\ H_2O}$$

The Sodium Reagent is a saturated solution of zinc acetate and uranyl acetate in acetic acid. Ammonium, magnesium, and potassium ions do not interfere with the test. The sodium ion imparts a yellow color to the Bunsen flame.

PROCEDURE 2. ***Solution from (1):*** ***K^+, Na^+, Mg^{++}, NH_4^+.*** **To 2 drops of the solution from (1) or Group V known or unknown, add 1 M HOAc until the solution is acid to litmus. Add 1 drop of this acidified solution to 5 drops of Sodium Reagent. Shake the mixture and set it aside for an hour. The formation of a yellow crystalline precipitate indicates the presence of sodium.**

49.3 Separation and Identification of Magnesium

To a second portion of the solution for analysis is added an excess of aqueous ammonia and disodium hydrogen phosphate. The formation of a white crystalline precipitate, $MgNH_4PO_4$, is evidence of the presence of the magnesium ion. The equation is

$$Mg^{++} + NH_4^+ + HPO_4^= \rightleftharpoons \underline{MgNH_4PO_4} + H^+$$

Note that the hydrogen ion is one product of the reaction. Completeness of precipitation of the magnesium ammonium phosphate is assured by making the solution basic with aqueous ammonia, which combines with the hydrogen ion and causes a shift of the equilibrium to the right.

After the magnesium ammonium phosphate is separated from the solution containing the sodium and ammonium ions, it is dissolved in acetic acid. This treatment with acid causes the following equilibrium to be shifted to the right.

$$MgNH_4PO_4 + H^+ \rightleftharpoons Mg^{++} + NH_4^+ + HPO_4^=$$

This results because the phosphate ion in a saturated solution of $MgNH_4PO_4$ is removed from the solution by combining with hydrogen ions, making the product of the concentrations of the Mg^{++}, NH_4^+, and PO_4^{-3} ions less than the solubility product constant. Magnesium Reagent and sodium hydroxide are added to the solution containing magnesium ions. The magnesium hydroxide which is formed adsorbs the Magnesium Reagent (a dye, p-nitrobenzene-azo-alpha-naphthol) and forms a blue precipitate, which confirms the presence of magnesium.

PROCEDURE 3. *Use 10 drops of the solution from (1) or 10 drops of Group V known or unknown: K^+, Na^+, Mg^{++}, NH_4^+.* **Add 4 M aqueous ammonia to the solution until it is alkaline to litmus and then add 1 drop in excess. Now add 2 drops of 1 M Na_2HPO_4 to the solution. The formation of a white crystalline precipitate, often slow in forming, confirms the presence of magnesium. Separate the mixture and save the solution for Procedure (4). Dissolve the precipitate in a mixture of 2 drops of 1 M HOAc and 3 drops of water. Add 1 drop of Magnesium Reagent and an excess of 4 M NaOH to the solution. The formation of a blue precipitate confirms the presence of magnesium.**

49.4 Identification of Potassium

The identification of potassium is made from the solution obtained from the separation of magnesium ammonium phosphate. Ammonium ions must be removed prior to the test for the potassium ion because the precipitant for potassium ions will also precipitate ammonium ions. Concentrated nitric acid is added to the solution, it is evaporated to dryness, and then it is ignited to expel volatile ammonium salts.

$$NH_4Cl \rightarrow NH_3\uparrow + HCl\uparrow$$
$$NH_4NO_3 \rightarrow NH_3\uparrow + HNO_3\uparrow$$
$$NH_3 + HNO_3 \rightarrow N_2O\uparrow + 2\ H_2O\uparrow$$

The potassium ion is precipitated from solution in the form of the yellow complex salt, $K_2Na[Co(NO_2)_6]$, upon the addition of a solution of $Na_3[Co(NO_2)_6]$.

$$2\ K^+ + Na^+ + [Co(NO_2)_6]^{-3} \rightarrow \underline{K_2Na[Co(NO_2)_6]}$$

Potassium gives a characteristic violet flame test which is masked by the intense yellow color produced by the sodium ion. By observing the flame through cobalt glass, which filters out the yellow color of the sodium ion, one may detect the potassium ion in the presence of the sodium ion.

PROCEDURE 4. *Solution from (3): K^+, Na^+, NH_4^+.* **Add 4 drops of concentrated HNO_3 to the solution held in a casserole, evaporate it to dryness, and then heat the dry residue for several minutes. After the casserole is cool, add 1 drop of 1 M HCl and 5 drops of 4 M HOAc to the residue and boil the resultant solution. Now add 2 drops of this solution to 5 drops of a saturated solution of $Na_3[Co(NO_2)_6]$. The formation of a yellow precipitate confirms the presence of potassium.**

PROCEDURE 5. *Original Known or Unknown Solution for Group V or Solution from Procedure (1).* **Make flame tests on this solution and compare with known solutions of the ions in question. When testing for potassium, observe the flame through a cobalt glass. Sodium ions impart an intense yellow color to the flame. A trace of the sodium ion as contaminant will give a yellow coloration to the flame, so do not rely entirely upon the flame test in reporting the presence of sodium ions. Potassium ions give a violet color to a flame.**

49.5 Identification of Ammonium Ions

Since ammonium ions are added in the course of the analysis at various points, it becomes necessary to test for this ion on the original solution of a known or unknown. The presence of the ammonium ion in a solution may be detected by the addition of a strong, nonvolatile base such as sodium hydroxide, with subsequent heating of the solution and liberation of gaseous ammonia.

$$NH_4^+ + OH^- \text{ (from NaOH)} \rightleftharpoons NH_3 \uparrow + H_2O$$

The gaseous ammonia may be detected by moist red litmus paper and by its characteristic odor.

$$NH_3 + H_2O \rightleftharpoons NH_4^+ + OH^-$$

During the heating of the solution one must not permit the sodium hydroxide solution to come in contact with the litmus paper because this would void the test for ammonia.

PROCEDURE 6. ***Original Solution of the Known or Unknown.*** **Add 4 M NaOH to the solution until it is basic. Moisten a piece of red litmus with distilled water and place it on the convex side of a watch glass. Place the watch glass on a beaker containing the solution and warm the solution gently. Avoid spattering of the solution by overheating and do not permit the litmus to come into contact with the solution. If the litmus turns blue within a short time, the presence of the ammonium ion is confirmed.**

QUESTIONS

1. Why is Group V often referred to as the soluble group?
2. Explain why the test for the ammonium ion must be made on a portion of the original sample during the analysis of either a Group V known or unknown or a general unknown involving all of the groups.
3. Why must the ammonium ion be removed before making the chemical test for the potassium ion?
4. Write the equation for the dissolution of $MgNH_4PO_4$ in an acid. Explain this reaction in terms of solubility product constant and ionic equilibria theory.
5. Why are $(NH_4)_2SO_4$ and $(NH_4)_2C_2O_4$ added prior to the analysis of Group V?
6. Explain the use of cobalt glass in the flame test for potassium.
7. What is the chemistry of the chemical test for potassium?
8. Why may red litmus turn blue upon prolonged exposure to the air of the laboratory?

PROBLEMS

1. How many ml. of NH_3 gas measured at 25° C and 740 mm. pressure will be evolved when a solution containing 10.0 mg. of NH_4Cl is treated with NaOH and heated? *Ans.* *4.7 ml.*
2. What weight of $MgNH_4PO_4$ can be formed from 5.0 mg. of Mg^{++}? *Ans.* *28 mg.*

CHAPTER FIFTY

Anion Analysis

50.1 Introduction

Thirteen of the more common and important negative ions are included in this scheme of anion analysis. The anions considered are carbonate, sulfide, sulfite, nitrite, sulfate, nitrate, phosphate, metaborate, oxalate, fluoride, chloride, bromide, and iodide. Among the anions that were given consideration in the cation scheme of analysis are arsenite, arsenate, stannite, stannate, permanganate, aluminate, chromate, dichromate, and zincate.

Although several schemes of anion analysis involving the separation of the ions into groups have been developed, the procedures are in general more complicated and unreliable than are those for cation analysis. Instead of using a systematic scheme of analysis on the same solution throughout the analysis, the procedures outlined below involve a series of elimination tests which prove the absence of certain anions. Tests are then made on different samples of the unknown solution for the presence of the anions whose absences were not indicated in the preliminary elimination tests. (A flow sheet of the anion elimination tests is given on page 798.)

The properties of the acids and their anions have been considered in Part 1 of the text in connection with the descriptive chemistry of the nonmetals. The student will find it necessary to refer to those earlier chapters in order to answer some of the questions which arise concerning the chemistry of the anions.

The anion knowns and unknowns are in general furnished in the form of mixtures of dry salts due to the fact that some of the anions react with one another in solution. Thus, certain anions may be detected in freshly prepared solutions, whereas, upon standing, these same anions may have undergone decomposition. Certain combinations of anions react almost immediately in alkaline solutions while still other anions cannot exist together in acidic solutions. As an example of anion incompatibility, strong oxidizing anions usually react with strong reducing anions upon acidification.

PRELIMINARY ELIMINATION TESTS FOR THE ANIONS

50.2 Anion Elimination Chart

Prepare an Anion Elimination Chart like that shown on page 799. As you perform each elimination test, check off in the appropriate spaces those anions

ANION ELIMINATION Flow Sheet

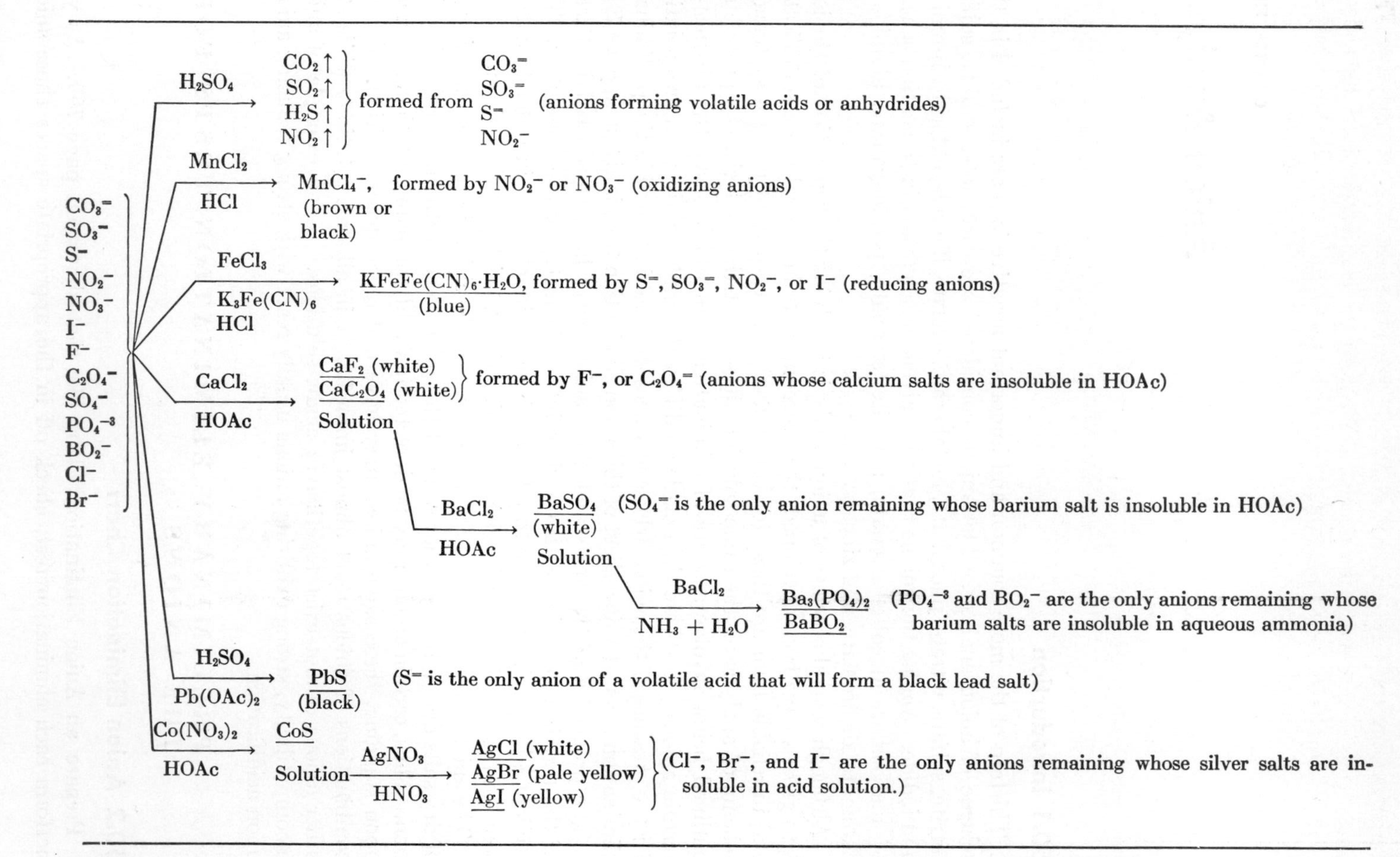

which you have found to be absent. When all the elimination tests have been made, it will be apparent which anions may be present. Tests will then be made for the anions which have not been eliminated.

Name: ______________________ *Section:* __________ *Date:* __________

Instructor's Approval: ______________________ *Ions Found:* __________

Grade: __________

ANION ELIMINATION CHART

Anions	*Test I*	*Test II*	*Test III*	*Test IV*	*Test V*	*Test VI*	*Test VII*	*Test VIII*	*Make Confirmatory Tests for*
$CO_3^{=}$									
$SO_3^{=}$									
$S^{=}$									
NO_2^-									
NO_3^-									
I^-									
F^-									
$C_2O_4^{=}$									
$SO_4^{=}$									
PO_4^{-3}									
BO_2^-									
Cl^-									
Br^-									

50.3 Elimination of the Anions Forming Volatile Acid Anhydrides

The ions $CO_3^{=}$, $SO_3^{=}$, $S^{=}$, and NO_2^- are anions derived from the weak acids, H_2CO_3, H_2SO_3, H_2S, and HNO_2, respectively. As acids in solution, H_2CO_3, H_2SO_3, and HNO_2 are unstable and decompose, producing gases. Hydrogen sulfide does not decompose but has a limited solubility in water. When salts of these anions are treated with strong acids, the anions, being strong bases according to the proton theory of acids and bases, readily combine with the hydrogen ions from the strong acids. The equilibria are

$$CO_3^{=} + H^+ \rightleftharpoons HCO_3^-$$
$$HCO_3^- + H^+ \rightleftharpoons H_2CO_3$$
$$H_2CO_3 \rightleftharpoons H_2O + CO_2 \uparrow$$
$$SO_3^{=} + H^+ \rightleftharpoons HSO_3^-$$
$$HSO_3^- + H^+ \rightleftharpoons H_2SO_3$$
$$H_2SO_3 \rightleftharpoons H_2O + SO_2 \uparrow$$
$$S^{=} + H^+ \rightleftharpoons HS^-$$
$$HS^- + H^+ \rightleftharpoons H_2S \uparrow$$
$$NO_2^- + H^+ \rightleftharpoons HNO_2$$
$$3\ HNO_2 \rightleftharpoons H^+ + NO_3^- + 2\ NO \uparrow + H_2O$$
$$2\ NO + O_2 \rightarrow 2\ NO_2 \uparrow$$

The high concentration of hydrogen ion furnished by the sulfuric acid used in this elimination test serves to shift the equilibrium to the right in each case. When the solubility of each gas is exceeded, it will escape from solution in the form of bubbles. Gentle heating decreases the solubility of the gases and aids in the test for gas-forming anions. Boiling of the solution should be avoided because bubbles of steam may be mistaken for bubbles of gaseous reaction products.

If no gas is evolved upon acidification and gentle heating of an unknown sample, $CO_3^{=}$, $SO_3^{=}$, $S^{=}$, and NO_2^- are absent. If a gas is evolved, then one or more of the gas-forming anions is present, and it becomes necessary to make tests for the presence of each of these ions unless they are proved absent by other elimination tests.

TEST I. ***Elimination of Anions Forming Volatile Acid Anhydrides, $CO_3^{=}$, $SO_3^{=}$, $S^{=}$, and NO_2^-.*** **Treat 25 mg. of the solid unknown contained in a test tube with 2 drops of 1.5 M H_2SO_4. Examine the mixture for the formation of gas bubbles. If no gas is evolved, heat the mixture in the hot water bath. If no gas is evolved, then $CO_3^{=}$, $SO_3^{=}$, $S^{=}$, and NO_2^- are proved to be absent. If these anions are absent, place a checkmark after the formula for each of these anions in the Test I column of your anion chart; leave these spaces blank if a gas is evolved.**

If a gas is evolved, note its odor and color. Carbon dioxide is colorless and odorless. Sulfur dioxide is colorless and has the odor of burning sulfur. Hydrogen sulfide is colorless and exhibits a characteristic odor. If the nitrite ion is present, nitrogen dioxide, with a reddish-brown color and characteristic odor, is evolved. The solution may be pale blue in color because of the presence of HNO_2 if the nitrite ion is present.

50.4 Preparation of the Solution for Analysis

The procedures outlined for the detection of the anions are applicable, in general, to salts containing only the alkali metals as cations. It is obvious that complications in the anion analysis will arise if certain metal ions are present to form precipitates, or possibly colored solutions, with the anions being detected.

Most of the metal ions may be removed from solution as insoluble carbonates, hydroxycarbonates, hydroxides, or oxides by treating a solution of the unknown with sodium carbonate. The ammonium ion, NH_4^+, is converted to NH_3, which is evolved from the hot solution. Since the carbonate ion is added in excess, the identification of this ion must be made on the original sample. The $CO_3^{=}$ must be removed before certain other tests are made.

PREPARATION OF THE SOLUTION FOR ANALYSIS. ***Removal of Heavy Metal Ions by Na_2CO_3.*** **Place 100 mg. of the powdered unknown in a test tube and add 2 ml. of 1.5 M Na_2CO_3 solution. Heat the mixture for 10 minutes in the hot water bath. If ammonia is given off, continue the heating until no more gas is evolved. Separate any precipitate that forms. The solution will contain the anions in the form of sodium salts and will be referred to as the "prepared solution."**

50.5 Elimination of Oxidizing Anions

It will be noted that the nitrite ion is included in both the elimination tests for oxidizing anions and reducing anions. The oxidation potential of the nitrite ion in acid solution is intermediate in value, thus making the ion an oxidizing agent in the presence of strong reducing agents, and a reducing agent in the presence of strong oxidizing agents.

The prepared solution is tested for oxidizing anions, NO_2^- and NO_3^-, by means of a saturated solution of manganese (II) chloride in concentrated hydrochloric acid. The development of a dark brown or black color is the result of the oxidation, in strongly acidic solution, of the manganese (II) ion, Mn^{++}, to the manganese (III) ion, Mn^{+++}. The manganese (III) ion then unites with chloride ions and forms the dark colored complex, $MnCl_4^-$.

$$Mn^{++} + HNO_2 + H^+ + 4\ Cl^- \rightarrow MnCl_4^- + NO\uparrow + H_2O$$
$$3\ Mn^{++} + 4\ H^+ + NO_3^- + 12\ Cl^- \rightarrow 3\ MnCl_4^- + NO\uparrow + 2\ H_2O$$

Test II. ***Elimination of Oxidizing Anions: NO_3^- and NO_2^-.*** **Add 6 drops of a saturated solution of $MnCl_2$ in 12 M HCl to 4 drops of the prepared solution and heat the mixture to boiling. The formation of a dark brown or black coloration, due to $MnCl_4^-$, indicates the presence of NO_3^-, NO_2^-, or a mixture of these ions. Record the results of the test on your anion chart.**

50.6 Elimination of Reducing Anions

A sample of the prepared solution is acidified with hydrochloric acid and then iron (III) chloride and potassium hexacyanoferrate (III) are added to the solution. The prompt appearance of a blue to blue-green color or precipitate proves the presence of one or more of the reducing anions $S^=$, $SO_3^=$, NO_2^-, or I^-.

Iron (III), Fe^{+++}, forms a brown solution when fresh, and a green solution when old, with $Fe(CN)_6^{-3}$. In the presence of a strong reducing agent the Fe^{+++} may be reduced to Fe^{++}, or the $Fe(CN)_6^{-3}$ reduced to $Fe(CN)_6^{-4}$, with the formation of $KFeFe(CN)_6 \cdot H_2O$, a blue pigment. The equations are

$$2\ Fe^{+++} + S^= \rightleftharpoons 2\ Fe^{++} + \underline{S}$$
$$2\ Fe^{+++} + SO_3^= + H_2O \rightleftharpoons 2\ Fe^{++} + SO_4^= + 2\ H^+$$
$$2\ Fe^{+++} + 2\ I^- \rightleftharpoons 2\ Fe^{++} + I_2$$
$$2\ Fe(CN)_6^{-3} + NO_2^- + H_2O \rightleftharpoons 2\ Fe(CN)_6^{-4} + 2\ H^+ + NO_3^-$$
$$K^+ + Fe^{++} + Fe(CN)_6^{-3} + H_2O \rightleftharpoons KFeFe(CN)_6 \cdot H_2O$$
$$K^+ + Fe^{+++} + Fe(CN)_6^{-4} + H_2O \rightleftharpoons KFeFe(CN)_6 \cdot H_2O$$

TEST III. ***Elimination of Reducing Anions:*** $S^=$***,*** $SO_3^=$***,*** I^-***, and*** NO_2^-***.*** **Mix 2 drops of a recently prepared saturated solution of** $K_3Fe(CN)_6$ **with 1 drop of 0.1 M** $FeCl_3$**, and add 2 drops of 6 M HCl. Add 2 drops of the prepared solution to this mixture and let the mixture stand for a few minutes. The development of a blue color or the formation of a blue precipitate indicates the presence of a reducing agent (**$S^=$**,** $SO_3^=$**,** I^-**,** NO_2^-**). Run a blank test with the same reagents but leave out the prepared solution and compare the colors and intensities of color of the unknown and blank test solutions.**

50.7 Elimination of Fluoride and Oxalate

Of the thirteen anions which may be involved in these procedures, only fluoride and oxalate form calcium salts which are insoluble in 4 M acetic acid.

$$Ca^{++} + F^- \rightleftharpoons \underline{CaF_2} \text{ (white)}$$

$$Ca^{++} + C_2O_4^= \rightleftharpoons \underline{CaC_2O_4} \text{ (white)}$$

If no precipitate forms when calcium chloride is added to an acetic acid solution of the unknown, then fluoride and oxalate are absent.

TEST IV. ***Elimination of Fluoride and Oxalate.*** **To 20 drops of the prepared solution add 4 M HOAc (count the drops) until the solution is just acid to litmus. Now add an equal number of drops of 4 M HOAc in excess. Tap the test tube repeatedly until the excess of** CO_2 **from the** Na_2CO_3 **present is expelled. Add 8 drops of 0.1 M** $CaCl_2$ **and shake the contents of the tube. If a precipitate forms after a few minutes, it may be** CaF_2**,** CaC_2O_4**, or a mixture of these compounds. If no precipitate forms,** F^- **and** $C_2O_4^=$ **are absent. Separate the precipitate and use the solution for Test V. Save the precipitate for the confirmatory tests for** $C_2O_4^=$ **and** F^-**.**

50.8 Elimination of Sulfate

After the separation of fluoride and oxalate as insoluble calcium salts, barium chloride is added to precipitate the sulfate ion as the white, crystalline barium sulfate in the solution which is still acidic with acetic acid. If the sulfite ion is present in relatively large amounts, barium sulfite may precipitate. $BaSO_4$ is insoluble in dilute hydrochloric acid, whereas $BaSO_3$ will dissolve and evolve SO_2 when treated with hydrochloric acid.

Owing to the ease with which the sulfite ion is oxidized to the sulfate ion by oxygen of the air, if sulfite is present in the original solution, you may obtain a test for sulfate although none was present at the outset.

TEST V. ***Elimination of Sulfate.*** **Test for completeness of precipitation in the solution from Test IV by adding 1 drop of 0.1 M** $CaCl_2$**. Now add 8 drops of 0.1 M** $BaCl_2$**. Shake the mixture and let it stand for 5 minutes. If** $SO_4^=$ **is present, a precipitate of** $BaSO_4$ **will form. Separate the mixture and reserve the solution for Test VI. If** $SO_3^=$ **was present in the original solution, you may obtain a test for** $SO_4^=$ **because sulfite is oxidized to sulfate by oxygen of the air.**

50.9 Elimination of Phosphate and Metaborate

The solution from the barium sulfate separation is acidified with hydrochloric acid and heated to expel CO_2 from $CO_3^=$ and SO_2 from $SO_3^=$, if present. If they were not first removed, these ions would be precipitated as barium salts in the ammoniacal solution used to precipitate barium phosphate and barium metaborate.

$$3\ Ba^{++} + 2\ PO_4^{=} \rightleftharpoons \underline{Ba_3(PO_4)_2}\ \text{(white)}$$
$$Ba^{++} + 2\ BO_2^{-} \rightleftharpoons \underline{Ba(BO_2)_2}\ \text{(white)}$$

It should be noted that phosphate and metaborate are insoluble in water, but did not precipitate as their calcium or barium salts in the acetic acid solutions in which CaF_2, CaC_2O_4, and $BaSO_4$ were formed. Barium phosphate does not precipitate in an acetic acid solution due to the low concentration of free phosphate ions in such a solution. The phosphate ion is a strong proton acceptor

$$PO_4^{-3} + H^+ \rightleftharpoons HPO_4^{=}$$

making its concentration so low that the solubility product constant of $Ba_3(PO_4)_2$ is not exceeded. Raising the pH of the solution by adding aqueous ammonia, on the other hand, increases the concentration of the phosphate ion

$$HPO_4^{=} + OH^- \rightleftharpoons PO_4^{-3} + H_2O$$

and permits the solubility product constant of $Ba_3(PO_4)_2$ to be exceeded.

TEST VI. ***Elimination of Phosphate and Metaborate:*** ***PO_4^{-3} and BO_2^-.*** **Transfer the solution from Test V to the casserole, add 6 drops of 12 M HCl and heat to expel SO_2 and CO_2. Make the solution alkaline with aqueous ammonia and then add 5 drops in excess. A white precipitate may be $Ba_3(PO_4)_2$, $Ba(BO_2)_2$, or a mixture of these. Because barium metaborate is prone to form supersaturated solutions, it is necessary to carry out the confirmatory test for BO_2^- even though no precipitate forms in Test VI.**

50.10 Elimination of Sulfide

The addition of dilute sulfuric acid to a sample of the prepared solution causes hydrogen sulfide gas to be evolved if the sulfide ion is present. Hydrogen sulfide interacts with lead acetate and forms a black precipitate of lead sulfide.

$$Pb^{++} + H_2S \rightleftharpoons \underline{PbS} + 2\ H^+$$

This elimination test also serves to confirm the sulfide ion if it is present.

TEST VII. ***Elimination of Sulfide: $S^=$.*** **To 4 drops of the prepared solution contained in a small beaker add sufficient 1.5 M H_2SO_4 to make the solution acidic. Cover the beaker with a watch glass to the underside of which is attached a small piece of moist lead acetate paper. The appearance of a black stain of PbS on the paper after a few minutes indicates the presence of the $S^=$ ion.**

50.11 Elimination of Chloride, Bromide, and Iodide

If the sulfide ion is present, it is first removed as the insoluble CoS before attempting to eliminate chloride, bromide, and iodide. Silver nitrate is then added to precipitate the halides as AgCl (white), AgBr (pale yellow), and AgI (yellow). Silver chloride is completely soluble in the mixture of aqueous ammonia and silver nitrate solutions described in Test VIII, silver bromide is partially dissolved, and silver iodide is insoluble in this reagent.

$$AgCl + 2\ NH_3 \rightleftharpoons [Ag(NH_3)_2]^+ + Cl^-$$
$$AgBr + 2\ NH_3 \rightleftharpoons [Ag(NH_3)_2]^+ + Br^- \text{ (partially soluble)}$$
$$AgI + NH_3 \rightleftharpoons \text{no reaction}$$

These facts reflect the decreasing solubility of the silver halides with increasing atomic weight of the halogen. The solubility product constants are 1.2×10^{-10} for AgCl, 3.3×10^{-13} for AgBr, and 1.5×10^{-16} for AgI.

If a white precipitate forms upon the acidification of the aqueous ammonia extract of the silver halide precipitate, then the presence of the chloride ion is confirmed.

$$[Ag(NH_3)_2]^+ + Cl^- + 2\ H^+ \rightarrow \underline{AgCl} + 2\ NH_4^+$$

A slight precipitate, yellow in color, may be silver bromide.

TEST VIII. ***Elimination of Chloride, Bromide, and Iodide.*** **If the sulfide ion is present, treat 10 drops of the prepared solution with 4 M HOAc until the solution is acid to litmus. Now add, dropwise, with shaking, 10 drops of 1 M $Co(NO_3)_2$. Heat in the hot water bath for five minutes and separate the precipitate of CoS. The solution may contain Cl^-, Br^-, and I^-. To the solution (or, if sulfide is absent, to 10 drops of the prepared solution acidified with 1 M HNO_3), add 5 drops of 1 M HNO_3. Now add to this solution 0.1 M $AgNO_3$ until precipitation is complete. Separate and wash the precipitate with 10 drops of water. Discard the solution. Mix 10 drops of 0.1 M $AgNO_3$, 6 drops of 4 M aqueous ammonia, and 4 ml. of water. Add this mixture to the precipitate and stir thoroughly. If the precipitate dissolves completely, Br^- and I^- are absent, and Cl^- is indicated. Acidify the solution with 4 M HNO_3. A white precipitate confirms chloride. If the precipitate did not dissolve completely in the aqueous ammonia and silver nitrate mixture, it may have partially dissolved. Separate and acidify the solution with 4 M HNO_3. If no precipitate forms, Cl^- is absent. The formation of a heavy white precipitate confirms the presence of Cl^-. A slight precipitate or turbidity, yellow in color, may be silver bromide.**

CONFIRMATORY TESTS FOR THE ANIONS

50.12 Identification of Carbonate

A sample of the original unknown is treated with hydrogen peroxide to oxidize any sulfite or nitrite which might be present. Then dilute sulfuric acid is added to decompose the carbonate and liberate carbon dioxide gas. The carbon dioxide gas which is evolved is permitted to come in contact with a drop of barium hydroxide solution which is held in a platinum wire loop and suspended above the reaction mixture. The formation of a definite turbidity in the drop of barium hydroxide indicates carbonate.

$$CO_3^{=} + 2\ H^+ \rightleftharpoons H_2O + CO_2 \uparrow$$
$$CO_2 + Ba^{++} + 2\ OH^- \rightarrow \underline{BaCO_3} + H_2O$$

If the sulfite and nitrite were not removed by oxidation to sulfate and nitrate respectively, sulfur dioxide and nitrogen dioxide would escape upon acidification, enter the drop of barium hydroxide solution, and either prevent the formation of barium carbonate or mask its presence.

PROCEDURE 1. ***Identification of $CO_3^{=}$.*** **To 25 mg. of the powdered solid unknown add 10 drops of hydrogen peroxide and heat the mixture in the hot water bath. Place a drop of $Ba(OH)_2$ solution in a loop of platinum wire. Add 3 drops of 4 M H_2SO_4 to the unknown mixture and immediately hold the drop of $Ba(OH)_2$ over the reaction mixture. The formation of a definite turbidity in the $Ba(OH)_2$ solution indicates the presence of $CO_3^{=}$.**

50.13 Identification of Sulfate and Sulfite

The formation of a white precipitate of barium sulfate upon the addition of barium chloride to a hydrochloric acid solution of the unknown serves to confirm the sulfate ion. Barium salts of the other anions are soluble in 6 M hydrochloric acid.

To the solution obtained from the separation of barium sulfate is added bromine water for the purpose of oxidizing the sulfite ion to sulfate.

$$SO_3^{=} + Br_2 + H_2O \rightleftharpoons SO_4^{=} + 2\ Br^- + 2\ H^+$$

The appearance of a white precipitate (barium sulfate) indicates the presence of the sulfite ion in the original solution.

PROCEDURE 2. ***Identification of $SO_4^{=}$.*** **Acidify 5 drops of the prepared solution with 6 M HCl and add 2 drops in excess. Heat in the hot water bath to expel the excess of CO_2. Add 0.1 M $BaCl_2$ until precipitation is complete; then allow the mixture to stand. A white, finely divided precipitate of $BaSO_4$ confirms the presence of $SO_4^{=}$. Separate the mixture and save the solution for the $SO_3^{=}$ test.**

PROCEDURE 3. ***Identification of $SO_3^{=}$.*** **Add 5 drops of bromine water and 2 drops of 0.1 M $BaCl_2$ to the solution from (2). Heat in the hot water bath and allow to stand for 5 minutes. A white precipitate of $BaSO_4$ shows the presence of sulfite in the original solution.**

PROCEDURE 4. ***Identification of $S^{=}$.*** **The sulfide ion is confirmed in elimination Test VII.**

50.14 Identification of Nitrite

Use is made of the oxidizing power of the nitrite ion in acid solution in the confirmatory test for this ion. The nitrite ion oxidizes iron (II) to iron (III), and nitric oxide is formed as the reduction product of the nitrite ion.

$$NO_2^- + Fe^{++} + 2\ H^+ \rightleftharpoons Fe^{+++} + NO + H_2O$$

The nitric oxide produced combines with some of the excess iron (II) ions in the reaction mixture, forming the brown complex, $Fe(NO)^{++}$.

$$Fe^{++} + NO \rightarrow Fe(NO)^{++}$$

PROCEDURE 5. ***Identification of NO_2^-.*** **To 5 drops of prepared solution add 4 M H_2SO_4 dropwise until the solution is acidic. Now add 5 drops of freshly prepared 0.1 M $FeSO_4$ solution. If NO_2^- is present the solution will assume a dark brown color.**

50.15 Identification of Nitrate

In the event that nitrite, bromide, and iodide ions are absent, one may identify the nitrate ion by the brown ring test. Iron (II) sulfate is added to a sample of the prepared solution which has been acidified by means of dilute sulfuric acid. Then concentrated sulfuric acid is introduced into the test tube containing the solution in such a manner as to form a layer of acid in the bottom of the tube (Fig. 50–1). If the nitrate ion is present, a brown ring will form at the junction

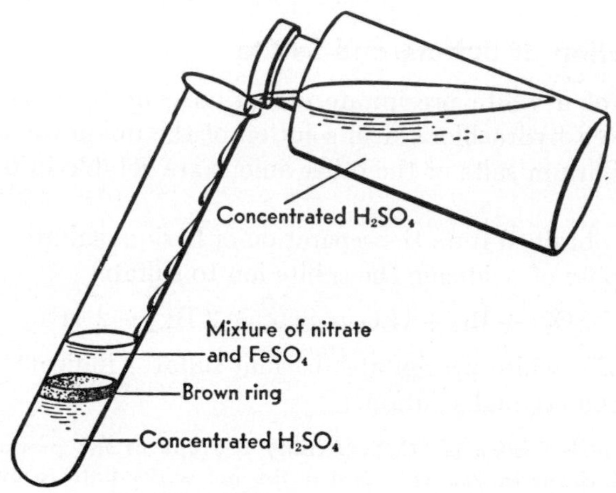

Fig. 50–1 The brown ring test for nitrates.

of the two phases in a short while. The reduction of the nitrate ion to nitric oxide by iron (II) ions takes place rapidly only in a solution of very high hydrogen ion concentration and at relatively high temperatures, conditions which prevail at the interface of the two liquids.

$$3\ Fe^{++} + NO_3^- + 4\ H^+ \rightleftharpoons 3\ Fe^{+++} + NO + 2\ H_2O$$
$$Fe^{++} + NO \rightarrow Fe(NO)^{++}$$

If the nitrite ion is present, then it must be removed prior to the nitrate test because the entire solution will turn brown and the development of the brown ring will be obscured. The removal of the nitrite ion is accomplished by adding ammonium sulfate and evaporating nearly to dryness over a flame. The added ammonium ion reacts with the nitrite ion and forms nitrogen and water.

$$NH_4^+ + NO_2^- + \text{heat} \rightarrow N_2\uparrow + 2\ H_2O$$

The residue is taken up in water and the brown ring test for nitrate is conducted on the solution.

If bromide or iodide ions are present, they will be oxidized by the concentrated sulfuric acid used in the test for nitrate, forming bromine and iodine respectively, both of which form colored layers. Therefore, these ions must be removed before making the brown ring test for nitrate. This is accomplished by the addition of solid, nitrate-free, silver sulfate to an acidified sample of the prepared solution to precipitate the bromide and iodide ions as their silver salts.

$$Ag_2SO_4 + Br^- \rightarrow \underline{AgBr} + SO_4^=$$
$$Ag_2SO_4 + I^- \rightarrow \underline{AgI} + SO_4^=$$

PROCEDURE 6. ***Identification of NO_3^- in the Absence of NO_2^-, Br^-, and I^-.*** **To 5 drops of prepared solution in a test tube add 4 M H_2SO_4 dropwise until the solution is acidic. Now add 5 drops of freshly prepared 0.1 M $FeSO_4$ solution. Add 5 drops of 18 M H_2SO_4, holding the test tube in an inclined position so that the sulfuric acid may run down the side of the test tube and form a separate layer on the bottom of the tube. If the NO_3^- is present, a brown ring will form at the junction of the two liquids within a few minutes.**

PROCEDURE 7. ***Identification of NO_3^- in the Presence of NO_2^-. Removal of NO_2^-.*** **To 6 drops of the prepared solution add 4 M H_2SO_4 until the solution is acidic and then add 4 drops of 1 M $(NH_4)_2SO_4$ solution. Place the mixture in a casserole and slowly evaporate the solution until only a moist residue remains (do not evaporate to dryness). Add 4 drops of water and evaporate to a moist residue a second time. Dissolve the residue in 10 drops of water and transfer the mixture to a small test tube. Repeat the brown ring test for NO_3^- as described in Procedure (6) on the mixture resulting from the removal of NO_2^-.**

PROCEDURE 8. ***Identification of NO_3^- in the Presence of Br^- and I^-.*** **Removal of Br^- and I^-. To 6 drops of the prepared solution in a test tube add 10 drops of water. Acidify the solution with 4 M HOAc and then add 80 mg. of powdered Ag_2SO_4 (NO_3^- free). Stir and grind the mixture in the test tube for 2–3 minutes. Separate the precipitate and transfer the solution to a test tube. Repeat the brown ring test for NO_3^- as described in Procedure (6) on the solution obtained from the removal of Br^- and I^-.**

50.16 Identification of Oxalate

The precipitate formed during the elimination test for oxalate and fluoride ions is used for the identification of the oxalate ion. It consists of CaC_2O_4 and CaF_2 if both ions were present in the original solution. Treatment of the precipitate with sulfuric acid serves to dissolve the calcium oxalate and form oxalic acid.

$$CaC_2O_4 + 2\ H^+ \rightleftharpoons Ca^{++} + H_2C_2O_4$$

Oxalic acid is a weak reducing agent that is readily oxidized to carbon dioxide and water by potassium permanganate in sulfuric acid solution. A dilute solution of the pink permanganate is employed, and the permanganate ion is reduced to the colorless manganese (II) ion by the oxalic acid. This bleaching of the colored permanganate solution shows the presence of the reducing agent, oxalic acid.

$$5\ H_2C_2O_4 + 2\ MnO_4^- + 6\ H^+ \rightarrow 10\ CO_2 \uparrow + 2\ Mn^{++} + 8\ H_2O$$

PROCEDURE 9. ***Identification of $C_2O_4^=$.*** **Wash the precipitate obtained in preliminary elimination Test IV twice. Use 10 drops of water each time and discard the washings. To the residue add 10 drops of water and 10 drops of 4 M H_2SO_4, and shake the mixture. Add 0.002 M $KMnO_4$ dropwise until 1 drop imparts a permanent pink color to the solution. If $C_2O_4^=$ is present, several drops of $KMnO_4$ should be required to give a permanent pink coloration to the solution. Run a blank by repeating the test but leaving out the precipitate from elimination Test IV.**

50.17 Identification of Fluoride

In the confirmatory test for the fluoride ion, a sample of the solid unknown is treated with concentrated sulfuric acid in the presence of silica, SiO_2.

$$2\ NaF + H_2SO_4 \rightarrow Na_2SO_4 + 2\ HF \uparrow$$

The hydrofluoric acid produced reacts with the silica present and forms gaseous silicon tetrafluoride, SiF_4.

$$SiO_2 + 4\ HF \rightarrow SiF_4 \uparrow + 2\ H_2O$$

The gaseous SiF_4 thus generated is permitted to come in contact with a drop of water contained in a loop of platinum wire suspended over the reaction mixture. The development of a white precipitate, H_4SiO_4, in the water confirms the presence of the fluoride ion.

$$3\ SiF_4 + 4\ H_2O \rightarrow \underline{H_4SiO_4} + 4\ H^+ + 2\ SiF_6^=$$

PROCEDURE 10. ***Identification of F^-.*** **Place 25 mg. of powdered sample in a test tube and add an equal volume of powdered silica. Select a cork to fit the test tube. Cut a notch on the side and a hole in the center of the cork. Through the hole, insert a glass rod to one end of which has been sealed a platinum wire looped at the end. Add 2 drops of 18 M H_2SO_4 to the mixture in the tube. Now place the platinum wire loop with a drop of water hanging to it in the test tube directly above the reaction mixture. Warm the test tube in the hot water bath and then set it aside to cool. The formation of a white precipitate or cloudiness in the drop of water confirms the presence of the F^- ion.**

50.18 Identification of Phosphate

Magnesia mixture ($MgCl_2$, NH_4Cl, and aqueous ammonia), when added to a slightly acidic solution of the unknown, will precipitate the phosphate ion as the white crystalline magnesium ammonium phosphate. Since this compound is prone to form supersaturated solutions, the precipitate may be slow in appearing.

$$Mg^{++} + NH_4^+ + HPO_4^= \rightleftharpoons MgNH_4PO_4 + H^+$$

PROCEDURE 11. ***Identification of PO_4^{-3}.*** **Dilute 4 drops of prepared solution with 10 drops of water. Make the solution just acidic with 4 M HNO_3 and add 10 drops of magnesia mixture. A white precipitate, often slow in forming, confirms the presence of the PO_4^{-3} ion.**

50.19 Identification of Metaborate

A sample of the prepared solution is evaporated to a small volume and then treated with methyl alcohol and sulfuric acid. The sulfuric acid converts the metaborate ion to orthoboric acid.

$$BO_2^- + H^+ + H_2O \rightarrow H_3BO_3$$

In the presence of the dehydrating agent, concentrated sulfuric acid, orthoboric acid reacts with methyl alcohol and forms the volatile methyl orthoborate.

$$H_3BO_3 + 3\ CH_3OH \rightleftharpoons B(OCH_3)_3 \uparrow + 3\ H_2O$$

The sulfuric acid present takes up the water produced in the reaction and shifts the equilibrium to the right. Methyl orthoborate burns with a characteristic green flame when ignited.

$$2\ B(OCH_3)_3 + 9\ O_2 \rightarrow B_2O_3 + 6\ CO_2 + 9\ H_2O$$

PROCEDURE 12. ***Identification of BO_2^-.*** **Evaporate 6 drops of the prepared solution to a small volume in the casserole. Add 1 ml. of methyl alcohol and 5 drops of 18 M H_2SO_4. Transfer the mixture to a test tube and place the tube in the hot water bath. When the alcohol begins to boil, ignite the vapors. A green tinge to the flame confirms the presence of the metaborate ion.**

50.20 Identification of Iodide, Bromide, and Chloride

The confirmatory test for chloride was outlined in the elimination test for chloride, bromide, and iodide; no further test for this ion is necessary.

In general the methods used for the detection of the halide ions in the presence of one another depend upon the differences in the reduction potentials of the ions. Of the three ions, chloride, bromide, and iodide, the iodide ion is most easily oxidized, the bromide ion is second, and the chloride ion is the most difficult to oxidize.

The iodide ion may be oxidized to iodine by iron (III) in acid solution without affecting the bromide or chloride ions.

$$2\ I^- + 2\ Fe^{+++} \rightleftharpoons I_2 + 2\ Fe^{++}$$

The elementary iodine is then extracted from the aqueous solution by carbon tetrachloride in which it exhibits a characteristic violet color.

After the complete removal of the iodide ion, a stronger oxidizing agent than iron (III) is used to oxidize the bromide to bromine. A dilute solution of potassium permanganate in the presence of nitric acid will oxidize bromide to bromine without interference from chloride.

$$10\ Br^- + 2\ MnO_4^- + 16\ H^+ \rightleftharpoons 5\ Br_2 + 2\ Mn^{++} + 8\ H_2O$$

The free bromine is extracted with carbon tetrachloride to which it imparts a yellow or orange color, depending upon the concentration.

PROCEDURE 13. ***Identification of I^-.*** **Dilute 6 drops of the prepared solution with 12 drops of water. Add 4 M HNO_3 until the solution is just acid to litmus and then add two drops of the acid in excess. Treat the solution with 1 ml. of 0.1 M $Fe(NO_3)_3$ and 10 drops of CCl_4 and shake the test tube. The development of a violet color in the CCl_4 layer proves the presence of I^-. Remove the CCl_4 layer by means of a capillary syringe and discard it. Add 10 more drops of CCl_4, shake, and remove the CCl_4 layer. Repeat the extraction until the CCl_4 layer remains colorless and use the aqueous solution for the identification of Br^-.**

PROCEDURE 14. ***Identification of Br^-.*** **Add to the solution from (13) 2 drops of 4 M HNO_3, then 0.1 M $KMnO_4$ solution drop by drop until the solution remains pink. Extract the solution with CCl_4. A yellow or orange coloration in the CCl_4 layer indicates the presence of Br^-.**

QUESTIONS

1. In terms of solubility product constant and ionic equilibria theory, explain the following: (a) $Ca_3(PO_4)_2$ is soluble in HCl while $BaSO_4$ is not. (b) $CaCO_3$ is soluble in HOAc while CaC_2O_4 is not.

2. Explain why the nitrite ion will respond to both the test for oxidizing agents and that for reducing agents.

3. If an anion unknown contains the sulfite ion, one may obtain a test for the sulfate ion even though sulfate was not used in making up the unknown. Explain.

4. What is meant by "incompatibility of anions"? Give an example.

5. What principle is involved in the tests for the halide ions in the presence of one another?

6. Explain how the nitrite ion interferes with the test for nitrate. How is the nitrite ion removed prior to the test for nitrate?

7. Make a list of anions which are reducing agents and list their oxidation products.

8. Make a list of anions which are oxidizing agents and list their reduction products.

9. If a solution is strongly acidic, what anions cannot be present in appreciable concentrations?

10. An acidic solution contains silver ions. What anions are probably absent?

11. A neutral solution contains calcium ions. What anions are probably absent?

12. A solution is slightly acid and contains sulfide ions. What cations are probably absent?

13. Why is it necessary to extract the iodine in the confirmatory test for the iodide ion?

14. Outline a simple test to distinguish between each of the following pairs: (a) $CO_3^{=}$ and $SO_4^{=}$, (b) Cl^- and I^-, (c) F^- and BO_2^-, (d) PO_4^{-3} and Br^-, (e) $S^{=}$ and $SO_3^{=}$, (f) $C_2O_4^{=}$ and Cl^-.

15. A solution known to contain either Na_2CO_3 or Na_2SO_4 turns red litmus blue. Which salt is present?

CHAPTER FIFTY-ONE

The Analysis of Solid Materials

The analytical procedures which have been outlined for cations and anions in the preceding chapters are usually applicable to solutions of the substances being analyzed. However, many substances are not readily soluble in water or even in acids. Thus it becomes necessary to use special procedures for effecting the dissolution of certain solid substances before proceeding with the analyses.

51.1 The Dissolution of Nonmetallic Solids

The procedures outlined in this section are applicable to solid inorganic materials other than metals and alloys. The analysis of metals and alloys is described in Section 51.2.

PROCEDURE 1. ***For Samples Soluble in Water.*** **Grind the sample of solid to a fine powder. Treat 100 mg. of the solid with 1 ml. of water. If no dissolution is apparent, heat the mixture in the hot water bath for a few minutes. If none of the sample appears to dissolve, evaporate a few drops of the supernatant liquid on a watch glass to determine whether partial dissolution has occurred. If a solid residue remains on the watch glass, heat the sample with fresh portions of water until complete dissolution has been effected. Concentrate the combined extracts by evaporation and proceed with the analyses for cations and anions as outlined in the preceding chapters. It should be recalled that certain solid substances, such as $BiCl_3$ and $SbCl_3$, hydrolyze when treated with water to form new solid substances. In such cases proceed as with samples soluble in water.**

PROCEDURE 2. ***For Samples Not Soluble in Water.*** **Warm a small sample of the solid substance with 6 M HCl or, if this has no effect, with 12 M HCl. If dissolution does not occur, or if it is incomplete, try 6 M HNO_3, 15 M HNO_3, and aqua regia (1 part 15 M HNO_3 to 3 parts 12 M HCl) in succession on small samples of the solid until a suitable solvent is found. If dissolution has been effected by any of these reagents, dissolve 100 mg. of the sample in the solvent selected. Evaporate the solution nearly to dryness and then take up the residue in 2 ml. of water. Use this solution for the analytical procedures.**

PROCEDURE 3. ***Treatment of the Residue with Na_2CO_3 Solution.*** **If HCl, HNO_3, or aqua regia do not completely dissolve the solid, the residue remaining after the acid treatment may be treated with a Na_2CO_3 solution. Treat the residue with 2 ml. of 1.5 M Na_2CO_3 in a casserole and boil the mixture for ten minutes, replacing the water that is lost during evaporation. This procedure will convert many insoluble salts such as $BaSO_4$, $CaSO_4$, $PbSO_4$, and many oxides into acid-soluble carbonates. Separate the mixture and discard**

the solution unless it is to be used for anion analysis. Wash the precipitate with water and then dissolve it in a few drops of 6 M HNO_3. Dilute the solution with 1 ml. of water and add it to the original acid solution which is to be evaporated. If dissolution of the residue was not complete, repeat the Na_2CO_3 treatment. The halides of silver, silicate salts, some oxides, and calcined salts are not dissolved by this procedure.

PROCEDURE 4. ***Reduction of Silver Halides with Zinc.*** **Suspend the residue containing the insoluble silver halides in 5 drops of water, add 1 ml. of 1 M H_2SO_4 and a few granules of zinc metal. Warm and stir the mixture for several minutes. Add more zinc if the evolution of hydrogen ceases. Separate the residue of precipitated silver. Wash the residue with water, dissolve it in 6 M HNO_3, and test the solution for the Ag^+ ion. Conduct tests for the halide ions on the solution from the silver separation.**

PROCEDURE 5. ***Fusion with Sodium Carbonate.*** **Silicates and certain oxides and calcined salts may not be taken into solution by treatment with acid, Na_2CO_3 solution, or by reduction with zinc. Fusion with Na_2CO_3 is effective with many of these substances. Transfer the residue remaining after the zinc reduction of silver halides to a small nickel crucible. Add to the residue 100 mg. of anhydrous Na_2CO_3, about half as much K_2CO_3, and a few mg. of $NaNO_3$. Place the crucible in a small clay triangle and heat it in the hot flame of a Meker burner until the mixture fuses. Cool the crucible, add 1 ml. of water, and warm the mixture until the solid mass has disintegrated. Separate the mixture and reserve the solution. Treat the residue with 8 drops of 6 M HNO_3 and warm in the hot water bath for a few minutes. Separate and add this nitric acid solution to the original solution. Analyze the solution for its cations.**

51.2 Analysis of Metals and Alloys

All of the common metals except Al, Cr, Mn, Fe, Sb, and Sn may be taken into solution with dilute nitric acid. Al, Cr, Mn, and Fe are attacked superficially by nitric acid with the formation of an oxide film which makes solution of these metals too slow to be practical. Metastannic acid, H_2SnO_3, and the insoluble oxides of antimony, Sb_4O_6, Sb_2O_4, and Sb_2O_5, are formed when nitric acid reacts directly with tin and antimony, respectively. Although these compounds are insoluble in nitric acid, they may be readily converted to the corresponding sulfides which are soluble in nitric acid. Hydrochloric acid is in general not suitable as a solvent for alloys of unknown composition since the volatile hydrides of sulfur, arsenic, phosphorus, and antimony may be formed; and consequently, these elements could escape detection. On the other hand, nitric acid oxidizes the first three of these elements to sulfate, arsenate, and phosphate, respectively, and antimony to oxides, all of which are nonvolatile. Aqua regia will generally dissolve alloys which resist the action of nitric acid alone.

PROCEDURE 1. ***Preparation of the Sample for Dissolution.*** **Convert the metal sample into a finely divided state with a large surface for interaction with the solvent. This may be accomplished by means of a steel file, a mortar and pestle for brittle metals, a hammer for malleable metals, or a knife for soft metals.**

PROCEDURE 2. ***Selection of a Suitable Solvent.*** **Treat a small sample of the metal with 6 M HNO_3 in a test tube and warm the mixture if necessary. If the sample reacts completely, with or without the formation of a white precipitate, proceed to (3). If the sample does not dissolve readily, try aqua regia (1 part of 15 M HNO_3 and 3 parts of 12 M HCl).**

If aqua regia fails to attack the sample, it may be treated with a mixture of concentrated HCl and Br_2, or fused with solid NaOH in a silver crucible.

PROCEDURE 3. *Dissolution by HNO_3.* Place 20 mg. of the sample in a test tube, add 1 ml. of 6 M HNO_3, and heat the mixture in the hot water bath. If a white residue forms, stir the mixture to remove the coating from the surface to the undissolved metallic particles. Add more HNO_3 if that is necessary to complete the reaction. After the metal has dissolved, transfer the solution or mixture to a casserole and evaporate it nearly to dryness. Add 5 drops of 15 M HNO_3 and again evaporate the solution nearly to dryness. Now add 5 drops of 6 M HNO_3 and 1 ml. of water and transfer the solution to a test tube. If a clear solution is obtained, analyze it according to the procedure for the cations. If there is a residue (H_2SnO_3, Sb_2O_5, or a mixture of these), separate and analyze the solution according to the procedures for the cations, omitting the tests for tin and antimony. Add 10 drops of 4 M NaOH and 5 drops of 5 per cent thioacetamide solution to the residue. Heat the mixture in the water bath for 5 minutes. Separate any residue and analyze the solution for tin and antimony.

PROCEDURE 4. *Dissolution by Aqua Regia.* Place 20 mg. of the sample in a test tube, and add 10 drops of 15 M HNO_3 and 30 drops of 12 M HCl. Heat the mixture in the hot water bath until the reaction is complete. Transfer the reaction mixture to a casserole and evaporate it to a small volume (not to dryness). When it is cool, add 2 ml. of water and 4 drops of 6 M HCl. Separate any precipitate that forms. Analyze the centrifugate, or the clear solution if no precipitate forms, by the procedures for Groups II, III, IV, and V. The precipitate may consist of AgCl, $PbCl_2$, and SiO_2. Analyze the precipitate for Group I.

PROCEDURE 5. *Dissolution by Br_2 and HCl.* If neither HNO_3 nor aqua regia will dissolve the metallic sample and a preliminary test has shown that Br_2 and HCl will do so, place 20 mg. of the sample in a casserole. Add 1 ml. of 12 M HCl and then a few drops of liquid bromine to the sample. Heat the mixture gently until reaction is complete and then evaporate it to dryness. Add 5 drops of 6 M HNO_3 to the residue, dilute the solution with 2 ml. of water, and then proceed with the cation analysis.

PART 5

Appendices

APPENDIX A Chemical Arithmetic

In the study of general chemistry, elementary mathematics is frequently used. Of particular importance and wide application in the calculations that the student makes in chemistry are exponential arithmetic, significant figures, and logarithms.

A.1 Exponential Arithmetic

In chemistry we use the exponential method of expressing very large and very small numbers. These numbers are expressed as a product of two numbers. The first number of the product is called the digit term. This term is usually a number not less than 1 and not greater than 10. The second number of the product is called the exponential term and is written as 10 with an exponent. Some examples of the exponential method of expressing numbers are given below.

$$1000 = 1 \times 10^3$$
$$100 = 1 \times 10^2$$
$$10 = 1 \times 10^1$$
$$1 = 1 \times 10^0$$
$$0.1 = 1 \times 10^{-1}$$
$$0.01 = 1 \times 10^{-2}$$
$$0.001 = 1 \times 10^{-3}$$
$$2386 = 2.386 \times 1000 = 2.386 \times 10^3$$
$$0.123 = 1.23 \times 0.1 = 1.23 \times 10^{-1}$$

The power (exponent) of 10 is equal to the number of places the decimal is shifted to give the digit number. The exponential method is particularly useful as a shorthand for big numbers. For example, $1{,}230{,}000{,}000 = 1.23 \times 10^9$; and $0.000{,}000{,}000{,}36 = 3.6 \times 10^{-10}$.

1. *Addition of Exponentials.* Convert all the numbers to the same power of 10 and add the digit terms of the number.

EXAMPLE. Add 5×10^{-5} and 3×10^{-3}

SOLUTION. $3 \times 10^{-3} = 300 \times 10^{-5}$

$(5 \times 10^{-5}) + (300 \times 10^{-5}) = 305 \times 10^{-5} = 3.05 \times 10^{-3}$

2. *Subtraction of Exponentials.* Convert all the numbers to the same power of 10 and take the difference of the digit terms.

EXAMPLE. Subtract 4×10^{-7} from 5×10^{-6}

SOLUTION. $4 \times 10^{-7} = 0.4 \times 10^{-6}$

$(5 \times 10^{-6}) - (0.4 \times 10^{-6}) = 4.6 \times 10^{-6}$

3. *Multiplication of Exponentials.* Multiply the digit terms in the usual way and add algebraically the exponents of the exponential terms.

EXAMPLE. Multiply 4.2×10^{-8} by 2×10^3

SOLUTION.
$$\begin{array}{r} 4.2 \times 10^{-8} \\ 2 \times 10^{3} \\ \hline 8.4 \times 10^{-5} \end{array}$$

4. *Division of Exponentials.* Divide the digit term of the numerator by the digit term of the denominator and subtract algebraically the exponents of the exponential terms.

EXAMPLE. Divide 3.6×10^{-5} by 6×10^{-4}

SOLUTION. $\frac{3.6 \times 10^{-5}}{6 \times 10^{-4}} = 0.6 \times 10^{-1} = 6 \times 10^{-2}$

5. *The Squaring of Exponentials.* Square the digit term in the usual way and multiply the exponent of the exponential term by 2.

EXAMPLE. Square the number 4×10^{-6}

SOLUTION. $(4 \times 10^{-6})^2 = 16 \times 10^{-12} = 1.6 \times 10^{-11}$

6. *The Cubing of Exponentials.* Cube the digit term in the usual way and multiply the exponent of the exponential term by 3.

EXAMPLE. Cube the number 2×10^3

SOLUTION. $(2 \times 10^3)^3 = 2 \times 2 \times 2 \times 10^9 = 8 \times 10^9$

7. *Extraction of Square Roots of Exponentials.* Decrease or increase the exponential term so that the power of ten is evenly divisible by 2. Extract the square root of the digit term by inspection or by logarithms and divide the exponential term by 2.

EXAMPLE. Extract the square root of 1.6×10^{-7}

SOLUTION. $1.6 \times 10^{-7} = 16 \times 10^{-8}$

$$\sqrt{16 \times 10^{-8}} = \sqrt{16} \times \sqrt{10^{-8}} = 4 \times 10^{-4}$$

A.2 Significant Figures

A bee keeper reports that he has 525,341 bees. The last three figures of the number are obviously inaccurate, for during the time the keeper was counting the bees, some of them would have died and others would have hatched; this would have made the exact number of bees quite difficult to determine. It would have been more accurate if he had reported the number 525,000. In other words, the last three figures are not significant, except to set the position of the decimal point. Their exact values have no meaning.

In reporting any information in terms of numbers, only as many significant figures should be used as are warranted by the accuracy of the measurement. The accuracy of measurements is dependent upon the sensitivity of the measuring instruments used. For example, if the weight of an object has been reported as 2.13 g., it is assumed that the last figure (3) has been estimated and that the weight lies between 2.125 g. and 2.135 g. The quantity 2.13 g. represents three significant figures. The weight of this same object as determined by a more sensitive balance may have been reported as 2.134 g. In this case one would assume the correct weight to be between 2.1335 g. and 2.1345 g., and the quantity 2.134 g. represents 4 significant figures. Note that the last figure is estimated and is also considered as a significant figure.

A zero in a number may or may not be significant, depending upon the manner in which it is used. When one or more zeros are used in locating a decimal point, they are not significant. For example, the numbers 0.063, 0.0063, and 0.00063 each have two significant figures. When zeros appear between digits in a number they are significant. For example, 1.008 g. has four significant figures. Likewise, the zero in 12.50 is significant. However, the quantity 1370 cm. has four significant figures provided the accuracy of the measurement includes the zero as a significant digit; if the digit 7 is estimated, then the number has only three significant figures.

The importance of significant figures lies in their application to fundamental computation. When adding or subtracting, the last digit that is retained in the sum or difference should correspond to the first doubtful decimal place (as indicated by underscoring).

EXAMPLE. Add $4.38\underline{3}$ g. and $0.002\underline{3}$ g.

SOLUTION.

$$\begin{array}{l} 4.38\underline{3} \text{ g.} \\ 0.002\underline{3} \\ \hline 4.38\underline{5} \text{ g.} \end{array}$$

When multiplying or dividing, the product or quotient should contain no more digits than the least number of significant figures in the numbers involved in the computation.

EXAMPLE. Multiply $0.623\underline{8}$ by $6.\underline{6}$

SOLUTION. $0.623\underline{8} \times 6.\underline{6} = 4.\underline{1}$

In rounding off numbers, increase the last digit retained by one if the following digit is five or more. Thus 26.5 becomes 27, and 26.4 becomes 26 in the rounding-off process.

A.3 The Use of Logarithms and Exponential Numbers

The common logarithm of a number is the power to which the number 10 must be raised to equal that number. For example, the logarithm of 100 is 2 because the number 10 must be raised to the second power to be equal to 100. Additional examples are as follows:

Number	*Number Expressed Exponentially*	*Logarithm*
10,000	10^4	4
1,000	10^3	3
10	10^1	1
1	10^0	0
0.1	10^{-1}	−1
0.01	10^{-2}	−2
0.001	10^{-3}	−3
0.0001	10^{-4}	−4

What is the logarithm of 60? Because 60 lies between 10 and 100, which have logarithms of 1 and 2, respectively, the logarithm of 60 must lie between 1 and 2. The logarithm of 60 is 1.7782; i.e., $60 = 10^{1.7782}$.

Every logarithm is made up of two parts, called the characteristic and the mantissa. The characteristic is that part of the logarithm which lies to the left of the decimal point; thus the characteristic of the logarithm of 60 is 1. The mantissa is that part of the logarithm which lies to the right of the decimal point; thus the mantissa of the logarithm of 60 is .7782. The characteristic of the logarithm of a number greater than 1 is one less than the number of digits to the left of the decimal point in the number.

Number	*Characteristic*	*Number*	*Characteristic*
60	1	2.340	0
600	2	23.40	1
6000	3	234.0	2
52840	4	2340.0	3

The mantissa of the logarithm of a number is found in the logarithm table (see Appendix B), and its value is independent of the position of the decimal point. Thus 2.340, 23.40, 234.0, and 2340.0 all have the same mantissa. The logarithm of 2.340 is 0.3692, that of 23.40 is 1.3692, that of 234.0 is 2.3692, and that of 2340.0 is 3.3692.

The meaning of the mantissa and characteristic can be better understood from a consideration of their relationship to exponential numbers. For example, 2340 may be written 2.34×10^3. The logarithm of (2.34×10^3) = the logarithm of 2.34 + the logarithm of 10^3. The logarithm of 2.34 is 0.3692 and the logarithm of 10^3 is 3. Thus the logarithm of $2340 = 3 + 0.3692$, or 3.3692.

The logarithm of a number less than 1 has a negative value, and a convenient method of obtaining the logarithm of such a number is given below. For example, we may obtain the logarithm of 0.00234 as follows: When expressed exponentially, $0.00234 = 2.34 \times 10^{-3}$. The logarithm of 2.34×10^{-3} = the logarithm of 2.34 + the logarithm of 10^{-3}. The logarithm of 2.34 is 0.3692 and the logarithm of 10^{-3} is -3. Thus the logarithm of $0.00234 = 0.3692 + (-3) = 0.3692 - 3 = -2.6208$. The abbreviated form for the expression $(0.3692 - 3)$ is $\bar{3}.3692$. Note that only the characteristic has a negative value in the logarithm $\bar{3}.3692$, and that the mantissa is positive. The logarithm $\bar{3}.3692$ may also be written as $7.3692 - 10$.

To multiply two numbers we add the logarithms of the numbers. For example, suppose we multiply 412 by 353.

$$\begin{aligned} \text{Logarithm of } 412 &= 2.6149 \\ \text{Logarithm of } 353 &= \underline{2.5478} \\ \text{Logarithm of product} &= 5.1627 \end{aligned}$$

The number which corresponds to the logarithm 5.1627 is 145400 or 1.454×10^5. Thus 1.45×10^5 is the product of 412 and 353.

To divide two numbers we subtract the logarithms of the numbers. Suppose we divide 412 by 353.

$$\begin{aligned} \text{Logarithm of } 412 &= 2.6149 \\ \text{Logarithm of } 353 &= 2.5478 \\ \text{Logarithm of quotient} &= \overline{0.0671} \end{aligned}$$

The number which corresponds to the logarithm 0.0671 is 1.17. Thus 412 divided by 353 is 1.17.

Suppose we multiply 5432 by 0.3124. Add the logarithm of 0.3124 to that of 5432.

$$\begin{aligned} \text{Logarithm of } 5432 &= 3.7350 \\ \text{Logarithm of } 0.3124 &= \bar{1}.4948 \\ \text{Logarithm of the product} &= \overline{3.2298} \end{aligned}$$

The number which corresponds to the logarithm 3.2298 is 1697 or 1.697×10^3.

Let us divide 5432 by 0.3124. Subtract the logarithm of 0.3124 from that of 5432.

$$\begin{aligned} \text{Logarithm of } 5432 &= 3.7350 \\ \text{Logarithm of } 0.3124 &= \bar{1}.4948 \\ \text{Logarithm of the quotient} &= \overline{4.2402} \end{aligned}$$

The number which corresponds to the logarithm 4.2402 is 17390 or 1.739×10^4.

The extraction of roots of numbers by means of logarithms is a simple procedure. For example, suppose we extract the cube root of 7235. The logarithm of $\sqrt[3]{7235}$ or $(7235)^{\frac{1}{3}}$ is equal to $\frac{1}{3}$ of the logarithm of 7235.

$$\begin{aligned} \text{Logarithm of } 7235 &= 3.8594 \\ \tfrac{1}{3} \text{ of } 3.8594 &= 1.2865 \end{aligned}$$

The number which corresponds to the logarithm 1.2865 is 19.34. Thus, 19.34 is the cube root of 7235.

A.4 The Solution of Quadratic Equations

Any quadratic equation can be expressed in the following form:

$$aX^2 + bX + c = 0$$

In order to solve a quadratic equation, the following formula is used.

$$X = \frac{-b \pm \sqrt{b^2 - 4\,ac}}{2a}$$

EXAMPLE. Solve the equation $3\,X^2 + 13\,X - 10 = 0$. Substituting the values $a = 3$, $b = 13$, and $c = -10$ in the formula, we obtain

$$X = \frac{-13 \pm \sqrt{(13)^2 - 4 \times 3 \times (-10)}}{2 \times 3}$$

$$X = \frac{-13 \pm \sqrt{169 + 120}}{6} = \frac{-13 \pm \sqrt{289}}{6} = \frac{-13 \pm 17}{6}$$

The two roots are therefore

$$X = \frac{-13 + 17}{6} = 0.67 \quad \text{and} \quad X = \frac{-13 - 17}{6} = -5$$

Equations constructed upon physical data always have real roots, and of these real roots only those having positive values are of any significance.

PROBLEMS

1. Carry out the following calculations:
   (a) $(1.56 \times 10^{-5}) \times (1.8 \times 10^{-4})$
   (b) $(2.3 \times 10^{-4}) \times (2.0 \times 10^{4})$
   (c) $(4.8 \times 10^{-4}) \div (2.4 \times 10^{-8})$
   (d) $(6.4 \times 10^{-4}) \div (3.2 \times 10^{4})$
2. Perform the following operations:
   (a) $\sqrt{90 \times 10^{-3}}$ (c) $(1 \times 10^{6})^{4}$
   (b) $\sqrt[3]{2.7 \times 10^{-2}}$ (d) $(4.1 \times 10^{-2})^{2}$
3. Add the following numbers: 2.863, 42.580, 0.02316, and 41.33. (Observe the principle of significant figures.)
4. Multiply 7.150 by 2.1; divide 6.4 by 2.141. (Observe the principle of significant figures.)
5. Write the characteristic and mantissa of each of the following logarithms:
   (a) $\log 3 = 0.4771$ (c) $\log 0.03 = \bar{2}.4771$
   (b) $\log 300 = 2.4771$ (d) $\log 0.3 = \bar{1}.4771$
6. Find the logarithms of the following numbers:
   (a) 47.6 (c) 983 (e) 47,600 (g) 476
   (b) 0.476 (d) 98.3 (f) 0.0476 (h) 0.00983
7. Make the following calculations using logarithms:
   (a) 26.3×6.79 (e) $\dfrac{56.3 \times 497}{3.06 \times 283}$
   (b) 72.9×0.0463 (f) $\dfrac{0.0469 \times 25.7}{12.1 \times 0.0157}$
   (c) $64.5 \div 5.98$
   (d) $\sqrt[5]{1.251}$

APPENDIX B Four-Place Table of Logarithms

No.	0	1	2	3	4	5	6	7	8	9	1	2	3	4	5	6	7	8	9
10	0000	0043	0086	0128	0170	0212	0253	0294	0334	0374	4	8	12	17	21	25	29	33	37
11	0414	0453	0492	0531	0569	0607	0645	0682	0719	0755	4	8	11	15	19	23	26	30	34
12	0792	0828	0864	0899	0934	0969	1004	1038	1072	1106	3	7	10	14	17	21	24	28	31
13	1139	1173	1206	1239	1271	1303	1335	1367	1399	1430	3	6	10	13	16	19	23	26	29
14	1461	1492	1523	1553	1584	1614	1644	1673	1703	1732	3	6	9	12	15	18	21	24	27
15	1761	1790	1818	1847	1875	1903	1931	1959	1987	2014	3	6	8	11	14	17	20	22	25
16	2041	2068	2095	2122	2148	2175	2201	2227	2253	2279	3	5	8	11	13	16	18	21	24
17	2304	2330	2355	2380	2405	2430	2455	2480	2504	2529	2	5	7	10	12	15	17	20	22
18	2553	2577	2601	2625	2648	2672	2695	2718	2742	2765	2	5	7	9	12	14	16	19	21
19	2788	2810	2833	2856	2878	2900	2923	2945	2967	2989	2	4	7	9	11	13	16	18	20
20	3010	3032	3054	3075	3096	3118	3139	3160	3181	3201	2	4	6	8	11	13	15	17	19
21	3222	3243	3263	3284	3304	3324	3345	3365	3385	3404	2	4	6	8	10	12	14	16	18
22	3424	3444	3464	3483	3502	3522	3541	3560	3579	3598	2	4	6	8	10	12	14	15	17
23	3617	3636	3655	3674	3692	3711	3729	3747	3766	3784	2	4	6	7	9	11	13	15	17
24	3802	3820	3838	3856	3874	3892	3909	3927	3945	3962	2	4	5	7	9	11	12	14	16
25	3979	3997	4014	4031	4048	4065	4082	4099	4116	4133	2	3	5	7	9	10	12	14	15
26	4150	4166	4183	4200	4216	4232	4249	4265	4281	4298	2	3	5	7	8	10	11	13	15
27	4314	4330	4346	4362	4378	4393	4409	4425	4440	4456	2	3	5	6	8	9	11	13	14
28	4472	4487	4502	4518	4533	4548	4564	4579	4594	4609	2	3	5	6	8	9	11	12	14
29	4624	4639	4654	4669	4683	4698	4713	4728	4742	4757	1	3	4	6	7	9	10	12	13
30	4771	4786	4800	4814	4829	4843	4857	4871	4886	4900	1	3	4	6	7	9	10	11	13
31	4914	4928	4942	4955	4969	4983	4997	5011	5024	5038	1	3	4	6	7	8	10	11	12
32	5051	5065	5079	5092	5105	5119	5132	5145	5159	5172	1	3	4	5	7	8	9	11	12
33	5185	5198	5211	5224	5237	5250	5263	5276	5289	5302	1	3	4	5	6	8	9	10	12
34	5315	5328	5340	5353	5366	5378	5391	5403	5416	5428	1	3	4	5	6	8	9	10	11
35	5441	5453	5465	5478	5490	5502	5514	5527	5539	5551	1	2	4	5	6	7	9	10	11
36	5563	5575	5587	5599	5611	5623	5635	5647	5658	5670	1	2	4	5	6	7	8	10	11
37	5682	5694	5705	5717	5729	5740	5752	5763	5775	5786	1	2	3	5	6	7	8	9	10
38	5798	5809	5821	5832	5843	5855	5866	5877	5888	5899	1	2	3	5	6	7	8	9	10
39	5911	5922	5933	5944	5955	5966	5977	5988	5999	6010	1	2	3	4	5	7	8	9	10
40	6021	6031	6042	6053	6064	6075	6085	6096	6107	6117	1	2	3	4	5	6	8	9	10
41	6128	6138	6149	6160	6170	6180	6191	6201	6212	6222	1	2	3	4	5	6	7	8	9
42	6232	6243	6253	6263	6274	6284	6294	6304	6314	6325	1	2	3	4	5	6	7	8	9
43	6335	6345	6355	6365	6375	6386	6395	6405	6415	6425	1	2	3	4	5	6	7	8	9
44	6435	6444	6454	6464	6474	6484	6493	6503	6513	6522	1	2	3	4	5	6	7	8	9
45	6532	6542	6551	6561	6571	6580	6590	6599	6609	6618	1	2	3	4	5	6	7	8	9
46	6628	6637	6646	6656	6665	6675	6684	6693	6702	6712	1	2	3	4	5	6	7	7	8
47	6721	6730	6739	6749	6758	6767	6776	6785	6794	6803	1	2	3	4	5	5	6	7	8
48	6812	6821	6830	6839	6848	6857	6866	6875	6884	6893	1	2	3	4	4	5	6	7	8
49	6902	6911	6920	6928	6937	6946	6955	6964	6972	6981	1	2	3	4	4	5	6	7	8
50	6990	6998	7007	7016	7024	7033	7042	7050	7059	7067	1	2	3	3	4	5	6	7	8
51	7076	7084	7093	7101	7110	7118	7126	7135	7143	7152	1	2	3	3	4	5	6	7	8
52	7160	7168	7177	7185	7193	7202	7210	7218	7226	7235	1	2	2	3	4	5	6	7	7
53	7243	7251	7259	7267	7275	7284	7292	7300	7308	7316	1	2	2	3	4	5	6	6	7
54	7324	7332	7340	7348	7356	7364	7372	7380	7388	7396	1	2	2	3	4	5	6	6	7
	0	1	2	3	4	5	6	7	8	9	1	2	3	4	5	6	7	8	9

APPENDIX B Four-Place Table of Logarithms (*Continued*)

No.	0	1	2	3	4	5	6	7	8	9	1 2 3	4 5 6	7 8 9
55	7404	7412	7419	7427	7435	7443	7451	7459	7466	7474	1 2 2	3 4 5	5 6 7
56	7482	7490	7497	7505	7513	7520	7528	7536	7543	7551	1 2 2	3 4 5	5 6 7
57	7559	7566	7574	7582	7589	7597	7604	7612	7619	7627	1 2 2	3 4 5	5 6 7
58	7634	7642	7649	7657	7664	7672	7679	7686	7694	7701	1 1 2	3 4 4	5 6 7
59	7709	7716	7723	7731	7738	7745	7752	7760	7767	7774	1 1 2	3 4 4	5 6 7
60	7782	7789	7796	7803	7810	7818	7825	7832	7839	7846	1 1 2	3 4 4	5 6 6
61	7853	7860	7868	7875	7882	7889	7896	7903	7910	7917	1 1 2	3 4 4	5 6 6
62	7924	7931	7938	7945	7952	7959	7966	7973	7980	7987	1 1 2	3 3 4	5 6 6
63	7992	8000	8007	8014	8021	8028	8035	8041	8048	8055	1 1 2	3 3 4	5 5 6
64	8062	8069	8075	8082	8089	8096	8102	8109	8116	8122	1 1 2	3 3 4	5 5 6
65	8129	8136	8142	8149	8156	8162	8169	8176	8182	8189	1 1 2	3 3 4	5 5 6
66	8195	8202	8209	8215	8222	8228	8235	8241	8248	8254	1 1 2	3 3 4	5 5 6
67	8261	8267	8274	8280	8287	8293	8299	8306	8312	8319	1 1 2	3 3 4	5 5 6
68	8325	8331	8338	8344	8351	8357	8363	8370	8376	8382	1 1 2	3 3 4	4 5 6
69	8388	8395	8401	8407	8414	8420	8426	8432	8439	8445	1 1 2	2 3 4	4 5 6
70	8451	8457	8463	8470	8476	8482	8488	8494	8500	8506	1 1 2	2 3 4	4 5 6
71	8513	8519	8525	8531	8537	8543	8549	8555	8561	8567	1 1 2	2 3 4	4 5 5
72	8573	8579	8585	8591	8597	8603	8609	8615	8621	8627	1 1 2	2 3 4	4 5 5
73	8633	8639	8645	8651	8657	8663	8669	8675	8681	8686	1 1 2	2 3 4	4 5 5
74	8692	8698	8704	8710	8716	8722	8727	8733	8739	8745	1 1 2	2 3 4	4 5 5
75	8751	8756	8762	8768	8774	8779	8785	8791	8797	8802	1 1 2	2 3 3	4 5 5
76	8808	8814	8820	8825	8831	8837	8842	8848	8854	8859	1 1 2	2 3 3	4 5 5
77	8865	8871	8876	8882	8887	8893	8899	8904	8910	8915	1 1 2	2 3 3	4 4 5
78	8921	8927	8932	8938	8943	8949	8954	8960	8965	8971	1 1 2	2 3 3	4 4 5
79	8976	8982	8987	8993	8998	9004	9009	9015	9020	9025	1 1 2	2 3 3	4 4 5
80	9031	9036	9042	9047	9053	9058	9063	9069	9074	9079	1 1 2	2 3 3	4 4 5
81	9085	9090	9096	9101	9106	9112	9117	9122	9128	9133	1 1 2	2 3 3	4 4 5
82	9138	9143	9149	9154	9159	9165	9170	9175	9180	9186	1 1 2	2 3 3	4 4 5
83	9191	9196	9201	9206	9212	9217	9222	9227	9232	9238	1 1 2	2 3 3	4 4 5
84	9243	9248	9253	9258	9263	9269	9274	9279	9284	9289	1 1 2	2 3 3	4 4 5
85	9294	9299	9304	9309	9315	9320	9325	9330	9335	9340	1 1 2	2 3 3	4 4 5
86	9345	9350	9355	9360	9365	9370	9375	9380	9385	9390	1 1 2	2 3 3	4 4 5
87	9395	9400	9405	9410	9415	9420	9425	9430	9435	9440	0 1 1	2 2 3	3 4 4
88	9445	9450	9455	9460	9465	9469	9474	9479	9484	9489	0 1 1	2 2 3	3 4 4
89	9494	9499	9504	9509	9513	9518	9523	9528	9533	9538	0 1 1	2 2 3	3 4 4
90	9542	9547	9552	9557	9562	9566	9571	9576	9581	9586	0 1 1	2 2 3	3 4 4
91	9590	9595	9600	9605	9609	9614	9619	9624	9628	9633	0 1 1	2 2 3	3 4 4
92	9638	9643	9647	9652	9657	9661	9666	9671	9675	9680	0 1 1	2 2 3	3 4 4
93	9605	9609	9694	9699	9708	9708	9713	9717	9722	9727	0 1 1	2 2 3	3 4 4
94	9731	9736	9741	9745	9750	9754	9759	9763	9768	9773	0 1 1	2 2 3	3 4 4
95	9777	9782	9786	9791	9795	9800	9805	9809	9814	9818	0 1 1	2 2 3	3 4 4
96	9823	9827	9832	9836	9841	9845	9850	9854	9859	9863	0 1 1	2 2 3	3 4 4
97	9868	9872	9877	9881	9886	9890	9894	9899	9903	9908	0 1 1	2 2 3	3 4 4
98	9912	9917	9921	9926	9930	9934	9939	9943	9948	9952	0 1 1	2 2 3	3 4 4
99	9956	9961	9965	9969	9974	9978	9983	9987	9991	9996	0 1 1	2 2 3	3 3 4
	0	1	2	3	4	5	6	7	8	9	1 2 3	4 5 6	7 8 9

APPENDIX C List of Apparatus for Qualitative Analysis

50 Reagent bottles, dropper type, 10 ml.
1 Rack for 50 reagent bottles
1 Test tube block
1 Flask, Florence, 250 ml.
2 Beakers, 250 ml.
2 Beakers, 50 ml.
2 Beakers, 20 ml.
1 Graduate, 10 ml.
1 Casserole, 15 ml.
6 Centrifuge tubes
6 Test tubes, 65 × 10 mm.
6 Test tubes, 75 × 10 mm.
1 Metal rack for a water bath
1 Micro burner
1 Bunsen burner
2 Watch glasses, 2.5 cm.
1 File
1 Box of labels
1 Bottle of litmus, red
1 Bottle of litmus, blue
1 Test tube holder, small
1 Test tube brush, small, tapered
1 Test tube brush, small, not tapered
1 Wire, platinum, 2 inches
1 Wire gauze
1 Ring stand (with ring), small
1 Spatula, micro (Monel metal)
1 Forceps
1 Two-hole rubber stopper to fit 250 ml. flask
1 Wing top
1 Box matches
1 Towel
1 Box of detergent, small
6 Medicine droppers, 1 ml.
6 Capillary syringes
100 cm. Glass tubing, 6 mm.
100 cm. Glass rod, 3 mm.
1 Cobalt glass

APPENDIX D List of Reagents for Qualitative Analysis

GROUP I Reagents

Hydrochloric acid, HCl, 6 M
Nitric acid, HNO_3, 4 M
Aqueous ammonia, $NH_3 + H_2O$, 4 M
*Potassium chromate, K_2CrO_4, 1 M
(*Fill reagent bottles only about one-fourth full of starred reagents.)

GROUP II Reagents (in addition to those listed for Group I)

Aqueous ammonia, $NH_3 + H_2O$, 6 M
Hydrochloric acid, HCl, 0.1 M
Thioacetamide, CH_3CSNH_2, 5 per cent solution
Sodium hydroxide, $NaOH$, 4 M
Ammonium nitrate, NH_4NO_3, 1 M
Sulfuric acid, H_2SO_4, 4 M
Acetic acid, $HOAc$, 1 M
Oxalic acid, $H_2C_2O_4$, 1 M
Ammonium acetate, NH_4OAc, 1 M

Aqueous ammonia, $NH_3 + H_2O$, 15 M
*Potassium hexacyanoferrate (II), $K_4Fe(CN)_6$, 0.1 M
Potassium cyanide, KCN, 1 M
Hydrogen peroxide, H_2O_2, 3 per cent solution
*Magnesia mixture: Dissolve 50 g. of $MgCl_2 \cdot 6\ H_2O$ and 70 g. of NH_4Cl in 400 ml. of water. Add 100 ml. of 15 M aqueous ammonia and dilute to 1 liter. Filter.
*Aluminum wire, Al
Mercury (II) chloride, $HgCl_2$, 0.2 M
Sodium hypochlorite, NaOCl, 5 per cent solution

GROUP III Reagents (in addition to those listed for Groups I and II)

Hydrochloric acid, HCl, 12 M
Hydrochloric acid, HCl, 1 M
Nitric acid, HNO_3, 14 M
*Dimethylglyoxime, 1 per cent solution, dissolve 10 g. in 1 liter of alcohol
Acetic acid, HOAc, 4 M
*Ammonium thiocyanate, NH_4CNS, solid
Acetone, $(CH_3)_2CO$
*Sodium fluoride, NaF, 1 M
*Potassium nitrite, KNO_2, solid
*Sodium nitrite, $NaNO_2$, 1 M
*Sodium bismuthate, $NaBiO_3$, solid
*Aluminum Reagent: Dissolve 1 g. of the ammonium salt of aurin-tricarboxylic acid in 1 liter of water
Lead acetate, $Pb(OAc)_2$, 0.1 M
Ammonium carbonate, $(NH_4)_2CO_3$, 1 M

GROUP IV Reagents (in addition to those listed for Groups I–III)

Ethyl alcohol, C_2H_5OH
*Ammonium oxalate, $(NH_4)_2C_2O_4$, 0.4 M

GROUP V Reagents (in addition to those listed for Groups I–IV)

*Ammonium sulfate, $(NH_4)_2SO_4$, 1 M
*Sodium Reagent: Mix 30 g. of $UO_2(OAc)_2 \cdot 2\ H_2O$ with 80 g. of $Zn(OAc)_2 \cdot 2\ H_2O$ and 10 ml. of glacial acetic acid. Dilute the solution to 250 ml., let it stand for several hours, and filter. Use the clear solution.
*Sodium hexanitrocobaltate (III), $Na_3Co(NO_2)_6$: Dissolve 30 g. of $NaNO_2$ in 97 ml. of water; add 3 ml. of glacial HOAc and 3.3 g. of $Co(NO_3)_2 \cdot 6\ H_2O$. Filter and use the clear solution.
*Disodium hydrogen phosphate, Na_2HPO_4, 1 M
*Magnesium Reagent, p-nitro-benzene-azo-alpha-naphthol: Dissolve 0.25 g. of this reagent and 2.5 g. of NaOH in sufficient water to make 250 ml. of solution.

Reagents for Anion Analysis (in addition to those listed for the Cation Analysis)

*Sulfuric acid, H_2SO_4, 1.5 M
Sodium carbonate, Na_2CO_3, 1.5 M
*Manganese (II) chloride, $MnCl_2$: Saturate 12 M HCl with $MnCl_2$.
*Potassium hexacyanoferrate (III), $K_3Fe(CN)_6$, a freshly prepared saturated solution
*Iron (III) chloride, $FeCl_3$, 0.1 M
Calcium chloride, $CaCl_2$, 0.1 M
Barium chloride, $BaCl_2$, 0.1 M
*Cobalt (II) nitrate, $Co(NO_3)_2$, 1 M
*Silver nitrate, $AgNO_3$, 0.1 M
*Bromine water, $Br_2 + H_2O$, saturated solution
*Barium hydroxide, $Ba(OH)_2$, a saturated solution
*Iron (II) sulfate, $FeSO_4$, 0.1 M
*Sulfuric acid, H_2SO_4, 18 M
*Silver sulfate, Ag_2SO_4, solid (nitrate free)
*Potassium permanganate, $KMnO_4$, 0.002 M
*Silica, SiO_2, powdered
*Methyl alcohol, CH_3OH
*Iron (III) nitrate, $Fe(NO_3)_3$, 0.1 M
*Carbon tetrachloride, CCl_4
*Potassium permanganate, $KMnO_4$, 0.1 M
*Lead acetate paper, filter paper moist with 0.1 M $Pb(OAc)_2$

APPENDIX E Preparation of Solutions of Cations

E.1 Stock Solutions

It is recommended that all stock solutions contain the cations in question at a concentration of 50 mg. per ml. These stock solutions may be prepared by grinding to a powder the weight of salt given below and adding enough water (or acid if specified) to make the volume 100 ml. Solution of the salts may be hastened by heating.

E.2 Known and Unknown Solutions

To prepare known or unknown solutions of cations, mix 20 ml. of the stock solutions (40 ml. of $AsCl_3$) of the cations desired and dilute the solution to 100 ml. with water. This solution will contain 10 mg. of cation per ml. This procedure allows for a maximum of five cations at a concentration of 10 mg. of cation per ml. Dilution to 200 ml. will allow a maximum of ten cations at a concentration of 5 mg. per ml. Give each student about 1 ml. of solution.

Stock Solutions of Cations (50 mg. of cation per ml.)

Group	*Ion*	*Formula of Salt*	*Grams per 100 ml. of Solution*
I	Ag^+	$AgNO_3$	8.0
	Pb^{++}	$Pb(NO_3)_2$	8.0
	Hg_2^{++}	$Hg_2(NO_3)_2$	7.0 (dissolve in 0.6 M HNO_3)
II	Pb^{++}	$Pb(NO_3)_2$	8.0
	Bi^{+++}	$Bi(NO_3)_3 \cdot 5\ H_2O$	11.5 (dissolve in 3 M HNO_3)
	Cu^{++}	$Cu(NO_3)_2 \cdot 3\ H_2O$	19.0
	Cd^{++}	$Cd(NO_3)_2 \cdot 4\ H_2O$	13.8
	Hg^{++}	$HgCl_2$	6.8
	As^{+++}	As_4O_6	3.3 (heat in 50 ml. of 12 M HCl, then add 50 ml. of water)
	Sb^{+++}	$SbCl_3$	9.5 (dissolve in 6 M HCl, and dilute with 2 M HCl)
	Sn^{++}	$SnCl_2 \cdot 2\ H_2O$	9.5 (dissolve in 50 ml. of 12 M HCl. Dilute to 100 ml. with water. Add a piece of tin metal)
	Sn^{++++}	$SnCl_4 \cdot 3\ H_2O$	13.3 (dissolve in 6 M HCl)
III	Co^{++}	$Co(NO_3)_2 \cdot 6\ H_2O$	24.7
	Ni^{++}	$Ni(NO_3)_2 \cdot 6\ H_2O$	24.8
	Mn^{++}	$Mn(NO_3)_2 \cdot 6\ H_2O$	26.2
	Fe^{+++}	$Fe(NO_3)_3 \cdot 9\ H_2O$	36.2
	Al^{+++}	$Al(NO_3)_3 \cdot 9\ H_2O$	69.5
	Cr^{+++}	$Cr(NO_3)_3$	23.0
	Zn^{++}	$Zn(NO_3)_2$	14.5
IV	Ba^{++}	$BaCl_2 \cdot 2\ H_2O$	8.9
	Sr^{++}	$Sr(NO_3)_2$	12.0
	Ca^{++}	$Ca(NO_3)_2 \cdot 4\ H_2O$	29.5
V	Mg^{++}	$Mg(NO_3)_2 \cdot 6\ H_2O$	52.8
	NH_4^+	NH_4NO_3	22.2
	Na^+	$NaNO_3$	18.5
	K^+	KNO_3	13.0

APPENDIX F Composition of Commercial Acids and Bases

Acid or Base	*Specific Gravity*	*Percentage by Weight*	*Molarity*	*Normality*
Hydrochloric	1.19	38	12.4	12.4
Nitric	1.42	70	15.8	15.8
Sulfuric	1.84	95	17.8	35.6
Acetic	1.05	99	17.3	17.3
Aqueous ammonia	0.90	28	14.8	14.8

APPENDIX G Solubility Product Constants

Substance	K_{sp} *at 25°*	*Substance*	K_{sp} *at 25°*
Aluminum		Cu_2S	1.6×10^{-48}
$Al(OH)_3$	1.9×10^{-33}	$Cu(OH)_2$	5.6×10^{-20}
Barium		CuS	8.7×10^{-36}
$BaCO_3$	8.1×10^{-9}	$CuCO_3$	1.37×10^{-10}
$BaC_2O_4 \cdot 2\ H_2O$	1.1×10^{-7}	Iron	
$BaSO_4$	1.08×10^{-10}	$Fe(OH)_2$	7.9×10^{-15}
$BaCrO_4$	2×10^{-10}	$FeCO_3$	2.11×10^{-11}
BaF_2	1.7×10^{-6}	FeS	1×10^{-19}
$Ba(OH)_2 \cdot 8\ H_2O$	5.0×10^{-3}	$Fe(OH)_3$	1.1×10^{-36}
$Ba_3(PO_4)_2$	1.3×10^{-29}	Lead	
$Ba_3(AsO_4)_2$	1.1×10^{-13}	$Pb(OH)_2$	2.8×10^{-16}
Bismuth		PbF_2	3.7×10^{-8}
$BiO(OH)$	1×10^{-12}	$PbCl_2$	1.7×10^{-5}
$BiOCl$	7×10^{-9}	$PbBr_2$	6.3×10^{-6}
Bi_2S_3	1.6×10^{-72}	PbI_2	8.7×10^{-9}
Cadmium		$PbCO_3$	1.5×10^{-13}
$Cd(OH)_2$	1.2×10^{-14}	PbS	8.4×10^{-28}
CdS	3.6×10^{-29}	$PbCrO_4$	1.8×10^{-14}
$CdCO_3$	2.5×10^{-14}	$PbSO_4$	1.8×10^{-8}
Calcium		$Pb_3(PO_4)_2$	3×10^{-44}
$Ca(OH)_2$	7.9×10^{-6}	Magnesium	
$CaCO_3$	4.8×10^{-9}	$Mg(OH)_2$	1.5×10^{-11}
$CaSO_4 \cdot 2\ H_2O$	2.4×10^{-5}	$MgCO_3 \cdot 3\ H_2O$	1×10^{-5} ca.
$CaC_2O_4 \cdot H_2O$	2.27×10^{-9}	$MgNH_4PO_4$	2.5×10^{-13}
$Ca_3(PO_4)_2$	1×10^{-25}	MgF_2	6.4×10^{-9}
$CaHPO_4$	5×10^{-6}	MgC_2O_4	8.6×10^{-5}
CaF_2	3.9×10^{-11}	Manganese	
Chromium		$Mn(OH)_2$	4.5×10^{-14}
$Cr(OH)_3$	6.7×10^{-31}	$MnCO_3$	8.8×10^{-11}
Cobalt		MnS	5.6×10^{-16}
$Co(OH)_2$	2×10^{-16}	Mercury	
$CoS(\alpha)$	5.9×10^{-21}	$Hg_2O \cdot H_2O$	1.6×10^{-23}
$CoS(\beta)$	8.7×10^{-23}	Hg_2Cl_2	1.1×10^{-18}
$CoCO_3$	1.0×10^{-12}	Hg_2Br_2	1.26×10^{-22}
$Co(OH)_3$	2.5×10^{-43}	Hg_2I_2	4.5×10^{-29}
Copper		Hg_2CO_3	9×10^{-17}
$CuCl$	1.85×10^{-7}	Hg_2SO_4	6.2×10^{-7}
$CuBr$	5.3×10^{-9}	Hg_2S	1×10^{-45}
CuI	5.1×10^{-12}	Hg_2CrO_4	2×10^{-9}
$CuCNS$	4×10^{-14}	HgS	3×10^{-53}

Substance	K_{sp}
Nickel	
$Ni(OH)_2$	1.6×10^{-14}
$NiCO_3$	1.36×10^{-7}
$NiS(\alpha)$	3×10^{-21}
$NiS(\beta)$	1×10^{-26}
$NiS(\gamma)$	2×10^{-28}
Potassium	
$KClO_4$	1.07×10^{-2}
K_2PtCl_6	1.1×10^{-5}
$KHC_4H_4O_6$	3×10^{-4}
Silver	
$\frac{1}{2}$ $Ag_2O(Ag^+ + OH^-)$	2×10^{-8}
$AgCl$	1.2×10^{-10}
$AgBr$	3.3×10^{-13}
AgI	1.5×10^{-16}
$AgCN$	1.2×10^{-16}
$AgCNS$	1.0×10^{-12}
Ag_2S	1.0×10^{-51}
Ag_2CO_3	8.2×10^{-12}
Ag_2CrO_4	9×10^{-12}
$Ag_4Fe(CN)_6$	1.55×10^{-41}
Ag_2SO_4	1.18×10^{-5}
Ag_3PO_4	1.8×10^{-18}
Strontium	
$Sr(OH)_2 \cdot 8\ H_2O$	3.2×10^{-4}
$SrCO_3$	9.42×10^{-10}
$SrCrO_4$	3.6×10^{-5}
$SrSO_4$	2.8×10^{-7}
$SrC_2O_4 \cdot H_2O$	5.61×10^{-8}
Thallium	
$TlCl$	1.9×10^{-4}
$TlCNS$	5.8×10^{-4}
Tl_2S	1.2×10^{-24}
$Tl(OH)_3$	1.5×10^{-44}
Tin	
$Sn(OH)_2$	5×10^{-26}
SnS	8×10^{-29}
$Sn(OH)_4$	1×10^{-56} ca.
Zinc	
$ZnCO_3$	6×10^{-11}
$Zn(OH)_2$	4.5×10^{-17}
ZnS	1.1×10^{-21}

APPENDIX H Dissociation Constants for Complex Ions

Equilibrium	K_d
$AlF_6^{-3} \rightleftharpoons Al^{+++} + 6\ F^-$	2×10^{-24}
$Cd(NH_3)_4^{++} \rightleftharpoons Cd^{++} + 4\ NH_3$	2.5×10^{-7}
$Cd(CN)_4^{=} \rightleftharpoons Cd^{++} + 4\ CN^-$	7.8×10^{-18}
$Co(NH_3)_6^{++} \rightleftharpoons Co^{++} + 6\ NH_3$	1.2×10^{-5}
$Co(NH_3)_6^{+++} \rightleftharpoons Co^{+++} + 6\ NH_3$	2.2×10^{-34}
$Cu(CN)_2^- \rightleftharpoons Cu^+ + 2\ CN^-$	1×10^{-16}
$Cu(NH_3)_4^{++} \rightleftharpoons Cu^{++} + 4\ NH_3$	8.5×10^{-13}
$Fe(CN)_6^{-4} \rightleftharpoons Fe^{++} + 6\ CN^-$	1×10^{-37}
$Fe(CN)_6^{-3} \rightleftharpoons Fe^{+++} + 6\ CN^-$	1×10^{-44}
$Fe(CNS)_6^{-3} \rightleftharpoons Fe^{+++} + 6\ CNS^-$	3.1×10^{-4}
$HgCl_4^{=} \rightleftharpoons Hg^{++} + 4\ Cl^-$	8.3×10^{-16}
$Ni(NH_3)_6^{++} \rightleftharpoons Ni^{++} + 6\ NH_3$	5.7×10^{-9}
$Ag(CN)_2^- \rightleftharpoons Ag^+ + 2\ CN^-$	1×10^{-20}
$Ag(NH_3)_2^+ \rightleftharpoons Ag^+ + 2\ NH_3$	6.8×10^{-8}
$Zn(CN)_4^{=} \rightleftharpoons Zn^{++} + 4\ CN^-$	1×10^{-19}
$Zn(OH)_4^{=} \rightleftharpoons Zn^{++} + 4\ OH^-$	3.5×10^{-16}

APPENDIX I Ionization Constants of Weak Acids

Acid	*Formula*	*K_i at 25°*
Acetic	HOAc (CH_3COOH)	1.8×10^{-5}
Arsenic	H_3AsO_4	4.8×10^{-3}
	$H_2AsO_4^-$	1×10^{-7}
	$HAsO_4^=$	1×10^{-13}
Arsenous	H_3AsO_3	5.8×10^{-10}
Boric	H_3BO_3	5.8×10^{-10}
Carbonic	H_2CO_3	4.3×10^{-7}
	HCO_3^-	7×10^{-11}
Formic	HCOOH	1.8×10^{-4}
Hydrazoic	HN_3	1×10^{-4}
Hydrocyanic	HCN	4×10^{-10}
Hydrofluoric	HF	7.2×10^{-4}
Hydrogen peroxide	H_2O_2	2.4×10^{-12}
Hydrogen selenide	H_2Se	1.7×10^{-4}
	HSe^-	1×10^{-10}
Hydrogen sulfate ion	HSO_4^-	1.2×10^{-2}
Hydrogen sulfide	H_2S	1.0×10^{-7}
	HS^-	1.3×10^{-13}
Hydrogen telluride	H_2Te	2.3×10^{-3}
	HTe^-	1×10^{-5}
Hypobromous	HBrO	2×10^{-9}
Hypochlorous	HClO	3.5×10^{-8}
Nitrous	HNO_2	4.5×10^{-4}
Oxalic	$H_2C_2O_4$	5.9×10^{-2}
	$HC_2O_4^-$	6.4×10^{-5}
Phosphoric	H_3PO_4	7.5×10^{-3}
	$H_2PO_4^-$	6.2×10^{-8}
	$HPO_4^=$	1×10^{-12}
Phosphorous	H_3PO_3	1.6×10^{-2}
	$H_2PO_3^-$	7×10^{-7}
Sulfurous	H_2SO_3	1.2×10^{-2}
	HSO_3^-	6.2×10^{-8}

APPENDIX J Ionization Constants of Weak Bases

Base	*Ionization Equation*	*K_i at 25°*
Ammonia	$NH_3 + H_2O \rightleftharpoons NH_4^+ + OH^-$	1.8×10^{-5}
Dimethylamine	$(CH_3)_2NH + H_2O \rightleftharpoons (CH_3)_2NH_2^+ + OH^-$	7.4×10^{-4}
Methylamine	$CH_3NH_2 + H_2O \rightleftharpoons CH_3NH_3^+ + OH^-$	4.4×10^{-4}
Phenylamine (aniline)	$C_6H_5NH_2 + H_2O \rightleftharpoons C_6H_5NH_3^+ + OH^-$	4.6×10^{-10}
Trimethylamine	$(CH_3)_3N + H_2O \rightleftharpoons (CH_3)_3NH^+ + OH^-$	7.4×10^{-5}

APPENDIX K Electromotive Series

	Electrode Reaction			*Standard Electrode (Oxidation) Potential (volts)*
	Reduced form		*Oxidized form*	
Potassium	K	$\rightleftharpoons$	$K^+ + e^-$	2.925
Calcium	Ca	$\rightleftharpoons$	$Ca^{++} + 2\ e^-$	2.87
Sodium	Na	$\rightleftharpoons$	$Na^+ + e^-$	2.71
Magnesium	Mg	$\rightleftharpoons$	$Mg^{++} + 2\ e^-$	2.37
Aluminum	Al	$\rightleftharpoons$	$Al^{+++} + 3\ e^-$	1.66
Manganese	Mn	$\rightleftharpoons$	$Mn^{++} + 2\ e^-$	1.18
Zinc	Zn	$\rightleftharpoons$	$Zn^{++} + 2\ e^-$	0.76
Chromium	Cr	$\rightleftharpoons$	$Cr^{+++} + 3\ e^-$	0.74
Iron	Fe	$\rightleftharpoons$	$Fe^{++} + 2\ e^-$	0.44
Cadmium	Cd	$\rightleftharpoons$	$Cd^{++} + 2\ e^-$	0.40
Cobalt	Co	$\rightleftharpoons$	$Co^{++} + 2\ e^-$	0.28
Nickel	Ni	$\rightleftharpoons$	$Ni^{++} + 2\ e^-$	0.25
Tin	Sn	$\rightleftharpoons$	$Sn^{++} + 2\ e^-$	0.14
Lead	Pb	$\rightleftharpoons$	$Pb^{++} + 2\ e^-$	0.13
Hydrogen	H_2	$\rightleftharpoons$	$2\ H^+ + 2\ e^-$	0.00
Copper	Cu	$\rightleftharpoons$	$Cu^{++} + 2\ e^-$	−0.34
Iodine	$2\ I^-$	$\rightleftharpoons$	$I_2 + 2\ e^-$	−0.54
Mercury	Hg	$\rightleftharpoons$	$Hg^{++} + 2\ e^-$	−0.79
Silver	Ag	$\rightleftharpoons$	$Ag^+ + e^-$	−0.80
Bromine	$2\ Br^-$	$\rightleftharpoons$	$Br_2\ (l) + 2\ e^-$	−1.06
Platinum	Pt	$\rightleftharpoons$	$Pt^{++} + 2\ e^-$	−1.2
Oxygen	$2\ H_2O$	$\rightleftharpoons$	$O_2 + 4\ H^+ + 4\ e^-$	−1.23
Chlorine	$2\ Cl^-$	$\rightleftharpoons$	$Cl_2 + 2\ e^-$	−1.36
Gold	Au	$\rightleftharpoons$	$Au^+ + e^-$	−1.68
Fluorine	$2\ F^-$	$\rightleftharpoons$	$F_2 + 2\ e^-$	−2.87

Index

Index

N

P

Q

R

S

T

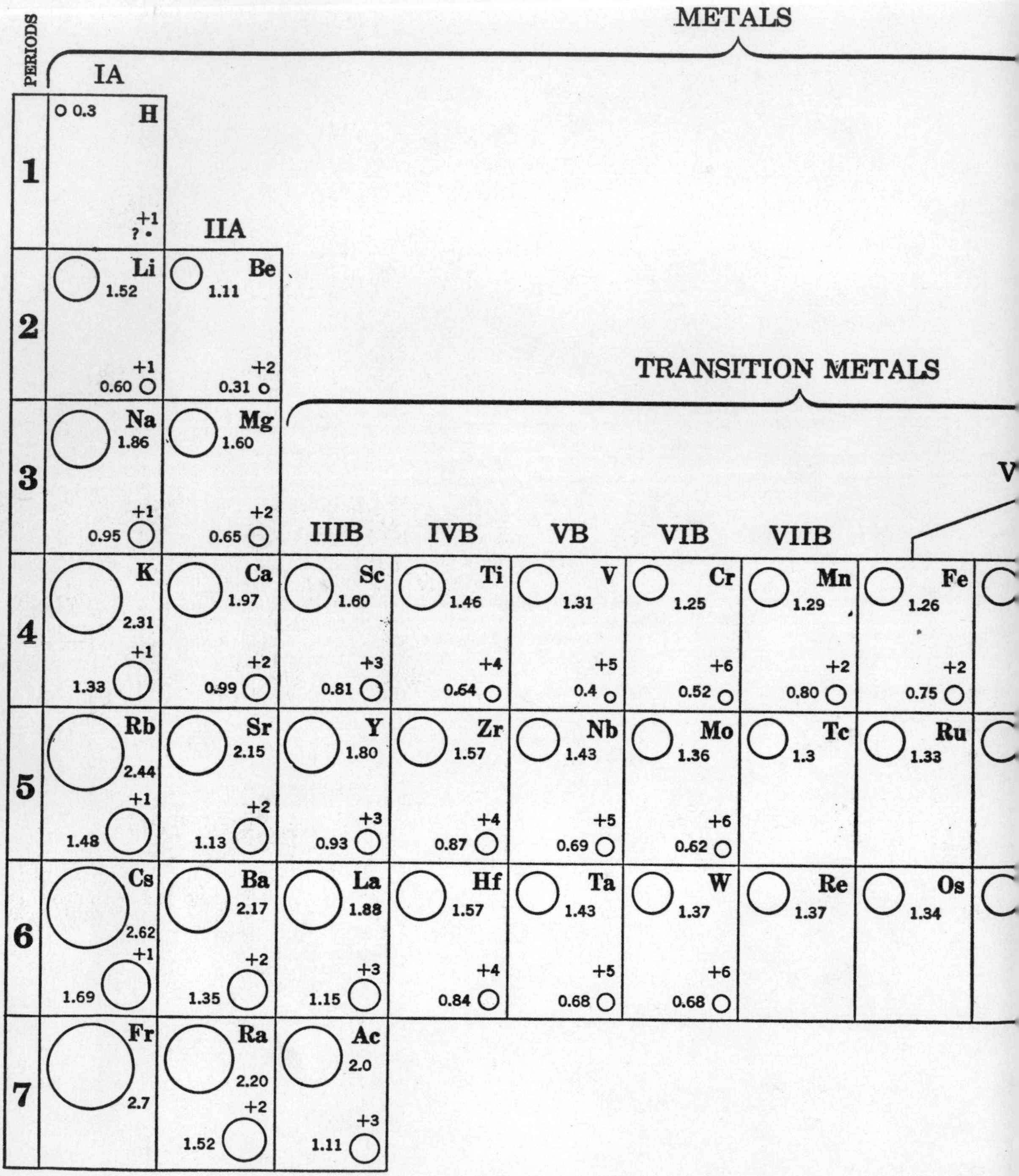

METALS

TRANSITION METALS

PERIODS	IA	IIA	IIIB	IVB	VB	VIB	VIIB	V
1	H 0.3; +1 ?							
2	Li 1.52; +1 0.60	Be 1.11; +2 0.31						
3	Na 1.86; +1 0.95	Mg 1.60; +2 0.65						
4	K 2.31; +1 1.33	Ca 1.97; +2 0.99	Sc 1.60; +3 0.81	Ti 1.46; +4 0.64	V 1.31; +5 0.4	Cr 1.25; +6 0.52	Mn 1.29; +2 0.80	Fe 1.26; +2 0.75
5	Rb 2.44; +1 1.48	Sr 2.15; +2 1.13	Y 1.80; +3 0.93	Zr 1.57; +4 0.87	Nb 1.43; +5 0.69	Mo 1.36; +6 0.62	Tc 1.3	Ru 1.33
6	Cs 2.62; +1 1.69	Ba 2.17; +2 1.35	La 1.88; +3 1.15	Hf 1.57; +4 0.84	Ta 1.43; +5 0.68	W 1.37; +6 0.68	Re 1.37	Os 1.34
7	Fr 2.7	Ra 2.20; +2 1.52	Ac 2.0; +3 1.11					